Life by Design

CHARLES DETWILER
Liberty University

KIMBERLY MITCHELL
Liberty University

NORMAN REICHENBACH
Liberty University

 CENGAGE
Learning·

Australia • Brazil • Japan • Korea • Mexico • Singapore
Spain • United Kingdom • United States

CENGAGE
Learning·

Life by Design
Charles Detwiler, Kimberly Mitchell,
Norman Reichenbach

Senior Manager, Student Engagement:
 Linda deStefano
 Janey Moeller

Manager, Student Engagement:
 Julie Dierig

Marketing Manager:
 Rachael Kloos

Manager, Production Editorial:
 Kim Fry

Manager, Intellectual Property Project Manager:
 Brian Methe

Senior Manager, Production and Manufacturing:
 Donna Brown

Manager, Production:
 Terri Daley

Compositor:
 MPS Limited, a Macmillan Company

For product information and technology assistance, contact us at
Cengage Learning Customer & Sales Support, 1-800-354-9706

For permission to use material from this text or product,
submit all requests online at **cengage.com/permissions**
Further permissions questions can be emailed to
permissionrequest@cengage.com

Library of Congress Control Number: 2011940744

ISBN-13: 978-1-285-13090-3

ISBN-10: 1-285-13090-1

Cengage Learning
5191 Natorp Boulevard
Mason, OH 45040
USA

Cengage Learning is a leading provider of customized learning solutions with
office locations around the globe, including Singapore, the United Kingdom,
Australia, Mexico, Brazil, and Japan. Locate your local office at:
international.cengage.com/region

Cengage Learning products are represented in Canada by
Nelson Education, Ltd.

Visit Signature Labs online at **signaturelabs.com**

Visit our corporate website at **cengage.com**

Printed in the United States of America

Contents

Chapter 1   Life Is Significant by Design   1

1.1   Design That Talks   1
Its Glory 1
Its Speech 2
Its Mandate 2

1.2   Design at Multiple Levels   4
Microbiological Architecture 4
Macrobiological Systems 8

1.3   Unity within Diversity   12
Diversity of Styles 12
Unity in Essence 14
Toward a Description of Life 17

1.4   Teleology, Start to Finish   20
To Summarize 22

Questions for Review 22
Questions for Thought 23
Glossary 23

Chapter 2   Understanding Life's Design   25

2.1   How Design Is Understood   25
Doing Science 25
Results as Puzzle Pieces 27

2.2   Rational Experimentation: Two Examples   29
The Effect of Sleep on Disease Resistance 29
Experimenting with Prayer 31

2.3   Seeing a Bigger Picture   33
Approaching Truth 33

Comparing Truth Sources 33
Limits to Truth 34
The Value of Truth from Two Sources 34

Questions for Review 35
Questions for Thought 36
Glossary 36

Chapter 3   Complexity I: Versatile Elemental Structure   38

3.1   A Brief History of Understanding Matter   38
Revealing Matter's Complexity 38
Revealing Continuity between Living and Nonliving Matter 41

3.2   Atomic Structure   43
What's an Atom? 43
What Are Its Parts? 43
How Do Atoms Differ from Each Other? 43
Do Neutrons Make any Difference? What's an Isotope? 44
How Are the Parts of an Atom Arranged? 44

3.3   Chemical Bonding   47
Ion Formation and Ionic Bonding 47
Covalent Bonding 48
Polarity in Water Molecules and Hydrogen Bonding 49

3.4   Water was Designed!   51
High Heat Capacity 51
As a Solvent 51
Its Cohesion 52

Questions for Review 54
Questions for Thought 54
Glossary 54

Chapter 4 Complexity II: Molecular Efficiency and Variety   56

4.1 The Centrality of Carbon to the Organic Molecules of Life   58

4.2 Construction and Degradation of Organic Molecules   61

4.3 Carbohydrates: Structure and Function   64
Sugars 64
Carbohydrate Polymers 65

4.4 Lipids: Structure and Function   68
The Wonderfully Functional Fat Molecule 68
The Amazing Phospholipid 71
Mighty Testosterone 72

4.5 Proteins: Structure and Function   75
A Glorious Structure Supports Myriads of Functions 75
Crossing Biomolecular Class Lines 78

4.6 Proteins Conceal Wisdom   80

4.7 Nucleic Acids: Structure and Function   83
Nucleotides: The Monomers 83
The Polymers: DNA and RNA 84

4.8 Living Things Need Just a Few Good Molecules   86
Questions for Review 87
Questions for Thought 87
Glossary 88

Chapter 5 Complexity III: The Glory of the Cell   90

5.1 What Is a Cell?   93
Definition 93
Cell Theory 93
Generalizations: At Once Brilliant and Naïve 95

5.2 Living Cells Are Complex   97
Prokaryotic Intricacies 98

Prokaryotic Organization 101
Eukaryotic Intricacies 103
Eukaryotic Organization 113

5.3 Complexity at the Cellular Level: Are There Limits?   117
Questions for Review 119
Questions for Thought 119
Glossary 120

Chapter 6 Energy-Driven Inventions   122

6.1 Living Systems Require a Flow of Energy   122

6.2 Laws of Energy Flow in the Living World   126

6.3 Energy Flows in Chemical Reactions   128

6.4 Enzymes Direct Energy Flow   130

6.5 Energy Flow in Reaction Pathways: Metabolism   132

6.6 Energy Pools in the Cell: ATP   135

6.7 Energy Flow from Carbohydrates to ATP: Respiration   136
Aerobic Respiration: Stage 1—Glycolysis 137
Aerobic Respiration: Stage 2—The Krebs Cycle 137
Aerobic Respiration: Stage 3—Electron Transfer Phosphorylation 139

6.8 Energy Flow from Carbohydrates to ATP: Fermentation   142

6.9 Energy Flow from Photons to Carbohydrates: Photosynthesis   144
Photosynthesis: Stage 1—Light-Dependent Reactions 145
Photosynthesis: Stage 2—Light-Independent Reactions 149

6.10 Energy Flow: An Integrated Picture   153
Questions for Review 155
Questions for Thought 156
Glossary 157

Chapter 7 Information and Its Expression in the Cell 160

7.1 The Need for Biological Information 160

7.2 The Nature of Biological Information 164
Biological Information Is Stored in the Base Sequence of DNA 164
Biological Information Is Stored in Chromosomes 170

7.3 The Expression of Biological Information 173
A Context for Understanding Gene Expression 173
Transcription: Using Some Genes Now and Some Not At All 175
Translation: Making Proteins 181
The Genetic Code 188

7.4 The Application of Information Expression 190
Our Deep Desire to Control Information Expression 190
Information Expression as Problem Solving 191
Essentials of Recombinant DNA Technology 195
The Sobering Early History of Human Gene Therapy 204

7.5 A Hidden Drama: Information Expression at Its Very Best 207
Questions for Review 207
Questions for Thought 208
Glossary 209

Chapter 8 Informational Continuity in Cells 213

8.1 A Thin Skin of Life Chasing Death 213

8.2 Cell Division: A Requirement of Life 216

8.3 Cell Division Is Part of a Cycle: The Cell Cycle 220

8.4 Mitosis 224
The Reason for Mitosis: Chromosomes 224
The Process of Mitosis: A Sequence of Stages 224

8.5 Cytokinesis 230

8.6 Cancer: Mutation Threatening Design 233
The Unifying Basis of Cancer 233
A Tale of Two Cancer Genes 234
Questions for Review 238
Questions for Thought 239
Glossary 240

Chapter 9 Complexity IV: From Cell to Organism 242

9.1 Development: Decoding a Master Plan 242
What Can Be Done with a Fertilized Egg? 242
Getting from One Cell to You or to a Tree 243

9.2 *Gingko Biloba*: How to Make a Tree 250
Early Development 250
Cell Specialization: Tissue Types Emerge 253
Morphogenesis: Organ Formation 255

9.3 Development of a Human Being 259
Early Events 259
Embryonic Differentiation of Organ Systems 262
Organogenesis of the Brain 267
Cooperation of Organs in Organ Systems 270

9.4 Asking and Answering Questions 273
Elegant Experiment #1 — Induction 273
Elegant Experiment #2 — Genomic Potency 275
Questions for Review 277
Questions for Thought 277
Glossary 278

Chapter 10　The Internally Integrated Human Animal　282

10.1　The Integrated Human　282

10.2　The Muscular System　286
Muscle Structural Organization 286
Muscle Contraction 287
Control of Contraction: Ions, Gradients, and Membrane Potentials 288
Control of Contraction: The Nervous System 290
Contraction of Cardiac and Smooth Muscle 292

10.3　The Cardiovascular System　293
Blood: A Medium of Exchange 293
Blood Vessels: The Body's Avenue of Life 294
The Heart: The Dynamo of Human Life 296

10.4　Basic Concepts of Immunity　300
Your First Line of Defense 300
Your Second Line of Defense 301
Your Third Line of Defense 303
Preparing Your Immune System: The Preemptive Strike 306

10.5　The Human Digestive System　308

10.6　The Human Urinary System　312

10.7　Neurons at Work　315
Neuron Structure and Function 315
Nervous Reflexes 318

10.8　The Human Nervous System　320
The Central Nervous System 321
The Peripheral Nervous System 324
The Nervous System Is Internally Integrated 327

10.9　Drugs and the Nervous System　328
Alcohol: The Oldest Sedative 328
Caffeine: Catalyst of the Technological Revolution 331
Fluoxetine Hydrochloride: Chemical Joy 332

10.10　Life Is Internally Integrated: The Amazing ATP Molecule　334
Questions for Review 336
Questions for Thought 337
Glossary 339

Chapter 11　Elegant Responsiveness　345

11.1　Life's Responsiveness　348

11.2　Responsiveness at the Transcriptional Level　351

11.3　Responsiveness at the Cellular Level　354

11.4　Responsiveness at the Hormonal Level　356

11.5　Responsiveness at the Organ System Level　362

11.6　Responsiveness at the Behavioral Level　366

11.7　A Reality Behind Responsiveness　369
Questions for Review 370
Questions for Thought 370
Glossary 371

Chapter 12　Informational Continuity in Organisms　373

12.1　Reproduction: Asexual and Sexual　376
Asexual Reproduction 376
Sexual Reproduction 377

12.2　Preparing Reproductive Cells for Multicellular Organisms　382
The Challenge of Making a Reproductive Cell 382
How Can This Ploidy Problem Be Solved? 382
Meiosis: A Triumph of Genome Reduction and Genetic Variability 384
Differentiation of Reproductive Cells: A Biological Context 387

12.3　Reproduction in Humans　391
Oogenesis in Humans 392
Spermatogenesis and Fertilization 397

12.4 Reproduction Constrained,
Part I: Control of Birth   404

12.5 Reproduction Constrained,
Part II: Destruction of Life   408
*Philosophers and Theologians Attempt to Define
Personhood 408*
Biologists Work to Define the Human Individual 409
Destruction of Human Life Takes Various Forms 411

12.6 Reproduction Constrained,
Part III: Mendel and His Laws   412
A Brilliant Empiricist 412
A Brilliant Law: Segregation of Alleles 413
A Brilliant Law: Independent Assortment 417
Brilliant Laws: Variations on the Theme 419

12.7 Reproduction Explained:
The Chromosomal
Basis of Heredity   423
Questions for Review 427
Questions for Thought 428
Glossary 430

Chapter 13 Life Is Ultimate Art   434

13.1 Life and Its Diversity: Ultimate
Art or Ultimate Accident?   435
Life as Ultimate Art 435
Life as Ultimate Accident 436

13.2 Can Life Originate without
Artistry?   442
Evolution's First Goal: The Smallest Cell 442
*Evolution's Starting Materials:
Small Geochemicals 445*
*Evolution's Highest Hurdle: Creating and Storing
Information 448*
*Evolution's Final Challenge: Spatial Ordering of
Biological Activity 451*

13.3 Can Life's Diversity Increase
without Artistry?   454
*The Gap to Be Bridged: Invention of Novel
Complex Structures 454*
*Bridging the Gap I: Random Mutation in
Primitive Feather Keratinocytes 460*
*Bridging the Gap II: Natural Selection in
Primitive Feather Keratinocytes 464*
Evaluation of the Naturalistic Hypothesis 469

13.4 Did Life's Diversity Increase
without Artistry?   471
The Cambrian Explosion 471
The Evidence from Homology 474

13.5 What Is the Product and
Value of Evolution?   483
Mutations Harmful, Neutral, and Helpful 483
What Does Nature Select? 486
Adding in Revealed Truth 489
Questions for Review 493
Questions for Thought 494
Suggested Reading List 495
Glossary 496

Chapter 14 An Infinity of Diversity   500

14.1 The Challenge of Classifying
Life's Diversity   500

14.2 Classification: Engaging the
Challenge   504

14.3 Characteristics Used in
Classification   508
Characteristic #1: Does It Do Photosynthesis? 509
Characteristic #2: Is It Multicellular? 510
Characteristic #3: Has It Got a Nucleus? 512
Characteristic #4: Has It Got Flagellae and Where? 512
Characteristic #5: What Are Its Mitochondria Like? 512
Characteristic #6: Can It Flow (Go) Places? 512
*Characteristic #7: What Are Some of the
Cell's Gene Sequences? 513*

14.4 Using Characteristics: Priorities
and Presuppositions   514

14.5 Using Characteristics to
Derive Groups   516
Group #1: The Bacteria 516
Group #2: The Archaea 517
Group #3: The Excavata 518
Group #4: The Rhizaria 519
Group #5: The Discicristates 520
Group #6: The Alveolata 521
Group #7: The Stramenopiles 523
Group #8: The Amoebozoa 524
Group #9: The Plants 525
*Group #10: The Opisthokonta, a Home for
Humans 527*

14.6 Classification:
     Persistent Problems   530

14.7 Classifying Man   532
Questions for Review 535
Questions For Thought 536
Glossary 536

Chapter 15 Ecology: Interactivity by Design   540

15.1 Thinking Like an Ecologist:
     Exploring a Lake   544

15.2 Hierarchical Organization in
     Ecology   546

15.3 Organismal Ecology   547

15.4 Population Ecology   548
Population Size and Density 548
Population Distribution Patterns 549
Age Structure and Sex Ratios 551
Population Growth 551

15.5 Community Ecology   556
Interspecific Competition 557
One Species Benefits and the Other Is Adversely
   Affected 561
Both Species Benefit 566

15.6 Ecosystems: Energy Flow through
     Sets of Interacting Organisms 569

15.7 A Final Word about Our
     Interaction with God's
     Household   575
Questions for Review 576
Questions for Thought 577
Suggested Reading 577
Glossary 578

Chapter 16 Life Is Finite   580

16.1 Definitions   582

16.2 Theories of Aging   584

16.3 Observations:
     Cellular Processes   585

16.4 Observations: Organ-Systemic
     Processes   590

16.5 Theory Evaluation   592

16.6 Why Do We Die? Programmed
     Aging from two Perspectives 594
Questions for Review 597
Questions for Thought 597
Glossary 598

Introduction

THE CONCEPT of this book—*Life by Design*—is so traditional that it is now novel! Encyclopedic texts crafted for the generic college biology course are everywhere available along with the online search engines that are powerfully superseding them. Yet all such resources are symptomatic of "the big problem" in college biology classes: too much content for students to learn. Compounding this problem is the inherent character of naturalistic philosophy, which finds few things in the living world more or less important than all of the rest. And everything is interesting! The inherent wisdom of each life-form fully engages us. The result is that even most of the smaller introductory texts still feebly attempt an encyclopedic coverage, skimming the surface with anecdotal illustrations that tend to fragment the discipline.

Life by Design possesses a unity of purpose absent from most of these encyclopedic survey texts. It seeks a unifying logia both within and above the biology it explores.* One result of this is a distillation of biology into 12 principles of life. A few in-depth examples of interest to the student become rich context in which each principle is manageably unpacked and rejoiced in. A predictable result of our approach is that many well-studied systems in biology are ignored. But the logic of life is woven deeply into the pages of this text. Especially for new instructors who wish to see biology from the perspective of unifying concepts, we offer these 12 principles.

Scientists steeped in the frigidity of the last century's philosophical mechanism often feel constrained to eliminate any emotion from their prose. We cannot do this. For us there is only rejoicing in works that show such glory. As a result, there is constant use of the terms such as *design* and *glory* throughout the text. Such vocabulary is scientifically unorthodox. But the authors are more than scientists. Observing the living world with

Sanford/Agliolo/Corbis

rationality calls forth these terms as a reasonable solution to the purposeful complexity the biologist is faced with. J.B.S. Haldane aptly caricatured the modern naturalist's dilemma, "Teleology is like a mistress to a biologist: he cannot live without her but he's unwilling to be seen with her in public." By contrast, the authors of *Life by Design* are happily wed to her and proud of her pervasiveness. They contend that random changes in nucleic acid polymers fed to a sequence of unpredictable changes in the environment fail to explain life's splendor.

The theist-evolutionist apostatizes from pristine evolutionary principles. At some elemental level, providential control is brought in to influence the course of mutational events. In this text we've chosen to respond rather to evolutionary materialism in its pure Darwinian form. In Darwinism, only selection controls design. All else is heresy.

In this introduction, allow us go beyond the word *Designer* to affirm that from the prescient character of the Hebrew Biblical text, there is adequate evidence to be able to name the Designer. This will be horrifying to many in the Intelligent Design (ID) movement since we merely reinforce here a theistic stereotype that materialists have saddled it with. We apologize to our ID friends. We have found a precision and virtuosity in the Biblical text that pleasingly matches that of the natural world. It is difficult for us to repress or ignore this wonderful correspondence.

The Designer is Yahweh, the God of Abraham, Isaac, and Jacob. Through His Son, Jesus Christ, these designs have been gloriously created and sustained. The redemptive work of Christ on His cross has produced within us a deep desire that our God should have His rightful place above and before the nature He designed and created. We further desire that through this work, Christ should be exalted in the reader's own heart. May this exaltation draw the reader toward an embrace of Christ's further redemptive work—a work that finally restores the reader to the biological life that was originally designed for him.

Comments are heartily solicited. While a work of this sort places less emphasis on recent, tentatively interpreted discoveries, there is the hope that future versions of the text will keep pace with consensus wherever it flourishes in the scientific community. It is the simple prayer of the authors that such consensus will someday include a strong conviction that living things, to quote Richard Dawkins, "are too improbable and too beautifully 'designed' to have come into existence by chance."

Many adult learners lament the superficiality of their high school biology education. In response, we've attempted to craft the prose here so that a reader with a very minimal background in science can at least appreciate the broad concepts being proposed.

Acknowledgements

WE WOULD like to thank our colleagues, spouses and students for their support in the production of this text. C. Detwiler thanks Dr. Ben Gutierrez for his vision for this text and the granting of time for hours of writing. Dr. Paul Sattler is thanked for help with photography. Drs. Doug Oliver, Robert C. Newman and Miss Amy Hetrick reviewed various chapters of the text. Beverly Detwiler assisted us with readability issues. Drs. Gary Isaacs, Gene Sattler, Randall Davy, Martin Offield and Marcus Ross all gave valuable assistance in helping us to understand various concepts dealt with in the text.

We would also like to thank project manager Kim Fry, Michael Stranz, Steve Esworthy, Carla Lomax and the staff of Cengage Publishing Company for their patient work on this project.

About the Authors

CHARLES DETWILER is a Pennsylvania German boy who grew up loving nature and spending many enjoyable hours in it long before studying it formally. His postgraduate work at Cornell University and Cambridge University focused on gene fine structure using the common vinegar fly, *Drosophila melanogaster,* as a model system. His Christian faith has strongly informed and enriched his study of the living world.

KIMBERLY MITCHELL is originally from Michigan but moved to Lynchburg in 1995 to attend Liberty University for her undergraduate education and has remained in central Virginia. Her research interests include nucleoside diphosphate kinase (NDPK; a protein involved in many cellular functions and linked to cancer) and primary cilia (cellular organelles involved in development and kidney disease). She holds an M.S. and Ph.D. from the University of Virginia. When she's not in the lab or classroom, Dr. Mitchell enjoys hiking, running, reading, gardening, sewing, and caring for her many pets. In addition, she teaches cake decorating and (during the summer and holidays) operates a specialty cake business.

NORMAN REICHENBACH teaches ecology, zoology, and environmental science to undergraduate students. His research interests range from toxicology to ecology to community development, and he has worked with a wide variety of organisms, ranging from insects to sea cucumbers to snakes. His current research projects, which typically engage teams of undergraduate students, have an ecological/conservation emphasis and include work on the Peaks of Otter salamander, red-spotted newt, eastern box turtle, timber rattlesnake, and Plains garter snake. He is a native of Ohio and received all his degrees, including a B.S. and M.S. in zoology and a Ph.D. in entomology, from Ohio State University. He and his wife, Susan, have been married 21 years and have two children, Faith and Keith.

All three authors are members of the Department of Biology at Liberty University in Lynchburg, Virginia.

Life Is Significant by Design

1.1 DESIGN THAT TALKS

Its Glory

What do you see when an oak tree towers above you as its branches resist the winds of an approaching storm, or when your dog stares penetratingly into your eyes while you're enjoying a roast beef sandwich? What do you hear in the majestic orchestral harmonies of Handel's chorus, "And the Glory of the Lord"? **Biology,** the study of life, is fascinating because it reveals to us legions of such wonders! Nature is replete with them. In the tropics, we're dumbfounded by ant colony-cities reaching to hundreds of cubic feet in size with finely tuned underground humidity and gas flow climate controls to optimize growth of their cultivated fungal food source. In the oceans, we gasp at the muscular coordination that launches 180 tons of blue whale out of the water as it breeches. Such sources of amazement abound in the living world.

Well then, what about journeying below the level of human sensation? Perhaps phenomena there will become highly unified and much simpler. Study utterly falsifies that speculation. The intricacy of a modern automobile with all of its computerized components pales by comparison with the interworkings of a tiny vertebrate liver cell (see Figure 1.1). Communication between swarming bacterial cells amazes us with both its responsiveness to the environment and its value to the survival of the population.

Survey Questions

1.1 Design That Talks
- Does nature show the observer complexity only, or is there evidence of design?
- What does the apparent design of nature "say" to the observer?

1.2 Design at Multiple Levels
- What challenges exist when attempting to design a system that functions at multiple levels of organization?
- What names are given to the levels of organization seen in living things?
- Does design at one level influence or account for design at other levels?

1.3 Unity within Diversity
- How diverse is life on this planet?
- How have we attempted to order or organize this diversity?
- How are life's unifying features related to its diversity?
- What are some examples of unifying features of all life-forms?

1.4 Teleology, Start to Finish
- What does the term *teleology* mean?
- Is teleology an appropriate concept to use when studying life?

biology—the study of life and of those objects that possess the quality of being alive.

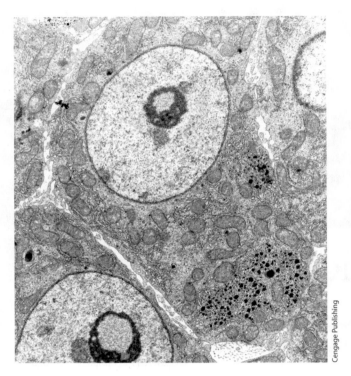

Figure 1.1 Portions of two adjacent liver cells taken from a vertebrate animal. Tissue was sliced through with a sectioning device, stained, and viewed under an electron microscope at 4000 times actual size. The large circular regions are cell nuclei.

Well then, perhaps on a large scale beyond the purview of human senses, living systems are chaotic in organization. Again, scientific study dismisses such speculation (see Figure 1.2). The community of living things in a forest may seem superficially random in distribution or activity. Yet within a myriad of interactions among many species of life, discrete rules govern all of the relationships we uncover. These rules show us an interrelatedness of life-forms that is sophisticated and coordinated in response to the challenges of the environment.

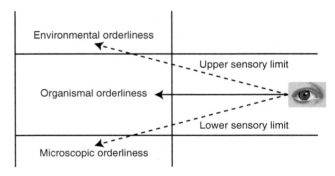

Figure 1.2 When we use instruments or techniques to extend the limits of our sensory systems, we find orderliness wherever we look.

What is the meaning of all of this organizational pageantry? Is there anything in our daily experience of life that would teach us that such glorious order and interaction are just "there"?

Its Speech

In civilization's greatest written work, the Holy Bible, we find these words, penned by a Jew named Paul of Tarsus: "(God's) invisible attributes are clearly seen, being understood by the things that are made . . ." These ancient words call us to see a glory—a wisdom—in the design of an ant colony, a whale's muscular system, or a human cranium. They declare that the ants, the whales, the mind are products of a powerful ordering Force external to themselves. This declaration is not audible. It is not detectable in any way by the scientist's senses or his instrumentation. Yet Paul argues that it is deeply rational. Experience and logic teach us to reject the notion that life's wonders can result from a sequence of seemingly random changes that occur in nature.

> *(God's) invisible attributes are clearly seen, being understood by the things that are made..."*
> —ROMANS 1:20

The structural design of the Brooklyn Bridge speaks of a power and intellect that go beyond the work of a single human being. In the oak tree under duress, the molecular structure of the wood whispers a similar message. It reveals an intellect that did not resort to random attempts at fortuitous combinations of atoms. So Mother Nature's intricacy speaks of a powerful Designer. And for reasons that lie to one side of rationality, some hear her voice and some do not.

Its Mandate

What does the "speech" of nature's design call us to? What demand does it impose on us? Does it call us to abandon our science—to view nature solely as a means to enhance our faith or our worship? Not at all! It simply reminds us that our finite senses and minds limit our methods of doing science. It calls us to look beyond these limitations and into

Figure 1.3 There are 70 species of water lilies around the world. Each part of this flower is elegantly designed for the role it performs in the reproduction of the plant. In fact, it's hard to rid ponds of this plant.

© 2007 John Foxx Images/Jupiterimages Corporation

the glories of a limitless Designer (see Figure 1.3). It urges us to explore artistic intricacies, to expect to see purpose and ingenuity underlying even the apparent randomness we at times observe.

Nature's design further calls us to form our view of what the Designer is like based on what He has made. Since this book is devoted primarily to the study of life, one might be offended by this call to learn more about the Designer as well! The study of life-forms is an arduous process. Why add to it further study of a supposed Designer? But would it

not be foolish to work hard studying living things and then not use such knowledge to better understand the Designer Himself? Consider that those with technological interests have applied their knowledge of life-forms to the betterment of man. They have found this a worthy concomitant goal. The power of antibiotics or genetically engineered plants, for example, attests to the worth of applying biological knowledge to the problems humans face. Might there also be value in applying biological knowledge to a deeper understanding of the Designer? The context of the quote from Paul of Tarsus strongly indicates that such a pursuit is worthy, even mandatory. His words reveal to us both a deep need to worship the Designer and the self-destructive result of refusing to do so.

So in this text, we will examine the details of nature as interpreted by the last 200 years or so of scientific investigation. But we will also be noting instances where we are confronted with the glory of magnificent design.

We will note some of the implications of design as it speaks to us of the purposes of the Designer. We will discover what we had suspected: That for reasons beyond the mere diversity and intricacy of living things, **Life Is Significant** in its revelation to us of the greatness of its Designer and the purposes He has for the creations of His Mind.

Life Is Significant—one of 12 principles of life on which this book is based.

IN OTHER WORDS

1. Biology, the study of living things, reveals countless fascinating designs to us.
2. These designs are detected in every size range from the microscopic to the global arena.
3. The greatest book in the history of civilization argues that life's designs point forcefully to the existence of a Designer.
4. The designs of life teach us about life itself, but they also teach us of the character of the Designer.

Microbiological Architecture

Picture a computer architect brooding over her model of a new design for a processor. It's a wonderful new chip with circuits made from parts of bacterial cells. It will be another breakthrough in the efficiency of information storage (see Figure 1.4).Now, imagine the great Designer fashioning man in a similar way. Instead of using silicon and bacterial parts, He uses dust. This simple comparison misses much of the transcendent power of the Designer of man. You see, the computer chip designer has no control over the structure of the silicon wafer itself or the bacterial cells because someone else designed those. She only wrestles with the arrangement of the cell's parts in a circuit pattern on the chip. She creates on only two levels of reality: the chip, or molecular level, and the level of the processor chip as a unit. To improve our analogy, we must imagine the computer architect designing structural features of the bacteria, features of the molecules within the cells, and patterns of silicon compounds within the chip. Further, she must simultaneously see new architectural possibilities for other related components of both the computer as a whole and the computer network it will be part of. By analogy, that is closer to what the Designer of the human body has done.

And so you, as a human being, are structured as an interwoven assembly of highly complex **systems.** Your muscular system helps you to procure nutrients. Your digestive system processes the nutrients. Your circulatory system distributes the nutrients throughout your body, and so on (see Figure 1.5). You are an interwoven collection of 11 different body systems, but each system is composed of integral parts called **organs.** Your heart is an organ that fulfills one of the

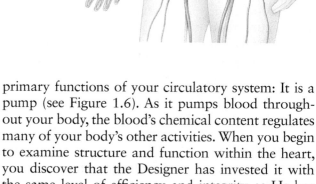

Figure 1.5 The circulatory system is a collection of organs like arteries, veins, and the heart that work together to get nutrients and oxygen to and waste products and CO_2 from all parts of the body. That is the role of this body system.

primary functions of your circulatory system: It is a pump (see Figure 1.6). As it pumps blood throughout your body, the blood's chemical content regulates many of your body's other activities. When you begin to examine structure and function within the heart, you discover that the Designer has invested it with the same level of efficiency and integrity as He has

Brand X Pictures

Figure 1.4 Computer chips "evolve" very quickly because human intelligence is used to create them. The one shown here is rather "primitive".

system—a combination of body organs that performs some significant body function.

organ—a combination of body tissues that performs some significant body function.

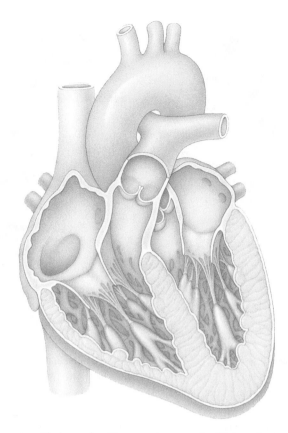

Figure 1.6 The human heart is an amazing pump; the thin boundary layer lining the inner chambers represents its endothelium, a tissue critical to maintaining blood pressure and healthy blood flow.

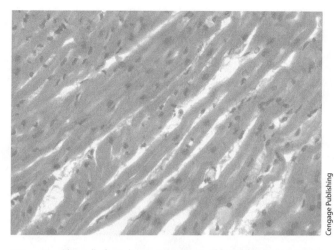

Figure 1.7 The wall of your heart contains powerful muscle **tissue**, shown here as strands of inter-connected muscle fibers (composed of cells.) They are stained pink for better visibility of cell parts. Nuclei of individual cells appear dark pink. Magnification here is about 400 times actual size.

the entire circulatory system of which it's a part. For example, heart muscle function is elegantly controlled from outside the heart using parts of the nervous system that enervate the heart. Hormones also affect the work of the heart, as does the chemistry of the blood. All of this control is finely tuned. So the Designer is an Artist-Engineer at multiple levels! Each separate design is so integrated within all of the others that we generalize this to say that **life is internally integrated.** The current version of evolutionary theory possesses no ordering force powerful enough to generate the levels of integration we are currently observing. (We have not observed them all.)

Your heart is composed of various **tissues.** A tissue is a large group of cells that serves a constituent role within an organ (See Figure 1.7). For example, muscle tissue contracts to propel blood forward. Another tissue lines and lubricates the inner heart surfaces to enhance blood flow. Still another tissue adds structural toughness to the exterior of the heart so the muscles have something to contract against.

All of these tissues are composed of individual **cells.** Cells are the smallest units of tissue structure that can

be said to be independently alive. For example, we can tease apart the cells of the tissue that lines your heart. In a supportive (cell culture) medium, we can keep individual cells alive. If we examine them closely using a microscope (see Figure 1.8) and various biochemical tests, we make another amazing discovery. An individual cell in the lining of our heart "solves" each of life's fundamental problems at its own structural level. And this requires a complexity far greater than we once thought possible or necessary. Once again, while the Designer was fashioning the glory of an organ that beats 2.5 billion times in a human lifetime, He was simultaneously crafting the architectural intricacies of the cells that comprise it.

Consider now that tiny, invisible, problem-solver cell that, with billions of others like it, helps line the interior of your heart's chambers. Let's imagine expanding that cell to the size of a basketball. Then within it, we would be able to see directly vast arrays of intricate structures called **organelles.** These intracellular parts cooperate in multiple, intricate, and interdependent ways, to keep the individual cell thriving

Life Is Internally Integrated—one of the 12 principles of life on which this book is based.

tissue—a combination of body cells that performs some role important to the correct functioning of an organ.

cell—the smallest unit part of a tissue that, of itself, possesses the quality of life.

organelle—a specialized part of a cell that performs some important function for it.

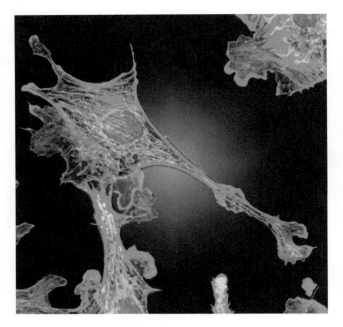

Figure 1.8 Individual endothelial cells grown in artificial culture and stained to reveal various cell parts: nucleus (blue), structural tubules (green), energy-generating organelles (orange).

University of Pennsylvania, School of Engineering and Applied Sciences, Bioengineering Imaging Core Facility

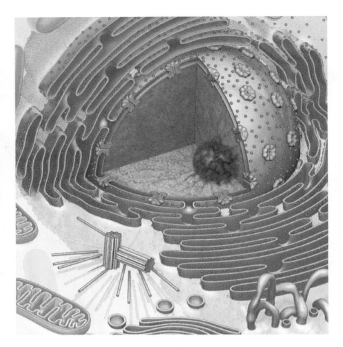

Figure 1.9 This "stylized" diagram from within a single animal cell depicts a variety of organelles within its structure. Each type of organelle helps to keep the cell alive.

and growing (see Figure 1.9). On this scale, organelles would range in size from a baseball down to a grain of sand. Some of them process information, others harness energy, still others are sites of synthesis. Others are sites of import and export. The cell is like a molecular city in three dimensions. Its inhabitants have no knowledge of each other, yet they interact seamlessly with each other in patterns of life maintenance and in

response to the cell's changing environment. And these patterns are truly elegant.

But each organelle is composed of a collection of **macromolecular structures** (see Figures 1.10)! These

macromolecular structure—a component part of a cell's organelle composed of two or more kinds of biomolecules.

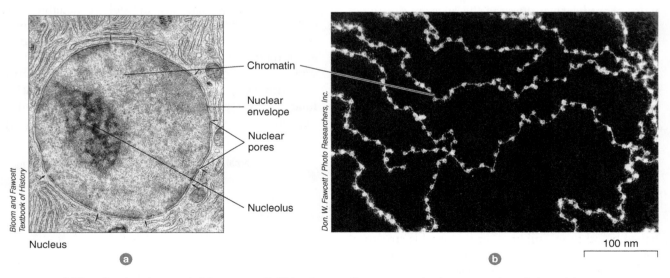

Figure 1.10 **(a)** The cell nucleus shown on the left is an organelle. Within this organelle, two macromolecular structures: the nucleolus and chromatin are indicated. **(b)** Chromatin seen at enormous magnification.

structures contribute specific processes and functions to the organelle they serve. The nucleus of a cell, for example is known to carry the hereditary instructions for building and operating that cell. When we peer inside the nucleus with an **electron microscope** to see the form the information takes, we find it arranged within long, macromolecular strands having a particulate, granular profile. We call these strands **chromatin**. As the cell approaches its time to divide, the chromatin is condensed into shorter, thicker, **chromosomes** that can be distributed neatly to daughter cells.

But each macromolecular structure is composed of a collection of **biomolecules** (see Figure 1.11)! These molecules have, in turn, been precisely designed with the shape and alterability requisite to the function they perform (see Chapter 4). One such biomolecule has a water-loving and a water-fearing side so that it participates in the formation of a membrane surface (an inside-outside boundary for organelles and whole cells). Another biomolecule is long and can be tightly coiled. It holds information in the sequence of smaller molecular subunits of its structure. The biomolecules of a million kinds of cells have been grouped into just a few broad structural classes that are represented in virtually all cells. These classes—carbohydrates, lipids, proteins, and nucleic acids—are the colors on the palette of the Artist painting the glory of the functional organelle.

But biomolecules are constructed from **atoms** (see Figure 1.12)! For atoms, there are just three simple definitions for their best known parts. And so the naïve student might guess that here, finally, the infinite creativity of the Designer distills down to a pleasing simplicity. Alas, nothing could be more wrong. Subatomic particles have still smaller constituent particle-forces! On and on the complexity goes into a reality hardly detectable by very costly machines. We could wander further down this size scale to explore little-known features of subatomic particles. But atoms are the organizational level of matter at which biologists typically stop. Most biological processes can be studied either at or above the level of the atoms that support them. Of the 92 naturally occurring kinds of atoms, the Designer has selected about 25 or so of them to fashion the vast variety of biomolecules we find in nature.

By now we can see that an apparently simple biological action, like the beating of the heart within your chest, results from a multiple-level integration of all of the component categories we've just summarized (see Figure 1.17). One fundamental concept in all of biology is that **Life Is Complex.**

electron microscope—a device that magnifies objects sufficiently such that internal structures of cells are easily seen.

chromatin—strands of informational DNA and structural protein within the nucleus of the cell; the genetic material.

chromosomes—discrete lengths of chromatin, usually highly condensed into visible, stainable structures that are easily apportioned to daughter cells during cell division.

biomolecule—a collection of atoms bonded together into a structure that serves some biological function within a living cell or organism.

atom—the smallest particle of an element having all the properties of that element; capable of combining with such particles of other elements.

Life Is Complex—one of 12 principles of life on which this book is based.

IN OTHER WORDS

1. Humans design their technology at one or a few ascending levels of reality. The Designer of life took at least 12 levels of reality into account as living things were fashioned.
2. Your body is organized into at least 11 systems that work together to support your life.
3. Each system of your body is composed of separate organs that support its function.
4. Each organ in your body is composed of separate tissues that support its function.
5. Each tissue in any organ of your body is composed of separate cells that cooperate to serve that tissue's role.
6. Each cell in your body is composed of a variety of organelles that support its life functions.
7. Each organelle we've studied is fashioned from macromolecular structures that carry out the organelle's role in the cell.
8. Each macromolecular structure is assembled from biomolecules that the cell has made or acquired from other cells.
9. Each kind of biomolecule is a collection of specific atoms bonded together in a way that enables the biomolecule to serve its unique role in the life of the cell.
10. Life Is Complex.

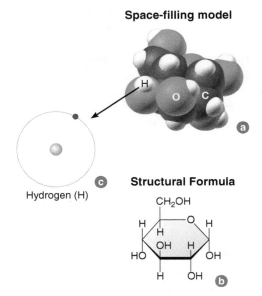

Figure 1.11 **(a)** If we take the outer lining (membrane) of the cell nucleus in the previous figure and greatly magnify its size, we see that it's composed of millions of component biomolecules, each of which serves some role in helping the membrane do its job. **(b)** this biomolecule (DNA) is designed to store information in the sequence of its internal base pairs (yellow).

Space-filling model

c

Hydrogen (H)

Structural Formula

CH$_2$OH

Figure 1.12 Two models of a glucose molecule and one of a hydrogen atom. Glucose is the most common sugar in your bloodstream. **(a)** each sphere represents a single atom. Black: carbon atom Red: oxygen atom White: hydrogen atom. **(b)** each atom is represented by the first letter of its element's name. The lines are bonds between atoms. **(c)** a simplistic model of a hydrogen atom, showing its two sub-atomic "particles". Chapters 3 and 4 have more detailed information on atoms and molecules.

Macrobiological Systems

Perhaps your mind is now reeling, wondering how many atoms it must take to make a human being. Hang on. We must now stare off in the opposite direction! Let's make you the "atom" in our description and build up from there! You are one of over 6 billion humans alive on this planet at this moment. All of these humans are distributed into somewhat discrete groups of individuals. They live in localized areas geographically, where they are more likely to interbreed with each other. These interbreeding, and hence biologically meaningful groups, are called **populations** (see Figure 1.13). The flow of genetic information (by mating), the day to day behavioral interactions between

population—all the members of a kind of organism (or species) that are proximate enough to each other to potentially interbreed.

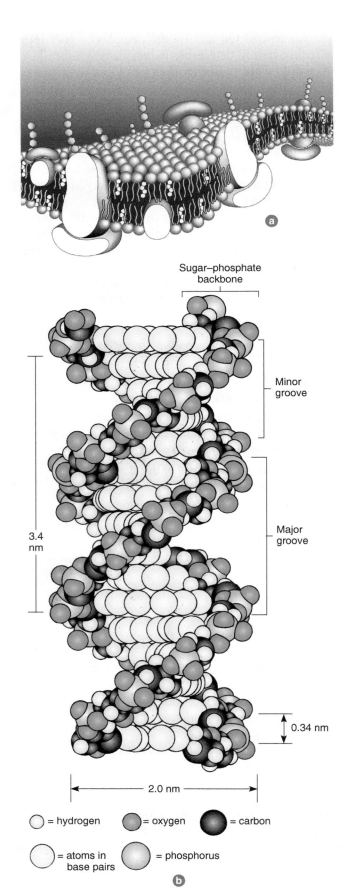

Sugar–phosphate backbone

Minor groove

Major groove

3.4 nm

0.34 nm

2.0 nm

◯ = hydrogen   ◯ = oxygen   ● = carbon

◯ = atoms in base pairs   ◯ = phosphorus

b

Figure 1.13 These male and female blue-lined snappers are potentially interbreeding—so they constitute a population of organisms.

Figure 1.15 A well-defined ecosystem. This campus courtyard has sharp structural boundaries. All the plant, animal, and microbial species, plus soil, water, light, temperature and other non-living features constitute this courtyard **ecosystem**.

individuals and the transmission of disease pathogens are all significant biological processes that occur at the populational level.

But no population exists in isolation. Consider Manhattan Island in New York City. Surely only one kind of population exists there, correct? But wait. Some residents have dogs as pets. Others have snakes. A few have gerbils or albino rats. And all of us have tiny mites living in our eyebrows and over 500 different kinds of bacteria in our bowels, with a somewhat separate variety in our mouths and upper respiratory tracts. People raise tomatoes on their roofs and clean pigeon droppings off of sidewalks. Some of those droppings contain viruses that might infect a human being. No matter where you go on Earth, separate, diverse populations of organisms live in proximity to each other and interact biologically with each other. We call these assemblages **communities** (see Figure 1.14). There are pond communities, forest

communities, desert communities, and inside your mouth, an oral community whose member species require a microscope for study.

Communities interact with the physical world around them. A pond community is radically different from a prairie community. One reason for this is the huge difference in the amount of water present. Features such as moisture content, mineral content, or solar radiation levels vary from place to place. So in any given area, we combine the living community and these non-biological features and call their summation an **ecosystem** (see Figure 1.15). A pond community would be all of the organisms that live in a pond. A pond ecosystem includes all of those organisms plus the water, the mineral content of the mud in and around it, and the incident solar radiation it receives.

Ecosystems cover this planet. Sometimes we need to refer to all of them at once. Politicians and global ecologists do this a lot. So we have developed the term **biosphere** to refer to the total collection of ecosystems on the planet (see Figure 1.16). It is presumed that there are no life-forms in the

Figure 1.14 A freshwater pond. The grasses, rushes, trees, and all the animal life (insects, fish, birds, mammals) that live and interact with each other here are termed a community.

community—the sum total of all the populations of living organisms in a given area and the interactions that occur among them.

ecosystem—all the living organisms, and nonliving factors in a given area and the interactions among them.

biosphere—the totality of all ecosystems on and within planet earth.

Figure 1.16 All of the deserts, rainforests, grassland, temperate forests, tundra and other ecosystems of the earth's surface are together called the biosphere.

magma of a volcano. Should the interior of a volcano be considered part of the biosphere?

As you work with various parts of this text, be aware of two things. First, our study of biology will, in general, take us up through this progression of levels from atoms to the higher levels of organization mentioned (see Figure 1.17). So secondly, try to be overtly aware of the level of organization at which we are studying. Most of us strongly desire a framework within which to build our biological awareness. Classifying what we learn according to the organizational level at which we are studying is a highly useful way of advancing our understanding!

IN OTHER WORDS

1. All the individuals of a species like our own, are arranged in large, potentially interbreeding groups called populations.
2. All the populations of species in a given area—populations that have the potential to interact with each other—are together called a *community*.
3. An ecosystem is a community of life-forms and its interactions with all the nonliving features of its surroundings
4. The sum of all ecosystems that comprise the "thin skin" of life on the surface of planet Earth are referred to as the *biosphere*.

organ

composed of a variety of tissues whose collective function supports the major role of the organ.

organ system

composed of organs working together to perform a major function within an individual.

tissue

composed of many identical cells working together at a common function.

individual

somehow this level appears to be a "frame of reference" about which the Creator is ultimately concerned.

cell

composed of assorted organelles appropriate to the type of cell.

population

composed of a typically large number of individuals that are potentially inter-breeding.

organelle

composed of a large variety of macro-molecular structures.

community

a collection of populations whose members interact by "eating and being eaten."

macro-molecular structure

composed of various kinds of biomolecules.

ecosystem

the community in a given area plus the non-living aspects of the environment.

molecule

composed of differing atoms of naturally occurring elements.

biosphere

all of the ecosystems on planet earth taken together.

Figure 1.17 If God is the Creator, and if His creation is complex, then "life" will be subject to description at the many interlocking, inter-nested levels of organization pictured above. The arrows point toward increasing levels of complexity. Note that the cellular level is the lowest level that can be independently "alive". Scholars who study life tend to select one or two of these 12 levels at which to study it.

atom

composed of sub-atomic particles: protons, neutrons, electrons.

Diversity of Styles

When early naturalists began to examine living things, one of the first observations they must have made was the profuse diversity of life-forms around them. One of the most basic principles in the study of living things is their extreme diversity. **Life Is Diverse.** There are millions of different kinds or **species** of living things on this planet, perhaps 100 million. One major challenge, then, has been to classify the various kinds of organisms for further study.

Aristotle, the Greek philosopher (384–322 BC) (see Figure 1.18), has been widely recognized as the "father of biology." His writings elucidated the structural and behavioral distinctions between plants and animals. Yet far earlier (by about 1300 BC), the Hebrew prophet Moses wrote an account of the origin of life that clearly placed the origin of plant and animal forms on separate days of creation. The same document granted the plant forms to the animal forms as

Life Is Diverse—one of 12 principles of life on which this book is based.

species—a group of organisms capable of interbreeding and producing fertile offspring.

Figure 1.18   Aristotle (left) (384-322 BC), (here imagined in Rennaissance garb!), an ancient Greek philosopher, and secular father of the science of biology. Moses (right) (1391-1271 BC) the Hebrew law-giver whose characterization of life forms derived from Yahweh, life's Designer.

Figure 1.19   Swedish naturalist Carl von Linne who Latinized his own name to Carolus Linnaeus (1707 – 1778).

plant species based on significant shared features they all possessed. He termed these larger groups *genera* (**genus**, singular).

Thus, in his system, each kind of organism was assigned a twofold, genus and species name. That is how the tomato came to be called *Solanum lycopersicum* and the potato came to be called *Solanum tuberosum* (see Figure 1.20). They share characteristics common to their genus but are distinct enough to be considered separate species. Once a species is formally named in a given context, repeated references to it may be made using only the first letter of the genus name, as for example, *S. lycopersicum* for the tomato.

Similar genera soon came to be grouped into larger **classes** (see Figure 1.21) and classes into still higher groups. These higher levels of grouping are much more subjective. It is becoming clear that one would need the wisdom and knowledge of the Designer Himself, in order to objectively render a consistent, broad-based classification scheme for all organisms.

food. So this basic distinction, found first in the Bible, and then in the writings of Aristotle, has until recent times been a mainstay in the classification of living forms relative to one another.

Working from the opposite extreme, the Swedish naturalist Carl von Linne (Linnaeus; 1707–1778; see Figure 1.19), began grouping together similar

genus—a grouping employed by taxonomists that includes closely related species.

class—a grouping employed by taxonomists that includes closely related genera.

common name/*scientific name*

tomato/*Solanum lycopersicum*   potato/*Solanum tuberosum*

Figure 1.20   The common names suggest two species that are quite different from each other. The scientific name reminds us that both plants found their way into the same Genus (originally named by Linnaeus). DNA studies are showing this Linnaean grouping of (now) over 1500 species to be artificial—not very biological.

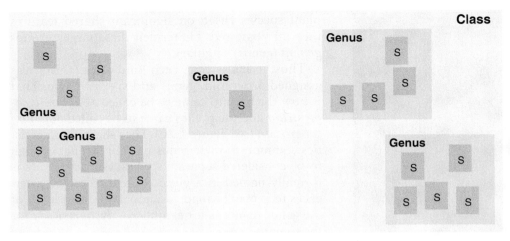

Figure 1.21 Linnaeus used structural (morphological) features of plants to define species ("S" in the diagram) and assign related ones into Genera. Later systematists attempted to group related Genera into Classes. A more dynamic definition of a species includes all individuals capable of inter-breeding to form fertile offspring. What might cause a naturalist to describe a Genus having only one species in it?

It is not surprising, therefore, that students of biological classification vary considerably in how they prefer to classify organisms at higher levels. Over the centuries, the traditional Aristotelian groupings of plants and animals slowly expanded into three and then five major groups.

One currently popular scheme, born in the late 1900s, places all organisms into three large domains. Two of these domains, the **Bacteria** and the **Archaea** have small, simpler cells lacking a well-defined nucleus. **Animals, plants, fungi,** and **protists** all have well-defined nuclei in their cells so they represent separate kingdoms within a third large domain of organisms called the **Eukarya.** These major groups of life-forms are represented in Figure 1.22

In this scheme, then, the protists are defined as one-celled and colonial forms of life, yet like animals and plants, with cells large enough to contain organelles like a **nucleus.** Yet when we begin to compare all of the cells having these protistan features, we discover a diverse and deeply dissimilar grab bag of otherwise unrelated species. Are structural (microscopic) comparisons alone in revealing this dissimilarity among protists? The answer is, "No."

Comparisons of important molecular components of individual protist species are also leading to a re-grouping of not only protistan forms, but of the other kingdoms as well. These newer groupings show protists to be too diverse to be a singular group. The problem is that the number of basic, important features of individual cells is great enough that workers disagree as to which of them ought to be most important for classifying. Evolutionary assumptions are generally used to decide which characteristics are most primitive and therefore most important. There is some consensus on what those features are. These comparisons along with microscopic fossil finds, which are very difficult to interpret, are then subjected to conjectural evolutionary reasoning. Long, sometimes heated, arguments are the result. Classification of living things will remain a challenging and conjectural area of research as long as scientists have finite minds.

Bacteria—a domain of structurally small and simpler, walled cells, widely distributed in nature; distinguished from Archaeans by their molecular structure.

Archaea—a domain of structurally small and simpler, walled cells, widely distributed in extreme environments in nature.

animal—a macroorganism distinguished from plants by its loco-motion and nonphotosynthetic metabolism.

plant—a macroorganism distinguished from animals by its lack of locomotion and its photosynthetic metabolism.

fungus—a nonmotile, nonphotosynthetic organism having large cells that are structurally complex (yeasts, molds, mushrooms).

protist—microscopic but structurally complex cells often possessing a loose, colonial form of association.

Eukarya—a domain of organisms whose cells are larger and contain membrane-enclosed organelles; includes animals, plants, fungi and protists.

nucleus—the large, membrane-enclosed, usually central portion of a higher cell that contains its hereditary instructions.

Unity in Essence

Two hundred years of biological study has led us to a very powerful generalization. Hidden beneath all of this amazing diversity is a highly pleasing unity of life at the subcellular and molecular levels!

Three Domains:

| Bacteria | Archaea |

Six Kingdoms:

Bacteria — Archaea

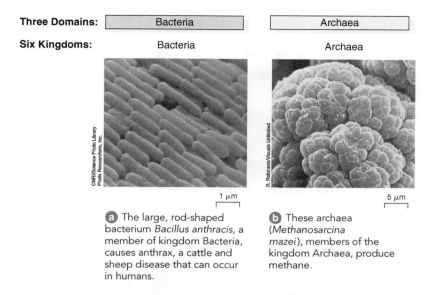

1 μm

a The large, rod-shaped bacterium *Bacillus anthracis*, a member of kingdom Bacteria, causes anthrax, a cattle and sheep disease that can occur in humans.

5 μm

b These archaea (*Methanosarcina mazei*), members of the kingdom Archaea, produce methane.

| Eukarya |

Protista — Plantae — Animalia — Fungi

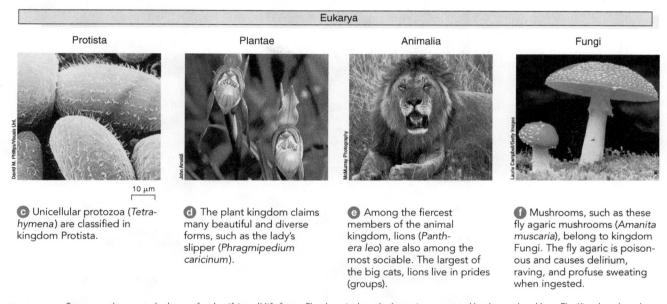

10 μm

c Unicellular protozoa (*Tetrahymena*) are classified in kingdom Protista.

d The plant kingdom claims many beautiful and diverse forms, such as the lady's slipper (*Phragmipedium caricinum*).

e Among the fiercest members of the animal kingdom, lions (*Panthera leo*) are also among the most sociable. The largest of the big cats, lions live in prides (groups).

f Mushrooms, such as these fly agaric mushrooms (*Amanita muscaria*), belong to kingdom Fungi. The fly agaric is poisonous and causes delirium, raving, and profuse sweating when ingested.

Figure 1.22 Two currently accepted schemes for classifying all life forms. The domain-based scheme is represented by three colored bars. The Kingdom-based scheme is represented by the names indicated above each photo.

Those who see design in nature assume that this unity of pattern traces back to efficient, thematic thinking in the mind of a single Designer. The evolutionist sees this same unity as evidence for a singular, primitive life-form from which we have all derived by Darwinian evolution (see Chapter 13).

Early perceptions of this unity of design in life-forms predate modern science. Dogs grow and oak trees grow. In both cases this growth is accompanied by significant increases in the complexity of the organism. What drives this growth?

In all life-forms, growth and maintenance of life require energy. **Life Is Energy-Driven.** Scientists began to describe the molecules that growth is driven by. They discovered that in plants, animals, and bacteria the variety of energy-carrying molecules (especially the carbohydrates) was small.

Life is Energy-Driven—one of twelve principles of life on which this book is based.

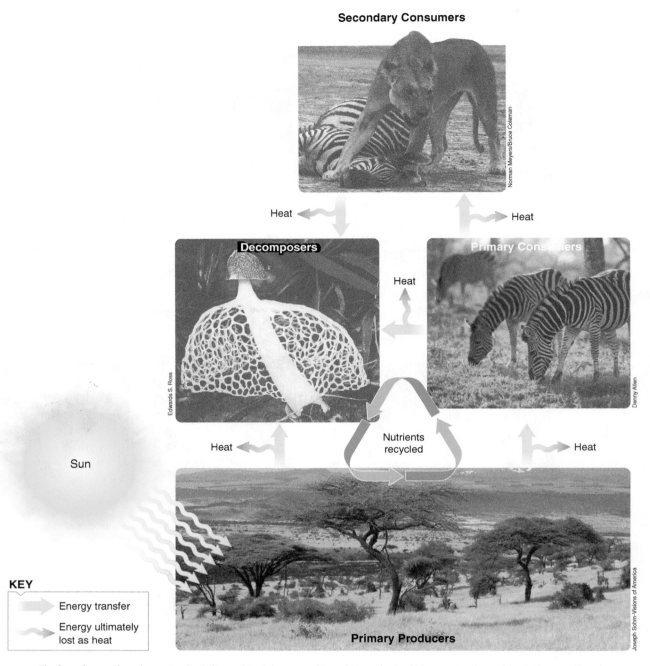

Secondary Consumers

Heat

Heat

Decomposers

Heat

Primary Consumers

Heat

Nutrients
recycled

Heat

Heat

Sun

KEY

Energy transfer

Energy ultimately
lost as heat

Primary Producers

Figure 1.23 The flow of energy from the sun to a lion's dinner plate. Solar energy drives photosynthesis which generates the nutrients in the grass. The zebra ingests those nutrients and then becomes nutrients for the lion. Where do the nutrients go after the lion utilizes them?

For example, glucose, a simple sugar (see Figure 1.12), is found in a wide variety of life-forms. And the flow of energy from the sun to the plants, bacteria, and to the animals (see Figure 1.23) is efficiently handled by a unified set of energy-transforming and energy-transferring molecules like chlorophyll, glucose, and adenosine triphosphate (ATP), whose structure we'll note a bit later).

The pathways of chemical reactions that move energy along from molecule to molecule within the cell are termed **metabolism.** Not only do metabolic reactions move energy around within

metabolism—the sum total of all of the chemical reactions and their inter-relationships within a living organism.

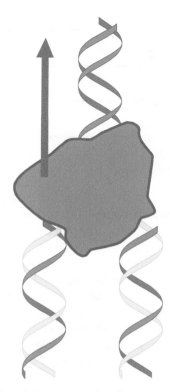

Figure 1.24 The blue shape, shown astride this duplicating strand of DNA, represents a protein molecule. This protein is the enzyme DNA polymerase that copies existing strands of DNA in order to make new ones. See chapter 8 for further details. Actual replication of DNA is far more complex than represented here!

the cell, they also result in the production of all the different kinds of carbohydrates, lipids, proteins, and nucleic acids that a cell needs to sustain life. With time, scientists have discovered that many aspects of metabolism are similar or identical across large groups of living organisms.

We also assumed early on that growth is directed by information. Since both growth and maintenance of life require information, we say that **Life Is Information Expressed.** We now believe there is enough information in the nucleus of one cell of your body to remake an entire "you." Scientists in the mid-1900s discovered that the information for growth resided in a class of biomolecules called *nucleic acids.* The specific nucleic acid molecule holding our biological (genetic) information is termed **DNA** (deoxyribonucleic acid). With time, except in a subgroup of viruses, DNA has been shown to be the archival informational molecule in virtually all life-forms! This warns us that information expression is likely to be a unified process in all of these organisms! One common way in which DNA's information is expressed is in the formation of **proteins.** Everywhere in the world of the cell, proteins are important both structurally and in many other ways. **Enzymes** are proteins. Within their structures they have catalytic sites that facilitate specific chemical reactions. Hence, when you study the function of a common enzyme like DNA polymerase (the enzyme that builds DNA) (see Figure 1.24) you are studying a molecule that does this in the majority of organisms on planet Earth—a pleasing and unifying thought.

Finally, growth results in size increase to a point where the cell or multicellular organism can reproduce itself. Again, information is required for this. We say that **Life Is Informational Continuity.** A gloriously designed process exists to precisely replicate and distribute the DNA information of the parent organism into the daughter organism(s). In this way, species identity is retained into subsequent generations.

Toward a Description of Life

Can we define the term *life?* We have just seen a vast diversity of living things unified by some core structural and functional elements of formidable complexity. The result—as you might guess—is that two-sentence, dictionary definitions of terms like *life* or *living organism* are beyond our ability to compose. Lacking such a definition, the best we can hope to do is to so carefully *describe* living things that no nonliving entity remains that fits our description. So far, we have described life as significant, complex, internally integrated, diverse, energy-driven, information expressed, and informational continuity. But there are two more unifying features of life that arise gloriously from all of this diversity. They

Life is Information Expressed—one of twelve principles of life on which this book is based.

DNA—an abbreviation for deoxyribonucleic acid. This nucleic acid is the archival repository of information for building the majority of all life-forms.

protein—a relatively large biomolecule composed of a sequence of amino acids; they performs some life functions usually at the chemical or cellular level of organization.

enzyme—a type of protein molecule that serves as an organic catalyst in solution. It reproducibly converts one specific sort of molecule into another: a specific substrate into its product.

Life Is Informational Continuity—one of 12 principles of life on which this book is based.

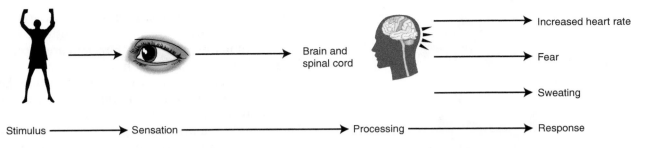

Stimulus ⟶ Sensation ⟶ Processing ⟶ Response

Figure 1.25   The responsive quality of life in higher organisms

help us to describe life more exclusively, and they bring still more tribute to its Designer.

Life Is Responsive. A universal feature of living things is their ability to moderate or correct their own internal activities in response to changes within themselves or within their surroundings. If you were to look up from this page and suddenly see the face and hear the voice of a person you knew to be dead, within seconds your heart rate would quickly increase (see Figure 1.25). Your mind would inform you of a severe incongruity. This would cause the amygdala region of your brain to generate an intense fear response that includes the ability to fight or flee from the circumstance. This would involve an increased heart rate, sweating, a fearful facial expression, and other potentially useful responses. Among millions of species on this planet, every one of them has a variety of ways in which its members respond to cold, to decreased oxygen, to heat, to starvation, to ultraviolet light. The list goes on and on. Living things differ from most nonliving things in their diversified abilities to respond to change. Well then, why don't we simply define life as the ability to respond to changes in the surrounding environment? Can you think of anything nonliving that can respond to changes in its environment? If not, try flushing your toilet.

Another feature of life that amazes us is the widespread interactivity in nature among organisms of different species. When we say that **Life Is Interactive,** we mean that cows eat grass, humans drink their milk, and bacteria in your gut break down the milk sugar you may fail to degrade. We mean that photosynthetic bacteria live inside the cytoplasm of larger protozoan cells. We mean that *Phytophthora infestans* (a fungus that caused the Irish potato blight) was responsible for sending the Kennedy family to America and ultimately giving us John F. Kennedy as the 35th president of the United States of America.

Interactivity between life-forms is something science will never comprehensively understand because the variety and extent of interspecific interaction is almost infinite. The best we can do is to explore specific examples of how one type of organism relates to and influences other types of organisms either directly or by means of changes it produces in the nonliving environment (see Figure 1.26). Such studies are undertaken in the discipline of **ecology**, a subdiscipline of biology where our increased knowledge is revolutionizing agriculture, urban planning, and numerous other facets of our civilization.

Figure 1.26   An ecologist studying the effects of species *Homo sapiens* (us) on fish in an Adirondack lake.

Life Is Responsive—one of 12 principles of life on which this book is based.

Life Is Interactive—one of 12 principles of life on which this book is based.

ecology—the science of the relationships among populations of organisms and their environments.

1. There may be as many as 100 million kinds (species) of life-forms on this planet presently. They are all in need of being organized into a system for study.
2. Moses and Aristotle, in ancient times, ordered life-forms into two large groups, plants and animals.
3. In the 1700s, Linnaeus began describing individual species of life-forms and collecting them into groups of related species called *genera* (*genus*, singular)
4. Large groupings of organisms are far more subjective. In one scheme, plants, animals, fungi, and protists are grouped into one of three domains called *Eukarya*.
5. Two other domains, the Bacteria and Archaea, contain simpler life-forms.
6. One of these groups, the protists, is particularly artificial in nature.
7. Underlying this vast diversity of life-forms is a unity found in the molecules that are most basic to life processes.
8. The fuel sugar glucose and the energy storage compound ATP are two metabolically important molecules broadly distributed across nature's life-forms.
9. The vast majority of life-forms appear to store their information in DNA molecules.
10. Enzyme molecules composed of protein catalyze metabolic reactions in the cells of virtually all life-forms.
11. All life-forms are able to alter their own metabolism and physical activities in response to changes in their environments that threaten their stability.
12. The discipline of ecology is a study of the vast array of interactions that occur between the different forms of life and nonliving aspects of their environments on Earth.
13. Life Is Highly Interactive.

1.4 TELEOLOGY, START TO FINISH

When a bush sends longer branches away from a wall, and shorter branches toward the wall, we assume that the bush is favoring growth in the direction of its light source. When a mouse flees to a dark corner of a room, when a bacterial cell swims toward a higher concentration of sugar molecules or away from some toxic substance, we again assume that we know reasons for these behaviors. There are endless examples in nature of what appears to be purposeful activity. Since the Greek word for *end* or *purpose* is *telos*, we refer to nature's apparent purposiveness as **teleology**.

For a biologist who is also a Design theorist, teleology is an entirely predictable concept. The various life-forms all have a Creator who had a purpose for creating them in mind. The bush may not want to grow toward light, but the purpose of moving toward light is inherent in its design. Mice were given feet because it was desired that they should be able to run.

Many philosophers, called naturalists, assert that a God cannot be known to exist and that nature alone is real. They assert that the phenomenon of running exists only because a mouse has feet to do so (see Table 1.1). The mouse happens to have feet because mice without them do not survive in nature as well as mice with them. Therefore the mouse was not given feet so that it could run; rather, it runs because it happens to have feet. Most scientists would probably agree with this naturalistic view of life. The method they use to obtain knowledge from the natural world is amazingly powerful and predictive!

Table 1.1 A theist assumes that purpose lies behind (and outside of) the elegant act of running. A naturalist observes only that without feet, the mouse might not survive. Having feet, it runs and thus, perhaps survives.

Presupposition	Observation	Interpretation
Theism	Mouse runs using feet	Running requires feet
Naturalism	Mouse runs using feet	Feet enable running

They have come to trust it deeply, in part because of these virtues. Unhappily, this method is entirely incapable of establishing that anything possesses a purpose external to itself. Yet some naturalists are so enamored of this approach to truth that they go further. They assume that any approach to knowledge lying outside the scope of science's method is *also outside the bounds of rationality*. They would say, "Since we cannot establish ultimate purpose using our method, it makes no sense to speak of purpose. So we will not."

Can we be certain that our scientific method is the only rational approach to nature? Science is limited to the realm of what we can sense with our five senses either directly or indirectly through instruments. Is it legitimate to limit logic to the realm of things sensed? Among early naturalists like Aristotle, deductions flowed as much from reason as from observation. They did make some serious errors, but they came to some important and valid conclusions as well, like the fundamental difference between plants and animals. Design theorists argue that the order and complexity evident in nature can reasonably support the existence of a Designer Who accords purpose to what He designs. True, we cannot jam this Designer into a test tube to measure Him. But it is also myopic to decide that our senses are the sole path to truth. A clean room belonging to a consistently sloppy child is evidence that a parent probably exists. A less rational explanation is that a window in the room was left open and the room's contents were blown to their correct positions. Our eyes may not show us the parent, but our minds can reason that the child is being helped.

This sort of reasoning, then, leads us to another major principle of life: **Life Is Ultimate Art**. This principle is a result of observation, limited experimentation, and rational thinking. We simply cannot allow the limitations of our experiments to

teleology—the philosophical study of design and purpose.

Life Is Ultimate Art—one of 12 principles of life on which this book is based.

leave us in ignorance regarding the origin of something as elegant as life. Honest, careful rationality leads us to accept life's dependence on a sufficient cause. This principle, in turn, will guide our later examination of the origin of living things.

Finally, if the main purpose of living things is to live, we are faced with the odd reality that all but the simplest of them die. (Single-celled life-forms generally do not die, they simply divide to form daughter cells.) The processes supporting life are so elegant that naturalists have had a terrible time of it, trying to explain why life-forms die (see Table 1.2, Chapter 16). Yet the occurrence of death is so pervasive and the result so frustrating that we encapsulate this oddity in our last principle of life, **Life Is Finite**. Scientific methodology provides us a detailed physical description of several aspects of death and it is also beginning to help us to understand how we deteriorate physically to this terminus. Of course, civilization's greatest written work, the Bible, purports to tell us *why* Life Is Finite—why death occurs. As we complete our treatment of life, we will try to bring together the how and why of death into a satisfying picture of this troubling process, if there can be such a thing (see Chapter 16).

If you have read the introduction to another biology text, you will sense that the picture of biology presented here is a richer, more satisfying one. It is certainly more purposive. Perhaps as a nonscientist, you value this venture that lies both outside and within the scientific method. It assembles a more robust picture of life. Rational extrapolation from life's complexity to its purpose will allow us to face scientific issues like environmental pollution and resource conservation with more than mere human selfishness as guide. However, our venture beyond the scientific method is not meant to belittle the tremendous value of that approach to truth. In the next chapter we will return explicitly to the scientific method in order to observe how the bulk of our scientific understanding has been derived.

Table 1.2 Scientific methodology searches for causes within the organism itself and ends up with wonderful accidents. A bit of additional humble rationality rescues our sanity and our society.

birth	→	life	→	death:
design	→	triumph	→	tragedy
matter	→	accident	→	accident #2

Life Is Finite—one of 12 principles of life on which this book is based.

IN OTHER WORDS

1. Most activities that we observe in living things appear to have a purpose behind them, usually relating to the ultimate welfare of some organism.
2. Philosophers of science argue with each other about the ultimate cause of these apparently purposive activities.
3. The methods scientists use are incapable of establishing the reality of purpose behind the activities of living things.
4. Some progress in understanding nature has resulted simply from rational reasoning in regard to the living things observed.
5. It is dangerous to assume that the scientific method is the only route to truth available.
6. Observation and deductive reasoning can lead one to the conclusion that living things are derived from and dependent upon a Designer.
7. Most living things eventually deteriorate and die. Life Is Finite. Scientific study and revelation together help us to understand how and why this is so.
8. The limitations of the scientific method should not be taken as a reason for belittling or ignoring the valuable results it has achieved.

TO SUMMARIZE

We can summarize the content of our introduction by simply listing the 12 Principles of Life that form the framework upon which succeeding chapters are arranged:

1. Life Is Significant. It's worth studying (Chapter 1).
2. Life Can Be Understood. When we study it, progress is made (Chapter 2).
3. Life Is Complex. There are too many intricacies to begin to grasp (Chapters 3, 4, 5, 9).
4. Life Is Energy-Driven. Eating facilitates playing; starving is deadly (Chapter 6).
5. Life Is Information Expressed. Here's where design is most clearly seen (Chapter 7).
6. Life Is Informational Continuity. Your parents produced you and informed your trait structure (Chapters 8, 12).
7. Life Is Internally Integrated. Parts assist all other parts in enabling organismal activities (Chapter 10).
8. Life Is Responsive. When the ball's pitched, you hit it, sometimes (Chapter 11).
9. Life Is Ultimate Art. Your properties aren't predictable from molecular properties (Chapter 13).
10. Life Is Diverse. We are ignorant of how many millions of species there are on this planet (Chapter 14).
11. Life Is Interactive. You eat fish and sharks eat you (Chapter 15).
12. Life Is Finite. The healthiest old woman eventually dies (Chapter 16).

QUESTIONS FOR REVIEW

1. Explore your own memory. List three wonders of nature that have piqued your curiosity in the past. What is it that you would like to understand about each of them?
2. In this chapter, the Bible has been singled out from among other ancient literary works as a source for comments on the complexity and order of the living world. Is it fair to ignore other such sources? Have you encountered any evidence that the Bible is worthy of such exclusive attention?
3. Make up a nonsensical sentence where each succeeding word in the sentence begins with the letters A-B-M-O-C-T-O-S-I-P-C-E-B (i.e., *A Big Monster On Crutches*, etc.). What will you be able to remember in sequence when you're finished?
4. Watch out for words that biologists borrow from society in general and then use differently! What is the difference between the way society uses the word *community* and the way biologists use it?
5. Life Is Information Expressed. What sort of biomolecule contains this information within its structure? What sort of biomolecule represents the most common form of expression of that information?
6. Life Is Responsive. List three examples you are aware of in which your own body responds to changing environmental conditions.
7. Explain how farmers will benefit from the studies done by ecologists.
8. "A mouse has feet so that it can run." Is that statement more agreeable to a theist or to a naturalist? Why?

QUESTIONS FOR THOUGHT

1. Consider the alternative to the principle Life Is Significant. Life Is Not Significant; life simply exists. Which alternative seems more rational to you? Why?
2. Suppose you were able to design a human skin cell that was able to use sunlight to do photosynthesis. What sort of problems might you encounter trying to incorporate that cell into a normal, healthy human being?
3. Consider the following organization of all living things: domain Bacteria, domain Archaea, and domain Eukarya (containing the kingdoms of the animals, plants, fungi, and protists). What strikes you as odd about this sort of organization? Save your thoughts about this for Chapter 14, which delves into the diversity of life.
4. Explain how a dentist is an ecologist.
5. The scientific method has shown itself to be highly powerful in providing explanations for how nature works. What weakness is hidden within that power?
6. Life Is Finite. Who has an easier time explaining this problem, a theist or a naturalist? Explain your position.

GLOSSARY

animal—a macroorganism distinguished from plants by its locomotion and nonphotosynthetic metabolism.

Archaea—a domain of structurally small and simpler, walled cells, widely distributed in extreme environments in nature.

atom—the smallest particle of an element having all the properties of that element; capable of combining with such particles of other elements.

Bacteria—a domain of structurally small and simpler, walled cells, widely distributed in nature; distinguished from Archaeans by their molecular structure.

biology—the study of life and of those objects that possess the quality of being alive.

biomolecule—a collection of atoms bonded together into a structure that serves some biological function within a living cell or organism.

biosphere—the totality of all ecosystems on and within planet earth.

cell—the smallest unit part of a tissue that, of itself, possesses the quality of life.

chromatin—strands of informational DNA and structural protein within the nucleus of the cell; the genetic material.

chromosomes—discrete lengths of chromatin, usually highly condensed into visible, stainable structures that are easily apportioned to daughter cells during cell division.

class—a grouping employed by taxonomists that includes closely related genera.

community—the sum total of all the populations of living organisms in a given area and the interactions that occur among them.

DNA—an abbreviation for deoxyribonucleic acid. This nucleic acid is the archival repository of information for building the majority of all life-forms.

ecology—the science of the relationships among populations of organisms and their environments.

ecosystem—all the living organisms, and nonliving factors in a given area and the interactions among them.

electron microscope—a device that magnifies objects sufficiently such that internal structures of cells are easily seen.

enzyme—a type of protein molecule that serves as an organic catalyst in solution. It reproducibly converts one specific sort of molecule into another: a specific substrate into its product.

Eukarya—a domain of organisms whose cells are larger and contain membrane-enclosed organelles; includes animals, plants, fungi and protists.

fungus—a nonmotile, nonphotosynthetic organism having large cells that are structurally complex (yeasts, molds, mushrooms).

genus—a grouping employed by taxonomists that includes closely related species.

Life Is Complex—one of 12 principles of life on which this book is based.

Life Is Diverse—one of 12 principles of life on which this book is based.

Life is Energy-Driven—one of twelve principles of life on which this book is based.

Life Is Finite—one of 12 principles of life on which this book is based.

Life is Information Expressed—one of twelve principles of life on which this book is based.

Life Is Informational Continuity—one of 12 principles of life on which this book is based.

Life Is Interactive—one of 12 principles of life on which this book is based.

Life Is Internally Integrated—one of the 12 principles of life on which this book is based.

Life Is Responsive—one of 12 principles of life on which this book is based.

Life Is Significant—one of 12 principles of life on which this book is based.

Life Is Ultimate Art—one of 12 principles of life on which this book is based.

macromolecular structure—a component part of a cell's organelle composed of two or more kinds of biomolecules.

metabolism—the sum total of all of the chemical reactions and their inter-relationships within a living organism.

nucleus—the large, membrane-enclosed, usually central portion of a higher cell that contains its hereditary instructions.

organ—a combination of body tissues that performs some significant body function.

organelle—a specialized part of a cell that performs some important function for it.

plant—a macroorganism distinguished from animals by its lack of locomotion and its photosynthetic metabolism.

population—all the members of a kind of organism (or species) that are proximate enough to each other to potentially interbreed.

protein—a relatively large biomolecule composed of a sequence of amino acids; they performs some life functions usually at the chemical or cellular level of organization.

protist—microscopic but structurally complex cells often possessing a loose, colonial form of association.

species—a group of organisms capable of interbreeding and producing fertile offspring.

system—a combination of body organs that performs some significant body function.

teleology—the philosophical study of design and purpose.

tissue—a combination of body cells that performs some role important to the correct functioning of an organ.

Understanding Life's Design

2.1

HOW DESIGN IS UNDERSTOOD

Doing Science

It's Christmas morning. Herbie jumps out of bed and heads for the Christmas tree. There is a package—just the right size—and two smiling parents to go with it. Tearing into the wrapping reveals a new laptop computer. Within minutes Herbie is exploring. Each screen in virtually every program he opens contains a link to a help menu that describes exactly how each aspect of the program works. In addition, Herbie's parents have purchased a reference book to help him grapple with procedures and options. Herbie ignores both the book and the help screens. Within an hour or two he has mastered a game and some drawing software. How does he do this without reference to any instructions? Herbie lives in a computer world. His mind is filled with computer experiences. He thinks as programmers do. He wants the kind of understanding that comes from working directly with the software itself—not reading about it! He is not concerned with the writer's agenda for the reference book. Herbie has his own reasons for exploring the software. Herbie is a scientist at heart (see Figure 2.1).

Brute exploration of a computer game is similar to brute exploration of the living world. Processes are occurring. You get as close to and as involved in those processes as possible, trying to figure out how they work. As Herbie struggles with his new game,

Survey Questions

2.1 **How Design Is Understood**
  - What approach or method is used by biologists in order to understand life?
  - What are the different parts or aspects of this method?
  - What does it mean to understand something? What words do we use to describe something that is well understood?

2.2 **Rational Experimentation: Two Examples**
  - How does one rationally design an experiment in biology?
  - What two examples are illustrated in this section?
  - In each example, how was the experiment set up, what were the results, and what new information was gained?

2.3 **Seeing a Bigger Picture**
  - Where is truth found?
  - Is the scientific method the only acceptable route to truth?
  - How do other methods of seeing the big picture compare to the scientific method?
  - Can different routes to the big picture be complementary in nature?

Figure 2.1 Biology is not "done" by reading textbooks. Text reading is looking in from the outside. Biology "arises" from data. This worker is having fun gathering some of that data from the top of a redwood forest.

he is using several mental tools that scientists use every day:

1. Today, he is interested in a particular character or player in his new game. He has **questions** about several aspects of the role this player has in the game.

2. When he gets stuck, he gives up and checks the manual just long enough to see if his question is answered. Then he goes back to the game immediately. If he has his answer he moves on to the next question.

3. But if his question was not answered in the manual, he goes back to the game with a hunch—an idea about how the player he's interested in functions in a given situation. Scientists call this hunch an **hypothesis.**

4. The hypothesis is hardly formed before he begins guessing as to how he can verify his hunch. "If I press these two buttons in this sequence (it's worked in other games), I'll bet he'll move to the next level." We refer to this momentary thought as a **prediction.**

5. Herbie quickly manipulates the keys to see if his prediction is born out. His manipulation of the system is called a *test* or an **experiment.** Notice here that Herbie is less dependent on the verbal descriptions of some author. He is more dependent on his fingers and his eyes. His senses inform him of whether or not his hunch is correct. He's getting **results** that address his hypothesis. He's learning how the system works and he knows that it will work for anyone else in the same way, regardless of how the written directions might have been interpreted.

6. Herbie discovers more and more individual moves for his player, and their utility becomes apparent. A **model** for how to use this particular player to win the game forms in Herbie's mind. A model, then, is a big picture that explains how the actions of all the parts of a system cooperate to determine the overall behavior of the system.

7. If trying certain buttons fails to work as Herbie had expected, then other combinations of buttons are attempted. These attempts will be based on what Herbie knows of other games, and what he recalls from the help screens he's read.

What goes through Herbie's mind as he explores the game? Is he thinking in terms of words like *hypothesis, prediction,* or *experiment?* No, he does not, nor do scientists. For example, in understanding how one whale communicates with another whale 100 miles away, scientists jump into the inquiry process at different stages. They participate in the part of the inquiry process where they are most gifted or interested. Some well-read and curious types ask more questions than anyone could answer in a lifetime! Others love to design elegant experiments around their choice of a good question. Still others enjoy technology and simply gather lots of data (results) very carefully. There is always a critical thinker in the group who loves to **interpret** the results. "Hah! You thought those results would support your hypothesis." But our thinker shows how those same results

question—an expression of inquiry regarding how something in nature works. In science, this inquiry must be testable.

hypothesis—an educated guess; a speculation regarding how something in nature works.

prediction—an assertion made in advance of the analysis that will validate or discredit it.

experiment—a test that is performed in order to evaluate the validity of an hypothesis.

results—data derived from an experiment that are used to validate a prediction and evaluate an hypothesis.

model—an explanation, based on experimentation, regarding how something in nature works.

interpretation—to clarify or explain the meaning of data from an experiment.

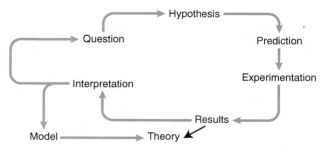

Figure 2.2 Science doesn't happen in neat circles like this one. However, the relationships in this diagram will help you to understand how science progresses. Good theories are very vulnerable to new results. Is evolution a good theory?

can support a rather different hypothesis, taking the model in a whole new direction. Meanwhile, the experiment designer listens carefully to this new interpretation, which now becomes a new hypothesis. She constructs a new experiment that can better distinguish between the now competing interpretations (see Figure 2.2). Suppose then, we were to place these scientific activities on a circle (see Figure 2.2) and start by asking a question, then gathering information, then forming an hypothesis, then making a prediction, then testing it, then harvesting results, then interpreting them, and finally asking a new, more penetrating question, starting around the circle again. Does scientific work follow in that precisely sequenced fashion? Sometimes it does, but rarely perfectly. If there really is a singular scientific method, it is a highly dynamic and fluid process in which sudden hunches, unexpected discoveries, and personal rivalries all influence the rate, pattern, and growth of knowledge. This is true in virtually all areas of the life sciences.

Results as Puzzle Pieces

Results enable us to evaluate a specific hypothesis. For example, receiving devices exist that can detect sounds emitted by whales. Data from such a device provides credence to the hypothesis that communication among whales may be based on the sounds they emit. But more ways of testing the hypothesis soon emerge. As more results come in, the hypothesis becomes formalized: We call it a model. Next we begin to speculate about how sounds of specific frequencies are received and responded to by a whale. As more data consistent

with the model come in, the model becomes more attractive, more likely to be correct. Slowly, with time, scientists treat the model as though it were very probably true; they begin to refer to it as a **theory**. A theory then evolves from an hypothesis that has generated so many predictions and has explained so many experimental results so well that the scientific community broadly accepts it as the probable explanation for a phenomenon or a system.

$$\text{Hypothesis} \rightarrow \text{Model} \rightarrow \text{Theory}$$

Does this mean that the theory is true? Historically, truth is an absolute term. It assumes the existence of a God—an ultimate Arbiter, an ultimate Knower. Man is finite. He is always guessing about how things exist and relate to each other. Scientific methodology is simply a very orderly way of fashioning guesses and then promoting them slowly toward the notion of truthfulness. We can never know if a theory has finally arrived—has become truth. The universality of gravity on the Earth's surface is a highly respected theory. But it is remotely possible that tomorrow, when you turn on a faucet, the water will simply float out into the air. We cannot know that this will not happen. But certain theories—like oxygen being the driving force of respiration, and cell nuclei being repositories of cellular information—are widely accepted. Rarely are these theories seriously questioned anymore. They have been tested so many times.

Unhappily, the word *theory* is abused because of its intrinsic dignity. Historians use it. They derive this or that theory to explain how the idea of a global flood could show up in the folklore of so many ancient cultures. Natural historians use it too. They have a theory for how a wide diversity of life-forms could have evolved from only one or a few original life-forms. The historical sciences weaken the concept of theory by applying it to strictly untestable hypotheses. It is impossible to return to the past to apply rigorous tests to the two hypotheses described above. So when we use the term *theory*, it is important to note the context.

theory—an idea that has survived much testing and analysis.

Is its subject testable like cell respiration? Or does it derive from an historical context like natural history? (See Table 2.1.) In the historical sciences, hypotheses can be elaborated, and observations assembled to favor or discredit them, but rigorous testing is not possible. Many biologists are virtually certain that all life-forms have evolved from a single progenitor cell. But this notion encompasses so much time that it never has been rigorously tested, nor will it ever be.

Table 2.1 Theories in Science

Theory—Historical Science	"soft science"
"Cats and dogs had a common ancestor."	untestable
Theory—Empirical Science	**"hard science"**
"Cats and dogs are intersterile."	testable

IN OTHER WORDS

1. Scientists investigate the living world by interacting physically and very closely with it.
2. They usually have a burning question in their minds and an hypothesis (a hypothetical answer) for that question.
3. They design experiments to test their hypothesis and carefully interpret the results to see how well their hypothesis survives.
4. The scientific method, as illustrated in Figure 2.2, is a sequence of activities that is rarely followed in the orderly fashion indicated by the diagram.
5. An hypothesis that repeatedly survives experimentation with minimal modification eventually becomes referred to as a model. Continued success graduates the model to a theory.
6. The term *theory* has a tentative meaning in the historical sciences; it's most precise meaning is found in the strongly empirical sciences.

2.2 RATIONAL EXPERIMENTATION: TWO EXAMPLES

Biologists usually engage life's complexity by studying something of personal interest. They do this within the framework of one of the levels of biological complexity described in Chapter 1. Study usually begins in the literature, noting what earlier workers have discovered about the system—its **structures** and the processes (or **functions**) these structures support. The biologist then begins to either build on, or question, what has been written.

For any structural part or functional process in nature that is being studied, many, many factors (other structures, other processes) influence it. These factors are called **variables.** An hypothesis is made as to which variable or variables affect the structure or process of interest. Which variable modulates, alters, inhibits or accelerates the process under study? An experiment is then designed to examine the effects on the system of one variable at a time. Biologists have a powerful way of doing this. First, they design a part of their experiment in which, for the process they are studying, they retain all the variables as they would be under normal circumstances. They call this their **control conditions.** In the other part of their experiment they select one variable of interest and alter its presence, magnitude, or some other feature of the variable. This part of the experiment is called the **experimental condition.** Let's observe

the utility of such an approach by examining two specific examples. First, let's consider an experiment from sleep research.

The Effect of Sleep on Disease Resistance

A group of scientists wanted to know how the variable "hours of sleep per night" relates to a person's resistance to common illnesses like the flu. Influenza, or flu, is caused by a viral infection. The hypothesis was that decreasing sleep time would have an inhibitory effect on the subjects' abilities to combat disease.

For their control conditions, they selected a group of 25 young men who slept between 7.5 and 8.5 hours per night. The scientists considered this a normal amount of sleep per night. (Studies suggest that as many as one-fourth of American teens average 6.5 hours per night or less. That is what adds interest to this experiment.) After four days of normal rest, the subjects' immune systems were challenged with a vaccine that contained parts of the influenza virus' outer surfaces. How well would they mount an immune response against the vaccine? Just before receiving the vaccine and 10 days after receiving it, their blood serum was analyzed to determine the levels at which they produced antibodies against the flu virus structures that were in the vaccine. So the first check on antibody levels on vaccination day is a control or baseline against which to measure how high antibody levels will go after being challenged with structural parts of the virus (see Figure 2.3).

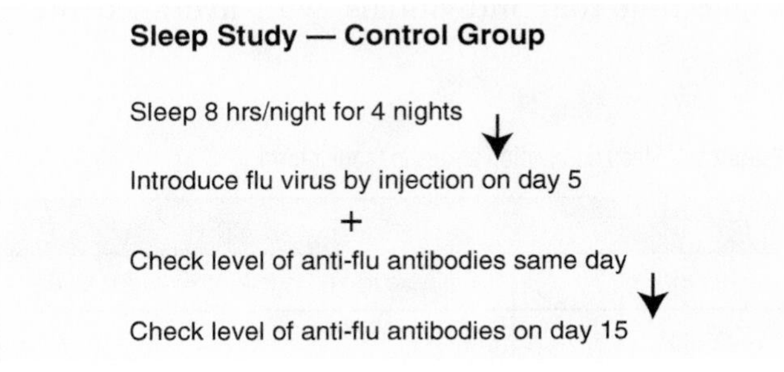

structure—any physical part or aspect of a living organism that in some way contributes to the viability of that organism or its offspring.

function—an activity performed or a role served by a structure that contributes to the viability of the organism or its offspring.

variable—an aspect of an organism or its environment that changes with time or context.

control conditions—a part of an experimental system in which all variables are maintained in a state most nearly corresponding to what is normal or typical.

experimental conditions—a part of an experimental system in which all variables, except for one of interest to the scientist, are maintained in a state most nearly corresponding to what is normal or typical.

Sleep Study — Control Group

Sleep 8 hrs/night for 4 nights

Introduce flu virus by injection on day 5

Check level of anti-flu antibodies same day

Check level of anti-flu antibodies on day 15

Figure 2.3 Sleep Study – Control Group

Sleep Study — Experimental Group

Sleep 4 hrs/night for 6 nights

Introduce flu virus by injection on day 7

+

Check level of anti-flu antibodies same day

Check level of anti-flu antibodies on day 17

Figure 2.4   Sleep Study – Experimental Group

For the experimental conditions, a second group of subjects was selected that was similar to the control group in sex, age, body mass index, and ethnic background. (All of these potential variables were kept constant.) However, the experimental individuals were allowed just 4 hours' sleep per night for six successive nights. Notice that two more nights of sleep deprivation are added to the experimental conditions. (The control conditions take advantage of the fact that 8 hours of sleep per night is closer to what the control individuals were getting anyway; therefore less adjustment time was needed.) The experimental subjects were then challenged with the vaccine in the same way as the group under control conditions (see Figure 2.4).

The antibody levels in the control group at 10 days after vaccination averaged out to 1.15×10^6 times the initial level determined just before vaccination. The levels in the experimental group averaged out to 0.50×10^6 times their initial levels (see Table 2.2, Figure 2.5). In other words, the sleep-deprived individuals made less than half the antibody response compared to the control individuals. We may interpret these results to mean that individuals who constantly deny themselves the amount of sleep they would naturally enjoy will be less able to resist infection by influenza virus. This conclusion may be compared with results of an unrelated study suggesting that individuals who averaged more

Table 2.2   Sleep deprivation results in tabular form

Results:	
Group	Relative increase in Anti-viral Ab levels
Control	1.15×10^6
Experimental	0.50×10^6

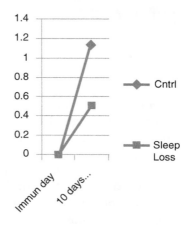

Relative anti-viral Antibody Levels

Figure 2.5   Sleep deprivation results in graphic form.

than 9 hours of sleep per night have a slightly shorter life expectancy. Apparently, there is a range of values for an optimal night's sleep that centers around 8 hours. Figure 2.6 summarizes

Question

How does loss of sleep relate to one's ability to resist flu virus infection?

Hypothesis

Sleep deprivation will make a person more susceptible to viral infection.

Prediction

A sleep deprived individual will produce fewer antibodies against an influenza virus vaccine.

Experiment

Control Conditions	Experiment Conditions
Sleep 7.5–8.5 hrs/night	Sleep 4 hrs/night

Results

1.15×10^6 fold increase in antibody levels	0.50×10^6 fold increase in antibody levels

Interpretation

Sleep deprivation results in a decreased ability of the body to challenge foreign antigens like viruses and bacterial pathogens.

Figure 2.6   Sleep deprivation, methodologically dissected

the sleep deprivation study by dissecting it into methodological steps.

Experimenting with Prayer

It is difficult to physically study a phenomenon that is essentially spiritual. But what if the spiritual phenomenon begins in a physical activity and has physical effects as a result? In one fascinating study, Dr. William Harris, at the Mid-America Heart Institute, asked this provocative question: Would continuous prayer for cardiac patients have any effect on the course of their disease during their hospital stay? The question itself had to be carefully defined. Harris didn't want to know about the length of the hospital stay, or even the final result of the stay in isolation. He wanted to focus on the progression of the patients' disease states during their stays. So he developed a coronary care unit course score, or CCU score. This value would be based on careful scoring of both the seriousness of the forms of intervention used on the patients and the outcome in terms of the patient's health.

The hypothesis was simple: Prayer can improve the experience and outcome in the cardiac patient's life. From this hypothesis we make a prediction. If intercessors believe that their prayer can influence another person's life and are given cardiac patients to pray for, then that prayer will lower the patients' CCU scores. The prediction is worded so as to exclude intercessors whose prayers would have no spiritual component to them.

Patients from two extreme groups—those receiving heart transplants and those who were in the hospital for less than 24 hours—were eliminated. The rest were randomly distributed into two groups, one containing 466 patients who received systematic prayer. The control group consisting of 524 patients did not receive systematic prayer. Other associated health problems such as diabetes or high blood pressure were fairly evenly distributed across both groups. That is, a variety of potentially important variables was being controlled for by being equalized across the two groups. Thus the only significant difference between the control and experimental groups is the presence or absence of prayer.

The CCU score of the control group receiving no (known, systematic) prayer was 7.13 ± 0.27, whereas the experimental group receiving systematic prayer was 6.35 ± 0.26. This was an 11% difference. Because of the small variation (± 0.27 or 0.26) of individual scores around these average values (7.13 and 6.35) and because the number of individuals studied was large, this 11% difference was statistically meaningful.

For many experiments, interpretation of data is a complicated process. For this experiment, the complicated part was designing the CCU scoring regime. Once this regime suited the goals of the study, interpretation of the results was simple. To quote the authors: "This result suggests that prayer may be an effective adjunct to standard medical care" (see Figure 2.7).

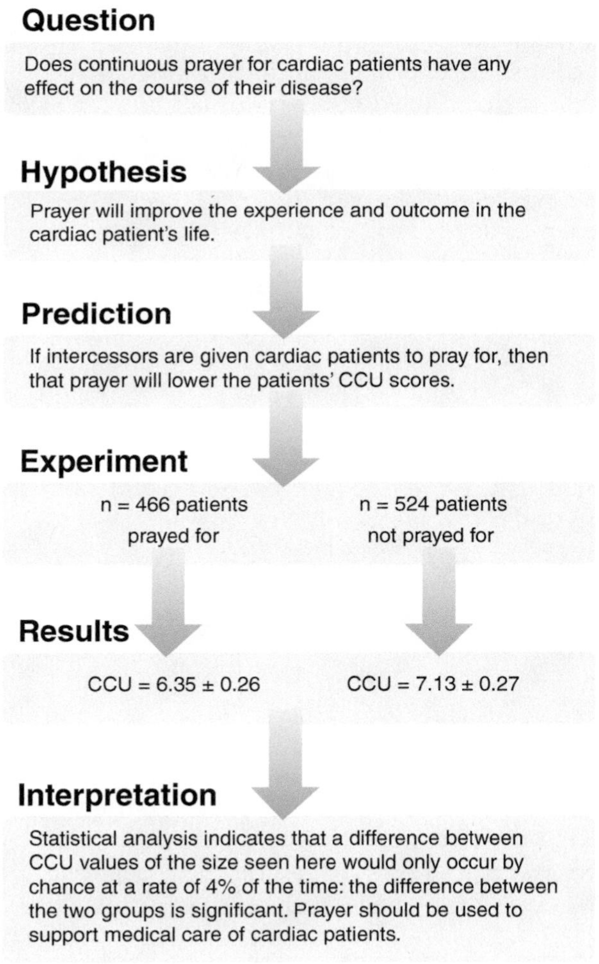

Question

Does continuous prayer for cardiac patients have any effect on the course of their disease?

Hypothesis

Prayer will improve the experience and outcome in the cardiac patient's life.

Prediction

If intercessors are given cardiac patients to pray for, then that prayer will lower the patients' CCU scores.

Experiment

| n = 466 patients prayed for | n = 524 patients not prayed for |

Results

| CCU = 6.35 ± 0.26 | CCU = 7.13 ± 0.27 |

Interpretation

Statistical analysis indicates that a difference between CCU values of the size seen here would only occur by chance at a rate of 4% of the time: the difference between the two groups is significant. Prayer should be used to support medical care of cardiac patients.

Figure 2.7 Effects of prayer on cardiac patients, methodologically dissected

1. When designing an experiment, we divide subjects into separate experimental and control groups.
2. We try to keep all structural and functional variables across the two groups identical except for one variable, which is altered in the experimental group.
3. We then examine the results of our experiment to see the effects of the one altered variable on the system we are studying.
4. If the altered variable is the amount of sleep a subject receives, we can observe the effect of sleep deprivation on the subject's ability to respond immunologically to a flu virus challenge.
5. If the altered variable is the amount of prayer a cardiac patient is subjected to, we can observe the effect of prayer on the patient's progress toward recovery.
6. In either study, much effort is required to determine that all the other variables that could possibly affect the outcome vary equally in both the experimental and control groups.
7. Sometimes differences between experimental and control groups are not large and statistics must be employed to determine whether the difference between the two groups is real.

Approaching Truth

Are scientists allowed to ask questions about the meaning of life? Are they allowed to question why life exists at all? No, not as scientists. Their method cannot address such questions. But scientists are not primarily scientists. They are human beings whose rationality enables them to appreciate truth both from within and from beyond the boundaries of the method they employ in their livelihoods.

Broadly speaking, humans have two fundamental approaches to truth. One is to receive it directly from a Designer capable of communicating it. We call this approach **revelation** (see Figure 2.8). A clearly supernatural book, a clearly magnificent creation, and a powerful Spirit are the resources with which we approach revelatory truth. The other approach is the one we've been examining— **scientific methodology.** Philosophers call this second approach *empiricism*. The man on the street calls it common sense. Man's unaided rational mind and his sensory system are the tools used to make progress toward scientific truth.

revelation—a process by which truth from an ultimate source reaches finite human beings.

scientific method—a rational approach to solving problems that employs observation, experimentation, and interpretation of results.

Comparing Truth Sources

Revealed truth possesses an inherent objectivity— it derives from a singular Designer whose relationship to reality is creational. Hence, He is not limited by the finite perceptions of the human mind. The power of this objectivity is seen in the quality of laws, life principles, and descriptions of mankind this truth brings to us. The best features of civilization derive from truths revealed in the Old and New Testament documents of the Bible. These documents have also given us the confidence to believe in the constancy of natural law. This constancy is what has allowed, historically, for our other approach to truth—the scientific method—to experience any progress at all.

Scientific knowledge, by contrast, possesses an inherent subjectivity since it derives from the finite minds of many men, some of whom passionately disagree with each other. The weakness of this subjectivity is seen in the grueling difficulty, slow pace, and temporarily misguided theories by which science explains the reality around us. This slow pace, however, does eventually lead us closer and

Sources of Truth

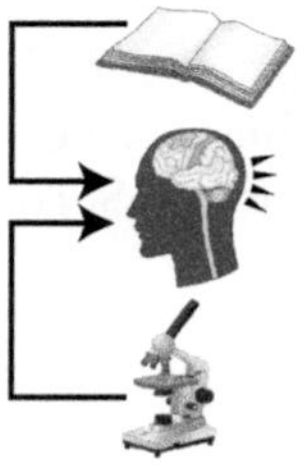

	CATEGORY	CHARACTER	LIMITATION
	revelation	source guarantees objectivity	human language; textual parameters
	scientific method	repeatability contributes objectivity	finite nature of human reason; intrusion of desires

Figure 2.8 Characterizing Truth

closer to truth. We're convinced of this because of the repeatability of our tests, the internal consistency of our best theories, and the pleasing utility of these theories in support of many technological improvements in our lives. The conviction that science really does lead us to truth is embodied in our second principle of life. It simply asserts that **Life Can Be Understood.**

Limits to Truth

Biologists sometimes view the repeatability of their results as a strong reason for believing that their approach to truth brings them closer to objectivity than do other approaches. They, even at times, disdain knowledge derived from more descriptive sciences such as psychology or political science. But repeatability of experimental results is not a royal road to objectivity. For example, the consistent results of many experiments with DNA in the mid-twentieth century pointed toward a model of DNA structure called the tetranucleotide hypothesis (see Figure 2.9). This model led researchers away from thinking of DNA as a possible frame for genetic information. Eventually, further experimentation, arguments, model-building, and newer physical-chemical analyses of DNA led us

past the tetranucleotide model for DNA structure. The currently held double-helical model for DNA structure is now quite well supported. And it nicely explains DNA's ability to bear genetic information. This model shift only happened, however, after seemingly well-worked-out interpretations were reluctantly set aside. The scientific approach to truth clearly participates in the mental and perceptual limits the scientist brings to it.

But the study of revealed truth has some inherent difficulties as well. Here again, man brings his finitude with him. The moral character of some scientists causes them to belittle or ignore revealed truth, missing its value entirely. On the other hand, some scientists who highly respect revealed truth cast aside important cultural and literary constraints, attempting to reason from biblical truth as though it were delivered in the form of scientifically technical writing. Such textual abuse at one point caused the Roman church to rashly defy Galileo and other Renaissance scientists. Galileo's view of the Earth's revolution around the sun was presumed not to accord with scripture. Passages like Psalm 93:1 appeared to teach that the Earth was the unmovable center of the solar system. But the Bible speaks its truth to humble men and it does so phenomenologically. For example, it allows the sun to "rise and set" each day. In this case, then, careful astronomy helped biblical scholars to further refine the manner by which they receive truth from the biblical texts.

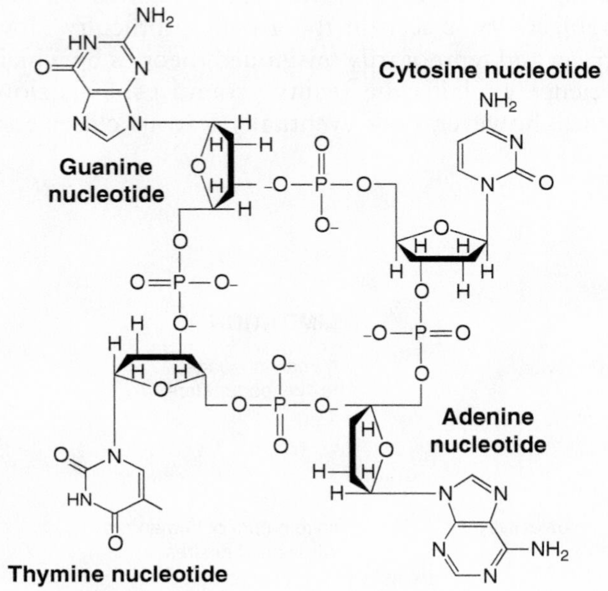

The Value of Truth from Two Sources

Today, areas of ideological conflict continue to exist between the interpreted truth of the Bible and the approximate truth of science. These areas include the process of life's origin, the motivational structure of personality, the nature of sexuality, the causes of aging, and death. For each such issue, much effort is required to harmonize, where possible, these two truth sources. Scholars argue as to how Scripture's

Figure 2.9   The tetra-nucleotide model for the structure of DNA (shown here) was abandoned as new experimental results cast doubt on its accuracy.

Life Can Be Understood—one of 12 principles of life on which this text is based.

truth informs the issue on one hand, and on the other, how to sort the data of science from the subjective interpretation of it. Consider the question of origins, as an example. The Bible reveals that God has supplied the creativity and power necessary to explain the diversity of life-forms on Earth. Science, on the other hand, has discovered a process that can change existing life-forms, doom some to extinction, and help others to weather environmental changes. The careful student must sort through data and interpretations to see what the physical process of evolution is capable of. She must also allow the Biblical text to be determinative where it truly places constraints on how living things originated.

Both revealed truth and scientific discoveries have greatly served society in the past. Great Biblical concepts like the "rule of law" have granted society a stability in which it can flourish. Great scientific discoveries like antibiotics have likewise contributed to the stability of society. It is the God of the Bible Who clarifies for us His desire that humans should have full lives as a result of applying truth from both sources. At one point He states: "Man shall not live by bread alone, but by every word that proceeds from the mouth of God." Human life is threatened in serious, even ultimate ways when God's words are ignored. On the other hand, God's command to "replenish the earth and subdue it" implies that we must understand and control nature if we are to manage our environmental resources for our good as He intends.

This text is a call to nonscientists to be fair and balanced in their scrutiny of truth from complementary sources. To do otherwise is to twist the Divine mandates into extreme and contradictory world and life views. That result will either degrade our concept of humanity or leave it at the mercy of nature's harsh realities.

IN OTHER WORDS

1. To scientists and nonscientists alike, at least two ways are available for seeking truth: the scientific method and revelation.
2. Revealed truth comes with an objectivity inherent in the nature of the Revealer of that truth; scientific truth comes with a subjectivity inherent in the finite minds that pursue that truth.
3. Since both revealed truth and scientific truth must be processed by a finite human mind, there are limits to what we can discern from either source.
4. Two truth sources—Scripture and nature—can be compared critically, but finally, both should be accepted as great gifts. Each source informs our lives in a way complementary to the other. Culturally and practically rich lives are the result.

QUESTIONS FOR REVIEW

1. Playing computer games is just one arena in (American) life where the enthusiast jumps into the discipline without ever reading anything about it first. List three other practical projects in life where great expertise is sometimes gained by direct manipulation of the system without ever reading anything about it.
2. List in logical order, the activities that are part of the scientific method.
3. "Automobiles contribute significantly to urban air pollution." From what you have read or been told, would this statement best be characterized as (a) an hypothesis, (b) a model, or (c) a theory? Explain your choice.
4. Which of the following two theories is a stronger theory?
   a. All life-forms have derived from a single common ancestral life-form.
   b. The sun is ultimately responsible for most of the free oxygen in the atmosphere of our planet.
   Defend your choice.

5. Explain why some scientists believe that getting enough sleep at night is a source of strength for the human immune system.
6. What are two contrasting sources of truth available to anyone trying to understand the living world?

7. Which is more inherently subjective in nature: scientific knowledge or revealed truth? Explain your reasoning.
8. If revealed truth comes from an infinite Source, what sort of limitations might still limit its use?

QUESTIONS FOR THOUGHT

1. What is true of nature and the human mind that enables science to move forward even when scientists do not follow in careful sequence the steps of the scientific method?
2. Which of the following generally requires the least knowledge and creativity: forming an hypothesis, designing an experiment, carrying out an experiment, or interpreting the results of an experiment? Support your choice.
3. In the study on cardiac patient recovery, name one variable: (a) whose magnitude could not be known, (b) whose magnitude could not be controlled, and (c) whose increase in number would result in a smaller difference between patients who were prayed for and those who were not.
4. Suppose a scientist, using available biomolecules, creates a living cell in a Petri plate in a laboratory.

Does this verify the theory that living cells evolved from nonliving molecules many years ago? Explain your reasoning.
5. In a study designed to prove that prayer improves the rate of recovery of cardiac patients, explain why it is important that the number of obese, diabetic, smoking, or chronic bronchial infection patients be approximately evenly distributed over both experimental and control groups.
6. Human behavior is exceedingly complex. Psychologists have a challenging time trying to systematize and study it! Explain how truth from two different sources—revealed truth and scientific truth—could be useful in attacking this problem.

GLOSSARY

control conditions—a part of an experimental system in which all variables are maintained in a state most nearly corresponding to what is normal or typical.

experiment—a test that is performed in order to evaluate the validity of an hypothesis.

experimental conditions—a part of an experimental system in which all variables, except for one of interest to the scientist, are maintained in a state most nearly corresponding to what is normal or typical.

function—an activity performed or a role served by a structure that contributes to the viability of the organism or its offspring.

hypothesis—an educated guess; a speculation regarding how something in nature works.

interpretation—to clarify or explain the meaning of data from an experiment.

Life Can Be Understood—one of 12 principles of life on which this text is based.

model—an explanation, based on experimentation, regarding how something in nature works.

prediction—an assertion made in advance of the analysis that will validate or discredit it.

question—an expression of inquiry regarding how something in nature works. In science, this inquiry must be testable.

results—data derived from an experiment that are used to validate a prediction and evaluate an hypothesis.

revelation—a process by which truth from an ultimate source reaches finite human beings.

scientific method—a rational approach to solving problems that employs observation, experimentation, and interpretation of results.

structure—any physical part or aspect of a living organism that in some way contributes to the viability of that organism or its offspring.

theory—an idea that has survived much testing and analysis.

variable—an aspect of an organism or its environment that changes with time or context.

3

Survey Questions

3.1 A Brief History of Understanding Matter

- What has our history of trying to understand matter revealed to us about its nature?
- Who attempted to sort out nature's complexity, and how did he accomplish this?
- What general terms are used to describe the basic forms matter takes?
- What is the simplest form that matter can assume?
- Is the matter of living things fundamentally different from that of nonliving things?

3.2 Atomic Structure

- What is an atom? Of what parts is it composed? What is an ion?
- How do the various kinds of atoms in nature differ from one another?
- What role do neutrons play in atomic structure? What are isotopes?
- How are the parts of the atom arranged relative to each other?
- What is an orbital? How are orbitals arranged?

3.3 Chemical Bonding

- Can any kind of atoms bond to any other kind?
- What causes one atom to tend to form a bond with another kind of atom?
- What is the nature of an ionic bond, and how does one form?
- What is the nature of a covalent bond, and how is one formed?

Complexity I: Versatile Elemental Structure

3.1 A BRIEF HISTORY OF UNDERSTANDING MATTER

Revealing Matter's Complexity

Before history was ever recorded, man must have tried to understand and work with substances like earth, air, fire, and water and the vast variety of living things. We humans love to control things. So it was always hoped that the parts of nature we worked with would be just complex enough to serve us but simple enough for us to easily control. The history of scientific discovery has been sobering in this respect. It has revealed that nature can be understood and, to a degree, controlled. But it also turns out that nature is unutterably complex and therefore not susceptible to the complete control we long for.

Consider soil. It's just jam-packed with various granules and flecks of minerals, living organisms, and microorganisms as well as decayed parts of previously existing organisms, microorganisms and their products (see Figure 3.1). It contains water, the chemicals humans add to it, and even bits and remnants of things humans used long ago. Soil is incredibly complex! Water is just H_2O, correct? Not pond water! A mere cupful contains thousands of different compounds and microbial life-forms swimming in it. Soil, water, air, and the rest of the biosphere represent a magnitude

- How do the nuclei of two atoms affect the nature of the covalent bond that forms between them?
- What is a hydrogen bond? How are the properties of water affected by hydrogen bonding?
- How is hydrogen bonding important in living systems?

3.4 Water Was Designed!

- What is *heat capacity,* and what makes the heat capacity of water so high?
- What effect does water's high heat capacity have on the living world?
- How do water molecules bring other atoms, ions, and molecules into solution?
- What causes the high level of cohesion between water molecules in the liquid state?
- What value does water's cohesiveness have in the living world?

Though the chemicals of living things are not "alive", they are a rich source of information about living things. Note that the design of the testube, the rack, and the clamp all symbolize our fascination with and success in controlling nature.

Figure 3.1 Soil—possibly the most complex mixture that exists in nature. It has been called "the placenta of life". But it is also life's graveyard. Both roles are implied if we call it nature's super recycling center.

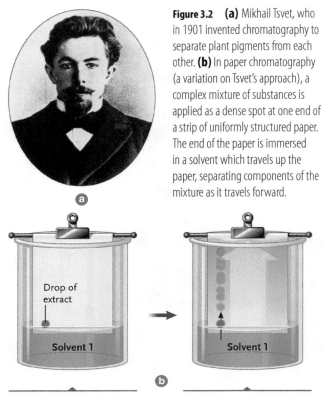

Figure 3.2 **(a)** Mikhail Tsvet, who in 1901 invented chromatography to separate plant pigments from each other. **(b)** In paper chromatography (a variation on Tsvet's approach), a complex mixture of substances is applied as a dense spot at one end of a strip of uniformly structured paper. The end of the paper is immersed in a solvent which travels up the paper, separating components of the mixture as it travels forward.

ⓐ

Drop of extract

Solvent 1 → Solvent 1

ⓑ

❶ A drop of solution containing extracted molecules is placed at the corner of a piece of chromatography paper. The edge of the paper is placed in a solvent.

❷ The solvent rises in the paper and separates the extracted molecules into a vertical row of spots. This is the first dimension of the technique.

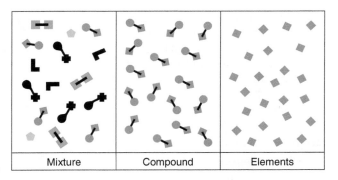

| Mixture | Compound | Elements |

Figure 3.3 This diagram uses shapes to represent three forms that matter can take. In the "element" panel individual atoms are seen. These atoms appear in the molecules of the compound shown in the middle panel. The left-hand panel contains this compound along with molecules of other compounds and atoms of another element. It's a mixture.

of complexity that we aren't even in a position to estimate yet. To describe complex substances such as soil, we use the term **mixture**. For many years, one major activity of scientists has been to develop ways of sorting out the pure component parts or elemental substances from these mixtures.

For example, in 1901, Mikhail Tsvet (see Figure 3.2), an Italian-born, Russian scientist, was studying plant pigments at the Russian Academy of Sciences in St. Petersburg. As part of his work, he inserted pulverized calcium carbonate, a common mineral, into a glass tube and used it as a matrix on which to separate from each other the distinct plant pigments he was studying. Since the plant pigments differed from each other in color, he named his technique **chromatography.** Historical circumstances buried his new method in the scientific literature for almost four decades—science sometimes does this. But upon its rediscovery, chromatography was developed into a science of its own using many chemical and physical varieties

of separating matrix. Chromatography has been included in a vast variety of purification projects. All along, the goal has been to purify substances out of these horribly complex mixtures so that their properties can be studied in isolation.

Components purified from mixtures always fell into one of two categories. Some substances, once purified, could be degraded to still simpler substances using chemical means such as heating or reacting with other substances. Other substances could not be degraded further by these means. We call the former substances **compounds** (see Figure 3.3). The smallest unit bit of a compound that retains all the properties of that compound is called a **molecule.** In a cup of the compound water, there are 7,500,000,000,000,000,000,000,000 individual molecules of water—approximately!

Though a purified compound is stable at moderate temperatures, it is composed of two or more simpler substances. If you supply enough energy to the molecules of a compound, they

mixture—a collection of two or more substances, each of which retains its chemical identity and specific properties.

chromatography—the science of separating the components of a mixture using such media as paper, gels, beads or various physical processes.

compound—a pure substance whose molecules are composed of more than one kind of atom.

molecule—a unit of two or more atoms held together by strong covalent or ionic bonds.

will come apart into simpler substances with properties unlike those of the parent compound. One of the substances Tsvet was able to purify was carotene. Carotene is a stable compound at moderate temperatures. When its molecules absorb light, they make a carrot appear orange in color. But if you "burn" carotene in a device called a bomb calorimeter, you can degrade it to simpler substances like carbon, oxygen, and hydrogen.

These simpler substances, then, can come either directly from a mixture or from chemically degrading a compound that was in a mixture. They are called **elements** (see Figure 3.3). Elements can't be degraded further by ordinary physical or chemical means. You can try to burn an element or to chemically cause it to react. In so doing, you may cause it to *combine* with other substances to contribute to a compound. But by these processes you will never degrade or simplify it any further. The concept of "element" (taken from the Latin term *elementum*) reflects the scholar's optimism that here finally is a substance so basic that it cannot be decomposed into anything simpler. To represent the tiniest, most miniscule, indivisible bit of such a pure elemental substance, scientists use the term **atom**. Atoms are small—the period at the end of this sentence could contain 5 trillion carbon atoms. In the next section of the chapter, we will further develop our concept of the atom. But first, we need to note one other feature of the compounds and elements that scientists were discovering, purifying, and characterizing.

Revealing Continuity between Living and Nonliving Matter

Nested within the almost unutterable complexity of the nonliving world is the living world. Living things have taught us that **Life** also **Is Complex**. Scientists began to dissect matter taken from living things—an intellectual voyage that led them from biology to chemistry, from cells to atoms and molecules. It is a truly fascinating story with many seemingly unrelated characters. Surely one of these was a handsome young chemist at the Polytechnic School in Berlin in 1828. His name was Friedrich Wohler (see Figure 3.4). He was the first human being in history to produce urea without urinating. He synthesized it chemically (and accidentally) in his laboratory. Urea is a compound. And his synthesis of it was from simpler substances that

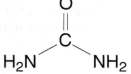

Figure 3.4 Friederich Wohler (1800–1882) and the urea molecule he synthesized. It has atoms of hydrogen, nitrogen, carbon and oxygen in it's structure. The bonds that hold the hydrogen atoms to the nitrogen atoms are not shown.

were known to be nonliving. So without planning to, Wohler was breaking down a huge conceptual barrier. It had long been assumed that when living things were created, an entirely separate realm of (more sophisticated) "organic" components must have been used. These components were supposed by some to explain the sense of self humans seemed to have. Yet here was evidence that the organic world of human metabolism was generating a substance that Wohler could create using entirely nonliving substances. As more and more syntheses of this sort succeeded, man's physical body was slowly to become an integral part of the physical world around him. Whatever it meant for man to believe himself to have been created in God's image, he began to see that physically, he was made *entirely* of the same stuff as dolomite and diamonds. If the carbon atoms in a man are no different than those in a diamond or in the compound carbon dioxide, then it is reasonable for our study of living things to begin with nonliving atoms.

element—a pure substance that cannot be decomposed by a chemical change.

atom—the smallest part of an element that can enter into a chemical reaction.

Life Is Complex—one of 12 principles of life on which this book is based.

1. Because of nature's complexity, it is challenging to understand and difficult to control.
2. Soil, water, and air each contain many components and are complex mixtures.
3. Mikhail Tsvet typifies many scientists; he invented chromatography, a technique that separates the components of a mixture so their properties can be studied in isolation.
4. Substances purified from a mixture are either compounds or elements. Compounds are further degradable into elements.
5. The unit part of a compound is a molecule; the unit part of an element is a molecule or an atom.
6. The carbon atoms in a diamond are identical to those in a dandelion.

ATOMIC STRUCTURE

What's an Atom?

The term *atom* comes from the Greek *átomos,* which means unable to be cut, something that cannot be divided further. Ahh! Have we finally arrived at some minimal structural end point? Is the atom the smallest thing that the Designer created with? The very names we give to the phenomena around us betray the naïveté of man and the overwhelming glory of a truly Great Artist. Not only is the atom divisible into constituent parts, but to understand how life works at the metabolic-chemical level, we will need to dissect the atom and consider those parts.

What Are Its Parts?

An atom consists of a dense, centrally positioned **nucleus** with a cloud of negatively charged **electron**s spinning around it (see Figure 3.5). The overall picture is somewhat like the planets in a solar system. Physicists, who invest millions of (your) dollars in this, tell us that the tiny, dense nucleus holds a collection of positively charged particles called **protons** and neutrally charged particles called **neutrons.** They also tell us that protons and

neutrons are themselves composite particles built up from still simpler particles. We will not chase down the identities and properties of these simpler particles. To do so is to peer into what may well be an infinite regress of particles within particles. This would take us further and further beyond the realm of biology, which is the collection of levels of reality that we've chosen to study.

Protons and electrons have a net *charge.* This word means that these tiny particles have electrical properties. Since each electron has a unit negative charge, it continually orbits the nucleus to which it is attracted by the positively charged protons found there. Electrical neutrality within the atom is maintained because the number of protons in the nucleus equals the number of electrons in the cloud about the nucleus. If the number of electrons and protons ever becomes unequal, then the entire atom takes on a net electrical charge and is called an **ion.**

How Do Atoms Differ from Each Other?

Atoms differ from each other in the number of protons, electrons, and neutrons they contain. Over the years, chemists have discovered that the totality of compounds on Earth, taken to bits, are composed of a much smaller collection of only

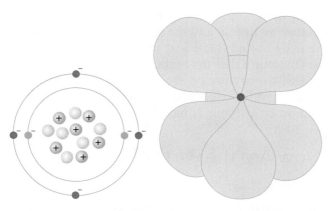

Figure 3.5 The earlier Bohr model of the atom (left) and the more recent Schrodinger model (right). Recent models use balloon-like orbitals to indicate that we will never know exactly where an electron is at any given time. The nucleus on the left contains purple protons and light purple neutrons. The entire nucleus on the right is represented by the tiny blue dot indicating its very small part of the atom's volume.

nucleus—the central region of an atom occupied by protons and neutrons.

electron—a particle of negligible mass and negative charge that occupies an orbital around the nucleus of an atom.

proton—a subatomic particle in the nucleus of the atom. It has a positive charge.

neutron—a subatomic particle in the nucleus of the atom. It has no net charge.

ion—a particle that results when an atom either loses or gains electrons relative to the number of protons present in the nucleus.

Table 3.1 Some Common Elements in the Human Body

Element	# of protons	% of human body by weight
Hydrogen	1	10.0
Carbon	6	23.0
Nitrogen	7	2.6
Oxygen	8	61.0
Sodium	11	0.15
Phosphorus	15	1.1
Sulfer	16	0.2
Potassium	19	0.2
Calcium	20	1.4

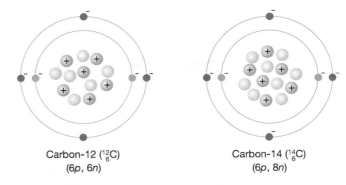

Carbon-12 ($^{12}_6$C)
(6*p*, 6*n*)

Carbon-14 ($^{14}_6$C)
(6*p*, 8*n*)

Figure 3.6 Both atoms diagrammed here are carbon atoms because they each have six protons and six electrons. They differ however in their number of neutrons and hence their mass. They are isotopes of each other.

92 naturally occurring elements. The atoms of each of these elements differ from the atoms of all other elements by the number of protons they contain. An atom with one proton is named *hydrogen*. An atom with six protons is carbon. Table 3.1 lists some of the atoms used frequently in living systems and the numbers of protons they contain.

Do Neutrons Make any Difference? What's an Isotope?

We said that all the atoms of an element have the same number of protons. The atoms of an element may differ, though, in the number of neutrons they contain. Neutrons and protons are equally heavy and contribute virtually all of the mass of an atom. (An electron weighs about a thousand times less than a proton—the mass they contribute to the atom is "peanuts" by comparison.) So atoms of the same element, but having different numbers of neutrons, differ in their atomic weight (see Figure 3.6). These differing versions of the same kind of atom are called **isotopes.**

Consider a typical carbon atom. It has 6 protons and 6 neutrons, yielding an atomic weight of 12. We call it ^{12}C or carbon-12. Carbon-12 is by far the most common isotope of carbon in nature. But nature also has small amounts of carbon-14

isotopes—atoms of an element that are identical in proton number and chemical properties but that, because of differing neutron numbers, differ in mass.

orbital—a mathematically defined space within an atom where a pair of electrons is likely to be found.

whose atoms contain 6 protons and 8 neutrons (see Figure 3.6). Carbon-14 is less stable than carbon-12. In fact, it is radioactive. Slowly, over time, radioactive atoms throw off energetic particles, or radiation. Often this involves loss of a proton and decay of the radioactive atom into a nonradioactive atom *of a different element,* which is more stable. For example, uranium-238 deteriorates to lead-208 at a rate such that after 4.5 billion years only half of the original sample of uranium-238 remains—the other half has all converted to lead.

These decay processes have been used widely in diagnostic medicine—radioactive elements can be followed throughout the human body using detection devices. Their decay can allow us to measure the rates of the metabolic processes they are involved in. Radioactive decay processes have also been used to attempt to determine the age of the planet we live on and the ages of some of the fossils that lie buried in ancient rock layers. Some scholars maintain that the biblical text, by its inferences, places constraints on estimates of the Earth's age. They therefore question the assumptions on which radiometric dating is based.

How Are the Parts of an Atom Arranged?

We stated that an atom is composed of a centrally located nucleus containing positively charged protons that attract and hold in orbit negatively charged electrons arranged around the nucleus in a large cloud. The positions the electrons take within this "cloud" are fairly well defined physically and are referred to as **orbitals** (see Figure 3.5). How are these orbitals

Figure 3.7 Protons like pizza are "positively" attractive. Electrons, like hungry boys, are drawn right in. In the perfect three dimensional analogy, the pizzas would float in mid-air and the boys would be able to fly, but these elements aren't needed to make the point. In this diagram, the boxes (neutrons) have been removed. . . .

arranged? Consider this wonderful olfactory analogy: Imagine a large dining room filled with small, round dining tables (see Figure 3.7). Each table contains at least one pizza. Some tables contain several pizzas. A few contain many pizzas.

There are no chairs. The tables are the nuclei. The pizza represents protons, the boxes separating the pizzas from each other can be thought of as neutrons. Now, throw open the doors and allow the room to fill with electrons—starving college boys. Electrons neatly surround all the nuclei. At the tables with one pizza, only two boys can easily consume what's there. Tables containing many pizzas are soon surrounded—at quite regular intervals—by a few boys. But behind these individuals is another, larger layer of boys who—at precise spots—throw long arms in toward the table to get their share of the food.

At the tables with the most pizzas, the second layer of boys is surrounded by yet another, third row of boys who can't physically get to the food, but its scent keeps them attracted to the table, hoping to get closer. Spatially each boy is at a spot—the orbital—where he optimally senses the pizza. Right up at the table, energy levels are low—pizza moves slowly, predictably into mouths. The further away from the table a boy is the more frustrated—or energetic—he is. He's trying to get at the food and not certain he's in exactly the right spot.

Let's complicate things. Every now and then, a waitress coming from outside the room hands a

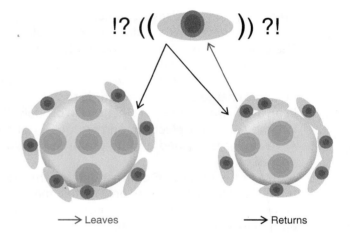

→ Leaves   → Returns

Figure 3.8 Extra energy causes "electron-boy" to leave the table he was attracted to. As energy declines, he seeks to rejoin some nearby pizza table.

small glass of caffeine-laced soft drink—a burst of energy—to select "electron boys" who consume it immediately. Even a boy right near a table—given enough sugar and caffeine—will jump away from the table in excitement, wandering if there's more pizza at another table. But soon (see Figure. 3.8) the energy is gone, and he wanders closer to the nearest table where food is.

With apologies to college freshmen, we now have a crude picture of how positively charged protons (pizza + aroma) and solar energy (soft drink) affect the behavior of electrons (boys). When we get to the process of photosynthesis, all you'll have to imagine is a soft drink–excited electron (boy) jumping far enough away from his nucleus (table) so that when he settles down, he ends up going to another, larger table. If you can imagine this, then you can understand the engine that drives photosynthesis.

Keep imagining—you're doing well! Now, picture a room full of pizza-laden tables that are rolling about on the floor in random directions. The boys must move with them. Soon, two tables approach each other and boys at both of them are attracted to food on the two adjacent tables simultaneously (see Figure 3.9). The resultant grabbing process tends to hold the two tables near each other. We are now in a position to use our analogy as a way of understanding **chemical bonding.**

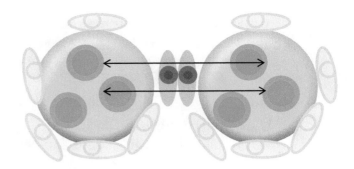

Figure 3.9 Pizza is so close at hand, both boys are attracted to both tables.

chemical bond—a relationship between two atoms in which electrons are either transferred or shared creating an attraction between the atoms.

IN OTHER WORDS

1. An atom is indeed divisible; it consists of a small, dense, central nucleus surrounded by much space in which electrons move within discrete orbitals.
2. The atomic nucleus contains two kinds of subatomic particles of approximately equal mass: protons and neutrons. Protons have a unit positive charge. Neutrons are uncharged.
3. In an atom, the overall charge is balanced because electrons, although of diminutive mass, have a unit negative charge equal in magnitude to the positive charge of a proton.
4. In an atom, the number of electrons in orbitals equals the number of protons in the atom's nucleus; in an ion, the number of electrons and protons is not equal.
5. An element is defined and its properties are determined by the number of protons and electrons it possesses.
6. Atoms of the same element that differ in the number of neutrons they possess are termed *isotopes.* Isotopes differ from each other only in their mass.
7. Some isotopes are radioactive, and as such, have been used for medical purposes and for studying the ages of rocks containing them.
8. Orbitals containing electrons occupy approximate locations around the nucleus of the atom.
9. Energy from an external source can cause individual electrons to become more excited and spin temporarily in an orbital that is further away from their nucleus.

3.3 CHEMICAL BONDING

Like layers of boys around a table, electrons fill systematically into orbitals that are arranged somewhat like concentric shells around the nucleus of the atom. Around a nucleus with only one or two protons, the shell is small, and it's filled by only two electrons. In atoms with more than two protons, there is enough positive charge to attract a second shell or layer of electrons. This second shell lies outside of the first one and the arrangement of the orbitals determines that this second shell has a capacity of up to eight electrons. (Here, the relative confusion of our pizza-lover analogy breaks down.) Recall that each atom has the same number of electrons and protons in it. Atoms like helium (2 protons, 2 electrons) or neon (10 protons, 10 electrons) have no "chemistry" at all. They just wander around bumping unproductively into other atoms. In both cases, they present to other atoms a complete outer shell of electrons (see Figure 3.10). They do not relate to other atoms in any way. They are chemically stable.

But among small atoms, those with one proton or with from three to nine protons in their nuclei will have their outer shell only partially filled with electrons. These atoms are unstable—so unstable that we don't find them in nature. They quickly either lose or gain or share electrons with other unstable atoms. These electron exchanges result in an increase in stability—outer shells can become more like those of helium or neon. When electrons shift their position so that two atoms can share them, or when they jump from one atom to another, a **chemical bond** forms. The bond has two effects: (1) atoms have joined together to form a molecule, and (2) each atom in the new molecule now has an outer shell stable having a full complement of electrons. Molecular oxygen (O_2) and water (H_2O) are two examples of molecules whose atoms each have complete outer shells of electrons because of the new chemical bonds formed. The electron shell's stabilities within these molecules are represented in Figure 3.11.

Ion Formation and Ionic Bonding

Let's consider some specific examples of how molecules result from atoms with outer electron shell stability. In Figure 3.12, the sodium atom has 11 protons and 11 electrons. Stability could be gained if some other atom would just "steal" that lone, high-energy electron. True, it would then no longer be an atom—its excess of protons over electrons would make it a positively charged ion. But the result (represented as Na^+) would now have a stable outer shell of electrons. What sort of atom might

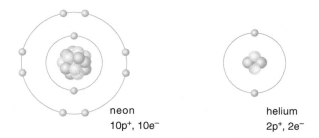

neon
$10p^+, 10e^-$

helium
$2p^+, 2e^-$

Figure 3.10 Electrons fill the outer shells of helium and neon making them chemically stable. They do not react with other elements chemically.

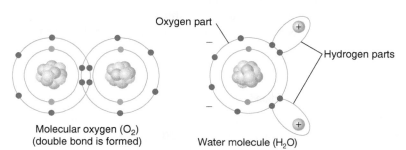

Oxygen part

Hydrogen parts

Molecular oxygen (O_2)
(double bond is formed)

Water molecule (H_2O)

Figure 3.11 Electron rearrangements that promote stability. Note how outer shells in all atoms now have either 2 or 8 electrons. In oxygen and water this is achieved by sharing electrons.

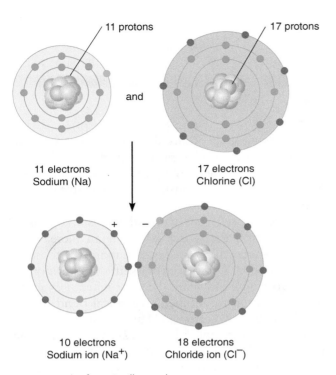

11 protons / 17 protons

and

11 electrons
Sodium (Na)

17 electrons
Chlorine (Cl)

+   −

10 electrons
Sodium ion (Na⁺)

18 electrons
Chloride ion (Cl⁻)

Figure 3.12 Ion formation illustrated.

Crystals of sodium chloride (NaCl)

Cl⁻
Na⁺

1 mm

Figure 3.13 Salt from your salt shaker at enormous magnification. Just lots of ions packed together in neat arrays.

do the stealing? Nature also contains rare, momentarily unstable, chlorine atoms. They have 17 protons and 17 electrons, leaving them with 7 electrons in their outer shell. An extra electron would convert the chlorine atom into a chloride ion (Cl⁻) but a stable outer shell of electrons would again result. So, if sodium metal atoms and chlorine gas atoms are combined, there is a wonderful explosion (why?), and this white powdery residue called sodium chloride (table salt) results. The chlorine atoms have stolen the extra electron dangling from the surface of the sodium atoms and the resulting ions are now highly stable. The negatively charged chloride ion is now attracted to the positively charged sodium ion. They stick together by means of an electrostatic attraction called an **ionic bond.** Within a sodium chloride crystal, each sodium ion is ionically bonded to all the chloride ions it is adjacent to (see Figure 3.13).

Covalent Bonding

What happens when unstable atoms of carbon and hydrogen approach each other? For both of these atoms, gaining an electron would contribute to further stability. The hydrogen has one electron in its only shell. Two would make it stable. The carbon

has four electrons in its outer shell—four more would yield stability. Thus a very stable arrangement could be achieved if *four* hydrogens were to combine with a single carbon atom somewhere in nature (see Figure 3.14). Each hydrogen could share its lone electron with carbon, granting an outer shell stability of eight electrons for the carbon atom and shell stability for each hydrogen atom as well. A molecule of methane gas (CH_4) would result. Methane gas appears as bubbles rising to the surface of a pond from bottom mud where bacteria are busy producing it. It's also a wonderful fuel to cook with.

Within the methane molecule, the sharing of a pair of electrons is termed a **covalent bond.** Methane has four covalent bonds. Why don't ionic bonds occur here? Why don't electrons simply leave the hydrogen atoms and transfer to the carbon atom? The answer seems to depend on how strongly the carbon

ionic bond—an attraction between two ions of opposite charge.

covalent bond—a stabilizing attraction between two atoms based on a sharing of a pair of electrons between them.

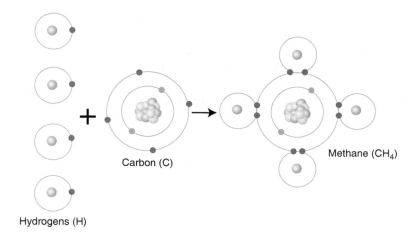

Carbon (C) Methane (CH₄)

Hydrogens (H)

Figure 3.14 Covalent bond formation between 4 hydrogen atoms and one carbon atom. Electrons are shared between nuclei. Electrons are represented by black circles (a), or lines (d), or the space their shells consume (c). In b) they are not shown.

and hydrogen nuclei pull on each electron involved in the bonding. The attraction each electron feels toward either of these nuclei is about equal. So the sharing of electrons is what's going to happen here.

Notice in Figure 3.14 how the electrons in these sharing relationships can be represented. Review Figure 3.11 again. Notice that these molecules also have shared pairs of electrons (covalent bonds) between their atoms. The individual atoms alone would be unstable. Why is that?

Polarity in Water Molecules and Hydrogen Bonding

Let's now take a closer look at a molecule that represents over half the mass of your body—the water molecule. It is held together by two covalent bonds between one oxygen and two hydrogen atoms (see Figure 3.15). The outer shell of the oxygen atom has six electrons. It thus has orbital space for two more electrons, which, when present, yield shell stability. The arrangement of the oxygen atom's outer shell electrons determines how electron sharing will occur with the two hydrogen atoms. The architecture of the sharing gives the water molecule its characteristic shape: It has ends—an oxygen end and a hydrogen end. Let's see how those ends differ from each other.

Recall that the electrical charges on protons and electrons are opposite in character but equal in magnitude. Imagine a pair of electrons being shared between a hydrogen nucleus (one proton) and an oxygen nucleus (eight protons). If opposites attract, where in the molecular space around and between those two nuclei will the electrons spend

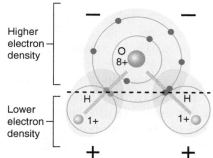

Higher electron density

Lower electron density

Figure 3.15 Electrons are shared between each hydrogen atom and the oxygen atom. But greater attraction by the oxygen nucleus means that electrons spend more time in the "oxygen end" of the molecule. The outer surface of this end is correspondingly more negative in charge than the "hydrogen end".

most of their time? They will feel more strongly the pull of the eight protons in the oxygen nucleus, and therefore spend more time around it. They will spend less time around a single proton (the hydrogen nucleus). Because of this, we draw the water molecule as shown in Figure 3.15. The bonds between hydrogen and oxygen are said to be **polar covalent bonds** because the electrons are not shared equally—along the bond distance, they gravitate toward the oxygen nucleus pole. If we step back now and look at the outside surface of the water molecule, this polarity has major consequences.

Consider the two ends of a water molecule. The oxygen end will command greater attention from outer shell electrons; therefore its surface will be slightly more negative. The hydrogen end of the molecule has very little to attract electrons with (one personal-size pizza?). Therefore that end of the molecule will be relatively positive. Think about what these

polar covalent bond—an unequal sharing of electrons between atoms—the electrons spend more time around the nucleus to which they are more strongly attracted.

slight surface charge differences mean for a water molecule.

Most of the time in the living world, a water molecule will be surrounded by other water molecules. If the ends of these molecules have slight charges—oxygen, negative; hydrogen, positive—then each molecule will orient itself such that the oxygen end will be attracted to the hydrogen end of several other water molecules. The hydrogens, conversely, will be attracted to oxygen ends of other water molecules. Each water molecule ends up attracting four other water molecules. These associations are pictured in Figure 3.16. These attractions do not have the strength of a covalent bond or even an ionic bond. However, collectively, they become very important in biological systems. We call them **hydrogen bonds.** These ubiquitous but weak bonds are partly responsible for the amazing properties of water we will describe in the next section. But these weak bonds

between hydrogen and oxygen or nitrogen atoms on other molecules are responsible for many other important structural and functional parts of the biochemistry of your body. You may have learned that the information-bearing molecule DNA is double-stranded. This feature is critical to the molecule's function. The two strands of a DNA molecule are held together by a long sequence of hydrogen bonds. So in the world of chemical bonding (as in other areas of life), weakness must not be equated with unimportance.

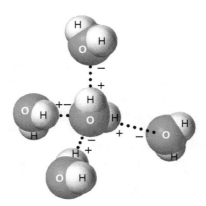

Figure 3.16 Weak hydrogen bonds form between the partially negative and partially positive ends of water molecules in the liquid state. These bonds help stabilize the structure of liquid water and are responsible for water's unique properties.

hydrogen bond—an electrostatic attraction between a partially positive hydrogen atom in one molecule and a partially negative atom (like oxygen) in another molecule.

IN OTHER WORDS

1. Inside of an atom, electrons orbit within shells. The shell closest to the nucleus has a capacity of two electrons; moving away from the nucleus, the next shell out has a capacity of eight electrons.
2. Atoms with 2 or 10 electrons (filled outer shell) are chemically inert. They simply collide ineffectively with other atoms as they have no tendency to share or acquire additional electrons.
3. Atoms with unfilled electron shells are electrically unstable and gain stability by forming chemical bonds with other unstable atoms.
4. Combinations of atoms chemically bonded to other atoms are called *molecules.*
5. Sometimes, stability results from electrons leaving a shell of one atom and entering a shell in another atom. This generates ions, which, because of opposite net charges, form ionic bonds with each other.
6. When the outer shells of two atoms are partially filled, stability is gained by sharing electrons between them. Electron sharing between shells of two atoms is called a *covalent bond.*
7. Electrons shared between nuclei having widely differing numbers of protons will be shared unequally. The greater attraction of the electrons to the nucleus with more protons results in unequal sharing, termed a polar covalent bond.
8. Polar covalent bonds cause an unequal distribution of positive and negative charges over the surface of the molecules that contain them. Usually, the lonely proton of a hydrogen atom (often deserted by its original electron) represents the partially positive surface region of the molecule.
9. Weak attraction between the partially positive surface region of one molecule and the partially negative surface region of another molecule is termed a *hydrogen bond.*
10. The stability of double-stranded DNA molecules and of liquid water is the result of hydrogen bonding.

3.4 WATER WAS DESIGNED!

Water is a highly improbable substance! Oh, yes, it's widely distributed on our planet. You'll drink 9500 gallons of it in your lifetime. But if you consider its molecular structure and properties, it is the most amazing, fortuitous substance you could imagine. Very few other substances are present on Earth in all three physical states—gas, liquid, and solid—at one time. All of these states are achievable within the narrow range of temperatures that the Earth's surface normally experiences.

High Heat Capacity

Water, like any other form of matter, contracts as it condenses from a gas to a liquid. But then, because of its hydrogen bonding properties, it *expands* by 1/11 of its volume as it transitions from liquid to ice (see Figure 3.17). This is unique among nature's substances. It is also critical to our existence. It means that ice, being less dense, floats instead of sinking. And that means that ice is quickly melted by solar radiation in spring. Were ice denser than water, almost the entire quantity of water on the planet would be tied up all year long in the form of unmelted ice and thus would be unavailable for our use as a liquid. There would be no fish on your restaurant menu!

Once ice melts to form water, the hydrogen bonding between the molecules means that a very large amount of heat energy must be put into the structure of liquid water to convert it to the gaseous state. This high **heat capacity** of water means that the huge daily influx of solar energy on this planet can be absorbed effectively by water with only a slight increase in Earth's surface temperature. Spending one day and one night in the temperature extremes of a desert will convince you of the value of water's high heat capacity.

As a Solvent

A crystal of sodium chloride (NaCl) is held together by many strong ionic bonds as described previously. Yet a tablespoon of salt crystals swirled into water is quickly dissolved into a uniform mixture (solution) of salt ions and water molecules. Water has this

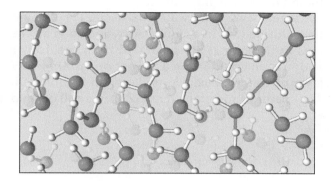

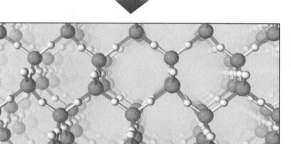

Figure 3.17 Water becoming ice. Note the transition from the denser disorder of water to the open hexagonal crystals of ice. Lower temperatures give added stability to the hydrogen bonds (in red) between the partially negative and partially positive ends of water molecules. This contributes to the additional space within the crystalline structure of ice.

wonderful solvent property. Most molecules of biological importance either have polar covalent or ionic bonds in them. These **solute** molecules, as we call them, are easily dissolved in the **solvent** water.

heat capacity—the quantity of heat that is required to increase a body of matter by 1 degree Celsius.

solute—a substance that is dissolved (separated to the level of individual molecules) within another substance (the solvent).

solvent—a substance (usually a liquid) that can dissolve another substance.

How are the ionic bonds in the salt crystal overcome? Again, hydrogen bonding is responsible for this. When the crystal first enters water, the partially negative oxygen ends of many water molecules back up to the positively charged sodium ions and collectively overcome the few ionic bonds that hold the ion in the crystal. The hydrogen ends of water molecules surround the chloride ions in a similar way, and soon all the ions in the crystal are separated from each other and held in solution by a *sphere of hydration*—a layer of water molecules as shown in Figure 3.18. The chemical reactions that occur in a cell depend entirely on the ability of the reacting substances to float up to each other—to find each other. An aqueous (water) solution is the "polar soup" that allows individually hydrated molecules of reactants to float toward each other separately from other solute molecules. Water is the medium in which the cell's chemistry takes place.

Its Cohesion

Finally, the vast number of hydrogen bonds in the structure of water gives it the property of surface

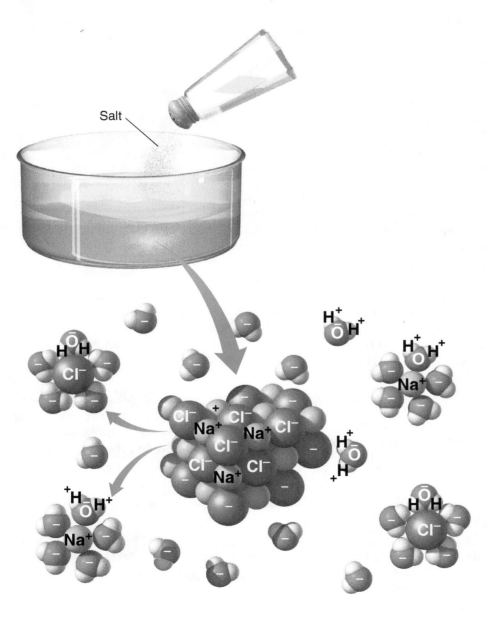

Figure 3.18 Salt dissolves in water. The corner of a crystal of sodium chloride is shown. Partially negative or positive ends of many water molecules associate with sodium and chloride ions along the free edges of the crystal and "coax" them out of the crystalline structure based on charge attraction.

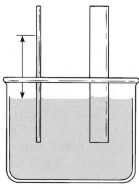

Figure 3.19 The high cohesiveness of water molecules generates spherical drops (left) and strong adhesion to walls of glass container (right).

tension or **cohesion.** Only the metallic element mercury has a greater surface tension than water. You see this tension when a drop of water forms as a pebble enters a still pool of water. It appears almost as though it has a membrane around it (see Figure 3.19). When the drop breaks free of the pool of water, the membrane appears to snap around the surface of the drop so that it leaves the pool as a nice, neat sphere. This inward pull of the water molecules on each other is incredibly strong. If you created a cylindrical column of absolutely pure water 1 inch in diameter, it would take the force of 210,000 lbs of tension along the column axis to produce a break in the water column. This tension also causes water to adhere strongly to polar surfaces. In a small glass test tube, the water at the top surface is higher around the edges of the glass than in the center of that surface (see Figure 3.19). As tube diameters get smaller and

smaller this attraction of water molecules to the glass surfaces gets more and more pronounced until finally, water actually rises within the tube. In biological conduits like the capillaries of your bloodstream or the xylem tubes in tall trees, the physiology of fluid flow is designed around this amazing property of water. Water evaporation occurring in tree leaves combines with these powerful cohesive forces to raise large amounts of water from a tree's roots hundreds of feet into the air. This is how water—a major raw material for photosynthesis—gets to all the aerial parts of a tree!

The polarity of electron sharing along the hydrogen-oxygen bonds in water is, in magnitude, precisely the value it needs to be in order for life on Earth to be possible. Virtually no variance in design could be tolerated here. If the polarity were only a few percent stronger, too much energy would be required to convert ice back to water; hence, life on Earth would be impossible. If the polarity were only slightly weaker, water would lose its excellent solvent properties and life chemistry would be prohibitively limited. Somehow the most basic subatomic particles were designed so that, among many other constraints, the polarity of the bonds in water would be just right. Nature at her most basic level is revealing Genius to us. Can we see it? Or will we not?

cohesion—the tendency of certain kinds of molecules to adhere to each other, often due to hydrogen bonding.

IN OTHER WORDS

1. Water moves freely from its liquid state to either the gaseous state or the solid state over the narrow temperature ranges found on planet Earth.
2. Due to hydrogen bonding, water expands slightly becoming less dense as it freezes.
3. In evaporation, the energy required to overcome ubiquitous hydrogen bonds causes water to have a high heat capacity; it absorbs much heat energy in converting to the gaseous state.
4. Hydrogen bonding causes water to have superior quality as a solvent for the many substances in living systems whose molecules have polar covalent bonds. The polarity of the water molecule enables it to coax the solute ions, or molecules, away from each other.
5. Hydrogen bonding between water molecules increases their cohesion to each other. This in turn drives water transport in plants and plasma movement in capillaries of the bloodstream.

QUESTIONS FOR REVIEW

1. What is the difference between a mixture and a compound? What does chromatography paper do to the mixture you apply to it?
2. If you burn or chemically degrade a compound, what kind of substances are you left with?
3. The term *nucleus* is used at several different levels of organization in the living world. What are the components of an atomic nucleus?
4. Describe what you have learned about where an electron is normally found.
5. What is an ion? How does it differ from an atom?
6. What is an isotope? How do the two isotopes of carbon differ from each other?
7. Inside of a neon sign particles of neon are bouncing around. Are these particles atoms or molecules? Explain.
8. Explain how an ionic bond forms.
9. How many atoms of hydrogen does carbon covalently bond with in methane? Explain why carbon always binds the same number of hydrogen atoms when forming methane.
10. Explain why polar covalent bonds form.

QUESTIONS FOR THOUGHT

1. Why is the term *atom* a misnomer?
2. A materialist says to you, "What you call a spirit is simply a highly modified area of your thought processes in your cranium (your brain) which we know to be made of the same carbon, oxygen and hydrogen atoms found in nonliving things." Respond to her by defining for her what you believe a spirit to be.
3. If, in radioactive decay, one element, like uranium gets converted to a simpler element like lead, what must part of the decay process involve?
4. Extend the pizza analogy. How might you explain ionic bonding using pizzas, moving boys, and perceptions about which tables' pizza will last the longest amount of time before being eaten.
5. Water striders are insects that walk on water. What property of water enables them to do this? What is the molecular basis for this property?
6. When a water molecule evaporates from the bottom surface of a leaf—that is, when a water molecule separates from the liquid state in the leaf and becomes part of a gaseous vapor—it tugs a bit on the water molecules it separates from. What explains the tugging? Now think about soil, water, and the high energy output of the sun. Can you explain how a leaf wilts on a hot day?

GLOSSARY

atom—the smallest part of an element that can enter into a chemical reaction.

chemical bond—a relationship between two atoms in which electrons are either transferred or shared creating an attraction between the atoms.

chromatography—the science of separating the components of a mixture using such media as paper, gels, beads or various physical processes.

cohesion—the tendency of certain kinds of molecules to adhere to each other, often due to hydrogen bonding.

compound—a pure substance whose molecules are composed of more than one kind of atom.

covalent bond—a stabilizing attraction between two atoms based on a sharing of a pair of electrons between them.

electron—a particle of negligible mass and negative charge that occupies an orbital around the nucleus of an atom.

element—a pure substance that cannot be decomposed by a chemical change.

heat capacity—the quantity of heat that is required to increase a body of matter by 1 degree Celsius.

hydrogen bond—an electrostatic attraction between a partially positive hydrogen atom in one molecule and a partially negative atom (like oxygen) in another molecule.

ion—a particle that results when an atom either loses or gains electrons relative to the number of protons present in the nucleus.

ionic bond—an attraction between two ions of opposite charge.

isotopes—atoms of an element that are identical in proton number and chemical properties but that, because of differing neutron numbers, differ in mass.

Life Is Complex—one of 12 principles of life on which this book is based.

mixture—a collection of two or more substances, each of which retains its chemical identity and specific properties.

molecule—a unit of two or more atoms held together by strong covalent or ionic bonds.

neutron—a subatomic particle in the nucleus of the atom. It has no net charge.

nucleus—the central region of an atom occupied by protons and neutrons.

orbital—a mathematically defined space within an atom where a pair of electrons is likely to be found.

polar covalent bond—an unequal sharing of electrons between atoms—the electrons spend more time around the nucleus to which they are more strongly attracted.

proton—a subatomic particle in the nucleus of the atom. It has a positive charge.

solute—a substance that is dissolved (separated to the level of individual molecules) within another substance (the solvent).

solvent—a substance (usually a liquid) that can dissolve another substance.

4

Complexity II: Molecular Efficiency and Variety

Survey Questions

4.1 The Centrality of Carbon to the Organic Molecules of Life

- How prominent is carbon in the structure of living things?
- What features of the carbon atom make it so useful for the design of biological molecules?
- How many molecules of life are there, and how are they organized for discussion and study's sake?

4.2 Construction and Degradation of Organic Molecules

- How important is construction and degradation of organic molecules to the living cell?
- How is construction of a large organic molecule carried out?
- Why would organic molecules need to be degraded? How is this accomplished?

4.3 Carbohydrates: Structure and Function

- What are carbohydrates? What does that term denote?
- Why is sugar considered to be a carbohydrate? What are some examples of carbohydrates?
- How are larger carbohydrates built from smaller ones?
- What are some important examples of large carbohydrates?

4.4 Lipids: Structure and Function

- What are the defining characteristics of a lipid? What are some examples of lipids?

Life Is Complex—one of the 12 principles of life on which this text is based.

When you have opportunity, watch a squirrel work its way into a sunflower seed that's fallen from a bird feeder (see Figure 4.1). Or watch an otter "on a lunch break" cracking its way into a mussel's shell with a pebble. It is fascinating to observe how elegantly the parts of the organism suit the process that is being carried out. One major purpose of this chapter is to extend your awareness. This high level of elegance in form-facilitating function stretches all the way back to the level of the biological molecules that comprise the individual cells of the squirrel or otter. Just as in organisms where the structure of organs determines their function, so it is with molecules: the way the atoms are bonded to each other determines what function the molecule will have. One molecule is built in a way that is optimal for storing information. Another molecule's structure perfectly suits it for breaking a specific covalent bond in a specific kind of molecule generating a specific product. Form determines function in molecules too.

Life Is Complex. In those living things that possess many levels of organization, the functions at one level determine what is functionally possible at higher levels. Molecular form and function determine cellular form and function and so on. The squirrel skillfully gets rid of the sunflower seed hull and ingests the starchy interior only because there is a corresponding elegance of organ, tissue, cellular, organellar, and molecular structure that support this feeding process.

Imagine that you are Mother Nature. You are given a mutant squirrel that knows how to feed on sunflower seeds but has no forelimbs. All you have to do is to design a set of forelimbs that will support this process. But you must do this by selecting individual molecules

- What role does fat play in living systems?
- How are plant fats distinct from animal fats?
- How much dietary fat is good for humans?
- What is a phospholipid, and where are they used in cells?
- What features of a phospholipid's structure highly suit it to its role in the cell?
- What hormones are lipids by structure?
- What effect(s) does the hormone testosterone have on the male human organism?

4.5 Proteins: Structure and Function

- What roles do proteins play in living systems?
- How does their structure support such roles?
- What are the structural elements or building blocks of proteins?
- What features of these elements suit them to the high level of variability of function observed in proteins?
- What are the separate levels of complexity in protein structure, and why are such complicated concepts needed in protein study?
- Are all biomolecules clearly either carbohydrates, lipids, or proteins? Are there hybrid molecules that have features of more than one class?

4.6 Proteins Conceal Wisdom

- What is hemoglobin, and what is its role in living systems?
- How does its design wonderfully suit the challenges inherent in its role in living things?

4.7 Nucleic Acids: Structure and Function

- How are nucleic acids structured?
- What are the structures and some examples of nucleotides? What roles do they perform?
- What are two different roles for the molecule ATP?
- How is the informational molecule DNA structured?

4.8 Living Things Need Just a Few Good Molecules

- How many molecules were produced in the prebiotic simulations of Miller and Urey?
- What critical feature is lacking in these studies that would make the production of life a more plausible outcome?

© 2007 John Foxx Images / Jupiterimages Corporation

Figure 4.1 A squirrel, (*species Sciurus carolinensis*) strips a sunflower seed of its hull so quickly, it's difficult to observe the process.

compatible with squirrel chemistry. You must break and form bonds in them until the squirrel forelimb exists and can support the feeding behavior that the squirrel already knows! Where would you begin? No modern scientist would know where to begin nor would any of the founders of evolutionary theory. So please observe the molecular form and function in this chapter with a bit of reverence. If you fail to see design inherent in these molecules, you may trap yourself into a philosophical perspective that is conceptually unproductive and personally degrading.

4.1 THE CENTRALITY OF CARBON TO THE ORGANIC MOLECULES OF LIFE

Mere molecules are the stuff that constitutes a cell. Yet a cell is hundreds of thousands of times their size! So if molecules are built of atoms and if structure at the cellular level is on a scale much larger than that of atoms, then it follows that at least some of the molecules we observe will be huge by comparison with the atoms that compose them. How are these huge biomolecules to be constructed?

Of the 90 or so naturally occurring elements, only about 28 of them find their way into significant amounts of cellular structure. And of those, only four—carbon (C), oxygen (O), hydrogen (H), and nitrogen (N)—compose 95% of the mass of the cell! Among these four kinds of elements is one whose atoms are incredibly versatile for the purpose of building large biological molecules. That element is carbon.

Carbon has 6 protons and 6 electrons (see Figure 4.2). Two of these electrons fill an inner shell leaving four electrons to populate its outer shell. As a result, carbon tends to form covalent bonds—to share its four electrons. This is useful for building biological molecules because covalent bonds are directed—giving specific shapes to the molecules formed from them. The fact that carbon forms four

such bonds means it can bond easily to four other atoms. And if carbon atoms readily bond to other carbon atoms, we can begin to understand how molecules of enormous size and elegantly crafted shape can be designed.

This versatility of structure can be further refined by using the other three kinds of elements mentioned above; all of whose atoms are light and easily form covalent bonds as well. Hydrogen forms one covalent bond, oxygen forms two, and nitrogen forms three (see Figure 4.2). So virtually any shape of molecule can be designed with these wonderful and versatile subunits.

From life's vast diversity of species, we may infer the existence of millions of different sorts of molecules out there supporting all of it. And now we can see how the versatile bonding potentials of carbon, hydrogen, nitrogen, and oxygen atoms well serve the production of that diversity. This inference causes us to wonder (fearfully!) how many of these diverse molecules we will have to study before even a rudimentary understanding of life is possible! Yes, biochemical life is complex, but we are in for a pleasant surprise.

It is true that huge biological molecules are composed of thousands of individual atoms. But most of them are built from a small collection—perhaps 40 or so distinct kinds—of simpler molecules containing only 10 to 100 atoms. We call these simpler building block molecules **monomers** (*mono* in Greek = one). The much larger molecules assembled from these monomers are called **polymers** (*poly* in Greek = many). Some of the common monomers are pictured in Figure 4.3. Once we've learned the names and structures of a few of the most important monomers, we start finding them in the polymers

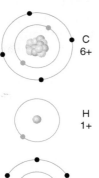

Figure 4.2 The carbon atom, with four electrons in its outer shell is constructed so that it readily bonds covalently with four other atoms. This makes large molecules possible. Hydrogen's shell fills by bonding to one other atom, oxygen by bonding with two other atoms, and nitrogen, three other atoms. How convenient! These 4 kinds of atoms compose 95% of cell structure by mass.

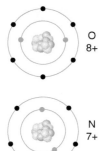

monomer—any chemical compound that can be used as a building block or structural subunit in the assembly of a much larger molecule called a *polymer*.

polymer—a large chemical compound formed by assembly of repeating structural units called *monomers*.

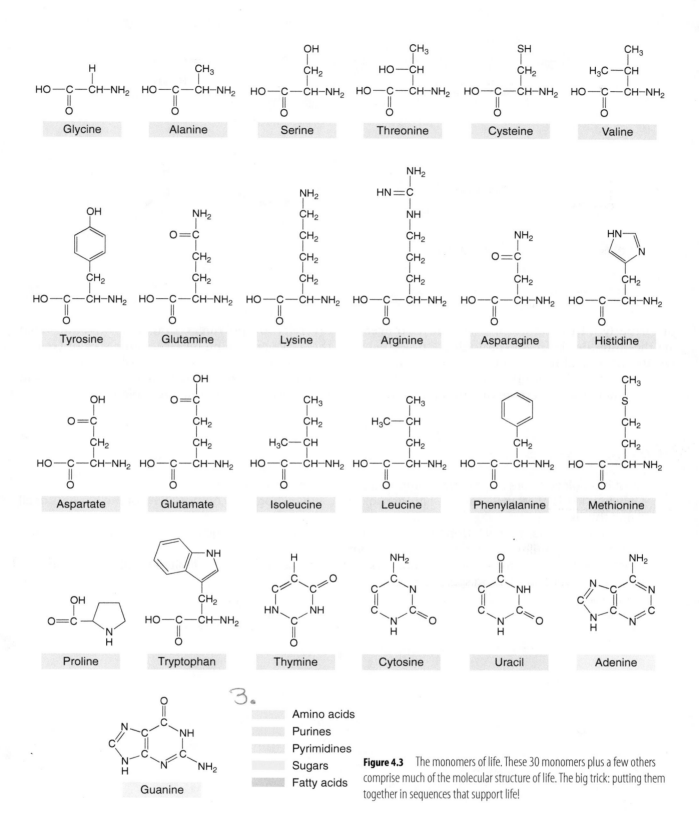

Figure 4.3 The monomers of life. These 30 monomers plus a few others comprise much of the molecular structure of life. The big trick: putting them together in sequences that support life!

Glycine | Alanine | Serine | Threonine | Cysteine | Valine

Tyrosine | Glutamine | Lysine | Arginine | Asparagine | Histidine

Aspartate | Glutamate | Isoleucine | Leucine | Phenylalanine | Methionine

Proline | Tryptophan | Thymine | Cytosine | Uracil | Adenine

Guanine

Amino acids
Purines
Pyrimidines
Sugars
Fatty acids

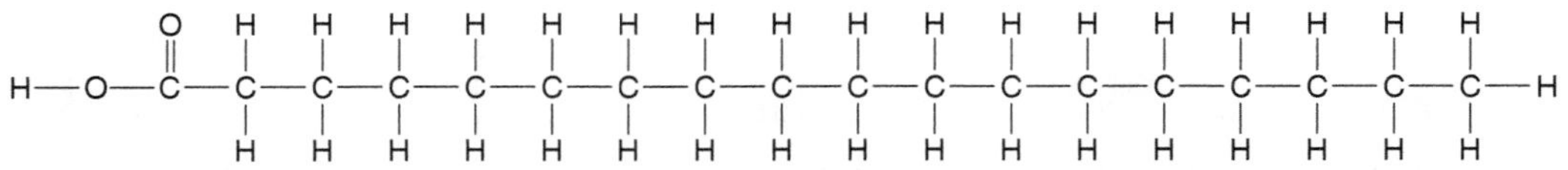

Stearic acid

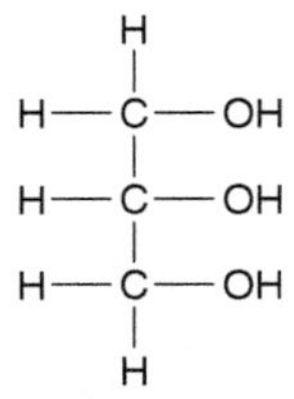

Glycerol

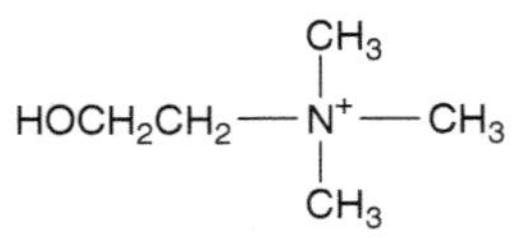

Choline

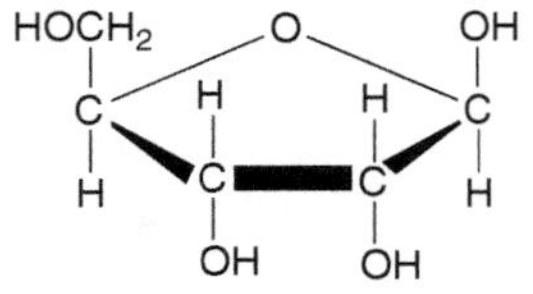

Ribose

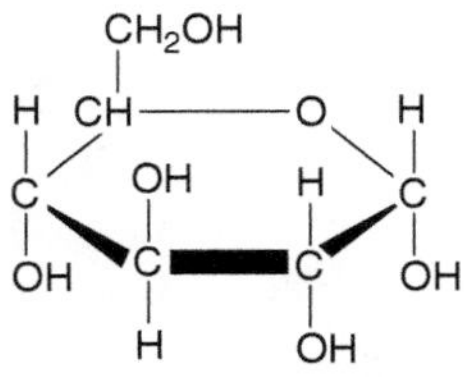

Glucose

Figure 4.3 (*Continued*)

of virtually all the organisms we study. So even at the humble level of biological molecules, we discover a glorious unity concealed within diversity. There is a unity structurally in the set of monomers used to create life but an incredible diversity of polymers that can be built from them. We are seeing here the same sort of Genius that can take a few basic oil colors on a palette and generate an infinite variety of colors and paintings using the same few pigments.

IN OTHER WORDS

1. Most biomolecules are huge in size compared to the atoms that compose them.
2. Only four kinds of atoms—carbon, nitrogen, oxygen, and hydrogen—compose 95% of the biomass of all living things.
3. Because carbon has four electrons in its outer shell, it is well suited to bind covalently to four other atoms. This predicts its utility for constructing large biomolecules.
4. Most large biological molecules are polymers that are constructed from a limited number of monomers commonly found in all living systems.

4.2 CONSTRUCTION AND DEGRADATION OF ORGANIC MOLECULES

A major portion of the cell's metabolism is the set of chemical reactions involved in synthesizing, changing, and degrading biological molecules. A cell living in the sheltered environment of your body receives the raw materials it needs for molecular synthesis in the form of monomers (simple sugars, fatty acids, amino acids, or nucleotides). A single, independent cell like a bacterium living in a pond must build even these monomers from still simpler molecules like ammonia, carbon dioxide, and water (see Figure 4.4).

Once any cell has the monomers needed for growth, metabolic reactions link these monomers together into polymers. These reactions are essentially the same in all cells. In each case, a large catalytic molecule called an *enzyme* (see Section 4.5) attaches to two monomers. It removes an oxygen and hydrogen atom from one monomer and a hydrogen from the other. Then it covalently bonds the two monomers together. The two hydrogens and the oxygen are combined to form water. The entire process is termed a **condensation** reaction (see Figure 4.5).

Consider, for example, the formation of the polymer starch—the major sort of molecule that was in your breakfast cereal this morning. The cereal plant cell uses an enzyme called *starch synthase* to take two simple sugar molecules, called glucose, and bond them together to form a **dimer** (*di* in Greek = two). The synthase enzyme continues to add glucose monomers to the dimer to lengthen the growing chain until a large polymer of starch is assembled.

And if you like observing genius in design, isn't it exceedingly efficient that the molecular by-product of forming all the various monomers into polymers is simply water—the universal solvent of the cell? If a system is very, very carefully designed, there is no categorical waste anywhere in it. Everything is useful somewhere!

At times, polymers need to be degraded back to monomers. Again, across legions of kinds of cells, the process is essentially the same. An enzyme binds to a polymer and breaks a covalent bond between two monomers. It then takes an oxygen and a hydrogen that were once part of a water molecule and binds them to one of the monomers. Another hydrogen from a water molecule is bound to the other monomer. The two monomers, now bound to new atoms, float freely and stably in solution (see Figure 4.6).

This process, the reverse of condensation, is termed **hydrolysis** because the atoms from a water molecule are used to stabilize the breaking (lysing) of a bond in a polymer molecule. When a portly gentlemen goes on a diet, deep within his adipose tissues, the process of hydrolysis degrades fat molecules—polymers—into monomers. These monomers can be further broken down to generate cellular energy.

---

condensation—a chemical reaction in which two molecules combine to form one with loss of a small molecule—usually water in biological systems.

dimer—the result of a condensation reaction in which two monomers are bonded together.

hydrolysis—a chemical reaction in which water is split (lysed) into a hydrogen ion and an —OH ion. In polymer degradation, these ions are added to each product stabilizing the resulting monomer and smaller polymer.

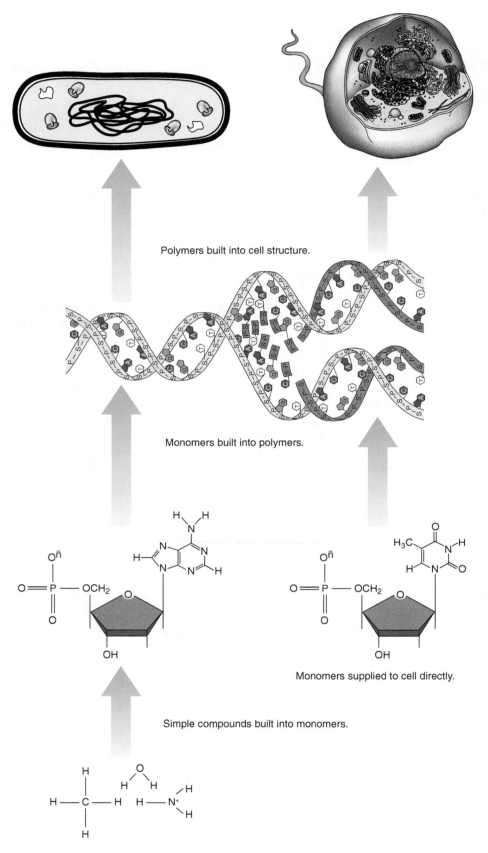

Figure 4.4 Biosynthesis starts with what is available. For the bacterial cell in a pond (left-hand side) more enzymatic machinery is needed because starting materials are simpler. A cell in your brain (right-hand side) has an easier time of it with monomers supplied directly in the bloodstream.

Polymers built into cell structure.

Monomers built into polymers.

Monomers supplied to cell directly.

Simple compounds built into monomers.

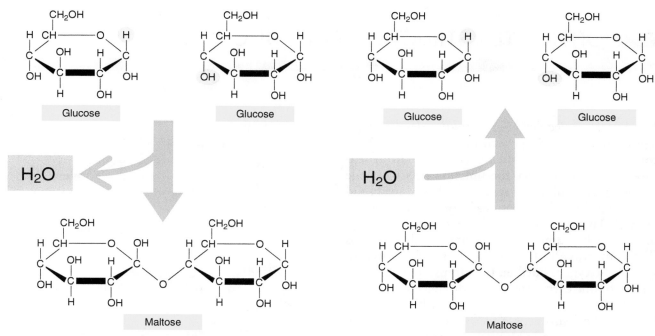

Figure 4.5 Condensation of two monomers to form a dimer. Addition of further monomers will generate a polymer, starch. An enzyme carries out this reaction.

Figure 4.6 Hydrolysis of a dimer to form two monomers. Water is needed. It is split into a hydrogen and an —OH group which are added to the resulting monomers to chemically stabilize them. The enzyme that carries out this reaction is often not the same enzyme that performed the (reverse) condensation reaction shown in Figure 4.5.

IN OTHER WORDS

1. Building, altering, and degrading the cell's biological molecules is a major component of metabolism.
2. Building cell structure requires either the acquisition or construction of molecular monomers followed by condensation reactions that polymerize these monomers into large polymeric molecules.
3. Hydrolysis reactions are used by the cell to disassemble polymers for subsequent reuse or transport of the resulting monomers.

CARBOHYDRATES: STRUCTURE AND FUNCTION

Biological molecules or *biomolecules,* though legion in variety, have been organized into about four broad classes based on their structural features (Table 4.1). Since the function of a molecule is the direct result of its structure, these four broad classes tend to differ from each other functionally as well. The class of biomolecules called *carbohydrates* got its name from the three kinds of atoms that comprise all of its molecules: carbon, hydrogen, and oxygen. Further, the atoms are present in a ratio of one carbon to two hydrogens to one oxygen $(CH_2O)_n$, where n can be any whole number. Usually, the hydrogens and oxygens in the molecules are peripherally bonded to carbon atoms that are more centrally arranged within the molecule.

Sugars

The monomeric molecules (the building blocks) among the carbohydrates are the simple sugars or **monosaccharides** (*saccharo* in Greek = sugar). By far, the most important of these in all living systems is **glucose,** the form of sugar found in the human bloodstream. Its molecular formula is $C_6H_{12}O_6$ (see Figure 4.7). Notice the 1:2:1 ratio of carbons, hydrogens, and oxygens that make it a carbohydrate.

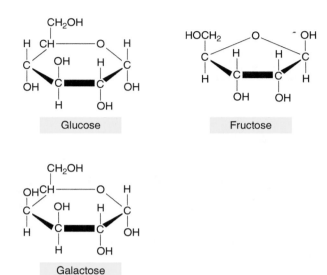

Glucose

Fructose

Galactose

Figure 4.7   Three common monosaccharides with identical molecular formulas but very different structural formulas. Carbon atoms are represented by apices at corners of each polygon.

The milk sugar galactose and the sugar **fructose,** found in fruit and in honey, both have the same molecular formula as glucose, $C_6H_{12}O_6$. The -OH groups (hydroxyl groups) that form common parts of the structure of these sugars make them very soluble in water and, therefore, in bodily fluids, such as blood (glucose) or milk (galactose). Look again at Figure 4.7. Though the molecular formulas are identical for these three sugars, the structural formulas and their resulting shapes are quite distinct. The manner in which the atoms are bonded to each other makes a difference in living systems. Enzymes

Table 4.1   Classes of Biomolecules

Class	Diagnostic Features
carbohydrates	molecules contain atoms of carbon, hydrogen, and oxygen in a ratio of 1:2:1
lipids	molecules are hydrophobic, insoluble in water, oils, fats
proteins	polymers of amino acids, linked in linear chains, contain nitrogen
nucleic acids	polymers composed of nucleotide monomers, includes informational molecules DNA and RNA

monosaccharide—a simple sugar built on a structure of anywhere from three to seven carbon atoms with associated hydrogen and oxygen atoms.

glucose—a monosaccharide sugar that is central to cellular metabolism, the form of sugar found in the human bloodstream.

fructose—a monosaccharide sugar that is found in many foods; fruits rich in the disaccharide sucrose have high levels of fructose, a component of sucrose.

in the body encounter these differences in shape between sugars and will only utilize the one they fit and bind to. Throughout nature, simple sugars are a ready source of energy for driving biological processes. They also serve as building blocks in larger polymers for energy storage and structural purposes.

The most widespread sugar found in nature is a disaccharide or double sugar called sucrose ($C_{12}H_{22}O_{11}$). Sugarcane stalks and sugar beet roots are loaded with it. It is our common table sugar. Planet Earth generates over 1 billion tons of it per year. Plant cells manufacture it enzymatically by doing a condensation reaction. They link together the monosaccharides glucose and fructose, discarding a water molecule in the process (see Figure 4.8). Sucrose is an efficiently transportable form of energy in plants.

In the cuboidal cells of human female breast tissue, yet another disaccharide is formed. There, the monosaccharides glucose and galactose are condensed enzymatically to form the disaccharide lactose ($C_{12}H_{22}O_{11}$), or milk sugar (see Figure 4.8b). Happily, in your infantile digestive tract you had an enzyme that hydrolyzed lactose to glucose and galactose. You were able to absorb these sugars and use their energy to generate neural tissues that would eventually enable you to read this sentence.

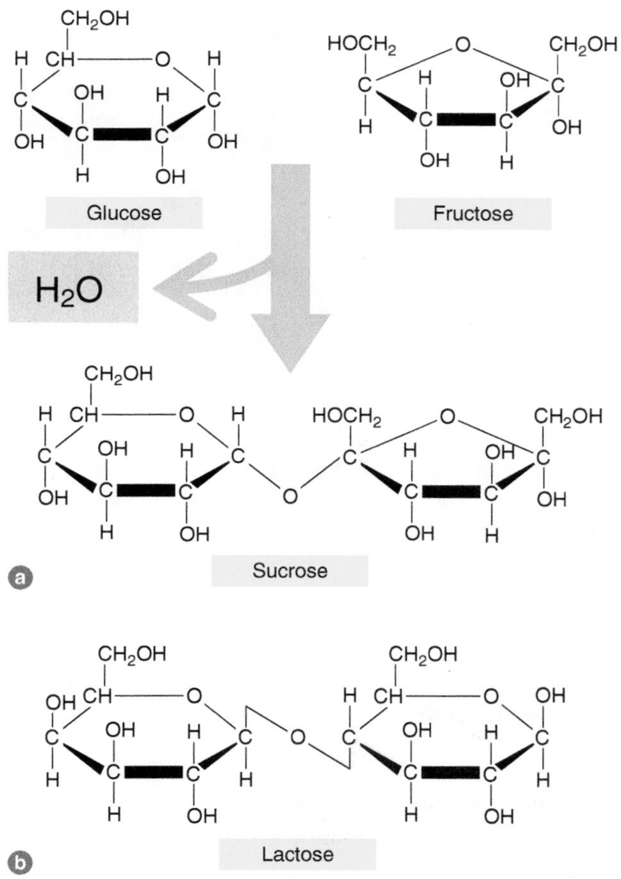

Carbohydrate Polymers

Simple sugars can be covalently bonded together to form disaccharides or they can be linked to each other in larger numbers to become much longer polymeric molecules. The sugar glucose, when polymerized in this way, gives rise to molecules containing thousands of individual atoms. The most common of these polymers are starch, glycogen, and cellulose. Though all three of these polymers are composed exclusively of identical glucose monomers, they are quite distinct in structure and in solubility because of the way in which the glucoses are bonded to each other in each of these molecules.

Starch (see Figure 4.9a) can be a relatively simple straight-chained amylose polymer up to several hundred glucose units in length. Or it can be a branched-chain amylopectin polymer in which, at about every 30th glucose, a side chain of additional glucoses branches off. Starch polymers fold into spiral coil arrangements that render them insoluble in water. This makes them an excellent immobile storage form of energy. Plant cells within a potato tuber (see Figure 4.9b) are loaded with granules composed entirely of starch. When you ingest potatoes, rice, wheat, or oats, you receive that stored energy. In your digestive tract, an enzyme

Figure 4.8 **(a)** Condensation reaction between glucose and fructose to generate sucrose and water. **(b)** the structure of lactose, the sugar found in mammalian milk.

disaccharide—two monosaccharide sugars covalently bonded together by a condensation reaction.

sucrose—a disaccharide sugar; energy storage form in plants; table sugar.

lactose—a double sugar or dissacharide found in mammalian milk; milk sugar.

starch—a polysaccharide polymer of glucose sugar units; energy storage form in plants; major portion of human diet.

amylose—a linear polymer of glucose subunits, a component of plant starch molecules.

amylopectin—a highly branched polysaccharide polymer of glucose units in starch; product of plant metabolism.

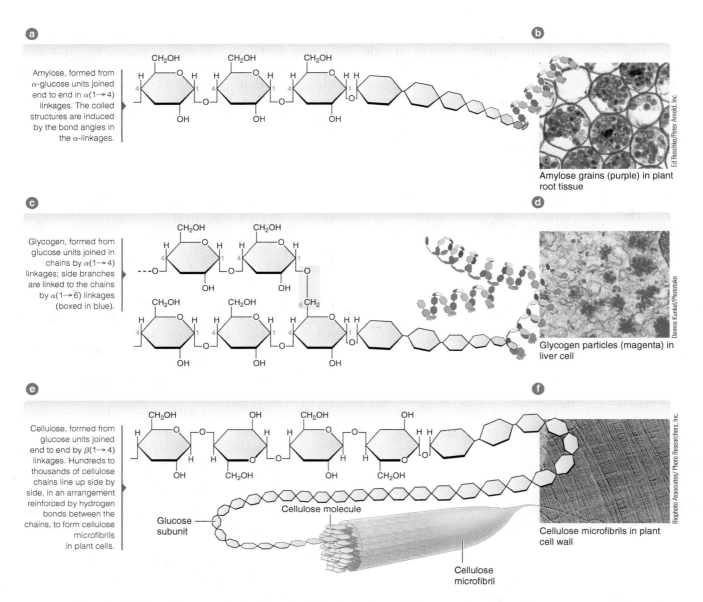

(a) Amylose, formed from α-glucose units joined end to end in α(1→4) linkages. The coiled structures are induced by the bond angles in the α-linkages.

Amylose grains (purple) in plant root tissue

(c) Glycogen, formed from glucose units joined in chains by α(1→4) linkages; side branches are linked to the chains by α(1→6) linkages (boxed in blue).

Glycogen particles (magenta) in liver cell

(e) Cellulose, formed from glucose units joined end to end by β(1→4) linkages. Hundreds to thousands of cellulose chains line up side by side, in an arrangement reinforced by hydrogen bonds between the chains, to form cellulose microfibrils in plant cells.

Glucose subunit

Cellulose molecule

Cellulose microfibril

Cellulose microfibrils in plant cell wall

Figure 4.9 Polysaccharides **(a)** amylose, a straight-chain form of starch. Covalent linkages in the chain cause it to coil up as the chain grows in size. **(b)** starch (amylose) grains in plant tissue **(c)** a branched chain of glycogen **(d)** glycogen particles (magenta) in liver cells. **(e)** chain in a cellulose molecule. Many separate chains bond to each other within a cellulose microfibril. **(f)** microfibrils are visible under an electron microscope as the warp and woof of a plant cell wall. All subunits in all of these molecules are glucose. Bonds between the glucoses vary however.

called *amylase* hydrolyzes starch molecules down to their component glucose monomers so that their energy is more readily available to you.

Sometimes animals need to store energy efficiently, as for example, when an excess of glucose is present in the blood. In your liver (and in skeletal muscle), excess glucose from your breakfast starch load is removed from the blood. By condensation, it is assembled to form a highly branched polymer called **glycogen** (see Figure 4.9c). Later in the morning, as circulating glucose gets used for energy, glycogen is enzymatically degraded and the resulting glucose is released into the bloodstream to keep blood sugar levels within an acceptable range.

The most abundant organic molecule in the world is the polymeric carbohydrate, **cellulose** (see

glycogen—a polysaccharide formed from glucose primarily in muscle and liver tissue; serves as a temporary storage form of energy.

cellulose—a polymeric carbohydrate whose subunits are monomers of glucose. It is probably the most common organic molecule on the face of the earth.

Figure 4.9e). It makes up most of the supportive structure of plant tissue. Wood is approximately 65% cellulose. Cotton is 91% cellulose. A single cellulose molecule can have anywhere from 300 to 15,000 glucose monomers in its structure depending on the species of organism it comes from. Plants need tough, sturdy cell walls both to support their aerial growth and to protect them from cellular bursting when they are submerged in water (see Figure 4.9f). The distinct bonding of glucose units in cellulose supports these functions.

Each successive glucose monomer in cellulose is bonded such that it is "upside down" from the one next to it. This arrangement allows additional covalent bonds to form *between* strands of the polymer, generating a strong, net-like structure (note the interior of the microfibril in Figure 4.9e). Humans have taken this wonderfully designed molecule and modified it for use in everything from explosives, to movie film, to building insulation, where it is proving safer for humans than traditional fiberglass insulation.

IN OTHER WORDS

1. Carbohydrates are biomolecules composed of carbon, hydrogen, and oxygen atoms in a ratio of 1 carbon to 2 hydrogens to 1 oxygen.
2. The simplest carbohydrates are the monosaccharides or simple sugars. Two examples are the six-carbon molecules glucose and fructose.
3. Although glucose and fructose have identical molecular formulas, their structural formulas and resulting recognition by cellular enzymes are distinct, giving them distinct roles to play in life.
4. Sucrose and lactose are two examples of disaccharides or double sugars that function as temporary transport and storage forms of energy.
5. The carbohydrate polymer starch is a plant polysaccharide composed of many glucose units that serves as a more permanent form of energy storage within plant tissues.
6. A corresponding form of energy storage in animals is the polysaccharide glycogen whose glucose subunits can be transported to tissues where immediate chemical energy needs exist.
7. The most abundant polysaccharide in the world is cellulose. Its major role is structural support in plant tissues.

4.4 LIPIDS: STRUCTURE AND FUNCTION

A second broad class of biomolecules, the lipids, derives its name from the term *lipos* in Greek, which referred to animal fat or vegetable oil. Unlike other classes of biomolecules, lipids are defined by their insolubility in water. Instead, they dissolve in solvents whose molecules are composed of nonpolar covalent bonds—solvents like benzene or chloroform. Lipids and their solvents are said to be **hydrophobic.** If you pour oil into water, it will separate itself from the water and form a discrete layer above the water. The large number and arrangement of nonpolar (H–C–H) bonds in the oil predict that this will happen. Polar molecules like water tend to attract each other and to exclude nonpolar oil molecules from their intervening spaces.

Lipids, then, include all substances that feel greasy or oily (see Figure 4.10). But this single solubility criterion means that the lipids include a wide diversity of molecules structurally and functionally. All fats, oils, waxes, and steroids are lipids. Functionally, lipids participate in membrane structure as protective outer coatings on the surfaces of many organisms, as storage forms of metabolic energy, and as signal molecules that diffuse toward, and recognize molecules on the cell surfaces of many organisms. Rather than classify the lipids into subgroups, we will examine three specific examples of lipids noting a truly pleasing correspondence between structure and function.

The Wonderfully Functional Fat Molecule

Many Americans are fat. This means that their tissues harbor a disproportionately large amount of a lipid polymer whose technical name is **triglyceride** (or triacylglycerol). This polymer (see Figure 4.11) is composed of three monomers of **fatty acid,** covalently bonded to a three-carbon **glycerol** molecule. Fatty acids are long chains of carbon atoms bonded to (and surrounded by) hydrogen atoms. They become attached to the glycerol molecule by the condensation reaction discussed in Section 4.2. A hydroxyl group (-O-H) from each fatty acid and a hydrogen atom from

> **hydrophobic**—water-fearing—descriptive of any molecule that water effectively excludes from its own surroundings due to the extensive hydrogen bonding that occurs between water molecules.
>
> **triglyceride**—a glycerol bonded to three fatty acids; the main constituent of plant and animal fats.
>
> **fatty acid**—a long chain of carbons and hydrogens that is a monomer from which fat polymers are constructed.
>
> **glycerol**—a three-carbon molecule with three —OH side groups to which fatty acids are attached in triglyceride synthesis.

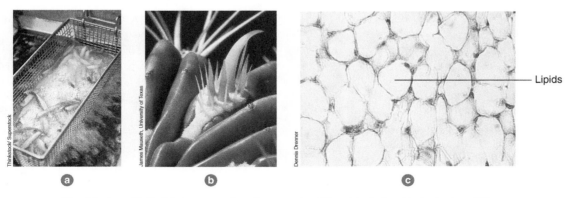

Thinkstock/ Superstock

James Mauseth, University of Texas

Dennis Drenner

(a)

(b)

(c)

Lipids

Figure 4.10 The oil foods are fried in **(a)**, the waxy surface of a cactus plant **(b)**, and the fat found in the droplets within these adipose cells **(c)** are all examples of lipids.

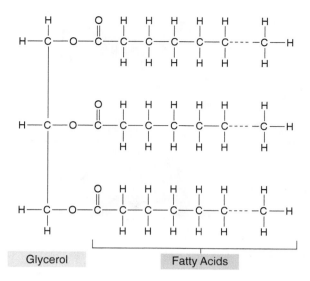

Figure 4.11 A triglyceride or fat molecule possesses only three kinds of atoms. But notice that there are far fewer oxygen atoms than would be present in a carbohydrate molecule this size. The dotted lines within the fatty acids represent many more —CH2 groups than are shown here.

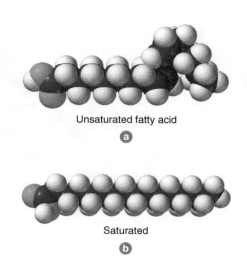

Unsaturated fatty acid

a

Saturated

b

Figure 4.12 **(a)** Linoleic acid, an unsaturated fatty acid with two double bonds adding to its structural rigidity. (red atoms = oxygen, black = carbon, white = hydrogen) **(b)** Palmitic acid, a saturated fatty acid; all carbon atoms are singly bonded to hydrogens or to each other giving free rotation of the molecule around any covalent bond in the chain.

the glycerol molecule are removed to form water, and the fatty acid is linked to one of the carbons on the glycerol molecule. So then, three separate condensation reactions take us from three fatty acids and one glycerol to a single fat molecule.

Let's consider those monomers in more detail. Fatty acids vary in structure. They range in length from as few as 4 carbons to as many as 24. They are produced in many kinds of plant and animal cells. Two of them, linoleic acid and alpha-linolenic acid, have been shown to be essential to humans. This means that we must have them for our normal metabolic processes, but we can't synthesize them so they must be supplied in our diets. (You don't need a triple cheeseburger to get them—in fact, you get far more of them in nuts and grains.)

Fatty acids from plant tissue often have one to several double covalent bonds between their carbon atoms (see Figure 4.12). Since this involves binding fewer hydrogen atoms, these fatty acids are said to be *unsaturated* (with hydrogen atoms).

Saturated fatty acids, by contrast, have carbon atoms singly bonded to each other and thus to a full complement of surrounding hydrogen atoms (see Figure 4.12). A double bond inhibits free rotation around itself for the atoms to either side of it. So it adds a certain rigidity to the fatty acid containing it. Fat molecules containing unsaturated fatty acids in their structure are termed *unsaturated fats*. Their rigidity tends to inhibit their tangling

through each other, so they remain liquids (oily) at room temperature and at body temperature.

Saturated fats, by contrast, are more frequently the product of animal tissue. Since their fatty acids have free rotation around every single carbon in their chain, they tend to rotate their way through other nearby fatty acids forming a wonderfully messy network that's a pasty solid at room temperature. Dairy products, creams, cheeses, and animal fats are high in saturated fats (see Figure 4.13). There's a positive correlation between a diet high in saturated fat and **atherosclerosis** with accompanying heart disease. On the other hand, a diet more respective of the Biblical (Genesis 1) mandate to eat a variety of fruits and vegetables is healthier for the heart and blood vessel walls. The Biblical text also inveighs against ingestion of animal fat. Fascinating! What other life wisdom might this amazing resource contain?

What function do fatty acids serve in the tissues where they are found? They are a wonderfully designed and highly concentrated source of energy. Energy? Yes. Carbon-hydrogen bonds are fairly easy to break—little energy is required to do so. And when

atherosclerosis—a thickening of the walls of arterial blood vessels as a result of the accumulation of fatty materials being transported in the blood.

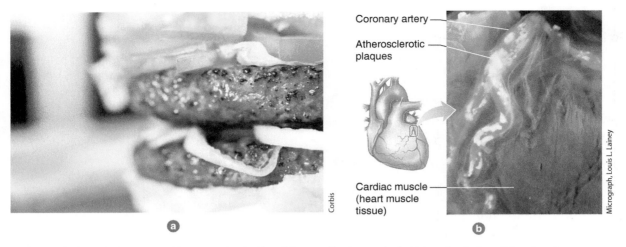

Coronary artery

Atherosclerotic plaques

Cardiac muscle (heart muscle tissue)

Micrograph, Louis L. Lainey

Corbis

(a)

(b)

Figure 4.13 **(a)** Diets high in saturated fats can result in buildup of fibrous and lipid material called "plaque" on the inner lining of arteries. **(b)** Plaque appears as zones of lighter color in this coronary artery.

Charles Detwiler

Figure 4.14 An ignited cashew nut's oil has many energy-rich C-H bonds that support prolonged burning.

new bonds form, oxygen is often involved, so lots of energy is given off in the formation of the new bonds.

A large cashew nut (see Figure 4.14), once lit with a match will burn for several minutes on the fatty acids in its oils. But fat energy is also concentrated. We said that fatty acids are hydrophobic. That means they can be efficiently

(tightly) packed or stored with no water molecules or "water weight" between them. That extra 10 lbs of fat you are storing right up front would have to be almost 70 lbs if you were to store that energy as a hydrophilic carbohydrate like glycogen with all its associated water weight.

Why don't we just store energy as fatty acid monomers? Why are they polymerized three at a time into fat molecules? Recall that unlike carbohydrates, fats are a long-term storage form of energy. Hence, there are (active) sites metabolically and (lean) times nutritionally when fatty acid degradation is needed. At other times they are not needed. Fats need to be stored and then transported to those sites where carbohydrate energy sources have run low. The body participates in a wisdom

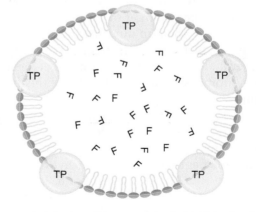

Figure 4.15 A chylomicron. This macro-molecular "glob" of various lipids and proteins, transports fat molecules (the small interior "F"'s) from sites of production or absorption to sites of use. TP = protein that transports fat molecules into or out of the chylomicron.

that has designed the monomers for immediate degradation for energy and the polymers as efficient transport to degradation sites. A variety of macromolecular bodies (see Figure 4.15) construct, recognize, incorporate, and transport fat polymers at precise times and places to locations where they are to be broken down and utilized. At appropriate sites, as, for example, muscle cells, the polymers are hydrolyzed and the monomers degraded for energy as carbohydrate energy pools are exhausted. It is a glorious system.

The Amazing Phospholipid

We said that fat molecules, like oils and waxes, are hydrophobic. Water excludes them (see Figure 4.16). But what if we take a triglyceride polymer, remove one fatty acid, and replace it with a much smaller organic molecule that has a phosphate group on the end of it (see Figure 4.17)? The collection of oxygen atoms in the phosphate group make it a very polar group, and perching this group on the one end of a triglyceride converts it into a **phospholipid**—a large polymeric molecule that is now nonpolar over most

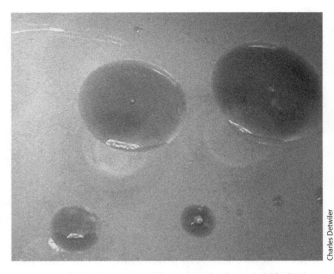

Charles Detwiler

Figure 4.16   Oil droplets on water. The water molecules exclude the lipid molecules into droplets.

phospholipid—a glycerol molecule attached to two fatty acids and a third, small organic molecule containing a phosphate group; a major component of animal cell membranes.

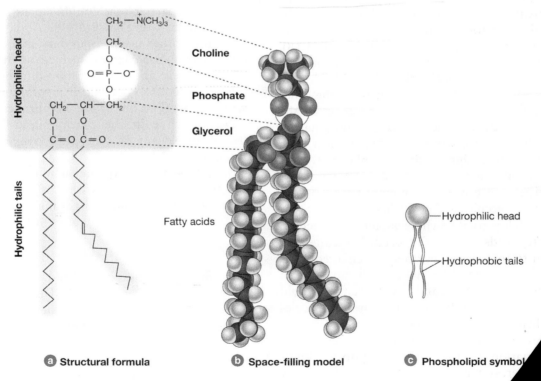

a **Structural formula**   b **Space-filling model**   c **Phospholipid symbol**

Figure 4.17   Three diagrams of a phospholipid; the major parts are labelled. Notice in **(c)** how the phospholipid is represented wh of them are drawn together in one diagram.

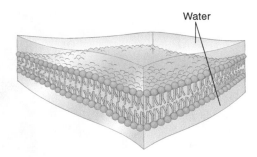

Figure 4.18 A bilayer of phospholipids. The red spheres represent the phosphate-containing group bound to glycerol. The light blue lines are fatty acids. A water layer has been added to each side to represent the bilayer's environment.

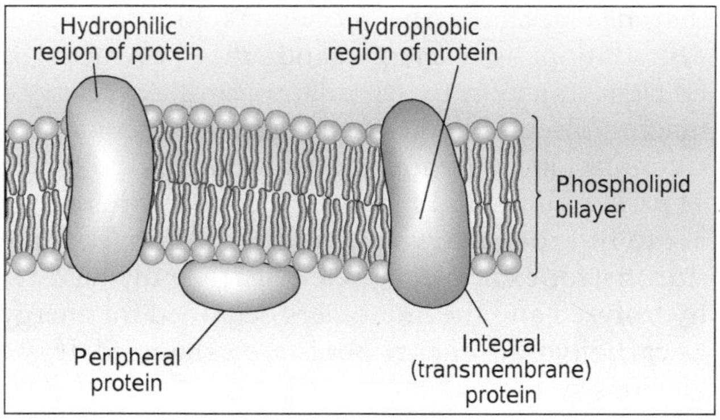

of its structure but very polar at one end. What utility has a molecule of this sort?

Much as school activity goes on inside and just outside of a school building, life's chemistry occurs both inside of and just outside of a cell. And water is the wonderfully superior solvent for the chemistry of life. Because very different activities occur inside and outside of these enterprises, we require a discrete boundary or barrier in both cases. For the school building, the boundary is a wall. What works to separate the internal aqueous and external aqueous environments for the cell? Could phospholipids be used for that purpose? Suppose we build two layers of phospholipids next to each other (see Figure 4.18). If we orient the layers so that the polar groups in each layer lie close to each other, their like charges will repel each other. But if we put them the other way round with the large nonpolar areas of the polymers toward each other, we have a truly amazing design—one so ingenious that someone must have seen this before designing the phospholipid itself. Note how this neatly compartmentalizes internal and external aqueous environments. The nonpolar parts of the molecules will be attracted to each other ⬦ stability to the whole system. The length ⬦ ⬦ty acids would give needed thickness or ⬦ the barrier. Further, the charged parts ⬦ would be facing both into the cell ⬦ surroundings where they would ⬦ all the water molecules ⬦ndary!

⬦ls more perfection! ⬦ phospholipids ⬦ vast variety ⬦ interior ⬦ cross this ⬦ through a

Figure 4.19 label text:
Hydrophilic region of protein
Hydrophobic region of protein
Phospholipid bilayer
Peripheral protein
Integral (transmembrane) protein

Figure 4.19 A bilayer of phospholipids in which three protein molecules are positioned. Some proteins serve as gates controlling what crosses from one side of the bilayer to the other.

thick nonpolar interior to do so. Yet very small but useful polar molecules like oxygen and water itself can diffuse freely; that is, they can move from where they are in high concentration across the membrane to where they are in lower concentration. Still another powerful advantage of this bilayer is that it is both elastic and fluid in nature. It is possible to build gates—we'll do this with proteins later—that will selectively allow certain substances across our barrier that couldn't pass through our lipid bilayer (see Figure 4.19). And those gates, as well as other useful boundary markers, can be given hydrophobic lateral surfaces so that they will wander freely about in the two-dimensional lipid bilayer sheet that is the cell membrane. But they will *not* just float out of the membrane.

So we have in the phospholipid a powerful use of an elegant idea repeated over and over in thousands of iterations. One phospholipid is miniscule—invisible to the light microscope user. But the cell membrane is something we can easily observe with an ordinary light microscope.

Mighty Testosterone

Our final example of a lipid is the hormone **testosterone** (see Figure 4.20). Despite its obvious structural difference from either fatty acids or glycerol, testosterone is a "good" lipid: It is freely

testosterone—a steroid hormone secreted by the sex organs in males and to a lesser degree in females.

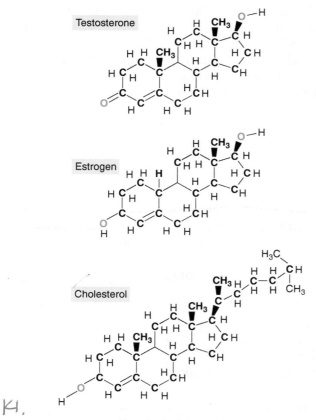

Figure 4.20 Structural formulas for the steroid hormones testosterone, estrogen, and the steroidal lipid cholesterol. Hydrogen atoms are covalently bonded to adjacent carbon atoms.

fat-soluble but not soluble in water. **Hormones** with the general structural formula shown in Figure 4.20 are called **steroid** hormones. Testosterone, because it induces the formation of secondary sexual characteristics in males, is termed an *androgenic steroid hormone*. The simplest assumption we could make about hormone structure is that hormones with radically different functions would have radically different structures. Amazingly, this is not so. If we remove just one –CH₃ group and convert one –C=O group to a –C–O–H group, testosterone becomes estrogen (see Figure 4.20), the hormone that produces the secondary sexual characteristics of the female! In fact, that removal process is exactly what happens in females. They

hormone—a chemical generated in one cell that has its effect in cells elsewhere in the organism.

steroid—a lipid that consists of four fused carbon rings with additional atoms bonded around the exterior of the rings.

first produce testosterone. But then, by just two little enzymatic changes, estrogen is formed and the wonderful human female with all her reproductive capabilities is the result! Eve was formed from Adam: Her estrogen is formed from testosterone. Yet her radical departure from Adam's appearance results from a hormone that appears almost exactly like his.

If, instead, we were to add a simple eight-carbon chain to one end of the basic four-ring structure, we would convert testosterone to cholesterol (see Figure 4.20). Cholesterol inserts into membranes between fatty acids contributing to membrane permeability and fluidity. So small changes in these steroid molecules have a huge effect on where they're found and what they do there. Why is this so?

How do hormone molecules play such powerful roles in living organisms? Testosterone is generated in and secreted from the human male testes. From there it travels to all of the body's tissues through the bloodstream. Its role in these tissues is to slip through lipid membranes (it is lipid soluble!), bind to its own receptor molecule within the cell, and change the behavior of any cell in which that receptor is found (see Figure 4.21). Think of all the various, scarcely related changes that occur as a male transitions from boyhood to manhood! Tissues in the axillary, pubic, and facial areas start generating thicker hair. Vocal cord tissues

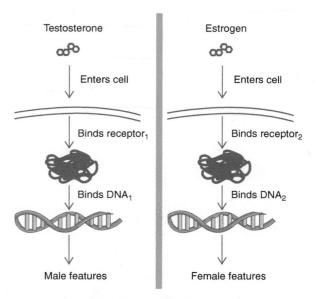

Figure 4.21 Hormonal effects on tissues. If a slightly different hormone binds an entirely different receptor, then the information sampled and the resulting changes in information expression can be quite large!

thicken, muscle mass increases, and bones lengthen at a faster rate while also becoming more dense. Brain size increases proportionately as compared to the female of the species. (Biologists often make sexist comments without even planning to.) Subcutaneous facial fat decreases. Sperm cell production begins. How can one hormone and its receptor cause all of these diverse changes to occur in many body tissues? All of this different expression of information in different tissues of the body is in response to one single (rather small) lipid molecule—the mighty testosterone.

IN OTHER WORDS

1. Lipids are a class of biomolecules defined by their insolubility in water; they include oils, fats, waxes, and steroids.
2. Common functions for lipids include long-term energy storage, structural parts of membranes, surface coatings of plant and animal tissues, and signal molecules within living systems.
3. A fat molecule is constructed from three fatty acids and a glycerol molecule by a set of three condensation reactions.
4. Unsaturated fatty acids contribute to fat molecules that remain liquid at physiological temperatures; these fatty acids are more common in plant tissues.
5. Dietary consumptions of excess saturated fat can result in atherosclerosis in the human circulatory system and in the heart in particular.
6. Fatty acids are readily degradable into two-carbon fragments representing readily available energy; fatty acids are polymerized into fat molecules for storage or for transport.
7. Phospholipids differ from fats in that one fatty acid is replaced by a hydrophilic functional group containing a phosphate; they are a major constituent of membrane structure.
8. Steroid hormones are lipids used for signaling purposes in both plant and animal tissues; testosterone, a sex hormone, is an example.
9. Testosterone is similar in structure to cholesterol and estrogen, yet it has a wide variety of signaling roles unique to the male organism.

4.5 PROTEINS: STRUCTURE AND FUNCTION

By far, the most complicated, powerful, elegant, and diverse class of biomolecules is the proteins. Proteins have been designed to bind every imaginable sort of molecule—from simple ions to complex molecules like sugars, nucleic acids—even other proteins. They compose 50% or more of your cells by weight and they are distributed through virtually every part of every cell in your body. They support a legion of life functions (see Table 4.2). Among the enzyme are thousands of different known types of proteins that catalyze over 4000 known chemical reactions. Other proteins transport substances in biological systems. Still others store amino acids nutritionally or serve as structural elements of muscle or as defensive antibodies in your immune system. They can be toxins, hormones, regulatory, or structural proteins. Yet amazingly, though there may be as many as 10^{12} different kinds of proteins in the organisms on this planet; most of them are built from only about 20 different building block monomers called **amino acids.**

A Glorious Structure Supports Myriads of Functions

Proteins are enormous in size compared to the atoms that compose them. A single molecule of the human enzyme DNA polymerase β (see Figure 4.22) is 39,000 times the mass of a hydrogen atom! Most proteins, structurally, are composed of single, long, unbranched chains of monomers—the amino acids—that are typically about 150 times the mass of a hydrogen atom. Chains of these amino acid residues, also called

> **amino acid**—a monomeric molecule used in synthesis of polypeptide chains or proteins. Contains both amino and acidic functional groups.
>
> **polypeptide**—a polymer formed from the covalent bonding of amino acids in a defined sequence. Small polymers are called *peptides*, larger ones *polypeptides* and still larger ones are referred to as *proteins*.

Table 4.2 Functional Classes of Proteins

Class with Examples	Function
Enzymes DNA polymerase amylase lactase lipase	synthesize new DNA digest starch degrades milk sugar breakdown of fat
Storage Proteins ovalbumin casein gliadin zein ferritin	source of amino acids in egg white in milk in wheat in corn iron storage in spleen
Transport Proteins hemoglobin myoglobin serum albumin β – lipoprotein	transports oxygen in blood oxygen in muscle cells fatty acids in blood lipids in blood
Contractile Proteins myosin actin dynein	for movement: filament, muscle cell filament, muscle cell filament in cilia
Protective Proteins antibodies complement	in blood and lymph "tag" foreign proteins kills some bacteria
Toxins botulinum toxin diphtheria toxin ricin	secondarily: poison food, bacterial kills cells, bacterial stops protein synthesis
Hormones insulin growth hormone	regulates glucose metabolism growth in bones
Structural Proteins virus coat protein	protective surface of virus particles
Regulatory Proteins *lac* repressor	control of lactose degradation
Receptor Proteins gp120	promotes viral binding to host cells

polypeptides, can be anywhere from 100 to 300 amino acids in length. But these chains fold into highly specific three-dimensional shapes. It is these shapes that are key to understanding how they work.

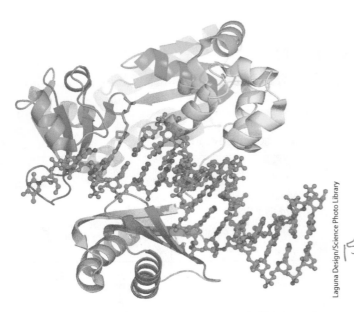

Laguna Design/Science Photo Library

Figure 4.22 The enzyme DNA polymerase. This enzyme rebuilds portions of a DNA molecule (a double helix showing individual atoms) during a DNA repair process. Separate polypeptide chains within the polymerase molecule are shown in different colors. Their individual amino acid monomers are not delineated.

What does a Designer do when He wants polymers for millions of specific functional roles He has in mind? Consider the ingenious structure of an amino acid monomer (see Figure 4.23). Each of 20 common amino acids has a single central carbon atom that is the structural base for four discrete functional groups bonded to it: (1) an "amino" group (–NH₂) that contributes to bonding between amino acids, (2) a carboxylic ("acid"ic) group (–COOH) that also contributes to bonding between amino acids, (3) a hydrogen atom that contributes versatility to the spatial direction in which bonds are formed, and (4) one of 20 different side groups (**R groups**) that are varying collections of atoms that determine the shape of the final polymer and thus its overall function. This is brilliant! Twenty different amino acids are distinguished by the chemical nature of the 20 distinct R groups that are possible (see Figure 4.3).

Much as 20 or so different orchestral instruments contribute to a wealth of distinct symphonic sounds, the 20 different amino acid R groups contribute to a wealth of chemical-structural possibilities in shaping

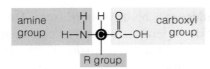

Figure 4.23 The generalized structure of an amino acid. See text for details.

a protein polymer. R groups vary all the way from a simple hydrogen atom in glycine to the complexity of the tryptophan R group. Some R groups' chemical arrangement leaves them with net charges and they are more stable in a polar aqueous environment—they are **hydrophilic**. Others, like leucine's, are entirely carbons and hydrogens making it hydrophobic or water-fearing. Since proteins require a stable, final shape in an aqueous environment, hydrophobic R groups will be found toward the interior of the protein and hydrophilic groups will project toward the outside. It is all so elegant …

As in other biomolecules, proteins are assembled from amino acid monomers by condensation reactions. The structure of an amino acid suggests, in part, how this process works (see Figure 4.24). Notice that a hydrogen atom can be removed from the amino group of one amino acid, and an oxygen and hydrogen, from the carboxyl group of another. These generate water and the two amino acids are then covalently bonded together in what is termed

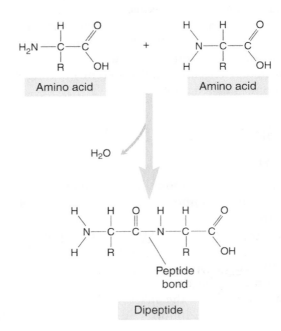

Figure 4.24 The generalized formation of a peptide bond. This is a condensation reaction—water is a product.

R group—the functional group of atoms peculiar to a specific kind of amino acid. It determines the unique function of that kind of amino acid.

hydrophilic—a molecule or region of a molecule to which water molecules are attracted because of the presence of polar bonds.

a **peptide bond.** In the reverse process, when you digest protein, you use enzymes to hydrolyze these peptide bonds so that the amino acids can be absorbed as nutrients.

In one respect, proteins are like college textbooks. A college textbook is a complex thing. To be useful to you, it exists in discrete levels, structurally. You can review the book as a whole or master a chapter of it, or you can refer to a page of, or simply read individual words of it. Protein molecules vary enormously in shape, size, and complexity. So it has been necessary to define at least four discrete levels of structure for the most complex proteins. All proteins participate to some degree in the first two of these levels. Let's define them.

The first or **primary** level of protein **structure** is simply the sequence of amino acids in its structure (see Figure 4.25). A cell uses its DNA sequences (genes) to determine how to place amino acids into the correct sequence to form a given protein. And just as the words of a book completely determine what the entire book is about, so the properties of each amino acid and their correct sequencing must be understood by the Designer in order to achieve a final folded form that will have the desired biological function.

During "construction," as the polypeptide chain lengthens, it begins to rotate around its many peptide bonds, twisting and folding as it does so. Certain sequences of amino acids respond to this folding process by specifying helical regions of structure (see Figure 4.25). Stability exists because every amino acid is hydrogen bonded to another one that is four amino acids away along the primary structure. We call this folding **secondary structure.** It takes us from the linearity of simple amino acid sequence to simple but three-dimensional molecules whose shape has the potential to rise above the chemistry of atoms and to begin to have a biological function. The α-keratin protein of lamb's wool exhibits long runs of repeated helical structure. Other amino acid primary sequences call for a flat, pleated sheet–like structure (see Figure 4.25). Silk fibers are composed of side-by-side amino acid chains in which individual amino acids of adjacent chains are hydrogen bonded to each other. α-Keratin and silk fibroin are examples of structural proteins. How amazing is a structure that, before it does its work, assembles itself!

For most protein molecules, biological function is only achieved at a still higher **tertiary** level of **structure.** At this structural level, the primary amino acid sequence of the protein is determining fine nuances of shape that allow for hundreds of different shapes and resultant functions (see Figure 4.25). The result of bending secondary helical regions at just the right places could become, for example, a molecule of myoglobin (see Figure 4.26) that effectively carries oxygen into muscle cells and then releases it for use there. Pleated-sheet regions, on the other hand, can be folded into barrel-like molecules that can serve as channels through membranes. Many enzymes possess a tertiary level of structure.

However, some biological functions are simply too complex to be carried out by a single polypeptide chain, no matter how long it is. These functions require the support of multiple, globular polypeptide chains associated intimately as subunits of a complex. This represents a **quaternary** level of protein **structure.**

An enzyme that repairs copies of DNA molecules (see Figure 4.22) in human cells is a widespread example. One polypeptide chain clamps onto the DNA molecule, another reads and inserts a new nucleotide (see below), and yet another chain removes the old damaged portion of the molecule. Here, we reach overwhelming levels of organizational creativity. The sequence of amino acids in each polypeptide chain determine (1) how that chain will fold to the tertiary shape that will support its own function and (2) how regions on the surface of that chain will associate with the other chains in the complex so as to enable the suite of functions of the overall complex—DNA copying, for example. Amazing. Life is very complex!

---

peptide bond—a covalent bond between the amino group of one amino acid and the acidic group of another amino acid. Water is a product of peptide bond formation

primary structure—the sequence of amino acids in the structure of a polypeptide or protein. The most basic level of protein structure.

secondary structure—the folding of an amino acid sequence into α-helical regions or planar sheets of amino acids. The folding that occurs is determined by the sequence of amino acids in that region of the polypeptide.

tertiary structure—the folding of regions of helical or pleated sheet secondary structures within a polypeptide chain into a unique higher-order shape that contributes function to the mature protein.

quaternary structure—multiple polypeptide chains associated with each other to form a complex, multimeric protein.

Figure 4.25 Proteins can exist at any of at least four increasingly levels of complexity. Rotation around peptide bonds allows for this. Folding, hydrogen bonding and occasional intra-strand covalent linkages account for higher level structures. Some small peptide hormones have only secondary structure. Many large enzyme complexes have quaternary structure.

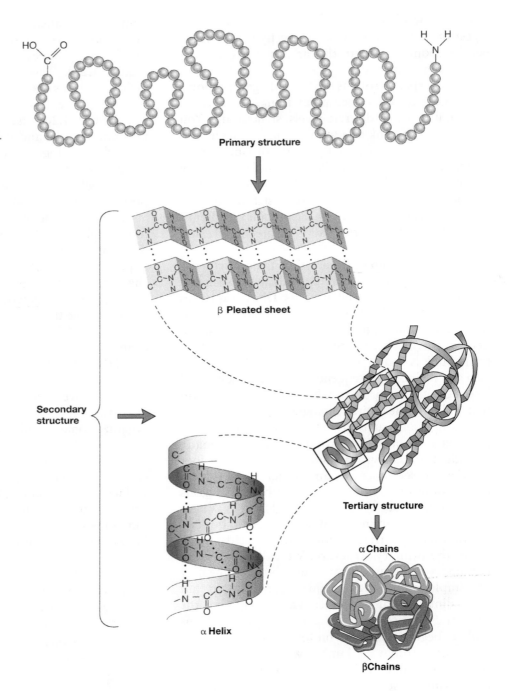

Primary structure

β Pleated sheet

Secondary structure

Tertiary structure

α Helix

αChains

βChains

Crossing Biomolecular Class Lines

How are thousands of biological functions carried out by biomolecules in only a few basic classes like carbohydrates, lipids, and proteins? Just as an artist combines primary colors to form fascinating new hues, individual molecules from different broad classes of biomolecules have been elegantly combined to serve unique biological roles in nature.

Adding short chains of simple sugars (**oligosaccharides**) onto the R groups of amino acids in proteins is one very common combination

oligosaccharide—polymers of 3 to 10 simple sugars attached to proteins or membranes; they serve a variety of functions including cell recognition.

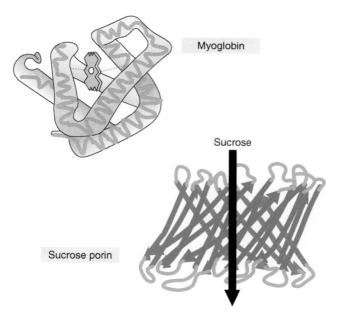

Myoglobin

Sucrose

Sucrose porin

Figure 4.26 Two models for proteins with radically different structures. Myoglobin tertiary structure is built largely from regions of α-helical structure (orange) while the sucrose porin protein's circular "pore" through a membrane is built largely of β – pleated sheet regions (blue). Sucrose diffuses across a membrane through this pore.

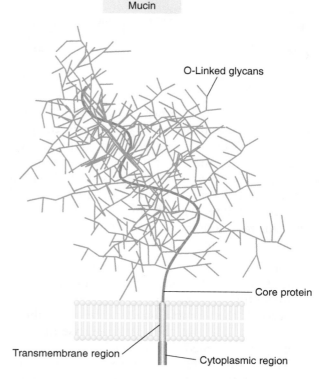

Mucin

O-Linked glycans

Core protein

Transmembrane region

Cytoplasmic region

Figure 4.27 The glycoprotein mucin. In the part of the protein projecting from the membrane, the purple strand represents a sequence of amino acids. All of the pink monomers are sugars—thousands of them—polymerized into long branching chains!

in living things (see Figure 4.27). The resulting **glycoproteins** have critical roles as enzymes or hormones or structural proteins that the chemistry of polypeptide chains alone could not perform.

Consider the glycoprotein mucin, found in the mucous secretions of your respiratory and digestive tracts. A small portion (20–30%) of the molecule is a sequence of amino acids folded to a tertiary level of structure. To this are linked hundreds of oligosaccharide chains. The presence of many, many sugar residues in these chains greatly enhances the water-holding capacity of these proteins, helping mucus to retain moisture. They also help mucin to resist

digestion by acids and protein-degrading enzymes in your gut. In this way, large aggregates of mucin protect your digestive system from self-digesting.

glycoprotein—an amino acid chain (protein) that has oligosaccharide sugar side chains attached to some of its amino acid R groups.

IN OTHER WORDS

1. Proteins are the largest, most diverse form of biomolecule both structurally and functionally.
2. Proteins (or polypeptides) are polymers composed of monomers drawn from a pool of about 20 common amino acids.
3. The diverse chemical character of the various amino acid side groups makes possible an enormous number of distinct shapes among the many polypeptide chains that exist in nature.
4. The structure of a protein can be described at four distinct levels: the primary sequence of amino acids, the local manner in which the primary sequence folds up, the extended shape of an entire polypeptide chain, and (sometimes) the grouping of polypeptide chain subunits in a complex *multimeric* protein.
5. Hybrid biomolecules are common in nature; sugar residues attached to a protein, for example, comprise a glycoprotein.

4.6 PROTEINS CONCEAL WISDOM

A protein molecule is either an evolutionary series of fortuitous accidents, or it is a finely designed machine. Let's use the amazing hemoglobin protein to see which of these two origin scenarios seems more attractive. Hemoglobin represents 97% of the mass of a red blood cell. It solves a seemingly simple problem: getting oxygen from where it's relatively abundant to where it's needed. However, that simple challenge is jam-packed with potential pitfalls:

1. First, our molecule must freely pick up oxygen molecules at the concentration of oxygen normally found in our lungs.
2. Second, this combining must be reversible—our molecule must be able to release the oxygen when needed in our tissues.
3. Third, the difference in oxygen concentrations in the lungs and tissues may not be all that great. Yet both the combining with and release of oxygen must be quick and efficient. If not, only a fraction of our molecules will be binding and releasing oxygen when they're supposed to.
4. Fourth, the releasing process must be sensitive to alteration in oxygen need when the body is at rest or is working hard.

These demanding functional constraints are all elegantly addressed in the intricate structure of the hemoglobin molecule.

Hemoglobin binds oxygen using a flat assemblage of atoms called a **heme group** (see Figure 4.28). The group has an iron atom right near the center to which an oxygen molecule freely binds. The other atoms attach the heme group to a polypeptide chain of 141 amino acids that comprise a hemoglobin subunit. The specific sequence of amino acids found there generates a tertiary structure that creates a highly specific binding environment for oxygen. Amazingly, that environment happens to favor the binding of oxygen at the concentrations found in the lungs but nicely favors release of oxygen at the concentrations found in tissues lacking oxygen.

There is still a problem, however. The higher oxygen concentration in the lungs is not different

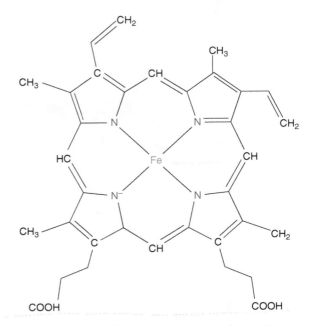

Figure 4.28 Heme group. Four nitrogen atoms suspend a central iron atom in such a way that it can bind to a free oxygen molecule. You need dietary iron in order to build this group.

enough from that in the tissues to allow a single protein chain to bind and release oxygen abruptly and efficiently enough. The binding and releasing would be equilibrium processes that would be slow and inefficient. Some hemoglobin subunits would leave the lung having not been charged with oxygen. Others would leave the tissues not having released their "cargo." There are limits to what a single polypeptide chain can do.

But the hemoglobin molecule is not a single polypeptide chain (see Figure 4.29)! It has quaternary structure in which four separate subunit polypeptide chains are bound to each other by large numbers of weak, noncovalent bonds (hydrogen bonds among them). Each chain has its own heme group and

heme group—a planar (flat) assemblage of atoms surrounding a central iron atom; the group is covalently attached to a polypeptide chain and is used to bind and transport oxygen molecules.

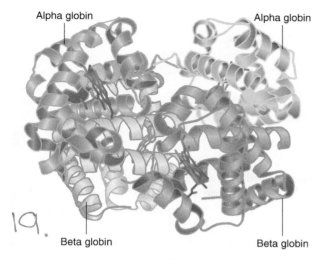

Alpha globin   Alpha globin

19.

Beta globin   Beta globin

Figure 4.29 Hemoglobin, a protein with quaternary structure, consists of four polypeptide chains (2 shown in blue, 2 in brown). Notice that each chain has its own heme group (red) capable of binding O_2. Notice also how closely each polypeptide chain associates with the two to either side of it. These regions of contact allow oxygen-binding-induced changes in one subunit to cause small structural changes in adjacent subunits. These changes alter the oxygen-binding capacities of the adjacent subunit.

binds one oxygen molecule. How does this complex arrangement of protein chains solve our efficiency problem? Here is where an amazing cooperation between subunits comes into play.

As the hemoglobin molecule arrives in the lungs, the tendency of its subunits to bind oxygen is appreciable though limited. But once one of the four subunits binds an oxygen molecule, the binding to the heme group causes a shift in the structure of its supporting polypeptide chain (see Figure 4.30). Through interchain contact, this structural change causes slight structural alterations in the other three subunits. The other subunits now bind oxygen much more readily than the first subunit did! This binding-dependent increase in affinity for oxygen

ensures that although the binding of oxygen will be initially somewhat slow, when the hemoglobin leaves the lungs it will be 98% saturated with oxygen. All four subunits will have their own oxygen molecule in tow.

This wonderful solution works backward when the hemoglobin arrives in the tissues. The release process is also coordinated. Again, the sequence of amino acids that support the heme group in each subunit cause the heme to tend to release oxygen at the lower concentrations found in the tissues where oxygen is being consumed. But the cooperative structural alterations among the subunits now improves release of the oxygen. Once one oxygen molecule has been released, shape changes in that subunit generate shape changes in the other subunits causing their affinity for oxygen to drop dramatically. The other three subunits then release their oxygen more quickly (see Figure 4.30). This increases the probability that when hemoglobin leaves the tissues on the way back to the lungs, it will have released its entire load of oxygen molecules.

Finally, the release of oxygen by each hemoglobin subunit is sensitive to the level of CO_2 in the tissue (see Figure 4.31). This sensitivity results from the ability of the hemoglobin polypeptide chains to bind to CO_2 at their ends. The binding results in shape changes within the chain that further reduce the affinity of the heme group for its oxygen molecule. Thus, if respiration is happening quickly, more CO_2 will be present. This will further lower hemoglobin's oxygen affinity resulting in even more rapid oxygen release.

What an amazing tribute to design technology! Here is a protein with subunit amino acid sequences that (1) cause oxygen to bind and release at appropriate concentrations, (2) can transmit and receive signals from other subunits to change its binding and release pattern, and (3) can change its

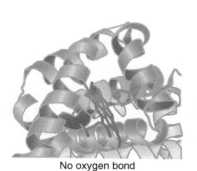

No oxygen bond

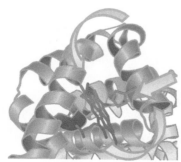

Oxygen bond

Figure 4.30 Close up of oxygen binding in hemoglobin. The heme group is red. The red pentagon-shaped ring is part of the R group of a nearby amino acid. As an oxygen molecule is bound to the iron ion (moving left to right in the diagram), that its presence attracts the R group closer to the iron ion. This causes the shift in the tertiary structure (arrows) of the polypeptide that will promote corresponding shifts in the other three associated polypeptide chains.

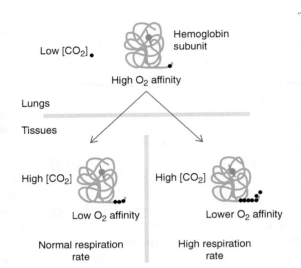

Low [CO₂] •

Hemoglobin subunit

High O₂ affinity

Lungs

Tissues

High [CO₂]

Low O₂ affinity

Normal respiration rate

High [CO₂]

Lower O₂ affinity

High respiration rate

Figure 4.31 A hemoglobin subunit's tertiary structure can be altered slightly by binding at one end to carbon dioxide molecules. The more molecules bound, the more the shape alters. The altered shape has a lower affinity for oxygen at it's heme iron site, releasing oxygen to the surrounding tissues more readily.

binding and release patterns in response to CO_2 levels! How can one sequence of amino acids do all of this? How would you begin to design hemoglobin? This molecule is shockingly wonderful. And your life is entirely dependent on its wisdom.

IN OTHER WORDS

1. Hemoglobin has the delicate function of maximally absorbing oxygen molecules in the lungs where they are abundant and releasing them optimally in the tissues where they are most needed.
2. Hemoglobin molecules accomplish this oxygen delivery by both precise physical interactions between their polypeptide subunits and by subunit sensitivity to CO_2 levels in the tissues.

4.7 NUCLEIC ACIDS: STRUCTURE AND FUNCTION

Our final broad class of biomolecules, the nucleic acids, is similar to proteins in that the class name refers principally to the large polymers within the class. Yet some of the nucleic acid monomers, called **nucleotides,** have highly interesting functions in their own right. Let's examine the structure of nucleotides and then note their functions. Then we will turn to the well-known polymers in this class: DNA and RNA.

Nucleotides: The Monomers

What monomers are used to build nucleic acid polymers? The structural formula for a very common nucleotide monomer, **adenosine triphosphate (ATP),** is shown in Figure 4.32. Notice that it possesses a five-carbon sugar (carbohydrate). In ATP this sugar is ribose. In other nucleotides the sugar may be deoxyribose if it has one less oxygen atom in its structure. The right-hand portion of the molecule is a nitrogen-containing base. In ATP, this base is **adenine,** having a double-ring structure. In other nucleotides it can be a single-ringed structure. On the left-hand side of the nucleotide, attached to the sugar residue, there can be anywhere from one to three phosphate groups ($-PO_3$) present.

What role can such a molecule have in the cell? The bond between the second and third phosphates is called a *high-energy phosphate bond* (see Figure 4.32). Little energy is needed to break this bond, and lots of energy is given off when the new bonds form. So ATP is like cellular energy currency. There are many vital places in the cell's chemistry where transfer of this phosphate group to some

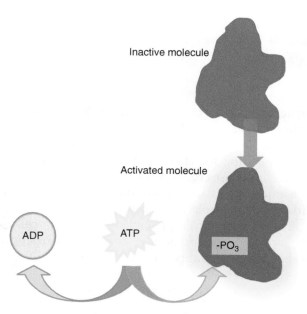

Figure 4.33   ATP activates a molecule within a cell. The high-energy bond in ATP is broken leaving behind a low-energy ADP (adenosine diphosphate). The high energy phosphate, when transferred to the inactive molecule activates it so that it can more easily enter into some reaction within the cell.

other cellular molecule (see Figure 4.33) activates that molecule and causes it to more readily enter into some desired cellular reaction.

Suppose we take this ATP molecule and make two simple changes. Let's remove two of the three phosphates (leaving one) and bond that remaining phosphate back to the sugar with two covalent bonds instead of one (see Figure 4.34). The result is a molecule of cyclic adenosine monophosphate, or

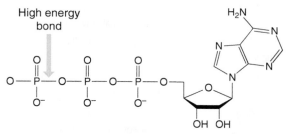

Figure 4.32   ATP. Adenine, the nitrogenous base is in the upper right hand corner. Attached to it are a five-carbon sugar, ribose, followed by three phosphate groups, each containing one phosphorus atom.

21. **nucleotide**—monomeric unit of nucleic acid, composed of a phosphate, a five-carbon sugar, and a purine or pyrimidine nitrogen-containing base.

   ATP (adenosine triphosphate)—a type of nucleotide that temporarily stores energy. It is also used as a monomer in RNA synthesis.

   adenine—an organic molecule with two nitrogen-containing rings' that are chemically basic a structural part of DNA and RNA polymers.

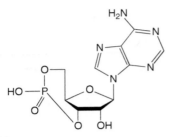

Figure 4.34 The molecular structure of cyclic adenosine monophosphate (AMP), a nucleic acid that is a common signal molecule within many types of cells.

cyclic AMP. In the cell, this molecule has an entirely different role from ATP. Cyclic AMP is a signal molecule. It travels over very short distances within the cell calling for changes in chemical activity at the site it diffuses to. How can such a small change in a nucleotide's structure make such a profound difference in its role in the cell?

A third major role of nucleotides in the cell is that they serve as monomers for the construction of the informational polymers DNA and RNA.

The Polymers: DNA and RNA

At the National Archives in Washington, DC, is a sequence of characters—letters comprising words—in a document called the Constitution of the United States. Millions of copies of this document exist so that students and even politicians can understand how the country is supposed to be run! There are only 26 letters in the alphabet, but ordered properly, they are sufficient for explaining how a country should operate.

We have referred previously to **DNA** as the informational molecule. Over 10 trillion copies of it inform the cells of your body how they are supposed to be run. In the monomer alphabet of the DNA molecule, there are only four different kinds of nucleotides (the Designer was very efficient). They are distinguished from each other by the structure of the nitrogenous base each contains. The structures of the four bases—**adenine, thymine, cytosine,** and **guanine**—are shown in Figure 4.3. In the nucleotides, each kind of base is attached to a deoxyribose sugar molecule with three phosphates attached (as in Figure 4.32). As they are being built into the polymer, two phosphates are lopped off (energizing the process) and a condensation reaction occurs in which the phosphate of one nucleotide is bonded to the sugar of the next nucleotide (see Figure 4.35). Again, a water molecule is given off.

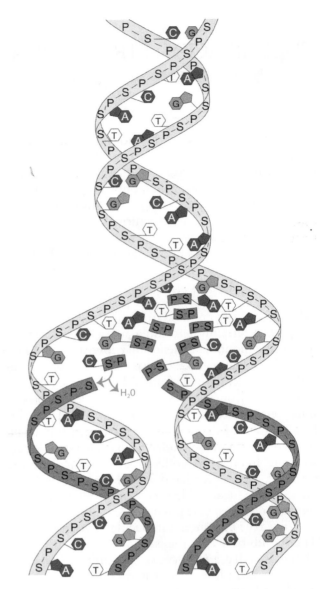

Figure 4.35 Adding nucleotides to DNA. Nucleotides are here shown as a nitrogenous base (C, A, G, or T) attached to a gray rectangle labelled, "S-P" or "P-S". The "P" represents a single phosphate. The other two phosphates have been removed to drive the process forward.

cyclic AMP—a nucleoside monophosphate that acts as an intracellular message molecule. When a signal arrives at the external boundary of a cell. Its effect within the cell is often mediated by this signal molecule.

thymine—a nitrogen-containing base with a single-ring pyrimidine structure, found in nucleotides in DNA only.

cytosine—a nitrogen-containing base with a single-ring pyrimidine structure; found in nucleotides in both DNA and RNA.

guanine—a nitrogen-containing base with a two-ring purine structure; found in nucleotides in both DNA and RNA.

When nucleotides are polymerized into very long chains, the resulting molecules are sometimes tens of billions of times the mass of a single hydrogen atom! A DNA molecule is actually two long nucleotide strands coiled around each other. These amazingly long sequences of nucleotides reside in the nucleus of a cell and determine how the cell will structure itself and how it will behave under any circumstance it encounters. Since you are a huge collection of these cells, the nucleotide sequence in DNA is specifying both the attributes that make you human and those that are specific to you (and possibly your twin brother). DNA's role in a living system will be discussed further in Chapter 7.

Information processing in most living systems requires two kinds of nucleic acid polymer: DNA and RNA. **RNA** is a single-stranded polymer similar in structure to a single strand of DNA (see Figure 4.36). There are differences between the two, however. The sugar ribose is used in its nucleotides instead of deoxyribose. Also, the nitrogenous base **uracil** (see Figure 4.3) is substituted in RNA nucleotides for the nitrogenous base thymine that's used in DNA nucleotides. These differences enable cellular enzymes to distinguish DNA and RNA from each other in cellular activities. The cell's information flows from DNA in the cell's nuclear archives out into the cytoplasm in the more expressible form of

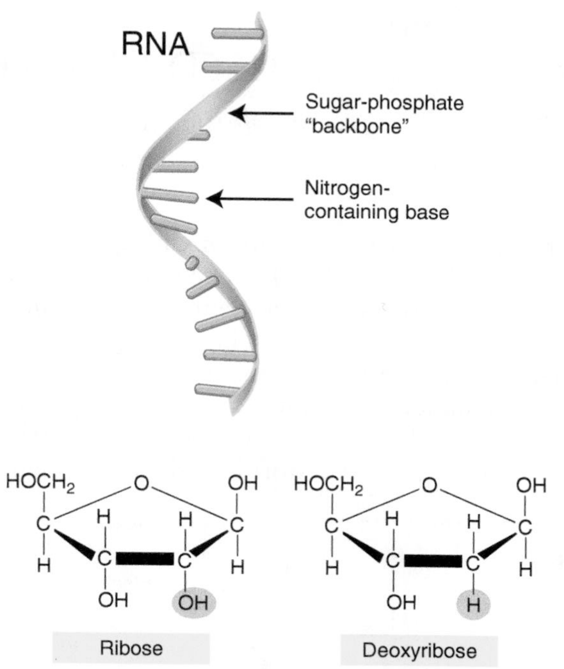

Figure 4.36 A schematic of an RNA molecule. Hidden in the brown strand are sugars and phosphates alternating in sequence. The four types of nitrogenous bases are all shown in blue. The sugars are of the ribose type (see below).

RNA. RNA polymers tend to be much shorter than DNA strands—more on the order of a single gene (segment of information) in length.

Scholars over the centuries have seen the great wisdom of collecting all of learning in large archival libraries from which individual intellectual tasks can be undertaken by careful selection of discrete passages of information. Long before the first library existed, the cell participated in this same wisdom using the informational polymers DNA and RNA.

23.

RNA (ribonucleic acid)—a single-stranded nucleic acid that can carry genetic information and is involved in protein synthesis.

uracil—a nitrogenous base found in nucleotides within the structure of RNA. The base uracil is found in the structure of RNA where thymine would be found in DNA.

IN OTHER WORDS

1. The monomers used to construct nucleic acids are called *nucleotides*; each one consists of a nitrogenous base, a five-carbon sugar, and one to three phosphates.
2. The nucleotide adenosine triphosphate (ATP) is used by the cell as both an immediate energy source and as a monomer for the construction of RNA.
3. Cyclic adenosine monophosphate (cAMP) is similar to adenosine monophosphate (AMP) in structure but functions as a signal molecule within many types of cells.
4. Deoxyribonucleic acid (DNA) is a double-stranded polymer in which each strand has a structural backbone of alternating phosphates and sugars that support genetic information in the form of a sequence of four kinds of nitrogenous bases.
5. Ribonucleic acid (RNA) is typically a single-stranded polymer with a structural backbone of alternating phosphates and sugars that temporarily support genetic information in the sequence of its nitrogenous bases.

4.8 LIVING THINGS NEED JUST A FEW GOOD MOLECULES

In the 1950s, two University of Chicago scientists, Harold C. Urey and Stanley L. Miller, conducted a fascinating series of experiments in an attempt to simulate conditions they believed might have existed early in the Earth's history (see Figure 4.37). They circulated a gaseous vapor rich in ammonia, methane, and hydrogen past a recurring electric arc that simulated electric storms in the atmosphere of

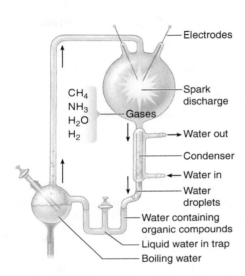

Figure 4.37 A glass-enclosed system designed to mimic in crude outline possible conditions on the early earth. If oxygen-containing molecules like water and carbon dioxide are increased in concentration within the system, the results are less favorable to life's origins.

the early planet. After a week of sparking this mixture of simple prebiotic molecules, they were able to isolate from the resulting mix a collection of 11 of the 20 common amino acids used to make proteins. This was exciting because it suggested that perhaps molecules with biological utility could be generated by random processes. Later, more precise analysis of these early samples has given more predictable and troubling results. At least 22 different amino acids are detectable in the mixtures resulting from these prebiotic experiments, suggesting that additional minute amounts of still other amino acids and their derivatives will be found.

These results are what would be expected from such an experiment: Every sort of amino acid that can be formed will be formed. But if no life-forms yet existed during Earth's early history, there was no biological context to determine which amino acids would finally be more useful for living systems and which would be less so. In forming primitive proteins, far too many kinds of monomers would exist. The results would be prebiotic chaos. To save this random soup from cybernetic oblivion, a brilliant Designer would need to intervene. He might choose about three or four dozen monomers out of the huge mix and design enzymes that could build everything from His standard set of monomers. Such a critical choice would set biomolecules on a path that could lead to the biomolecular uniformity we observe across the biotic world. There is here, then, a clear need and clear evidence for Life by Design.

IN OTHER WORDS

1. In the mid-twentieth century, Stanley Miller and Harold Urey conducted an early Earth atmosphere simulation experiment in which they successfully generated a wide variety of amino acids and other organic molecules.
2. Their system lacked a means of selecting for further use only those amino acids that would contribute optimally to the structuring of proteins.

QUESTIONS FOR REVIEW

1. What are two specific levels of organization in the biological world where we've observed that form wonderfully supports function?
2. What features of the carbon atom adapt it so elegantly to its central role in the structure of biological molecules?
3. Contrast the role of water in a condensation reaction and in a hydrolysis reaction.
4. Write down the term *carbohydrates*. Beneath it, draw three short branching lines that represent the classes of carbohydrates discussed in this chapter. Name those classes at the end of each line. Under each name, list the names of examples mentioned in the carbohydrates section of the chapter.
5. What are the four components of a triglyceride or fat molecule?
6. What features of a phospholipid perfectly suit it to be a part of a biological membrane?
7. What two classes of biological molecules make up most of the structure of a membrane?
8. List some of the changes in the human male brought about by signals from the hormone testosterone.
9. Which class of biomolecules is functionally the most diverse?
10. At which level of protein structure are amino groups and carboxyl groups employed? At which level are alpha helices and beta-pleated sheets formed?
11. What is a glycoprotein? In its own way, a glycoprotein is a bit of a threat to our scheme for classifying and describing biological molecules. Why do we say that?
12. List four functional constraints your body places on a hemoglobin molecule in your bloodstream (four things your body needs to have hemoglobin do properly) within its role as an oxygen transport machine.
13. Where is the available energy focused in the structure of an ATP molecule?
14. What do the four bases in a DNA molecule have in common with the 26 letters of the English alphabet?
15. The role of DNA in the cell is information archiving. What is the role of RNA in the cell?

QUESTIONS FOR THOUGHT

1. Glucose, glycine, glycerol, and cholesterol are found in a wide variety of organisms. Evolution suggests that this is because these organisms all have a single, common, original ancestor. An infinite Designer, on the other hand, could have easily made the chemistry of each species entirely different. Why might He not have chosen to do this? If there is no good answer to this question, then perhaps do all living things have a common ancestor?
2. To break a covalent bond, energy is required. A carbon-hydrogen covalent bond is easier to break than an oxygen-hydrogen covalent bond. When new bonds form, energy is given off. Survey some diagrams of carbohydrates and lipids in this chapter. Which class of molecule stores more energy more efficiently? Explain your choice.
3. Both starch and cellulose are polymers of glucose monomers. At night when they need additional energy to live, why don't plant cells accidentally degrade cellulose and use the glucoses for energy?
4. Explain why saturated fats are solids at room temperature and unsaturated fats are not.
5. All proteins in nature are built from about 20 different amino acids. Why 20? Why not 10? Why not 40? Speculate a bit. After working through Chapter 7, you may have more ideas to offer at this point.
6. What changes (speaking functionally) at a heme sight on a hemoglobin subunit when the subunit next to it binds an oxygen molecule?
7. Why would the Miller-Urey experiment have been more useful for evolutionary theory if 20 and only 20 kinds of products, all of them amino acids, had been produced?

GLOSSARY

adenine—an organic molecule with two nitrogen-containing rings' that are chemically basic a structural part of DNA and RNA polymers.

amino acid—a monomeric molecule used in synthesis of polypeptide chains or proteins. Contains both amino and acidic functional groups.

amylopectin—a highly branched polysaccharide polymer of glucose units in starch; product of plant metabolism

amylose—a linear polymer of glucose subunits, a component of plant starch molecules.

atherosclerosis—a thickening of the walls of arterial blood vessels as a result of the accumulation of fatty materials being transported in the blood.

ATP (adenosine triphosphate)—a type of nucleotide that temporarily stores energy. It is also used as a monomer in RNA synthesis.

cellulose—a polymeric carbohydrate whose subunits are monomers of glucose. It is probably the most common organic molecule on the face of the earth.

condensation—a chemical reaction in which two molecules combine to form one with loss of a small molecule—usually water in biological systems.

cyclic AMP—a nucleoside monophosphate that acts as an intracellular message molecule. When a signal arrives at the external boundary of a cell. Its effect within the cell is often mediated by this signal molecule.

cytosine—a nitrogen-containing base with a single-ring pyrimidine structure; found in nucleotides in both DNA and RNA.

dimer—the result of a condensation reaction in which two monomers are bonded together.

disaccharide—two monosaccharide sugars covalently bonded together by a condensation reaction.

fatty acid—a long chain of carbons and hydrogens that is a monomer from which fat polymers are constructed.

fructose—a monosaccharide sugar that is found in many foods; fruits rich in the disaccharide sucrose have high levels of fructose, a component of sucrose.

glucose—a monosaccharide sugar that is central to cellular metabolism, the form of sugar found in the human bloodstream.

glycerol—a three-carbon molecule with three –OH side groups to which fatty acids are attached in triglyceride synthesis.

glycogen—a polysaccharide formed from glucose primarily in muscle and liver tissue; serves as a temporary storage form of energy.

glycoprotein—an amino acid chain (protein) that has oligosaccharide sugar side chains attached to some of its amino acid R groups.

guanine—a nitrogen-containing base with a two-ring purine structure; found in nucleotides in both DNA and RNA.

heme group—a planar (flat) assemblage of atoms surrounding a central iron atom; the group is covalently attached to a polypeptide chain and is used to bind and transport oxygen molecules.

hormone—a chemical generated in one cell that has its effect in cells elsewhere in the organism.

hydrolysis—a chemical reaction in which water is split (lysed) into a hydrogen ion and an –OH ion. In polymer degradation, these ions are added to each product stabilizing the resulting monomer and smaller polymer.

hydrophilic—a molecule or region of a molecule to which water molecules are attracted because of the presence of polar bonds.

hydrophobic—water-fearing—descriptive of any molecule that water effectively excludes from its own surroundings due to the extensive hydrogen bonding that occurs between water molecules.

lactose—a simple sugar or monosaccharide found in mammalian milk; milk sugar.

Life Is Complex—one of the 12 principles of life on which this text is based.

monomer—any chemical compound that can be used as a building block or structural subunit in the assembly of a much larger molecule called a *polymer*.

monosaccharide—a simple sugar built on a structure of anywhere from three to seven carbon atoms with associated hydrogen and oxygen atoms.

nucleotide—monomeric unit of nucleic acid, composed of a phosphate, a five-carbon sugar, and a purine or pyrimidine nitrogen-containing base.

peptide bond—a covalent bond between the amino group of one amino acid and the acidic group of another amino acid. Water is a product of peptide bond formation

phospholipid—a glycerol molecule attached to two fatty acids and a third, small organic molecule containing a phosphate group; a major component of animal cell membranes.

polymer—a large chemical compound formed by assembly of repeating structural units called *monomers*.

polypeptide—a polymer formed from the covalent bonding of amino acids in a defined sequence. Small polymers are called *peptides*, larger ones *polypeptides* and still larger ones are referred to as *proteins*.

primary structure—the sequence of amino acids in the structure of a polypeptide or protein. The most basic level of protein structure.

quaternary structure—multiple polypeptide chains associated with each other to form a complex, multimeric protein.

oligosaccharide—polymers of 3 to 10 simple sugars attached to proteins or membranes; they serve a variety of functions including cell recognition.

R group—the functional group of atoms peculiar to a specific kind of amino acid. It determines the unique function of that kind of amino acid.

RNA (ribonucleic acid)—a single-stranded nucleic acid that can carry genetic information and is involved in protein synthesis.

secondary structure—the folding of an amino acid sequence into α-helical regions or planar sheets of amino acids. The folding that occurs is determined by the sequence of amino acids in that region of the polypeptide.

starch—a polysaccharide polymer of glucose sugar units; energy storage form in plants; major portion of human diet.

steroid—a lipid that consists of four fused carbon rings with additional atoms bonded around the exterior of the rings.

sucrose—a disaccharide sugar; energy storage form in plants; table sugar.

tertiary structure—the folding of regions of helical or pleated sheet secondary structures within a polypeptide chain into a unique higher-order shape that contributes function to the mature protein.

testosterone—a steroid hormone secreted by the sex organs in males and to a lesser degree in females.

thymine—a nitrogen-containing base with a single-ring pyrimidine structure, found in nucleotides in DNA only.

triglyceride—a glycerol bonded to three fatty acids; the main constituent of plant and animal fats.

uracil—a nitrogenous base found in nucleotides within the structure of RNA. The base uracil is found in the structure of RNA where thymine would be found in DNA.

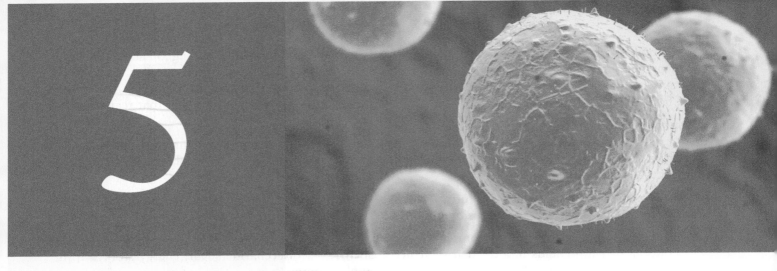

5

Complexity III:
The Glory of the Cell

Survey Questions

- How is a cell different from a molecule or an atom?
- What does it mean to say that a cell is alive? What is life?

5.1 What Is a Cell?

- What is the definition of the term *cell* in a biological context?
- Are there problems in defining the term *cell* as there are in defining the term *life*?
- Who first saw cells? How widespread are they?
- How do cells relate to whole organisms?
- Where do cells come from?
- Why are cells microscopic in size?

5.2 Living Cells Are Complex

- How are the many kinds of cells organized for study?
- What is the outer boundary of a cell like?
- How are cellular activities controlled?
- How are the parts of a cell produced?
- How is the interior of a cell organized?

cell—the structural and functional unit of a living organism. Some organisms consist of only a single cell. Others, like humans, are multicellular.

The late physicist Phillip Morrison once quipped, "The discovery of life on one other planet—e.g. Mars—would transform the origin of life from a miracle to a statistic." Thus far then, life is still a miracle. We have been preparing to explore this miracle. "Preparing . . . ?" you say. "Four arduous chapters were all just preparation?" Yes. Chapter 1 taught us that Life Is Significant. It asked us to see design in the biological world. Chapter 2 explained that Life Can Be Understood and demonstrated how a scientist explores it. Chapters 3 and 4 took us into the complexity of structure and function at the molecular level of the living world.

But atoms and molecules are not alive! While their appreciation is critical to understanding life, life occurs at a level of complexity far above the level of molecules (see Figure 1.17). Molecules are organized into larger polymeric molecules. Polymers unite into macromolecular structures. These higher-order structures are built into a variety of organelles that finally comprise the cell—the *living* cell (see Figures 5.1, 5.2). So Chapter 5 is about living things because cells appear to be the smallest indivisible bits of self-contained life. We have seen structural intricacy underlying the wide diversity of biomolecules. It was wonderfully improbable, was it not? Our discussion now moves from the biomolecule to the cell—from the improbable to the miraculous.

And since cells have this higher-order property called *life*, we life scientists are obliged to define our term, are we not? What is life? We said in Chapter 1 that life is currently indefinable. Oh, the dictionary is bound to give you a phrase or two, but the use of words like *vital* and *living* in the definition are the clue that its complexity still renders it a mystery. One dictionary describes life as a "tendency toward negative entropy." But when a definition focuses on a single feature of life (like its tendency to generate more order from chaos), there is usually some nonliving system (like salt crystal formation)

- How do the parts of a living cell interact in order to support the cell's functions?
- How do substances get into and out of cells?
- Where is all the information for making a cell in the human body stored?
- Are cells eternal? What happens when parts of them wear out?
- How do substances and cell parts move around inside of a cell?
- How do cells derive energy from nature? Where in the cell does this energy-handling occur?
- What is an acinar cell? What is its role in my body?
- How is the activity of an acinar cell controlled?

5.3 Complexity at the Cellular Level: Are There Limits?

- How much complexity is possible within the context of a single cell? Can there be cells within cells?
- How would the cells cooperative in such an arrangement?
- How could two cells ever start such a relationship?

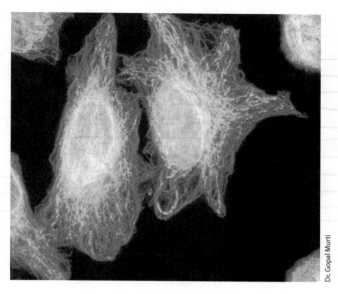

Figure 5.1 Fluorescent antibodies developed against specific cell structures are a wonderful technological contrivance that here glorify a brilliant Designer of cell parts. Nucleus = blue, cytoskeleton = green, mitochondria = orange.

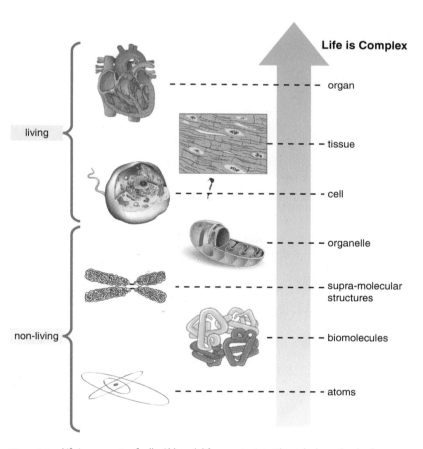

Figure 5.2 Life is a property of cells. Although life cannot exist without the lower levels of complexity that contribute to it, these lower levels are not, themselves alive.

that is inadvertently being described as well. It is appropriately humbling to us scholars that a simple definition of life eludes us.

Lacking a definition, we turned to *describing* life by accumulating a list of its characteristics. This worked quite nicely. We can affirm that anything that grows, exchanges energy with its environment, reproduces itself, and responds to stimuli from its environment is categorically alive. It has life in it.

Yes, **Life Is Complex.** We can define individual threads of its tapestry, but nothing in our vocabulary captures its essence. Sola Gloria Dei.

Life Is Complex—one of the 12 principles of life on which this text is based.

Definition

Defining the biological term *cell* is impractical for the same reason. We still try, though. One dictionary uses a multicellular organism as a frame of reference. It states that a cell is "the smallest unit of an organism capable of independent functioning, composed of a membrane enclosing a nucleus, cytoplasm and inanimate matter" (see Figure 5.3). This phrase sounds cogent but is fraught with difficulties. Your own cells die apart from your body unless a complex culture medium is constructed to support them. Most cells in our biosphere are too simple to possess a nucleus, strictly speaking. And the undefined word *cytoplasm* tells us nothing. So here again, we shall have to walk into the world of cell biology short of a definition. And once again, scientists have managed to develop a cell theory without doing any serious defining.

Cell Theory

Most cells are small. They were not observable until exploration with microscopes began. By 1665, Robert Hooke, an Oxford scholar and member of the Royal Society in London, had made drawings from microscopic observations of thinly shaved cork bark (see Figure 5.4). He used the term *cellulae* to describe what he saw: small, regularly shaped spaces, each surrounded by a boundary. They reminded him of the confining rooms of a prison or monastery. The term *cell* slowly became an integral part of the literature, even though workers later realized that in living cork tree cells, those spaces were filled with all of the complex molecular architecture that, taken together, is alive.

Through the 1700s and into the 1800s, more and more observations of cells were made. In the 1830s, a

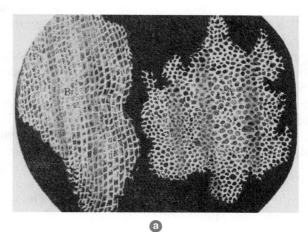

(a)

(b)

Figure 5.4 **(a)** One of Robert Hooke's drawings of cells. **(b)** Robert Hooke, 1635–1703, was a British natural philosopher and microscopist who first used the term "cell".

Cell membrane

Cytoplasm

Nuclear membrane

Nucleus

"the smallest unit of an organism capable of independent functioning, composed of a membrane enclosing a nucleus, cytoplasm and inanimate matters"???

Figure 5.3 The Cell as drawn in the late 1800's. The term "cell" has yet to be accurately defined. Life is Complex.

Bettmann/CORBIS;

Getty Images

Figure 5.5 Mathias Schleiden (1804–1881) and Theodore Schwann (1810–1882) were two principle contributors to what is now called "cell theory".

Wellcome Library, London

Figure 5.6 Robert Remak (1815–1865) a Prussian embryologist who first described the third element of cell theory: All cells come from pre-existing cells.

Scottish botanist, Robert Brown, clearly saw what he called a **nucleus**—a large central body that appeared regularly in all of the cells he examined. But, as is common in science, someone was needed to draw these observations together into a satisfying model that would mature into a theory. In the late 1830s two German biologists, Mathew Schleiden and Theodor Schwann, assumed that role (see Figure 5.5). In 1838, Schleiden, a lawyer-turned-botanist (!), went out on a limb somewhat and published a single study from which he derived two elements of cell theory: (1) all plants and animals are composed of cells, and (2) the cell is the unit of life (see Table 5.1). Though his paper contained erroneous concepts of how a cell develops, he managed to get two aspects of cell theory correct.

The following year, in his paper, "Microscopical Researches on the Similarity in Structure and Growth of Animals and Plants," Schwann, a seasoned and careful scholar at the University of Berlin, released years' worth of study that gave significant substance to Schleiden's two broad generalizations. He also gave us the term *metabolism* to represent all of the chemical reactions that occur in a living cell.

It remained for a Prussian neurologist—also working in Berlin in the early 1840s—to add the last essential feature of cell theory. From his observations of early development of frog embryos, Robert Remak (see Figure 5.6) advanced the generalization that all cells come from preexisting cells by a process of cell division. Remak's discoveries and interpretation were accurate and came at a time and place propitious for their acceptance. But in science as in the rest of society, prejudice lurks. Remak was Jewish. As a result, he was repeatedly denied academic promotion and his work was regarded as doubtful for years after its completion. Finally, in the late 1850s the widely respected German pathologist Rudolph Virchow plagiarized Remak's work, bringing to acceptance the last element of cell theory: cells come only from preexisting cells (see Table 5.1). This final generalization makes every cell a *creator*—a creator of daughter cells. This notion bedevils Darwinian thinkers who seek to contradict it just once! They sincerely hope to learn how nature might have used less than a cell to select the machinery of the very first cell that ever was. Their sorely questionable source: randomly generated mutations in some primordial information system.

Table 5.1 Elements of cell theory.

1. All organisms are composed of cells.
2. The cell is the unit of life.
3. All cells come from pre-existing cells.

nucleus, pl. nuclei—a centrally located, visible body within a eukaryotic cell that houses archival information in the form of linear, DNA-containing chromosomes.

Generalizations: At Once Brilliant and Naïve

The living world reveals a wide variety of organisms that calls into question even our most basic generalizations. Consider the theory: "All organisms are composed of cells." Even in the early years, Schwann discovered noncellular material within the bones of animals. He needed to modify the theory to assert that "all organisms are composed of cells *and materials secreted by those cells.*" Since his day, a variety of fungi and slime molds have been discovered that, strictly speaking, lack cells! (See Figure 5.7.) Some of these, like *Physarum polycephalum*, can reach a diameter of 20 cm or more. Yet their structure is a network of protoplasmic veins in which nuclei and other organellar and cytoplasmic materials stream freely past each other as though the entire organism were one huge cell. So the elements of cell theory have great value as generalizations: They guide our experimental work in many fruitful ways. But they don't constitute a precise theory.

We said above that most cells are small. Microscopes reveal them and their dimensions are measured in micrometers. (A **micrometer** is one one-thousandth of the smallest visible division on a millimeter ruler.) But here again is a generalization with limited meaning! Notice the wide variation in size along the logarithmic scale shown in Figure 5.8. Cells range in size from the tiny **mycoplasma** that

Figure 5.7 A slime mold of genus *Physarum* growing on a log—one huge "cell" with many, many nuclei and organelles.

threatens you with walking pneumonia to an ostrich egg that could supply your breakfast table for a week. Those two cell types range from 0.3 up to 150,000 micrometers in diameter! Your cells fall neatly within the lower-middle portion of that

micrometer—a metric unit of measure for objects similar in size to a cell. There are 1000 micrometers in a single millimeter.

mycoplasma—a bacteria-like prokaryotic cell that has the smallest genome known to support cellular function; many are pathogenic, some to humans.

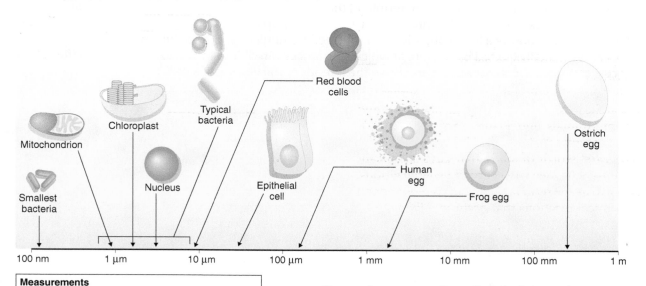

Measurements		
1 meter	=	1000 millimeters (mm)
1 millimeter	=	1000 micrometers (µm)
1 micrometer	=	1000 nanometers (nm)

Figure 5.8 Diameters of some common cell types. Notice that the horizontal measurement scale is logarithmic. Subcellular structures of larger cells overlap in size the entire diameter of smaller bacterial cells.

range from about 10 to 50 micrometers in diameter (with some exceptions!).

Why must cells be so small, generally? There may be many reasons. One factor is that molecules must move promptly into, out of, and within cells in order for processes to function normally. Often this movement is driven solely by **diffusion**—the random movement of molecules due to their thermal energy. Diffusion distributes molecules so that they spread out evenly into all available space. But diffusional forces are not rapid enough to support life over distances greater than about 1000 micrometers or 1 millimeter (see Figure 5.9). So cell diameters need to fall well below that size range. This is fortunate for many sociopolitical reasons as well. For most of human history, individual human cells have been beyond the experimental reach of those who would exploit our species for their private purposes. A revolution in biological research is now eroding that protection.

The diversity of the living world yields to few sweeping statements. For cell size, it's hard to generalize.

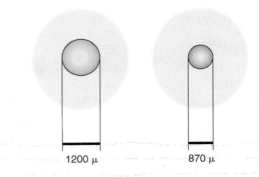

1200 μ   870 μ

Figure 5.9   Two large "cells" of diameter 1200 μ and 870 μ are placed for 10 seconds into a solution of a green dye capable of crossing the cell membrane. The dye is then removed. It successfully penetrates to the core of the smaller cell but cannot, in 10 seconds, reach the center of the larger cell. Diffusion rates place upper limits on the size of cells.

diffusion—the tendency of any substance to move through a liquid or solid medium from a region where its concentration is higher to a region where it is lower.

IN OTHER WORDS

1. Defining the term *cell* is practically impossible. Describing the parts of a typical cell is more achievable.
2. Robert Hooke was the first to use the term *cell* for observable microscopic units of structure and function in living organisms.
3. Two German scientists, Mathias Schleiden and Theodor Schwann, asserted that all living things are composed of cells and that the cell is the unit—the simplest entity—of life.
4. Robert Remak and Rudolph Virchow determined that cells come from preexisting cells by cell division.
5. There are many exceptions to the three generalizations comprising cell theory. Human bone tissue, a primary example, is part of a living organism, yet much of it is nonliving, extracellular material.
6. Cell size is generally limited by the rate at which substances can diffuse in aqueous solution. Diffusion is a process by which substances enter and leave the interior or the vicinity of a cell.

5.2 LIVING CELLS ARE COMPLEX

Of the 12 principles of life introduced in Chapter 1, an early and obvious principle is that Life Is Complex. Complexity in an organism like yourself cannot be properly appreciated until the daunting intricacy of its component parts—the cells—is at least touched on. Light and electron microscopy over the past 100 years have revealed thousands of kinds of cells. There are surely many more out there to discover. Most of the ones we've found (so far!) fall into two somewhat discrete levels of complexity (see Figure 5.10). The simpler, smaller ones lack a discrete membrane-bound nucleus and are termed **prokaryotic** cells (*pro* = before; *kary* = kernel, or nucleus). A major portion of these cells go by the common name **bacteria**. The larger, more complex cells, like our own, sport a much larger, membrane-bound nucleus. They are thus termed **eukaryotic** cells (*eu* = true). These are the cells of **protistans**, fungi, higher plants, and animals. We will explore these two classes of cells separately.

Cellular complexity implies at least two separate features. First, cells have many intricate structures within them. Second, those intricacies are highly organized and they interact thoroughly with each other. So for both classes of cells we will first list the more prominent subcellular structures they contain. Then we will explore one example of how several of these structures interact to serve the cell as a whole.

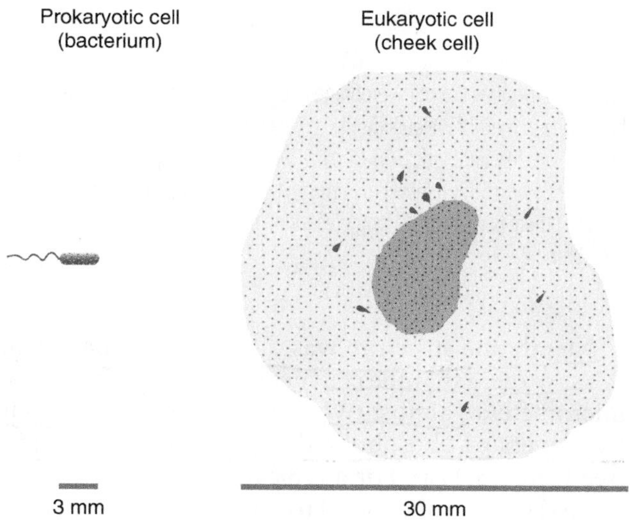

Prokaryotic cell
(bacterium)

Eukaryotic cell
(cheek cell)

3 mm

30 mm

Figure 5.10 Prokaryotic and eukaryotic cells represent two somewhat discrete size classes of cells. Again, generalization is difficult. At least one kind of bacterium found in a surgeonfish's gut is over 600 μm in length. You can easily see it without a microscope.

prokaryotic—descriptive of the smaller, simpler sort of cell that contains no true membrane-bound nucleus and few if any membrane-bound organelles; bacteria are common examples.

bacteria—a common form of prokaryotic cell lacking a membrane-bound nucleus and usually much smaller in size than higher eukaryotic cells.

eukaryotic—descriptive of a cell that contains a true membrane-bound nucleus, generally larger than prokaryotic cells.

protistans—unicellular or colonial forms of life that possess eukaryotic cells; the amoeba and paramecium are examples.

IN OTHER WORDS

1. There appear to be two fundamental levels of complexity in cell size and structure: smaller prokaryotic cells that lack a membrane-delimited nucleus and larger eukaryotic cells that possess a wider variety of membrane-delimited organelles, including the nucleus.
2. Prokaryotic cells include all Bacteria and Archaea. Eukaryotic cells include protists, fungi, plants, and animals.
3. Cell complexity is characterized by both a wide variety of intricate internal structures and functions and by a high level of organization that ties these structures and functions together.

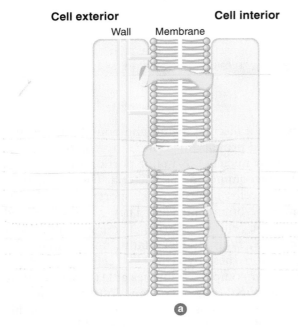

Cell exterior   **Cell interior**
Wall   Membrane

(a)

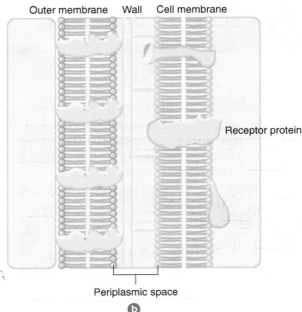

Cell exterior   **Cell interior**
Outer membrane   Wall   Cell membrane

Receptor protein

Periplasmic space

(b)

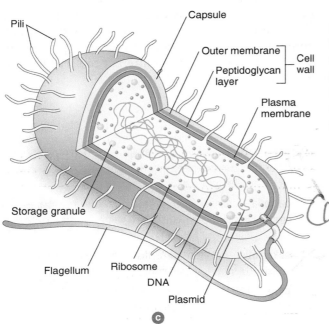

Pili

Capsule

Outer membrane
Peptidoglycan
layer

Cell
wall

Plasma
membrane

Storage granule

Flagellum   Ribosome
DNA
Plasmid

(c)

Figure 5.11 The prokaryotic cell. **(a)** a close look at the boundary surrounding the cell which includes the cell membrane and a cell wall **(b)** In some cases the cell has a second membrane outside the cell wall that helps protect the cell from toxic substances like antibiotics. **(c)** cutaway view of a prokaryotic cell showing a variety of cell structures referred to in the text. In many prokaryotic cells (as shown here) there is an almost complete lack of any membranes internal to the cell membrane.

Membrane structure was discussed in Chapter 3. We saw there that the cell membrane is a thin (0.008 micrometers), almost two-dimensional sea in which two layers of phospholipids swim and spin around (see Figure 5.11a). For a typical bacterium, it covers a (vast) surface area of 10 to 15 square micrometers. A bacterium's internal content is 60% to 70% water, and in the aqueous world where life is lived, this lipid bilayer forms a wonderful boundary. Separate chemical environments exist inside and outside of the cell, and the bilayer effectively isolates them from one another. Processes can be contained within the cell without having the components simply diffuse away from each other like cologne from an unwashed college freshman.

Prokaryotic Intricacies

All structural parts of a typical bacterial cell are contained within a limiting boundary. Inside of this boundary the complexity is extraordinary. Outside, relatively speaking, randomness reigns. The boundary must be both chemically and physically protective of the cell's internal complexity. Chemical protection is afforded by a **cell membrane**.

cell membrane—a phospholipid bilayer containing proteins that serves as a boundary around a cell defining its chemical limits and controlling movement of substances into and out of the cell.

Table 5.2 Functions of membrane-bound proteins

1. Receptor proteins	receive and respond to signals from outside the cell.
2. Transport proteins	allow specific substances or classes of substances into or out of the cell.
3. Respiratory proteins	transfer and receive electrons in a process that generates cellular energy.
4. Binding proteins	enable a cell to bind to other cells like itself or to specific or general cellular or even non-biological surfaces.
5. Ion Channels	either allow or actively pump specific ions across the membrane as part of critical cellular activities.
6. Attachment point proteins	serve as anchor points for parts of the cells' internal structural skeleton.
7. Enzymes	catalyze reactions that need to occur just inside of or outside of the cell membrane.

Perched within the thin bilayer are rather larger protein molecules with a wide diversity of shape and size (see Figure 5.11a). Many of these proteins have regions, or *domains*, that project out of the membrane in both directions. The structural shape of each protein in or on a membrane controls what that protein does for the cell. Their roles are legion (see Table 5.2). They can be (1) gates that passively allow or actively pump needed substances into the cell, (2) gates that remove excess waste products from the cell, (3) respiratory enzymes that generate chemical energy, (4) **receptor proteins** that are involved in recognizing signals from the environment or from other cells, (5) binding proteins that enable a bacterium to adhere to other bacteria or to nonliving surfaces, or (6) various other exquisitely fashioned molecular tools that functionally need to be close to the cell's external environment.

Lying just outside the cell membrane, most prokaryotic cells have a structurally rigid **cell wall** that physically protects a bacterial cell that often finds itself in water with few dissolved substances (see Figure 5.11a). As water rushes into the cell from high outer concentrations to lower inner concentrations, the cell begins to swell. A cell membrane alone would simply rupture. The firm, multilayered wall restrains this swelling and thus retains the bacterium's cellular integrity. Despite its strength, however, the wall has a very open structure, chemically. Chemical discrimination is the membrane's job.

Many bacteria, including some that are pathogenic to humans, contain a second membrane lying outside the cell wall. This outer membrane is chemically discriminatory somewhat like the inner one. As such it creates a compartment between the inner and outer membranes called the **periplasmic space** (see Figure 5.11b). The cell wall lies within this space. Also within this space lies a host of cell-secreted enzymes involved in procuring and altering nutrients

as they enter the cell. Also enzymatically controlled wall-building processes occur there.

This complex boundary of the prokaryotic cell houses an inner volume of viscous fluid called the **cytoplasm** (see Figure 5.11c). In *Escherichia coli (E. coli)*, a bacterium that lives in your bowel, the cytoplasmic volume is about 1 cubic micrometer. This fluid is a site where much of the cell's metabolism occurs that results in the growth and structuring of the cell's architecture. And near the geometric center, at the hub of all this activity, lies the principle site from which it is all directed!

Just as a good library is the functional center of a good university, the cell has an elegantly structured aggregate of DNA and scaffolding proteins called the **nucleoid** region (see Figure 5.11c). Here the archival information in the base sequence of DNA is maintained within a surprisingly sophisticated

receptor protein—a protein found within a cell membrane that recognizes and binds to some signal molecule from another source; the protein changes shape as a result and this transmits the signal to the inside of the cell displaying it.

cell wall—a mechanically rigid outer polymeric surface of some cells; in aqueous environments it keeps the influx of water from bursting the cell.

periplasmic space—a region lodged between the inner (cell) membrane and the outer membrane of certain varieties of bacteria; specialized enzymatic processes occur within this space.

cytoplasm—the interior volume of a cell excluding the cell's nucleus; composed of a wide variety of chemical substances participating in the cell's metabolism; organelles or microcompartments are suspended within it.

nucleoid—a central region of a prokaryotic cell where genetic information is localized.

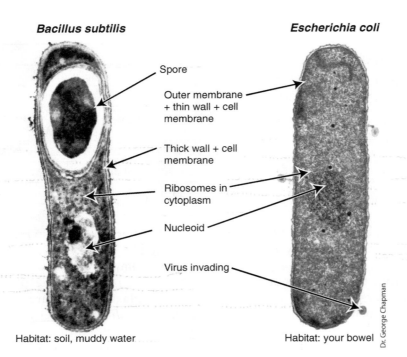

Bacillus subtilis   **Escherichia coli**

Spore

Outer membrane
+ thin wall + cell
membrane

Thick wall + cell
membrane

Ribosomes in
cytoplasm

Nucleoid

Virus invading

Dr. George Chapman

Habitat: soil, muddy water   Habitat: your bowel

Figure 5.12 Slices through two quite different bacteria showing some structural distinctions. Bacteria living in your bowel experience a fairly constant environment. Cells living in a mud puddle need to be able to form protective spores when the puddle dries up!

chromosome of RNA and protein molecules. This structure allows selected regions of DNA to be uncoiled and accessed for information much as a file drawer is opened to extract a file folder. Imagine a file cabinet with 100 different drawers. . . . Copies of the accessed information flow outward from the nucleoid region to sites of information expression. Suspended in the cytoplasm are small, roughly spherical structures called **ribosomes**. These amazing machines, composed largely of protein molecules (and a few RNAs), are responsible for building all the protein molecules for the entire cell: the structural proteins, the enzymes, receptor proteins, regulatory proteins, ribosomal proteins—all of the proteins!

The cytoplasm of the prokaryotic cell is not totally occupied with information expression however. Distributed within the cytoplasm of many prokaryotic cells are protein-encased compartments or organelles called **microcompartments** in which specialized metabolism occurs (see Figure 5.11c). They are typically about 0.1 to 0.15 micrometers in diameter and can have thousands of proteins as part of their outer boundary. For example, the carbon source for the growth of many bacteria is carbon dioxide in the air. These cells have a microcompartment called

a **carboxysome**, which houses the enzymes that enable them to trap carbon dioxide and bind it to larger substrate molecules.

Many types of prokaryotic cells exist with a wide variety of included structures that are not discussed here. Figure 5.12 reviews for you the internal structure of two common bacteria, one found in your bowel and the other found in a puddle of water near your home.

ribosomes—aggregates of protein and ribosomal RNA molecules that together read messenger RNA sequences from the cell's nucleus and construct polypeptide chains (proteins) according to the sequence of nitrogenous bases in the messenger RNA.

microcompartment—a protein-enclosed compartment or space within a prokaryotic cell that specializes in some particular metabolic function like combining with carbon dioxide or degrading some unusual nutrient or chemical substrate.

carboxysome—a microcompartment found in photosynthetic bacterial cells; its component parts remove carbon dioxide molecules from the air and attach them to larger substrate molecules.

1. The cell membrane, composed of phospholipids, proteins, and steroids maintains cellular organization by controlling which substances leave and enter the cell and which substances are retained within or outside the cell.
2. Proteins within a membrane can serve as receptors for signals, gates/pumps for transporting substances, enzymes supporting cell respiration, or adhesive substances that bind cells to surfaces or each other.
3. Cells living in watery environments where solute concentrations are low often possess a structural wall external to their membrane to keep influx of water from bursting the cell.
4. Some bacteria possess a second membrane external to their walls. This membrane protects the cell from host cell defensive molecules and other antibiotics.
5. The cytoplasm of a cell is where most of the chemistry of growth, maintenance, and cell-specific functions occur.
6. The nucleoid of prokaryotic cells houses much of the hereditary information that guides the structuring and activity of the cell.
7. A ribosome is a machine composed of protein and RNA that reads informational molecules in order to produce amino acid sequences that will form proteins of use to the cell or the whole organism.
8. Many prokaryotic cells contain microcompartments within their cytoplasm that are encased within protein and within which specialized reaction sequences occur.

Prokaryotic Organization

Let's now select a specific example from a prokaryotic cell's life and observe how the intricacies described above cooperate to enable the cell to successfully exploit the environment it resides in. Consider cells of the species *Streptococcus pyogenes* (*pyo* = pus; *gen* = gives rise to) (see Figure 5.13). Let's watch what goes on inside of them as they cause a virulent case of strep throat.

Streptococcus cells grow and divide just as your cells do. In 10% of us, they grow slowly as a small proportion among the variety of bacterial cells that normally stick to the surfaces of the cells in our oropharynx (throat). Let's suppose that a new, virulent strain shows up in your throat as the result of the wrong kiss, a child's probing fingers, or proximity to a very badly executed cough. Or we could assume that one of us who normally carries a *Streptococcal* strain around in our throat is having a bad time of it stress-wise and our immune system just is not doing very well. In any case, the *Streptococcus* cells begin to grow more rapidly.

To cause an infection and not simply get washed away by saliva, *Streptococcus* cells must adhere to your surfaces and to the surfaces of each other. Within the nucleoid of the *Streptococcus* cell is information that codes for two kinds of proteins.

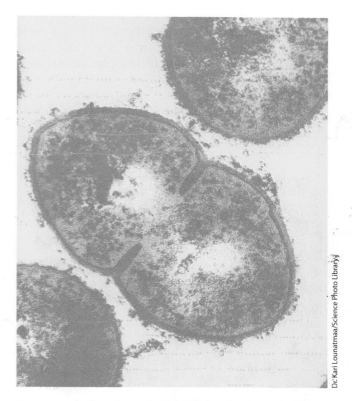

Figure 5.13 Electron microscopic view of the bacterium *Streptococcus pyogenes* showing cell division. At this magnification, the human cells it adheres to would, by comparison, be a bit larger in cross section than the size of your open textbook.

Dr. Kari Lounatmaa/Science Photo Library

One kind, called **adhesins,** sticks to receptor proteins on the surfaces of your throat-lining (epithelial) cells. The other kind of protein is a structural subunit for building long, fibrous tendrils called **fimbriae** (see Figure 5.14).

The information in the nucleoid is accessed by copying enzymes and the resulting information travels to the cell cytoplasm where it is read by streptococcal ribosomes (see Figure 5.11c). The product of this reading process is adhesin proteins and subunit proteins, which are assembled in the cytoplasm into extensions of the cell membrane. They extend out through the cell wall. The assembly appears to be carefully and deliberately designed with the final infection in mind. The adhesins get tacked onto the ends of the fimbriae, the *Streptococcus* cell and its daughter cells stick effectively to your own cells, and the localized infection begins.

Normal growth of the *Streptococcus* cells involves all parts of the cell. Information is constantly extracted from the nucleoid region, expressed by cytoplasmic ribosomes, and the products contribute either structurally or metabolically to increase the number of microcompartments, the size of the membrane and wall, and ultimately the content of the nucleoid itself. We are moving toward cell division—making more *Streptococcus* cells.

All of this growth requires carbohydrates, amino acids, and other vitamins and minerals. These must come from your secretions and your cells. Again,

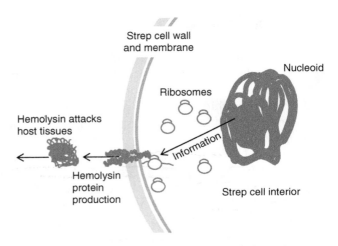

Figure 5.15 Hemolysin is a protein enzyme that degrades host red and white blood cells. Here it's production by a Strep cell is represented. Information flows from the nucleoid to the enzyme's production site on ribosomes. It's then secreted to the Strep cell's environment.

the nucleoid is accessed for information to produce proteins called **hemolysins** (see Figure 5.15). After their production on cytoplasmic ribosomes, hemolysin structure causes them to be recognized as destined for secretion; they are secreted right through secretion protein gates in the cell membrane to the outside of the cell. Once outside, they bind to your local red and white blood cells from your capillary beds and rupture the membranes of these cells! As your blood cells die, their contents become the nutrients for the growing *Streptococcus* cells. For example, your red cells supply much needed iron ions for microbial growth. You are bacterial food!

You have defensive cells called **macrophages** that are designed to eat and destroy these nasty *Streptococcus* cells. (Why can't we have peaceful coexistence in this world? Even at the molecular level, warfare is intense.). But the *Streptococcus* cells are designed to hide from these macrophages! In their

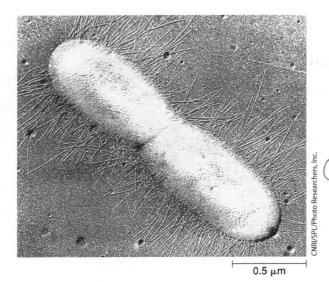

0.5 μm

CNRI/SPL/Photo Researchers, Inc.

Figure 5.14 Fimbriae are built from proteins. They are extensions of a bacterial cell surface that help to tether the cell to host cell and tissue surfaces long enough so that cell duplication and invasion can occur.

adhesin—molecule, often a protein, found on the surface of one cell enabling it to adhere to another cell.

fimbriae—tendril-like extensions of a bacterial cell's membrane used to adhere to substrates like a host cell; composed of proteins.

hemolysin—protein molecule produced in one cell, usually a bacterium, that can rupture the membrane and destroy the integrity of another cell, often a blood cell.

macrophage—large amoeboid-like cell in the vertebrate immune system that recognizes, engulfs, and digests foreign cells or small objects that gain entry to the host tissues.

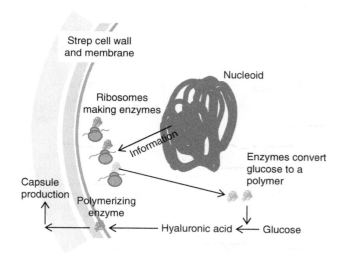

Figure 5.16 Capsule Production in *Streptococcus pyogenes.* Information is accessed for enzymes to convert glucose to hyaluronic acid (HA) and to polymerize the HA as part of capsule production.

nucleoid they access information that is expressed on ribosomes to form enzymes (see Figure 5.16). Some of these enzymes remain in the cytoplasm and begin converting some of the cell's glucose into hyaluronic acid. Another kind of enzyme is synthesized and placed right into the cell membrane. From there it can build the altered glucose into hyaluronic acid residues to be linked together in a huge polymer on the outside of the cell wall. There the polymer forms a sticky **capsule** that coats the entire cell. But hyaluronic acid is used by your own cells to hold themselves together in their own tissues. So now the macrophage is stumped! Many foreign "Trojan horse" streptococcal structures are hiding inside that capsule. But the macrophage can't feel them. It only senses hyaluronic acid—self surface—and it simply moves on. How tricky is that?

In this fight-to-the-death between your epithelial cells and streptococcal bacterial cells, all the intricate structures of the humble bacterial cell cooperate to threaten a much larger enemy. In this battle, it is not sufficient, for example, to imagine an enzyme that just helps to make hyaluronic acid. That is not enough. The enzyme must also be capable of (1) fitting into the molecular structure of the cell's membrane so that it can (2) be placed there; (3) it must recognize the sugar it's to operate on coming from the cytoplasm side, and (4) as it converts it to hyaluronic acid, it must (5) get this product into the right orientation on the outside to become part of the polymer in the capsule. Life Is Complex! (And death is the alternative.)

> **capsule**—a loose or formed gelatinous layer of carbohydrate and protein molecules that surrounds some bacteria. Usually grants some protection from a host's immune cells.

IN OTHER WORDS

1. *Streptococcus pyogenes* is a species of bacterium that often causes strep throat in the pharynx of an infected individual.
2. The *Streptococcus* cells use their own cellular information to generate adhesion molecules that coat their fimbriae and enable them to stick to human epithelial cells.
3. They also produce enzymes called *hemolysins* that leave the *Streptococcus* cell and degrade host cells in surrounding tissue, creating nutrients for strep cell growth and multiplication.
4. Cells in your immune system called *macrophages* are designed to engulf and destroy bacterial cells, but the invaders are hard to detect when they are coated with hyaluronic acid–containing capsules.
5. The enzymatic machinery that builds capsules is highly intricate in design and operates in both the cytoplasm and the membrane of the bacterial cell.

Eukaryotic Intricacies

In nature, there are probably many more kinds of eukaryotic cells than prokaryotic cells. Each prokaryotic cell is, by itself, a single organism possessed of one cell type. Conversely, *each* kind of higher organism possesses its own variety of eukaryotic cell types. There are conservatively over 200 kinds of eukaryotic cells that compose your own body. And eukaryotic cells include those of all protists, fungi, plants, and animals (see Figure 5.17). In exploring eukaryotic intricacies, therefore, we will be able to select only a few of the most common, most important aspects of cell structure.

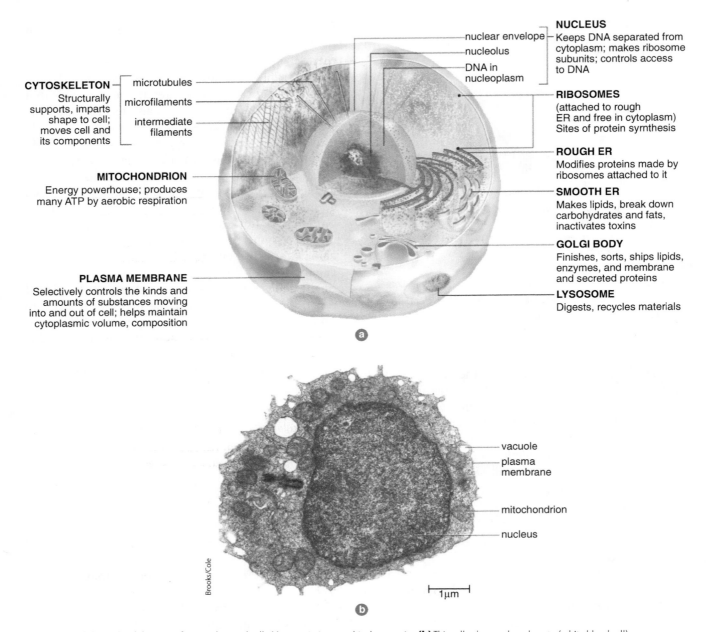

CYTOSKELETON — microtubules, microfilaments, intermediate filaments
Structurally supports, imparts shape to cell; moves cell and its components

NUCLEUS
Keeps DNA separated from cytoplasm; makes ribosome subunits; controls access to DNA

nuclear envelope
nucleolus
DNA in nucleoplasm

RIBOSOMES
(attached to rough ER and free in cytoplasm) Sites of protein synthesis

ROUGH ER
Modifies proteins made by ribosomes attached to it

MITOCHONDRION
Energy powerhouse; produces many ATP by aerobic respiration

SMOOTH ER
Makes lipids, break down carbohydrates and fats, inactivates toxins

GOLGI BODY
Finishes, sorts, ships lipids, enzymes, and membrane and secreted proteins

PLASMA MEMBRANE
Selectively controls the kinds and amounts of substances moving into and out of cell; helps maintain cytoplasmic volume, composition

LYSOSOME
Digests, recycles materials

a

vacuole
plasma membrane
mitochondrion
nucleus

1μm

Brooks/Cole

b

Figure 5.17 **(a)** A stylized drawing of a typical animal cell. Many variations on this theme exist. **(b)** This cell, a human lymphocyte (white blood cell), was photographed using an electron microscope.

The eukaryotic cell is surrounded by a cell membrane whose structure is fundamentally similar to that of a prokaryotic cell—a lipid bilayer "sea" in which a wide variety of proteins floats about in two dimensions (sideways but not into or out of the bilayer). The membrane separates an internal orderliness and high density of molecular machinery from an external environment that may have a similar concentration of molecules. Therefore a wall is not needed. But outside the cell membrane a far lower level of orderliness is found. Once again, orderliness is maintained by membrane proteins

that serve as gates, each allowing some appropriate class of substances in or out of the cell.

The eukaryotic membrane has a mechanism for bulk transport of substances not known to occur in prokaryotic cells called **endocytosis** (see Figure 5.18). In the process of endocytosis, molecules outside of

endocytosis—bulk transport of molecules or structures into a cell by a regulated bulging in of the cell membrane with final pinching off of the membrane's bleb to form an endocytotic vesicle.

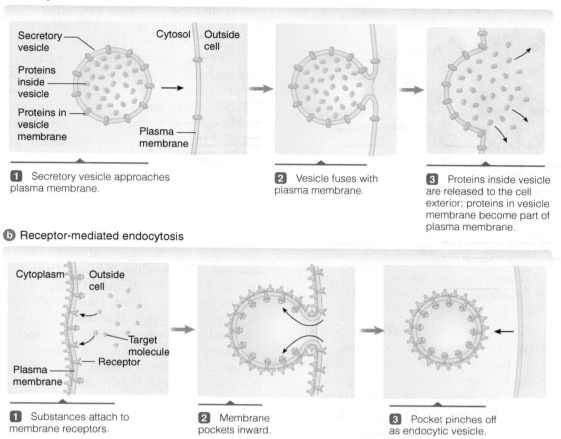

a Exocytosis

Secretory vesicle

Cytosol   Outside cell

Proteins inside vesicle

Proteins in vesicle membrane

Plasma membrane

1 Secretory vesicle approaches plasma membrane.

2 Vesicle fuses with plasma membrane.

3 Proteins inside vesicle are released to the cell exterior; proteins in vesicle membrane become part of plasma membrane.

b Receptor-mediated endocytosis

Cytoplasm   Outside cell

Target molecule

Receptor

Plasma membrane

1 Substances attach to membrane receptors.

2 Membrane pockets inward.

3 Pocket pinches off as endocytic vesicle.

Figure 5.18 **(a)** A secretory vesicle travels toward the cell membrane, the phospholipid bilayer of the vesicle "melts into" the phospholipid bilayer of the cell membrane releasing vesicle content to the cell exterior. **(b)** A substance of value to the cell binds to receptor proteins designed specifically for it. Binding causes the membrane in the area of binding to fold inward. The membranes pinch off and a new vesicle is formed.

the cell bind to membrane surface receptor proteins thus signaling their presence. In response, that area of the cell membrane folds in to form a vesicle that pinches off and is now inside the cell. In this way, large molecules, aggregates of molecules, or even whole cells can be taken into the cell cytoplasm. In a complementary process called **exocytosis**, large numbers of cellular products like hormones, antibodies, or digestive enzymes can be efficiently exported from the cell in which they are produced.

Inside the eukaryotic cell membrane is a complex world of great proportion compared to a prokaryotic cell. You could jam over 100 *Streptococcus* cells into a single one of your cells. Your larger cell size requires and supports a higher level of compartmentalization. Most of the compartments of the eukaryotic cell are membrane-enclosed and are referred to as **organelles**.

The largest compartment of a eukaryotic cell is generally the nucleus. This functionally critical core area of the cell is surrounded by a membrane that is doubled in thickness (see Figure 5.19) and festooned with complex pores. Within the nucleus lies the **nucleoplasm**. The nuclear membrane thus separates information access and processing from the cytoplasm where information expression and generalized metabolism occur. The membrane

exocytosis—bulk transport of molecules or structures out of a cell by a regulated fusion of a vesicle containing the molecules or structures with the cell membrane. The interior of the vesicle opens to the exterior of the cell, spilling its content outside the cell.

organelle—membrane-enclosed compartment within a eukaryotic cell.

nucleoplasm—the volume of fluid within the cell nucleus where the chromatin is suspended. It is somewhat continuous with the cytoplasm through large nuclear pores that connect the nucleus and cytoplasm.

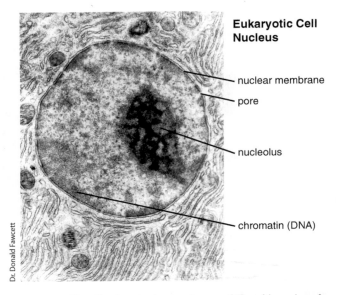

Eukaryotic Cell Nucleus

— nuclear membrane

— pore

— nucleolus

— chromatin (DNA)

Dr. Donald Fawcett

Figure 5.19   The cell nucleus. An electron microscope image of the nucleus of an acinar cell from your pancreas. The nucleus is about 6–7 microns in diameter.

pores control the flow of information (RNA) and proteins from the nucleus to the cytoplasm.

But the nucleus is further compartmentalized. While the nucleoplasm contains many enzymes and building blocks involved in information handling, much of the space there is taken up by the information itself—the DNA. Eukaryotic cells need more information to control a much larger living system. The DNA in a single human cell nucleus would unravel to about 2 meters in length! By comparison, that of a prokaryotic cell might run about 2 millimeters. So, just as shelving and aisles are critical to the value of a library, so an elaborate system of protein scaffolding exists to provide support and access to the DNA sequences. Because of its enormous length, the cell's DNA and its scaffolding, collectively referred to as **chromatin**, are divided up into discrete unit lengths of sequence called **chromosomes**. In human cells, the chromatin is divided into two sets of 23 chromosomes.

Most eukaryotic nuclei also contain one or more darkly staining regions called **nucleoli** (**nucleolus**, singular). This is a high-activity region along the chromatin where the DNA sequences code for the RNA molecules found in ribosomes (see Figure 5.19). For reasons not yet understood, the protein parts of ribosomes are synthesized in the cytoplasm (on ribosomes!) and exported to the nucleolus. There, the RNA portion of the ribosome (synthesized in the nucleolus) and the imported protein portions are combined to form both large and small ribosomal subunits. The completed subunits are returned to

the cytoplasm, via nuclear pores, where they will finally function as mature ribosomes.

Like a complex factory with separate production areas, the cytoplasm of eukaryotic cells has a single large internal membrane system organized into separate regional areas. Each area consists of complex systems of membrane-lined channels whose principal function is the synthesis and modification of proteins and lipids of importance to the cell. During synthesis, proteins or lipids move through these channels, transitioning from one area to another in membrane-enclosed sacs called **vesicles** (see Figure 5.22). What follows is a description of the major regions of this vast inner complex of membrane compartments.

In cells heavily responsible for making proteins, much of the endomembrane system consists of a network of channels and sacs called the **rough endoplasmic reticulum (RER)** (*reticulum* in Latin = fine network; see Figure 5.20). The channels appear rough because their outer surfaces are densely coated with **ribosomes**. Information from the nucleus travels through the cytoplasm to the ribosomes. They then read it to synthesize sequences of amino acids into proteins with the protein product extruded into the lumen (or interior) of the endoplasmic reticulum. As the protein next diffuses along the channel of the RER, it is folded into its final form with additional carbohydrate or lipid groups attached to it. At the end of the channel the proteins enter a newly forming vesicle that blebs from the RER and moves to the next portion of the endomembrane system: the **Golgi complex.**

chromatin—general term for a cell's informational content—its DNA—plus the molecular scaffolding that supports it.

chromosome—a single long piece of DNA and the molecular scaffolding that supports it.

nucleolus—a region within the cell nucleus, visible by electron microscopy, composed of protein and nucleic acid. It is the site where ribosomal RNA is transcribed and processed for inclusion into ribosomal subunits.

vesicle—a small, membrane-enclosed sac with a cell where some activity or substance is sequestered from the rest of cellular activity. Substances are frequently transported intracellularly with vesicles.

rough endoplasmic reticulum—a network of membrane-lined channels within the eukaryotic cell cytoplasm where proteins are synthesized and processed.

Golgi complex—a sequence of flattened membrane-bound sacs found in the eukaryotic cell cytoplasm. They are sites of protein and lipid processing and packaging.

Eukaryotic Cell

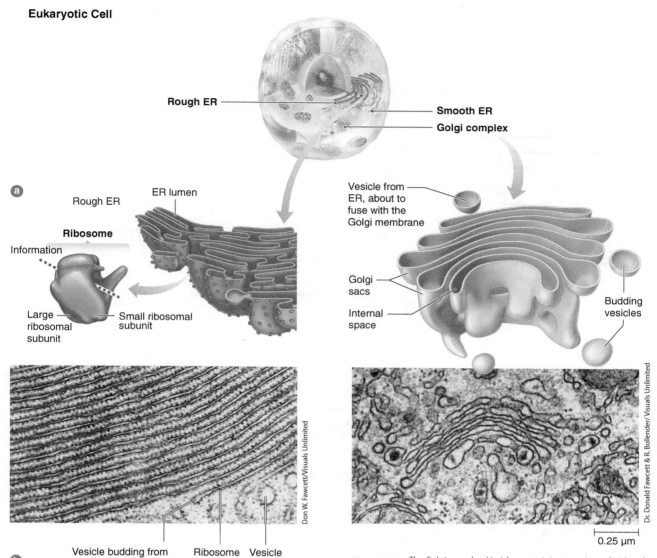

Figure 5.20 The rough endoplasmic reticulum (RER) is the site where information from the nucleus is used to produce protein products. **(a)** The ribosomes (red dots.......processing will occur. **(b)** An electron microscope image of rough endoplasmic reticulum.

Figure 5.21 The Golgi complex. Vesicles containing proteins or lipids to be processed arrive at the inner-most sac and fuse with it. As sacs approach the outer-most position (closest to cell exterior), processing reaches completion and vesicles can bleb off of the last sac and proceed to transport either within or outside of the cell.

The Golgi complex is a series of membrane-enclosed, flattened sacs that look like a stack of pancakes without a plate (see Figure 5.21). Vesicles arrive at the first sac at the end of the complex that's closest the nucleus. The vesicle membrane fuses with the sac membrane, increasing its size and dumping its protein contents into the sac. As new sacs form and older ones work their way through the complex, protein products within them are sorted and further modified. Amino acid segments may be removed. Further nonprotein side groups may be added. Once a sac reaches the far end of the complex, protein maturation is complete. The content of the last sac breaks up into vesicles transporting their protein content to its destination.

Some vesicles will carry protein to the cell membrane (see Figures 5.18a, 5.22). There, the vesicle membrane will fuse with the cell membrane. If the proteins in the vesicle were embedded into the vesicle membrane, then those proteins will now be part of the cell membrane's protein inventory. They

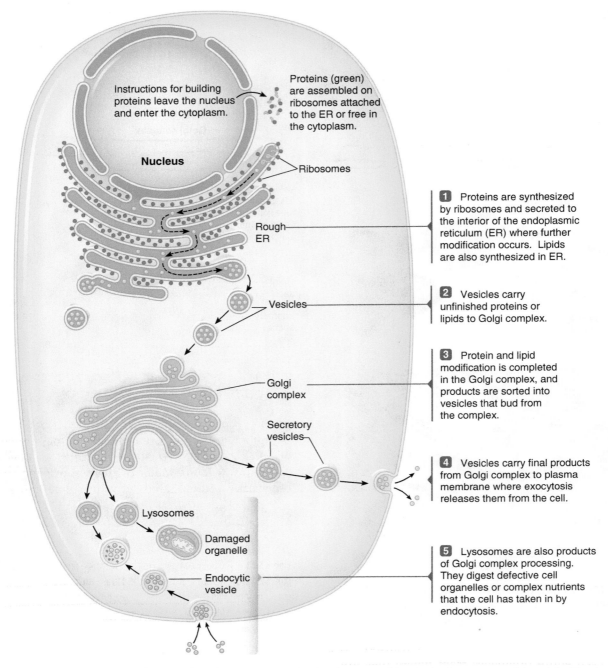

Instructions for building proteins leave the nucleus and enter the cytoplasm.

Proteins (green) are assembled on ribosomes attached to the ER or free in the cytoplasm.

Nucleus

Ribosomes

Rough ER

Vesicles

Golgi complex

Secretory vesicles

Lysosomes

Damaged organelle

Endocytic vesicle

1 Proteins are synthesized by ribosomes and secreted to the interior of the endoplasmic reticulum (ER) where further modification occurs. Lipids are also synthesized in ER.

2 Vesicles carry unfinished proteins or lipids to Golgi complex.

3 Protein and lipid modification is completed in the Golgi complex, and products are sorted into vesicles that bud from the complex.

4 Vesicles carry final products from Golgi complex to plasma membrane where exocytosis releases them from the cell.

5 Lysosomes are also products of Golgi complex processing. They digest defective cell organelles or complex nutrients that the cell has taken in by endocytosis.

Figure 5.22 A cellular "assembly line". Nuclear information is accessed and used to generate biomolecules that are processed through the ER and Golgi complex. Vesicles are used to move biomolecular products within the assembly line and to appropriate destinations at it's end.

will contribute to membrane functions there! If, on the other hand, the proteins were free, suspended within the vesicle, then fusion with the cell membrane will dump the proteins (secrete them) outside the cell as a protein product to be used elsewhere in the tissues of the organism's body.

Sometimes the vesicle simply remains within the cell cytoplasm to form what's called a **lysosome** (see Figure 5.22). These are membrane-bound

vesicles whose internal proteins are a broad catalog of digestive enzymes. In different cells they serve different purposes. In most cells they fuse with old

lysosome—in eukaryotic cells, a membrane-enclosed organelle containing hydrolytic enzymes capable of degrading either cell parts, invasive cells, or some inorganic substances.

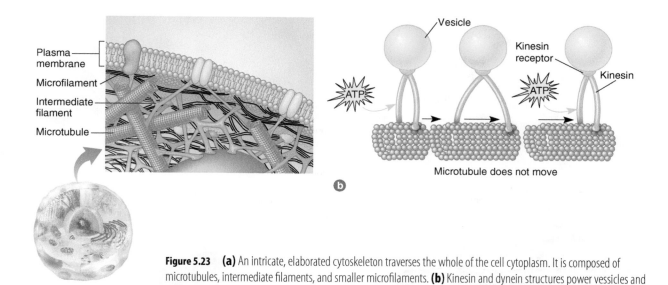

Figure 5.23 **(a)** An intricate, elaborated cytoskeleton traverses the whole of the cell cytoplasm. It is composed of microtubules, intermediate filaments, and smaller microfilaments. **(b)** Kinesin and dynein structures power vessicles and other organelles from place to place within the cell along the cytoskeletal network. ATP energy drives this movement.

Labels in figure (a): Plasma membrane, Microfilament, Intermediate filament, Microtubule

Labels in figure (b): Vesicle, Kinesin receptor, Kinesin, ATP, ATP, Microtubule does not move

organelles that are no longer functioning properly and degrade their structures so that the component parts can be salvaged and reused by the cell. In cells of your immune system they wait about within large macrophage cells till a new virus or bacterium has been engulfed by the process of endocytosis. They then fuse with the new vesicle and digest the virus or bacterium for "lunch." Finally, in independent cells in an aqueous environment, they fuse with vesicles that have brought in some smaller microbe or portion of a dead microbe to form a "cyto-stomach" that digests the micro-meal with the molecular results diffusing out into the cytoplasm where they feed the cell's own synthetic processes.

This whole business of synthesizing and modifying proteins, and of directing them to their physical destination, involves considerable intracellular movement, especially of vesicles. The entire cytoplasmic "warehouse" is neatly traversed by a system of molecular "cables" and "winches" that transport vesicles, even entire organelles from where they are to where they need to be (see Figure 5.23). These protein cables are called **microtubules.** Vesicles or organelles are attached to microtubules by means of protein "motors" called **dyneins** and **kinesins** that "walk" along the microtubule either away from or toward the center of the cell. The microtubules, along which cell structures move, are in turn supported within a cytoskeletal framework occupying the entire cytoplasm—another protein-based framework constructed from supporting "struts" called **intermediate filaments.** The whole internal architecture is a wonderful factory built of biological molecules!

If this all sounds like a highly energetic system, your intuition is correct. The cell is consuming millions of ATPs per second to keep things going. This consumption is supported by a series of enzyme-driven reactions that generate fresh ATP supplies. These reactions, termed **cell respiration,** occur largely within a cytoplasmic organelle called the **mitochondrion** (see Figure 5.24). Some cells have one huge mitochondrion filling much of the cytoplasmic space; other cells have hundreds of smaller ones. Since the

microtubule—a part of the cell's cytoskeleton (support structure) composed of 25-nanometer thick fibers composed of tubulin proteins. These are used to move chromosomes during cell division.

dynein—a micro-scale motor device constructed of protein; it attaches to and moves cellular structures along the length of microtubules toward the center of the cell.

kinesin—a micro-scale motor device constructed of protein; it attaches to and moves cellular structures along the length of microtubules toward the periphery of the cell.

intermediate filament—structural elements within and outside of cells having thicknesses on the order of 10 nanometers. Component parts of nails, hair, horns, scales, and parts of sarcomere structure in muscle cells.

cell respiration—a sequence of chemical reactions within a cell that transfers electrons to oxygen and results in the phosphorylation of ADP to produce ATP, a cellular form of immediate energy.

mitochondrion—an organelle within the cytoplasm of eukaryotic cells bound by two separate membranes within which the major reactions of cell respiration take place.

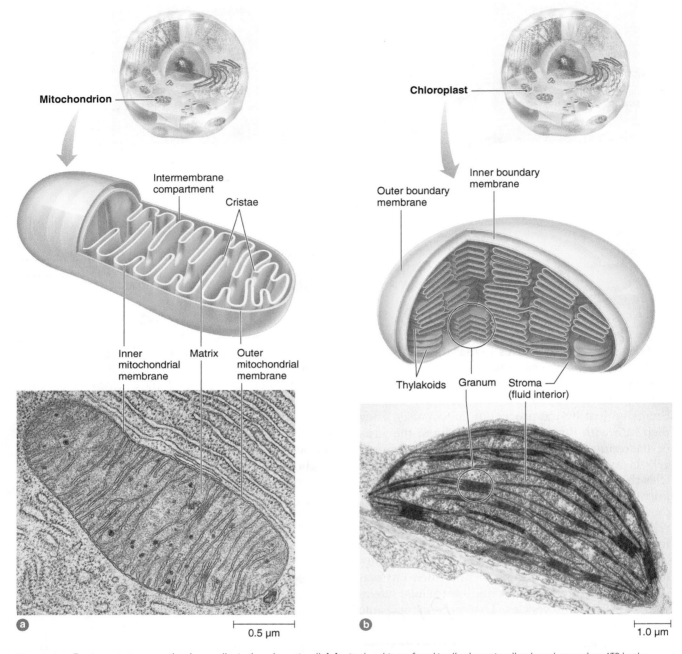

Mitochondrion

Intermembrane compartment

Cristae

Inner mitochondrial membrane

Matrix

Outer mitochondrial membrane

a   0.5 µm

Chloroplast

Inner boundary membrane

Outer boundary membrane

Thylakoids   Granum   Stroma (fluid interior)

b   1.0 µm

Figure 5.24 Two important energy related organelles in the eukaryotic cell. **(a)** mitochondria are found in all eukaryotic cells where they produce ATP by the process of cellular respiration. **(b)** chloroplasts, found in plant cells and some protists, are sites of photosynthesis.

respiratory reactions themselves are complex and subject to multifaceted control, the mitochondrial compartment is itself further subdivided. It is surrounded by both an outer and an inner membrane creating an intermediate space where one set of reactions occurs. A second set of reactions occurs on the surface of the inner membrane itself. This second set of reactions is a highly directed pathway that occurs many, many times relative to other respiratory reactions. It works best when the component enzymes

are linearly arranged on a surface—a membrane surface. As a result, the inner membrane has a highly folded structure. The compartments that result are called **cristae**. As we saw in Chapter 4, when viewing

cristae—folds within the inner membrane system of the mitochondrion; on these folds are arranged the enzymes that participate in the final sequence of reactions involved in cellular respiration.

molecular structure, here again at the cellular level, shape, and form are precisely arranged for the nature of the task to be carried out. The mitochondrion is a beautifully crafted machine.

The ATP supplied by the mitochondrial power plant can be generated only if there are some carbs around to fire the process. Glucose is preferred. So your cells have to have a continuous supply of sugar (fuel) to keep mitochondrial production at its peak. That's why you ingest carbohydrates. But there are some cells that don't need to import glucose because they can *make* it! These are the plant cells (and some kinds of prokaryotic/bacterial cells). This process of making burnable fuel molecules is called **photosynthesis.** In eukaryotic cells, a separate, special organelle supports the many reactions that comprise photosynthesis. That organelle is the **chloroplast** (see Figure 5.24).

Chloroplast function is complementary to mitochondrial function. The former uses sunlight to drive the formation of stable, energy-rich glucose molecules. The latter harvests that energy from the glucose in order to replenish less stable ATP stores. The complexity of photosynthesis has the structure of chloroplasts appearing in some ways similar to mitochondria. There is again, an outer membrane and an inner one creating a discrete inter-membrane space. The reactions within the "inner sanctum" again work best on a two-dimensional membrane surface. So the interior of the chloroplast has a grainy appearance; it is jam packed with grana—stacks of membrane-bound sacs called **thylakoids** (see Figure 5.24). The syrupy fluid surrounding these stacks is called the **stroma.** One set of reactions occurs within the

thylakoid; another occurs in the stromal space. It is all elegantly arranged to support a reaction pathway that ultimately feeds you your meals three times a day.

The eukaryotic pattern has been fashioned into so very many cellular forms and sizes that there is simply no space here to speak of smooth endoplasmic reticulum, vacuoles, plastid classes, centrioles, light sensors, flagellae, cilia, and a host of other subcellular machines that neatly perform a variety of functions critical to some cell's survival. Table 5.3 summarizes some of these organelles and their functions. If this array of sophisticated equipment appears complicated, it is because **Life Is Complex.** Such complexity intimidates the lazy scholar. But the curious one senses that this exploration is not just a tour inside the "unit of life." It is also a tour inside of an amazing Mind who saw this all as a single unit of life, and then produced it . . .

photosynthesis—a sequence of chemical reactions by which autotrophic cells and organisms use solar energy to generate carbohydrate energy from carbon dioxide and water.

chloroplast—a membrane-bound organelle in the cytoplasm of eukaryotic cells where the reactions of photosynthesis take place.

thylakoid—a membrane-enclosed sac within the chloroplast; within the sac membrane are enzymes that carry out the transformation of solar energy into ATP energy.

stroma—the fluid within a chloroplast that surrounds and bathes the thylakoids; within it ATP energy is used to generate more stable carbohydrate energy.

Table 5.3 Component parts of cells in prokaryotes and eukaryotes.

Structure	Function	Pro	Euk
1. Cell Membrane	retains cell contents, regulates inward and outward flux of substances, site of cellular respiration in prokaryotes	+	+
2. Cell Wall	protects cell from osmotic rupture, influences cell shape	M	S
3. Outer Membrane + periplasmic Space	retains critical substances within periplasmic space, protects cell from toxins, antibiotics	S	−
4. Nucleoid	site of information storage and retrieval	+	−
5. Nucleus	site of information storage and retrieval, site of synthesis of ribosomal subunits.	−	+
6. Chromosomes	contain the hereditary information that determines or influences the structure and function of the cell	+	+
7. Nucleolus	synthesis of RNA molecules used in construction of ribosomes; site of ribosome subunit assembly	−	+
8. Ribosomes	site of protein synthesis	+	+

(Continued)

Table 5.3 (*Continued*)

Structure	Function	Pro	Euk
9. Microcompartments	protein-encased regions of specialized function with the cytoplasm; often these functions are specific metabolic reaction pathways.	+	–
10. Rough Endoplasmic Reticulum	site of ribosomes and their function; protein production and modification; source of vesicles that transport unfinished synthetic products	–	+
11. Smooth Endoplasmic Reticulum	site of lipid synthesis; calcium ion storage in some cells, drug detoxification in others	–	+
12. Golgi Complex	finishing stage of protein and lipid modification; sorting and secretion by means of vesicles occurs here	–	+
13. Lysosomes	intracellular breakdown of old organelles, ingested cells and particles.	–	+
14. Vacuoles	storage of water, minerals, wastes, support of plant cell structure	S	+
15. Mitochondria	site of majority of reactions of cellular respiration; principle site of ATP production	–	+
16. Chloroplasts	site of conversion of light energy to chemical energy in sugar molecules	–	S
17. Thylakoids (isolated)	site of conversion of light energy to ATP energy for use in the cell	S	–
18. Peroxisomes	membrane-bound organelle that helps degrade toxic products of cell respiration; fatty acid degradation also occurs here	–	+
19. Eyespot	a photoreceptive organelle found in many photosynthetic algal forms; its pigments allow the cell to swim toward a light source.	–	S
20. Microfilaments	part of cytoskeletal structure; provide physical support for cells' architecture; assist in movement of organelles and in cell division	–	+
21. Intermediate Filaments	help to stabilize and reinforce cell shape	–	+
22. Microtubules	provide physical support for cell's architecture; assist in cellular and organellar movement, structural parts of cilia, flagellae, centrioles.	–	+
23. Centrioles	organizing centers of microtubule arrays within the cell cytoplasm; of critical importance during cell division	–	S
24. Fimbriae (pili)	surface extensions of bacterial cells facilitating adhesion to host cell surfaces; some allow transfer of genetic information from cell to cell	S	–
25. Capsule	surface layer of polysaccharides and proteins; hides foreign surfaces of a bacterium making it less visible to host immune system cells	S	–
26. Cilia	enable movement of some protistan cells; movement of materials over the surface of some human cells.	–	+
27. Flagella	provides motility for many bacterial and protistan cells and for sperm cells	+	+

Note:- + = most forms possess this, – = most forms do not, S = some forms possess this, M = many forms possess this

IN OTHER WORDS

1. There is an almost endless diversity of eukaryotic cells in the living world.
2. Besides having membrane proteins that control the influx/efflux of substances, eukaryotic cells can move bulk quantities of substances across their membranes by exocytosis and endocytosis, processes that involve vesicle formation and degradation.
3. The eukaryotic nucleus is surrounded by a double membrane containing elaborate pore structures that facilitate information flow from the chromatin sequestered inside.
4. The nucleolus is a darkly staining nuclear structure where ribosomal RNA is produced and fitted into ribosomal subunits.
5. Large quantities of molecules that need to be moved from place to place during processing within a eukaryotic cell are transported within membrane-bound vesicles.

6. The rough endoplasmic reticulum (RER) is an elaborate network of membrane-lined channels in which newly synthesized proteins begin to be modified into their final usable form.

7. The Golgi complex is a series of concentric, flattened sacs that receive and deliver the content of vesicles. That content is protein or lipid molecules that complete their processing into mature form while within the complex.

8. Vesicles emerging from the Golgi complex can have various fates: They can transport substances to the membrane for secretion, or they can remain in the cytoplasm as lysosomes for the purpose of digesting the content of still other vesicles with which they fuse.

9. Protein motors called *dyneins* and *kinesins* use cellular energy to move vesicles and organelles from place to place within the cell along the surfaces of microtubules.

10. Microtubules, along with intermediate filaments, form much of the interior skeletal support for the shape and strength of the eukaryotic cell.

11. Most of the reactions of cell respiration and the majority of ATP production occur within the fluid and membrane array (cristae) inside of mitochondria.

12. Cells of plants and some protists are able to make their own carbohydrate supply by carrying out photosynthesis within the structure of a green organelle called the *chloroplast*.

13. Two component parts of photosynthesis are compartmentalized within the chloroplast with solar energy capture occurring in thylakoids, and the actual sugar production occurring in the stromal fluid within the chloroplast.

Eukaryotic Organization

Now let's go inside of your **pancreas.** We will observe how the amazing intricacies of eukaryotic cellular life work in common to support you in a singularly pleasurable task: the consumption of a pizza. Deep within the tissues of the pancreas are collections of enzyme-secreting cells called **acinar cells** (see Figure 5.25).

Pizza is mostly starch. Starch can't be absorbed directly in your digestive system—its molecular structure is too large to enter the epithelial cells lining your small intestine. An enzyme (protein) called **amylase** needs to be present and waiting in your small intestine in order to degrade the starch molecules to glucose units in order for them to be absorbed. Let's see how the acinar cell plays a part in this.

Acinar cells are constantly producing the enzyme amylase along with a variety of other digestive enzymes (see Figure 5.26). Information that codes for these enzymes is found within the chromosomes in the cell nucleus. This information is accessed, and copies of it find their way out past the nuclear membrane through its pores to the ribosomes on the surface of the RER. The amino acid sequence of amylase is generated by the ribosome, and the product is secreted into the lumen (interior) of the reticulum. Further along, the amylase is collected into vesicles that bud off of the RER

and carry it further away from the site of synthesis. Eventually, these vesicles fuse with a sac in the Golgi complex where the amylase reaches its final mature form. From the Golgi complex, the amylase is again sequestered into specialized vesicles called *zymogen granules*. These vesicles become attached to microtubules and are walked along them toward the acinar cell membrane, where they begin to accumulate in the cytoplasm on the side of the cell nearest its opening into a tiny pancreatic duct. The amylase is ready for that pizza!

But when and how are these vesicles released? It would be foolish to simply release digestive enzymes all the time whether they were needed or not. That would represent an unacceptable waste of material, machinery, and energy for both the

pancreas—a body organ that produces and secretes digestive enzymes into the small intestine and that generates and secretes hormones such as insulin into the bloodstream.

acinar cell—a type of cell within the pancreas that produces and secretes digestive enzymes.

amylase—an enzyme in saliva and in the small intestine that degrades starch to disaccharides and trisaccharides that will be further degraded to form glucose units suitable for absorption in the small intestine.

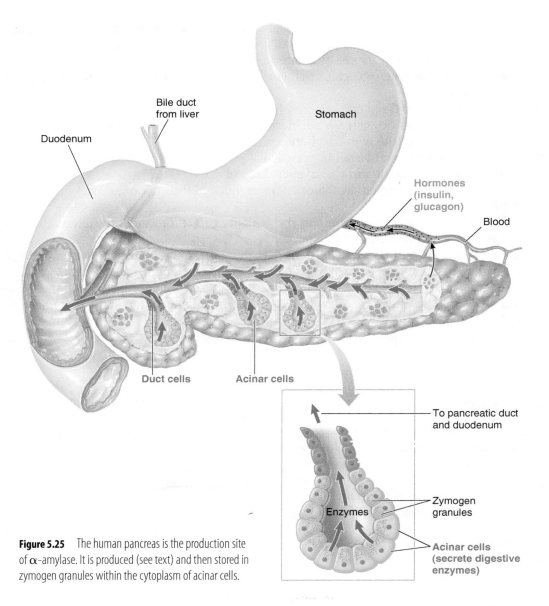

Figure 5.25 The human pancreas is the production site of α-amylase. It is produced (see text) and then stored in zymogen granules within the cytoplasm of acinar cells.

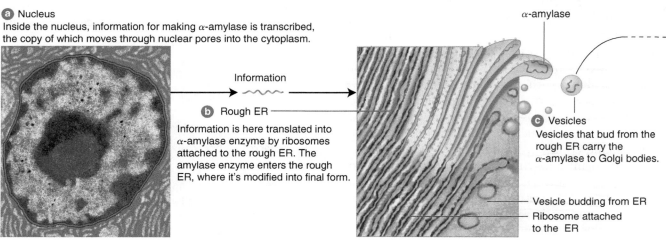

a Nucleus
Inside the nucleus, information for making α-amylase is transcribed, the copy of which moves through nuclear pores into the cytoplasm.

Information

b Rough ER
Information is here translated into α-amylase enzyme by ribosomes attached to the rough ER. The amylase enzyme enters the rough ER, where it's modified into final form.

c Vesicles
Vesicles that bud from the rough ER carry the α-amylase to Golgi bodies.

Figure 5.26 Production of α-amylase in an acinar cell.

cell and its Designer. Suppose you could put some careful, conscious thought into this system. How would you get the system to secrete amylase just as it was needed? The process actually occurs in stages—Life Is Complex.

It is very hard for a large pizza to surprise your nose. As visual and olfactory stimuli begin to assault your nervous system, it sends a signal to your acinar cells. For most of the distance from your nose to your pancreas that signal travels along the membranes of highly specialized cells called **neurons**. But when the signal arrives within about 0.030 micrometers from your acinar cell, the signal becomes a diffusible chemical called **acetylcholine**. When the acetylcholine is released next to the acinar cell, it very quickly diffuses up to the cell surface and binds to a receptor protein there—a surface protein designed to specifically fit the structure of acetylcholine (see Figure 5.27). When the portion of the receptor protein on the outside of the membrane binds acetylcholine, it changes its shape. This change includes part of the receptor protein that is inside the cell membrane. This means that the signal is now a change that has occurred *inside* the cell.

Somehow this shape change in the surface receptor results in a significant change in the calcium ion concentration within the acinar cell cytoplasm. This change in turn starts the vesicles with their digestive enzymes moving up to the inside of the cell membrane. As we saw before, when the vesicle membrane merges into the cell membrane, the vesicle actually fuses with—becomes a part of—the cell membrane dumping its amylase content (along with other digestive enzymes) into the nearest tiny branch of the pancreatic duct. This duct will carry the enzymes to the small intestine, where they will be waiting when the (remains of the) pizza arrive there.

As we saw with testosterone back in Chapter 4, acetylcholine is doing an amazing thing here. It is starting a whole cascade of cell reactions/activities that will be of great benefit to the organism—that will enhance the organism's survival. What is amazing is that acetylcholine is a very common molecule in your body. Cells in your stomach, heart, eyes, brain, salivary glands, and skeletal muscles all respond to its presence. Yet each cell type responds to acetylcholine in its own unique way, all of which are beneficial to the organism in different ways. It is difficult to imagine how such an elegant system could come together piecemeal without some highly gifted Designer seeing the bigger picture ahead of time.

So secretion of enzyme begins with anticipation. But most of the secretion is designed to result from a thoughtfully more conservative stimulus that requires the pizza to have already been eaten. (Who has not smelled a pizza they were not in fact entitled to?) Once fragments of pizza actually arrive at the beginning of your small intestine, their presence chemically induces a major hormonal

neuron—the cellular unit of the nervous system; a cell characterized by long narrow processes extending away from the cell body. Signals along the length of processes take the form of electrical impulses.

acetylcholine—a neurotransmitter substance; a chemical signal formed at the end of a neuronal axon that diffuses across a synaptic space and stimulates a response in the receiving cell.

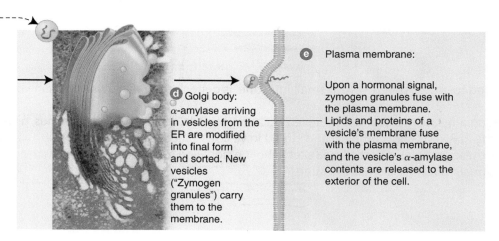

d Golgi body: α-amylase arriving in vesicles from the ER are modified into final form and sorted. New vesicles ("Zymogen granules") carry them to the membrane.

e Plasma membrane:

Upon a hormonal signal, zymogen granules fuse with the plasma membrane. Lipids and proteins of a vesicle's membrane fuse with the plasma membrane, and the vesicle's α-amylase contents are released to the exterior of the cell.

Figure 5.26 *(Continued)*

Amylase Release in Stages: 1) stimulation from nervous system releases acetylcholine near acinar cells 2) a small number of vesicles containing amylase undergo exocytosis 3) hormones arrive from small intestine signalling that starch is present 4) many vesicle containing amylase undergo exocytosis releasing digestive enzymes into the pancreatic duct.

Figure 5.27 Amylase Enzyme is realeased from Acinar cells of the pancreas in stages. The movement of vesicles ("zymogen granules") up to the cell membrane inner surface and the exocytosis of the amylase enzymes is signalled for by hormones from the nervous system and digestive system.

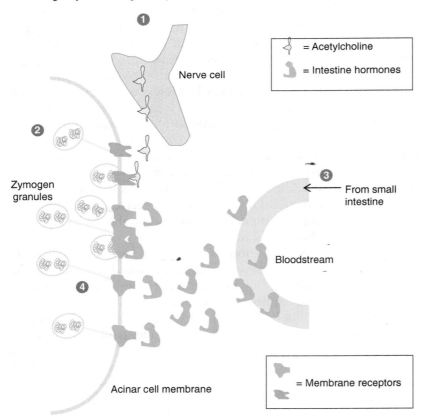

signal. Two hormones travel from the small intestine where they are produced to the acinar cells by way of the bloodstream (see Figure 5.27). These hormones again bind to receptors on the acinar cell surfaces and cause massive rupturing of zymogen granules with release of sufficient amylase to entirely degrade that pizza starch you so enthusiastically ingested. What an elegant and efficient system for turning a gastronomic delight into simple nutrients for you to absorb and profit from! It almost seems as if there is benevolence hidden in the structuring of this system.

IN OTHER WORDS

1. The enzyme amylase, used to digest starch in your small intestine, is generated within acinar cells in your pancreas.
2. Information for generating amylase molecules is retrieved from the nucleus, translated on ribosomes, processed to final form in the RER and Golgi complex, and stored in vesicles called *zymogen granules*.
3. Control of the release of these granules is partially via acetylcholine signaling from the nervous system and partially via hormonal signaling from the small intestine.

We have just finished exploring a wide array of subcellular compartments and organelles, each of which is an intricate and interwoven collection of macromolecules that supports the compartment's activities. In turn, the organelles themselves act cooperatively in a cellular context, which represents a still higher level of complexity. Does cellular life get any more complex than this? It's time for a trip to the pond.

Swimming in and about the quiet surface waters of your local pond is a frighteningly complex eukaryotic **protozoan** named *Paramecium bursaria* (see Figure 5.28). Protozoan cells are so large and replete with varied and unusual organelles that some workers have made the (semantic) argument that they are small "acellular animals." Well this 125-micrometer-long "cell animal" has a surprise for us: It is green in color—like a plant. Microscopic examination reveals an entirely new category of reality for us to think about: The green comes from small cells—algal cells—that live within the larger host *Paramecium* cell! We call this relationship **endosymbiosis** (*endo* = within; *sym* =

together). This is clearly beyond the concept of compartments within a cell. A chloroplast within one of these algal cells represents a compartment within a cell within a compartment within a larger (host) cell!

Studies reveal that 100 or more small algal cells of genus *Zoochlorella* each exist within its own vacuole-like organelle within the cytoplasm of *Paramecium*. The vacuole is surrounded by its own membrane, which thus elegantly controls the flow of substances back and forth between the algal cell and its host animal cell. The arrangement functions wonderfully for both parties (See Figure 5.29).

The algal cell is protected by its host cell from any other kind of cell that would engulf it by endocytosis and then degrade (eat) it. The alga is nonmotile, but it gets a free ride from place to place. The paramecium uses its own cilia to take the whole menagerie to places where ample sunlight and fresh carbon dioxide sources keep photosynthesis going. The paramecium also imports glutamine (an amino acid) into its cytoplasm, which then diffuses into Chlorella's vacuolar recluse, where the alga used it to build its own amino acids and proteins.

The host Paramecium does not need to always actively forage by taking food into its cytopharynx. Such food would require a complete digestion process. Instead, the host cell can get energy from the sugars generated by the algal cell: The sugar maltose moves freely across the vacuolar membrane from alga to Paramecium. And, oddly enough, the presence of the algal cell results in the construction of a protein gate in the outer membrane of the *host* cell that now allows ammonium ions (NH_4^+)

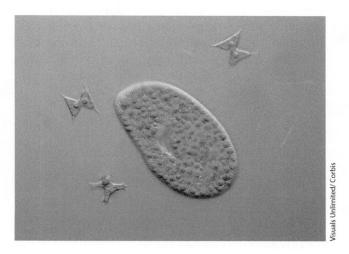

Visuals Unlimited/ Corbis

Figure 5.28 The protistan, *Paramecium bursaria*. The Paramecium cell by itself has no green color. But many individual algal cells of Genus *Chlorella* "live" endosymbiotically inside the cytoplasm of the host Paramecium cell. They make food for the host cell and get a free ride in return. The clear area in the center of the *Paramecium* cell is the oral groove where smaller Protists and bacteria are ingested "for lunch".

protozoan—single-celled microorganisms that are eukaryotic and possess animal-like characteristics, particularly motility.

endosymbiosis—a relationship between two disparate types of cells in which one cell type exists within the cytoplasm of the other cell type. At least one of the two cell types will benefit from this relationship.

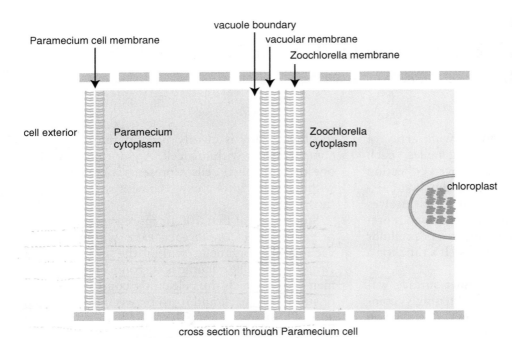

cell exterior

Paramecium cell membrane

vacuole boundary
vacuolar membrane
Zoochlorella membrane

Paramecium cytoplasm

Zoochlorella cytoplasm

chloroplast

cross section through Paramecium cell

Figure 5.29 Compartmental relationships between the cytoplasm of the *Zoochlorella* cell and it's host cell *Paramecium bursaria.* See text for details.

into both host and symbiont cell for use in building nitrogen-containing compounds.

We are touching only the surface of a broad array of ways in which these two cell types intimately serve each other while maintaining their separate chemistries. And already the obvious question haunts us: If many or most cells in nature exist independent of any such relationships, why do these complicated symbioses occur and how did they ever begin? When Life Is Complex, answers are meager indeed! We can assume in the highly competitive world of nature that no endosymbiotic relationship would occur unless it brought significant advantage to at least one of the two parties.

But how could that ever happen? A Paramecium cell of *any other type* that engulfs an algal cell will either digest the algal cell and utilize it for nutrition or starve if it isn't able to. Complex mutualistic relations like this do not accidentally fall out of random engulfment events!

Endosymbiosis in its ultra-high-order complexity is showing us that there is a Designer whose creative style is far, far beyond our abilities to conceive such systems. The observer is left watching this graceful "multicellular cell" bathing itself in a microscope's rich light source, cilia beating synchronously, chemistries amply stocking the machine with ATP. It is time to worship.

P. 19

IN OTHER WORDS

1. The protistan cell *Paramecium bursaria* houses photosynthetic algal cells of genus *Zoochlorella* within its cytoplasm.
2. This relationship, in which each cell type's metabolism is intimately related to the other's, is termed *endosymbiosis.*
3. The algal cell receives physical protection and provides photosynthetic products to the Paramecium cell. The latter takes in nitrogen-containing compounds sufficient for itself and its algal symbionts.
4. No satisfactory explanation exists for how such symbiotic relationships came into existence apart from careful design, which is evident in the relationship itself.

QUESTIONS FOR REVIEW

1. State the three elements of cell theory.
2. Why is a concise definition of the term *life* impossible to generate?
3. What places upper limits on the size of most cells?
4. Are protistans prokaryotic or eukaryotic? Explain your answer.
5. Make a list of the various functions a cell membrane has based on the proteins that are found within the membrane. Now try to recall from Chapter 4 the functions that the phospholipid bilayer has. You now have a fairly complete picture of what a cell membrane does.
6. What is the function of a cell wall? What threat does it protect against?
7. What form does information take in the nucleoid of a bacterium? What form does it take in a mature protein?
8. What is a microcompartment? How does it differ from an organelle?
9. List two initial segments of information that a streptococcal cell requires in order to set up an infection in your throat.
10. Based on your knowledge of the capabilities of a typical eukaryotic cell, what does a macrophage cell in your immune system do to a streptococcal cell in order to inactivate it?
11. List in order the events that occur in a streptococcal cell that result in formation of a capsule.
12. Compare and contrast the way a nutrient molecule and a nutrient cell are taken into a hungry host cell.
13. Distinguish between the terms *chromatin* and *chromosome*.
14. What activity occurs in the nucleolus of a cell?
15. Consider the two terms *rough endoplasmic reticulum* and *kinesis*. Classify each of these terms as either structural or functional and explain your reasoning.
16. Summarize the function of the chloroplast. Where are they found in nature? Are there any cells in nature that lack chloroplasts but that still carry out the function assigned to them?
17. What is the role of a zymogen granule?
18. What are the sources of the stimulus that releases amylase into the pancreatic duct?
19. Make a list of the chemical interactions that occur between *Paramecium bursaria* and *Zoochlorella* species.

QUESTIONS FOR THOUGHT

1. The three elements of cell theory are generalizations. Find a specific example in nature that would contradict each of the three elements.
2. Most cells in our biosphere do not have a nucleus. Explain how this can be a true statement.
3. Use a popular online search engine to search the phrase, "the largest bacterium on earth." Why must this bacterium be considered prokaryotic in nature?
4. The cell wall surrounding many bacteria in the human body is very thin. Yet bacteria in nature often have much thicker cell walls. Why might this be the case?
5. Ribosomes are largely protein in composition. Yet they make proteins! Think of some examples in which a human machine makes another human machine. What can we say of the origin of the machine? the origin of the ribosome?
6. What is the basis for the argument that there are more kinds of eukaryotic than prokaryotic cells in the biosphere?
7. Are the protein products found within a vesicle mature proteins or immature proteins? Explain.
8. Provide a physical description of a cell that is totally devoid of any microtubules or intermediate filaments.
9. What could you assume to be true of a cell whose cytoplasm contained a high density of mitochondria?
10. If you chew saltine crackers for long enough, they begin to taste sweet in your mouth. What must be happening to the crackers? What must be present with them in your mouth?
11. Should *Paramecium bursaria* be considered a photosynthetic cell? Support your contention.

GLOSSARY

acetylcholine—a neurotransmitter substance; a chemical signal formed at the end of a neuronal axon that diffuses across a synaptic space and stimulates a response in the receiving cell.

acinar cell—a type of cell within the pancreas that produces and secretes digestive enzymes.

adhesin—molecule, often a protein, found on the surface of one cell enabling it to adhere to another cell.

amylase—an enzyme in saliva and in the small intestine that degrades starch to disaccharides and trisaccharides that will be further degraded to form glucose units suitable for absorption in the small intestine.

bacteria—a common form of prokaryotic cell lacking a membrane-bound nucleus and usually much smaller in size than higher eukaryotic cells.

capsule—a loose or formed gelatinous layer of carbohydrate and protein molecules that surrounds some bacteria. Usually grants some protection from a host's immune cells.

carboxysome—a microcompartment found in photosynthetic bacterial cells; its component parts remove carbon dioxide molecules from the air and attach them to larger substrate molecules.

cell—the structural and functional unit of a living organism. Some organisms consist of only a single cell. Others, like humans, are multicellular.

cell membrane—a phospholipid bilayer containing proteins that serves as a boundary around a cell defining its chemical limits and controlling movement of substances into and out of the cell.

cell respiration—a sequence of chemical reactions within a cell that transfers electrons to oxygen and results in the phosphorylation of ADP to produce ATP, a cellular form of immediate energy.

cell wall—a mechanically rigid outer polymeric surface of some cells; in aqueous environments it keeps the influx of water from bursting the cell.

chloroplast—a membrane-bound organelle in the cytoplasm of eukaryotic cells where the reactions of photosynthesis take place.

chromatin—general term for a cell's informational content—its DNA—plus the molecular scaffolding that supports it.

chromosome—a single long piece of DNA and the molecular scaffolding that supports it.

cristae—folds within the inner membrane system of the mitochondrion; on these folds are arranged the enzymes that participate in the final sequence of reactions involved in cellular respiration.

cytoplasm—the interior volume of a cell excluding the cell's nucleus; composed of a wide variety of chemical substances participating in the cell's metabolism; organelles or microcompartments are suspended within it.

diffusion—the tendency of any substance to move through a liquid or solid medium from a region where its concentration is higher to a region where it is lower.

dynein—a micro-scale motor device constructed of protein; it attaches to and moves cellular structures along the length of microtubules toward the center of the cell.

endocytosis—bulk transport of molecules or structures into a cell by a regulated bulging in of the cell membrane with final pinching off of the membrane's bleb to form an endocytotic vesicle.

endosymbiosis—a relationship between two disparate types of cells in which one cell type exists within the cytoplasm of the other cell type. At least one of the two cell types will benefit from this relationship.

eukaryotic—descriptive of a cell that contains a true membrane-bound nucleus, generally larger than prokaryotic cells.

exocytosis—bulk transport of molecules or structures out of a cell by a regulated fusion of a vesicle containing the molecules or structures with the cell membrane. The interior of the vesicle opens to the exterior of the cell, spilling its content outside the cell.

fimbriae—tendril-like extensions of a bacterial cell's membrane used to adhere to substrates like a host cell; composed of proteins.

Golgi complex—a sequence of flattened membrane-bound sacs found in the eukaryotic cell cytoplasm. They are sites of protein and lipid processing and packaging.

hemolysin—protein molecule produced in one cell, usually a bacterium, that can rupture the membrane and destroy the integrity of another cell, often a blood cell.

intermediate filament—structural elements within and outside of cells having thicknesses on the order of 10 nanometers. Component parts of nails, hair, horns, scales, and parts of sarcomere structure in muscle cells.

kinesin—a micro-scale motor device constructed of protein; it attaches to and moves cellular structures along the length of microtubules toward the periphery of the cell.

Life Is Complex—one of the 12 principles of life on which this text is based.

lysosome—in eukaryotic cells, a membrane-enclosed organelle containing hydrolytic enzymes capable of degrading either cell parts, invasive cells, or some inorganic substances.

macrophage—large amoeboid-like cell in the vertebrate immune system that recognizes, engulfs, and digests foreign cells or small objects that gain entry to the host tissues.

microcompartment—a protein-enclosed compartment or space within a prokaryotic cell that specializes in some particular metabolic function like combining with carbon dioxide or degrading some unusual nutrient or chemical substrate.

micrometer—a metric unit of measure for objects similar in size to a cell. There are 1000 micrometers in a single millimeter.

microtubule—a part of the cell's cytoskeleton (support structure) composed of 25-nanometer thick fibers composed of tubulin proteins. These are used to move chromosomes during cell division.

mitochondrion—an organelle within the cytoplasm of eukaryotic cells bound by two separate membranes within which the major reactions of cell respiration take place.

mycoplasma—a bacteria-like prokaryotic cell that has the smallest genome known to support cellular function; many are pathogenic, some to humans.

neuron—the cellular unit of the nervous system; a cell characterized by long narrow processes extending away from the cell body. Signals along the length of processes take the form of electrical impulses.

nucleoid—a central region of a prokaryotic cell where genetic information is localized.

nucleolus—a region within the cell nucleus, visible by electron microscopy, composed of protein and nucleic acid. It is the site where ribosomal RNA is transcribed and processed for inclusion into ribosomal subunits.

nucleoplasm—the volume of fluid within the cell nucleus where the chromatin is suspended. It is somewhat continuous with the cytoplasm through large nuclear pores that connect the nucleus and cytoplasm.

nucleus, *pl.* **nuclei**—a centrally located, visible body within a eukaryotic cell that houses archival information in the form of linear, DNA-containing chromosomes.

organelle—membrane-enclosed compartment within a eukaryotic cell.

pancreas—a body organ that produces and secretes digestive enzymes into the small intestine and that generates and secretes hormones such as insulin into the bloodstream.

periplasmic space—a region lodged between the inner (cell) membrane and the outer membrane of certain varieties of bacteria; specialized enzymatic processes occur within this space.

photosynthesis—a sequence of chemical reactions by which autotrophic cells and organisms use solar energy to generate carbohydrate energy from carbon dioxide and water.

prokaryotic—descriptive of the smaller, simpler sort of cell that contains no true membrane-bound nucleus and few if any membrane-bound organelles; bacteria are common examples.

protistans—unicellular or colonial forms of life that possess eukaryotic cells; the amoeba and paramecium are examples.

protozoan—single-celled microorganisms that are eukaryotic and possess animal-like characteristics, particularly motility.

receptor protein—a protein found within a cell membrane that recognizes and binds to some signal molecule from another source; the protein changes shape as a result and this transmits the signal to the inside of the cell displaying it.

ribosomes—aggregates of protein and ribosomal RNA molecules that together read messenger RNA sequences from the cell's nucleus and construct polypeptide chains (proteins) according to the sequence of nitrogenous bases in the messenger RNA.

rough endoplasmic reticulum—a network of membrane-lined channels within the eukaryotic cell cytoplasm where proteins are synthesized and processed.

stroma—the fluid within a chloroplast that surrounds and bathes the thylakoids; within it ATP energy is used to generate more stable carbohydrate energy.

thylakoid—a membrane-enclosed sac within the chloroplast; within the sac membrane are enzymes that carry out the transformation of solar energy into ATP energy.

vesicle—a small, membrane-enclosed sac with a cell where some activity or substance is sequestered from the rest of cellular activity. Substances are frequently transported intracellularly with vesicles.

6

Energy-Driven Inventions

6.1 LIVING SYSTEMS REQUIRE A FLOW OF ENERGY

Survey Questions

6.1 Living Systems Require a Flow of Energy

- What is energy? How is it best defined in living systems?
- What sorts of processes in a living thing require energy?
- What form will energy take in a living cell?

6.2 Laws of Energy Flow in the Living World

- What are the basic physical principles that govern the flow of energy in cells?
- What is the source of the energy flow in the living world?
- How efficient is energy flow in the living world? Is all of the generated energy useful?
- What form does solar energy take when it enters living things?

6.3 Energy Flows in Chemical Reactions

- What is a chemical reaction?
- How does a chemical reaction support the flow of energy in a cell?
- What are the essential characteristics of a chemical reaction?
- Do all chemical reactions give off energy?
- What controls whether a chemical reaction will happen (or not)?

Life Is Energy Driven—one of 12 principles of life on which this book is based.

energy—the capacity to do work; the capacity to make changes of importance to a living thing.

Magnificent architectural evidences of human ingenuity and grinding toil dot the landscape of the European Union states. To find one of them, try using an Internet satellite map program to focus on Great Britain; then look in the eastern part of the island for the city of Ely.

Ely Cathedral, an architectural gem of East Anglia, is breathtaking in size, scope, and intricacy of structure (see Figure 6.1). Built to glorify God, it absorbed the greater share of energy from the lives of thousands of men. We walk into the nave, look up, and sigh with wonder. We are tired just getting there! Who built all of this? It must have taken a tremendous amount of energy! Yet if you could become the size of a carbon dioxide molecule and diffuse into the glorious *Elodea* cell shown in Figure 6.1, you'd see the same magnitude, the same order, and have the same wonder as if you were standing in the nave of the cathedral. The living cell represents a huge investment of energy: **Life Is Energy-Driven.**

What is **energy?** Physicists define it as *the ability to do work*. This makes sense if we are building a cathedral or a cell. But this definition isn't comprehensive enough to help us to understand all that energy does in the context of a living cell. A cell needs a constant source of energy because many specific changes are needed for its survival and growth. So let's define energy as *the ability to make specific changes occur*. What sorts of changes need to take place within a cell (see Figure 6.2)?

6.4 Enzymes Direct Energy Flow

- What is an enzyme?
- How does an enzyme catalyze a chemical reaction?
- What happens to reactants within the structure of an enzyme?
- How do enzymes control the metabolism of a cell?

6.5 Energy Flow in Reaction Pathways: Metabolism

- What is a metabolic pathway?
- How is the flow of product from a metabolic pathway controlled?
- How can an enzyme's structure contribute to control of a metabolic pathway?

6.6 Energy Pools in the Cell: ATP

- Where does the cell get energy to run its endergonic reactions with?
- What does an ATP molecule look like?
- Where is energy stored within an ATP molecule?

6.7 Energy Flow from Carbohydrates to ATP: Respiration

- Why are carbohydrates considered to be "energy-rich"?
- What is the purpose of aerobic respiration?
- What substances enter glycolysis, and what substances leave it? What is its contribution to respiration?
- What substances enter the Krebs cycle, and what substances leave it? What is the cycle's contribution to respiration?
- What substances enter the electron transfer system? What substances leave it? What is the system's contribution to respiration?
- What process immediately generates the energy used to make ATP?
- How much ATP is produced from one carbohydrate molecule?

6.8 Energy Flow from Carbohydrates to ATP: Fermentation

- How is fermentation different from respiration? How are they the same?
- How much ATP results from fermentation?

6.9 Energy Flow from Photons to Carbohydrates: Photosynthesis

- How do photons become energy within a cell?

Figure 6.1 The cathedral and the cell—two glorious works of art potentially pleasing to the same set of eyes and mind. Light illuminates the interior of a cathedral but sadly, it obscures much of the fine structure of the cell interior.

Lee Frost/Robert Harding World Imagery/Corbis; Nik Wheeler/CORBIS; Visuals Unlimited/Corbis

- What does chlorophyll actually do in photosynthesis?
- How are the chemical reactions of photosynthesis ordered/organized?
- Where in the plant cell do the stages of photosynthesis take place?
- What carbohydrates are produced by photosynthesis?

6.10 Energy Flow: An Integrated Picture

- How do photosynthesis and respiration work together to support life?
- How did photosynthesis and respiration originate? What came first?
- What is the functional result or value of having photosynthesis limited to just some life-forms?

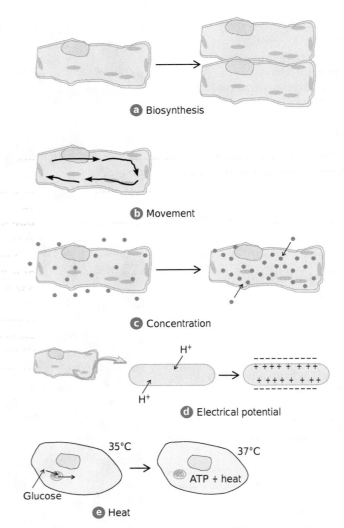

(a) Biosynthesis

(b) Movement

(c) Concentration

(d) Electrical potential

(e) Heat

Figure 6.2 Five major categories of energy change in the cell are shown here. **(a)** synthetic work is demonstrated by the making of daughter cells from a parent cell, **(b)** movement is represented by the streaming movement of the cytoplasm, **(c)** concentration of a substance within a cell is effected by active transport, **(d)** electrical potential is generated by ion movement across a membrane, **(e)** heat energy is generated by increasing the rate of respiration in the cell.

Standing in the middle of our *Elodea* cell and glancing around, the first change we would observe is that vast amounts of membrane and molecular machinery have been built up from simpler molecules. **Biosynthesis** of organic monomers, and their subsequent assembly into polymers and then into supramolecular structures, requires considerable energy.

But were we the size of a carbon dioxide molecule, our observation of synthesized structures would be made "on the run." The cytoplasm and many organelles within the cell are in constant motion, not the result of slow diffusional forces based on thermal energy of particles. Rather, the cell is investing energy to move its cytoplasm about by bulk flow—a streaming process that allows molecules and materials important to cellular reactions to be quickly circulated to where they need to go. Indeed, as we adjust the fine focus knob

biosynthesis—the building up of biomolecules or biological structures within a living cell; a process that requires energy.

of our microscope to better observe the *Elodea* cell, muscle cells in our fingers and eyes are also contracting, a form of movement that also requires energy.

Another change often required within cells is the movement of materials across membranes both into and within cells. If the molecules of a substance coming into a cell are in higher concentrations outside the cell, then the thermal energy of random motion will cause the molecules to diffuse into the cell either through the membrane or through special gates within the membrane (see Figure 6.3). But suppose the substance is a nutrient of great value to the cell. It is to the cell's advantage to bind to and take in that nutrient even if it is already in higher concentration inside the cell. As night approaches and sugar production in *Elodea* leaf cells subsides, cells in the stem of the plant will take in the last few circulating molecules of sugar even though its concentration is already higher within the cell. This pumping of substances against the diffusional forces that would carry them the other way requires energy: the **energy of concentration** of substances.

Sometimes a cell must move *ions* across a membrane. Often it moves them to the side where they are already more concentrated. Later in this chapter we will see how concentrating ions on one side of a membrane is a powerful way to generate large amounts of ATP in cell respiration. However, pushing ions to one side of a membrane not only requires energy for concentrating things: These ions are charged. So an **electrical potential** is building up across our membrane as well. The cell needs energy to push together charged particles that are repelling each other. Indeed, later on, release of this electrical potential across a membrane can be used to make ATP. The cell needs energy to do this *electrical* work.

Finally, although *Elodea* cells can live acceptably at a wide variety of temperatures, your cells cannot. Their processes require an internal temperature of 37°C. Sometimes outdoor temperatures are considerably below this value. You discover that your muscle cells are contracting, not in order to lift a weight or move food forward in your intestines, but simply to shiver. Shivering uses cellular energy to generate the metabolic heat needed to retain your body temperature close to the 37°C level at which it's designed to work. So sometimes cells need energy just to help maintain an optimal operating temperature.

A wide variety of kinds of cells, then, need energy for a variety of changes they are constantly making. Will there be a correspondingly wide variety of forms in which energy comes to these cells and in which it is handled by these cells? No. An elegantly unified process, governed by a few basic laws, describes energy conversions all across the living world. We'll now explore that unity.

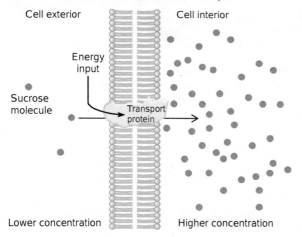

Elodea cell membrane in stem of plant

Cell exterior

Cell interior

Energy input

Sucrose molecule

Transport protein

Lower concentration

Higher concentration

Figure 6.3 Cells are designed to invest chemical energy to move carbohydrate molecules into their cytoplasm even against a concentration difference. Respiration of the carbohydrate will yield far more energy than that expended to acquire it.

energy of concentration—the work of moving molecules or ions against a concentration gradient, that is, moving them from where they are less concentrated to where they are already more concentrated.

electrical potential—a difference in charge across a membrane based on a difference in the concentration of positive and/or negative ions across the membrane.

IN OTHER WORDS

1. Cathedrals and cells both require energy for their construction.
2. Energy is the ability to make specific changes occur within a cell.
3. Energy is needed within cells for biosynthesis, movement, concentration of substances, generation of electrical potentials, and heat.
4. The generation of cellular energy is a unified process across the living world.

6.2 LAWS OF ENERGY FLOW IN THE LIVING WORLD

Life Is Energy-Driven. Wonderful structural products are the result. But where does the energy come from to generate those products? Most of it comes from the sun. And as it flows through living systems, two very basic laws govern its behavior. The first law is called the law of conservation of matter and energy. The law is simply diagramed and simply stated: Energy is freely convertible from one form to another, *but* energy can never be created or destroyed in normal processes. (The fire can't continue when the cardboard of the match is consumed.) Energy from the sun flows through nature obeying this basic law and finds its way into the living cell in the form of C–O–H and C–H bonds within the glucose molecule.

Energy: the ability to make specific changes occur.

Energy (form #1) ⇄ Energy (form #2)

The second law that governs the behavior of energy in the living world can be stated as follows: Systems that convert energy from one form to another are not 100% efficient. In each conversion event, the total amount of *useful* energy decreases because some energy becomes useless, typically in the form of heat (the random motion of individual particles of matter). These relationships are easily seen in the exchanges occurring in an automobile engine (see Figure 6.4). The chemical energy in the gasoline is converted to movement energy within the cylinders in the engine block. Why, then, is a water pump necessary for the engine to continue operating? More than half the energy resulting from the combustion of the octane is lost to the engine block as heat energy. This energy is useless. This same useless heat energy is felt in a crowded

Figure 6.4 Photograph of an automobile engine while running. Taken with a thermal camera. Yes, the crankshaft is turning, but that represents the minority of the energy given off by the combustion of octane. The combustion of glucose in our bodies has the same effect.

Tyrone Turner/National Geographic Society/Corbis

classroom at the end of the lesson period—and for much the same reason. The students burn glucose to maintain cell life and take notes. But the exchange isn't even 50% efficient. The rest of glucose's energy is lost to the room as heat.

Energy, then, flows from the sun through living systems. Eventually it all ends up in the form of heat (see Figure 6.5). It travels through organisms that are energetically classified as producers or consumers (like us). Producers convert solar energy to chemical energy—the energy of C–H and C–O–H bonds. When we ingest producer tissues—broccoli or sugared cereals—that chemical bond energy then gets us

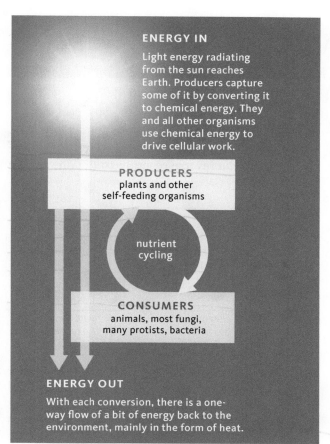

ENERGY IN

Light energy radiating from the sun reaches Earth. Producers capture some of it by converting it to chemical energy. They and all other organisms use chemical energy to drive cellular work.

PRODUCERS
plants and other self-feeding organisms

nutrient cycling

CONSUMERS
animals, most fungi, many protists, bacteria

ENERGY OUT

With each conversion, there is a one-way flow of a bit of energy back to the environment, mainly in the form of heat.

consumers going in the morning and takes us through our day. Since energy spends most of its time in the living world flowing within and between chemical bonds, we need to examine more closely the chemical reactions that break and form those bonds.

Figure 6.5 Energy flow through the living world is a one-way process. The vast majority of energy enters the living world as sunlight and departs as heat. By contrast, matter does not flow through the living world, it cycles around and back to where it started.

IN OTHER WORDS

1. Energy is freely convertible from one form to another, but energy can never be created or destroyed in normal processes.
2. In all energy conversions in living systems, some of the energy given off fails to be conserved as useful energy. It is lost as heat.
3. Energy flows from the sun into the chemical reaction pathways of living things and ends up as heat.

ENERGY FLOWS IN CHEMICAL REACTIONS

Energy in C–OH and C–H bonds can be removed and then utilized in biosynthesis only through **chemical reactions**. This means breaking existing bonds between atoms in a molecule called the **reactant** (or substrate) and forming new bonds between different atoms creating a **product** molecule. For example, some bacteria use the following reaction to gain energy:

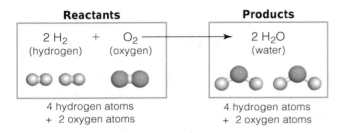

Reactants		Products
$2 H_2$ + O_2	→	$2 H_2O$
(hydrogen) (oxygen)		(water)

4 hydrogen atoms
+ 2 oxygen atoms

4 hydrogen atoms
+ 2 oxygen atoms

Notice in the diagram that atoms are simply shuffled around. No new atoms or electrons just appear or quietly disappear. Matter is conserved. But in this shuffle, energy is flowing. How does that happen? A chemical reaction has three characteristics we want to notice:

1. Chemical reactions proceed with energy changes. Whenever chemical bonds are broken, energy is required. Whenever chemical bonds are formed, energy is given off. Chemical reactions can be classified according to which is greater: the requirement for energy to break initial bonds or the energy generated when new bonds form. In the reaction pictured above, less energy is required to break initial bonds than is given off when the new bonds form. We term this sort of reaction **exergonic** (Gk. *ex-* = out or away from; Gk. *-gonic* = energy) because the extra energy given off comes *out* of the reaction and is available to do work for us. In fact, the energy from this single reaction is what the bacterium lives off of!

If greater energy is required to break initial bonds than is generated in forming the new ones, we call the reaction **endergonic** (Gk. *end-* = in or into) because outside energy must be

added *in* to drive the reaction forward. Suppose, for example, we wished to hydrolyze water in the reverse reaction to the one shown above.

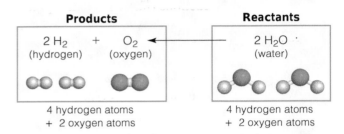

Products		Reactants
$2 H_2$ + O_2	←	$2 H_2O$
(hydrogen) (oxygen)		(water)

4 hydrogen atoms
+ 2 oxygen atoms

4 hydrogen atoms
+ 2 oxygen atoms

(Photosynthesis begins with a reaction similar to this one.) Here, more energy is required to break initial bonds in the water molecules than is given off in the formation of new bonds between two hydrogen atoms and two oxygen atoms. Photosynthesis is endergonic: You have to invest solar energy to split those stable water molecules.

2. Chemical reactions are reversible. Suppose we begin our reaction with high levels of reactants A and B and little or no C and D. The reaction will generally proceed in the forward

$$A + B \longrightarrow C + D \qquad (1)$$

direction as written. But reaction rates depend on the relative concentrations of the reactants

chemical reaction—a process in which bonds are broken in one kind of molecule (the reactant) and new bonds are formed to produce a product; energy change accompanies any chemical reaction.

reactant—an initial substance that absorbs energy and enters into a chemical reaction in which it is changed in structure.

product—a substance that is formed during a chemical reaction.

exergonic—descriptive of a chemical reaction in which free energy is given off; a spontaneous reaction.

endergonic—descriptive of a chemical reaction in which free energy must be added in order to get the reaction to take place.

and products. As the concentrations of C and D become higher compared with those of A and B, then the reaction will begin to run in the reverse direction.

$$A + B \xleftarrow{\hspace{2cm}} C + D \qquad (2)$$

Eventually, if no additional amounts of either A, B, C, or D are added to the system, the forward reaction will equal the reverse reaction in rate. The system will now be at equilibrium.

$$A + B \xrightleftharpoons{\hspace{2cm}} C + D \qquad (3)$$

Most cellular reactions run under non-equilibrium conditions in which products are being removed (used or discarded) such that the reaction continues in the forward direction as in reaction (1) above.

3. Chemical reactions are relatively uncommon and slow in the nonliving world. Consider the dead cellulose in the page you are now staring at or the dead cashews in the box on your desk. They could sit there for 100 years and seldom participate in a chemical reaction. For most reactant molecules in nature, the amount of energy required to break their bonds—to start a reaction—is simply not present in their environment. You could strike a match under either the page or the cashew (see Figure 4.14) and supply the initial energy to break a few of those bonds. Then an exergonic reaction would get going and liberated energy would spontaneously keep it going. (It could become a house fire if we don't meddle.) The energy needed to get a chemical reaction going is called its **activation energy**. In a diagram (see Figure 6.6) that shows the energy state of the

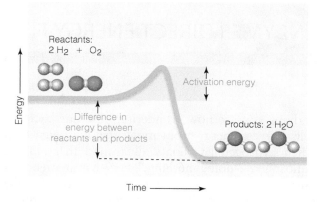

Figure 6.6 In an energy diagram (note the y axis) for a chemical reaction, how shall we represent the fact that energy must be invested to break bonds in the reactants? We use a small "hill" called the activation energy. That hill will prevent this reaction from running at temperatures common in living things.

reactants and their products through time, the activation energy looks like a hill to be got over. And while the size of the activation energy is different for every kind of reaction in nature, most of these energy hills are prohibitively high given the energy available at temperatures common on our planet. This is a good thing. It explains the stability of wood in houses and food on shelves. The world's forests would be aflame without these energy hills. No reaction can ever get going unless there's enough energy available to break bonds somewhere in the reactant molecules.

activation energy—an amount of energy necessary to break bonds in a reactant thus getting a chemical reaction started.

IN OTHER WORDS

1. In chemical reactions, energy changes occur when covalent bonds in reactant molecules are broken and new bonds in product molecules are formed.
2. If more energy is required to break old bonds than is given off when new bonds form, the reaction is endergonic.
3. If less energy is required to break old bonds than is given off when new bonds form, the reaction is exergonic.
4. Chemical reactions are reversible. The direction in which the reaction runs depends on the relative concentrations of reactants and products already in place.
5. A chemical reaction will never begin unless there is enough energy present to begin breaking bonds in reactant molecules. This amount of energy is termed the *activation energy*.

6.4 ENZYMES DIRECT ENERGY FLOW

Perhaps you are now wondering how our bacterial cells harvest energy from molecular hydrogen (H₂) when hydrogen gas floats all around them in the atmosphere "doing nothing." For that matter, you burn glucose for energy. Yet glucose sits around inside of grapes on vines all over the world doing nothing. Like the breakdown of hydrogen or glucose, most important cellular reactions do not proceed spontaneously at any significant rate when they are apart from the cells they normally occur in. But inside of cells are some very amazing protein molecules called **enzymes**. Enzymes catalyze chemical reactions. When we say, "George is a catalyst for change," what do we mean? We mean the changes we are seeing were possible before George showed up, but they just didn't occur at any significant rate until he did show up!

Consider the reaction diagram in Figure 6.7a. Of the two lines, focus on the brown one. The reaction—the breakdown of glucose—won't go at any significant rate at body temperature because its activation energy is too great. How does an enzyme help with this? The enzyme is a rather complicated molecule—usually a protein—that has within its structure an **active site** (see Figure 6.7b). The active site is highly selective for the specific shape of the reactant molecule it is designed to bind to. And it binds the reactant in such a way as to stress just the bond that needs to be broken to get the product that is desired! How in the world is such bond-breaking specificity

enzyme—a type of protein molecule that serves as an organic catalyst in solution. It reproducibly converts one specific sort of molecule into another—a specific reactant into its product.

active site—a precise three-dimensional space within the structure of an enzyme where a specific reactant or reactants selectively bind and are there converted to a product or products.

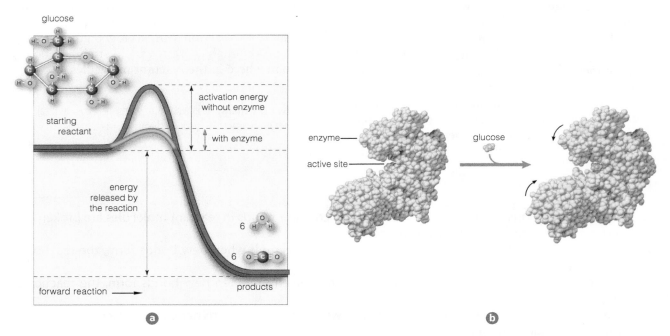

Figure 6.7 Enzymes and activation energy. **(a)** a chemical reaction diagrammed to show the energy of the reactants and products over the time course of the reaction. The height of the energy hill shown in brown is such that, at cellular temperatures, no bonds in the substrate will be energetically unstable enough to break. The green (enzyme catalyzed) energy hill is low enough that ordinary thermal energy within the cell will allow bonds in the reactant molecules to break freely. **(b)** Space-filling models showing how an enzyme combines with the reactant glucose to stress just the bond that needs breaking in order for glucose to begin the energy-yielding process of respiration.

achieved? When the reactant lodges within the active site, the precise internal shape of the site sets up weak attractions here and there with atoms in the reactant. But which atoms? The ones participating in precisely the bond to be broken! So that bond becomes weaker. But wait! How does stressing a bond in the reactant molecule help us to get over the energy hill in the diagram in Figure 6.7? By putting some stress on just the bond that needs breaking, the energy hill is greatly lowered (see the green line in Figure 6.7a). The thermal energy present in the cell is now sufficient to cause the bond to break. The reaction goes forward! In the case of glucose breakdown, that is how the whole process of cell respiration begins. In the case of hydrogen breakdown mentioned above, lots of useful energy is given off. The bacterium's metabolism—its life—is driven by this catalyzed breakdown or "burning" of hydrogen.

What elegantly designed pieces of machinery enzymes are! Do you understand their significance for cell metabolism? By their presence, enzymes control which reactions go at *significant* rates within the cell at normal temperatures. Now think: By controlling which enzymes are produced, the cell controls which reactions will occur. There are 24 covalent bonds in a glucose molecule—all of them breakable. If you burn crystalline glucose with a match, they all do break! And all the useful energy is lost as heat. But only one particular bond must be broken if we want to *slowly* degrade glucose in an orderly way so as to extract discrete amounts of useful energy from it (see Figure 6.8). So a Genius, familiar with cell chemistry and reactant molecules,

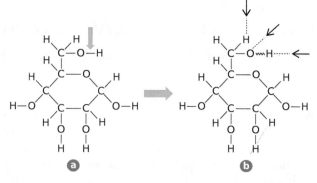

Figure 6.8 **(a)** Glucose has 24 different covalent bonds that, with energy input, could be broken. To degrade it in the orderly fashion described in Section 6.7, only the bond indicated by the arrow can be broken. **(b)** So, "happily" an enzyme exists whose active site holds glucose perfectly, and stresses just the bond that needs to be broken. At cellular temperatures, the available thermal energy will break this bond.

has to design an enzyme that will (1) selectively bind to just glucose and not some other molecule and (2) stress *just the bond in glucose* needed to produce its first orderly breakdown product. And this glucose degrading enzyme is just one small part of a much larger project in which the Designer surveys the entire set of reactions needed to run a cell. Thousands of enzymes are needed to specifically catalyze them. He then invents the enzymes, the information to code for them, and the system that will access that information at the correct time to generate all the enzymes as needed. It is nothing short of glorious!

IN OTHER WORDS

1. Most chemical reactions in nature do not proceed at any significant rate because the amount of energy present is less than the activation energy for these reactions.
2. An enzyme binds to a specific reactant when the reactant diffuses into the enzyme's active site.
3. Enzymes lower the activation energy hill for specific chemical reactions, enabling them to proceed at significant rates at low cellular temperatures.
4. Activation energy for a reaction is lowered when the bond in the reactant that initially needs breaking is stressed in some way by the active site of an enzyme.
5. The existence of many kinds of enzymes in a cell allows molecules to be transformed in orderly ways within cells, slowly generating useful free energy and useful structures.

As we implied earlier, it is rare that an energy-containing molecule can be utilized completely (or a cell structure constructed completely!) in a single step. Chemical reactions exist in sequences—**metabolic pathways**—within cells. Most of the cell's chemical reactions are arranged into this or that series of exergonic (energy yielding) or endergonic (energy requiring) reaction pathways. Consider Figure 6.9, which represents a metabolic pathway that has both linear and cyclical parts to it. Reactants A and B are converted into product C, which is itself a reactant for another enzyme that converts C to product D, and so on—and on and on. . . . ! Notice that products D and I are combined by some enzyme to make product E. Product G is split into products H and I, and H is polymerized into product J.

Is all of this controlled? Does the cell ever have too little of A or make too much of J for the cell to use? Do enzymes, glorious as they are, simply rush forward, converting every reactant molecule that comes their way into product? Biochemists have been amazed at both the intricacy and the variety of control mechanisms that govern these pathways. Consider a few ways in which traffic through a pathway like this can be controlled.

First, recall the principle of reversibility. If substance J (see Figure 6.9) at the end of the process is continually used up, making a cell part, for example, it will always be in low concentration. Even though the reactions in all the pathways are reversible, this low level of J will pull the *entire* set of reactions in the diagram in the forward direction to make more of J. By this same property of chemical reactions, too much of J will slow the entire pathway down.

But elegance of control rises above the level of simple availability of reactant or use of product. Most metabolic pathways in the cell have an enzyme near the beginning of the pathway that has a second binding site on it—an **allosteric site** (Gk. *allo* = other, different; Gk. *stere* = site; see Figure 6.10). This site is

> **metabolic pathway**—a series of chemical reactions in a sequence in which the product of one reaction is the reactant of the next reaction.
>
> **allosteric site**—a three-dimensional groove, pocket, or surface on or within an enzyme molecule; when a specifically shaped regulatory substance binds the site, the enzyme's active site is altered structurally.

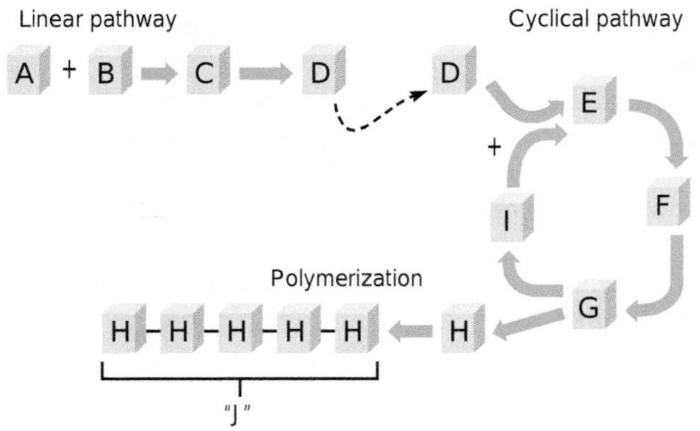

Allosteric inhibition

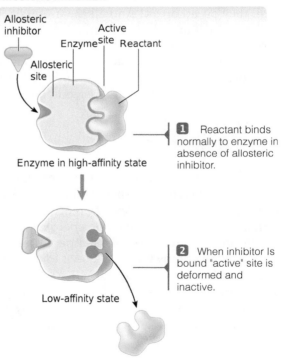

1 Reactant binds normally to enzyme in absence of allosteric inhibitor.

2 When inhibitor Is bound "active" site is deformed and inactive.

Enzyme in high-affinity state

Low-affinity state

Figure 6.9 Metabolic Pathways. Each block represent a reactant for the reaction (arrow) ahead of it while simultaneously being the product from the reaction (arrow) before it. The molecule "J" is a polymer composed of many monomers "H".

Figure 6.10 An Allosteric Enzyme. This enzyme possesses an active site that is alterable in shape as a result of binding an inhibitor molecule at a second site on the enzyme's surface.

physically distinct from the active site where reactants bind and products depart. The allosteric site is designed to bind very specifically to regulatory molecules from other strategic points within the cell's metabolic world. Binding of the regulatory molecule to the allosteric site changes the shape of the enzyme so that its active site is now deformed and reactant is no longer converted to product! Thus an entire metabolic pathway can be shut down by a specific kind of regulatory molecule. One obvious approach is to design the allosteric site into the first enzyme of a pathway such that it specifically binds to the product of the last enzyme in the pathway. Neat! Now, too much final product to be used up by normal means causes the product to accumulate. Extra product molecules start binding to the first enzyme's allosteric site, shutting down the whole pathway. We call this process **feedback inhibition** (see Figure 6.11). Of course, this causes reactant molecules at the beginning of the pathway to begin to accumulate. However, they may, in turn, be useful in some other pathway.

But the regulatory molecule that precisely fits an enzyme's allosteric site often turns out to be the product of some other metabolically related pathway or even an intracellular signal molecule arriving from the cell surface. Sometimes a cell needs to respond to a major change in its environment or its role in an organism. One strategy is to design a single regulatory protein that recognizes a carefully chosen set of enzymes, each of which begins a metabolic pathway that needs to be shut down—or started up. The regulatory protein then attaches a phosphate group to each enzyme altering the receptivity of its active site to reactant molecules (see Figure 6.12). Evidently, the control of metabolic pathways is elegant and finely tuned. You should be wondering at this point about the genius reflected in the design and linking together of these amazing things called *metabolic pathways*.

---

feedback inhibition—a form of rate regulation in metabolic pathways in which the product of some late reaction in the pathway controls the rate of catalysis by an enzyme earlier in the pathway.

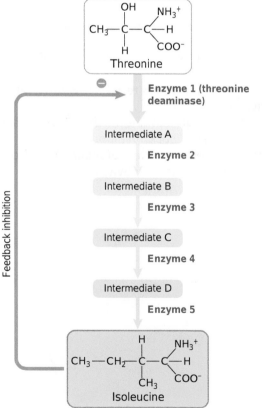

Figure 6.11 Feedback Inhibition. This metabolic pathway converts the amino acid threonine into the amino acid isoleucine by five sequential reactions. The end product, isoleucine can be used (removed) in protein sythesis. But if it begins to accumulate, it binds as an allosteric inhibitor to the first enzyme in the pathway, shutting down production of itself.

Initial Enzymes for Four Separate Metabolic Pathways

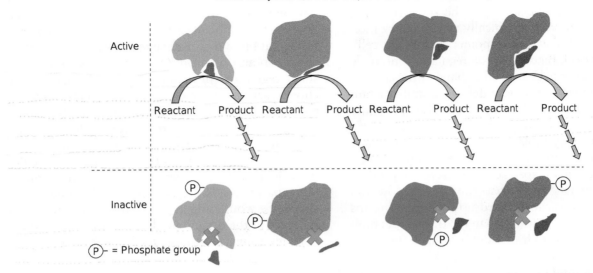

Figure 6.12 Pathway Inhibition by Enzyme Phosphorylation. Control of cell metabolism on a grand scale is sometimes effected by adding a phosphate group ($-PO_3$) to the first enzyme in a wide variety of metabolic pathways. The enzyme's active sites are all altered so as to shut down all of the pathways.

IN OTHER WORDS

1. Single chemical reactions make small changes in reactant molecules. Significant changes require a sequence of chemical reactions: a metabolic pathway.
2. Some metabolic pathways yield free energy as a product; they are exergonic. Others are endergonic.
3. Metabolic pathways can be linear or circular. A circular pathway regenerates one of the original reactants the pathway started with.
4. Removal of the end product of a metabolic pathway causes the entire pathway to be pulled in the direction of generating more of that end product.
5. Often an enzyme at the beginning of a metabolic pathway will have an allosteric site, which, when it binds a small, specific regulatory molecule, causes the enzyme's activity to be altered.
6. Often the regulatory molecule is the end product of the pathway and its binding to the allosteric site results in a deformed active site that is no longer catalytic; this is called *feedback inhibition*.
7. Sometimes, a single regulatory molecule phosphorylates initial enzymes in a variety of related metabolic pathways, altering their active sites so as to shut them all down or enhance their activity all at once.

6.6 ENERGY POOLS IN THE CELL: ATP

We have seen that metabolic pathways are of two fundamental types energetically. Exergonic ones go forward spontaneously and useful energy flows out of them. Endergonic ones (usually the ones that build cell parts) go forward only if energy flows into them and drives them forward. There is an obvious question here. Is there some way that we can harness the energy-releasing pathways to drive the biosynthetic ones? Could we have exergonic pathways depositing their free energy into a pool somewhere from which the endergonic pathways could draw out energy for bringing about all the needed changes outlined at the beginning of this chapter?

Consider Figure 6.13. The cell's metabolism is arranged such that the energy-requiring pathways are nicely driven by the energy-generating pathways (exergonic) shown to the right in the figure. But what is the energetic point of connection between these two types of reactions? Can any biosynthetic enzyme pick up energy from any exergonic reaction? No, that would be horribly complicated, both chemically and spatially within the cell. Instead (this is so brilliant), a few very common exergonic pathways work together to produce a single kind of transient, high-energy bond within an energy-storage molecule called **ATP** (**adenosine triphosphate**; see Figure 6.13). And the biosynthetic endergonic pathways are all designed to use ATP bond energy to drive their reactions forward! Isn't that neat?

Endergonic pathways, then, are driven forward by energy liberated by breaking the high-energy bond between the last two phosphates on ATP. That bond is easily broken (little energy is required) and lots of energy is given off when the new bonds form. ATP is the ultimate molecular connection between eating and working! You get out of bed at 6:00 a.m. because your cellular ATP pools allow you to.

> **ATP (adenosine triphosphate)**—the major energy-storage compound in most cells; energy is given off following the breaking of a covalent bond between the second and third phosphate groups.

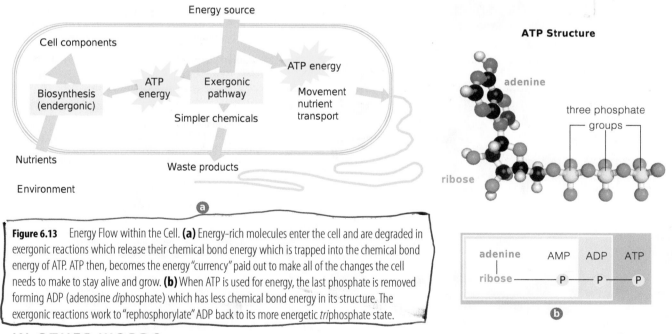

Figure 6.13 Energy Flow within the Cell. **(a)** Energy-rich molecules enter the cell and are degraded in exergonic reactions which release their chemical bond energy which is trapped into the chemical bond energy of ATP. ATP then, becomes the energy "currency" paid out to make all of the changes the cell needs to make to stay alive and grow. **(b)** When ATP is used for energy, the last phosphate is removed forming ADP (adenosine *di*phosphate) which has less chemical bond energy in its structure. The exergonic reactions work to "rephosphorylate" ADP back to its more energetic *tri*phosphate state.

IN OTHER WORDS

1. The exergonic reactions within a cell provide free energy for driving the endergonic reactions in the cell.
2. The medium of exchange between exergonic reactions and endergonic reactions is energy stored in the phosphate bonds of ATP molecules.

6.7 ENERGY FLOW FROM CARBOHYDRATES TO ATP: RESPIRATION

If they are to generate ATP, all organisms on Earth need stable energy-rich molecules: They must either find them or produce them. These energy sources—molecules that are rich in C–H, N–H, and S–H covalent bonds—are the starting point for the exergonic pathways that generate cellular ATP pools (see Figure 6.13). Higher plants and animals, including humans, use three interrelated exergonic pathways and oxygen to efficiently generate large amounts of ATP from small numbers of energy-rich glucose molecules. We call this process **aerobic respiration.** Figure 6.14 represents the entire process: Glucose is degraded all the way to water and carbon dioxide (CO_2) with the use of oxygen at the final step. Energy liberated from stable glucose molecules is neatly captured within the last phosphate bond in ATP molecules. Aerobic respiration is actually about 30 individual, sequential chemical reactions, which Figure 6.14 summarizes as just three metabolic pathways. We can further summarize the process into one simple chemical reaction showing only initial reactants and final products (see Figure 6.15). This summary reaction is highly useful for seeing the overall process of respiration. It takes us quickly from the energy of glucose to the energy

aerobic respiration—a metabolic pathway in which energy-rich molecules are degraded chemically with the generation of phosphate bond energy in ATP molecules; electrons from the energy-rich initial reactant end up combining with oxygen to form water.

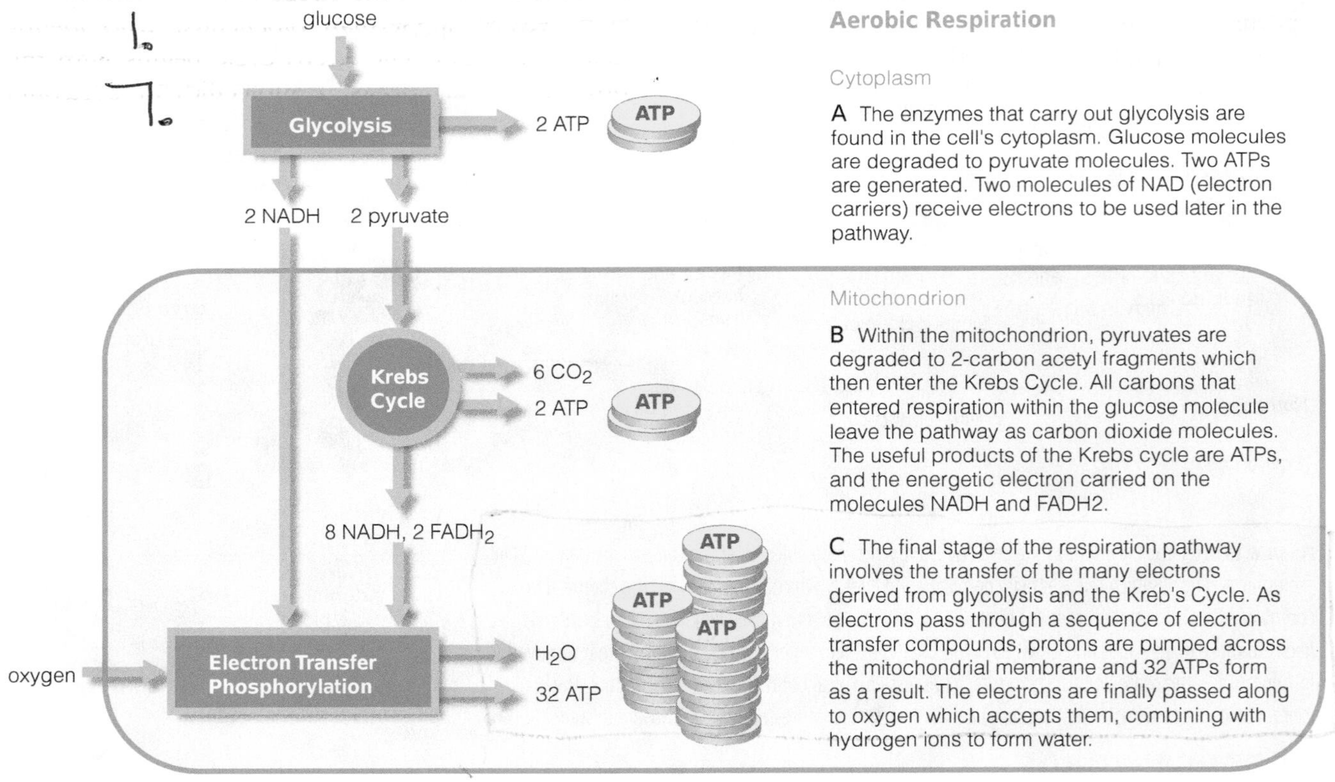
glucose
Glycolysis
2 ATP
ATP
2 NADH
2 pyruvate
Krebs Cycle
6 CO_2
2 ATP
ATP
8 NADH, 2 $FADH_2$
ATP
ATP
ATP
oxygen
Electron Transfer Phosphorylation
H_2O
32 ATP
Aerobic Respiration
Cytoplasm
A The enzymes that carry out glycolysis are found in the cell's cytoplasm. Glucose molecules are degraded to pyruvate molecules. Two ATPs are generated. Two molecules of NAD (electron carriers) receive electrons to be used later in the pathway.
Mitochondrion
B Within the mitochondrion, pyruvates are degraded to 2-carbon acetyl fragments which then enter the Krebs Cycle. All carbons that entered respiration within the glucose molecule leave the pathway as carbon dioxide molecules. The useful products of the Krebs cycle are ATPs, and the energetic electron carried on the molecules NADH and FADH2.
C The final stage of the respiration pathway involves the transfer of the many electrons derived from glycolysis and the Kreb's Cycle. As electrons pass through a sequence of electron transfer compounds, protons are pumped across the mitochondrial membrane and 32 ATPs form as a result. The electrons are finally passed along to oxygen which accepts them, combining with hydrogen ions to form water.

Figure 6.14 Aerobic Respiration within the Cell. The blue parts of this diagram outline the process of respiration itself. The orange sector contains the parts of the process that occur within the mitochondrion.

1.

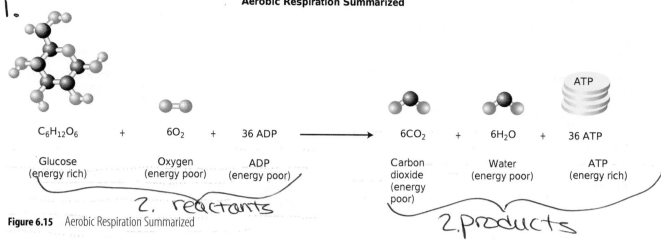

$C_6H_{12}O_6$ + $6O_2$ +   36 ADP   → $6CO_2$ + $6H_2O$ +   36 ATP

Glucose (energy rich)   Oxygen (energy poor)   ADP (energy poor)   Carbon dioxide (energy poor)   Water (energy poor)   ATP (energy rich)

2. reactants   *2. products*

Figure 6.15 Aerobic Respiration Summarized

of ATP. But the brilliance of energy manipulation can't be adequately appreciated unless we delve into the process in a bit more detail. Keep referring to Figure 6.14 while we look more closely at the first of the three stages in this process.

3. Aerobic Respiration: Stage 1— Glycolysis

For most organisms, extracting energy from C–H bonds commences with the sugar molecule glucose, which has seven such bonds. The first stage of the extraction process is an enzyme-catalyzed metabolic pathway termed **glycolysis** (see Figure 6.14). This pathway occurs in the cell cytoplasm and uses no oxygen. It's similar in some respects to a variety of pathways that are used by bacteria and yeast growing under **anaerobic** conditions (see Section 6.8). In glycolysis, each six-carbon glucose *—reactant* molecule is degraded and its parts rearranged to form two 3-carbon molecules of **pyruvate**. What makes this pathway exergonic? It's the tendency of electrons to be attracted out of bonds where they are *less* stable (like C–H bonds) and into bonds involving oxygen (like C–O bonds) where they will be *more* stable. More stability means less kinetic energy—the energy of motion. The kinetic energy lost to the electrons along the pathway is used to create the energy-rich phosphate bonds in ATP molecules. For each molecule of glucose degraded within glycolysis, the cell gains the energy of two ATP molecules while conserving some energy that remains in the bonds within two pyruvate molecules (see Figure 6.14). Also, two energetic electrons get transferred from glycolysis pathway reactants into more stable bonds on special diffusible carrier molecules called **NADH**. These carrier molecules

matter because later in respiration, in a pathway where oxygen is directly involved, they will release these electrons to still more stable molecules, resulting in additional ATP production.

3. Aerobic Respiration: Stage 2— The Krebs Cycle

The second stage of aerobic respiration (see Figures 6.14, 6.16) is the **Krebs cycle** (named for Sir Hans Krebs, a German biochemist who identified it in 1937). The Krebs cycle begins with the *4* products of glycolysis: 2 molecules of pyruvate, both of which have considerable potential energy remaining in their molecular structure. Pyruvate molecules diffuse from the cell cytoplasm into the mitochondrion, where the second and third stages

4.
products

glycolysis—the initial degradation of glucose molecules to pyruvate molecules with the generation of two molecules of ATP per molecule of glucose processed.

anaerobic—any environment or process in which oxygen is absent.

pyruvate—a three-carbon carbohydrate product of glycolysis whose continued degradation generates two-carbon fragments that serve as reactants in the Krebs cycle.

NADH (nicotinamide adenine dinucleotide)—a biomolecule that accepts electrons from reactants in glycolysis and the Krebs cycle and transports them in solution to an electron transfer system. The system accepts the electrons and uses them to generate ATP for the cell.

5. **Krebs cycle**—a metabolic pathway in which acetyl groups *—reactants* are stripped of energetic electrons and degraded to carbon dioxide; an integral part of aerobic respiration.

product

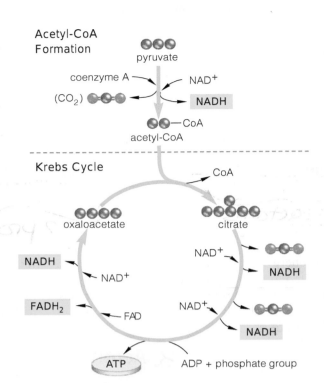

a Pyruvate enters the mitochondrion and loses one of its carbons in the form of CO_2. The remaining 2-carbon acetyl fragment is carries into the cycle by a coenzyme called CoA. At this point an electron is also conserved on an NADH carrier molecule.

b The two carbon fragment adds onto a 4 carbon compound to form the six carbon citrate molecule.

c Atoms rearranged on the reactant citrate cause another carbon to be lost as CO_2 (breathe out right now!) and again an electron is captured on another NADH.

Acetyl-CoA Formation

pyruvate

coenzyme A — NAD+

— NADH

(CO_2) —

— CoA

acetyl-CoA

Krebs Cycle

CoA

oxaloacetate — citrate

NADH — NAD+

NAD+ — NADH

FADH2 — FAD

NAD+ — NADH

ATP

ADP + phosphate group

d Further rearrangements on the reactant molecule cause another carbon to be lost as carbon dioxide and another electron to be captured in NADH.

e In rearrangements at the bottom of the cycle enough energy becomes available to phosphorylate an ADP directly to form an ATP molecule.

f Further electrons are captured and transferred to carrier compounds NADH and FADH2.

g The four carbon product of the cycle at this point is prepared to be the reactant in a second turn of the cycle.

Figure 6.16   The Krebs Cycle Summarized

of aerobic respiration take place. Once inside the mitochondrion, each pyruvate molecule loses one of its carbon atoms, which, along with two oxygen atoms, becomes carbon dioxide (see Figure 6.16). The remaining two-carbon fragment, called an *acetyl* group, is shown entering the cyclic pathway as part of a complex known as **acetyl-CoA** (see the top of Figure 6.16). Since glucose degradation in glycolysis gave us two molecules of pyruvate, the Krebs cycle reactions run twice for each glucose molecule degraded in glycolysis. Thus four of the carbon atoms that begin glycolysis in glucose end up entering the Krebs cycle.

The Krebs cycle, like glycolysis, is exergonic. What drives all these reactions forward, generating energy, is the tendency of electrons to jump from atoms in molecules like isocitrate. where they are less stable, to atoms in molecules like NADH. where they become more stable. Again, the electrons now on the NADH carrier molecules still contain considerable potential energy for generating ATP molecules, as we shall soon see.

The carbon atoms remaining from glucose that go into the Krebs cycle on acetyl-CoA leave the Krebs cycle one after the other in the form of CO_2 (see Figure 6.16). Review the summary equation for respiration given in Figure 6.15. The Krebs cycle is where

much of the CO_2 comes from that you breathe out all day long! "Does that mean I'm breathing out the carbons I ate in my oatmeal this morning?!" Yes, you've got it! The carbon atoms from your breakfast cereal are within the carbon dioxide you exhale each moment. If you see that, you are catching onto a major feature of the carbon cycle in nature.

What then are the products of the Krebs cycle? Two 3-carbon molecules of pyruvate have become six energy-poor, 1-carbon molecules of carbon dioxide. "Energy-poor? Well then, where is the energetic value in the Krebs cycle?" Notice in Figure 6.16 that for each turn of the cycle, enough energy is released in one of the reactions to generate an ATP molecule directly. All the rest of the cycle's energetic value is in the electrons bound to eight carrier molecules of NADH and two of **FADH2**.

5. **acetyl-CoA**—a two-carbon fragment resulting from degradation of pyruvate; the fragment is attached to a large cofactor molecule that transfers the acetyl fragment onto a reactant in the Krebs cycle.

FADH2 (flavin adenine dinucleotide)—a biomolecule that accepts electrons from reactants in the Krebs cycle and transports them in solution to an electron transfer system. The system accepts the electrons and uses them to generate ATP for the cell.

The matter and energy yield of the Krebs cycle is summarized in Figure 6.14.

3. Aerobic Respiration: Stage 3— Electron Transfer Phosphorylation

Also within the mitochondrion, anchored within its inner membrane, is a series of proteins that receive and transfer electrons (see Figure 6.17b). Electrons are all that connect glycolysis and the Krebs cycle to the electron transfer system—just electrons. The little NADH and $FADH_2$ "electron dump trucks" pull electrons from substrates around the Krebs cycle and travel (are soluble) to the electron transfer system, where they then lose their electrons to membrane-bound proteins that hold them even more tightly! Amazing. The whole system remains wonderfully exergonic as long as each electron "destination" attracts the electron more strongly than the molecule that currently holds it! Some Designer must have had fun seeing all of this! Aren't you? (Perhaps your brain is fun-fatigued. . . .)

This last stage of aerobic respiration is the most ingenious of all (see Figure 6.17)! As electrons

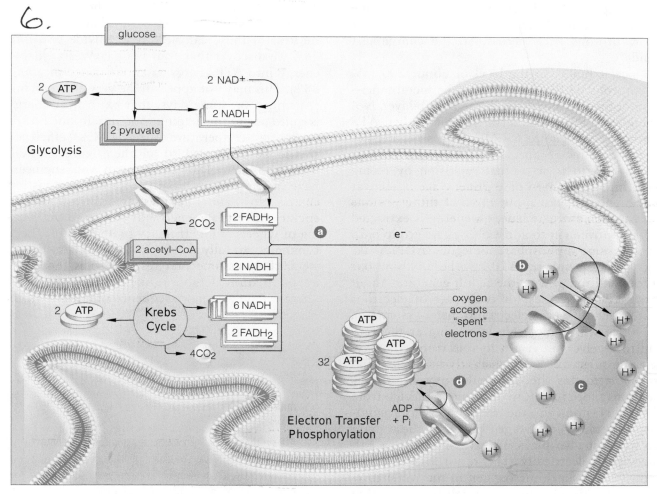

ⓐ Electron carriers transfer electrons from glycolysis and the Krebs Cycle to the Electron Transfer proteins in the mitochondrial membrane.

ⓑ As electrons are pulled forward by each successive transfer protein, the energy given off pumps protons across the inner mitochondrial membrane.

ⓒ A strong positive charge (potential energy) begins to develop outside the membrane.

ⓓ ATP synthase relieves this electrical potential by allowing protons to flow back into the organelle's interior. The energy of this flow is used to phosphorylate ADPs creating ATPSs—the desired product of the entire respiratory process.

Figure 6.17 Aerobic Respiration in relation to Mitochondrial Structure. Details of the electron transfer chain are represented.

transfer from protein to protein, each succeeding protein captures and holds the electrons more tightly than the previous protein. So with each step the electrons are held more stably and energy is given off as a result. This energy is used to pump protons (H$^+$ ions) from one side of the inner mitochondrial membrane to the other. Since the outer membrane keeps all of those protons from wandering away, the electrical potential across that inner membrane starts to rise until there's a 200-**millivolt** (mV) difference in charge across the membrane. There's a net positive charge on the outside—and a net negative charge on the inside (see Figure 6.17c). And the fatty acid interior of the phospholipid bilayer of the inner membrane insulates the inside from the outside; it doesn't allow protons back across. So the charge just builds.

Once it builds to the level of about 200 mV, the protons do cross back over the membrane—but not by escaping through the lipid bilayer. No! There exist these wonderful proteins called **ATP synthases** (see Figure 6.17d). They sit like gates across that membrane. They allow the protons to respond to their mutual repulsion by racing back into the inner compartment again—but at a price. Every time about three of those protons sail through the gate, enough energy is extracted by that movement to add a phosphate group onto an adenosine diphosphate molecule (ADP), making it a triphosphate (ATP)! So here is how our mitochondrion powers the cell: It generates about three ATP molecules for each pair of electrons that "ride down" the electron transfer system.

Notice which molecule is waiting at the very end to receive and retain the electrons: It's oxygen, the substance you constantly breathe in and transport to this site. Molecular oxygen attracts electrons more forcefully than any molecule from any other point in the entire aerobic respiratory system. When oxygen picks up these extra electrons, it also picks up extra protons to balance itself electrically. The result is water (see Figure 6.14). Since the oxygen in the water molecule holds the electrons very tightly, we say that water is energy-poor. But the ATP we generated is energy-rich. Metabolically, a fine exchange has just occurred.

Let's summarize the energetics of the whole of respiration (see Figure 6.14). For each molecule of glucose fuel that we "burn," we have a net return of 2 ATP from glycolysis, 2 ATP from the Krebs cycle, and 32 ATP from the transfer of electrons supplied by the 12 carrier molecules. That's 36 ATPs harvested from the breakdown of a single glucose molecule.

How much energy is that? Energy can be measured in units called **calories**. One kilocalorie is equal to 1000 calories' worth of energy. When your body degrades 6.5 ounces of glucose in respiration, 686 kilocalories of energy are released. Of that amount, 263 kilocalories are retained in ATP bond energy. According to the second law of energetics (see Section 6.2), what happens to the rest of those calories? If we divide 686 into 263, we discover that your body converts glucose energy into ATP energy at an efficiency of about 38%. This may not appear to be very efficient, but remember, on some days, that extra heat energy is quite useful for helping to maintain our body's operating temperature. That 38% efficiency should be compared to another figure as well. Since the early 1800s, designers and engineers have labored to perfect the internal combustion engine. Now, many decades later, the automobile engine converts the energy of octane to the turning of wheels at an efficiency of about 25%. Let's ruminate carefully on these two numbers before we blithely assume that respiration is the product of an unpredictable sequence of environments operating on a random sequence of mutations.

millivolt—a unit of electrical potential energy equal to 1/1000 of a volt.

ATP synthase—a protein within the mitochondrial membrane; it relieves a proton gradient by allowing protons to flow back across the membrane. It uses the resulting energy production to phosphorylate ADP making energy-rich ATP molecules.

calorie—the amount of energy required to raise the temperature of 1 gram of water by 1°C.

1. Aerobic respiration is a metabolic pathway that degrades carbohydrates capturing their stored energy in the phosphate bonds of ATP.

2. In glycolysis, the first stage of respiration, glucose is degraded to pyruvate and some of its energy is stored in the phosphate bonds of two ATP molecules and in electrons on the carrier molecule NADH.

3. In the Krebs cycle, portions of pyruvate molecules are further degraded to carbon dioxide with energy stored in electrons on the carrier molecules NADH and $FADH_2$.

4. Carrier molecules from glycolysis and the Krebs cycle transport electrons to the electron transfer system, where they release their potential energy during the transfer process.

5. The transfer of electrons from compound to compound in the transfer system causes protons to be pumped from the interior of the mitochondria, creating an electrical potential.

6. The electrical potential is relieved by an inward flow of protons through the ATPase enzyme that phosphorylates ADP, generating ATP.

7. Respiration generates 36 ATP from the breakdown of a single glucose molecule; in energy conversion, respiration is 38% efficient at conserving glucose bond energy.

6.8 ENERGY FLOW FROM CARBOHYDRATES TO ATP: FERMENTATION

In exergonic reaction pathways, electrons are always moving. And they always have to end up stored somewhere on some molecule. In nature, the most stable place for electrons to end up is on oxygen molecules (making water). Water is a highly stable, energy-poor molecule. But there are many places on Earth that have little or no oxygen—the bottoms of ponds, or oceans, or wine vats! Living things or their parts die and decay in all of these areas; their bodies contain many energy-rich molecules, such as glucose in grapes (see Figure 6.18). Shall we just give up on using these nutrients because no oxygen is available to respire (burn) them? That would be a major design flaw in a biosphere where most life-forms die. Dead organisms would simply accumulate in these anoxic zones. Eventually, the world's carbon supply would be tied up in those places. But in principle, life is *energy*-driven not *oxygen*-driven. Can't energy be derived from C–H bond–containing molecules even if no oxygen is present? The answer is "yes," and the process is called **fermentation.**

A variety of microbes inhabit places in the world's environments where there is no oxygen. These bacteria and yeasts use large numbers of energy-rich molecules in short exergonic pathways to generate modest amounts of ATP that they can survive on (see Figure 6.19). Fermentation pathways vary depending on the energy-rich molecules

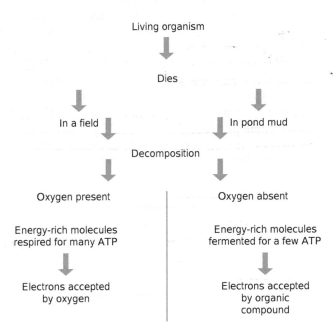

Figure 6.18 Fate of Energy-rich Molecules in Organisms that have Died.

fermentation—a short metabolic pathway in which electrons transferred to NADH carrier molecules are finally accepted, not by oxygen but by some organic molecule.

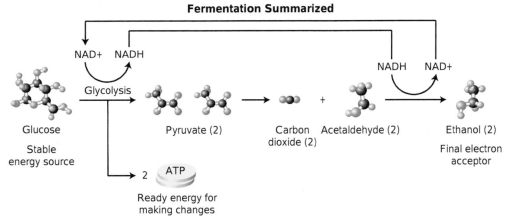

Fermentation Summarized

Glucose
Stable energy source

Glycolysis

NAD+ NADH

Pyruvate (2)

Carbon dioxide (2) + Acetaldehyde (2)

NADH NAD+

Ethanol (2)
Final electron acceptor

2 ATP
Ready energy for making changes

Figure 6.19 Alcoholic Fermentation. This process requires no oxygen. In the initial decay process, complex carbohydrates are degraded to the glucose shown here. Glucose is them degraded through glycolysis as in aerobic respiration with a net production of 2 ATP. Electrons are pulled off of reactants along the glycolytic pathway and are finally dumped onto the small organic molecule acetaldehyde to generate ethyl alcoholic. The entire baking and brewing industry rest upon this reaction. The bakers run it to get the carbon dioxide which raises the bread. The brewers run it to get the alcohol.

available for use. Some of these pathways are very much like glycolysis—especially when glucose is available. But what do such pathways end with? If oxygen's not the final electron acceptor (as in aerobic respiration), then where are the electrons "dumped"? One very common molecule that acts as a terminal electron holder in anaerobic energy generation is **ethanol** (ethyl alcohol, grain alcohol, "juice"!). Yeast cells, of species *Saccharomyces cerevisiae,* do fermentation at the bottom of wine vats all over Europe and upstate New York (see Figure 6.19).

Ethanol, then, is a major ingredient in a fungal (yeast) waste product that our society concentrates and drinks! If you took a yeast cell and dropped it into a bottle of bourbon whiskey, it would die marinating in a concentrated form (70% ethanol) of its own metabolic waste. Suppose we were to concentrate urine—human metabolic waste—to that same degree. Many of us, who wouldn't consider drinking such a product, are quite casual about drinking a yeast cell's metabolic waste. Think about that one a bit. (There are bacteria in nature that neatly degrade ethanol to simpler compounds: Our services were never needed for this task.)

> **ethanol**—a two-carbon alcohol formed when electrons on NADH are transferred to a molecule of acetaldehyde; beverage alcohol.

IN OTHER WORDS

1. The Earth has many anoxic (oxygen deficient) environments where respiration cannot take place.
2. Fermentation derives ATP energy from energy-rich carbohydrates in the absence of any oxygen.
3. The final electron acceptor in fermentation is usually a small organic molecule like ethanol or acetic acid (vinegar).

The flow of energy we have traced out thus far prepares us to take in an even bigger picture: The way in which the sun drives all of life! Many microbes and higher plants are called **autotrophs** (GK. *auto* = self; Gk. *troph* = feed on). Autotrophs need energy-rich molecules containing C–H bonds just as we do and for all the same reasons. But oak trees don't eat the squirrels inside of them, and yet, their ATP supplies are just fine. What is the source of energy-rich molecules for autotrophs? They build their own using solar energy. Then, to meet their own energy needs, they turn round and degrade these molecules, using the same respiration pathway we use. (see Figure 6.5). Autotrophs possess an amazing collection of molecules called **chlorophylls**, which channel solar energy into the production of high energy carbohydrates in a process called **photosynthesis.** Like respiration, this process has separate stages and represents something like 30 separate sequential reactions. Once again, the process can be summarized by the single expression in Figure 6.20. The glucose product of this pathway is then degraded by respiratory pathways in the same cell to generate all the ATP needed for biosynthesis, movement, and transport of materials. Just imagine over 300,000 widely differing species of plants—everything from roses to redwood trees—all carrying out photosynthesis and respiration in essentially the

same way using the same enzymes and organellar compartments! A glorious Designer envisioned it all first! Then . . . then . . . we made sense of it!

We slowly discovered that photosynthesis is really two somewhat separate processes. In the first process, called the **light-dependent pathway,** solar energy is used to split water molecules, generate free oxygen and the temporary energy storage molecules ATP and NADPH (see Figure 6.21a). In the second process, the **light-independent pathway** (see Figure 6.21b), the ATP energy and the electrons

autotroph—any organism capable of taking in carbon dioxide gas from nature and using it to generate energy-rich carbohydrates.

chlorophyll—a green pigment biomolecule capable of absorbing solar photons and using the resultant energy to break and form covalent bonds.

photosynthesis—a metabolic pathway in which light energy is used to generate carbohydrates from carbon dioxide gas and water.

light-dependent pathway—a sequence of reactions within photosynthesis that utilize light energy to generate ATP molecules and to transfer electrons to NADP generating NADPH.

light-independent pathway—a cyclical sequence of reactions within photosynthesis that utilize ATP bond energy and electrons from NADPH to generate energy-rich carbohydrates.

Photosynthesis Summarized

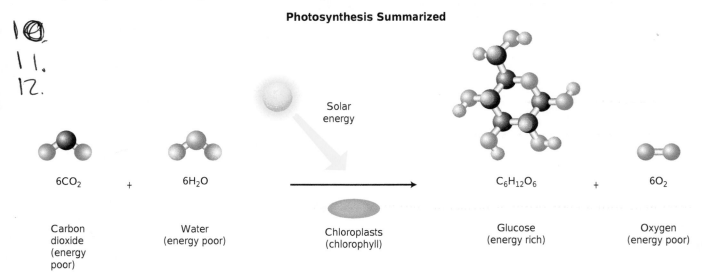

| $6CO_2$ | + | $6H_2O$ | | $C_6H_{12}O_6$ | + | $6O_2$ |

Carbon dioxide (energy poor)   Water (energy poor)   Solar energy   Chloroplasts (chlorophyll)   Glucose (energy rich)   Oxygen (energy poor)

Figure 6.20 Photosynthesis Summarized.

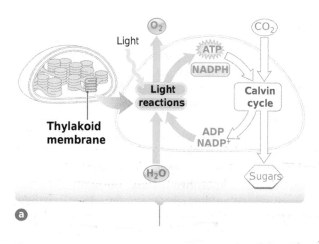

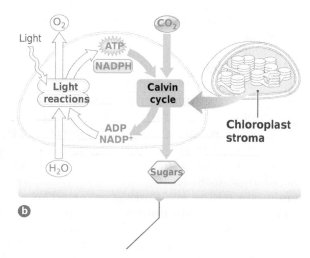

a

b

Figure 6.21 Photosynthesis Dissected. **(a)** Light-Dependent Reactions. To the left a chloroplast is shown in a cut-away view that reveals the thylakoids within. The reactions shown in color take place within the thylakoid and across the thylakoid membrane. **(b)** Light-Independent Reactions. To the right, a chloroplast is shown in a cut-away view that reveals the stromal fluid and space around the thylakoids. The reactions shown in color take place within the stromal fluid of the chloroplast.

Figure 6.22 Light Energy. **(a)** The sun emits energy from a broad range of the electromagnetic spectrum, including all the visible wavelengths of light. **(b)** Visible light is only a small portion of the total electromagnetic spectrum of wavelengths of energy that exist. It is most convenient to measure visible wavelenths of light in nanometers (10^{-9} meters). Radio waves can be as long as 20 kilometers in length.

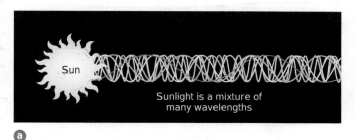

Sunlight is a mixture of many wavelengths

a

on NADPH are used to attach carbon dioxide to a small, existing sugar molecule making it larger and generating the additional C–H bonds that make it more "energetic." So the light-dependent pathway converts solar energy into chemical energy. The light-independent pathway uses this chemical energy to "grow" sugar molecules one carbon at a time. Let's dissect these two processes a bit starting with the first.

Photosynthesis: Stage 1— Light-Dependent Reactions

Generating energy-rich carbohydrates begins with light. Visible light from the sun can be described either as energetic particles or as waves. If you bend light with a glass prism, it breaks up into its constituent wavelengths, which appear to our eyes in all the colors of the rainbow (see Figure 6.22a). Each wavelength of light has its own energy level. The shortest visible wavelength of light (violet)

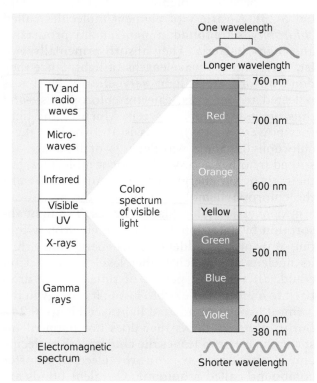

b

consists of particles with almost twice the energy of red light, which has the longest wavelength in the visible spectrum of light.

Life was designed with visible light in mind. Visible light is only a tiny portion of an exceedingly broad **electromagnetic spectrum** of radiation that extends from ultrashort and highly powerful gamma rays to much longer and lower-powered radio waves that surround us constantly (see Figure 6.22b). What is surprising is that wavelengths of radiation from most parts of this spectrum are minimally felt on the Earth's surface. The chemistry of space and our atmosphere absorb almost all electromagnetic radiation shorter or longer in wavelength than visible light. Yet visible light waves are just the ones that are most useful for transferring energy from light to electrons in organic molecules. Higher-energy wavelengths indiscriminately disrupt the structure and function of organic molecules—degrading the photosynthetic machinery itself. Lower-energy wavelengths increase overall molecular motion in fluids but aren't strong enough to encourage the breaking of specific covalent bonds. How wonderful! Precisely the wavelengths of energy we need for life are the ones that survive space and our atmosphere, arriving safely on the surface . . . of leaves.

Visible light enters the biological world when it is absorbed by **pigment molecules** (see Figure 6.23). A variety of pigment molecules called *chlorophylls* are found in plants, many protistans, and many bacteria. They absorb principally violet, blue, and red wavelengths of light. Since they don't absorb green light very effectively, this is reflected to our eyes, causing chlorophylls—and thus plants—to appear green. Much of the light that powers photosynthesis is absorbed by these chlorophylls. Some wavelengths of light are absorbed by other **accessory pigment** molecules, but their absorbed energy is then channeled toward the chlorophyll molecules, where the actual energy conversion takes place. The result of light absorption by chlorophyll is that an electron within one of its atoms suddenly gains energy and orbits its nucleus at a much higher level. This electron could, after a brief period of time, simply drop back to a more stable orbit, losing its energy in the form of heat or reradiated light (see Figure 6.24). But in photosynthesis that does not happen! Instead, the electron leaves the chlorophyll molecule and is transferred to a nearby electron transfer compound called a **quinone.** Covalent bonds are

broken and formed. What was previously solar energy has now become chemical bond energy.

How does the chlorophyll molecule always have a quinone adjacent to it to pass electrons to? The glorious photosynthetic chemistry is housed in a meticulously arranged set of compartments within the green cells of the lettuce leaves you ate for dinner tonight. Inside each cell (were!) many chloroplasts whose insides were packed with a stacked, convoluted system of (green) membranes called **thylakoids.** The membranes are green because the chlorophyll we've described is situated within them (see Figure 6.25). Within the thylakoid membranes hundreds of chlorophylls and accessory pigments are held together in clusters called **photosystems** (see Figure 6.26). The pigment molecules harvest light and channel it to two special chlorophyll molecules within each photosystem. These two molecules actually transfer their excited electrons along to electron-accepting quinones. There are two different kinds of photosystems in the membrane that possess chlorophylls differing in the wavelength of light that excites them. These two kinds of photosystems cooperate to generate a continuous flow of electrons between them. That flow results in the ATP production needed to drive the growth of sugar molecules.

electromagnetic spectrum—the entire range of radiation extending in frequency from approximately 10^{-13} centimeters to infinity and including cosmic-ray photons, gamma rays, X-rays, ultraviolet radiation, visible light, infrared radiation, microwaves, and radio waves.

pigment molecules—organic compounds that absorb and reflect wavelengths of light selectively such that they appear to the human eye to have a particular color.

accessory pigments—organic compounds such as carotenoids that absorb wavelengths of light not readily absorbed by chlorophyll; they transfer the energy of that absorption to nearby chlorophyll molecules, enhancing their excitation of electrons.

quinone—a class of yellow compounds found in thylakoid membranes; they accept electrons from chlorophyll molecules.

thylakoid—a membrane-enclosed sac within a chloroplast inside of which are the enzymes, pigments, and electron transfer compounds of the light-dependent reactions of photosynthesis.

photosystem—a membrane-bound collection of chlorophylls and accessory pigments that harvest light energy and make it available to the light-dependent pathway of photosynthesis.

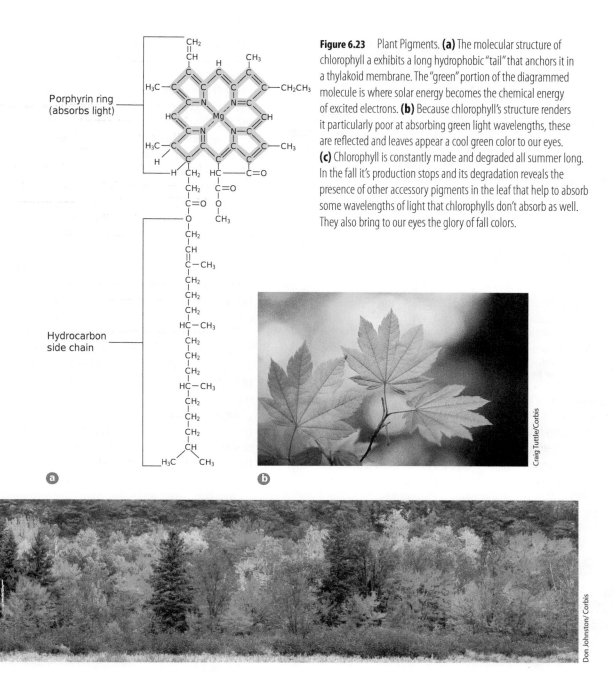

Porphyrin ring
(absorbs light)

Hydrocarbon
side chain

a

b

c

Figure 6.23 Plant Pigments. **(a)** The molecular structure of chlorophyll a exhibits a long hydrophobic "tail" that anchors it in a thylakoid membrane. The "green" portion of the diagrammed molecule is where solar energy becomes the chemical energy of excited electrons. **(b)** Because chlorophyll's structure renders it particularly poor at absorbing green light wavelengths, these are reflected and leaves appear a cool green color to our eyes. **(c)** Chlorophyll is constantly made and degraded all summer long. In the fall it's production stops and its degradation reveals the presence of other accessory pigments in the leaf that help to absorb some wavelengths of light that chlorophylls don't absorb as well. They also bring to our eyes the glory of fall colors.

Positioned right next to one of the photosystems, within the membrane, are the quinone molecules that quickly trap the excited electrons from a chlorophyll molecule. The electrons then enter an electron transfer system similar to the one described for aerobic respiration (see Figure 6.17, right-hand side of the diagram). As the electrons move from one transfer component to the next, they release energy used to pump protons (H^+ ions) from the exterior to the interior of the thylakoid membrane. A charge begins to build up across the membrane. But again that charge is relieved by a membrane-bound ATPase enzyme (see Figure 6.26) that uses the energy to generate ATP.

The first law—the conservation of matter—states that electrons cannot simply come from

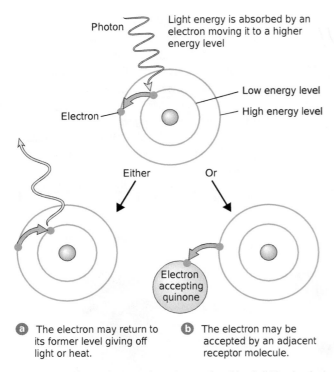

Figure 6.24 Photon Absorption by an Atom within Chlorphyll. The absorbed light energy promotes an electron to a higher energy level. (a) The electron could simply return to its more stable configuration with the energy given off either as re-emitted light or as heat. (b) If an appropriate acceptor molecule is nearby, the energized electron may jump to the acceptor molecule, resulting in a new energy-rich covalent bond. Light energy has become chemical energy.

nowhere. Once chlorophyll loses its electron to the nearby electron transport system, how does it acquire another electron for the next solar excitation event? An enzyme activity that is closely associated with the photosystem of chlorophyll molecules uses solar energy to drive an otherwise very unfavorable reaction—the splitting of (very stable) water molecules. There are plenty of water molecules around—the roots of the plant are always supplying more of them. The enzyme splits away protons (H^+ ions) from two water molecules and captures the now available electrons on behalf of the "wanting" chlorophyll molecule. The enzyme then goes on to combine the two remaining oxygens to form a molecule of oxygen gas (which makes your breathing worthwhile). But what a breath-takingly facile enzyme is this amazing machine that our lives are so entirely dependent upon!

Consider the electrons stolen from water. They take a long but very fast ride, chemically. They get excited by chlorophyll and travel down an electron transfer chain only to be picked up by a second, somewhat different, chlorophyll in the second of the two photosystems mentioned above. In this photosystem they are again excited by solar energy—but to a still higher energy level (see Figure 6.26). With this additional energy they are capable of being transferred to the soluble electron carrier NADPH

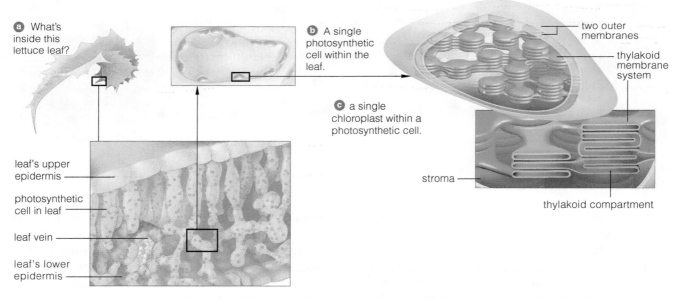

Figure 6.25 Finding Photosynthesis in a Leaf. Cells within leaves (a) are arranged in discrete layers or "tissues". Toward the leaf's upper surface is a high density of cells (b) filled with chloroplasts. In (c) the interior of a chloroplast is diagrammed. The compartments within a chloroplast remind us that Life is Complex.

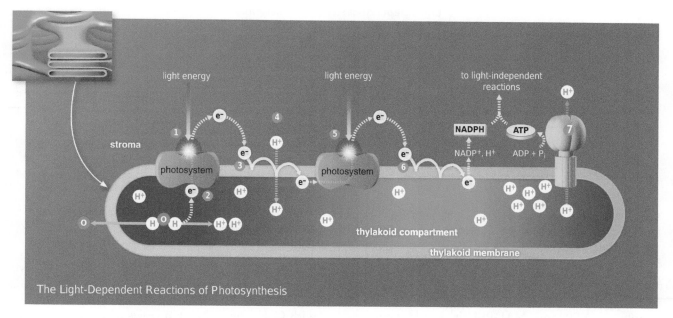

light energy   light energy   to light-independent reactions

stroma

photosystem   photosystem

NADPH   ATP

$NADP^+, H^+$ $ADP + P_i$

thylakoid compartment

thylakoid membrane

The Light-Dependent Reactions of Photosynthesis

Figure 6.26 The Light-Dependent Part of Photosynthesis. Two differently designed photosystems convert the energy of light into the energy of electron acceleration. The solid yellow lines represent how that added energy is relieved. The electrons are transferred from compound to compound, all the while their energy is used to pump protons (H^+ ions) into the thylakoid. The electrons, initially stolen from water molecules (energy poor) finally end up on a molecule of NADPH (energy rich). The ATPase enzyme (shown to the right in the thylakoid membrane) allows the protons back to the exterior. The energy given off in that flow is used to phosphorylate ADP to generate energy rich ATP.

which has a role similar to the NADH used in respiration. NADPH carries high-energy electrons to the second stage of photosynthesis where they are used to create energy-rich C-H bonds.

So then, fundamentally, the light dependent reaction of photosynthesis is simply a long flow of electrons. First they are pushed up an energy hill by the "power of the photon!." As they then flow down the energy hill, they pump protons. The displaced protons return across the membrane making ATP. Finally the electrons themselves generate NADPH once their transfer is complete.

You may be thinking, "Wait! Why not just have the light-dependent part of photosynthesis make lots of ATP and be done with it? The plant can get all its ATP from that source (instead of doing respiration), and then I'll get that ATP when I eat the plant tissue" (see Figure 6.27). But there is a design problem here. Many changes required by the cell involve substantial amounts of energy input at specific endergonic reactions. That energy can be made available to those reactions, concentrated into one single bond—*if* that bond is somewhat unstable. That's what we have with ATP. It delivers,

in a single bond, ample free energy to the many endergonic processes that require it. But the price is instability. ATP breaks down almost as soon as it's formed if you don't use it right away. Since it's needed within your individual cells, that's really where you need to produce it. Sugars like glucose are much more stable, absorbable, and transportable energy sources. So a brilliant Designer made photosynthesis complete enough to generate stable sugar molecules that we can then absorb and use at leisure to make unstable but highly useful ATP molecules.

Photosynthesis: Stage 2— Light-Independent Reactions

We must therefore invest our ATP and NADPH almost immediately into making stable sugar molecules. This requires the second stage of photosynthesis, the light-independent stage. We call it that because it needs only the products of the light-dependent stage to operate. If we were to supply the second stage of photosynthesis with a continuous

Light-Dependent Reactions Imagined

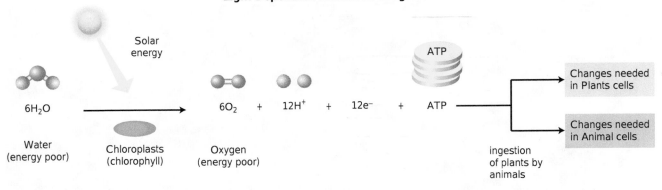

Figure 6.27 "If Only". ATP's available energy is highly concentrated in the covalent bond between the last two phosphates. The bond takes very little energy to break and much energy is given off when new bonds form. If only ATP were a more stable molecule, respiration and the light-independent part of photosynthesis would be entirely unnecessary—so much less to learn! It is the diffusely energetic but stable glucose and the highly energetic but unstable ATP molecule that require all the additional chemistry of respiration and photosynthesis. But an infinite Designer saw all of that and chose to use two molecular versions of energy storage—ATP and glucose.

supply of ATP and NADPH, it would generate sugar for us all day long with no input of solar energy whatever.

The light-independent reaction is simply a way of using ATP energy and NADPH's electrons to first add carbon dioxide to the structure of an existing sugar molecule and then to replace some of the energy-poor C–O bonds with energy-rich C–H bonds on that sugar molecule (see Figure 6.28a). How does this pathway begin? Land plants allow carbon dioxide into their leaves by **stomata** on the undersurface of the leaf. Algae use carbon dioxide dissolved in the surrounding water.

Carbon dioxide diffuses into the cytoplasm of photosynthetic cells and then into the chloroplast. There in the semifluid matrix of the chloroplast— called the **stroma**—the light-independent pathway takes place. The reactions in the pathway take the form of a cycle somewhat like the Krebs cycle, only here, as you might have expected, CO_2 is added to the substrate molecules rather than being taken off as in the Krebs cycle! The CO_2 gets added to the five-carbon sugar **ribulose 1,5-bisphosphate (RuBP)**, which is then regenerated by the end of the cycle. The enzyme that catalyzes this reaction, RuBP carboxylase, is believed to be the most abundant protein on the face of the Earth! Why might this be true?

Adding one carbon to a five-carbon sugar creates a six-carbon hexose (sugar) that immediately is split into two 3-carbon sugars within the cycle. These small carbohydrates then receive electrons from NADPH to enrich their structures chemically

with C–H bonds. Next, a series of cutting and pasting reactions then occur among three-, four-, five-, and seven-carbon sugars within the cycle in order to regenerate RuBP. The cycle must turn six times, capturing six carbon atoms as CO_2, in order to form the equivalent of one 6-carbon glucose molecule. The whole process can be represented with the summary statement shown in Figure 6.28b. Actually, glucose is not present in high concentrations within the cytoplasm of the plant cell. It is quickly combined with fructose to form **sucrose**, the major transported form of sugar in the plant, or it is polymerized into long molecules of **starch**, the major storage form of carbohydrate in the plant. Starch can be stored in the chloroplast itself until nighttime

> **stomata**—regulated openings on the undersurfaces of leaves that control the influx of carbon dioxide and efflux of water from internal leaf tissues.
>
> **stroma**—a syrupy fluid within chloroplasts that surrounds the stacks of thylakoids; the enzymes of the light-independent reaction are found in the stroma.
>
> **ribulose 1,5-bisphosphate**—a twice-phosphorylated five-carbon sugar that combines with carbon dioxide in the light-independent reaction of photosynthesis to form two 3-carbon sugars.
>
> **sucrose**—a disaccharide sugar composed of the monomers glucose and fructose; the sugar used for transporting energy throughout the tissues of a plant.
>
> **starch**—a polymer of glucose molecules; used as a storage form of energy in plant tissues.

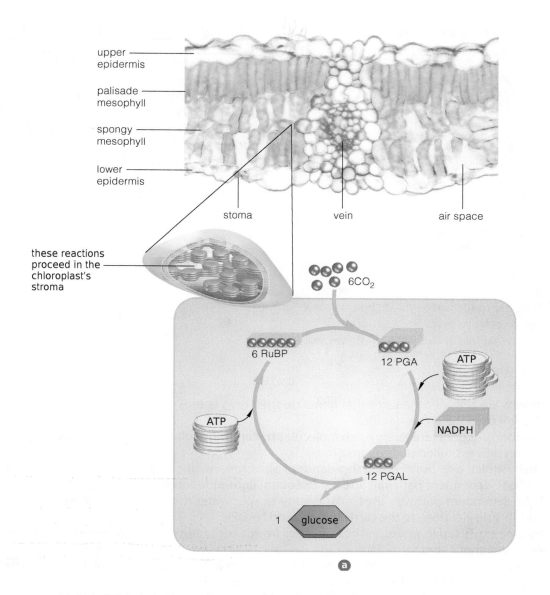

upper epidermis

palisade mesophyll

spongy mesophyll

lower epidermis

stoma   vein   air space

these reactions proceed in the chloroplast's stroma

$6CO_2$

6 RuBP

12 PGA

ATP

NADPH

ATP

12 PGAL

1 glucose

a

Light-Independent Pathway Summarized

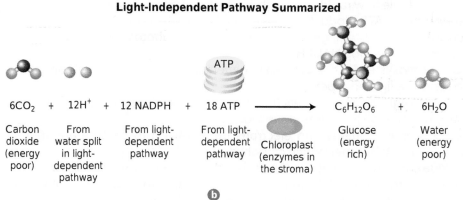

$$6CO_2 \; + \; 12H^+ \; + \; 12\,NADPH \; + \; 18\,ATP \longrightarrow C_6H_{12}O_6 \; + \; 6H_2O$$

| Carbon dioxide (energy poor) | From water split in light-dependent pathway | From light-dependent pathway | From light-dependent pathway | Chloroplast (enzymes in the stroma) | Glucose (energy rich) | Water (energy poor) |

b

Figure 6.28 The Light-Independent Reactions of Photosynthesis. **(a)** The brown spheres represent carbon atoms. Note that the $6CO_2$ molecules entering the reaction pathway require six "turns" of the cycle in order to generate one 6-carbon glucose molecule. **(b)** A summary of the reactants and products of the light-independent metabolic pathway.

when it's converted to sucrose and distributed as needed for energy throughout the plant.

Finally, as the preceding summary reaction suggests, more ATP than NADPH is needed to generate our glucose molecule. Continuous operation of the light-dependent pathway as we've described it here would thus lead to a surplus of NADPH. This problem is avoided, however, because a simpler version

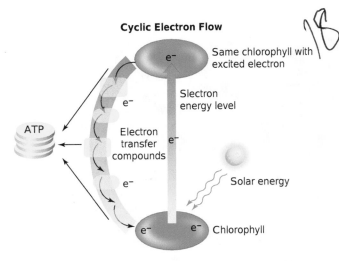

Cyclic Electron Flow

Same chlorophyll with excited electron

Slectron energy level

ATP

Electron transfer compounds

Solar energy

Chlorophyll

Figure 6.29 Cyclic Electron Flow. If NADPH supplies in the chloroplast are adequate, solar energy is sometimes used to simply excite electrons in chlorophyll. Their carefully crafted flow back through electron transfer compounds pumps protons into the thylakoid and results in extra ATP production. Only one photosystem is involved and no NADPH is generated.

of the light-dependent reaction exists that uses only the first photosystem. It is cyclic. Excited electrons leave chlorophyll from the first photosystem, travel an electron transfer sequence, and then return to the same photosystem, their energy spent (see Figure 6.29). The spent energy pumps protons and yields ATP. But because the second photosystem is not involved, no NADPH is generated. The chloroplast can shift freely between the simpler or more prolonged systems keeping the pools of ATP and NADPH is precise balance. Such elegant control!

IN OTHER WORDS

1. Autotrophs are cells or organisms that generate their own energy-rich molecules using energy-poor carbon dioxide from the environment.
2. Many autotrophs generate energy-rich molecules by capturing solar energy using chlorophyll in an energy conversion process called *photosynthesis*.
3. Essentially similar over hundreds of thousands of plant species, photosynthesis consists of two component parts, a light-dependent pathway, and a subsequent light-independent pathway.
4. The light-dependent pathway uses solar energy to split water molecules, release free oxygen, generate ATP, and shuttle electrons to the carrier compound NADPH.
5. The light energy used in photosynthesis derives from a very narrow portion of wavelengths of energy in the electromagnetic spectrum.
6. Excited electrons quickly lose their energy either as heat or as reradiated light unless they can be passed to an acceptor molecule that enables them to retain their added energy.
7. Electrons passed to an acceptor molecule flow rapidly through an electron transfer system formally similar to one in respiration with a similar result: ATP production.
8. The electrons leave the electron transfer system, get reexcited in a second photosystem and are finally accepted by a carrier molecule of NADP making NADPH.
9. The chloroplast can use just one photosystem or two of them to generate the products of ATP and NADPH in the proportions needed to serve the light-independent reaction.
10. The ATP molecules generated in the light-dependent reaction are too unstable chemically to serve as an energy source for the heterotrophic (animal) life-forms in the biosphere.
11. The light-independent pathway uses ATP energy and electrons from NADPH to capture energy-poor carbon dioxide and uses it to generate stable energy-rich carbohydrates.
12. In terrestrial plants, carbon dioxide enters the stomata on the underside of leaves; it then diffuses into plant cells, then into chloroplasts, where, in the stroma, it becomes chemically bound to existing carbohydrates.
13. The light-independent pathway is a cyclic series of chemical reactions that rearrange, cut, and paste carbohydrate molecules.
14. The pathway generates free carbohydrate energy sources and regenerates the five-carbon sugar that accepts carbon dioxide at the beginning of the cycle.

6.10 ENERGY FLOW: AN INTEGRATED PICTURE

Let's conclude our analysis of energy's "driving effect" on life processes by comparing the two processes of photosynthesis and respiration (see Figures 6.15, 6.20). You must have noticed by now that the summary reactions for these two processes are materially precisely the reverse of each other. What does that fact mean functionally and energetically? Photosynthesis and respiration are complementary processes within a global cycle called the **carbon cycle.** The major reservoirs of carbon in this cycle are atmospheric carbon dioxide, the Earth's water supply with its dissolved carbon dioxide, the organic matter in all of the living things on the surface of the planet, and all the residue of once-living organisms. This last category includes all coal and oil deposits (see Figure 6.30).

Photosynthesis is essentially an endergonic process. It requires the sun's energy to drive the uptake of energy-poor molecules—CO_2 and H_2O—from

heterotroph—any organism that gains its food by feeding on other organisms or their remains.

their respective reservoirs and convert them into energy-rich organic molecules (like glucose) with the elaboration of free oxygen. The energy-rich glucose is then burned by **heterotrophs** like us. We can't make our own fuel photosynthetically—we must depend on the autotrophs that can. The free oxygen they provide in photosynthesis can then be the final electron acceptors, pulling electrons off of energy-rich food molecules during the exergonic reactions of respiration.

Now that we've appreciated at least a bit of life's biochemical complexity, we dare to ask: How did all of this glorious machinery originate? Let's suppose, as many have, that metabolism evolved slowly from single chemical reactions to more complex pathways. We must imagine an early version of photosynthesis: just a few membrane-bound

carbon cycle—the circulation of carbon within the biosphere, sometimes as carbon dioxide, and at other times within organic molecules such as glucose; photosynthesis and respiration are central processes in this circulation.

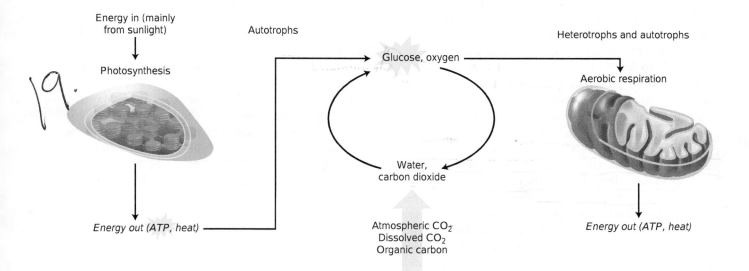

Figure 6.30   The Big Picture. The energy of the sun drives photosynthesis; the energy of glucose drives respiration. Respiration occurs in all higher plants and animals while photosynthesis occurs only in autotrophic forms. While matter cycles continuously between the two processes, energy flows vertically from light to chemical energy to heat.

Figure 6.31 Evolutionary Origin of Photosynthesis and Respiration. Microfossils and layers of rock that show the effects of free oxygen are demonstrable features of sedimentary rocks. Beyond these hard evidences most of the lower portion of this figure is conjectural. It is based on the assumption that evolution takes us from what is simple to what is more complex. The photographs here show both modern cells of the blue-green cyanobacterium, and fossil forms of these bacteria. We can't know what these fossil forms were capable of metabolically.

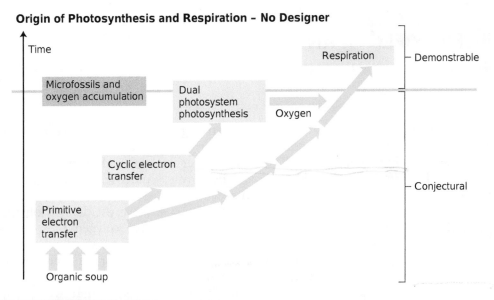

Origin of Photosynthesis and Respiration – No Designer

compounds that transfer electrons and that somehow learn to generate ATP as a result of electron transfer (see Figure 6.31). We next imagine that a more complex (non-cyclic) version of photosynthesis developed—one that generated oxygen. Our assumption further forces us to postpone arrival of cells capable of respiration until complex photosynthesizers fill the atmosphere with this oxygen. It is difficult to force current evidence to require this progression of pathway development. The oldest known fossil microbes look like early members of Phylum **Cyanobacteria** (see Figure 6.31). Modern cyanobacteria possess the more complex form of photosynthesis although they are capable of running just the simpler version. Since these ancient cyanobacteria exist only as fossils, they can't tell us what their metabolic abilities were. Yet if we assume life must have evolved from simple to complex, then we will assume that cyanobacteria came to have their present appearance well before they were capable of generating oxygen and NADPH since they are practically the earliest fossils we possess. So the simple-to-complex paradigm moves us to assume that respiring forms came far later than early photosynthetic forms even though geologic evidence

for early oxygen accumulation begins at about the same time as unequivocal evidence for the first cyanobacterial cells.

But for a moment, let's stop trying to derive one form from another. Let's turn our attention away from *when* these early forms began life and ask what a Designer might have had in mind for them. A truly fascinating functional divide in nature is observed. It is as though a Designer determined that one set of organisms—autotrophic bacteria and plants—would specialize in both energy capture and energy utilization. With their broad enzymatic capabilities, these "servant organisms" would be supremely adept in the whole business of energy handling, generating far more C–H bond energy than they would ever utilize (see Figure 6.32). Then, a whole range of heterotrophs from minimal microbes to the magnificence of man could,

cyanobacteria—prokaryotic cells, often colonial forms, that use chlorophyll to carry out photosynthesis with oxygen as a by-product; blue-green algae.

Figure 6.32 Independence and Dependence. Two highly sophisticated species each supremely adapted to its own role in nature. One is highly efficient at generating excessive amounts of stable chemical energy. The other simply utilizes that excess energy to work and to worship.

to support them. The one organism that we know has the ability to be proud is, upon study, given the knowledge that it he totally dependent on organisms that are completely independent of him. How fitting.

Each life-form, whether respiring, fermenting or photosynthesizing, complements every other life-form in nature. Each living thing supplies the global carbon cycle with precisely the molecules needed to render each other life-form a dynamic part of the biosphere. Powerful solar energy drives this wonderfully integrated machinery of life! How on earth could such a wondrous set of relationships originate? What would a biologist who knows St. Paul's writings answer to a question like that? There is only one answer—found in Romans 11:

"Oh the depths of the riches of the wisdom
and knowledge of God....
How unsearchable are His judgments
and His (metabolic) pathways beyond tracing out!"

with a much simpler energy metabolism, fill either humbler or more exalted roles in the biosphere with stable carbohydrate energy always available

IN OTHER WORDS

1. Photosynthesis uses solar energy and chlorophyll to convert energy-poor water and carbon dioxide to energy-rich carbohydrate with the evolution of free oxygen.
2. Respiration uses energy-rich carbohydrates to build up ATP resources, returning energy-poor water and carbon dioxide to the carbon cycle for photosynthesis to operate on again.
3. Evolutionary theorists believe that electron transport systems were the earliest elements of both respiratory and photosynthetic machinery.
4. The earliest fossil forms are similar to modern cyanobacteria that currently do both photosynthesis and respiration; they are some of the most metabolically capable cells that exist.
5. The contrast between heterotrophic and autotrophic life-forms appears to be one of the most basic distinctions in the mind of the Designer.
6. The man with the greatest faith attributes the wisdom inherent in the carbon cycle to environmental selective forces he is entirely unable to rigorously quantitate.

QUESTIONS FOR REVIEW

1. List some specific examples (from previous chapters if necessary) where movement occurs within a living cell.
2. State the two laws that govern the behavior of energy in living things.
3. Solar energy enters life-forms and most of it is lost as heat energy. How would you describe where the useful energy is retained within living systems?
4. Bonding two amino acids together while making a protein is an endergonic process. What does this term tell you about the process?
5. Why does glucose accumulate in grape cells but get used up in muscle cells?

6. Glucose can be degraded to energy-poor carbon dioxide and water using either enzymes or a match. If the cell could withstand high temperatures, why would the enzyme approach still be more useful to the cell?

7. What is the purpose of a metabolic pathway? Why must individual chemical reactions be linked together in such pathways?

8. If a product at the end of a pathway accumulates to a high concentration, what effect will that have on the reaction generating the product?

9. How many binding sites does an allosteric enzyme have? What are their functions?

10. Why are you perpetually breathing out carbon dioxide? Where does it originate?

11. Write out a summary equation (reaction) for the whole process of aerobic respiration.

12. In what form does energy emerge from glycolysis?

13. What is the connecting link between the Krebs cycle and the electron transfer compounds?

14. Once protons have been pumped across the inner mitochondrial membrane, what would cause them to tend to flow back to the interior? What would keep them from doing so? What enables them to do so?

15. If respiration is so much more efficient than fermentation at deriving ATP energy from glucose, why does fermentation exist at all?

16. List the reactants and products of the light-dependent pathway of photosynthesis; then do the same for the light-independent pathway.

17. Of what value are accessory pigments if chlorophyll molecules can themselves absorb photo energy and excite electrons with it?

18. Draw a slice through a chloroplast showing its interior structure. Label the following terms: thylakoid, stroma, photosystem, ATPase, site of light-dependent reaction, and site of light-independent reaction.

19. Explain in your own words why you and I cannot simply absorb, digest, and utilize ATP generated by the light-dependent reaction of photosynthesis.

20. Why is the light-independent reaction pathway so named?

21. How many times must the light-independent cycle of reactions turn to generate one molecule of glucose? Why?

22. Why would a thylakoid sometimes use just one photosystem and generate only ATP when the electrons involved could simply go on, given sunlight, to generate more NADPH as well?

23. Draw your own diagram of the carbon cycle using figures from this chapter and the following terms: carbon dioxide, glucose, water, oxygen, mitochondrion, chloroplast, autotrophs, heterotrophs, atmosphere, dissolved carbon dioxide, and fermentation.

24. Metabolically, which of the following organisms is most independent of any other organism: man, cats, heterotrophic bacteria, eagles, cyanobacteria, or mushrooms? Explain why.

QUESTIONS FOR THOUGHT

1. Consider a membrane within a cell where ions are being moved from one side of the membrane to the other (where they are already in higher concentration). Why would this require more energy than doing the same thing with glucose molecules?

2. Besides the water circulated by a water pump, what other critical substance in an automobile engine reminds us that most of combustion's energy ends up as heat?

3. Large "No Smoking" signs are found on gasoline pumps everywhere. Use the term *activation energy* to explain why.

4. In terms of atoms, electrons, and covalent bonds, explain how an enzyme's active site lowers a reaction's activation energy.

5. What is the advantage to a cell to have a metabolic pathway that is subject to feedback inhibition?

6. Why do we say that ATP is an energy-rich molecule when energy is actually required to break any covalent bond, including the phosphate bond of the ATP molecule?

7. Is respiration one metabolic pathway or is it three pathways? Explain your choice.

8. The process that causes bread to rise (found within the yeast *Saccharomyces*) is exactly the same fermentation pathway used to make wine. Why don't we get drunk eating bread?

9. Use an Internet search engine to answer these questions: How can some autotrophs make energy-rich molecules deep in the ocean depths where no solar energy exists at all? What is their energy source? *Hint:* They are called *chemoautotrophs*. Land plants are photoautotrophs.

10. If you believe in evolution, which of the following systems would have evolved first: respiratory pathways, photosynthetic pathways, or proton pumping? Why?

GLOSSARY

accessory pigments—organic compounds such as carotenoids that absorb wavelengths of light not readily absorbed by chlorophyll; they transfer the energy of that absorption to nearby chlorophyll molecules, enhancing their excitation of electrons.

acetyl-CoA—a two-carbon fragment resulting from degradation of pyruvate; the fragment is attached to a large cofactor molecule that transfers the acetyl fragment onto a reactant in the Krebs cycle.

activation energy—an amount of energy necessary to break bonds in a reactant thus getting a chemical reaction started.

active site—a precise three-dimensional space within the structure of an enzyme where a specific reactant or reactants selectively bind and are there converted to a product or products.

aerobic respiration—a metabolic pathway in which energy-rich molecules are degraded chemically with the generation of phosphate bond energy in ATP molecules; electrons from the energy-rich initial reactant end up combining with oxygen to form water.

allosteric site—a three-dimensional groove, pocket, or surface on or within an enzyme molecule; when a specifically shaped regulatory substance binds the site, the enzyme's active site is altered structurally.

anaerobic—any environment or process in which oxygen is absent.

ATP (adenosine triphosphate)—the major energy-storage compound in most cells; energy is given off following the breaking of a covalent bond between the second and third phosphate groups.

ATP synthase—a protein within the mitochondrial membrane; it relieves a proton gradient by allowing protons to flow back across the membrane. It uses the resulting energy production to phosphorylate ADP making energy-rich ATP molecules.

autotroph—any organism capable of taking in carbon dioxide gas from nature and using it to generate energy-rich carbohydrates.

biosynthesis—the building up of biomolecules or biological structures within a living cell; a process that requires energy.

calorie—the amount of energy required to raise the temperature of 1 gram of water by 1°C.

carbon cycle—the circulation of carbon within the biosphere, sometimes as carbon dioxide, and at other times within organic molecules such as glucose; photosynthesis and respiration are central processes in this circulation.

chemical reaction—a process in which bonds are broken in one kind of molecule (the reactant) and new bonds are formed to produce a product; energy change accompanies any chemical reaction.

chlorophyll—a green pigment biomolecule capable of absorbing solar photons and using the resultant energy to break and form covalent bonds.

cyanobacteria—prokaryotic cells, often colonial forms, that use chlorophyll to carry out photosynthesis with oxygen as a by-product; blue-green algae.

electrical potential—a difference in charge across a membrane based on a difference in the concentration of positive and/or negative ions across the membrane.

electromagnetic spectrum—the entire range of radiation extending in frequency from approximately 10213 centimeters to infinity and including cosmic-ray photons, gamma rays, X-rays, ultraviolet radiation, visible light, infrared radiation, microwaves, and radio waves.

endergonic—descriptive of a chemical reaction in which free energy must be added in order to get the reaction to take place.

energy—the capacity to do work; the capacity to make changes of importance to a living thing.

energy of concentration—the work of moving molecules or ions against a concentration gradient, that is, moving them from where they are less concentrated to where they are already more concentrated.

enzyme—a type of protein molecule that serves as an organic catalyst in solution. It reproducibly converts one specific sort of molecule into another—a specific reactant into its product.

ethanol—a two-carbon alcohol formed when electrons on NADH are transferred to a molecule of acetaldehyde; beverage alcohol.

exergonic—descriptive of a chemical reaction in which free energy is given off; a spontaneous reaction.

FADH2 (flavin adenine dinucleotide)—a biomolecule that accepts electrons from reactants in the Krebs cycle and transports them in solution to an electron transfer system. The system accepts the electrons and uses them to generate ATP for the cell.

feedback inhibition—a form of rate regulation in metabolic pathways in which the product of some late reaction in the pathway controls the rate of catalysis by an enzyme earlier in the pathway.

fermentation—a short metabolic pathway in which electrons transferred to NADH carrier molecules are finally accepted, not by oxygen but by some organic molecule.

glycolysis—the initial degradation of glucose molecules to pyruvate molecules with the generation of two molecules of ATP per molecule of glucose processed.

heterotroph—any organism that gains its food by feeding on other organisms or their remains.

Krebs cycle—a metabolic pathway in which acetyl groups are stripped of energetic electrons and degraded to carbon dioxide; an integral part of aerobic respiration.

Life Is Energy Driven—one of 12 principles of life on which this book is based.

light-dependent pathway—a sequence of reactions within photosynthesis that utilize light energy to generate ATP molecules and to transfer electrons to NADP generating NADPH.

light-independent pathway—a cyclical sequence of reactions within photosynthesis that utilize ATP bond energy and electrons from NADPH to generate energy-rich carbohydrates.

metabolic pathway—a series of chemical reactions in a sequence in which the product of one reaction is the reactant of the next reaction.

millivolt—a unit of electrical potential energy equal to 1/1000 of a volt.

NADH (nicotinamide adenine dinucleotide)—a biomolecule that accepts electrons from reactants in glycolysis and the Krebs cycle and transports them in solution to an electron transfer system. The system accepts the electrons and uses them to generate ATP for the cell.

photosynthesis—a metabolic pathway in which light energy is used to generate carbohydrates from carbon dioxide gas and water.

photosystem—a membrane-bound collection of chlorophylls and accessory pigments that harvest light energy and make it available to the light-dependent pathway of photosynthesis.

pigment molecules—organic compounds that absorb and reflect wavelengths of light selectively such that they appear to the human eye to have a particular color.

product—a substance that is formed during a chemical reaction.

pyruvate—a three-carbon carbohydrate product of glycolysis whose continued degradation generates two-carbon fragments that serve as reactants in the Krebs cycle.

quinone—a class of yellow compounds found in thylakoid membranes; they accept electrons from chlorophyll molecules.

reactant—an initial substance that absorbs energy and enters into a chemical reaction in which it is changed in structure.

ribulose 1,5-bisphosphate—a twice-phosphorylated five-carbon sugar that combines with carbon dioxide in the light-independent reaction of photosynthesis to form two 3-carbon sugars.

starch—a polymer of glucose molecules; used as a storage form of energy in plant tissues.

stomata—regulated openings on the undersurfaces of leaves that control the influx of carbon dioxide and efflux of water from internal leaf tissues.

stroma—a syrupy fluid within chloroplasts that surrounds the stacks of thylakoids; the enzymes of the light-independent reaction are found in the stroma.

sucrose—a disaccharide sugar composed of the monomers glucose and fructose; the sugar used for transporting energy throughout the tissues of a plant.

thylakoid—a membrane-enclosed sac within a chloroplast inside of which are the enzymes, pigments, and electron transfer compounds of the light-dependent reactions of photosynthesis.

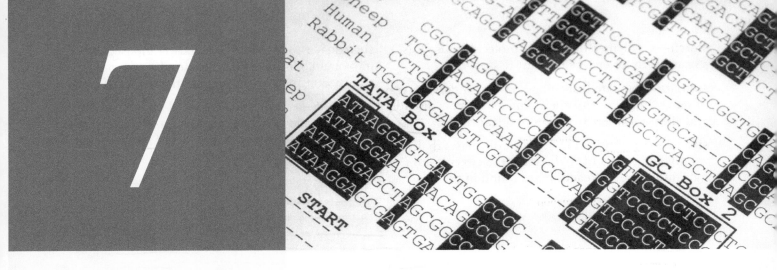

7

Information and Its Expression in the Cell

Survey Questions

7.1 The Need for Biological Information
- How much structure is there to a cell?
- What is information needed for within a cell?

7.2 The Nature of Biological Information
- What is biological information made of physically?
- How was the physical substance of information discovered?
- What is the physical structure of biological information?
- How is biological information stored within a cell?

7.3 The Expression of Biological Information
- What physical form does the expression of biological information take?
- Where does information expression start, and where does it end?
- What component processes are involved in information expression?
- What structures and molecules participate in transcription?
- What are the products of transcription and their roles in the cell?

nanometer—a distance of 1/1000 of a micrometer. Cells are measured in micrometers. Molecules are measured in nanometers.

algal—of or referring to algae, a diverse, relatively simple, autotroph form of life typically found in fresh water or marine habitat; they lack distinct organs.

7.1 THE NEED FOR BIOLOGICAL INFORMATION

Let's revisit Ely Cathedral in Cambridgeshire, England. In Chapter 6 we observed its grandeur and perhaps choked a bit considering the amount of energy required to build it. Today we walk the nave eastward to the great octagon and look straight up. Directly above us—142 feet up—is a massive 400-ton work of wood, lead, glass and glory called *the lantern*. A photograph of it appears on the next page. Sunlight descending through this artistry reveals symmetry in size, shape, and color, all carefully set into the beautiful fan-vaulting of a graceful octagonal ceiling. We are again seeing enormous energy expenditure over decades of years and lives. But a second realization intrudes. We are not seeing the random energy of violent explosion. Rather, the lantern is energy harnessed into myriads of measured activities. We are seeing the results of *information expressed*. Many hours were spent drawing, designing, and scaling the lantern before construction began. And in construction, information guided the use of tools, the procurement and fashioning of materials, and the movement of component parts into place. The lantern is a triumph of energy-driven information expression.

As is the cell. Imagine climbing into the ocular lens of a microscope focused on the glorious *Micrasterias* cell also in the illustration on the next page. Were we to become the size of a plant protein—perhaps 70 **nanometers** in height—we could wander up to the surface of this single-celled **algal** "cathedral" and be amazed at symmetrical

- How does the arrangement of the information support its efficient expression?
- What structures and molecules participate in translation?
- What are the products of translation, and does translation complete the process of information expression?
- How is biological information encoded in archival molecules?

7.4 The Application of Information Expression

- Why has society desired to control information expression in biological systems?
- What are some problems society has solved by engineering and expressing genes?
- What steps are involved in engineering and artificially expressing genes?
- How do scientists get genes from one organism into another?
- What risks are involved in these activities?
- What technologies had to be developed in order to do gene therapy?
- What has the recent history of gene therapy taught us about its prospects?

7.5 A Hidden Drama: Information Expression at Its Very Best

- What is the most dramatic display of information expression around us in nature?

Life Is Information Expressed—one of 12 principles of life on which this book is based.

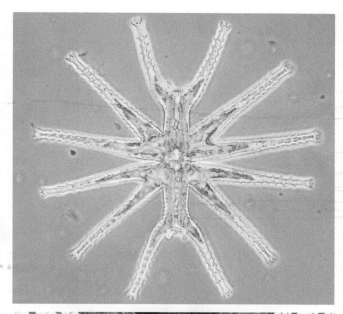

Circular symmetry pleases the eye. But the architectural masterpiece above is afterthought. It replaces a ceiling once collapsed. In the cellular masterpiece above, symmetry is intricately related to all major elements of cellular function.

patterns in the sculpting and ornamentation of its walls. Instead of saints, these walls are festooned with highly strategic combinations of membrane-bound proteins that regulate the internal biochemical milieu of the cell (see Figure 7.1). Wandering inside we would note the elaborate shaping of its two large chloroplasts, the distribution of its starch-containing bodies, and the precise centrality of its nucleus. *Micrasterias,* and a thousand million other types of cells in our biosphere, are a triumph of (energy-driven) information expression. **Life Is Information Expressed.**

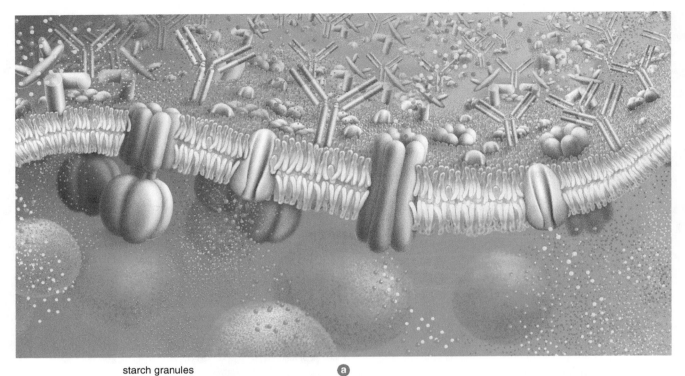

starch granules
chloroplast   cell wall

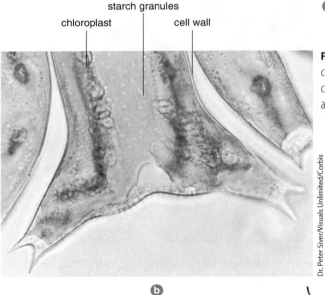

Dr. Peter Siver/Visuals Unlimited/Corbis

(b)

Figure 7.1 Information Expressed. **(a)** Externally, a wide variety of precisely crafted proteins float two-dimensionally in this phospholipid bilayer "sea" controlling which substances will enter and exit the cell. **(b)** Internally, organelles are optimally shaped to carry out their roles within the cell.

In terms of sheer brilliance, however, *Microsterias* has the cathedral lantern entirely trumped. The lantern required the design and efforts of hundreds of human minds. And it happened once. *Microsterias,* by contrast, builds itself! And it does so again and again, every day, in countless ponds and bogs the world over! But cells are not only the expression of information cobbled together somewhere in the past. They actually store the information they express within their own structure! They access this information and express it themselves according to a construction schedule that is *also* stored within their structure! (Excuse all our exclamation marks!)

Now, there are some nonliving things that can do this. Computers store and express internal information and can do so on schedule (see Figure 7.2). Computers and cells excel at this because they are designed things. But cells are uniquely facile here because the information they select and express is useful not only for themselves but for the organisms and biosphere they are a part of! We are bringing small minds to a very big picture here. . . . Where shall we begin?

In this chapter we'll look first at the physical nature of the information itself. We will then consider how it is stored and how it is expressed. Finally, we will consider how we can manipulate this process using recombinant DNA technology. The cell's ability to both possess and express information at the molecular level is amazing. It's like having both a huge library (possession) and a gifted scholar (expression) all in one micrometer-sized package.

System	Form of Information	Storage	Expression	Product
Architecture	Numbers, lines	Blueprints	→ Construction	→ Cathedral
Algal cell	DNA bases	Chromosomes	→ Transcription, translation	→ 2 algal cells
Computer	Bytes	Hard drive	→ Processing	→ Report, image
University	Words	Books	→ Research	→ Book, report

Figure 7.2 Examples of Information Expression. Why does cellular activity fit so neatly into a chart of otherwise human activities?

IN OTHER WORDS

1. Cathedrals and cells both require information for their construction.
2. Information is expressed in cellular structure on the exterior of and within the cell.
3. In cells, this information is stored and expressed from within the cell itself.
4. Information expression in the cell is carefully sequenced and timed.

Biological Information Is Stored in the Base Sequence of DNA

What is biological information? If it's stored inside the cell itself, it must have some physical basis in reality. What substance, what biomolecule is it associated with? Back in 1869, a Swiss physician-biochemist named Friedrich Miescher was collecting samples of human white blood cells (leucocytes) taken from the pus of discarded bandages from a hospital near Tübingen, Germany (see Figure 7.3). Using a variety of salts and precipitation techniques he was able to isolate a chemically novel sort of biomolecule containing **phosphorus**

and nitrogen but not **sulfur** (as is found in protein fractions). Since his new **fraction** was derived from the nuclei of the cells, he called it *nuclein*. He and his students continued their study of this fascinating substance until his death from tuberculosis at the age of 51. As is typical in scientific study, they had no idea at the time that the major component of nuclein would later be named deoxyribonucleic acid (DNA) and would in time be found to be the informational molecule of life.

If bandage refuse was an odd sort of raw material for discovering the secret of life, understanding DNA's importance began within the highly specialized world of bacterial pathology. Fred Griffith, a British microbiologist working in the Ministry of Health, made a seminal discovery (see Figure 7.4). His experimental system was two strains of bacteria of the genus *Diplococcus*. One strain (rough) was not **virulent**. Injecting it into a mouse simply stimulated the mouse's immune system to destroy it. A smooth (encapsulated and highly virulent) strain of the same bacterium, upon injection, quickly killed his mice. Griffith discovered that he could **transform** his nonvirulent rough strains to virulence by killing his virulent strain with heat and then incubating his nonvirulent cells with the remains of the heat-killed virulent strain. These transformed bacteria now gave rise to virulent bacteria. Whatever they had absorbed from the remains of the dead virulent cells was now hereditary! You could kill

Friederick Miescher
1844 – 1895
Physician-biochemist
discoverer of DNA

Science Photo Library

Figure 7.3   Friederick Miescher. While studying at the University of Tübingen, Germany he isolated a crude fraction from the nuclei of pus cells that he named nuclein. It was later shown to be DNA.

phosphorus—an element in nature widely distributed in nucleic acids but seldom found in newly synthesized proteins.

sulfur—an element in nature widely distributed in proteins (because of its presence in the amino acids cystine and cysteine) but never found in nucleic acids like DNA or RNA.

fraction—a single portion of a biological sample that is being separated into many such portions as part of a purification process.

virulent—possessing a highly increased ability to cause disease.

transform—to change a hereditary characteristic of an organism by introducing new DNA into its genome.

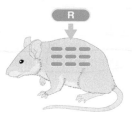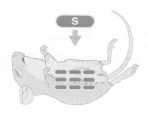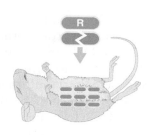

(a) Mice injected with live cells of harmless strain *R* do not die. Live *R* cells are in their blood.

(b) Mice injected with live cells of killer strain *S* die. Live *S* cells are in their blood.

(c) Mice injected with heat-killed *S* cells do not die. No live *S* cells are in their blood.

(d) Mice injected with live *R* cells plus heat-killed *S* cells die. Live *S* cells are in their blood.

Figure 7.4 Transformation in Mice. **(a)** A non-virulent strain of the diplococcus bacterium injected into mice grows briefly but is soon eliminated by the mouse's immune system. **(b)** Very small numbers of the virulent strains of the bacterium when injected, multiply rapidly and kill the mouse. **(c)** Heat-killing the virulent strain renders it non-virulent; when injected, the mouse survives. **(d)** If a mixture of heat-killed virulent cells and living non-virulent cells is injected into a mouse, the mouse dies, it's blood filled with virulent bacteria.

these virulent offspring and use *them* to transform still other nonvirulent bacteria of the same genus to virulence.

What was it that the nonvirulent strains were absorbing from the denatured remains of virulent cells? Oswald Avery at the Rockefeller Institute

gene—a segment of (usually) DNA that controls a single characteristic or trait of an organism.

DNase—an enzyme that catalyzes the breakdown of DNA either into smaller segments of DNA or completely down to its nucleotide subunits.

in New York was determined to find out. By the 1940s, a variety of degradative (digestive) enzymes were available in purified forms. One enzyme would degrade proteins. A different enzyme would degrade DNA. Still another degraded RNA. These enzymatic reactions, as you may recall, are highly specific for the class of molecules they degrade. Most biologists of the time believed that the hereditary material—the **genes**—would prove to be proteins, the biomolecules that were already known to have considerable complexity. To everyone's surprise, the highly purified "transforming factor" taken from virulent cells lost its transforming ability when incubated with the enzyme pancreatic **DNase** (see Figure 7.5)! The transforming factor

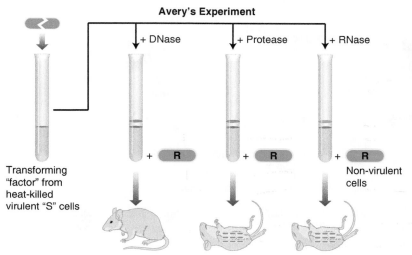

Avery's Experiment

Transforming "factor" from heat-killed virulent "S" cells

+ DNase

+ Protease

+ RNase

+ R

+ R

+ R

Non-virulent cells

Figure 7.5 DNA—the Transforming Principle. The transforming principle detected in part d) of Figure 7.4, could be destroyed by incubating it with the degradative enzyme Dnase before injecting it into a mouse. Protease or Rnase incubation leaves the transforming factor intact, killing the mice.

survived incubation with **proteinase** and **RNase** enzymes. The transforming factor had to be— DNA! DNA from the heat-killed virulent cells had got into the nonvirulent cells and supplemented their hereditary information—their genes—with genes for virulence! By the early 1950s, Dr. Avery at the Rockefeller Institute and Dr. Alfred Hershey, with his viral inheritance studies at Cold Spring Harbor Laboratories (see Figure 7.6), were convincing the scientific community that the nucleic acid DNA was indeed the hereditary material. It was an exciting time to be studying biology—and the power of being able to now focus attention on the nature and behavior of this one molecule has sustained that excitement in biology right up to the present day!

Biologists' thinking is not bound by their data. They like to speculate beyond it like anyone else. Some scientists were anticipating that DNA might

proteinase—an enzyme that catalyzes the breakdown of protein either into smaller segments of peptides or completely down to its amino acid subunits.

RNase—an enzyme that catalyzes the breakdown of RNA either into smaller segments of RNA or completely down to its nucleotide subunits.

The Hershey and Chase Experiment Demonstrating That DNA Is the Hereditary Molecule

Question: Is DNA or protein the genetic material?

Experiment: Hershey and Chase performed a definitive experiment to show whether DNA or protein is the genetic material. They used the phage T2 virus for their experiment; it consists only of DNA and protein.

1. Infect bacterial cells with viruses in the presence of nutrients containing either radioactive phosphorus or radioactive sulfur. Phosphorus goes only into DNA. Sulfur goes only into protein.

2. Harvest radioactive viruses and reinfect new cells with them.

3. Once infection is begun, knock virus particles from cell surface using a blender. Note where radioactiviy is found.

4. Search in offspring viruses for radioactivity.

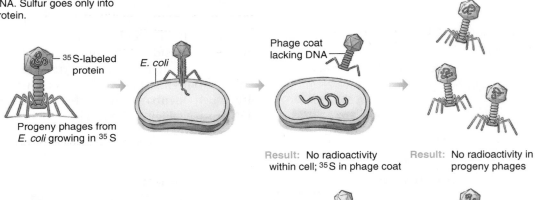

Progeny phages from E. coli growing in ^{35}S

^{35}S-labeled protein

E. coli

Phage coat lacking DNA

Result: No radioactivity within cell; ^{35}S in phage coat

Result: No radioactivity in progeny phages

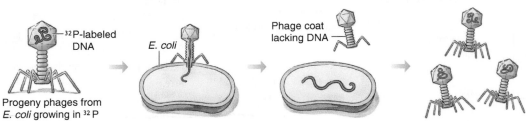

Progeny phages from E. coli growing in ^{32}P

^{32}P-labeled DNA

E. coli

Phage coat lacking DNA

Result: ^{32}P within cell; not in phage coat

Result: ^{32}P in progeny phages

Conclusion: DNA is the molecule that enters the bacterial cell and directs formation of new virus particles.

Figure 7.6 Hershey-Chase Experiment. Is life's informational molecule protein or is it DNA? Information is needed in order for a bacterial cell to construct new viruses from the virus that first infects it. But the T2 bacterial virus consists of only protein and DNA. And it is possible to radioactively label either DNA or protein and then follow the radioactivity during the viral infection.

Ratios of Base Composition in DNA	Values
[Adenine] / [Guanine]	Varies from species to species
[Adenine] / [Thymine]	1.0
[Cytosine] / [Adenine]	Varies from species to species
[Cytosine] / [Guanine]	1.0
[Thymine] / [Guanine]	Varies from species to species
[Cytosine] / [Thymine]	Varies from species to species

Brackets around the name of the base indicate the concentration or amount of base per weight of DNA

Figure 7.7 Chargaff's Data Summarized.

turn out to be the informational molecule and had worked to isolate it from cells, purify it and study its properties. At Columbia University in the late 1940's Erwin Chargaff used chromatography techniques (see Section 3.1) to separate the different kinds of nucleotides out of degraded segments of DNA molecules. He was able to show that the four component nucleotides of DNA (adenine, guanine, cytosine, and thymine) were all present but not in equal amounts. The amounts varied from species to species (which would have made sense if DNA were informational). But oddly enough, the amount of the base adenine in any sample *was* also equal to the amount of thymine, and the amount of cytosine was always equal to the amount of guanine (see Figure 7.7). What could that mean for the structure of DNA?

Scientists had assumed that if DNA were informational in nature, it would have to be some sort of long polymer, and several of them, for example, Francis Crick and James Watson at the Cavendish Labs in Cambridge University, were building speculative models of possible structures. Helical structures were being found in protein molecules. Could DNA be helical? Hard data were needed to help constrain the variations in their models. This was to be supplied by still other workers who had begun to study the structure of DNA using a technique called **X-ray crystallography.** This process involves firing powerful X-rays at highly purified samples of a protein or nucleic acid and seeing the pattern of rays that get through the structure of the molecule in order to strike photographic film (see Figure 7.8). Some of the best X-ray data were obtained by Rosalind Franklin working at King's College in London. The patterns on the film suggested to her that DNA polymers were in fact helical in nature and that DNA might be double-stranded. She even derived estimates of dimensions for the width of the helix and distance between nucleotides. Dr. Franklin was quite devoted to her work and understandably secretive in regard to her own carefully derived data. On a visit to the crystallography labs in London, Watson was secretly shown her latest data in her absence. It included the famous photograph seen in Figure 7.8. Because he'd spent

X-ray crystallography—a physical technique in which a purified sample of protein or nucleic acid is exposed to high-powered electromagnetic radiation to determine its molecular structure.

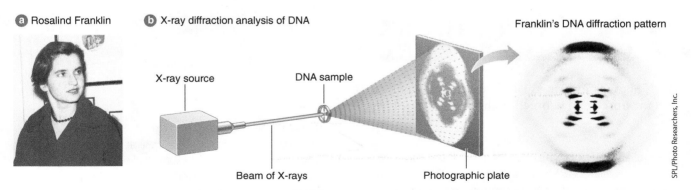

(a) Rosalind Franklin   **(b)** X-ray diffraction analysis of DNA   Franklin's DNA diffraction pattern

X-ray source   DNA sample

Beam of X-rays   Photographic plate

SPL/Photo Researchers, Inc.

Figure 7.8 X-Ray Diffraction Studies on DNA Fibers. **(a)** Rosalind Franklin **(b)** X-rays are focused on fibers of highly purified DNA. The DNA molecule diffracts the rays in a pattern based on DNA's structure. The X-rays diffracted by the DNA generate patterns on photographic film as seen to the right.

time building models with Crick, Watson quickly saw that Rosalind had the answer to his questions. Within weeks Watson and Crick submitted their now-famous paper to the journal *Nature* outlining the now generally accepted model for the structure of DNA. A very hard-working lady had supplied the critical data, and two highly intelligent model-builders were given most of the credit for the discovery. Sometimes science works like that.

DNA is a double helix consisting of two intertwined polymers of nucleotides (see Figure 7.9) that is incredibly long. The DNA in just one of your cells would approximate 2 meters—the size of a coffee table—in length! (We had better discuss below how it's folded, had we not!) Within each chain of nucleotides, sugars and phosphates alternate in supporting the strand structurally. One strand is structurally upside down compared with the orientation of the other. The nitrogen-containing bases point inwardly. The two chains are held together by multiple weak hydrogen bonds between these long sequences of bases. The pairing of the bases between the two strands is quite specific. On the first strand, wherever an adenine is present, a thymine will be opposite it on the other strand. Cytosine is always found opposite guanine. These pairing rules, A with T and G with C, form the basis for Chargaff's observations about equality of amount between the bases adenine and thymine on the one hand and between cytosine and guanine on the other. But more than that, these pairing rules mean that the base sequence in one strand determines the sequence of bases in the other strand. The one sequence will always be **complementary** to the other. Consider the diagram that follows. If the sequence along one helix is TGAGGACTCCTCTT, then, by the base-pairing rule, the sequence on the opposite strand must be ACTCCTGAGGAGAA.

one base pair	T	G	A	G	G	A	C		C	C	T	C	T	T
	A	C	T	C	C	T	G	A	G	G	A	G	A	A

This was exciting. The hypothetical genes that plant and animal breeders had studied for years

complementary—in nucleic acids, describes the appropriately sized nucleotide bases from opposite strands of a double-stranded DNA (adenine with thymine, guanine with cytosine) that pair via hydrogen bonds, thereby holding the double-stranded nucleic acid together.

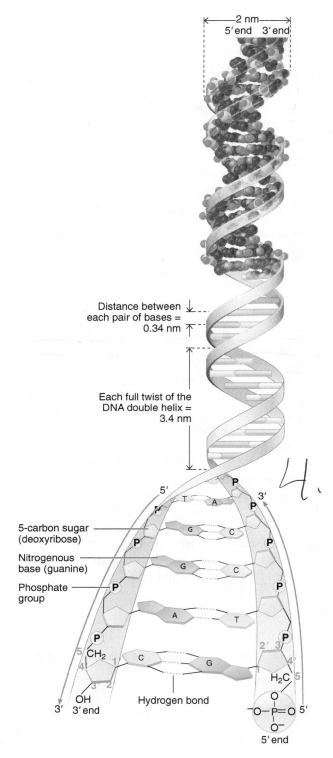

Figure 7.9 The Structure of DNA. A single monomer of DNA—a nucleotide—consists of a single 5-carbon sugar, an attached phosphate, and a nitrogenous base (pointing inward). Nucleotide sugars and phosphates linked together form the backbone of each of the two chains. Notice carefully the way the sugars and phosphates are drawn—the one chain is upside-down or "antiparallel" to the other. At the top of the diagram, individual atoms are represented by space-filling spheres.

now had an actual physical basis in reality. A gene is really a sequence of bases along one strand of a DNA molecule. It was something that in principle could eventually be isolated, studied, and even manipulated (see Section 6.5)! Yes, there were only four different kinds of bases, but the sequences of them could be thousands of bases in length. How many different words could you write given just two vowels, two consonants, and the freedom to use them in sequences up to 3000 letters in length?

And because there are two strands instead of one, Watson and Crick were able to predict how this molecule could be replicated to make identical copies of information for daughter cells. If the two strands are unwound, and new strands built against each parent strand (using the base pairing rule), then the two daughter copies of the double helix would be identical to each other and to the parent double helix (see Figure 7.10). How elegant is that! We'll say more about this replication process in Chapter 8.

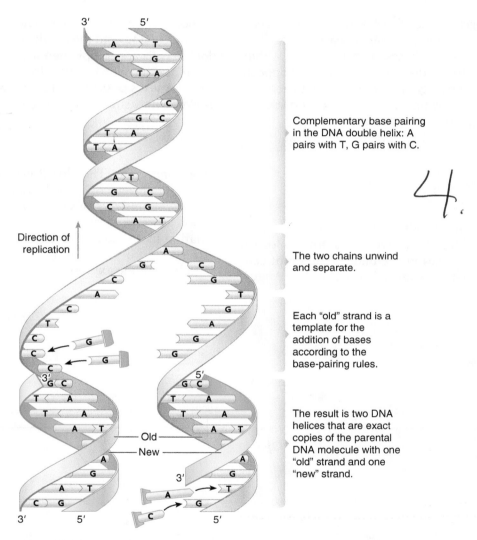

Complementary base pairing in the DNA double helix: A pairs with T, G pairs with C.

The two chains unwind and separate.

Each "old" strand is a template for the addition of bases according to the base-pairing rules.

The result is two DNA helices that are exact copies of the parental DNA molecule with one "old" strand and one "new" strand.

Direction of replication

Old
New

Figure 7.10 DNA Replication. The double helix modelled by Watson and Crick is shown in gray. If the helices are unwound, and new nucleotides (in red) are built into new strands following the base pairing rule, two DNA double helices will be generated, each of which has the same precise base sequence at the "parental" gray strands.

1. In the late 1860s, Friederich Miescher discovered DNA in leucocyte nuclei from bandages and named it *nuclein*.
2. Fred Griffith began to isolate DNA based on its ability to permanently transform nonpathogenic cells to pathogenic ones in mice.
3. Oswald Avery began to identify Griffith's transforming substance as DNA by discovering which classes of enzymes would degrade and deactivate it.
4. Erwin Chargaff contributed to our understanding of DNA's structure by studying the relative amounts of each nitrogenous base that were present in his DNA samples.
5. Watson and Crick contributed to our understanding of DNA's structure by building models of what DNA might look like based on information available to them.
6. Rosalind Franklin used X-ray crystallography to infer the secondary structure of DNA: a double helical molecule.
7. Each helical strand of a DNA molecule consists of a "backbone" of sugars and phosphates of adjacent nucleotide subunits, with the base of each nucleotide subunit projecting toward the interior of the double helix.
8. The nitrogenous bases at each position within the double helix are complementary to each other in size and structure. Adenine is always found opposite thymine, and guanine is always found opposite cytosine.
9. Complementarity of base pairing between the two strands makes possible replication of the DNA double helix by simply unwinding the existing strands and building new strands against each original one using the complementarity rule.

Biological Information Is Stored in Chromosomes

The mid to late 1800s in the German universities were highly productive years for biological theory and advances in the understanding of cells in particular. The biologists Ernst Haeckel, August Weismann, and Theodor Boveri were discovering that the nucleus of the cell was the location of its hereditary instructions (see Figure 7.11). This made good sense, structurally. By sequestering the information in an internal nucleus, it is kept unharmed from many other separate chemical processes that result from the expression of it.

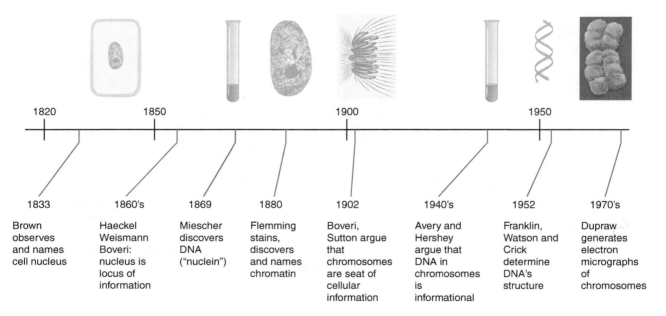

1833	1860's	1869	1880	1902	1940's	1952	1970's
Brown observes and names cell nucleus	Haeckel Weismann Boveri: nucleus is locus of information	Miescher discovers DNA ("nuclein")	Flemming stains, discovers and names chromatin	Boveri, Sutton argue that chromosomes are seat of cellular information	Avery and Hershey argue that DNA in chromosomes is informational	Franklin, Watson and Crick determine DNA's structure	Dupraw generates electron micrographs of chromosomes

Figure 7.11 Human Understanding of Information Storage

Figure 7.12 Coiling DNA into a Chromosome. In order to prepare DNA for distribution to a daughter cell, the DNA double helix is wound first around a collection of protein core particles (shown in green here) called nucleosomes. These "beads on a string" are further coiled to form a unit chromatin fiber, which is super-coiled still further to form the visible strands in the arm of a chromosome as seen under the electron microscope. Other structural proteins are used to maintain the integrity of these higher order fibers.

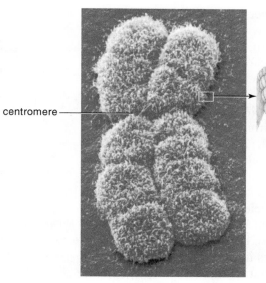

centromere

multiple levels of coiling of DNA and proteins

fiber

beads on a string

DNA double helix

core of protein

nucleosome

Staining cells improved their visibility under a microscope and revealed newly observable structures. Walther Flemming, another German biologist, first observed very thin darkly staining material within nondividing cell nuclei that he termed **chromatin**. As the nucleus progressed toward cell division, it would lose its membrane boundary, and its chromatin appeared to condense into much smaller darkly staining bodies called simply **chromosomes** (Gk. *chromos* = color; Gk. *soma* = body; see Figure 7.12). It soon became apparent that the cells of each species of organism studied had its own characteristic number and size of chromosomes. Working with sea urchin embryos, Theodor Boveri was able to show that a complete set of these chromosomes must be present in each embryo in order to support the normal development of the organism. In 1902, together with Walter Sutton in the United States, he advanced the theory that the chromosomes carry the information of the nucleus into daughter cells (see Figure 7.11). This process will be examined more closely in Chapter 8.

Meantime, as noted above, Miescher had isolated his nuclein from the nuclei of leucocytes. Workers such as Flemming at the University of Kiel,

chromatin—fibers within the cell nucleus consisting of DNA periodically stabilized by being wrapped around protein spheres called *nucleosomes*.

chromosome—a highly coiled and organized arrangement of a single DNA molecule within the nucleus of a cell; used to transport DNA to a daughter nucleus.

Edmund B. Wilson at Columbia University, and others, began to suggest that this nuclein was associated with the chromatin strands Flemming had first seen and named. Working in the later decades of the twentieth century, scientists eventually determined that in the cells of higher organisms, a chromosome is a single long, although compacted, DNA double helix, intricately arranged around and within several levels of protein scaffolding (see Figure 7.12).

The first level of folding involves stabilizing the structure and orientation of the DNA double helix by wrapping it around perfectly sized spherical conglomerations of proteins called **nucleosomes**. Electron microscope pictures of DNA coiled around these protein stabilizers look like beads on a string. This is the form that DNA takes in the relatively diffuse and decondensed chromatin found in the cell's nucleus during cell growth. When it is time to distribute copies of DNA to daughter cells, the nucleosomes are then precisely packaged into a higher-order fiber, which is then coiled to make a still higher-order string that becomes the visible fiber of which a chromosome is composed. One of your cells has 46 of these chromosomes.

In prokaryotic (bacterial) cells, chromosomal organization has both differences and similarities to that of higher cells like our own. As discussed previously, bacterial cells have no membrane-bound nucleus. Their DNA aggregates near the center of the cell in a region called the *nucleoid*. For many bacteria, the nucleoid contains a single long chromosome that takes the form of a closed circle rather than a linear structure as in eukaryotic chromosomes. These circular chromosomes lack the nucleosome structure that forms the most basic level of chromosome compaction (coiling) in eukaryotes. But bacterial chromosomes do possess the higher-order coiling of DNA seen in eukaryotic chromosomes so that, again, lots of information can be packaged into minimal space (see Figure 7.13). The humble

Bacterial Information Storage

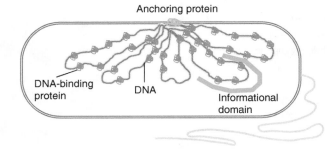

Figure 7.13 Coiling DNA in a Bacterial Cell. In order to compact long sequences of DNA into small spaces, the double helix is coiled up and stabilized in that state by DNA-binding proteins. The entire nucleoid region is stabilized by proteins that anchor the cell's genome to the membrane of the cell. DNA-binding protein location is not random within the genome but respects regions of information called domains that are expressed at given times for different purposes.

gut bacterium *E. coli* is cylindrical and is typically about 0.65 **microns** wide and 1.7 microns long. Yet its one circular DNA chromosome measures about 1300 microns in length. So if we were to squash that circular chromosome flat, its length would be several hundred times the length of the cell it's in! The fact that this chromosome can be easily unraveled for access to information or tightly coiled again for distribution purposes is a powerful testimony to two things: (1) the DNA of the chromosome is extraordinarily thin (only 0.0025 microns thick), and (2) the aggregation and coiling of the bacterial DNA within the nucleoid must follow a brilliant organizational scheme—though we've yet to unravel that scheme.

nucleosome—a structural repeat unit within chromatin in which 147 base pairs of DNA are wrapped around a spherical protein core for purposes of stability and protection.

micron (or micrometer)—is 1/1000 of a millimeter; the millimeter is the smallest division visible on a metric ruler.

IN OTHER WORDS

1. German scientists in the late 1800s discovered the nucleus, and in particular, chromatin, to be the locus of the hereditary instructions in a cell.
2. Theodor Boveri determined that a complete set of chromosomes was necessary for a sea urchin embryo to develop normally.
3. In eukaryotic chromosomes, DNA is highly coiled in at least two separate levels of complexity and stabilized in these super-coils by nucleosomes and other DNA-binding proteins.
4. Prokaryotic (bacterial) cells also have super-coiled DNA, and proteins are used to stabilize these higher-order fibers.

7.3 THE EXPRESSION OF BIOLOGICAL INFORMATION

A Context for Understanding Gene Expression

Suppose you live near Philadelphia, Pennsylvania, and need to travel to your sister's home just south of Atlanta, Georgia. What is the fastest route from your home to hers? You drive to the store (by the fastest route) and purchase a global positioning system—a GPS device. Entering two home addresses into its program soon gives you the precise route you need. The next morning the trip begins. The expression of biological information is similar to this process. Just as the GPS stores all the information you could need for any trip, the chromosomes store all the information a cell could need to become any sort of cell in the body. That collection of information—DNA base sequences, or genes—is called the cell's **genotype** (see Figure 7.14). In the production of an organism, cells divide many times. Each daughter cell needs to get from its initial undifferentiated state to a highly differentiated,

ordered state that we can call a bone cell or brain cell or blood cell. This developmental sequence of the expression of particular genes is like the sequence of roads the GPS directs you to drive on to get you to Atlanta. The result of following the GPS is a successful trip to Atlanta. The result of expressing a specific set of genes in a defined sequence is what we call a **phenotype**—the characteristics that make up the bone cell or brain cell.

But what is the phenotype actually composed of? Yes, a blood cell appears red; a muscle cell appears spindle-shaped. What controls these features? Over half of the biomass of the cell is protein. And the nonprotein parts of the cell—like vast amounts of phospholipids that comprise membranes—are built by enzymatically controlled reactions. And enzymes are proteins. So to control the proteins of a cell is to control the cell! And that is what the genotype of the cell does. It controls the phenotype by retaining the information for all of the proteins the cell employs. Proteins are built from sequences of amino acids. So somehow, according to a code we will examine later, the sequence of bases in the DNA—the genotype—controls or specifies the sequence of amino acids in the cell's proteins: its phenotype.

Consider red blood cells. The red color results from the reflection of light off of molecules of the protein **hemoglobin**. In the nucleus of the maturing red blood cell, there are two genes that code for the sequences of the two different kinds of polypeptide subunits in the hemoglobin protein of adults. The cell's machinery "reads" the DNA base sequence of each gene and sends messages

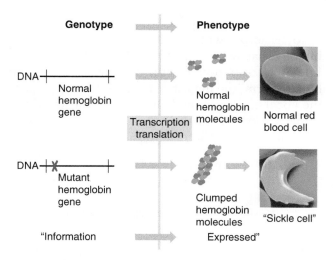

Figure 7.14 Information Expression. The genes that code for the oxygen-transporting protein hemoglobin represent it's genotype. The expression of the genes within a red blood cell—the hemoglobin molecule—is it's phenotype. Mistakes in the base sequence of the DNA-based genotype lead to alterations in the phenotype, such as the clumping of hemoglobin molecules within the cell. The red cell in the lower panel is from an individual with the disease sickle cell anemia.

genotype—the genetic makeup of—the informational specifications for—an organism.

phenotype—the physical appearance of an organism resulting from the expression of the organism's genotype.

hemoglobin—a protein with a quaternary level of structure consisting of four polypeptide chains, 2 α chains, and 2 β chains. It transports oxygen from the lungs to the tissues.

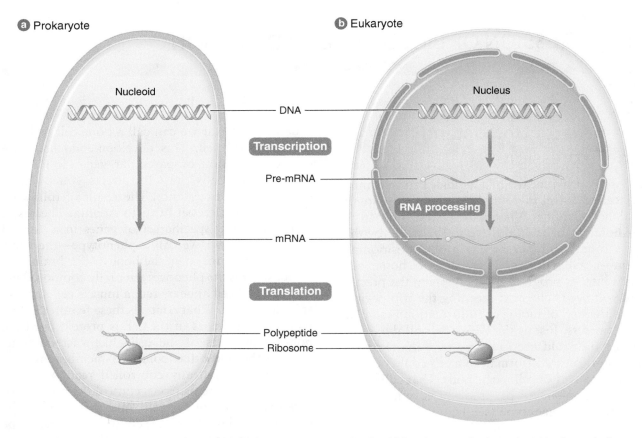

a Prokaryote

b Eukaryote

Nucleoid

Nucleus

DNA

Transcription

Pre-mRNA

RNA processing

mRNA

Translation

Polypeptide

Ribosome

Figure 7.15 The Central Dogma. The flow of information in **(a)** a prokaryotic (bacterial) cell and **(b)** a eukaryotic cell is depicted. mRNA in bacterial cells as transcribed is immediately ready for translation into protein. In higher cells, the mRNA undergoes modification before it is translated. The term "polypeptide" refers to a single chain of amino acids or a simple protein.

containing that sequence to the cytoplasm, where the base sequence in the message is used to generate a sequence of amino acids that folds up into a hemoglobin subunit (see Figure 7.15). As the subunits assemble and then aggregate into mature hemoglobin molecules, the cell begins to take on its characteristic red phenotype. Gene expression is essentially the same for all other protein-coding genes. Information is read from the archival DNA molecule in the chromosome. It is built into a transportable molecule—also made up of base sequences—called *messenger RNA*, or **mRNA**, or simply *message*. This reading/building process is termed **transcription**. The mRNA is then transported to cytoplasmic ribosomes, where its base sequence is decoded into a sequence of amino acids by a process termed **translation**. The sequence of amino acids, covalently linked together, becomes a protein that contributes to the phenotype of the cell. This flow of information from genes to proteins is termed *the central dogma*; it

is so basic, so widespread, and so important to biology that we've summarized it in the principle, Life Is Information Expressed. The glory of the human form, the majesty of the eagle's wing span, the vocal cords of a male lion, the intricacy of the spider's web are all the result of that exquisitely controlled flow of information.

mRNA—a class of RNA molecules that code for proteins and serve to direct the process of translation on ribosomes in the cell cytoplasm.

transcription—the process of reading a sequence of bases in DNA and generating from it a complementary sequence of bases in RNA.

translation—the process of reading a sequence of bases in RNA and generating from it an encoded sequence of amino acids that comprise a polypeptide chain or protein.

Information flow poses two serious challenges to biological systems. The first is the problem of *selectivity*. If we were to use all of the cell's information at the same time in the same place, we'd end up with a blood-nerve-muscle-bone-brain-gland-everything cell! We must have a way to use information selectively and sequentially. The second problem we face is the *limitation of space* for processing the information. Protein synthesis—information expression—takes many monomers, much energy, and a lot of space. We can't jam all those materials and ribosomes into the cell's nucleus. So those are our two major problems. In the next two sections of the chapter we'll start to solve them.

IN OTHER WORDS

1. A cell's genotype is the information it possesses for building and maintaining its structures. It is a linear sequences of bases in DNA.
2. A cell's phenotype is the quality and features of those structures. It is the genotype expressed in three dimensions.
3. Most of a cell's phenotype is proteins or structures created by proteins.
4. The DNA base sequence is transcribed into mRNA base sequence. The mRNA base sequence is then translated into an amino acid sequence, which is a protein.
5. Information expression in the cell faces two essential problems: expressing information selectively and finding space to express it.

Transcription: Using Some Genes Now and Some Not At All

The term *transcription* was carefully chosen by biologists to indicate that the first stage of information expression is, from beginning to end, entirely in the "language" of nucleotide bases, whether in DNA or mRNA (see Figure 7.16). But beyond this basic structural similarity, the functional difference between archival DNA and RNA messages is profound. Transcription is a wonderfully conceived process that starts with the entire archival information set of the cell and ends with selected gene-sized segments of information that are needed within the cell at the precise moment in time at which they are made. How is this selectivity achieved?

First, we need an enzyme that can work its way into the DNA double helix to begin reading the sequence of bases along one of the strands. It must make an RNA molecule whose base sequence is complementary to that in the DNA. We call this enzyme **RNA polymerase**. Then, we need regions of base sequence within the DNA that can "inform" RNA polymerase precisely where to start reading (see Figure 7.17). These sequences are termed **promoter** sequences. We also need an efficient way of informing RNA polymerase when it has finished copying the needed information from a given site so that it can terminate its copying work precisely. Together, promoter sequences and termination sequences or processes help direct and limit RNA polymerase activity to gene-sized RNA

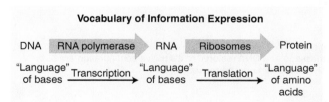

Vocabulary of Information Expression

Figure 7.16 Vocabulary of Information Expression. The use of the terms transcription and translation in biology is formally analogous to their use in human language. To transcribe is to rewrite in the same language. To translate is to render the meaning of words from one language into a second language. To translate in biology is to convert biological information from a sequence of bases to a sequence of amino acids.

RNA polymerase—a protein; an enzyme that builds RNA molecules using free ribonucleotides and using a strand of DNA as a sequence template (guide) against which to build.

promoter—a sequence of bases in DNA that guides an RNA polymerase to the precise position where initiation of transcription is to occur.

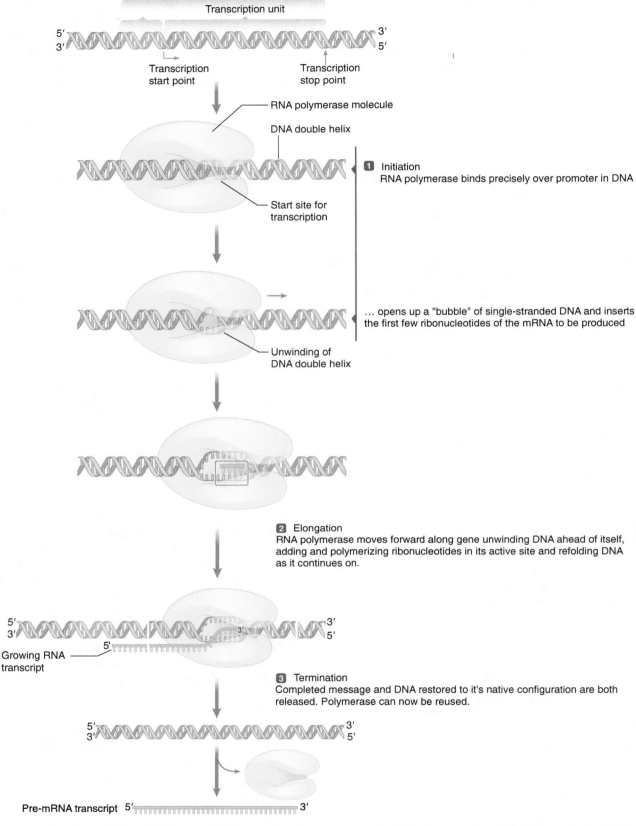

Figure 7.17 Transcription of DNA into RNA. One strand of DNA—the "sense" strand—is transcribed. (The other strand is useful only during replication of DNA.) The process has three stages—initiation, elongation and termination—as shown.

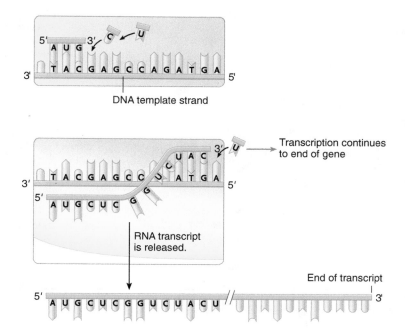

Figure 7.18 DNA and RNA Complementarity. Ribonucleotides are added according to the same base pairing rules respected by DNA except that the base uracil is substituted in RNA for thymine in DNA.

molecules. Finally, we need a collection of regulatory molecules—mostly proteins—that inform RNA polymerase concerning which promoters to transcribe at and which ones to ignore. Sometimes these regulatory molecules are protein subunits that bind directly to the RNA polymerase. In other cases, they bind specifically to regions of the DNA that need transcription. The result is differential expression of the DNA archives: messenger RNAs that are temporary, reusable copies of a gene whose product is needed just now to build or maintain cell structure.

The cell has no brain. Yet elegance is seen everywhere in the process of transcription. There are structural **domains** within the RNA polymerase enzyme whose precise three-dimensional shapes enable them to recognize specific base sequences in a DNA promoter region. This recognition enables the RNA polymerase to pause at a given place on the DNA long enough for **initiation** of transcription to occur. During initiation, RNA polymerase binds to the DNA double helix right over the promoter sequence (see Figure 7.17). The enzyme then opens up or unwinds a small portion of the double helix to form a "bubble" of single-strandedness within the DNA. Now the polymerase can read along a single strand of the DNA molecule. Once a region of about 10 DNA base pairs opens up, the enzyme begins using DNA base sequence as a template against which to begin positioning single

ribonucleotides according to the base-pairing rule. Recall from Chapter 4 that in RNA the base uracil is substituted for the thymine base used in DNA nucleotides. So if the polymerase senses the first 10 DNA bases to be as illustrated in red in Figure 7.18, then the first 10 bases in the message would be as illustrated in the green sequence in the same figure. Once an initial set of RNA nucleotides are in place and covalently bonded together, RNA polymerase moves into an **elongation** phase, where it pulls away from the promoter and continues "downstream" reading along the DNA molecule.

domain—a structural region of contiguous amino acids within a protein that performs a specific component function within the overall function the protein performs.

initiation (transcription)—the productive binding of RNA polymerase to DNA and the initial alignment of ribonucleotides such that transcription has begun.

ribonucleotide—a subunit of the nucleic acid polymer RNA; within RNA it is composed of a single phosphate attached to a ribose sugar that is attached to one of the nitrogenous bases adenine, cytosine, guanine, or uracil.

elongation (transcription)—the movement of RNA polymerase along the DNA template strand generating a single complementary strand of RNA.

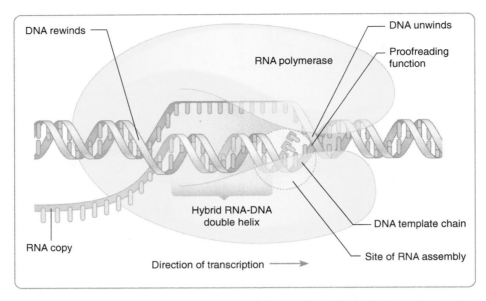

Figure 7.19 RNA Polymerase. This highly simplified diagram represents an enzyme that is actually a collection of polypeptide chains whose precise three-dimensional structures serve several dynamic and related roles.

Elongation is an enzymatic nightmare (see Figure 7.19):

1. The DNA helix must be unwound or opened up ahead of RNA polymerization.
2. The correct ribonucleotides must be sensed and incorporated into the new RNA strand.
3. The RNA strand must be dislodged from its (temporary) pairing with the DNA.
4. The new RNA strand must be proofread to remove and replace any errors made by the copying going on in the enzyme's active site.
5. The double strands of DNA must be reclosed as they were originally.
6. All of this must be done while negotiating around the protein structure of the nucleosomes that the DNA is wound around in chromatin.

Roles 1 through 5 are all deftly handled by the RNA polymerase and its associated subunits. The final role is played by separate proteins that unravel DNA from nucleosomes ahead of the polymerase and reassemble and reemploy the nucleosomes once transcription has passed by.

As RNA polymerase reaches the end of a gene, a **termination** process occurs (see Figure 7.17). In bacteria, a simple transcription termination sequence is read by RNA polymerase: The DNA is released and transcription stops. But in higher cells like our own, the process requires additional enzyme activity and is poorly understood. Somehow, the RNA transcript is released and has encoded within it a complete gene sequence complementary—base for base—to the gene sequence in the archival DNA.

The RNA product of transcription has a rather high fidelity with the DNA from which it was copied. Following the polymerase's proofreading function (item #4 above), there is about 1 error per 10,000 nucleotides incorporated. Given that multiple messages are transcribed from a single DNA gene, this error rate proves acceptable. Let us all in our own transcription activities strive for only one spelling error per 10,000 letters written!

The RNA products of transcription fall into three broad categories functionally (see Table 7.1). One set, the mRNAs, code for protein and are by far the largest in variety. But a second set of RNAs, the ribosomal RNAs (**rRNAs**) are transcribed from the nucleolar region of DNA (see Chapter 5, Section 2c). These RNAs are never translated into proteins. As RNAs, they are folded structurally into ribosome subunits, where they play a

termination (transcription)—the process by which transcription ends, including the disassociation of RNA polymerase from its DNA substrate and the release of the mRNA or pre-mRNA product.

rRNA (ribosomal RNA)—single-stranded nucleic acids composed using ribose sugars and containing the nitrogenous base uracil instead of thymine. They form structural parts of ribosomes assisting with alignment of other RNA classes.

Table 7.1 Functional classes of RNA molecule in the cell

Class	Location of RNA Genes in Genome	Structural Modifications After Transcription	Role in Cell
mRNA	scattered	in prokaryotes: none in eukaryotes: introns processed out	translated into protein
rRNA	within nucleolus	nucleotide sequence folds to correct shape for use in ribosome	incorporated into the structure of large and small ribosomal subunits
tRNA	clustered in various places	many bases are modified, folds to 3-dimensional "L" shape.	transfer amino acids to ribosome for incorporation into growing peptide chain.

critical role in helping ribosomes recognize how and where to begin their work. We will examine ribosome function shortly. A third important class of RNA "transcripts" is called *transfer RNAs* or **tRNAs.** These RNAs, after some modification, also function directly as RNA molecules by folding up into a three-dimensional L-shape, after which they are attached to specific amino acids. They transfer these amino acids to ribosomes for the translation of mRNA into protein. We will examine this process shortly as well.

Messenger RNA transcripts code for proteins. In bacterial cells, once the mRNA has been transcribed, it is immediately ready for translation into proteins. In fact, the front end of an mRNA is often already being translated before the tail end of the message even exists! One can play these tricks when no nuclear membrane exists to separate transcription from translation. But in higher cells like our own, mRNAs are a bit more complicated and require some processing before they are ready for translation. In your own cells, mRNAs just completing transcription are called **pre-mRNAs** (see Figure 7.15). At least three processing steps

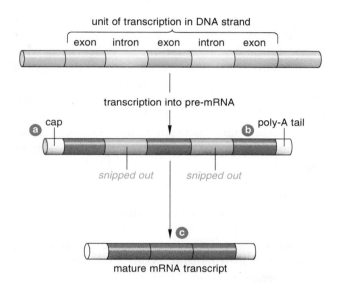

Figure 7.20 Processing of Pre-mRNA. There are three elements to pre-mRNA processing. **(a)** A single guanine nucleotide is added as a "cap" to facilitate initial alignment of the message on the ribosome. **(b)** a poly-adenine "tail" is added to the message to control its longevity in the cytoplasm. **(c)** Introns and some exons are excised from the message leaving only the exons that will encode the desired protein product.

are required to convert these RNAs into mature messages ready to be translated (see Figure 7.20). First, a guanine ribonucleotide containing several phosphate groups is attached to the front end of the mRNA. This **cap** will help the front end of the RNA to get properly aligned on the ribosome for its translation. Second, a long series of adenine ribonucleotides is added to the tail end of the message. The length of this **poly(A) tail** will determine how long the mRNA will survive for use in translation once it's reached the cytoplasm. The third processing step is more complex—more obviously designed.

Human genes contain interspersed regions of sequence that do not code for and will not contribute to the final sequence of amino acids in

tRNA (transfer RNA)—single-stranded nucleic acids composed using ribose sugars and containing the nitrogenous base uracil instead of thymine. They attach to and transport amino acids to ribosomes for incorporation into growing protein chains.

pre-mRNA—an RNA molecule that is an immediate product of transcription; it contains introns that must be removed before it can be translated into protein.

cap—a guanine ribonucleotide with three phosphate groups and an additional methyl group that is attached to a pre-mRNA during processing; this structure assists in ribosomal attachment to a mature mRNA.

poly(A) tail—a sequence of adenine ribonucleotides attached to a pre-mRNA following transcription; controls the length of time a mature mRNA will survive degradation in the cell's cytoplasm.

the protein product. These interspersed sequences are called **introns**. The sequences within the pre-mRNA that directly code for amino acid sequence are termed **exons**. In humans, most pre-mRNAs have alternating patterns of introns and exons in their sequences. It is thus necessary to have within the nucleus a collection of **splicing enzymes** and a corresponding processing step to remove all introns from the pre-mRNA, thereby generating a mature mRNA message ready for translation.

Perhaps you are now shouting at your textbook, wondering why on earth such a complicating and seemingly needless step is interposed between transcription and translation. Early workers, who began with a naturalistic bias, considered that the base sequences corresponding to introns were "**junk DNA**." It was necessary to get rid of these sequences from the pre-mRNA before translation so that a meaningful protein could be built. Soon evidence began to accumulate that the intron sequences were in some way involved in regulating the expression of genes they were found in. How they do this has been, by far, one of the most exciting discoveries since finding that genes are sequences of DNA. Even those whose bias was oriented toward design were amazed. It has been shown that introns and exons make it possible for one gene to code for more than one protein! Consider the example of the α-tropomyosin gene in mammals (see Figure 7.21). This protein has many functions, one of which is in muscle cells, where it helps control muscle contraction. Its pre-mRNA has 12 exons and 11 introns! The splicing machinery is different in cells of different tissues within the same animal. So in each tissue where it is needed, its mRNA is the result of a tissue-specific splicing pattern that produces a protein

uniquely designed for that tissue. In this way, the α-tropomyosin gene codes for at least six different but related proteins in different tissues! How widespread are intron-containing genes in humans? Recent estimates suggest that as many as three-fourths of all human genes show multiple splicing patterns. This suggests that a human genome containing about 25,000 different protein-coding genes could actually generate over 100,000 different proteins following pre-mRNA processing. We are only now beginning to understand how the pre-mRNA processing proteins are differentially employed in different tissues of the body. Clearly, there is a whole lot more to the control of gene expression than we had ever anticipated! But given the way information flows in the cell, it is efficient to have most of the control of gene expression occurring during this first stage: the transcription of DNA into RNA.

intron—a sequence of nucleotides in DNA that are transcribed into pre-mRNA and that separate protein-coding portions of a gene from each other; removed during processing to form mature mRNA.

exon—a sequence of nucleotides in DNA that are transcribed into pre-mRNA and that represent protein-coding portions of a gene; retained and joined together during processing to form a mature mRNA.

splicing enzyme—small particles composed of protein and RNA that attach to pre-mRNA at junction points between introns and exons; they cut RNA at these sites, remove intron sequences, leaving exon sequences contiguous to each other.

junk DNA—a sequence of DNA believed to have no useful function; some see usefulness for it in the past, other see usefulness for it in the future.

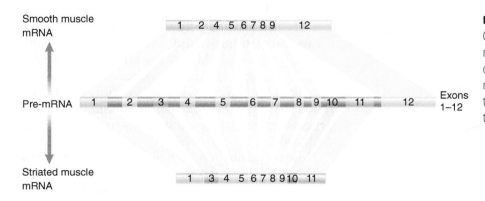

Figure 7.21 Alternate Proteins from the Same Gene. The protein α-tropomyosin exists in multiple forms in the human body. Here, two different splicing patterns are shown that will result in two distinct mature messages and therefore two distinct proteins for two different tissues. Elegant!

1. Transcription converts biological information in the base sequence of archival DNA into the base sequence of the ribonucleic acids mRNA, rRNA, and tRNA.
2. The enzyme RNA polymerase creates these RNAs by aligning and covalently bonding ribonucleotides in a sequence complementary to the DNA base sequence it is reading.
3. The process of transcription occurs in three stages: initiation, elongation, and termination.
4. Transcription begins at one end of a promoter sequence in the template DNA strand and concludes at the tail end of a transcript anywhere from one to several genes in length.
5. During elongation, RNA polymerase unwinds DNA, lengthens an RNA molecule against a DNA template, proofreads the RNA sequence, and then refolds the DNA double helix.
6. In bacteria, termination of transcription is signaled by a sequence of bases in DNA; in higher cells, termination is enzymatically more complicated.
7. In bacteria the product of transcription is a mature mRNA ready to be translated; in higher cells the product of transcription is pre-mRNA, which must be further processed before translation.
8. Pre-mRNA processing in higher cells involves capping the transcript, adding a poly-adenine tail, and removing all introns and a selection of exons from the pre-mRNA message.
9. Tissue-specific processing of pre-mRNA allows genes in higher cells to code for anywhere from two to many different polypeptide chains having related but distinct functional roles in different cells of the same organism.

Translation: Making Proteins

If well over half the biomass of a cell is protein, and if the rest of the cell's biomass is assembled by proteins, then we need to start making proteins! Since this process is a major part of the biosynthetic activity of the cell, and since, following translation, many proteins require considerable processing to reach their final mature form, we need much space for these activities. The nucleus is already filled with archival information and its processing enzymes. Protein synthesis will have to occur out in the cytoplasm; mRNA transcribed in the archives will have to travel to the cytoplasm to be translated (see Figure 7.15). Although in bacterial cells, the information level is lower and processing is simpler, protein synthesis is still largely peripheral to the nucleoid region.

The term *translation* is used for protein synthesis because the information we work from is a sequence of nitrogenous bases in mRNA, but the information as expressed takes the form of a sequence of amino acids in a protein (see Figure 7.16). Nucleotide bases and amino acids lie within two broadly distinct classes of biomolecules: nucleic acids and proteins. Since we are moving from one language (base sequence) to another (amino acid sequence) we use the term *translation*.

Using mRNA bases in sequence to specify a sequence of amino acids leads to an immediate coding problem (see Table 7.2). There are only 4 kinds of bases in DNA or mRNA, and there are at least 20 common amino acids found in proteins. Clearly, there cannot be a one-to-one coding correspondence between bases and amino acids.

Table 7.2 Coding for Amino Acids using base sequence.

Number of Bases	Bases per Codon	Possible Combinations of Bases	Possible Number of Codons	Number of Amino Acids needing Coding	Feasibility
4	1	4	4	20	–
4	2	4 × 4	16	20	–
4	3	4 × 4 × 4	64	20	+

Thus coding must involve using short sequences of bases to code for individual amino acids. These sequences of bases are called **codons**. Suppose a codon were two bases in length. The number of kinds of codons we could form taking four bases, two at a time, would be 4^2 or 16 codons. This would still be inadequate for amino acid coding. Keeping sequence efficiency in mind, it was thus predicted and later demonstrated that a codon in mRNA consists of a sequence of three bases that together code for a specific amino acid. The number of combinations of four bases taken three at a time is 4^3 or 64 combinations. This represents more than enough codons for all 20 amino acids. In the 1960s, the genetic code was elucidated by Drs. Marshall Nirenberg of the National Institutes of Health in Washington, DC, and Har Gobind Khorana at the University of Wisconsin (see Figure 7.22). They used ribosomes to translate simple, artificially constructed mRNAs as a means to crack the code. Details of the code's structure will be discussed below.

Given a coding relationship between bases and amino acids, what "biological hardware" is needed to actually "do" translation? Naturalistic thinkers beware! A formidable challenge faces us. We require (1) a properly processed mature mRNA containing a biologically meaningful sequence of codons; (2) a set of adapter molecules, each of which must recognize a codon in mRNA and provide the amino acid it codes for; (3) a set of corresponding enzyme molecules, each of which can attach the correct amino acid to its corresponding adapter molecule; and (4) a machine that can use an mRNA codon sequence to properly order adapter molecules in the correct sequence to generate a polypeptide chain containing amino acids in the correct sequence. Let's reflect on some specific aspects of these requirements:

1. As we've seen, the mature mRNA molecule is a succinct code that not only contains a meaningful sequence of codons but has a cap that attracts the translation machinery to the beginning of the message (see Figure 7.20). Its poly-adenine tail controls how many times it will get translated before cytoplasmic enzymes degrade it.

codon—a sequence of three adjacent nucleotide bases in mRNA that code for a single amino acid in a sequence within a polypeptide chain or protein.

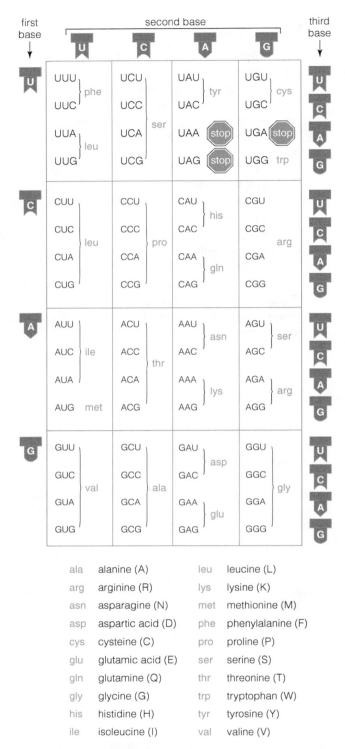

ala	alanine (A)	leu	leucine (L)
arg	arginine (R)	lys	lysine (K)
asn	asparagine (N)	met	methionine (M)
asp	aspartic acid (D)	phe	phenylalanine (F)
cys	cysteine (C)	pro	proline (P)
glu	glutamic acid (E)	ser	serine (S)
gln	glutamine (Q)	thr	threonine (T)
gly	glycine (G)	trp	tryptophan (W)
his	histidine (H)	tyr	tyrosine (Y)
ile	isoleucine (I)	val	valine (V)

Figure 7.22 The Genetic Code. Mentally construct an mRNA codon using any three bases you wish in sequence. Find the first base down the left-hand side of the chart to select a row. Now go across the top in search of the second base in your codon and select the large box from your selected row. Select the third base in your codon from the list down the right-hand side of the chart. Within the large box, you can now determine what amino acid your codon codes for. Abbreviations of amino acid names are given with their full names in the list below. Some codons like AUG or UAA start and stop translation. See the text for details.

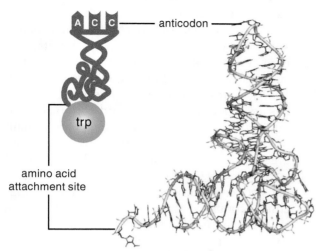

Figure 7.23 Transfer RNA. Shown here are two structural models of a molecule of tRNA carrying the amino acid tryptophan. It's anticodon, -ACC- is complementary (by base pairing) with the codon -UGG- in mRNA that codes for tryptophan. (see Figure 7.22)

2. The adapter molecules are now known to be transfer RNAs. Their existence was predicted and by the 1960s their presence and structure were elucidated as well. Each tRNA is about 85 nucleotides in length (see Figure 7.23). This chain of monomers folds up in solution and because of intrachain hydrogen bonding between matching base pairs, its three-dimensional folded form takes the shape of an L. At one end of the L, each tRNA contains a sequence of three bases called an **anticodon.** These three bases will be complementary in sequence to a particular codon within mRNA. Covalently bonded to the opposite end of the transfer RNA molecule is the amino acid corresponding to the codon in the mRNA message!

So the tRNA really is the translator molecule. It has (anticodon) bases on one end and the correct amino acid for the codon on the other. But how does the correct amino acid get attached to its own corresponding tRNA?

3. Here we require the specificity that enzymes possess. There is a set of 20 enzymes called **tRNA synthetases.** Each synthetase recognizes just one kind of amino acid and only the tRNAs specific for that amino acid (see Figure 7.24). (Some amino acids have more than one codon that calls for them.) We are here seeing an incredible example of design: an enzyme that "walks into the dress shop" of tRNA molecules, tries on many different tRNAs, but binds to—selects—only the ones with the shape that precisely fits the three-dimensional shape of its own active site. It also tries on all the different amino acids but

anticodon—a sequence of three adjacent nucleotide bases in tRNA that are complementary in sequence to an mRNA codon; the tRNA carrying it also carries the correct amino acid corresponding to the mRNA codon.

tRNA synthetase—an enzyme that recognizes the structure of from one to four tRNAs that specify a particular amino acid; the enzyme links them covalently to that correct amino acid.

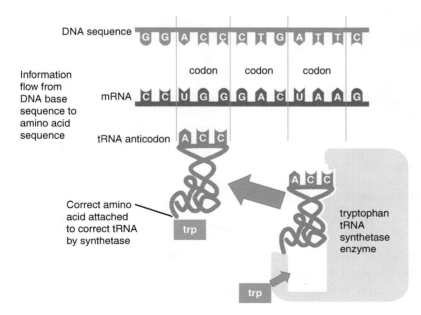

Figure 7.24 Preparing tRNA for Translation. Tryptophan tRNA Synethase is one of 20 synthetase enzymes that keep the entire collection or "pool" of tRNAs in the cell charged with their respective amino acids. Imagine having to design each of these enzymes such that its active site recognized only one "family" of tRNA and only the amino acid corresponding to that family. Three-dimensional shape of the active site is the key variable in the design of these enzymes.

again binds only to the one that fits another portion of its active site. And, by design, that amino acid is the one that the already-bound tRNA must be attached to—the one that the mRNA code calls for! So these synthetases are covalently loading amino acids onto their corresponding adaptor molecules and doing it such that the bond between the two is a high-energy bond useful for the energy-expensive amino acid polymerization process that follows. The error rate—1 mistake per 1000 tRNAs loaded—is amazing when you consider how similar some of the amino acids appear to each other (see Figure 4.3). So these synthetases are 20 works of art, each one capable of bonding the one amino acid it recognizes to any of the one to four tRNAs whose anticodons complement the correct codon for that amino acid. Amazing.

4. Given the carefully crafted association of correct amino acids with their cognate anticodons, all that remains is for some relatively witless machine to allow codons and anticodons to be matched up in sequence and to then form the resulting sequence of amino acids into a chain. That machine is the ribosome (see Figure 7.25). In higher cells, each ribosome is assembled in the nucleus from 50 proteins and 3 rRNAs. It then travels to the cytoplasm for use. It's a machine large enough to be easily seen with an electron microscope. Its proteins and RNAs are built into two subunits, one large and one small. These two subunits associate to begin translation and dissociate (fall apart) as translation ends. The large subunit has an active site that can bind amino acids to one another forming them into a peptide chain or protein. The small subunit has a decoding area where tRNAs are properly sequenced against mRNA codons such that amino acids get properly sequenced. This wonderful machine contains three separate sites where tRNAs can bind, two of which allow them to bind to the mRNA message. In all of these binding and catalytic sites, it is the rRNAs that play the key structural and catalytic roles. The ribosomal proteins are more or less supportive of the rRNA roles played in ribosomal function. When the two ribosomal subunits are associated together, they create two perfectly crafted channels: one that allows mRNA to enter, be read, and exit and one from which the growing protein chain emerges.

The process of translation occurs in three stages: initiation, elongation, and termination. Sound

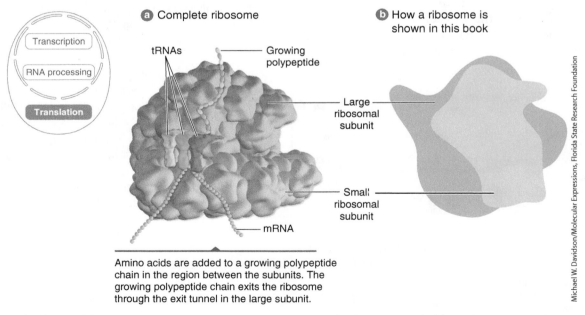

a Complete ribosome

Transcription

RNA processing

Translation

tRNAs

Growing polypeptide

b How a ribosome is shown in this book

Large ribosomal subunit

Small ribosomal subunit

mRNA

Amino acids are added to a growing polypeptide chain in the region between the subunits. The growing polypeptide chain exits the ribosome through the exit tunnel in the large subunit.

Michael W. Davidson/Molecular Expressions, Florida State Research Foundation

Figure 7.25 The Ribosome. **(a)** a computer-generated image in which three adjacent tRNA binding sites are used while translating the mRNA shown entering from below. The growing polypeptide chain emerges from the top of the large subunit. The mRNA is within the structure of the associated subunits. **(b)** an icon of an intact ribosome as we will represent it in subsequent figures.

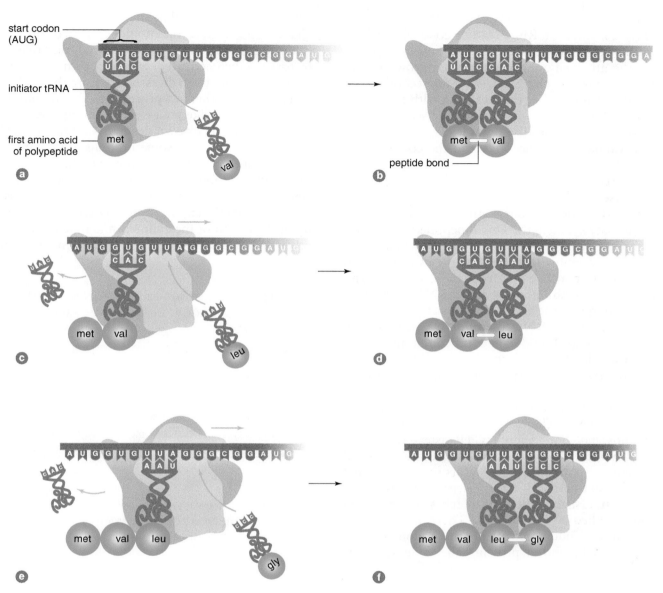

start codon (AUG)

initiator tRNA

first amino acid of polypeptide

met

val

a

peptide bond

met — val

b

met val

leu

c

met val — leu

d

met val leu

gly

e

met val leu — gly

f

Figure 7.26 Translation. **(a)** The initiation complex is complete and ready for elongation to begin. **(b)** Elongation, a peptide bond forms between the first two amino acids in our new protein. **(c)** Elongation, a spent tRNA exits and a new tRNA enters. **(d)** Elongation, a second peptide bond forms. **(e)** Elongation, the next tRNA exchange occurs. **(f)** Elongation, a third peptide bond forms. The process continues. The average polypeptide chain length in yeast cells is 466, so that's 466 elongation steps prior to termination.

familiar? **Initiation** begins with a mature mRNA getting correctly "into register" on the small ribosomal subunit (see Figure 7.26a). The first codon of every message has the base sequence AUG, which is called the **start codon.** This sequence codes for the amino acid methionine, which will be the first amino acid in the new protein chain. So the initiation complex waits until a tRNA with the correct anticodon (–UAC–) bearing methionine also finds its way to the small ribosomal subunit. A variety of soluble and attached proteins assist in setting up

this complex. When everything is in its place, the large ribosomal subunit binds the small one and the initiation of translation is complete.

initiation (translation)—the productive binding of mRNA, an initiator tRNA, and a small and large ribosomal subunit into a complex that enables translation to begin.

start codon—the base sequence –AUG- in mRNA that codes for the amino acid methionine. This sequence is the first translated codon in most mRNA molecules.

Elongation now begins. The ribosome will be moving along the mRNA, reading codons, matching them with anticodons on tRNAs, and incorporating the attached amino acids into a growing peptide chain (see Figure 7.26b–f). If the second codon in mRNA is –GUG–, then a tRNA with anticodon CAC will match up with it using the second tRNA binding site on the ribosome. It carries the amino acid valine, which, according to the code, should be the second amino acid in the peptide chain. The large ribosomal subunit now forms a peptide bond (see Chapter 4, Section 5a) between methionine and valine, and our peptide chain is now two amino acids in length. This dipeptide remains attached to the second tRNA, leaving the first tRNA free of any amino acid. The first tRNA is moved to an exit site that is away from the active site, and the ribosome shifts along the mRNA to bring a new codon into the active site. This creates an open space for a third tRNA to "try on" the third codon of the message. If codon and anticodon match, another peptide bond is formed, another tRNA exits, and the ribosome shifts again. As new codons are matched to anticodons, new amino acids are transferred to the ribosome and incorporated into the growing peptide chain. This entire process is driven by phosphate bond energy (**GTP** instead of ATP) at each peptide bond formation step, and it is guided by required soluble protein factors too complicated to represent here. It is a truly elegant process.

Eventually, the ribosome reaches a specialized codon called a **stop codon.** There is no tRNA with an anticodon recognizing this codon (see Figure 7.27). Instead, a protein called **release factor**

enters the tRNA binding site, recognizes the stop codon, and causes the now completed protein chain to separate from the ribosome. Other release factors are then activated, which, in turn, cause the ribosomal subunits to disassociate from the mRNA and from each other in a process called **termination.**

In higher cells like your own, the completed peptide chain signals its own destination. Immediately following translation, some proteins are complete and are simply released in the cytoplasm, where they will function. Others, based on their amino acid sequence, are destined for further processing and possibly export from the cell. These end up in the lumen of the endoplasmic reticulum. Still other peptide chains will signal their own insertion

elongation (translation)—the movement of the ribosome along the mRNA generating a single polypeptide chain composed of amino acids.

GTP—guanosine triphosphate; a nucleoside triphosphate whose covalent bond between the second and third phosphates contains as much potential energy as the same bond in the ATP molecule.

stop codon—one of three mRNA base sequences, –UAA–, –UAG–, or –UGA–, for which there is no corresponding amino acid; recognized by release factors that cause translation termination.

release factor—a protein that enters a tRNA binding site on the ribosome; sensing the presence of a stop codon, it causes translation to terminate.

termination (translation)—the process by which translation is ended, including the disassociation of ribosomal subunits, mRNA, and a completed polypeptide chain.

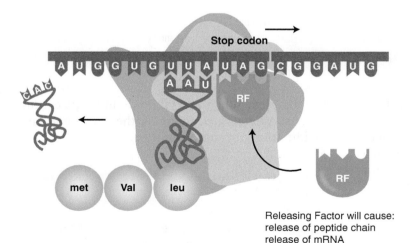

Figure 7.27 Termination of Translation. A class of proteins called "release factors" respond to the mRNA codons UAA, UAG and UGA. When any of these codons come into the ribosome's active site, release factors recognizes them and release first the peptide chain, then the mRNA and the ribosomal subunits.

Releasing Factor will cause:
release of peptide chain
release of mRNA
Dissociation ribosomal subunits

The Human Intracellular Protein Factory

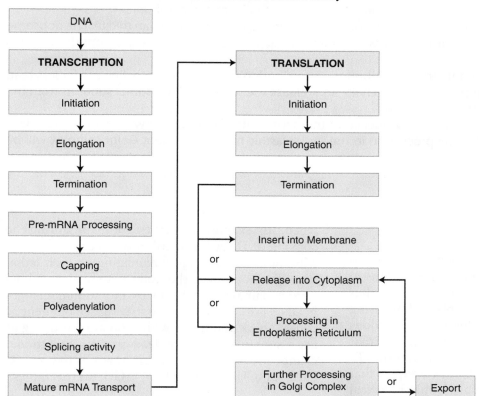

Figure 7.28 The Human Intracellular Protein Factory. The steps in the production of a mature protein as discussed in this chapter are listed in this flow chart along with some possible variations in processing. Cellular structures are able to determine from the "front end" sequence of amino acids in the protein whether or not it will enter the endoplasmic reticulum for processing or not.

into membranes within or outside of the cell" (see Figure 7.28).)

As you may recall, the journey through the endoplasmic reticulum and later the Golgi complex may involve the loss or modification of amino acids, cross-bonding between amino acids at other places in the peptide chain, or the addition of sugars or lipid groups. When all of these additional processing steps are complete, the result is a mature protein, processed and ready for use. Think of

the ribosome, the endoplasmic reticulum, and the Golgi complex as somewhat like a bicycle factory. The newly synthesized peptide chain is something like a basic bicycle: wheels, frame, handlebars, and pedals. It goes. But it would be nice to have a seat, fenders, and a horn. These extras make the working bicycle fully functional and safer. The processing steps add the nonprotein parts to the peptide chain making it ready to fulfill its function completely.

IN OTHER WORDS
....

1. Translation is the mRNA-guided process of synthesizing proteins; it occurs on ribosomes in the cytoplasm of the cell.
2. Information for amino acid sequence is stored in the base sequence of mRNA in a sequence of base triplets called *codons*.
3. Sixty-four different codons in mRNA control amino sequence and the start and termination of the translation process.
4. The five component parts of translation are a message, tRNAs, tRNA synthetases, amino acids, and ribosomes.
5. Each variety of transfer RNA in the cell contains a specific anticodon that is complementary in sequence to some codon in mRNA.
6. tRNA synthetase enzymes load each individual tRNA with the amino acid it is designed to carry.
7. Ribosomes are composed of two subunits, one large and one small. Together, these subunits contain three different molecules of rRNA and some 50 ribosomal proteins.

8. Translation begins with the formation of an initiation complex consisting of a mature mRNA, an initiator tRNA carrying the amino acid methionine, and the large and small ribosomal subunits.
9. Elongation of the polypeptide chain results from movement of a ribosome along an mRNA. The ribosome reads codons, matches them with anticodons in tRNA and peptide bonds amino acids from those tRNAs in the correct sequence.
10. Translation terminates when the ribosome brings a "stop" codon into its active site. Release factors read that codon, cleave the completed peptide chain, and release the mRNA and ribosomal subunits from the translation process.
11. Following translation the amino acid sequence of the peptide itself determines whether the peptide is complete or whether additional processing in the endoplasmic reticulum and/or Golgi complex will be required.

The Genetic Code

The genetic code is a marvelous piece of craftsmanship. In its simplest expression it relates codons in mRNA to amino acids in protein sequence. But as we've seen, there are 64 possible codons using four bases three at a time, and this excess of codons over amino acids has left us with enigmas that appear somewhat accidental to materialists. To those who embrace design however, we expect that these enigmas will someday clarify only to reveal precise reasons for code redundancies that today appear fanciful.

So we say that the code is **degenerate.** This simply means that most of the amino acids are specified by more than one codon (see Figure 7.22). With our limited understanding of the occasional instabilities of DNA, we can see some value to code degeneracy. Rarely, in the DNA "archives" do bases get altered or **mutated** (see Figure 7.29). This happens when, for example, mistakes are made during the copying of DNA for distribution to daughter cells. Mutations can be highly damaging or even lethal to cells. Examining the code closely shows how serious damage to proteins by mutational changes in DNA is minimized by the structure of our genetic code. (Think about this while you are out trying to get a suntan!) For example, suppose a mutational change in DNA alters the third base of the codons UUU or CUU or GUU or GGU (as examples).

degeneracy—absence of a one-to-one correspondence between codon sequence and the amino acid coded for; rather, several codons code for the same amino acid.

mutated, mutation—referring to changes in the base sequence of DNA; change of identity of one base for another, loss or addition of a base, loss or addition of multiple bases; some mutations result in serious functional loss or organismal death.

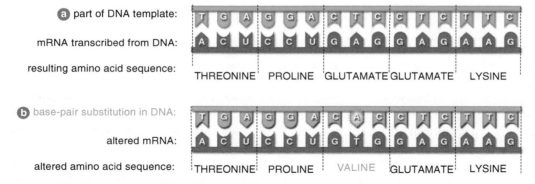

Figure 7.29 Effect of DNA Mutation on Protein Structure. **(a)** In this diagram we are lodged somewhere in the middle of a huge (gene) DNA sequence. **(b)** Notice the effect on the protein of substituting the base adenine for the base thymine. That one amino acid difference may have a profound effect on the three-dimensional shape of the protein because the amino acids glutamate and valine have very different structures. This alteration, as diagramed, actually occurs in sickle-cell anemia sufferers.

It wouldn't matter what base that final U mutated to; the code would still call for the same amino acid! Also, looking vertically through the chart, the structures of the amino acids in each column of the chart tend to be somewhat similar to each other. In this way, a mutational change in the first base of a codon will result in substituting an amino acid from the same column, again, minimizing the effect of the mutation. So the strategy inherent in the code clearly rises above the level of simply getting each amino acid represented by a few different codons in mRNA.

Finally, our genetic code is not universal. Figure 7.22 does not hold true for all organisms! Now, evolutionarily, it really should, you know. One would assume that coding relationships would be laid down very, very early in the history of life, after cells began to divide but before they began to diversify. Yet in certain groups of bacteria (prokaryotes), protozoa (single-celled eukaryotes), and yeasts (fungal forms), there are very slight differences in the code. For example, in the yeast *Candida,* the codon CUG codes for the amino acid serine rather than for leucine as it does in the normal code. Why in the world is this? If life-forms are designed, there will be an important reason for these (rare!) coding differences. But as of this writing, the reasons for these differences are not known.

IN OTHER WORDS

1. The degeneracy of the genetic code helps to protect cells and organisms from the harmful effects of mutations.
2. The genetic code is not universal. Scientists have just begun to uncover a variety of microorganisms whose codes show slight but significant variations from the normal code.

7.4 THE APPLICATION OF INFORMATION EXPRESSION

Our Deep Desire to Control Information Expression

One of humanity's most valuable stories tells of an ideal man and woman who were placed in a garden and told to "subdue and have dominion" over it and its component life-forms. The story goes on to describe how that man and woman made a choice and, as a result, lost their idyllic existence. Both their motives for action and their environment fell into a degeneracy that survives to this day. The story keeps alive the notion that a Designer had not desired life to take this foul turn and might yet have a remedy for it. His earlier directive to subdue and have dominion over the biosphere survived this loss of original dignity. Only now, the command must be carried out with tainted motivations. And the arena for its fulfillment would now both contain and develop many new trials and challenges to have dominion over!

With time, genes in human populations would take on harmful variations. Faulty versions of hemoglobin genes would give rise to sickle cell anemia. Faulty cell surface receptor genes would predispose their bearers to type 2 diabetes. In this fallen world, parasitic forms like viruses would now infect man and his domesticated animals (see Figure 7.30). Tobacco mosaic virus would eventually threaten his tomato crops. The ultimate challenge humans would face was their own demise. Death would now be programmed into them and all other life-forms. Civilization, in seeking to subdue and have dominion over this tragedy, has wrestled with these challenges for years. But in the twentieth century an understanding of DNA structure and its mutation led to a hope of correcting mutations. The power of gene expression began to yield fruit in the biotechnological suppression of parasitism. And the discovery of genes associated with aging has left some wondering if we might significantly postpone or even preclude organismal death.

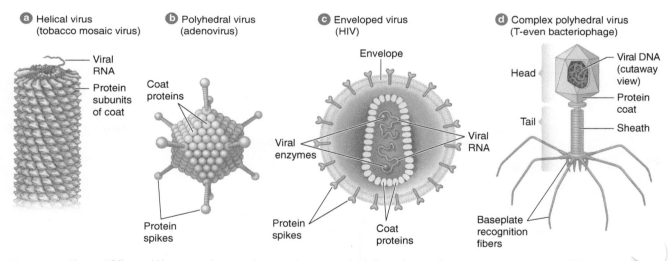

Figure 7.30 Viruses. A fallen world has viruses that cause disease and sometimes death. They take many forms. Here are some examples: **(a)** tobacco mosaic virus that infects plants **(b)** an adenovirus which causes some of your colds **(c)** the AIDS virus **(d)** even bacterial cells have their own viruses.

IN OTHER WORDS

1. Scientists have developed means to control or alter gene expression in an attempt to cure genetic diseases, control crop pests, and provide cheap protein sources to society.

Information Expression as Problem Solving

Such formidable disease states and challenges have prompted scientists to turn to life's most powerful resource: segments of pre-designed genetic information—genes! Consider some examples of using specific genes to solve difficult problems:

1. Researchers have inserted the gene for normal hemoglobin into the **genome** of **stem cells** from mice that have sickle cell disease. Mice that received this treatment were cured of the disease.

2. The gene for human **insulin** has been inserted into bacterial cells and more recently into the cells of the safflower plant, where it supports the production of human insulin. This insulin can be harvested and used as a drug for therapy in diabetes patients.

3. A human gene whose protein product inhibits blood clot formation has been injected into the nuclei of embryonic cells of goats (see Figure 7.31). Adult female goats grown from these embryos secrete the human anti-coagulant protein in their milk from which it is easily isolated.

4. A bacterial gene that promotes ice formation on the surface of plants has been rendered nonfunctional and inserted into plant-associated strains of the bacterium. When these strains colonize plant surfaces, ice formation requires a lower temperature, decreasing crop losses in cold weather.

5. A bacterial gene that codes for a protein toxic to insect pests has been inserted into tissues of economically important crop plants (see

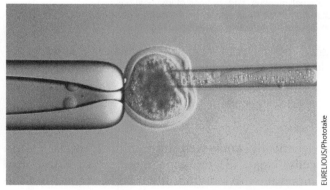

Figure 7.31 Genome Alteration. The glass tube on the right is introducing foreign DNA into the nucleus of a fertilized egg—a zygote. If the DNA successfully incorporates into the genome, it will be replicated into all the cells of the adult developing from this embryo.

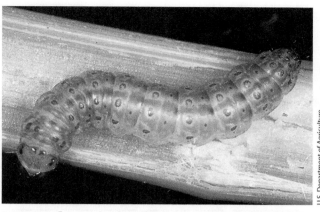

Figure 7.32 European Corn Borer. This pest of corn plants is now encountering a damaging neurotoxin in corn fields across North America. The toxin is engineered into corn tissues. It was taken from the genome of a soil bacterium.

Figure 7.32). The plants now have increased resistance to these pests.

Recombinant DNA research began in 1970. Research since that time has provided a host of examples comparable to those cited above (see Table 7.3). Each technological triumph results from making a series of component decisions:

1. The optimal gene sequence for the task must be selected or created.
2. The cell type in which the gene will be expressed must be selected.
3. The gene sequence and its flanking sequences must be appropriately modified to optimize expression in the cell it will function within (see Figure 7.33).
4. A method for inserting the gene into the target cells must be selected and sometimes modified to optimize gene delivery (see Table 7.4).
5. The cells must be assayed to determine that the gene is functioning as was hoped.

genome—the collection of all the genetic information (genes) in the cells of an organism

stem cells—undifferentiated cells found in most organisms; cells that are able to divide continuously by mitosis and eventually differentiate into any of the types of cells found in the mature organism.

insulin—a hormone in mammals that controls the absorption of glucose into the tissues from the bloodstream.

recombinant DNA—the use of nuclease and ligase enzymes to cut and join segments of DNA from the cells of two different species of organisms.

Year	Modification
1973	Salmonella bacterial gene expressed in E. Coli
1976	yeast genes expressed in bacteria
1977	bacteria produce human growth hormone
1978	human insulin gene expressed in bacteria
1979	multiple oil degradation genes inserted into a single bacterial strain
1980	ice-minus gene inserted into bacterial strain for crop protection
1983	bacterial toxin gene expressed in tomato plants
1985	mouse enzyme (reverse transcriptase) expressed in bacterium
1990	normal adenosine deaminase gene inserted into immunodeficient human cells
1994	genes added to tomatoes to help retain ripeness
2000	daffodil and bacterial genes inserted into "golden" rice
2009	human anti-thrombin genes expressed in goat mammary glands.

Table 7.3 Genetically engineered cells.

Typical Gene Modification

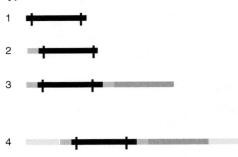

1. Begin with many copies of a purified gene of interest

2. Paste appropriate promoter sequence upstream

3. Paste additional gene (and promoter) coding for resistance to antibiotic. Cells grown in presence of antibiotic will now die unless they have incorporated this sequence (and probably our gene next to it!) into their genome

4. Paste on each end DNA sequences that are known (from DNA sequence studies) to be on either side of the gene that we wish to replace within the genome

The Cell's Response:

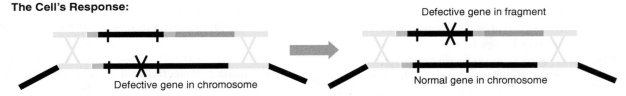

Defective gene in fragment

Defective gene in chromosome

Normal gene in chromosome

Enzymes within the cell nucleus "find" regions of identical base sequence to either side of the gene and move the normal gene into the chromosome discarding defective gene in the fragment.

Figure 7.33 Typical Gene Modification. There are many (!) variations on this general sequence. The ultimate purpose is to prepare a gene to precisely replace a defective one in the genome. All this design is useless unless there is already a well designed set of recombination enzymes present in the nucleus to insert the modified gene while discarding the old one.

For example, workers (in item 1 above) who wanted to replace the sickle cell gene in anemic mice with a normal gene, had to (1) select the normal hemoglobin gene source and isolate and purify the gene. Then (2) they had to determine in what cell population the normal gene would function. For this they used mouse tail cells, which they genetically converted into undifferentiated stem cells. Next, (3) the gene required an active promoter next to it so that it would be efficiently transcribed. They also arranged the DNA sequences adjacent to either side of the gene so that it would get inserted at the right place in the genome (see Figure 7.33). Enzymes in the cell nucleus would do

Method	Description
Chemical Transfection	use of calcium salts and organic buffers to precipitate DNA; precipitate is taken up by cells in culture use of positively-charged lipid-like molecules to complex with DNA and carry it through the cell's membranes
Viral Vectors	use of disabled viruses specific for the organism to receive the DNA; DNA is incorporated into their genome in place of genes that render the normal virus pathogenic to the cell being invaded
Liposomes	incorporate DNA within small lipid-lined spheres that fuse easily with cell membranes dumping their DNA content into the cell
Electroporation	mixed cells and DNA are subjected to electric current that generates transient pores in the membrane through which the DNA then passes.
Gene Gun	DNA is coupled to a microscopic particle of an inert solid (like gold) which is then "shot" directly into the target cell's nucleus

Table 7.4 Methods of Inserting DNA into Eukaryotic Cells.

this for them. They then (4) selected a way to get the genes into the stem cell population (a process called **transfection**). Lipid-like chemicals are often complexed with genes to carry them through membrane barriers and into the nucleus. Finally, (5) they examined the resulting mature red cells for any evidence of sickling (which would mean failure of the procedure).

Suppose, however, we desire (2) bacterial cells to generate a useful human protein for us such as human growth hormone. The human gene (1) for the hormone will require (3) replacement of an upstream human promoter sequence with a bacterial one so that bacterial RNA polymerase will transcribe it effectively. We may even need to alter codons in the gene in favor of ones typically used in the bacterial cell (recall the degeneracy of the genetic code mentioned above). For trickier problems like this we have "gene machines" that can manufacture gene sequences from solutions of nucleotides. The genes are moved into bacterial cells (4) in a procedure called **transformation**. Using calcium salts and a bit of temperature abuse, bacterial cells will take up DNA directly from solution. The bacterial culture soon produces large amounts of human growth hormone (5), which vastly exceeds the **nanogram** amounts available from the pituitary glands of human cadavers.

When therapeutic genes are being inserted into a human being, a fundamental choice must be made. This choice was defined for us back in the late 1800s by the German zoologist August Weismann. He argued that, at some early point during development, the fertilized egg—like the one you once were—gives rise to two separate populations of cells. One population, the **somatic** cells, differentiate into

all the functional tissues of your own body (see Chapter 9 for more discussion of this). The other population becomes your sex cells—egg or sperm cells—which are committed not to supporting your own function but to provide "germinal cells" for the next generation. Weismann called this latter group **germ line** cells (see Figure 7.34).

Should we insert therapeutic genes into just the specific somatic cells of an individual where the defective gene is currently being expressed? This would have its cost, but it would solve an immediate problem in a single individual. We could also, however, insert therapeutic genes into the germ line cells—egg or sperm cells—of the individual. This is similar to what was done in goats that now secrete human anticoagulation protein in their milk (example 3 above). Then, the defect is corrected in *all* the cells of the *next* generation of individuals. This is a difficult question to address. With germ line therapy, the possible beneficial effects could quickly move into the population at large and

transfection—the process of incorporating DNA from an external source into the nucleus of a eukaryotic cell.

transformation—the process of incorporating DNA from an external source into the genome of a bacterial cell.

nanogram—1/1000 of a microgram.

somatic cell—a cell from the body of an organism that carries out some contributory function there other than becoming a sex cell.

germ line cell—any cells within the developing embryo whose descendant cells will become sperm or egg cells in the mature adult

Germm Line Cells

Somewhere, early in development a cell arises in the embryo from which all precursor germ cells and eventually all sex cells in the mature adult will arise. This separate cell lineage does not contribute to the function of the organism. Rather it produces the new generation of individuals.

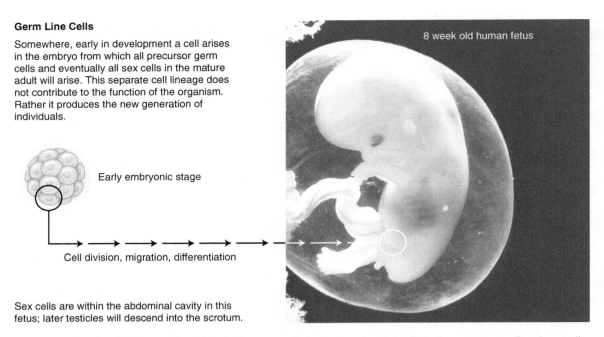

Early embryonic stage

8 week old human fetus

Cell division, migration, differentiation

Sex cells are within the abdominal cavity in this fetus; later testicles will descend into the scrotum.

Figure 7.34 Germ Line Cells. Somewhere, early in development a cell arises in the embryo from which all precursor germ cells and eventually all sex cells in the mature adult will arise. This separate cell lineage does not contribute to the function of the organism. Rather it produces the new generation of individuals.

might eventually eradicate the genetic defect from the population. Many individuals would be spared the disability as a result of one investment of effort. But possible serious side effects could also occur. Once human-engineered genes enter the germ line of the population, they would affect countless cells in an ever-expanding group of individuals. These genes could hardly be withdrawn from the population. A horrible, unstoppable error could be perpetuated in this way. By contrast, changes merely to somatic cells are lost when the individual harboring them dies. Current efforts at human gene therapy, despite growing sophistication, still lack critical controls. For these reasons, governmental authorities have required that human gene therapies respect the **Weismannian boundary** described here. Only alterations of human somatic cells are allowed and then only with careful review by peers. By contrast, gene engineering experiments in plants have no such boundaries. Those involving animals need respect only the boundary of cruelty to obviously sentient (self-conscious) forms.

Weismannian border—the conceptual divide between somatic cells and germ line cells; gene therapy in humans employs only somatic cells.

IN OTHER WORDS

1. Genes for hemoglobin, insulin, anticoagulation of blood, ice nucleation protein, bacterial toxins (and many other proteins) have been recombined with DNA from other sources and engineered into novel sites in new genomes.
2. Genetic engineering requires selecting a gene, selecting a cell type in which it will be expressed, creating useful flanking sequences for the gene, inserting the gene into the target cells, and assaying to determine that the gene is functioning as was hoped.
3. Scientists have used the normal gene for mouse hemoglobin to cure mice of sickle cell anemia.
4. Scientists have used bacteria and plants to generate large quantities of human insulin.
5. Insertion of genes into human cells has been restricted to somatic tissues only; placing novel gene combinations into human germ line tissue is currently not acceptable.

Essentials of Recombinant DNA Technology

The examples of genetic engineering just cited may leave you wondering if scientists are also magicians. Many elegant DNA technologies have been developed. Detailed descriptions are beyond the scope of our text. Instead, in question and answer format, lets observe some of the basic means by which DNA is manipulated and genes get engineered into new cellular environments.

How is DNA isolated away from the other parts of the cell?

Cells containing desired DNA are physically torn open in homogenizers or sonic wave generators (see Figure 7.35), or chemicals that disrupt cell membranes are used. We then employ salts and enzymes to get rid of polysaccharides and RNA. An organic compound, **phenol,** is often used to denature membranes and proteins. The goal is to remove other polymers leaving one polymer—DNA—in solution. DNA can then be brought out of solution using ethyl alcohol. This alcohol precipitation leaves many small monomeric molecules behind.

How are long polymers of DNA reduced to gene-sized segments?

A collection of enzymes called **restriction nucleases** have been isolated from a variety of bacterial and fungal cells. These enzymes were brilliantly designed to efficiently deactivate foreign (viral) genes entering a cell like invaders hiding in a Trojan horse. If viral DNA is expressed, the products take over the workings of the cell. How can viral DNA be quickly deactivated without some enzyme having to slowly chew off nucleotides from each end of a long viral genome? A given restriction nuclease recognizes a specific sequence of bases in the DNA that is usually six to eight base pairs in length. The

phenol—an organic compound that denatures membranes and proteins, bringing them out of solution so that they can be removed from the system, leaving highly polymerized DNA behind.

restriction nuclease—an enzyme that recognizes a specific sequence of six to eight base pairs along a double-stranded DNA molecule; it creates within the base sequence a staggered break in the DNA characterized by single-stranded DNA ends.

DNA Isolation

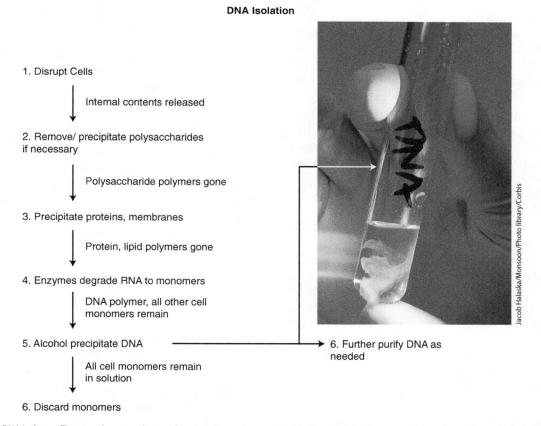

1. Disrupt Cells

    Internal contents released

2. Remove/ precipitate polysaccharides if necessary

    Polysaccharide polymers gone

3. Precipitate proteins, membranes

    Protein, lipid polymers gone

4. Enzymes degrade RNA to monomers

    DNA polymer, all other cell monomers remain

5. Alcohol precipitate DNA ⟶ 6. Further purify DNA as needed

    All cell monomers remain in solution

6. Discard monomers

Jacob Halaska/Monsoon/Photo library/Corbis

Figure 7.35 DNA Isolation. The procedure at each step of the isolation varies considerably depending on the nature of the cell type from which the DNA is isolated. Newer, proprietary approaches abound.

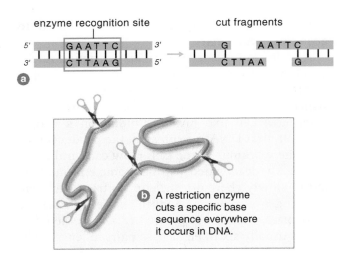

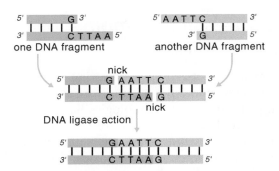

a

b A restriction enzyme cuts a specific base sequence everywhere it occurs in DNA.

Figure 7.36 Restriction Nucleases. **(a)** Amazing enzymes that are prepared to make a staggered cut through the DNA double helix, but only at sites where a precise DNA base sequence is present. Imagine the precision of design inherent in the active site of this enzyme! **(b)** Such breaks will occur randomly but fairly frequently within the genome of the cell.

Figure 7.37 Ligation. Ligase enzyme was created in order to repair single-stranded nicks or breaks in the sugar-phosphate backbone of the DNA molecule. How very useful it's become to genetic engineers. How fortunate that they did not have to design it before being able to use it!

nuclease makes a staggered cut at that sequence (see Figure 7.36a). Since the recognition sequence shows up (by chance?) only every 1000 base pairs or so, the nuclease, when incubated with a DNA sample will degrade long polymeric segments in the sample to gene-sized segments of various lengths (see Figure 7.36b). In nature, this means that critical viral genes cannot be transcribed. In the lab, a chosen sample of DNA from some cell of interest can be degraded such that one segment may well contain our gene of interest. If not, there are hundreds of different restriction nucleases with differing recognition sites that can be tried. One of them will leave our gene of interest in a gene-sized segment. Now it must be found!

How do these gene segments get chemically linked with genes from other organisms?

Suppose we place DNA from two separate sources into one tube. We then add a restriction nuclease isolated from the bacterium *E. coli* that lives in our bowel. That enzyme, EcoR1, recognizes the base sequence GAATTC/CTTAAG in double-stranded DNA and makes a staggered cut across the double helix exactly as shown in Figure 7.36a. The product of the cut is two segments of DNA with what we call "sticky ends." The two cut ends could easily base pair with each other: Their sequences are complementary. There just isn't enough available energy for them to covalently rejoin. However, if the complementary sticky ends do "find each other" briefly in solution, another DNA handling enzyme called

ligase (Lt., *liga-* = to bind or tie) could quickly glide over that base-paired region and reform the originally broken covalent bonds. Now remember, we're using DNA from two different sources. So sticky ends of two DNA molecules from the two different organisms can get together, and the ligase can join them. The result (see Figure 7.37) is recombinant DNA—a possibly quite novel gene combination.

How can you find the particular DNA segment you want?

We begin by controlling the DNA sources in the mixing experiment described previously. One source is the genome of the cells that contain the gene we wish to fish out—like a needle from a haystack. The other source of DNA is millions of copies of a single, small, circular, double-stranded DNA molecule called a **plasmid**. Plasmids were discovered in bacterial cells where their DNA codes for functions less "basic," more optional, than the genes on the bacterial chromosome. Small plasmids containing about 3 to 15 genes are a nice size for this work (see Figure 7.38). Because they are short, we have already learned the DNA base sequence of many of them. Before bacterial cells divide, they replicate their chromosomes and in some cases duplicate their plasmids

EcoR1—a restriction nuclease that recognizes the base sequence GAATTC/CTTAAG in double-stranded DNA; it creates single-stranded ends with the sequences—AATTC and CTTAA—

ligase—an enzyme that recognizes breaks in DNA molecules between sugars and phosphates along the DNA backbone; it repairs these breaks.

plasmid—a small, circular piece of double-stranded DNA found within a cell; it contains a far smaller number of (functionally less critical) genes than are found in a cell's chromosomal DNA.

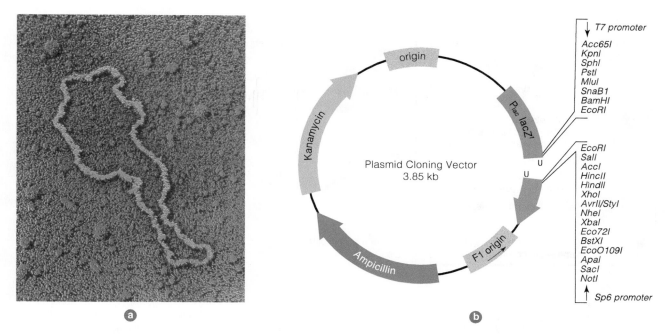

Figure 7.38 Plasmids. **(a)** a color-enhanced electron microscope image of a circular plasmid DNA isolated from a bacterium. A bacterial chromosome would be hundreds of times larger. **(b)** This plasmid has about 5 different genes carefully engineered onto it. The purple and blue ones enable the engineer to be certain a bacterial cell contains this plasmid. The red gene has cut sites for about 22 different restriction nucleases, any of which can be used to open up the plasmid for insertion of foreign DNA. Such insertion disrupts the *lacZ* gene, destroying it's function. Within a bacterial cell such loss indicates that foreign DNA is in the plasmid at that point.

up to a hundred or more copies per cell. Thus it is not difficult to get many copies of a single plasmid.

We carefully mix equal amounts of DNA from our two sources and add our selected restriction nuclease. Based on our knowledge of the plasmid's DNA base sequence, we already know that the nuclease will cut it open in exactly one place (see Figure 7.39). This will make our plasmid a linear, double-stranded piece of DNA. If we cut both our DNA and our plasmid with the same restriction nuclease, we'll have two sets of linear molecules all having the same sticky ends. Controlling the dilution of our DNA segment mixture, we then allow the sticky ends to bond with each other and we use a ligase enzyme to paste DNA segments together. The result is a whole **library** of different gene sequences, each one nested within a small plasmid whose DNA sequence we know (see Figure 7.39).

But how can a plasmid help you find your gene of interest?

We have extensively cut and pasted DNA sequences on these plasmids; they are highly engineered. Look again at Figure 7.38. This plasmid has a site where it can be cut open with a wide variety of restriction nucleases for insertion of our gene of interest. We well know the DNA sequence to either side of that cut site. We haven't isolated our specific gene yet. But that gene is now isolated into a plasmid away from all the other genes of its genome. Once we find it, our restriction nuclease that enabled it to combine with the plasmid will pop it back out and give it to us in pure form. What we have is like a school library's information neatly separated into discrete "books." But there's no catalog. So now we must find the one book we are looking for.

How might you find the gene that codes for insulin from a huge collection of plasmids?

Insulin is a small protein. It is fairly similar in cows and humans and biochemists can purify it from pancreas tissue. It is now possible to begin lopping off amino acids from the front end of the protein and identifying them. Because insulin is a small protein, its amino acid sequence has been known for years. But suppose we knew only the first seven amino acids in the protein. Using the genetic code we could write down a small variety

library—a collection of gene-sized pieces of DNA each inserted into a plasmid or other vector. The collection, taken from a single cell type, is large enough to include all the genes present in a cell's genome.

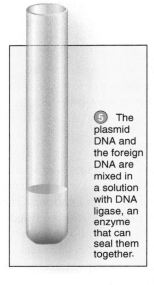

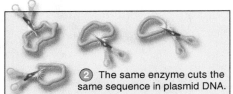

① A selected restriction enzyme cuts a specific base sequence everywhere it occurs in a chromosome.

② The same enzyme cuts the same sequence in plasmid DNA.

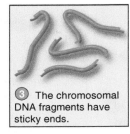

③ The chromosomal DNA fragments have sticky ends.

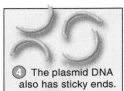

④ The plasmid DNA also has sticky ends.

Figure 7.39 Library Construction. Building a library of the genome of an organism involves cutting and pasting millions of randomly generated genomic fragments into millions of copies of the same, well studied plasmid. The plasmid is the "book cover". The "content" is the foreign DNA sequence.

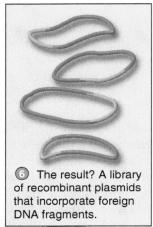

⑤ The plasmid DNA and the foreign DNA are mixed in a solution with DNA ligase, an enzyme that can seal them together.

⑥ The result? A library of recombinant plasmids that incorporate foreign DNA fragments.

encounter a gene whose first 21 nucleotides are complementary in base sequence to the probe, base paring will occur and this becomes the reactant in a gene-searching process known as the **polymerase chain reaction** (PCR).

What is PCR?

PCR is a process designed to search within a huge population of diverse gene sequences. The components of the process work together to find a specific sequence of interest and make so many copies of that single sequence that they become the dominant species of DNA in the sample (see Figure 7.41). The 21-nucleotide-long sequences of single-stranded DNA we have constructed (red, in the diagram) will be used as **primers** of DNA synthesis for the

of nucleotide sequences 21 base pairs long that would code for those seven amino acids (see Figure 7.40). Why could we not write down a single sequence? Suppose we designed several nucleotide sequences of single-stranded DNA. These could all be produced using current gene machine technology. We then use a population of millions of these 21-nucleotide-long sequences as probes. When they

polymerase chain reaction—a technique that replicates a single or few copies of a segment of DNA by several orders of magnitude, generating millions of copies of a particular DNA sequence.

primer—a short sequence of single-stranded DNA that, by base pairing with a much longer template strand of DNA provides a substrate for DNA polymerase to lengthen using the template sequence as a guide.

Finding the Gene for Insulin

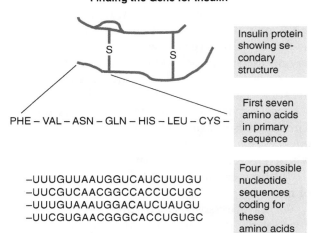

Insulin protein showing secondary structure

PHE – VAL – ASN – GLN – HIS – LEU – CYS –

First seven amino acids in primary sequence

–UUUGUUAAUGGUCAUCUUUGU
–UUCGUCAACGGCCACCUCUGC
–UUUGUAAAUGGACAUCUAUGU
–UUCGUGAACGGGCACCUGUGC

Four possible nucleotide sequences coding for these amino acids

Figure 7.40 Finding the Insulin Gene. Working backwards from the amino acids sequence, we infer nucleotide sequences and use these early sequences to "fish" the gene from our library using the polymerase chain reaction.

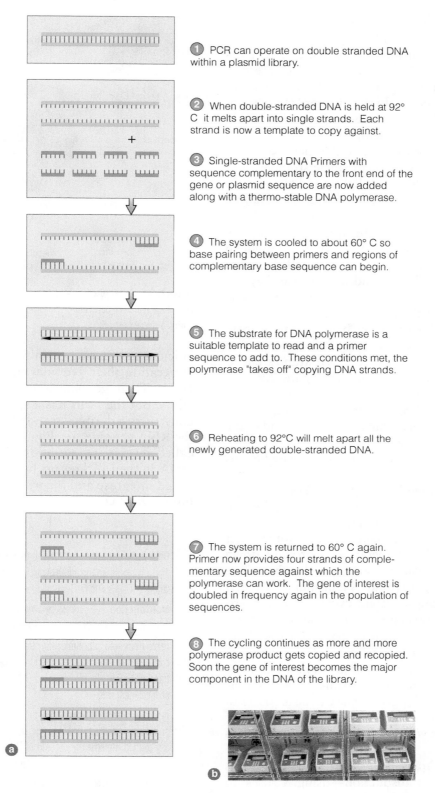

① PCR can operate on double stranded DNA within a plasmid library.

② When double-stranded DNA is held at 92° C it melts apart into single strands. Each strand is now a template to copy against.

③ Single-stranded DNA Primers with sequence complementary to the front end of the gene or plasmid sequence are now added along with a thermo-stable DNA polymerase.

④ The system is cooled to about 60° C so base pairing between primers and regions of complementary base sequence can begin.

⑤ The substrate for DNA polymerase is a suitable template to read and a primer sequence to add to. These conditions met, the polymerase "takes off" copying DNA strands.

⑥ Reheating to 92°C will melt apart all the newly generated double-stranded DNA.

⑦ The system is returned to 60° C again. Primer now provides four strands of complementary sequence against which the polymerase can work. The gene of interest is doubled in frequency again in the population of sequences.

⑧ The cycling continues as more and more polymerase product gets copied and recopied. Soon the gene of interest becomes the major component in the DNA of the library.

Figure 7.41 Polymerase Chain Reaction. **(a)** Small primer sequences of single-stranded DNA (shown in red) drift through melted, single-strand plasmid libraries binding to genomic DNA sequences that their base sequence is complementary to. A special DNA polymerase recognizes the ends of these primers and builds gene sequence onto them, making more copies of the gene being searched for. **(b)** Shelves of machines busily running PCR amplification of genes.

left-hand side of the insulin gene. Corresponding primers for the right-hand side of the gene can be made to be complementary to the first 21 base pairs in the plasmid DNA sequence after the insertion point where the insulin gene is located. This plasmid sequence is well known. In the PCR process, the entire population of plasmids we created earlier would be placed at 92°C. At this temperature, the hydrogen bonds between bases in the double helix of DNA melt apart and DNA becomes single stranded. The temperature is then lowered slightly and our primers are added along with **DNA polymerase,** an enzyme that makes new copies of DNA strands. The DNA polymerase used here is one that functions well at very high temperatures. The primers we added wander around within our sample of all the genes in the genome until they find a sequence they are complementary to—the front end of the insulin gene and the tail end of the plasmid just after the insulin gene. As soon as the primers base pair with these sequences, they become a reactant for the enzyme DNA polymerase. Because a DNA strand's chemistry has an orientation to it (see Figure 7.9), the polymerase will only copy forward on one strand of DNA into the front end of the insulin gene and backward on the other strand into the tail end of the insulin gene (see Figure 7.41).

How does replication of the insulin gene help us to find it?

After enough time has elapsed to copy through the insulin gene, the temperature of the system is suddenly raised to 92°C again. All DNAs melt apart again and become single strands. More primer is added. When the temperature is brought down again and strands can rebond to each other, there are now four single strands of insulin DNA that can be read during a second cycle of the process. If the process of raising and lowering temperature and adding primer is allowed to go on for about 30 cycles, there will soon be a billion copies of the insulin gene while all other genes in the genome remain essentially uncopied. At this point, a simple biochemical separation technique can be used to isolate the desired plasmid containing the insulin gene.

Once you have your gene, how do you get it into human cells?

Various techniques have been studied for this purpose. One is **transduction**—using viruses to carry genetic information into cells. Historically, the preferred technique has been to cut human genes from plasmids and ligate them into **retrovirus** genomes (see Figure 7.42). Retroviruses are very

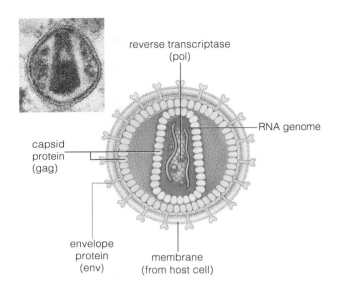

Figure 7.42 Retroviruses. Among these viruses are those that cause AIDS, and various cancers, particularly leukemias. Thousands of retroviruses could fit within a single host cell.

efficient at entering certain human cell types and integrating their genomes into our chromosomal DNA. Their genome is composed of RNA, not DNA. But the virus has a specialized enzyme that constructs a double-stranded DNA sequence from the RNA genome (see Figure 7.43). This process is called **reverse transcription.** The double-stranded DNA is then picked up by another viral enzyme called **integrase** and incorporated directly into the human host cell's DNA. Thus this difficult part of

DNA polymerase—an enzyme that reads a sequence of bases along a single strand of DNA and constructs a complementary strand of DNA using nucleoside-triphosphates as substrates.

transduction—a process by which a virus carries foreign DNA into a host cell; the DNA is then expressed within the host.

retrovirus—a subcellular infectious particle whose genome is composed of RNA. In the infection process, the RNA is reverse-transcribed into double-stranded DNA, which integrates into the host cell genome.

reverse transcription—the process of using RNA base sequence to construct, first a single strand of DNA, and from that, a second complementary strand of DNA thereby replacing RNA-based information with DNA-based information.

integrase—an enzyme that recognizes similarity of base sequence between two double-stranded DNA molecules and then breaks covalent bonds in each molecule such that the two strands exchange ends with each other; integrates viral genes into host cell DNA.

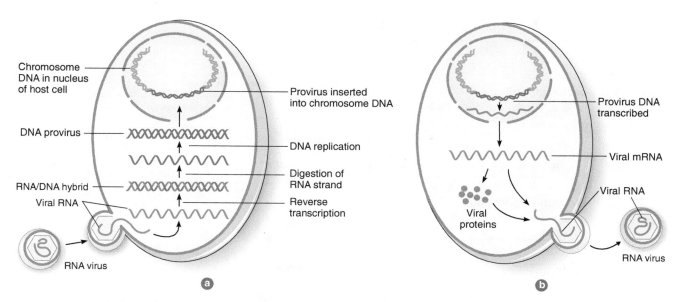

Figure 7.43   Retroviral Infection. **(a)** Viral Entry. The viruse's envelope protein binds to a host cell surface receptor protein (that has some other "normal" function.) This releases its RNA genome into the host cell cytoplasm where it is reverse transcribed into DNA and integrated into the host cell's DNA. This latent (quiet) proviral "presence" in the cell can last for days or years. **(b)** Stimulation of the cell to a high activity level can also promote return of the provirus to more activity. It's genome gets transcribed and translated to generate mature virus particles that then leave the host cell taking a bit of host cell membrane with them as they go.

gene therapy—getting the therapeutic gene incorporated into the cell's genome—has been designed for us! Retroviruses can be produced in cultured

cells from which the virus is harvested, disrupted, and the genome isolated.

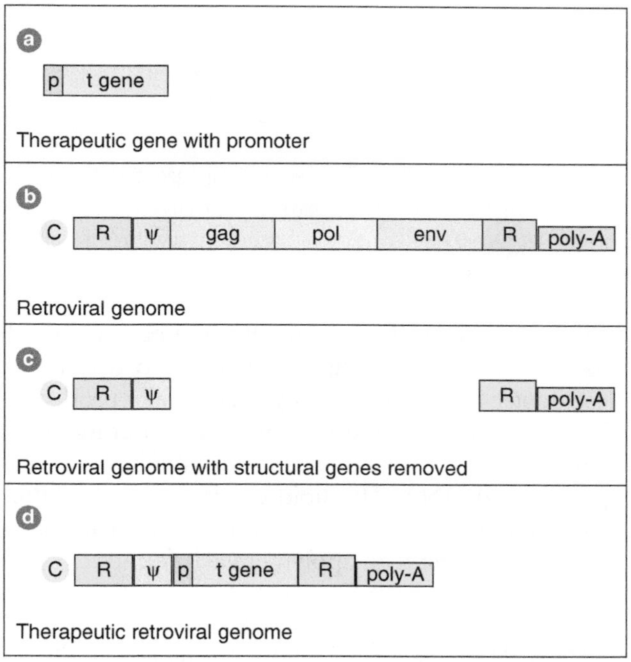

How does the retrovirus genome serve the genetic engineer?

The retroviral genome (see Figure 7.44b) contains highly useful repeated sequences at each end, which are read by a viral integrase enzyme. These same sequences occur in the human genome! The enzyme matches the human sequences up to the viral ones and then recombines the viral genome right into the host cell's DNA at that site. Also, within the viral genome, between the terminal repeat sequences, are four additional useful gene regions. One of these, called *psi* (Ψ), is a tag that is read during production of new virus particles. The psi sequence causes the virus' RNA genome to be properly packed into the outer protein coat that will protect it while the virus is outside the cell. The other gene regions, *gag, pol,* and *env* code for critical viral proteins: Gag codes for viral coat proteins, env codes for viral surface proteins that bind the virus to its host cell, and pol codes for the polymerase and integrase enzymes that process the viral genome and move it into the host cell DNA (see Figure 7.42).

How is a nasty retrovirus rendered "therapeutic"?

The trick is to produce a complete retrovirus with its surface proteins, coat, and enzymes all functioning properly. But in its genome, we will replace genes critical for further viral reproduction with a therapeutic human gene! We use a restriction

Figure 7.44   Recombining Genomes. **(a)** the therapeutic gene that has been found using PCR amplification. **(b)** the normal retroviral genome shown as an RNA ready for translation into viral proteins (note the cap and tail). **(c)** the parts of the viral genome that must be retained for proper packaging and integration later **(d)** the newly engineered retroviral genome with its therapeutic gene embedded.

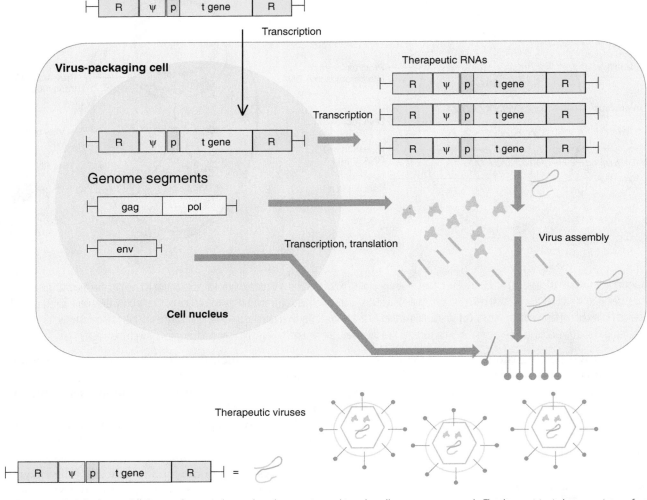

Figure 7.45 Virus Packaging Cell. Retroviral structural genes have been engineered into the cell genome permanently. The therapeutic viral genome is transfected into the packaging cell within which it is then transcribed into multipe copies. The psi function allows them to be packaged into newly assembled virus capsids. As they leave the cell, the viruses get enveloped with surface proteins that will gain them entry into patient's cells complete with enzymes that will repicate and integrate the therapeutic gene into the patient's cells genomes. Humans are "second generation" designers!

nuclease to cut out the gag, pol, and env genes and discard them (see Figure 7.44c). Then we use a ligase enzyme to paste a therapeutic human gene into the space between the two ends of the viral genome (see Figure 7.44d). The resulting virus will then neatly take that gene into our host cell, insert it into the genome, and then, lacking its structural gag, pol, and env genes, be unable to proceed any further with its infection process! The main problem with this is that we need the products of these structural genes to make functional therapeutic viruses in the first place.

How do we then make these therapeutic viruses?

Gene engineers have created what's called a *packaging cell line*. They keep these **cells** in **culture** (see Figure 7.45). The packaging cell has viral envelope, polymerase, and group antigen genes (gag) incorporated right within the cell's genome. But the packaging cell has no viral psi gene region—there is no way it can destroy itself ahead of time by accidentally producing viruses. Scientists then use a lipid-like **carrier molecule** to transfect the packaging cells with engineered therapeutic viral DNA. The lipid carrier takes the DNA through the cell membrane and the nuclear membrane where host RNA polymerase is found.

cell culture—the process of growing cells from a multicellular organism in dishes or bottles or on slides using a growth medium complex enough to support the growth and division of those cells apart from the host organism.

carrier molecule—a lipid-like polymer that attaches to DNA molecules and transports them into eukaryotic cells.

The packaging cell can do all the rest for us (see Figure 7.45). It transcribes the therapeutic virus genome into RNA copies appropriate for insertion into mature virus particles: The psi region was left intact in the therapeutic virus genome so it is present on these RNAs. A chemical signal added to the medium caused the packaging cell to transcribe and translate the in-house gag, pol, and env genes so that mature virus particles are generated. Each particle will have stuffed within it the therapeutic human gene plus the enzymes necessary to reverse transcribe the gene from RNA to DNA and the integrase needed to get the therapeutic gene incorporated into the human cell's DNA. What a triumph of human design technology!

What do we do with these therapeutic viruses?

We harvest them from the packaging cell culture (see Figure 7.46). They are used to infect a sample of the human somatic cells whose behavior we wish to correct. Again, this work is done by culturing the patient's cells apart from the patient. The cultured cell sample is then infected with the therapeutic virus. Finally, the genetic engineer must devise a simple way to select the cells that now have corrected function from among the remaining non-transduced defective cells. This may require getting individual patient cells into separate culture wells, growing them up as clones, and, for example, assaying individual clones for enzyme function.

Gene Therapy, Clinical Stages

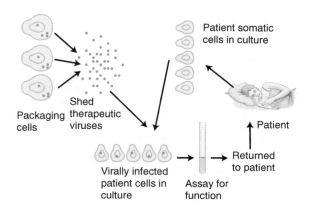

Figure 7.46 Gene Therapy, Clinical Stages. The therapeutic viruses generated by packaging cells are incubated with cells in culture taken from the patient. After infection occurs, the cells are assayed for correct functioning of the therapeutic gene and after several rounds of division are returned to the patient.

The cells with corrected gene function are then returned to the patient, where it is hoped that they compete favorably with the defective cell population remaining in the patient's body. In the cases where human gene therapy has been successful in the past (see below), patients required continuing occasional infusions of corrected cells to grow alongside of defective cells that continued to survive in the patient's body.

IN OTHER WORDS

1. DNA can be isolated from a variety of tissues using physical or chemical disruption of cells followed by various chemical purification steps.
2. Long polymeric DNA molecules can be reduced to gene-sized pieces with complementary base-pairing sticky ends. Restriction nucleases are used for this purpose.
3. Two separate populations of DNA molecules with such sticky ends can be mixed in one tube and ligated together such that recombinant molecules are produced having DNA from two distinct species.
4. Stable libraries of genomic DNA from a given cell type can be built by inserting DNA from that genome into the DNA of well-studied plasmids.
5. Information about the amino acid sequence of a protein can be used to construct primer sequences for the polymerase chain reaction process.
6. PCR is a process that uses primers and DNA polymerase to generate enormous numbers of DNA sequences built off of the same primer molecule.
7. A large uniform population of therapeutic genes can be ligated between the left and right ends of retroviral genomes to generate a therapeutic viral genome.
8. Packaging cells can incorporate the therapeutic genome into infectious virus particles in cell culture.
9. Therapeutic viruses can be incubated with cells from a patient needing gene therapy. The patient's cells can be assayed for successful virus integration and therapeutic gene function.
10. Cured patient cells can be reintroduced to the patient, where they must compete with noncured cells in order for the patient to experience relief from the genetic disease state.

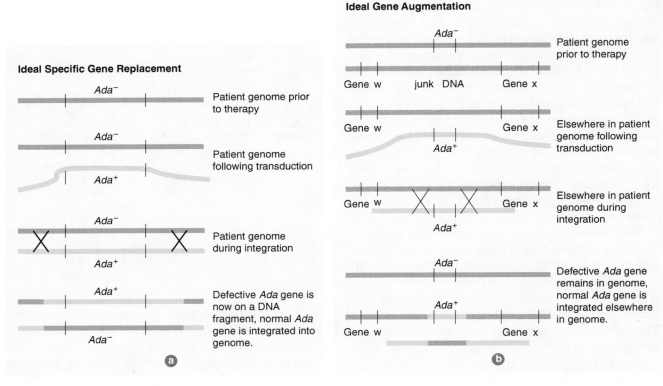

Figure 7.47 Approaches to Gene Therapy. **(a)** Specific replacement therapy involves precise intra locus replacement of a defective gene by a normal one. **(b)** Augmentation therapy seeks to stably add a normal gene to a cell without concern for the defective gene or the effects of its products. In both cases, some integrase enzyme is probably seeing base sequence similarities between sequences to either side of the therapeutic gene being inserted and sequences in genomic DNA. This is what results in the recombination events (the X's in the diagram) that brings the therapeutic gene into the genome.

The Sobering Early History of Human Gene Therapy

The first documented attempt at controlled human gene therapy was carried out in 1990 at the National Institutes of Health on a four-year-old girl named Ashanti DeSilva. At that time, two conceptual approaches to gene therapy were known. The one approach, called **specific replacement therapy,** would send a therapeutic gene into her cells in such a way that the defective gene would be removed from the nuclear DNA (see Figure 7.47a). The therapeutic gene would be recombined into the precise site from which the defective gene had been removed. In 1990, specific replacement therapy was not technically possible. So the only other approach—**augmentation therapy**—was followed (see Figure 7.47b). In this process, the more humble hope is to get a therapeutic gene incorporated and functioning somewhere within the genome. The mRNA from the therapeutic gene must outcompete or somehow compensate for mRNA coming from the defective gene that is still present. Was

this a simplistic assumption or was it a reasonable hope? Surely that would depend on the nature of defect in the nonfunctional gene.

Ashanti suffered from a genetic disease called *severe combined immunodeficiency* (SCID). She had very few functioning lymphocytes and, as a result, would be subject to a short life filled with endless infections, one of which would ultimately be her demise. Her particular version of the disease resulted from a defect in a single gene, *Ada,* coding for the enzyme adenosine deaminase. Since her *Ada* gene product was not working properly,

specific replacement gene therapy—a process by which a normal, functional gene is directly (spatially) substituted for a defective gene within a cell. The defective gene is removed and the normal one precisely takes its place within the genome.

augmentation gene therapy—a process by which a normal functional gene is permanently inserted and expressed within the genome of a defective cell. The defective gene in the cell remains; the location of the normal gene within the genome is not specified.

augmentation therapy seemed like a reasonable approach. After all, wouldn't a therapeutic version of the *Ada* gene simply enter the nucleus, get integrated, and begin functioning? If her defective gene produced either no mRNAs or mRNA coding for a nonfunctional enzyme, wouldn't a therapeutic gene product rescue her lymphocytes and get them functioning normally?

Modified retroviruses were used similar to those described in Section 7.4c. A helper cell population was transfected with a therapeutic viral-*Ada*⁺ genome and therapeutic viruses were made. A few surviving lymphocytes were isolated from Ashanti and transduced with therapeutic virus particles in culture. Joy abounded when her cell populations began to produce functional adenosine deaminase! These new healthy lymphocytes were given back to her by injection, and soon her disease symptoms began to wane. The day was a triumph for molecular medicine.

Subsequent results with SCID patients have seen guarded success. But most patients require subsequent infusions of corrected cells. They don't seem to be able to convert stably to the *Ada*⁺ condition. In some cases, their immune systems slowly destroy the corrected cells possibly because of residual viral (foreign) components (see Figure 7.48).

But a more insidious problem has surfaced. Back in the 1980s, when gene augmentation therapy was being considered, evolutionary assumptions about the organization of the human genome were naïve. It was hoped that the therapeutic *Ada* gene would integrate harmlessly somewhere in the large amounts of randomly distributed junk DNA that appeared to constitute much of the human genome. But such harmless, nonspecific integration events

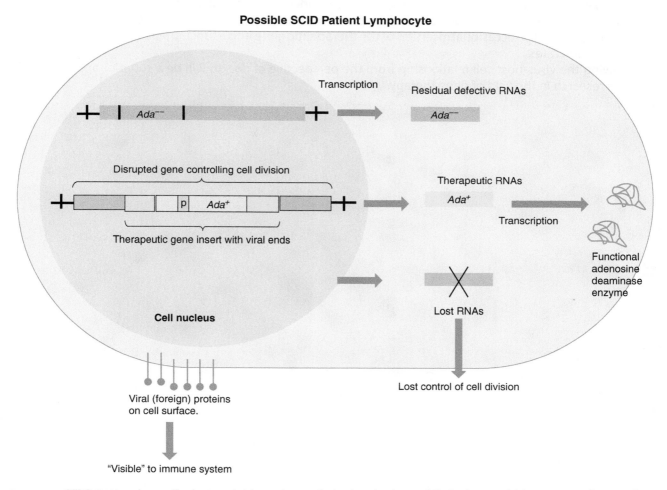

Figure 7.48 SCID Patient Lymphocytes. The theraupeutic Ada gene is transcribed and translated successfully. But the original defective gene is still present. The site of integration of the therapeutic gene is not controlled. This cell shows the gene inserted into a "proto-oncogene"—a gene whose malfunction results in the loss of control of cell division.

appear not to be the rule. Soon, patients who'd conquered SCID began developing leukemia—a form of lymphocytic cancer. Of 20 trials in Europe, five patients developed the disease. As a result, clinical trials in the United States were halted. It appears that the therapeutic viral genome is being integrated a bit more systematically than was hoped—integrating into the middle of genes whose consequent dysfunction is causing leukemia (see Figure 7.48). The relationship between the retrovirus and the human genome is more sophisticated than we'd supposed.

Specific gene replacement therapy is now being carried out successfully in mice. It will not be long before human studies succeed as well. Such therapies should avoid the errant integration events that predispose to leukemia. In retrospect, viewing the virus—human genome interaction from a design perspective rather than an evolutionary one may have enabled us to approach gene therapy in humans with a more appropriate caution. At the very least, secondary effects of the therapy might have been more prudently anticipated. Everywhere we look within the human cell and within the retrovirus, we see design. Specific gene replacement will completely succeed only when we take all of this design into account.

IN OTHER WORDS

1. Gene therapy has been successfully employed to temporarily cure severe combined immunodeficiencies (SCID) in cases where they are due to a dysfunctional adenosine deaminase gene.
2. Success in these efforts has been limited by the short-lived expansion of treated cell populations within the patient and the occasional insertion of the therapeutic gene into a functionally critical gene regulating cell division rates.
3. Viewing the virus-host cell relationship from the perspective of design will be a superior approach to future research in the field of gene therapy.

7.5 A HIDDEN DRAMA: INFORMATION EXPRESSION AT ITS VERY BEST

The prospects for biotechnology are bright! There are many exciting changes we will soon be making by expressing newly acquired information in novel ways. To save our dwindling modesty from morphing into undue presumption, let's finish this chapter on information expression by imagining a miracle. Imagine journeying to Ely, England and discovering two Ely cathedrals right next to each other, both just slightly smaller than the original one, both possessing all the intricacies and glory of the original one. What would the news media do with that one? (Who in the world could be responsible for such a spectacle?) Now, think again of the green alga *Micrasterias* or any other microbial lifeform. That wonderful miracle of self-replicating is happening constantly in mud puddles, in the backs of refrigerator drawers, and even within the microbial community in your own bowel. Complexity generating more complexity—this drama can only happen because living things have been provided with a vast and glorious store of information to express.

QUESTIONS FOR REVIEW

1. In what ways is information expression in a cell superior to that in the construction of an ornate part of a building?

2. Explain why the scientific community has at various times referred to the same molecule as nuclein, gene, and DNA.

3. Griffiths injected material from heat-killed virulent bacteria along with nonvirulent living bacteria into a mouse and discovered that the mouse soon dies. List two different control studies he must do, and the result he must get before his conclusions about transformation become justifiable.

4. What characteristic of enzymes makes their use in Avery's experiments so powerful in helping him reach his conclusions?

5. Consider some molecular details of Figure 7.9. What would be the effect on the double helix of allowing adenine to occasionally pair with guanine? cytosine with thymine? What feature of DNA's final structure was being constrained by Chargaff's findings about the relative amounts of adenine and thymine in his DNA samples?

6. Whose contribution to the discovery of the double helix was more important, Rosalind Franklin's or Watson and Crick's? Explain your response.

7. You have isolated a short piece of DNA. The base sequence of one of its strands is TGAGGAATCCTTCTT. Starting from the left-hand end, what would be the sequence of bases on the complementary strand?

8. In order for Theodor Boveri to assert that all of a sea urchin's chromosomes must be present and normal in order for development to proceed normally, what must he have been observing in his studies?

9. Look up the terms *transcription* and *translation* in a dictionary to see how they are used in relation to words. Why is the term *transcription* applied to mRNA production? Why is the term *translation* applied to the production of protein?

10. If the middle of an exon in a sense strand of DNA read as –GGTACCTAATT– what base sequence would be found in a pre-mRNA at that point? in a mature mRNA at that point?

11. List two possible structural differences between a ribonucleotide and a deoxyribonucleotide.

12. Predict what would happen to transcription in a bacterial gene if the termination sequence was altered (mutated) such that RNA polymerase would not recognize it.

13. List three differences between pre-mRNA and mature message.

14. After having read the section of the text on transcription, list two questions that are in your mind in regard to how gene expression is controlled.

15. In bacteria, transcription and translation can be happening to the same mRNA at the same time. How is this possible?

16. What are the four essential molecular components of the translation process?

17. Before tRNA's existence was demonstrated or its structure known, it was presumed to exist and was called the *adapter* molecule. Why was it given that name?

18. What is the functional role of a tRNA synthetase enzyme?

19. Which translation functions are served by the small ribosomal subunit? by the large subunit?

20. What is the role of tRNA in translational initiation? in elongation? in termination of translation?

21. Translate the following mRNA into a peptide chain:
   –AUGACACACACACACACACACUAAUGA–

22. A very important kind of cell surface protein is the glycoprotein, a protein that has sugar groups attached to it in its final form. List all the organelles involved in its production.

23. What is the value of having a genetic code that is degenerate?

24. Of the five examples of gene engineering in Section 7.4b, which ones represent genes now flowing in the germ line of engineered organisms?

25. List the steps involved in a typical gene therapy study.

26. What is transfection? How does it differ from transformation?

27. List the steps involved in making a plasmid library of the mouse genome.

28. What is the function of ligase? Use the phrase *covalent bond* in your answer.

29. When mixing cut plasmid DNA with cut genomic DNA, why is it critical to control the concentration of each DNA going into the mixture?

30. If you were asked to isolate from a genomic library the structural gene that codes for a protein that you've studied quite a bit, what would be your strategy for finding the gene?

31. For what purpose does a researcher use PCR?

32. Why were cancer-causing retroviruses chosen for development of a way of getting DNA into human cells?

33. Why is a packaging cell a necessary step in getting therapeutic viruses into human cells? Why not simply add a therapeutic gene to a virus genome and directly infect a patient's cells with it?

34. List two problems researchers have encountered in using the augmentation therapy approach to cure SCID patients.

QUESTIONS FOR THOUGHT

1. Consider the humble laborer standing beside a half-finished cathedral perfecting a stone to go into its wall. To which cellular organelle would he be most analogous?

2. You spent some time learning about atoms. Was that time wasted? Consider the atoms sulfur and phosphorus. How has our knowledge of these atoms helped us define and describe what DNA is and what its function is?

3. Assume for a moment that your body has 60 trillion human cells in it. (It has more bacterial cells than that within its structure.) Using the figure given in this chapter for DNA length per cell, what is the total length of the DNA in your body? (There are 1609 meters/mile.)

4. What function of a DNA molecule is principally served by coiling it up tightly through several levels of compaction? What function then is served by unwinding it to the relatively loose orientation seen in chromatin?

5. Since DNA has sufficient information for guiding protein structure and ribosomes are able to read base sequences directly, what would be the principle problem with using DNA directly to translate proteins?

6. Suppose a serious defect occurred in the promoter sequence of a gene. (We call these defects *mutations*). Which is more likely, that the mutation would result in a defective, nonfunctioning gene product or no gene product at all? Explain your choice.

7. The existence of transfer RNA was predicted a couple of years before it was discovered. How is that possible? What assumptions was the theoretician making?

8. What assumption is a scientist making when he refers to a sequence of DNA as *junk*?

9. Why are codons not two base pairs in length? Why are they not four base pairs in length?

10. How many different kinds of structures and molecules must a tRNA molecule fit or conform to structurally? What are the sources of constraint on its structure?

11. In order for translation to evolve so that proteins can be made, which must evolve first, synthetase enzymes or transfer RNAs? Explain your reasoning.

12. Is peptide bond formation an exergonic reaction or an endergonic reaction? Explain.

13. Think about the meaning of the genetic code. Think about the minority of organisms whose code varies from the normal one. Why might their codes vary in slight ways?

14. Which of the following diseases would probably be the most difficult to eradicate: sickle cell anemia, typhoid fever, or clinical depression? Explain your reasoning.

15. Which of the following examples are descended from germ line cells: liver tissue, ovarian follicle cells, sperm cells, pharyngeal epithelial cells, seminal vesicles, egg cells?

16. In bacterial cells where restriction nucleases are present for destroying the occasional intrusion of viral DNA, there is always another enzyme present called a *methylase*. This enzyme adds methyl groups ($-CH_3$) to DNA at the same sites where restriction nucleases normally make their cuts. What might be the purpose of such methylases?

17. Figure 7.38 diagrams a plasmid that has two antibiotic resistance genes on it. Where would you expect to find a bacterium that contains this plasmid?

18. The developer of PCR won a Nobel Prize for his efforts. Why is this procedure considered so valuable?

19. What is the value of infecting patient cells in culture? Why not simply introduce the therapeutic virus directly into a patient's bloodstream?

20. Suppose you had a young daughter with SCID. Would you be willing to submit her to currently available therapy and sign a document stating that you would not litigate against a clinic or a physician if the therapy does not yield the results you anticipate? Explain your position.

GLOSSARY

algal—of or referring to algae, a diverse, relatively simple, autotroph form of life typically found in fresh water or marine habitat; they lack distinct organs.

anticodon—a sequence of three adjacent nucleotide bases in tRNA that are complementary in sequence to an mRNA codon; the tRNA carrying it also carries the correct amino acid corresponding to the mRNA codon.

augmentation gene therapy—a process by which a normal functional gene is permanently inserted and expressed within the genome of a defective cell. The defective gene in the cell remains; the location of the normal gene within the genome is not specified.

cap—a guanine ribonucleotide with three phosphate groups and an additional methyl group that is attached to a pre-mRNA during processing; this structure assists in ribosomal attachment to a mature mRNA.

carrier molecule—a lipid-like polymer that attaches to DNA molecules and transports them into eukaryotic cells.

cell culture—the process of growing cells from a multicellular organism in dishes or bottles or on slides using a growth medium complex enough to support the growth and division of those cells apart from the host organism.

chromatin—fibers within the cell nucleus consisting of DNA periodically stabilized by being wrapped around protein spheres called *nucleosomes*.

chromosome—a highly coiled and organized arrangement of a single DNA molecule within the nucleus of a cell; used to transport DNA to a daughter nucleus.

codon—a sequence of three adjacent nucleotide bases in mRNA that code for a single amino acid in a sequence within a polypeptide chain or protein.

complementary—in nucleic acids, describes the appropriately sized nucleotide bases from opposite strands of a double-stranded DNA (adenine with thymine, guanine with cytosine) that pair via hydrogen bonds, thereby holding the double-stranded nucleic acid together.

degeneracy—absence of a one-to-one correspondence between codon sequence and the amino acid coded for; rather, several codons code for the same amino acid.

DNA polymerase—an enzyme that reads a sequence of bases along a single strand of DNA and constructs a complementary strand of DNA using nucleoside-triphosphates as substrates.

DNase—an enzyme that catalyzes the breakdown of DNA either into smaller segments of DNA or completely down to its nucleotide subunits.

domain—a structural region of contiguous amino acids within a protein that performs a specific component function within the overall function the protein performs.

EcoR1—a restriction nuclease that recognizes the base sequence GAATTC/CTTAAG in double-stranded DNA; it creates single-stranded ends with the sequences—AATTC and CTTAA—

elongation (transcription)—the movement of RNA polymerase along the DNA template strand generating a single complementary strand of RNA.

elongation (translation)—the movement of the ribosome along the mRNA generating a single polypeptide chain composed of amino acids.

exon—a sequence of nucleotides in DNA that are transcribed into pre-mRNA and that represent protein-coding portions of a gene; retained and joined together during processing to form a mature mRNA.

fraction—a single portion of a biological sample that is being separated into many such portions as part of a purification process.

gene—a segment of (usually) DNA that controls a single characteristic or trait of an organism.

genome—the collection of all the genetic information (genes) in the cells of an organism

genotype—the genetic makeup of—the informational specifications for—an organism.

germ line cell—any cells within the developing embryo whose descendant cells will become sperm or egg cells in the mature adult

GTP—guanosine triphosphate; a nucleoside triphosphate whose covalent bond between the second and third phosphates contains as much potential energy as the same bond in the ATP molecule.

hemoglobin—a protein with a quaternary level of structure consisting of four polypeptide chains, 2 α chains, and 2 β chains. It transports oxygen from the lungs to the tissues.

initiation (translation)—the productive binding of mRNA, an initiator tRNA, and a small and large ribosomal subunit into a complex that enables translation to begin.

initiation (transcription)—the productive binding of RNA polymerase to DNA and the initial alignment of ribonucleotides such that transcription has begun.

insulin—a hormone in mammals that controls the absorption of glucose into the tissues from the bloodstream.

integrase—an enzyme that recognizes similarity of base sequence between two double-stranded DNA molecules and then breaks covalent bonds in each molecule such that the two strands exchange ends with each other; integrates viral genes into host cell DNA.

intron—a sequence of nucleotides in DNA that are transcribed into pre-mRNA and that separate protein-coding portions of a gene from each other; removed during processing to form mature mRNA.

junk DNA—a sequence of DNA believed to have no useful function; some see usefulness for it in the past, other see usefulness for it in the future.

library—a collection of gene-sized pieces of DNA each inserted into a plasmid or other vector. The collection, taken from a single cell type, is large enough to include all the genes present in a cell's genome.

Life Is Information Expressed—one of 12 principles of life on which this book is based.

ligase—an enzyme that recognizes breaks in DNA molecules between sugars and phosphates along the DNA backbone; it repairs these breaks.

micron (or micrometer)—is 1/1000 of a millimeter; the millimeter is the smallest division visible on a metric ruler.

mRNA—a class of RNA molecules that code for proteins and serve to direct the process of translation on ribosomes in the cell cytoplasm.

mutated, mutation—referring to changes in the base sequence of DNA; change of identity of one base for another, loss or addition of a base, loss or addition of multiple bases; some mutations result in serious functional loss or organismal death.

nanogram—1/1000 of a microgram.

nanometer—a distance of 1/1000 of a micrometer. Cells are measured in micrometers. Molecules are measured in nanometers.

nucleosome—a structural repeat unit within chromatin in which 147 base pairs of DNA are wrapped around a spherical protein core for purposes of stability and protection.

phenol—an organic compound that denatures membranes and proteins, bringing them out of solution so that they can be removed from the system, leaving highly polymerized DNA behind.

phenotype—the physical appearance of an organism resulting from the expression of the organism's genotype.

phosphorus—an element in nature widely distributed in nucleic acids but seldom found in newly synthesized proteins.

plasmid—a small, circular piece of double-stranded DNA found within a cell; it contains a far smaller number of (functionally less critical) genes than are found in a cell's chromosomal DNA.

poly(A) tail—a sequence of adenine ribonucleotides attached to a pre-mRNA following transcription; controls the length of time a mature mRNA will survive degradation in the cell's cytoplasm.

polymerase chain reaction—a technique that replicates a single or few copies of a segment of DNA by several orders of magnitude, generating millions of copies of a particular DNA sequence.

pre-mRNA—an RNA molecule that is an immediate product of transcription; it contains introns that must be removed before it can be translated into protein.

primer—a short sequence of single-stranded DNA that, by base pairing with a much longer template strand of DNA provides a substrate for DNA polymerase to lengthen using the template sequence as a guide.

promoter—a sequence of bases in DNA that guides an RNA polymerase to the precise position where initiation of transcription is to occur.

proteinase—an enzyme that catalyzes the breakdown of protein either into smaller segments of peptides or completely down to its amino acid subunits.

recombinant DNA—the use of nuclease and ligase enzymes to cut and join segments of DNA from the cells of two different species of organisms.

release factor—a protein that enters a tRNA binding site on the ribosome; sensing the presence of a stop codon, it causes translation to terminate.

restriction nuclease—an enzyme that recognizes a specific sequence of six to eight base pairs along a double-stranded DNA molecule; it creates within the base sequence a staggered break in the DNA characterized by single-stranded DNA ends.

retrovirus—a subcellular infectious particle whose genome is composed of RNA. In the infection process, the RNA is reverse-transcribed into double-stranded DNA, which integrates into the host cell genome.

reverse transcription—the process of using RNA base sequence to construct, first a single strand of DNA, and from that, a second complementary strand of DNA thereby replacing RNA-based information with DNA-based information.

ribonucleotide—a subunit of the nucleic acid polymer RNA; within RNA it is composed of a single phosphate attached to a ribose sugar that is attached to one of the nitrogenous bases adenine, cytosine, guanine, or uracil.

RNA polymerase—a protein; an enzyme that builds RNA molecules using free ribonucleotides and using a strand of DNA as a sequence template (guide) against which to build.

RNase—an enzyme that catalyzes the breakdown of RNA either into smaller segments of RNA or completely down to its nucleotide subunits.

rRNA (ribosomal RNA)—single-stranded nucleic acids composed using ribose sugars and containing the nitrogenous base uracil instead of thymine. They form structural parts of ribosomes assisting with alignment of other RNA classes.

somatic cell—a cell from the body of an organism that carries out some contributory function there other than becoming a sex cell.

specific replacement gene therapy—a process by which a normal, functional gene is directly (spatially) substituted for a defective gene within a cell. The defective gene is removed and the normal one precisely takes its place within the genome.

splicing enzyme—small particles composed of protein and RNA that attach to pre-mRNA at junction points between introns and exons; they cut RNA at these sites, remove intron sequences, leaving exon sequences contiguous to each other.

start codon—the base sequence –AUG- in mRNA that codes for the amino acid methionine. This sequence is the first translated codon in most mRNA molecules.

stem cells—undifferentiated cells found in most organisms; cells that are able to divide continuously by mitosis and eventually differentiate into any of the types of cells found in the mature organism.

stop codon—one of three mRNA base sequences, –UAA–, –UAG–, or –UGA–, for which there is no corresponding amino acid; recognized by release factors that cause translation termination.

sulfur—an element in nature widely distributed in proteins (because of its presence in the amino acids cystine and cysteine) but never found in nucleic acids like DNA or RNA.

termination (transcription)—the process by which transcription ends, including the disassociation of RNA polymerase from its DNA substrate and the release of the mRNA or pre-mRNA product.

termination (translation)—the process by which translation is ended, including the disassociation of ribosomal subunits, mRNA, and a completed polypeptide chain.

transcription—the process of reading a sequence of bases in DNA and generating from it a complementary sequence of bases in RNA.

transduction—a process by which a virus carries foreign DNA into a host cell; the DNA is then expressed within the host.

transfection—the process of incorporating DNA from an external source into the nucleus of a eukaryotic cell.

transform—to change a hereditary characteristic of an organism by introducing new DNA into its genome.

transformation—the process of incorporating DNA from an external source into the genome of a bacterial cell.

translation—the process of reading a sequence of bases in RNA and generating from it an encoded sequence of amino acids that comprise a polypeptide chain or protein.

tRNA synthetase—an enzyme that recognizes the structure of from one to four tRNAs that specify a particular amino acid; the enzyme links them covalently to that correct amino acid.

tRNA (transfer RNA)—single-stranded nucleic acids composed using ribose sugars and containing the nitrogenous base uracil instead of thymine. They attach to and transport amino acids to ribosomes for incorporation into growing protein chains.

virulent—possessing a highly increased ability to cause disease.

Weismannian border—the conceptual divide between somatic cells and germ line cells; gene therapy in humans employs only somatic cells.

X-ray crystallography—a physical technique in which a purified sample of protein or nucleic acid is exposed to high-powered electromagnetic radiation to determine its molecular structure.

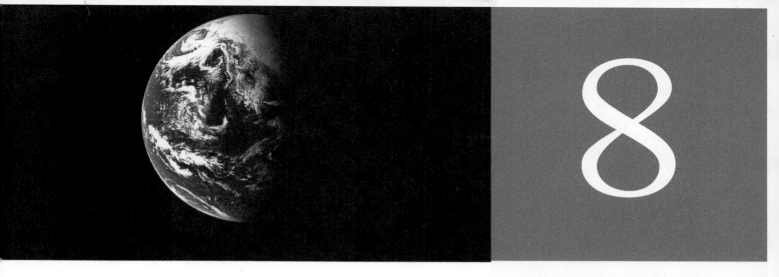

Informational Continuity in Cells

8.1 A THIN SKIN OF LIFE CHASING DEATH

He had never seen such a moon, so white, so blinding, and so large ... 'Weston,' he gasped, 'what is it? It's not the moon, not that size. It can't be, can it?' 'No,' replied Weston, 'it's the earth.' ...
—C. S. LEWIS, *OUT OF THE SILENT PLANET*

It suddenly struck me that that tiny pea, pretty and blue, was the Earth. I put up my thumb and shut one eye, and my thumb blotted out the planet Earth. I didn't feel like a giant. I felt very, very small.
—NEIL ARMSTRONG, FROM THE *APOLLO 11* SPACECRAFT, 1969

Somewhere, tucked far away in the cold dark emptiness of universal space is an incredibly tiny planet bearing life. You happen to be on it. Within its mere 8000-mile diameter, life's domain is only a few miles thick—a precariously thin skin on a cinder in the near infinity of cosmos. That's our biosphere.

Close examination of life-forms within this thin skin reveals that they all have death as a prospect. Life spans limit the large forms; predation and competition, the small ones. Since life spans of organisms are vanishingly brief compared with life's history on Earth, life

Survey Questions

8.1 A Thin Skin of Life Chasing Death
- What is the "thin skin of life"?
- How are the processes of life and death related in the living world?

8.2 Cell Division: A Requirement of Life
- What is the importance of cell division in the living world?
- What is the result of many cell divisions in a yeast cell or in a fertilized human egg cell?
- How does a cell prepare to divide?
- What does each daughter cell need to receive from the parent cell?
- How is the cell's DNA information copied prior to cell division?
- How are the copies managed during cell division?

8.3 Cell Division Is Part of a Cycle: the Cell Cycle
- What is a cell cycle?
- What aspects of cell life other than division are part of the cell cycle?
- What are the stages within the cell cycle?
- What occurs in each stage?
- Is cycling time constant or subject to control? How is the cycle controlled?

8.4 Mitosis
- What is the role of mitosis in the cell cycle?
- What happens to chromosomes before, during, and after mitosis?
- How is the process of mitosis organized?
- How do chromosomes actually get moved into daughter cells?

8.5 Cytokinesis

- How does cytokinesis differ from mitosis? from cell division?
- What changes occur during this process?
- How does a cell with a rigid wall get divided in half?

8.6 Cancer: Mutation Threatening Design

- What is a mutation?
- How many genes, when mutated, cause cancer?
- What do these genes normally do when not mutated?
- How can a mutation in DNA cause a cell to become cancerous?

Life's Essential Resources in Cell Division

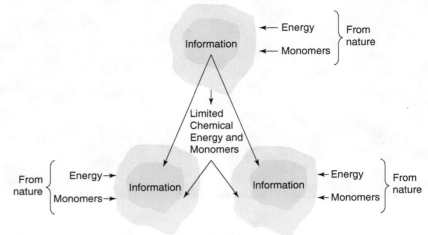

Figure 8.1 Life's Essential Resources. Newly divided cells bring all three essential resources along from the parent cell. But soon raw materials and energy are obtained from the cell's own environment. Information is not.

must have a rugged continuity to it. It has persisted through millennia! If, in its chase after death, life did not persist and prevail over it, Earth would become Mars. How does life manage to keep up?

The chase of life requires three essential resources for its success: a good supply of life's monomers (recyclables like sugars and amino acids), a persistent supply of energy (the sun will do . . .), and a continuous source of information to direct growth (see Figure 8.1). Now, some monomers, parts of other monomers, and the energy to use them are coming into life-forms from nature around them. But the information is not. It is internal. This most amazing, self-directing character of living things forms the basis for our sixth principle: **Life Is Informational Continuity.** To have life is to have inherited information from the past. To have robust life is to pass information into the future. Like some precious Biblical text, life's information creeps forward through time, carefully copied within cells, relentlessly protected from sources of change.

The chase of life in the skin of Earth is essentially cellular in nature. So is death. Just before a viewing, the funeral director clips the nails and trims a few hairs on the corpse. Not every cell finishes life at exactly the same moment! So this whole business of acquiring monomers and energy takes place at the microscopic level. In the chapter on cell structure we saw why this was necessary. Diffusion brings monomers and energy sources to the cell. Diffusion rates are quite adequate over microscopic distances. But for large organisms like ourselves, diffusional processes are hopelessly slow. Our cellularity delivers us from smearing peanut butter on our arms and waiting for it to diffuse to our bones. But if Earth's thin skin is cellular, then in order to win life's race, it is cells that do the absorbing, the processing, the growing, and the dividing. They must do this at a rate that at least matches the death rate. So to understand life's informational continuity, we must understand cell growth and division. We will find it to be a wonderfully timed, cyclical, integrated, and carefully controlled process.

Life Is Informational Continuity—one of 12 principles of life on which this text is based; DNA base sequence that is used to craft any cell came to that cell from a parental cell by DNA replication.

IN OTHER WORDS

1. The biosphere is a place where living things both die and yet persist.
2. Living things require monomers of life, an energy source, and information.
3. These resources are processed and used at the cellular level.
4. Understanding the balance of life requires an understanding of cell growth and division.

8.2 CELL DIVISION: A REQUIREMENT OF LIFE

The division of a parental cell into two daughter cells is a basic life process. Yet its significance depends heavily on its context. In single-celled organisms, cell division amounts to reproduction. The daughter cells are two new individuals in a population of largely independent cells. By contrast, in multicellular organisms, cell division is how the organism grows to its adult size and replaces its worn-out tissues (see Figure 8.2).

Consider the humble yeast cell. Some of its varieties have lived on us and within us. Others have matured our breads and wines for centuries. A common form of cell division in yeast is **budding** (see Figure 8.2). A daughter cell begins as a small bud on the end of the maternal cell. The bud acquires monomers and energy from the maternal cell, and eventually its own nucleus from the maternal nucleus. When the bud approaches the size of the maternal cell it normally breaks free, leaving behind a bud scar on the surface of the maternal cell. The mature bud is a complete version of the entire organism. Nothing is missing from the daughter cell. The maternal yeast cell has reproduced itself.

A single fertilized human egg cell is a quite different story. On its voyage through a masterful developmental program, it will divide its way to over 100 trillion cells in a period of 18 to 20 years (see Figure 8.2, Chapter 9). Along the way, daughter cells will grow, **differentiate**, and eventually cooperate to read this sentence! Only you—the resulting individual—have all of your properties. No one cell of your body could be called the "essential organism." In you, cell division is not reproduction of the individual; it is rather a means of growth—and replacement. Even before your adult form is reached, replacement processes begin. Your body's cells are entirely replaced with new ones in an average of seven years' time. For example, though your life expectancy may be 78 years, that of each of your 30 trillion red blood cells is only about

> **budding**—in yeast, the process by which a new daughter cell emerges from the surface of the larger maternal cell using materials and information from the maternal cell.
>
> **differentiation**—a process by which, through time and successive generations of cells, stem cells commit to utilizing a specific part of their genomes; this process transforms them into specific types of cells like neurons or epithelial cells.

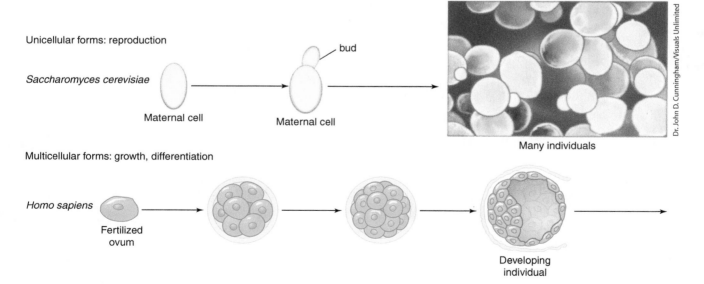

Unicellular forms: reproduction

Saccharomyces cerevisiae

Maternal cell → Maternal cell → bud → Many individuals

Dr. John D. Cunningham/Visuals Unlimited

Multicellular forms: growth, differentiation

Homo sapiens

Fertilized ovum → → → Developing individual →

Figure 8.2 Cell Division in Context. When unicellular yeast divides the result is reproduction of more yeast cells. When human egg cells divide, a new completely differentiated organism is the product. Various strains of the yeast *Saccharomyces cerevisiae* are used in baking bread and fermenting fruit juices. A different genus of yeast, *Candida*, contains species that grow on and in humans where they occasionally cause oral and vaginal infections.

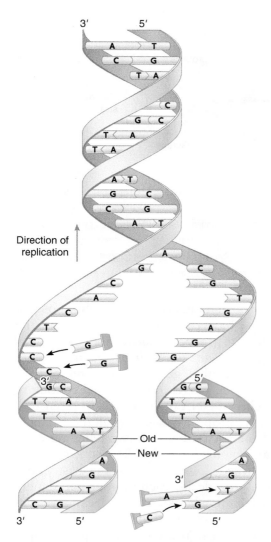

3'   5'

A — T
C — G
T — A

C
G — C
T — A
T — A

A — T
G — C
C — G
A — T

Direction of
replication

A
G — C
C
G
A
C — T
C
G
T
C — G
C
C
3' G — C
G C
T — A   T — A
T — A   T — A
A — T   A — T

Old

New

A   A
G   3'   G
A — T   A — T
C — G   A → T
G → G
C

3'   5'   5'

Figure 8.3 DNA Replication. The maternal DNA molecule is shown in gray. New daughter strands are shown in red. As maternal strands unwind they become the templates against which new daughter polynucleotide strands are built using the base pairing rules. Each daughter double helix will be half-maternal, half newly-synthesized polymer.

from its structure (see Figure 8.3). The two strands need only separate from each other through the breaking of the interior hydrogen bonds between the bases. Then, using the base-pairing rules (the base A pairs with T, T pairs with A, G with C, and C with G), each single DNA strand can serve as a **template** against which to build a new strand with a sequence complementary to that of the template. All that is needed is a supply of monomeric **nucleosides** (in their **triphosphate** forms) and enzymes to read along the parental template strands, building a new daughter strand against each of them.

The molecular components of the DNA replication system are highly sophisticated. A set of 10 or more different protein "machines," working in synchrony, opens up the double helix, reads both template (parental) strands (each in the opposite direction of the other), builds new daughter strands, and checks for errors! The result is two new identical daughter double helices with an error rate of less than 1 in a billion base pairs misincorporated (see Figure 8.4). And the process runs at about 300 nucleotides per minute! The enzymes that actually orient and bond the individual nucleotides into the new DNA strands are called **DNA polymerases.** These proteins, some with **molecular weights** more than 100,000 times that of a hydrogen atom, are complicated multisubunit machines that can both produce and repair the structure of DNA.

Now, the polymerase enzymes themselves are protein products of polymerase genes within the genome. Yes, we are peering in on machinery that builds itself! Imagine the glory of an elegant polymerase molecule—like a brand new high performance sports car—rolling through the genome, copying hundreds of genes, and among them the very genes that code for its own amino acid sequence. What a powerful picture of external design

0.30 years. So for life to successfully chase death here, we require about 1 million cell divisions or 2 million new red blood cells every second—every second!— within your bone marrow tissue. Cell division both produces you and keeps you alive!

For an animal cell to grow and mature to the point of division, it continuously absorbs monomers, parts of monomers, and chemical energy sources. It selectively transports these across its cytoplasmic membrane. Monomer and polymer construction inside the cell support its growth. But while this is happening, the cell is also enzymatically copying its entire genome within the nucleus.

Recall that structurally, the cell's genome is DNA. How DNA can be replicated is immediately apparent

template—a sequence of nucleic acid that is read by a polymerase enzyme such that it generates a new sequence of bases complementary to the one read.

nucleoside triphosphate—a subunit monomer for nucleic acids DNA or RNA that includes three adjacent phosphate groups in its structure. ATP is an example.

DNA polymerase—an enzyme that replicates an organism's DNA by adding free nucleotides to the ends of single DNA strands.

molecular weight—the total mass number of the atoms comprising a molecule. Each carbon would contribute a mass number of 12 to the molecule; each oxygen, 16.

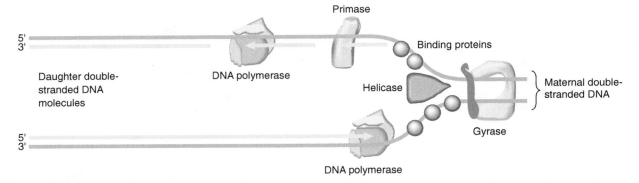

Figure 8.4 Enzymes of DNA Replication. Enzyme function is best understood in bacteria. After an opening is created in the maternal double-stranded DNA, a helicase enzyme inserts itself and begins to unwind the double strands. Binding proteins hop onto the DNA to keep it single-stranded transiently. Meanwhile, down ahead of the helicase a gyrase enzyme is twisting, breaking and resealing the DNA double helix so that helicase is able to continue unwinding the DNA strands. Primase enzyme creates a starting substrate for the DNA polymerase that has to work backwards along one strand of DNA while a second polymerase enzyme copies forward on the other strand. The reverse replication of the one strand is required by the fact that the one maternal DNA strand is upside down in orientation and chemistry relative to the other one.

imposing order on the randomness of nucleotide monomers in solution: a machine that copies code, copying its own code to generate more of itself!

One pair of polymerase enzymes starting DNA replication at one spot in the genome would be inefficient. The human genome at 3 billion base pairs would take over 10 years to replicate. Multiple polymerase systems start replicating the DNA at multiple **origins of replication** within the genome (see Figure 8.5). Replication proceeds in both directions from these points generating **bubbles** of replication, which grow larger and larger until they fuse to form one complete replicated genome. And what a pleasing result! Where we once had a

single complete maternal genome of billions of base pairs, we now have two double-stranded daughter genomes that are genetically identical to the original maternal genome *and to each other*. In fact, one strand of each daughter genome *is* a strand from the maternal genome. Life is informational continuity, and the fidelity of DNA replication is its essence.

But now we propose to separate all these daughter genes from each other into two daughter cells! The human genome has about 25,000 genes. Suppose you owned 25,000 books—the best books ever written! You decide each of your two daughters must have these books. So you spend a year or so accumulating a complete duplicate set of these same 25,000 books. You have to keep the duplicates next to each other while you are accumulating them so you know what to buy next. Now your daughters are leaving home. What process will you use to separate 50,000 books into two identical collections? Eat your breakfast that morning! Buy lots of small sturdy boxes! How in the world do cells sort their replicated genomes every time they prepare to divide?

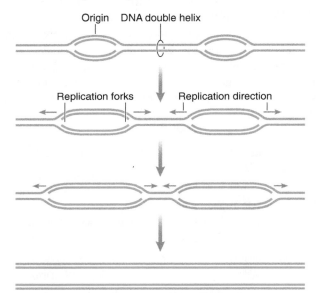

Figure 8.5 Chromosomal Replication. DNA replication begins at multiple sites within eukaryotic chromosomes.

origin of replication—a sequence of bases in DNA that is recognized by a helicase enzyme; the enzyme twists open the double helix at this point to allow a polymerase enzyme to begin replicating single DNA strands.

bubble—in DNA replication, the already-replicated region within the DNA molecule which begins at the origin of replication and expands as DNA is replicated in both directions from the replication origin.

Recall from Chapter 7, Section 2b, that multibillion base-pair genomes are organized into structures called *chromosomes*. You've seen their super-coiled structures (see Figure 7.12). Now, let's add a temporal context to this structuring. When is the genome loose, unraveled chromatin and when is it tightly packaged chromosomes (see Figure 8.6)? For the DNA replication process we've just discussed, the unraveled chromatin nicely allows the polymerase enzyme machinery access to all of the origins of replication in order to accomplish their roles. For a cell's growth and biosynthesis activities, the RNA polymerase machinery requires access to the genes' promoter regions as well. But a point is eventually reached in the cell's life where two genomes need to be taken in two separate directions—kind of like "packing the whole circus into the truck before moving to the next town." Prior to cell division, a period of condensation and packaging ensues that converts the DNA of chromatin into protein-scaffolded, tightly super-coiled chromosomes. The super-coiled DNA is so dense that stained chromosomes are easily visible with an ordinary light-illuminated microscope. However, when a genome as long as ours is tightly condensed to 46 more manageable chromosomes, it still requires a very elaborate system of microtubules to equally split and distribute them into daughter cells. We will

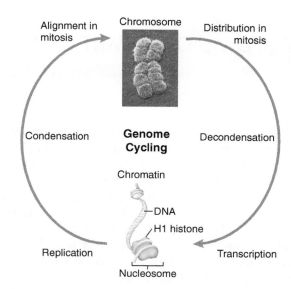

Figure 8.6 *Genome Cycling. Chromosome behavior coordinates immaculately with the roles required of it. When it is needed as an immediate information source, it assumes a decondensed form making the maximum amount of information accessible. When it is needed for allocating information to daughter nuclei it assumes a condensed form making distribution simpler.*

examine this distribution architecture in Section 8.4. Once their distribution is complete and cells have divided, chromosomes de-condense again making their DNA more accessible to the next round of transcriptional and replication activity.

IN OTHER WORDS

1. Cell division can represent reproduction or a component part of growth depending on the cellular complexity of the organism it occurs in.
2. One common method of reproduction in yeast cells is a form of cell division called *budding*.
3. Cells increasing in size, then dividing, and then differentiating transform a fertilized human egg into a human being.
4. In preparation for generating two daughter cells, a maternal cell must accumulate monomers and molecular forms of energy and must replicate its DNA.
5. DNA is replicated by polymerizing nucleotides into single strands of DNA; the single strands of the maternal DNA are used as templates against which to sequence daughter strands.
6. DNA replication is carried out by a collection of elegant proteins that unwind and stabilize maternal strands. DNA polymerase then builds the new strands.
7. Replication of DNA begins at multiple origins of replication distributed along each chromosome.
8. In the human genome, 25,000 genes' worth of DNA is replicated, then meticulously condensed into 46 chromosomes to be split, and their halves distributed into daughter cells.
9. DNA cycles from a highly condensed form suitable for distribution during mitosis to a de-condensed chromatin state suitable for its transcription and later replication.

8.3 CELL DIVISION IS PART OF A CYCLE: THE CELL CYCLE

Cell growth is the counterpart to cell division. Were there no growth, division would eventually reduce cell size to oblivion. Were there no division, cell growth would quickly render transport processes into and out of the cell ineffective. These two processes taken together are called the **cell cycle** (see Figure 8.7). The cycle begins when daughter cells emerge from a division event, and it ends when each daughter cell completes its own division process forming granddaughter cells.

Cell division is relatively brief and quite dramatic. Biologists in the 1800s observed it and meticulously characterized its structural changes (see Sections 8.4 and 8.5). They then rather dismissively gave the name **interphase** to the much longer, less spectacular growth interval that followed each division. In cultured mammalian cells, division may last the greater part of an hour, while interphase accounts for about 20 hours. In recent years, that 20 hours has been finely dissected.

Growth during interphase is a well-designed and carefully controlled process.

Right after division, the daughter cell enters a period of biosynthetic activity that usually continues throughout interphase. The result is growth of the cell from its size as a new daughter cell to an optimal size for its function. The first portion of this cell growth period is termed the **G$_1$ phase**

cell cycle—a sequence of stages that prepares a cell for and that carries it through cell division. It begins immediately within daughter cells following the division of a maternal cell.

interphase—that portion of the cell cycle when the cell is not in the process of dividing. It is characterized by biosynthesis and growth of the cell.

G$_1$ phase—an initial period of growth immediately following cell division that precedes DNA synthesis; highly variable in length in diverse cell types or under varying conditions of growth.

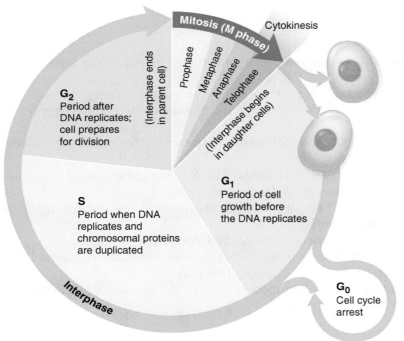

Figure 8.7 The Cell Cycle. A cell is either growing, dividing or arrested in its growth. These processes comprise the cycle. Growth takes the longer amount of time and is referred to as interphase. Interphase has it's functional subphases; see the text for details.

(see Figure 8.7). It is the part of interphase that varies most in length and where the most critical control over the cell cycle is exercised. The letter G stands for *gap* because, although many kinds of biomolecules are being synthesized apace, the DNA synthesis critical to future daughter cells has not yet begun. When will DNA synthesis begin? This is where control becomes important. Is this growing cell going to divide again? For many nerve cells in the human body, the answer may be "no." In this case, DNA synthesis never does begin and the cell seems to drop out of G_1 entering a holding pattern that is termed the G_0 **phase** (see Figure 8.7). The cell will continue to maintain itself biochemically for an indefinite period of time. It sits behind what is termed a **checkpoint**—a biochemical control point that will never allow it into the next phase of the cycle.

Logically, G_1 is the phase that most varies in length. If materials for growth are scarce, if some required hormonal signal does not arrive at the cell surface, or if some other genetically controlled roadblock is in place, the G_1 phase grows longer in response—the cell simply waits. But once the G_1 checkpoint is passed, the cell proceeds forward toward division at a constant rate limited only by availability of monomers and energy.

Your intestinal epithelial cells are an absorptive surface that replaces itself every five days. In such a cell population, continuous division is needed. These cells routinely pass the G_1 checkpoint and move into **S phase**, where *S* stands for *DNA synthesis* (see Figure 8.7). During this period of time, all of the cell's chromatin—the DNA and supportive proteins—is replicated to generate two complete copies of the genome. Also, in S phase, biosynthesis of other important cell structures and polymers continues simultaneously. In cultured mammalian cells, S phase lasts about 10 hours. Why is DNA synthesis accorded a phase of its own? Well, a single cell needs only its own genome. And once a cell begins this expensive genome duplication process, it has passed a critical checkpoint: It is now committed to making two daughter cells.

From the time DNA synthesis is complete until chromatin condenses just prior to cell division, there is another growth period called the G_2 **phase** (see Figure 8.7). In this phase, much of the cellular architecture needed to organize and distribute chromosomes into daughter cells is constructed.

Again, biosynthesis of other cellular organelles and structures continues. When entering both the S phase and the G_2 phase, checkpoints are being passed. The cell wastes nothing. It will not head into a division event unless and until the S and G_2 phases have been passed successfully. When they have, all is ready for the cell's final drama to begin. The first act will include the division of the nucleus and its component chromosomes—a process called **mitosis**. Along with or following mitosis, act two: the division of the cell's cytoplasm or **cytokinesis** occurs.

We've noted the three overlapping periods of growth and synthesis that characterize interphase. But before observing cell division, let's return to that critical checkpoint between G_1 and S phases and see what occurs there. What would stop a cell from mechanically moving ahead with division? How would you arrange the division machinery of the cell such that it would divide only if new daughter cells are needed and if it is materially possible to make them? This is a tall order; serious design is needed. First, the protein machinery that actually moves the cell cycle forward must be controllable. This is exactly what we find! Proteins controlling cycling will not signal DNA synthesis (the entering of S phase) to move forward

G_0 **phase**—an indefinite, usually long time period (formally within G_1 phase) during which a cell simply maintains its vitality because it is unable to pass a checkpoint leading to DNA synthesis.

checkpoint—a collection of interacting proteins that monitors conditions within a cell, inhibiting the cell from proceeding further into its cycle until conditions are favorable.

S phase—that portion of the cell cycle during which DNA and its scaffolding proteins are synthesized.

G_2 **phase**—that portion of the cell cycle following DNA synthesis during which cellular biosynthesis focuses on structures needed for division of the cell.

mitosis—the process of dividing a single maternal nucleus into two daughter nuclei distributing to each nucleus equal halves of replicated chromosomes. Cell division is usually concurrent or follows immediately.

cytokinesis—the division of the cytoplasm of a maternal cell resulting in two daughter cells. Mitosis precedes this process.

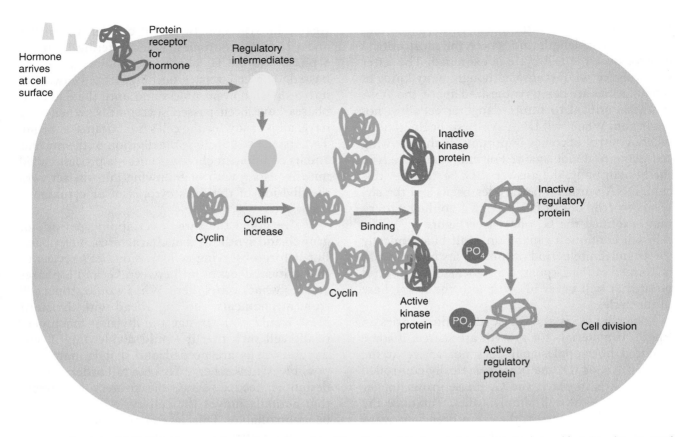

Figure 8.8 Regulating Cell Division. A hormonal signal arrives at the surface of the cell where it binds precisely to the receptor designed for it. A resulting structural alteration of the interior part of the receptor starts a cascading series of reactions between intracellular proteins or "intermediates" which results in increased cyclin concentrations. These in turn signal the phosphorylation of proteins that will cause the cell to cycle on into S phase toward division.

unless they are **phosphorylated**—that is, unless they have phosphate groups attached at critical points on their structure (see Figure 8.8). Then they function. Second, a group of **kinase enzymes** that add phosphates to these controlling proteins are always present, but they are themselves in an inactive form. Third, a group of proteins called **cyclins** are produced that can activate these kinase enzymes. But cyclins are produced only in response to the favorable conditions outlined previously. If a hormone signal arrives outside the cell, it will bind to a membrane receptor protein (see Figure 8.8). This binding will, in turn, cause the concentration of cyclins within the cell to rise. If nutrients levels are acceptable for DNA synthesis, a cyclin is generated. Cyclins are the activator function of an elegant "situation reporting network" whose details are still not entirely understood. This network involves various receptor proteins in the cell membrane and a huge collection of intracellular proteins that, by binding to each other, transmit molecular signals. But a go-ahead signal always involves activating

kinase enzymes, which then phosphorylate cycle-mediating proteins. The molecular signals cause the cell to do the sensible thing from the organism's perspective, not because the cell understands its own behavior or that of the organism as a whole. Rather a brilliant Designer crafted a protein network that mindlessly weighs alternatives at both the cellular and organismal levels and either holds the cell at the checkpoint or lets it by. When these systems work well, life is fun. When they're defective, the result is often cancerous (see Section 8.6).

phosphorylation—the attachment of a phosphate group $(-PO_3)$ to a molecule; often protein modification from inactive to active states is accomplished in this way.

kinase enzyme—a protein that catalyzes the addition of a phosphate group to some other protein or molecule. Addition or removal of the phosphate often results in altered regulation of some cell function.

cyclin—intracellular protein that activates kinase enzymes involved in moving the cell cycle forward.

IN OTHER WORDS

1. In the cell cycle, a relatively long period of growth precedes a shorter period of cell division.
2. The period of growth, termed *interphase,* is itself divided into three phases—G_1, S, and G_2—which are named for their temporal relationship to DNA synthesis.
3. Depending on circumstances, some cells move rather quickly through the G_1 phase; other cells enter it and never leave.
4. There are biochemically controlled checkpoints around the cell cycle that control how a cell proceeds through the cycle.
5. G_1 phase is most variable in length. Phases S, G_2, and M (Mitosis) proceed according to a more constant time frame from cell to cell.
6. While biosynthesis of most cell constituents occurs all through interphase, DNA synthesis is limited to the S phase.
7. Checkpoints are really collections of interacting proteins that sense when cell division is desirable and raise cyclin levels to signal a transition toward division.
8. Defects in checkpoint function are usually the basis for the cell's progression toward the cancerous state.

The Reason for Mitosis: Chromosomes

In a bacterial cell like *E. coli,* where mitosis is unnecessary, virtually all of the cell's genetic information resides on one circular chromosome, which is neatly replicated and distributed to two daughter cells. Eukaryotic life is more complex. There are larger genomes and longer chromosomes, which may number as high as 78 in the cells of your cocker spaniel or even 208 in king crab cells! Also, most eukaryotes, like yourself, have two copies of each kind of chromosome—and therefore of every gene they possess. You have two different versions of genes influencing eye color, skin color, height, intelligence, and so on. You got one set of these genes from your father and one from your mother (see Chapter 12). So the 46 chromosomes in each of your cells are really 23 matching pairs of chromosomes, one chromosome in each pair from your mother, the other from your father (see Figure 8.9). Only 23 chromosomes' worth of information is needed to generate a human being. We call this the **haploid** (or *n*) number of chromosomes. But your somatic cells contain 46 chromosomes—what we call the **diploid** number (or *2n*). It's sort of like having the luxury of buying two different biology texts in order to pass the course—one will do, but two give the richer perspective and correct each other's errors.

As you examine the process of mitosis, please realize that a maternal cell cannot simply duplicate its 46 chromosomes to 92 and then throw any 46 of them into each daughter cell! In this way, a daughter cell might miss both chromosomes of one or more given pairs while receiving unneeded duplicates for other pairs. Important information would be lacking—the daughter cells would never

haploid—refers to a cell (often a sex cell) that contains a single set of chromosomes or one copy of the cell's genome.

diploid—refers to a cell that contains two complete sets of chromosomes, usually inherited from two separate parent genomes.

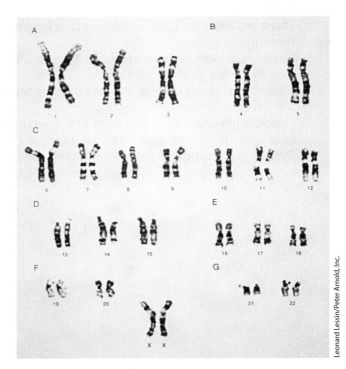

Figure 8.9 A Human Chromosomal Karyotype. The forty-six chromosomes of a human cell arranged by shape and size into 23 pairs. Similar chromosomes contain similar genes. One pair, at the bottom of the photo, is the sex chromosomes. They determine the sex of the individual. This cell has two X's and is therefore from a female. Were one of the X's replaced with a smaller Y chromosome, the cell would be from a male.

survive. Rather, each of the 46 chromosomes, once duplicated in a pre-mitotic S phase, must be systematically split during mitosis such that one copy goes to each daughter cell. The result is two daughter cells each with a genome that looks exactly like the genome of the maternal cell before its S phase. Hence, there is a necessary and severe elegance to the division process we are about to observe.

The Process of Mitosis: A Sequence of Stages

Once interphase checkpoints have been passed, the cell has signaled to itself that (1) it is large enough to divide, (2) its chromatin is entirely replicated, and (3) the machinery is in place for distributing halves of replicated chromosomes. The process of mitosis will now distribute these copies of genetic information into daughter nuclei in preparation for division of the rest of the cell (cytokinesis). Mitosis occurs in several stages based on the appearance and behavior of the now-condensed chromosomes. These stages are: **prophase, metaphase, anaphase,** and **telophase** (see Figure 8.7). For each stage in this sequence, let's examine the obvious structural changes that have been observed for years and, here and there, a few of the molecular changes that have been discovered more recently.

Prophase begins when the chromatin-to-chromosome transition reaches a point where chromosomes are now visible with a simple light microscope (see Figure 8.10). This high level of condensation is somewhat like taking cooked spaghetti in a bowl and reversing the cooking process to return each strand of pasta to its straight, precooked configuration. Just as it would be easy to separate the contents of a box of spaghetti into two pots of boiling water, it is easier to move halves of tightly coiled chromosomes into daughter cells. Each chromosome now has two duplicated daughter halves to its structure; these are called **sister chromatids.** They remain attached to each other through a small, complexed region of highly repeated DNA sequences called the **centromere** (see Figure 8.11). Bound to this region is *a pair* of protein complexes called **kinetochores,** which serve the same function for a chromosome as does a door handle for a door. (Door handles are usually paired as well.) Microtubules will soon attach to the kinetochore on each side of the centromere, preparing to pull each half of the replicated chromosome in opposite directions. Where do these microtubules come from? To answer this question, we must wander back in time a bit.

Next to the cell nucleus during the G_1 phase was a complex cytoplasmic structure called the **centrosome.** It functions as an organizing center for microtubule construction. During S phase, the centrosome is replicated into two centers. Now, in prophase, these two centers begin to move around the surface of the nuclear membrane to opposite ends or poles (see Figure 8.10). As they move, microtubules grow in length between them. During prophase, the nuclear membrane deteriorates and the microtubules extending between the centrosomes become a beautiful, symmetric, and dominant architectural frame called a **mitotic spindle** because of its overall shape. Microtubules also extend back away from the centrosomes toward the cytoskeleton just beneath the cell membrane in two more stunning, star-like,

astral arrays. These microtubules will anchor the spindle structurally for the work it is about to do.

When a tow truck pulls a car from a ditch, it's not enough to have an ultra-strong winch. Without ultra-strong brakes, the winch may take the tow truck into the ditch with the car. When a mitotic spindle pulls halves of chromosomes toward two different poles, the same pulling and restraining forces are used but in a much more elegantly orchestrated arrangement of winching and braking (see Figure 8.12). Three different groups of microtubules (cellular "cables"), and their associated **motor proteins** (cellular "winches and brakes"), are involved in chromosome distribution:

1. A set of kinetochore microtubules extend from opposite centrosomes to the kinetochores of

prophase—the first stage of mitosis during which chromosomes become visible, the nuclear membrane deteriorates, and the mitotic spindle apparatus takes shape

metaphase—the second stage of mitosis during which chromosomes reach the center of the maternal cell being arranged across an imaginary equatorial plate.

anaphase—the third stage of mitosis during which replicated chromosomes split and a daughter chromatid goes to each daughter cell; a period of chromosome movement.

telophase—the fourth stage of mitosis during which parted sister chromatids (now chromosomes) decondense, nuclear membranes form, and daughter nuclei take on an interphase appearance.

sister chromatid—half of a replicated chromosome; joined to a replica of itself by a centromere; splitting of the centromere converts each chromosomal half into a separate (now unreplicated) chromosome.

centromere—a region of a chromosome containing highly repeated, short DNA sequences that is structural, not informational. Kinetochores attach to this region.

kinetochore—a protein complex that binds centromeric regions of chromosomes; microtubules attach to it and pull the chromosome to a spindle pole during mitosis.

centrosome—a cellular microtubule organizing center. Microtubules radiate from this structure during mitosis.

mitotic spindle—arrangement of microtubules used to separate halves of replicated chromosomes into daughter nuclei.

motor proteins—an enzyme that uses ATP energy to do mechanical work within the cell; interacts with cytoskeletal elements to move cell parts.

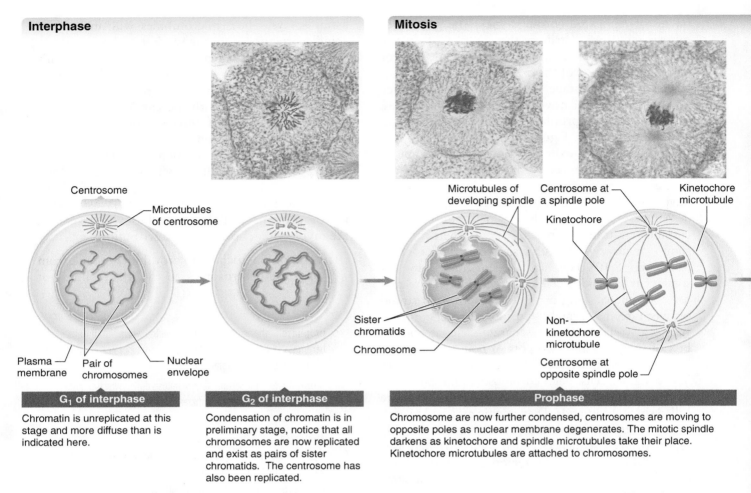

G₁ of interphase

Chromatin is unreplicated at this stage and more diffuse than is indicated here.

G₂ of interphase

Condensation of chromatin is in preliminary stage, notice that all chromosomes are now replicated and exist as pairs of sister chromatids. The centrosome has also been replicated.

Prophase

Chromosome are now further condensed, centrosomes are moving to opposite poles as nuclear membrane degenerates. The mitotic spindle darkens as kinetochore and spindle microtubules take their place. Kinetochore microtubules are attached to chromosomes.

Figure 8.10 Mitosis in Stages. The photographs are of cells in the embryo of the whitefish caught in various stages of mitosis. They were taken through a light microscope. The accompanying diagram uses just two pairs of chromosomes to illustrate what the larger number of (darkly stained) chromosomes in the photographs are doing.

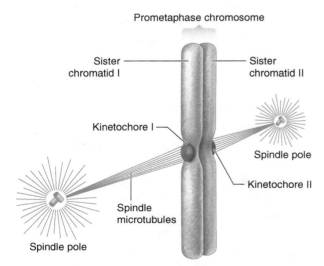

Figure 8.11 A Duplicated Chromosome at Metaphase. The two kinetochores are attached to the centromeric region of the chromosome. (Kinetochore) microtubules of the spindle attach to the kinetochores in preparation for the splitting/unravelling of the centromeric region that starts anaphase.

each chromosome. They extend by being built out, monomer by monomer, toward the kinetochores, where they attach by protein "hooks."

2. Another set of polar microtubules, form the outline of the spindle extending from each centrosome toward the other. They meet each other out in the center of the spindle and make productive contact with each other by means of shared motor proteins.

3. A third set of astral microtubules flare out from the centrosomes toward the cell's cytoskeleton, where motor proteins anchor them to the cell's periphery.

The subsequent movements of these microtubules are carefully coordinated.

Soon, the kinetochore microtubules begin to shorten by being disassembled at the centrosome poles. This places tension on the chromosomes since they are all attached to both centrosomes by

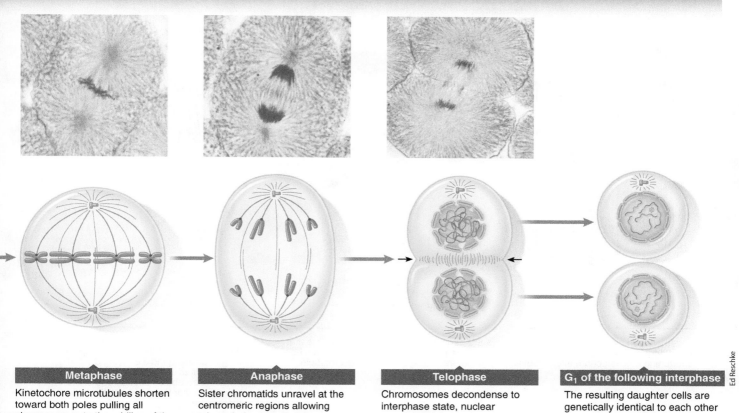

Metaphase	Anaphase	Telophase	G₁ of the following interphase
Kinetochore microtubules shorten toward both poles pulling all chromosomes to the midline of the spindle.	Sister chromatids unravel at the centromeric regions allowing microtubules to pull sister chromatids of each chromosome to opposite poles.	Chromosomes decondense to interphase state, nuclear membranes form around chromatin as cytokinesis begins.	The resulting daughter cells are genetically identical to each other and to the paternal cell from which they were derived.

Figure 8.10   (*Continued*)

their two kinetochore linkages. This pulling from both ends has the effect of bringing all the chromosomes to the midline of the spindle, a region called the **metaphase plate.** Once the chromosomes are neatly aligned there, the cell is said to be in metaphase. The system is neatly designed so that chromosome condensation reaches its maximum during this critical phase.

The shortest phase of mitosis is anaphase; it lasts only a few minutes in the hour consumed by division. It is a period of dramatic movement. At a critically timed moment (have we used this phrase before?) a collection of enzymes concentrated in the centromeric region of each chromosome alter the DNA conformation there so that the sister chromatids of each chromosome are able to separate from each other. (The mechanism is still being studied.) Now, kinetochore microtubules begin to be disassembled

(shortened) at both the centrosome and the kinetochore ends (see Figure 8.12b), pulling sister chromatids away from each other. Simultaneously, polar microtubules begin to lengthen, pushing the poles of the spindle further apart. Protein motors pull microtubules from opposite poles past each other. Both groups of microtubules contribute positively to a rapidly growing distance between the two daughter genomes. What is the result of all this movement? Consider, for example, a dividing cortical cell at the base of one of your body's hairs. It does anaphase

metaphase plate—an imaginary region, disc-shaped, often in the cell's geometric center, where all of the cell's chromosomes come to lie during the second stage of mitosis.

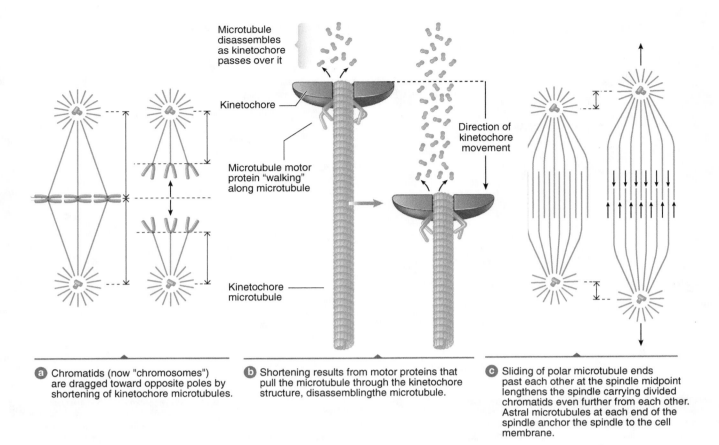

Microtubule disassembles as kinetochore passes over it

Kinetochore

Microtubule motor protein "walking" along microtubule

Kinetochore microtubule

Direction of kinetochore movement

a Chromatids (now "chromosomes") are dragged toward opposite poles by shortening of kinetochore microtubules.

b Shortening results from motor proteins that pull the microtubule through the kinetochore structure, disassemblingthe microtubule.

c Sliding of polar microtubule ends past each other at the spindle midpoint lengthens the spindle carrying divided chromatids even further from each other. Astral microtubules at each end of the spindle anchor the spindle to the cell membrane.

Figure 8.12   Mitotic Spindle Structure and Activity.

by abruptly ending 46 individual tug-of-war events for each of your 46 now-replicated chromosomes. Those events end with each future daughter cell getting precisely 46 halves of 46 replicated chromosomes. Each daughter cell is genetically complete, genetically identical to the other daughter cell—and your hair grows just a bit longer. . . .

Telophase could be called the *clean-up* or *restoration phase* (see Figure 8.10). Conditions revert to those of the non-dividing cell. Telophase begins once the chromosomes have arrived at the poles of the now larger mitotic spindle. As it progresses, the spindle microtubules are all disassembled and the nuclear membranes of two new nuclei begin to form around the daughter genomes. The chromosomes rapidly begin the de-condensation that will allow the genes to be transcribed again so that informed life can continue. It is while this nuclear drama winds down that the cytoplasmic division—cytokinesis—reaches full expression.

IN OTHER WORDS

1. Because of their relative complexity, eukaryotic cells require a highly elaborate and controlled system for distributing genetic information into daughter cells prior to cell division.
2. In the cell nuclei of most animals, the number of chromosomes is diploid; there are two complete sets of genetic information, one set derived from each parent.
3. Mitosis must divide human chromosomes such that each of the 46 chromosomes provides one of its sister chromatids to each of the two daughter nuclei.
4. Mitosis occurs only after the last checkpoint between G_2 and mitosis has been successfully passed.

5. In prophase of mitosis, duplicated chromosomes become visible as they become attached to kinetochore microtubules; the nuclear membrane deteriorates and a mitotic spindle takes shape.
6. Spindle architecture for dividing chromosomes includes three types of microtubules: kinetochore microtubules that pull chromosomes, polar microtubules that control the size of the spindle, and astral microtubules that support the spindle structurally.
7. In mitotic metaphase, microtubules are preliminarily shortened, generating a structural tension that pulls all chromosomes to the midline of the maternal cell.
8. In anaphase, sister chromatids physically separate and microtubules pull them to opposite poles of the mitotic spindle.
9. In telophase of mitosis, chromosomes de-condense to their chromatin state, nuclear membranes form around daughter genomes, and cytokinesis, if occurring, continues toward completion.

Cytokinesis accomplishes for the cell boundary and cytoplasm what mitosis does for the cell nucleus. Thus mitosis followed by cytokinesis results in complete division of a cell. Organellar structures, monomers for growth and intracellular energy sources, are distributed by cytokinesis into separate daughter cytoplasms, which become separated from each other by new cell boundaries. While cytokinesis typically begins during late anaphase or telophase of mitosis, the two processes are not strictly connected mechanically. Cytokinesis can, in some situations, follow along well after mitosis. In early insect development, for example, repeated mitotic events generate a multi-nucleate embryo with a common cytoplasm (see Figure 8.13). Following some cytoplasmic differentiation activities, cytokinesis then carves up all the nuclei into separate cytoplasms for subsequent development. Temporal separation of mitosis and cytokinesis is atypical however; close association of cytokinesis with mitotic telophase is the more common rule.

In animal cells, cytokinesis involves cleavage of the maternal cytoplasm into two daughter domains. What starts as a minor depression in the cell membrane above and below the former metaphase plate deepens into a **cleavage furrow** that surrounds the cell (see Figure 8.14). The furrow draws interiorly like purse strings, and eventually cleaves the cell

> **cleavage furrow**—a constricting region of cytoplasm in a maternal cell that encircles the cell and progressively deepens finally resulting in two separate daughter cells.

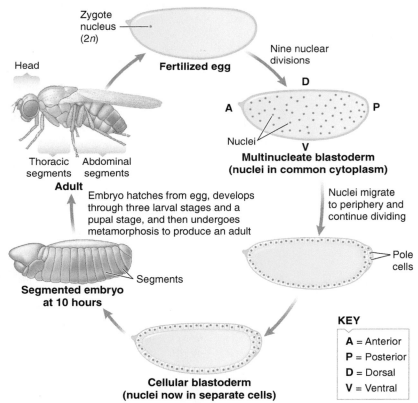

Figure 8.13 Mitosis Apart from Cytokinesis. Insect development begins with a fertilized egg containing a single diploid nucleus. This nucleus undergoes many rounds of mitosis, and daughter nuclei migrate to the periphery of the cytoplasm before the blastodermal stage of development when cytokinesis provides a separate cytoplasm for each nucleus. By this time, considerable regional differences exist in the cytoplasm so that different kinds of larval segments can subsequently form. The insect egg has been grossly enlarged compared to the adult form so that nuclear behavior can be represented.

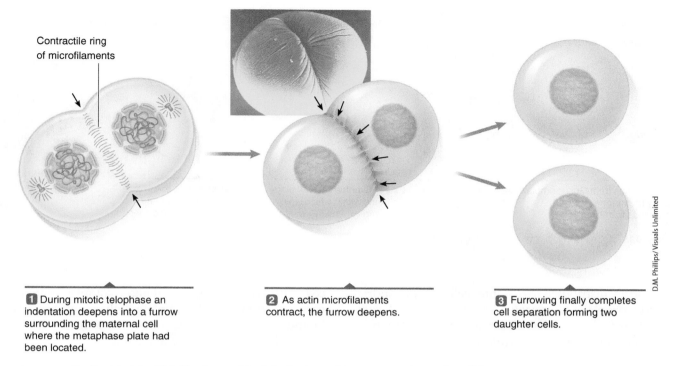

Contractile ring
of microfilaments

1 During mitotic telophase an indentation deepens into a furrow surrounding the maternal cell where the metaphase plate had been located.

2 As actin microfilaments contract, the furrow deepens.

3 Furrowing finally completes cell separation forming two daughter cells.

D.M. Phillips/Visuals Unlimited

Figure 8.14 Cytokinesis in Animal Cells. The photograph is of a fertilized egg cell beginning to undergo its first cell division

cytoplasm in two. Electron microscopy reveals that just beneath the cleavage furrow is a **contractile ring** composed of bundles of **actin** microfilaments whose orientation is parallel to the cleavage furrow. A dynamic process that involves both pulling on and rapid shortening of actin filaments (depolymerizing) leads to the observed constriction of the contractile ring. The ring eventually separates the cell into two daughter cells with one nucleus in each.

The challenge of separating a plant cell into two daughter cells is heightened by the existence of a tough, protective, supportive cell wall just outside the cell membrane. A constricting contractile ring would be inadequate in this situation for much the same reason that human hands are not effective in breaking tree branches in half. So an entirely different strategy is employed—one that works from the interior to the exterior of the maternal cell rather than the other way round as in animal cells (see Figure 8.15). During telophase of mitosis, vesicles containing molecular components for a new membrane and wall begin arriving at the center of what was the metaphase plate within the maternal cell. As these vesicles fuse with each other, they generate a growing internal structure called a **cell plate**. The plate slowly expands toward the exterior edges of the maternal cell boundary and eventually fuses with existing cell

wall components. The last step involves construction of cellulose fibers and insertion of them into the new partition being constructed. The final partition has two new membrane surfaces separated **medially** from each other by two distinct layers of wall material. This new wall structure becomes continuous with the preexisting wall material of what is now two daughter cells.

Many preliminary structural changes within a maternal cell support the subsequent process of cytokinesis. Large organellar structures and networks tend to fragment prior to cytokinesis so they can be

contractile ring—a visible structure within a cleavage furrow composed of actin microfilaments; responsible for the deepening of the cleavage furrow.

actin—a protein subunit of which microfilaments are composed. Together with myosin filaments, it is responsible for contractile events either in dividing cells or in muscle tissue.

cell plate—a medial, incipient, combined membrane and wall component preparatory to complete division of a maternal plant cell into two daughter cells.

medial—occurring or situated in the middle or between other structures or processes.

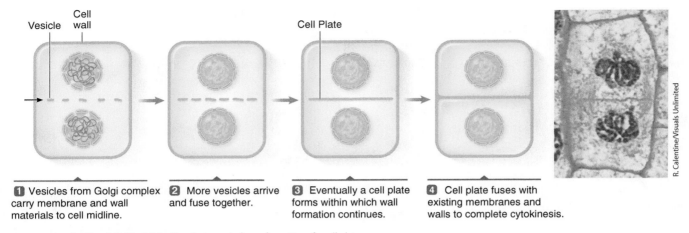

1 Vesicles from Golgi complex carry membrane and wall materials to cell midline.

2 More vesicles arrive and fuse together.

3 Eventually a cell plate forms within which wall formation continues.

4 Cell plate fuses with existing membranes and walls to complete cytokinesis.

R. Calentine/Visuals Unlimited

Figure 8.15 Cytokinesis in Plant Cells. The photograph shows formation of a cell plate.

uniformly distributed to daughter cells. Mitochondria and chloroplasts have grown and divided in sufficient numbers for appropriate distribution to each daughter cell. The final result of cytokinesis is two separate cell cytoplasms, each containing a complete diploid genome within a nucleus and enough energy sources, biomolecular monomers, and organellar structures for continued cell grow or maintenance.

IN OTHER WORDS

1. Once the cell nucleus has divided in mitosis, cytokinesis completes the cell division event by partitioning organelles and other cytoplasmic components into two separate daughter cells.
2. In animal cells, orchestrated microfilament contraction draws a cleavage furrow down through the maternal cell cytoplasm creating two daughter cells.
3. In plant cells, new membrane and wall components develop within the maternal cell partitioning it into two daughter cells.
4. The living cell is superior to any human contrivance in its ability to marshal resources, construct its own components and completely reproduce itself repeatedly using energy and information with unmatched efficiency.

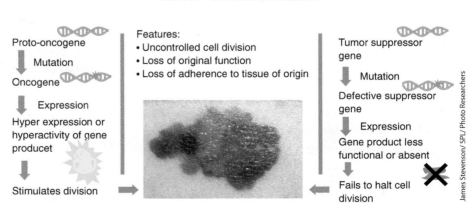

8.6 CANCER: MUTATION THREATENING DESIGN

The Unifying Basis of Cancer

Cancer is an unqualified enemy of the living world. In the United States alone it drains close to $50 billion from the economy per year and costs our species dearly both in emotional turmoil and in thousands of careers invested in diagnosis, treatment, and research. Cancer is a broad collection of molecular disease states characterized by cells that divide in an uncontrolled fashion and that no longer respect their role or confinement within their tissue of origin (see Figure 8.16). Despite the many environmental, hereditary, viral, dietary, and chemical causes of cancer, they all have one common root cause: mutational changes in genes that control cell division.

We know of about 150 genes whose mutation predisposes the cell to cancer. One hundred or so of these are called **proto-oncogenes**. Their products are entirely normal proteins that *activate* regulatory pathways that move a cell toward division. When these genes mutate, they become **oncogenes** (Gk. *oncos* = tumor), which move the affected cell toward the cancerous state (see Figure 8.16). Another 50 or so genes are called **tumor suppressor genes**. Their products are also normal proteins that tend to *inhibit* regulatory pathways, keeping a cell from moving toward division. As you might guess, proto-oncogenes that are over-expressed, or proto-oncogene proteins that mutate to hyperactivity are likely to cause the cell to divide uncontrollably.

On the other hand, tumor suppressor genes that (1) become underexpressed, (2) that are not expressed, or (3) whose protein products are non-functional are likely to allow cells to divide uncontrollably. In either case, again, cancer is a likely outcome.

Cancer rarely results from a single gene mutation. Recall that our genomes are diploid. We have, in our genome, two copies of every proto-oncogene and tumor suppressor gene. This is a wonderfully protective situation. Sometimes, when a gene mutates to the cancerous state, a normal copy of the gene is there to limit the effect of the cancerous one. It has also been shown that mutation is generally necessary in at least two different genes regulating cell division to initiate the cancerous state. So the frequency of cancer in the human population is happily limited by the need for multiple mutations in order for it to begin and progress.

> **proto-oncogene**—a normal cellular gene whose product helps control progress within the cell cycle toward cell division.
>
> **oncogene**—(Gk. *oncos* = tumor), a mutant proto-oncogene that predisposes the cell toward uncontrolled division.
>
> **tumor suppressor gene**—a normal cellular gene whose product inhibits progress toward cell division; its mutation or loss leads to cancer.

Figure 8.16 *Cancer — A Result of Mutation.* Shown here is a malignant melanoma, a fast-growing and invasive variety of skin cancer. Possible processes that contribute to cancer formation are outlined to each side of the photo. Characteristics of cancer cells are listed above the photo.

Cancer – a result of mutation

Proto-oncogene
↓ Mutation
Oncogene
↓ Expression
Hyper expression or hyperactivity of gene producet
↓
Stimulates division

Features:
• Uncontrolled cell division
• Loss of original function
• Loss of adherence to tissue of origin

Tumor suppressor gene
↓ Mutation
Defective suppressor gene
↓ Expression
Gene product less functional or absent
↓
Fails to halt cell division

James Stevenson/ SPL/ Photo Researchers

Figure 8.17 Control of Cell Division. Cells sense signals that control their rate of growth and division. In embryonic life, childhood, and later life cell division rates in each organ and tissue conform to the changing needs of the individual. Tissue specificity of cell division rate is one of many factors that contribute to control pathway complexity.

The protein products of proto-oncogenes and tumor suppressor genes participate in complex intracellular regulatory pathways. These pathways often link signaling functions that begin outside the cell membrane to transcriptional changes deep within the genome (see Figure 8.8). So the proto-oncogene that mutates might code for (1) external growth signal molecules, (2) receptors for those molecules, (3) numerous kinase enzymes that are intermediate controls along the pathway, or (4) transcriptional control factors that function within the nucleus to determine what constellation of genes will be read. We might complain here about why pathways that regulate cell division must possess so very many stages of activation or inhibition. If only regulation of cell division involved a mere two or three steps, there would be far fewer ways of getting cancer! The problem is that the cell needs to be ready to divide or not divide in response to many different environmental variables both within and outside of its boundaries (see Figure 8.17). So the regulatory pathways must be long enough to interact with all of the somewhat unrelated signals they are receiving. Life Is Complex!

KRAS—a proto-oncogene whose product, the Ras protein, functions in the control of cell division.

Ras—a regulatory protein whose activation stimulates a cascade of regulatory alterations that results in the movement of a cell from G_1 into S phase of the cell cycle.

A Tale of Two Cancer Genes

Let's consider two examples of genes that control cell division. Mutation in either of them will predispose a cell to becoming cancerous. One is a proto-oncogene; the other is a tumor suppressor gene.

The proto-oncogene **KRAS** (gene names are italicized) codes for a protein called **Ras**. Ras is an intermediate in the control pathway that moves a cell from G_1 phase in the cell cycle past a checkpoint and on into S phase. Suppose you've gone to the beach and gotten too much sun. As a result, many of your epidermal cells have been fried to death and you need to make new ones. How is this accomplished? Inside of millions of healthy dermal cells, the following stages in a regulatory process unfold (see Figure 8.18.):

1. Increased amounts of growth factor arrive at the surface of mature dermal cells that now need to divide. Growth factor complexes with a cell-surface receptor protein, part of whose shape is designed to specifically bind to the growth factor.
2. The binding of growth factor and receptor protein causes the internal part of the receptor protein to accept phosphate groups: It becomes phosphorylated.
3. Through an adapter protein, the phosphorylated receptor protein is now able to activate the Ras protein.
4. Ras then activates a cascade of intracellular protein kinase enzymes.
5. Their activation results in increased cyclin production.
6. Each cyclin binds to its own kinase protein called *Cdk*.

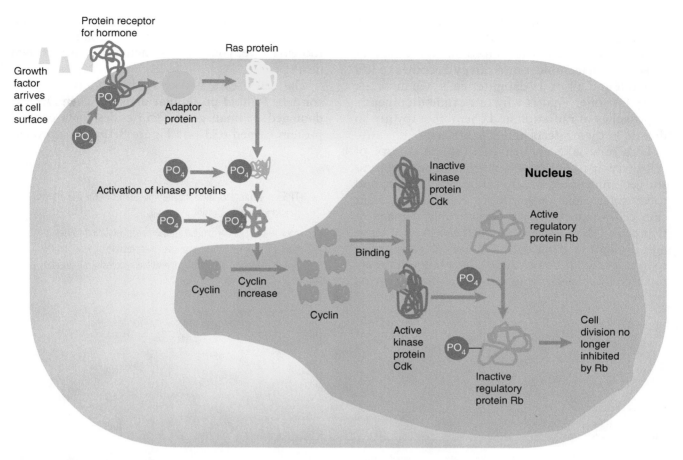

Figure 8.18 Ras Protein Control of Cell Division. At least eight steps are involved in this control pathway: 1. growth factor arrives from endocrine gland and binds to cell receptor protein. 2. Cell receptor protein binding alters internal protein structure resulting in receptor's susceptibility to being phosphorylated. 3. Phosphorylated receptor activates adapter protein which in turn activates the Ras protein. 4. Ras protein activates a series of pathway intermediate kinase proteins, the last of which, when phosphorylated causes an increased production of cyclin molecules. 5. Increased cyclin binds to cyclin-specific kinase enzymes in the nucleus activating them. 6. Activated Cdk-cyclins phosphorylate the Rb protein converting it to its inactive state. 7. Inactivate Rb protein no longer holds cell at checkpoint. 8. Cell moves into S phase, division is now one checkpoint closer.

7. The cyclin-bound Cdk kinases now add phosphate groups to an important regulatory protein called **Rb.** Rb has been keeping the cell at the G_1-S transition checkpoint.

8. The Rb protein, once phosphorylated, becomes inactive. This releases the cell into S phase so DNA synthesis can begin!

Since you are constantly replacing skin cells at a slower rate even in the absence of a good sunburn, this multistep process happens all the time in your skin cells (with no thought at all on your part)!

But suppose, during your day at the beach, ultraviolet rays from the sun hit the DNA in one of your cells causing some critical covalent bonds to break and reform. During replication of that DNA in an S phase, this might cause a base pair in the DNA of the *KRAS* proto-oncogene to be mutationally altered (see Figure 8.16). For example, an A=T pair in double-stranded DNA might be substituted with a G≡C pair at some point along the DNA sequence. If this results in a dangerous amino acid substitution in the structure of the Ras protein, then *KRAS* is now an oncogene. Its mutant protein product Ras becomes hyperactive. It is no longer responsive to activation by the adapter protein. It is now active *all the time!* It continually activates the protein kinase cascade, so cyclin levels remain abnormally high. The result is a cell that will not stop dividing. That is the hallmark of cancer.

Rb—a regulatory protein that, when phosphorylated, moves a cell from G_1 into S phase of the cell cycle.

Can you see how difficult it would be for some oncologist to find that tiny cell or to stop it from dividing? Once it has produced enough daughter cells to be detectable, our strategy becomes to kill that cell and all of its daughter cells. We must get every last one! That is why our crude therapeutic approaches of radiation and chemotherapy are so drastic in their effects and side effects.

Let's now take another look at the control of cell division to see how a normal tumor suppressor gene functions. We are at the beach again, and today solar radiation—without killing a particular skin cell—happens to do considerable damage to that cell's DNA. Depending on the degree of damage, it might be dangerous for that cell to continue to live. It could become cancerous or it could simply function improperly. Your cells are crafted in such a way that DNA damage can halt normal cell division until the DNA is repaired. If the repair needed is too extensive, your cell can actually cause its own death!

The cell uses a widely studied tumor suppressor gene to hold up cellular division when DNA is damaged. Human gene *TP53* codes for a control protein named **p53** (see Figure 8.19). This protein

TP53—a tumor suppressor gene whose product, the p53 protein, is used to suppress division of the cell.

p53—a regulatory protein whose phosphorylation causes it to bind the DNA sequences, resulting in expression of genes that will halt the cell cycle temporarily or result in apoptosis (cell suicide).

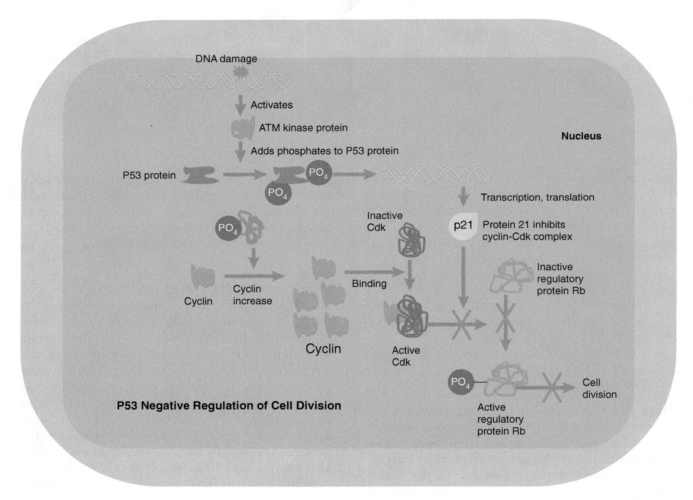

Figure 8.19 Protein Control of Cell Division. This pathway senses when cellular DNA has been damaged. 1. DNA damage activates a kinase protein called ATM. 2. Active ATM adds phosphate groups to p53 which cause p53 to bind to a particular site on DNA. 3. This binding causing transcription and translation of protein p21. 4. Protein p21 inhibits the activity of cyclin-dependent Cdk kinase. 5. With Cdk inactive, the control protein Rb remains active. 6. The result is that the cell cannot pass the checkpoint moving it from the G_1 phase to the S phase.

receives signals from other proteins such as **ATM,** a protein kinase that is activated when DNA is damaged. ATM, a kinase, activates p53 by adding phosphate groups to it. In its activated state, p53 now binds to DNA at a specific site coding for still another protein called **p21.** (Such romantic names for proteins!) DNA binding by p53 causes the gene for p21 to be expressed and soon the p21 protein is floating about in the cell's nucleus. The p21 inhibits the activity of the combined Cdk-cyclin proteins. Now, they can no longer inactivate the Rb protein whose continued activity keeps the cell behind the G_1-S phase checkpoint. So the cell gets stuck there. If it is a dermal cell meant to divide to produce new skin cells for you, then it will not do so. Amazing! All by itself, the cell is recognizing that it is damaged and should not go on to generate other damaged cells with its own genetic defects. Tumor suppressor genes code for wonderful products that may protect us from another new cancer that starts every other week or so!

But what if this protection is lost? Cancer researchers have estimated that more than half of the world's 10 million people diagnosed with cancer each year have mutations in the *TP53* gene. It is the most widely mutated gene associated with cancer in humans. In these people, damage to DNA is not clearly sensed. Protein p53 is defective: It either fails to be properly phosphorylated, or it fails to bind DNA properly—or it is simply absent (see Figure 8.16). In either case, the p21 protein is never produced. So cells that are damaged and should be stopped until repairs are done, go right on dividing. If a proto-oncogene in the DNA of such a cell has also been damaged—and is now oncogenic—p53 will not be there to stop it. Cancer will probably result.

Life at the cellular level is highly competitive and just generally a dangerous form of existence. Protozoa engulf other species of protozoa for lunch (see Figure 8.20). Bacterial cells attack and destroy human cells, then absorb their remains. Fungal cells enzymatically degrade the brain cells of the ants they invade. Yet poised in the midst of all this vital, even rabid cellular greed is this wonderful example of selflessness based on carefully crafted cellular control genes. *TP53* has been designed to guide a cellular process that is not in the best interest of the cell but rather of the organism

that owns it. The active p53 protein can call for the death of its own cell so that the rest of the cells in the organismal population can continue to live! It does so even though new mutations in its own cell might enable that cell to reproduce vigorously by comparison with its sisters! What an insight into the mind of the Designer! It is entirely appropriate at this point for the reader to feel a deep sense of thankfulness. The control of cell division, though focused on cellular perpetuity, clearly has the greater welfare of the organism in mind. You are that organism. The cell is dispassionately, mechanistically selfless in this example. As an organism, your selflessness is a choice. Might a caring Designer be showing you a better use of your life?

ATM—a protein kinase that is expressed and activated as a result of numerous breaks occurring in the double-stranded DNA of the cell's genome. It phosphorylates key regulatory molecules affecting cell division.

p21—a protein that inhibits the activity of Cdk-cyclins; their inhibition halts progress toward cell division.

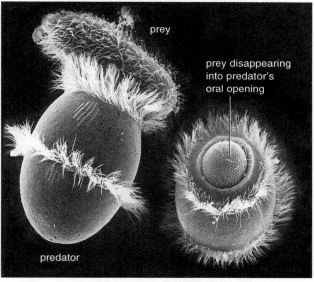

Gary W. Grimes and Steven L'Hernault

Figure 8.20 Cellular Predation. Protozoa don't have an easy life. Here a ciliate protozoan *Didinium* fires paralyzing "darts" into another type of ciliate, a *Paramecium*, turns it about and ingests it as you might a foot-long sub. It does so slowly and without teeth.

1. Cancer cells differ from normal cells by dividing uncontrollably, dedifferentiating, and spreading into other tissues of the body.
2. Cancer is caused by mutations in genes of two different types: proto-oncogenes and tumor suppressor genes.
3. Usually two or more mutations in at least two different genes are required to cause the cell to become cancerous.
4. Cancer-causing mutant genes typically code for proteins that are parts of highly elaborate control pathways that determine when or whether a cell will divide to form two daughter cells.
5. Control pathways usually possess a receptor protein within the cell's plasma membrane, a series of kinase enzymes that phosphorylate pathway intermediates, and DNA binding proteins that influence transcription of specific genes in the DNA.
6. The proto-oncogene *KRAS* codes for the protein Ras, an intermediate in the control pathway that allows a cell to move past a checkpoint from G_1 phase into S phase.
7. A common type of base substitution (point) mutation in *KRAS* DNA causes a change in the Ras protein so that it becomes hyperactive and no longer subject to control; the cell is now instructed to divide continuously.
8. Tumor suppressor genes normally code for protein products that work to inhibit cell division when there are good reasons for a cell not to divide.
9. The tumor suppressor gene *TP53* codes for the protein p53 that inhibits cell division when the cell's DNA is badly damaged.
10. The gene *TP53* is the most commonly mutated gene in human cancers.
11. Both positive and negative control pathways affecting the G_1-S transition checkpoint work by controlling the form of the Rb protein. When Rb is inactive, the checkpoint is passed; when it's active, the checkpoint is respected.
12. If a proto-oncogene mutates to oncogene status on a genetic background where *TP53* is already mutant, the host cell is likely to become cancerous.
13. The selfless character of the p53 regulatory pathway causes it to inhibit division or even kill the cell it functions in.

QUESTIONS FOR REVIEW

1. List three essential resources that any living thing must have to maintain its living state.
2. What is the source of energy-containing molecules for the bud forming on a maternal yeast cell? Be as comprehensive as possible.
3. Name three component processes that contribute to the program that starts with a fertilized egg and ends with a mature adult.
4. How many new red blood cells do you produce every second?
5. A DNA polymerase molecule encounters the following base sequence on a maternal template strand of DNA: –AATATCGATCCCTTAT-GAGA–. Write down the sequence of nucleotides it will build into the new daughter strand opposite this template strand.
6. When a DNA polymerase copies the base sequence that codes for its own structure, of what significance is this to the maternal cell it is working within? to the daughter cell in the next generation?
7. What is a replication bubble?
8. What functions of DNA are best served by its de-condensed chromatin state? its condensed chromosomal state?
9. Which process takes more time: cell growth or cell division? Why might this be so?
10. Explain the difference between the G_1 phase and a G_0 phase.

11. What do you know about the future of a cell that has started synthesizing daughter-strand DNA?
12. What is the function of a kinase enzyme, generally speaking?
13. What effect does the binding of a cyclin have on an intracellular kinase enzyme? What is the result of this binding?
14. Why is it accurate to say that your physical appearance is a blend of your mother's and your father's characteristics? Use boldface terms from this chapter in fashioning your response.
15. Fill in the blanks with summary terms of your choice: Mitosis is principally about the partitioning of _____. As such, prophase is a time of _____, metaphase, a time of _____, anaphase, a time of _____ and telophase, a time of _____.
16. List three types of microtubules in a mitotic spindle and describe the function of each.
17. Distinguish between the terms *mitosis, cytokinesis,* and *cell division.*

18. Why is the cleavage furrow mechanism not useful for cell division in plants?
19. What part of a vesicle coming from the Golgi complex is the most likely source of membrane material for the new partition that will divide two daughter plant cells?
20. List the three basic characteristics that differentiate a cancer cell from a non-cancerous, normal cell.
21. What is the functional difference between proto-oncogenes and tumor suppressor genes?
22. What is one important limit on cancer cell formation that keeps cancer relatively rare in the human population?
23. List the kinds of proteins that contribute to pathways that regulate cell division in normal body cells.
24. What is the precise function of the Ras protein? What does it immediately interact with?
25. Explain how changing a base pair in the *KRAS* DNA from A=T to G≡C can alter the structure of the Ras protein (consult Figure 7.14).
26. How is a p53 protein activated?

QUESTIONS FOR THOUGHT

1. A pointy-headed friend announces vociferously that life's race with death occurs essentially at the level of the organism, not the cell. Which two words in the previous sentence would immediately become the focus of subsequent debate?
2. The fertilized egg cell that gave rise to you went through many rounds of cell division with daughter cells eventually differentiating into a variety of cell types. Which cells in your body would have to retain the function of all of your genes in order to properly differentiate and serve their very important function?
3. Estimate the proportion of cells in your body that are red blood cells.
4. At what rate does DNA polymerase check its work for errors? How many base pairs per second does it check?
5. "Cells multiply by dividing." What biological process removes the paradox from this statement?
6. Some acellular slime molds are simply large masses of cytoplasm multiple centimeters in diameter that contain thousands of separate nuclei. How does this add meaning to the term *cytokinesis?*

7. In a nucleus containing 78 replicated chromosomes, how many centromeres are present? After the cell goes through a round of division, how many centromeres are present in each daughter cell? Explain again the phrase "cells multiple by dividing."
8. Why is it necessary for a centrosome to divide before anything else in the cell can divide?
9. Consider what you learned about microtubules in Chapter 5. What must happen to the microtubules of the mitotic spindle once cell division is completed? Work from your conclusion to evidence that the cell is a designed thing.
10. Why might cytokinesis be delayed during the repeated mitotic events of early insect embryo development?
11. Why do cell division control pathways involve 8 to 10 separate control proteins instead of only one or two such proteins?
12. What determines whether or not the gene for protein p21 will be expressed?
13. In the living world, is it advantageous for a cell to mutate such that it now grows faster than other cells around it?

GLOSSARY

actin—a protein subunit of which microfilaments are composed. Together with myosin filaments, it is responsible for contractile events either in dividing cells or in muscle tissue.

anaphase—the third stage of mitosis during which replicated chromosomes split and a daughter chromatid goes to each daughter cell; a period of chromosome movement.

ATM—a protein kinase that is expressed and activated as a result of numerous breaks occurring in the double-stranded DNA of the cell's genome. It phosphorylates key regulatory molecules affecting cell division.

bubble—in DNA replication, the already-replicated region within the DNA molecule which begins at the origin of replication and expands as DNA is replicated in both directions from the replication origin.

budding—in yeast, the process by which a new daughter cell emerges from the surface of the larger maternal cell using materials and information from the maternal cell.

cell cycle—a sequence of stages that prepares a cell for and that carries it through cell division. It begins immediately within daughter cells following the division of a maternal cell.

cell plate—a medial, incipient, combined membrane and wall component preparatory to complete division of a maternal plant cell into two daughter cells.

centromere—a region of a chromosome containing highly repeated, short DNA sequences that is structural, not informational. Kinetochores attach to this region.

centrosome—a cellular microtubule organizing center. Microtubules radiate from this structure during mitosis.

checkpoint—a collection of interacting proteins that monitors conditions within a cell, inhibiting the cell from proceeding further into its cycle until conditions are favorable.

cleavage furrow—a constricting region of cytoplasm in a maternal cell that encircles the cell and progressively deepens finally resulting in two separate daughter cells.

contractile ring—a visible structure within a cleavage furrow composed of actin microfilaments; responsible for the deepening of the cleavage furrow.

cyclin—intracellular protein that activates kinase enzymes involved in moving the cell cycle forward.

cytokinesis—the division of the cytoplasm of a maternal cell resulting in two daughter cells. Mitosis precedes this process.

differentiation—a process by which, through time and successive generations of cells, stem cells commit to utilizing a specific part of their genomes; this process transforms them into specific types of cells like neurons or epithelial cells.

diploid—refers to a cell that contains two complete sets of chromosomes, usually inherited from two separate parent genomes.

DNA polymerase—an enzyme that replicates an organism's DNA by adding free nucleotides to the ends of single DNA strands.

G_0 phase—an indefinite, usually long time period (formally within G_1 phase) during which a cell simply maintains its vitality because it is unable to pass a checkpoint leading to DNA synthesis.

G_1 phase—an initial period of growth immediately following cell division that precedes DNA synthesis; highly variable in length in diverse cell types or under varying conditions of growth.

G_2 phase—that portion of the cell cycle following DNA synthesis during which cellular biosynthesis focuses on structures needed for division of the cell.

haploid—refers to a cell (often a sex cell) that contains a single set of chromosomes or one copy of the cell's genome.

interphase—that portion of the cell cycle when the cell is not in the process of dividing. It is characterized by biosynthesis and growth of the cell.

kinase enzyme—a protein that catalyzes the addition of a phosphate group to some other protein or molecule. Addition or removal of the phosphate often results in altered regulation of some cell function.

kinetochore—a protein complex that binds centromeric regions of chromosomes; microtubules attach to it and pull the chromosome to a spindle pole during mitosis.

KRAS—a proto-oncogene whose product, the Ras protein, functions in the control of cell division.

Life Is Informational Continuity—one of 12 principles of life on which this text is based; DNA base sequence that is used to craft any cell came to that cell from a parental cell by DNA replication.

medial—occurring or situated in the middle or between other structures or processes.

metaphase—the second stage of mitosis during which chromosomes reach the center of the maternal cell being arranged across an imaginary equatorial plate.

metaphase plate—an imaginary region, disc-shaped, often in the cell's geometric center, where all of the cell's chromosomes come to lie during the second stage of mitosis.

mitosis—the process of dividing a single maternal nucleus into two daughter nuclei distributing to each nucleus equal halves of replicated chromosomes. Cell division is usually concurrent or follows immediately.

mitotic spindle—arrangement of microtubules used to separate halves of replicated chromosomes into daughter nuclei.

molecular weight—the total mass number of the atoms comprising a molecule. Each carbon would contribute a mass number of 12 to the molecule; each oxygen, 16.

motor proteins—an enzyme that uses ATP energy to do mechanical work within the cell; interacts with cytoskeletal elements to move cell parts.

nucleoside triphosphate—a subunit monomer for nucleic acids DNA or RNA that includes three adjacent phosphate groups in its structure. ATP is an example.

oncogene—(Gk. oncos = tumor), a mutant proto-oncogene that predisposes the cell toward uncontrolled division.

origin of replication—a sequence of bases in DNA that is recognized by a helicase enzyme; the enzyme twists open the double helix at this point to allow a polymerase enzyme to begin replicating single DNA strands.

p21—a protein that inhibits the activity of Cdk-cyclins; their inhibition halts progress toward cell division.

p53—a regulatory protein whose phosphorylation causes it to bind the DNA sequences, resulting in expression of genes that will halt the cell cycle temporarily or result in apoptosis (cell suicide).

phosphorylation—the attachment of a phosphate group ($-PO_3$) to a molecule; often protein modification from inactive to active states is accomplished in this way.

prophase—the first stage of mitosis during which chromosomes become visible, the nuclear membrane deteriorates, and the mitotic spindle apparatus takes shape

proto-oncogene—a normal cellular gene whose product helps control progress within the cell cycle toward cell division.

Ras—a regulatory protein whose activation stimulates a cascade of regulatory alterations that results in the movement of a cell from G_1 into S phase of the cell cycle.

Rb—a regulatory protein that, when phosphorylated, moves a cell from G_1 into S phase of the cell cycle.

S phase—that portion of the cell cycle during which DNA and its scaffolding proteins are synthesized.

sister chromatid—half of a replicated chromosome; joined to a replica of itself by a centromere; splitting of the centromere converts each chromosomal half into a separate (now unreplicated) chromosome.

telophase—the fourth stage of mitosis during which parted sister chromatids (now chromosomes) decondense, nuclear membranes form, and daughter nuclei take on an interphase appearance.

template—a sequence of nucleic acid that is read by a polymerase enzyme such that it generates a new sequence of bases complementary to the one read.

TP53—a tumor suppressor gene whose product, the p53 protein, is used to suppress division of the cell.

tumor suppressor gene—a normal cellular gene whose product inhibits progress toward cell division; its mutation or loss leads to cancer.

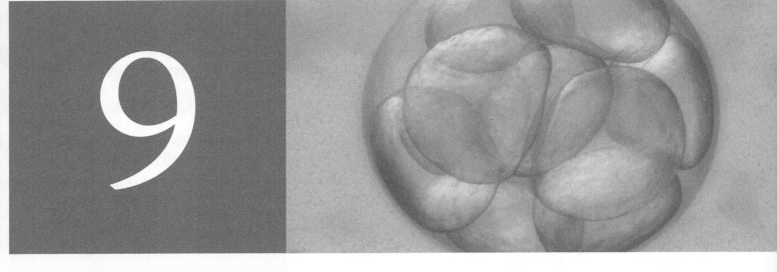

9

Complexity IV: From Cell to Organism

Survey Questions

9.1 Development: Decoding a Master Plan

- How does a single cell develop into a huge macroorganism? How does the acorn become the oak?
- Is development a process that can be subdivided into more intelligible subprocesses?
- What are these processes and how do they work together to produce an organism?
- How comprehensive is development? How is the final product, the organism, organized?

9.2 *Gingko biloba*: How to Make a Tree

- What is a *Ginkgo* tree?
- Where does development of the tree actually begin?
- How do plant and animal development differ?
- What controls the differentiation of the tree's cells into tissues and organs?
- How are leaves, stems, roots, and flowers differentiated?

9.3 Development of a Human Being

- In what structure does human development begin, and how does it begin?
- Do growth, cell division, differentiation, and morphogenesis all begin at once and continue at a constant rate?
- Through what sort of stages does human development progress?
- How does the process of differentiation begin and get maintained in human development?
- How does development progress from cells to tissues to organs?

DEVELOPMENT: DECODING A MASTER PLAN

9.1

What Can Be Done with a Fertilized Egg?

Thus far, your impression of biology is one of a vast assortment of carefully crafted biomolecules functioning within the membranes and "bowels" of even more intricate cells. Yet most of what our eyes observe in the living world is organismal. (Isn't biology about dissecting frogs and making leaf collections?) We have now explored cells and their workings just barely long enough to enable us to move on. On to where? To the subject of development—the use of cells to develop an organism.

The process of development is difficult to define. We might describe it as a trek of informational expression from a single cell—a fertilized egg—to a mature organism (see Figure 9.1). But this trek expresses itself in unfolding levels of internested complexity! (Life Is Complex.) Sporting a wonderful program that we still fail to comprehend, a single cell begins to grow, and divide, with the products developing first into tissues, then into organs, and finally into organ systems, presenting to us the mature organism.

Perhaps you've visited or worked at an assembly line in a factory. Computers and automobiles "develop" in this way (see illustration

- How do tissues and organs with the same genetic information get to be different from each other?
- How do whole systems like the digestive or nervous system develop?
- How does the human heart form?
- How can development start with a single-celled zygote and end up with a cerebrum that contemplates that process?
- What sort of chemical communication is involved in the process of development?
- How do the parts of an organ system work together?

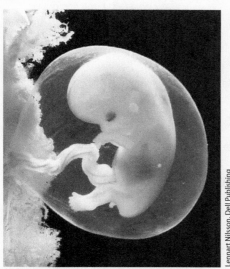

Imagine an automobile that, given sufficient energy and parts, makes itself. That would be close to imagining the hidden talent of the human embryo.

below). It is exciting (at first) to watch as the parts of a new automobile get spot welded into place. A high-performance engine and drive train, sophisticated electronic panels, and carpeting are added. Eventually, a key is turned, and the automobile takes on a life of its own—a triumph of human knowledge, mental creativity, and strength.

Far more amazing than that assembly line, is the ultrasound suite in a prenatal clinic. Like the automobile, the parts of the child are taking shape. But how highly superficial is our analogy! For all the time that the **embryo** develops it is also entirely alive! It respires without lungs. Without a brain it sends out neurons to appropriate places in the body. And as stated previously, the design is not found in file drawers in some model shop. And it is not implemented by some external skilled craftsmen. The design is *within* the embryo itself, and the construction, driven with placental support, is also directed from within! The embryo is the "auto-mobile" that makes itself. While it is becoming it is also *being*.

So development is the study of initiation and construction. Once the mature adult exists, we can then study a variety of maintenance functions. This will be the subject of Chapter 10. But far more amazing than the efficient function of the 11 organ systems that are you is the process that "pulled them out of the hat"—the single-celled **zygote** that you once were. The daunting complexity of organismal development is an integrating field in biology (see Table 9.1). Molecular, cellular, tissue, and organismal studies are all part of its province. Scientists trained in a variety of subdisciplines are drawn to the fascinating mysteries inherent in the process of development.

Getting from One Cell to You or to a Tree

In our relative ignorance of its nuances, we have attempted to categorize aspects of development that isolate and clarify the mysteries to be explained. Currently, we see four component parts to the process that commences with a zygote (a fertilized egg) and results in you. Some of them are obvious, some, more subtle.

1. The first is **growth.** Your first cell was the size of the point of a pin. What is your size now? (150 lbs? 220 lbs?). And some of us, with the help of ice cream and cookies, continue to grow. One fruitful question you might ask is why are there limits to growth in height? Why does the average human male in the United States reach a height of 5′ 9″ and then stop growing?

embryo—an organism in its early stages of developing toward maturity; immediately following fertilization, the cell has commenced this development.

zygote—a single diploid cell resulting from the fertilization of a haploid egg cell by a haploid sperm cell.

growth—accumulation of biomass in either a cell, a tissue, an organ or an individual.

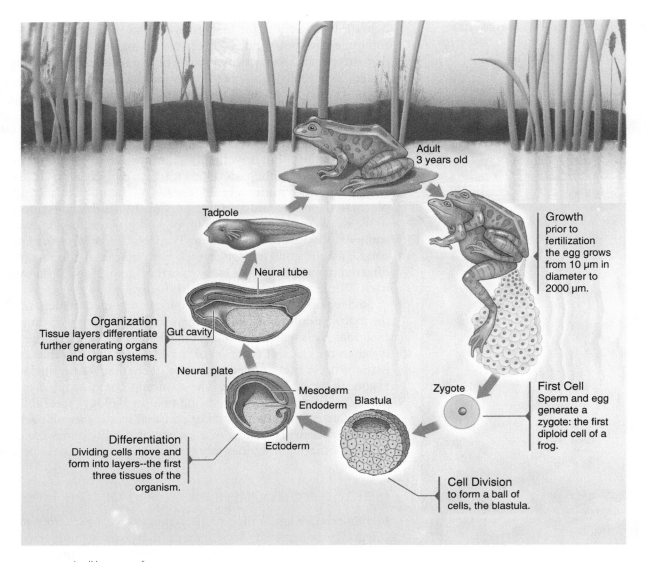

Figure 9.1 A cell becomes a frog.

One thing we know for certain. If growth were the only component to development, you'd be no larger than a single cell. Why is that? (Return to Section 5.1 for ideas.)

2. This huge mass we've become must have undergone cell division. This was critical so we could molecularly service all the parts of our bodies with oxygen, nutrients, and waste removal (see Figure 9.2). This is why the coffee you spill onto your hand isn't going to get the caffeine working in your fingertips! The developing organism is something like what happens to a grocery business when it graduates from a farm stand to a supermarket. In a farm stand everyone gathers around the goods, reaches in, and selects what they want. But in a supermarket, there're too

Table 9.1 Biological disciplines contributing to developmental biology

Sub-discipline of Biology	Interest in Development
anatomy	form of new structures
physiology	embryonic processes
genetics	informational control of development
histology	how tissue layers form and move
cell biology	how cells differentiate
microbiology	development of simpler multicellular organisms
molecular biology	the chemical basis of differentiation

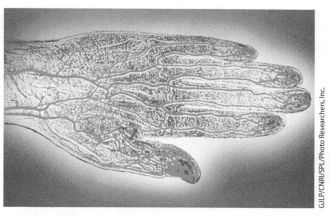

Figure 9.2 Servicing a Multicellular Hand. Blood vessels carry nutrients, oxygen, and hormones to billions of cells all throughout the hand.

Table 9.2 Differentiation in plant cells.

	Cell Type	Function
	Parenchyma cell	Secreation, storage, photosynthesis
	Collenchyma cell	Support
	Sclerenchyma cell (fiber)	Support
	Tracheid	Conduction of water and minerals; support
	Vessel element	Conduction of water and minerals; support
	Sieve-tube element	Conduction of dissolved food materials (carbohydrates)
	Companion cell (not shown)	Aids sieve-tube element
	Epidermal cells	Protective covering over surface

many goods to use that approach. So we have aisles separating various goods so everything is available to everybody. In a huge tree or a human body, growth must be followed by subdivision (cell division) with spaces in between so that bulk flow of materials can service all the parts.

3. But we can't get by with just one type of cell. In a macroorganism with many cells, there has to be **differentiation** of those cells into separate types, with each type serving the organism in its own way (see Table 9.2). We humans must have neurons to inform us, lymphocytes to fight our microbial battles, myocytes to lift things, erythrocytes to transport oxygen, and osteocytes to support us. Somehow, for each of the more than 200 different types of cells in your body, a select set of genes is activated, and all the other genes that would support the functions of all the other cell types are shut off. Someone has written an amazing developmental program! It was not any scientist I know.

4. But finally, we aren't just a grab bag of 200 cell types just strewn through the organism randomly. Cells are organized into tissues. Neurons are found in nerves. Osteocytes work *together* in bones (see Figure 9.3a). Tracheids form long water-conducting tubes of xylem in the stem of an alfalfa plant (see Figure 9.3b). When many cells of one type divide, grow, and move together in a process called **morphogenesis,** they become spatially organized into large ordered groupings like a stomach lining or a toenail. In this way, they can better serve an organism as large as a tree or a human being.

But the variety of tissue structures and functions is small compared to the diversity of activities required within an organism like a human or a tree.

differentiation—a process by which a generalized cell or tissue matures into a specialized cell or tissue.

morphogenesis—the development of the form of the organism; involves getting and keeping differentiated cells and tissues organized into productive groupings.

Bone tissue

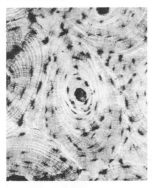

Figure 9.3   Morphogenesis leads to Organization. **(a)** Within a human bone is a dense array of concentric rings of bone cells arranged around central canals whose blood vessels and nerves service the surrounding cells. "Osteocytes" (bone cells) secrete the dense layers around them that give strength to the bone. **(b)** Within the stem of an alfalfa plant is a glorious arrangement of diverse tissue structures that together support the plant physically, conducts water and nutrients, and protect interior structures from dessication and parasites.

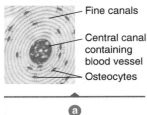

- Fine canals
- Central canal containing blood vessel
- Osteocytes

a

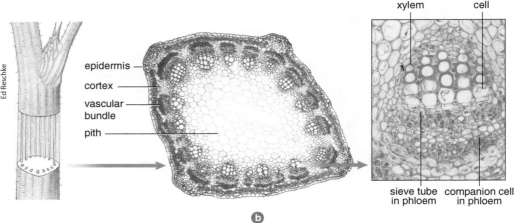

Ed Reschke

epidermis

cortex

vascular bundle

pith

vessel in xylem

meristem cell

sieve tube in phloem

companion cell in phloem

b

So tissues are arranged into higher-order structures called *organs,* whose diversity suits this myriad of activities. **Epithelial tissue, connective tissue,** glandular tissue, muscle tissue, and neural tissue work together to make an organ we call the *stomach* (see Figure 9.4a). Epidermal tissue, **mesophyll tissue,** and conducting tissues work together to form a leaf (see Figure 9.4b).

But how do miracles like leaves and stomachs ever get structured from their component tissues? Questions like this invade the realm of high mystery where developmental biology operates! Our current answers are crude but maturing year by year. The miracle of development is really a highly sophisticated program. As the program unfolds, movements of separate tissue layers cause them to change their relationships to each other spatially within the embryo (see Figure 9.5). Signal molecules from cells in a newly adjacent tissue can cause gene expression changes in cells of another tissue. We call this process **induction.** This sort of signal reception and response informs the process of patterning and structuring as tissues interact and mature into organs (see Figure 9.5).

In humans, as many as 78 organs serve 78 discrete functions. But these functions fall into natural groupings that suggest a still higher level of organization in the Mind of the Designer. In Chapter 1, we called this higher level the *organ system.* For example, the stomach, pancreas, liver, small intestine, and large intestine are all organs that cooperate to support nutritional intake of the organism. They are

an organ system: the **digestive system.** The human organism is composed of 11 such organ systems, which, although separately defined, are highly interrelated (see Figure 9.6)!

This, then, is a superficial description of how development uses a single cell to create a macro-organism. In summary, cells grow till they're large enough to divide. Once there are enough of them, they differentiate into different types of cells, but the various cell types organize into tissues and organs as the body grows, so that the whole organism is served. While a two-sentence summary of development may have a basic intellectual appeal to it, it does practically nothing to detract from the pleasant mystery the gardener anticipates as he drops a seed in a hole.

epithelial tissue—layers or groups of animal cells that cover body surfaces, line body cavities, and give rise to certain glands.

connective tissue—a collection of cells in an extracellular matrix of supportive material that adds structural strength to other nearby collections of cells.

mesophyll tissue—interior photosynthetic cells in a leaf.

induction—that chemical process by which one cell or tissue produces a change in behavior or structure in a second cell or tissue.

digestive system—that organ system in the animal body that takes in, breaks down, and absorbs the components of food.

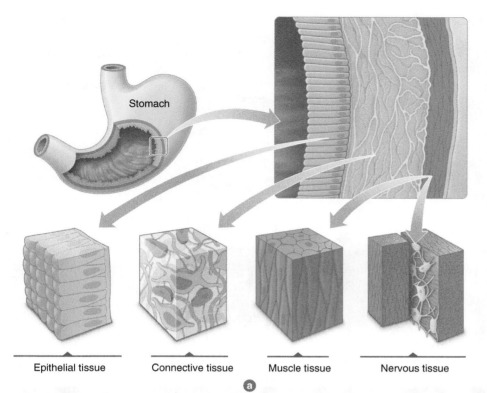

Figure 9.4 Tissue Structure of an Organ. **(a)** The stomach is an organ used for the mechanical and enzymatic degradation of food. Four of its supporting tissues are shown. Epithelial tissue: absorption, secretory glands. Connective tissue: blood vessels for transport, supportive structures. Muscle tissue: mixing and movement of food. Nervous tissue: intra-organ, inter-organ control and communication.

Epithelial tissue   Connective tissue   Muscle tissue   Nervous tissue

a

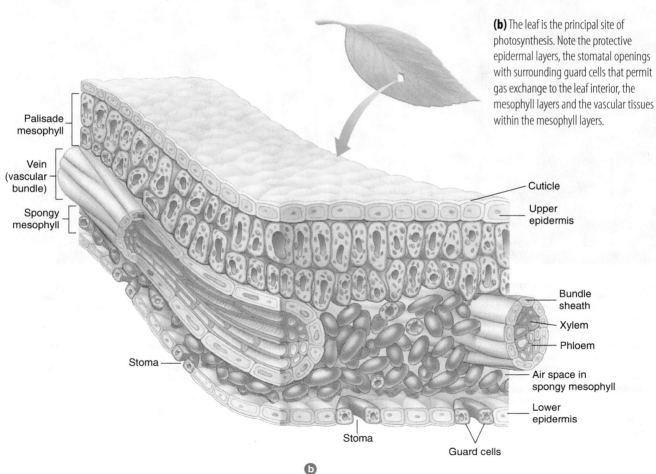

(b) The leaf is the principal site of photosynthesis. Note the protective epidermal layers, the stomatal openings with surrounding guard cells that permit gas exchange to the leaf interior, the mesophyll layers and the vascular tissues within the mesophyll layers.

Palisade mesophyll

Vein (vascular bundle)

Spongy mesophyll

Cuticle

Upper epidermis

Bundle sheath

Xylem

Phloem

Stoma

Air space in spongy mesophyll

Lower epidermis

Stoma

Guard cells

b

Embryonic induction

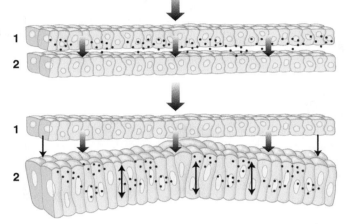

1. Morphogenetic movement brings two embryonic tissue layers into close proximity with each other.

2. The first tissue layer secretes a gene product (black dots) that has a signaling effect on the second tissue layer.

3. The second tissue layer responds to the signal substance by altering its own gene expression resulting in new morphological and functional patterns.

Figure 9.5 Embryonic Induction. Biomolecular signals elaborated from one embryonic tissue layer initiate structural changes and altered behaviors in another layer.

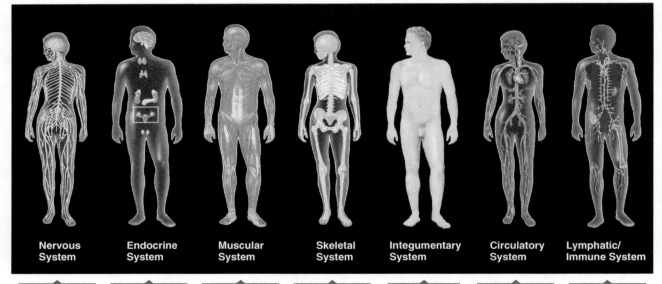

Nervous System	Endocrine System	Muscular System	Skeletal System	Integumentary System	Circulatory System	Lymphatic/ Immune System
Main organs: Brain, spinal cord, peripheral nerves, sensory organs	**Main organs:** Pituitary, thyroid, adrenal, pancreas, and other hormone secreting glands	**Main organs:** Skeletal, cardiac, and smooth muscle	**Main organs:** Bones, tendons, ligaments, cartilage	**Main organs:** Skin, sweat glands, hair, nails	**Main organs:** Heart, blood vessels, blood	**Main organs:** Lymph nodes, lymph ducts, spleen, thymus
Main functions: Senses internal and external stimuli; coordinates responses to stimuli; controls other organ systems.	**Main functions:** Cooperates with nervous system to control body function using hormonal signals.	**Main functions:** Movement of limbs and parts of internal organs; heat generation.	**Main functions:** Support and protection of body; leverage for muscle contraction; blood cell production.	**Main functions:** Protection from dehydration, pathogens, injury; temperature control; waste excretion.	**Main functions:** Services body cells with nutrients, oxygen, and waste removal; temperature and pH stabilization.	**Main functions:** Filters tissue fluids, monitors and protects against disease.

Figure 9.6 Organ Systems in the Human Body.

1. The process of development uses information in the nucleus of a single cell and the positional relationship of molecules in the cytoplasm of that cell to generate a complex multicellular organism.
2. The developing organism is entirely alive and functions all the time that it is in the process of maturing to adulthood.
3. The first cell of the developing organism is a fertilized egg, also called the *zygote*.
4. Organismal development can be dissected into four component processes: growth, cell division, differentiation, and morphogenesis (or organization).
5. Cell division permits growth of the organism beyond the limits of cell size imposed by exchange capabilities across the cell membrane.
6. Differentiation of cells into diverse types involves turning on separate, specific sets of genes in each cell type. Most genes are not expressed in most cells.
7. As cells differentiate, those of a given type tend to stay together to form tissues. Tissue movement and signalling in the embryo—the process of morphogenesis—yield body organs that can be classified into organ systems.
8. One tissue signaling another to alter its behavior is called *induction*.

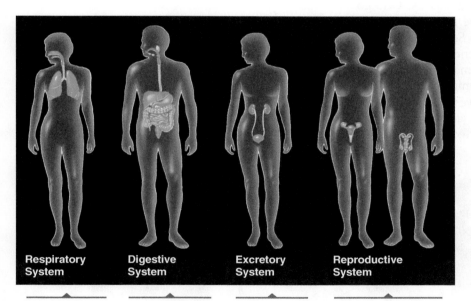

Respiratory System

Main organs:
Lungs, diaphragm, trachea, and other airways

Main functions:
Oxygen delivery to tissues, waste CO2 removal; pH regulation.

Digestive System

Main organs:
Pharynx, esophagus, stomach, intestines, liver, pancreas, rectum, anus

Main functions:
Ingestion of food; mechanical and chemical breakdown of food, nutrient absorption, waste elimination.

Excretory System

Main organs:
Kidneys, bladder, ureter, urethra

Main functions:
Controls volume and composition of internal fluids, removes excess water and metabolic wastes.

Reproductive System

Main organs:
Female: ovaries, oviducts, uterus, vagina, mammary glands
Male: testes, sperm ducts, accessory glands, penis

Main functions:
Production and union of sex cells; supports embryonic development; hormonal control of some body systems.

Figure 9.6 *(Continued)*

GINGKO BILOBA: HOW TO MAKE A TREE

We've just made some very broad generalizations about development. Let's apply them to two specific examples: the development of a tree and the development of you. What sort of tree might we select for our study? The maidenhair tree, scientific name *Ginkgo biloba,* is a fascinating tree for study (see Figure 9.7). A quick look at the structure of its graceful leaf supports what we know from other studies as well: No other trees alive today are quite like it. In fact, we're not really certain that it grows anywhere in the wild—perhaps in Eastern China, but even this particular location is debated. It's been cultivated by Chinese monks in this region for over 1000 years, perhaps out of interest in its culinary and medicinal properties. The glorious yellow color of the leaves in fall commends their rare beauty to us. Ginkgo trees exist that are claimed to be more than 2500 years in age! They're hardy too! Several individual trees survived the intense, high-energy radiation of the atomic bombing of Hiroshima in 1945. Little else did. And the medical community is highly interested in the chemistry of the leaves for a variety of pathological conditions. There is a certain satisfaction in studying the development of an organism so attractive, long-lived, durable, and medically useful. Let's have a look at how it begins life.

Early Development

Childhood experience suggests to us that a new plant results from the **germination** of a **seed.** But a closer look reveals that the life of a new plant formally begins deep within the female reproductive structures of the parent plant. Ginkgo trees are "good" plants, but they have some surprises for us. First, they are **dioecious**—they exist as separate male and female trees. Second, their female reproductive structure is unique. We hesitate to call it a *flower* or a *cone* (see

> **germination**—the beginning or resumption of growth in a seed, spore, or bud structure.
>
> **seed**—an embryonic plant together with its nutrient source enclosed within a protective coat of external tissue.
>
> **dioecious (Gk. *di-* = two, *oikos-* = house)**—a species of plant in which the reproductive organs of the two sexes are found on separate individuals.

Figure 9.7 *Ginkgo biloba.* **(a)** a beautiful specimen in a formal garden in England **(b)** the fall color of the leaves is glorious. On a single tree, they all drop (abscise) within a few days' time. **(c)** a Ginkgo leaf resting on a fossil of a Gingko leaf taken from Cretaceous sediments.

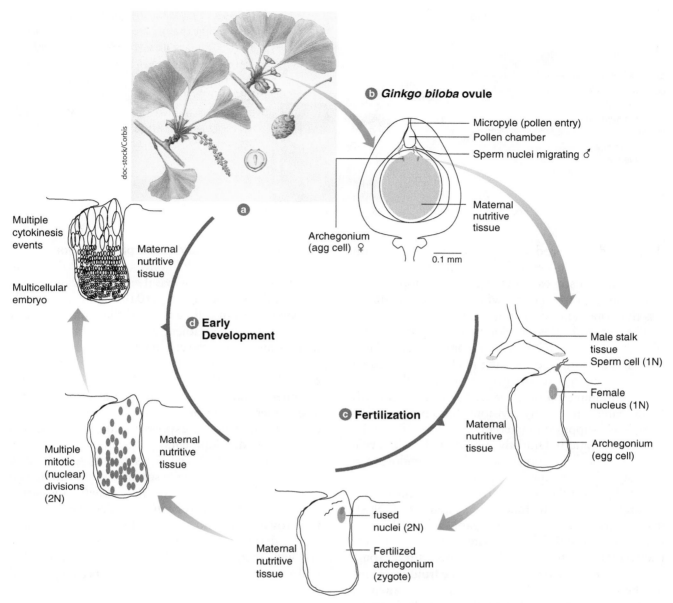

Figure 9.8 Ginkgo Reproduction. **(a)** In the upper right-hand corner of this diagram is a portion of a stem from a female tree. Note the ovules protruding from the stalks. In the lower lefthand corner is a portion of a stem from a male tree. Note the loosely arranged "cone" that forms pollen grains. In the lower right hand portion of the diagram a seed is shown both entire and sectioned through with a knife. **(b)** a diagramatic slice through an ovule at a time just prior to fertilization of an archegonium (or egg cell). **(c)** a diagramatic slice through an archegonium (egg cell) showing fertilization by a haploid sperm nucleus. **(d)** the same archegonium following multiple nuclear divisions and cytokinesis events that generate a 256 cell embryo.

Section 9.2b). It's a 1.5-cm-long stalk with a colorful swollen end that contains just one to two **ovules** in the end of it (see Figure 9.8a, b). Within each ovule is a haploid egg cell. When a **pollen grain** from a cone on a male tree (see Figure 9.8a) wanders by and lands there, male tissue arises from it, begins to invade the ovule and grows there. Soon, haploid sperm cells are produced and one of them migrates to and fertilizes the haploid egg cell (see Figure 9.8b–c). This **fertilization** event can occur while the ovule is still on the tree or after it has matured a bit and fallen to

ovule—a female reproductive structure in plants in which the haploid egg cell has matured. The mature ovule contains the new individual and is called a *seed*.

pollen grain—a spore-like structure in plants containing the haploid nucleus that will fertilize the female ovum to produce a zygote. It is carried from the male reproductive structure to the female one by wind, water, or other organisms.

fertilization—process by which a male sex cell and a female sex cell fuse to form a diploid first cell (zygote) of a new individual.

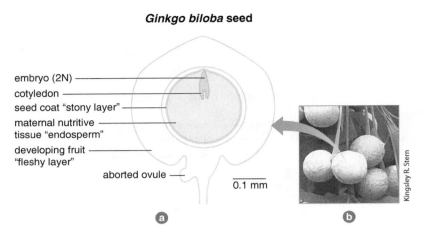

Ginkgo biloba seed

embryo (2N)
cotyledon
seed coat "stony layer"
maternal nutritive
tissue "endosperm"
developing fruit
"fleshy layer"
aborted ovule

0.1 mm

Kingsley R. Stern

a   **b**

Figure 9.9 *Ginkgo biloba* seed. **(a)** The seed and surrounding fruit have a shape similar to that of the ovule in Figure 9.8 because the seed develops within the ovule. The cotyledon is a primary embryonic leaf whose nutritive content is utilized once the seedling begins to grow. The actively dividing apical part of the embryo (toward the cotyledons) grows forward (downward) digesting maternal nutrient tissues as it grows. **(b)** photo of the seeds/fruit.

the ground. The product of fertilization—the fusion of egg and sperm—is a diploid cell (two complete sets of chromosomes)—the zygote. Development of a huge ginkgo tree begins with a zygote measuring less than one-tenth millimeter in length.

The zygote begins development with a sequence of eight nuclear divisions in a common cytoplasm (see Figure 9.8d). The resulting nuclei get distributed into separate cytoplasms generating an oblong embryo containing about 2^8 or 256 cells in it. Growth accompanies these early divisions. Both processes are completely supported materially and energetically by specialized maternal nutritive tissues within the ovule of the parent plant, sometimes called the **endosperm**. The ovule also synthesizes a tough outer seed coat that will protect the embryo from possibly harsh desiccating conditions to follow (see Figure 9.9). Next, it synthesizes a foul-smelling organic acid in the fruit that will surround the seed-coated embryo. It is suspected that this "rotting flesh" odor may attract some reptilian predators that then ingest the fruit, distributing the seeds unharmed in their feces. Other potential predators may be repelled by the odor. Without all this biologically "expensive" support from the parent plant, the embryo wouldn't have a chance in a cold, dry, external world filled with predatory fungi, insect, and avian forms.

Meanwhile, within the seed, the cells of the embryo are differentiating into distinct tissues. How does this happen? Signal molecules called **hormones** move cell populations in new directions structurally and functionally. They do this in at least two ways. First, they cause some cells to stop transcribing certain genes within their genomes and to start transcribing others. But hormones may also initiate new steps in development by interacting directly with molecules or structures to change how they will now function in the cell. Early on, within the maternal tissues surrounding

the new zygote, a gradient of a plant hormone called an **auxin** is set up—the concentration of the auxin being higher toward the basal end of the zygote than the apical end (see Figure 9.10a). Auxins are readily transported from cell to cell and they diffuse readily within cells. So a gradient is quickly established extending away from the cell in which the auxin is being generated. When the cell divisions occur that give rise to the 256-cell embryo, cells at the basal end will have a higher auxin concentration than at the other end. The higher concentration of auxin in basal cells will call different genes to expression and new structural parts of the developmental program to unfold. The result will be distinct cell types emerging in the new embryo. So it is maternally supplied information—an auxin gradient—that directs new genetic and structural information expression in the developing organism. Toward one end of the embryo (the apical end), tissues that form the **shoot** (future stem, leaves, flowers) will emerge; toward the basal end, the **root** (that will absorb water and mineral nutrients from the soil)

endosperm—a plant tissue within a seed that contains stored nutrients for a developing embryo. It forms from fertilization of nuclei in the ovule by a nucleus in the pollen grain.

hormone—within an organism, a (usually small) molecule generated in one kind of tissue that becomes a signal or message causing cells elsewhere in the organism to alter their behavior in response.

auxin—a class of plant hormones that tends to promote cell elongation leading to stem elongation and root initiation.

shoot—the portion of embryonic tissue that will give rise to aerial parts of the plant: the stems, leaves, and flowers.

root—the portion of embryonic tissue that will give rise to underground parts of the plant designed for absorption and anchoring of the plant.

Hormonal gradient in embryo

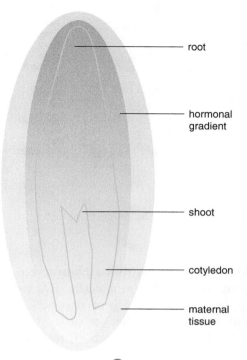

- root
- hormonal gradient
- shoot
- cotyledon
- maternal tissue

(a)

Figure 9.10 Differentiation in an Early Embryo. **(a)** Maternal tissues set up a gradient of auxin concentration within embryonic cells which defines an axis of polarity along which the embryo develops—the root to one end, the shoot tip to the other end. **(b)** After several weeks, the embryo within the seed has a clear polarity with structures as labelled. The cotyledons are loaded with starch granules which will provide nutrients once the seed germinates.

Ginkgo biloba embryo within the seed

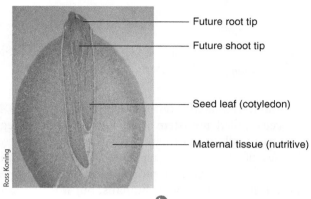

- Future root tip
- Future shoot tip
- Seed leaf (cotyledon)
- Maternal tissue (nutritive)

Ross Koning

(b)

will form. The cells at each end of the embryo have the same genetic information! But differential auxin signaling yields expression of different subsets of the genome in different cells. In Figure 9.10b you can see embryonic cells that will become the tip of the first shoot—the first stem of the seedling.

Development of the embryo within a seed reaches a point less commonly reached in animal development—a stopping point. In many plants, especially in temperate climates, by the time the seed coat has become fully protective of the embryo, environmental (seasonal) conditions no longer favor continued development. So the embryo simply stops developing, the seed remains dormant until optimal growth conditions resume. The seed then germinates, and development of the embryo into a seedling resumes.

Cell Specialization: Tissue Types Emerge

Within the maturing root and shoot, three basic types of cells differentiate from each other and organize as separate tissues. Later on, these three tissue types will be found in all organs of the plant: The **ground tissue** serves basic life-support functions such as photosynthesis and storage of food and water, **vascular tissue** distributes water and

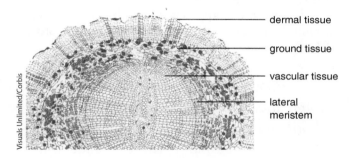

- dermal tissue
- ground tissue
- vascular tissue
- lateral meristem

Visuals Unlimited/Corbis

Figure 9.11 *Ginkgo biloba* root in cross section (cut through with a sharp blade and seen on end). The tissues are stained for better visibility.

solutes throughout the plant, and **dermal tissue** covers and protects plant surfaces (see Figure 9.11).

But there is one other sort of tissue, especially within stems and roots, that fascinates plant biologists: It is a

ground tissue—the fundamental tissue system of a plant excluding its epidermal and vascular tissues.

vascular tissue—those structures both cellular and cellular products that conduct fluids from one place to another in the plant body.

dermal tissue—those cellular layers that serve a protective function on the surface of the plant body; protection from desiccation and parasitic pests.

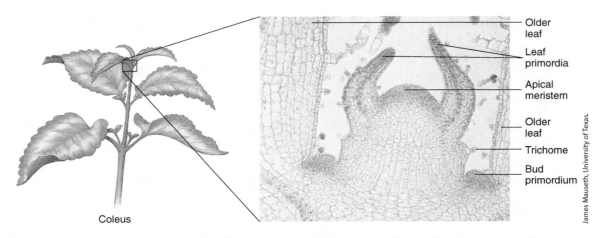

Coleus

Figure 9.12 Apical Meristem. This is a longitudinal slice through the tip of a stem in a plant of Genus *Coleus* showing a region of apical meristem. Other developing structures are noted as well

permanently **undifferentiated**, continuously dividing collection of cells called **meristem** (Gk. *meristo-* = divided). This tissue allows us to study the developmental processes of growth and cell division in the absence of any differentiation or morphogenesis. It is somewhat like **stem cell** tissue in humans, but unlike in humans, it enables the gingko tree to reach thousands of years in age instead of simply decades! This difference was appreciated by observers literally thousands of years ago. In the ancient Biblical story of Job we read:

> *For there is hope for a tree, if it is cut down, that it will sprout again, and that its shoots will not cease. . . . but a man dies and is laid low; man breathes his last and where is he? . . .* (JOB 14: 7, 10)

The mystery of the superior durability of meristem cells as compared with human stem cells is one that still challenges molecular biologists today. It is a quandary in the midst of which naturalistic biologists appeal to the accidental aspects of their theory. By accident, plant meristem has achieved this exceptional durability while, by accident, human stem cells only discover it in the cancerous state. Meristem durability means that for the entire life of an individual plant, growth is a more continuous process. In animals, by contrast, development leads to maturity and then maintenance. This results in entirely different lifestyles. In waging life's wars, animals go places whereas plants grow places.

Meristem exists within a plant in zones—small regions of cells that seasonally give rise to fresh stem, leaf, flower, and root tissues. Consider the **apical meristem** at the tip of a stem (see Figure 9.12). Cells in this region have high growth and division rates. As the rapidly dividing cell region moves up or forward, the cells left behind then begin to differentiate into the three tissue types discussed above. Apical meristems tend to lengthen stems and roots. By contrast, consider again Figure 9.11—a section through a root of *Ginkgo biloba*. Shown there is a thin layer (dark purple) of **lateral meristem**—undifferentiated cells that, by their division, thicken the root as the seedling grows. As cells divide horizontally away from these meristems, they differentiate into the various tissues that support function in the thickening

undifferentiated—referring to a cell or tissue that is committed to no specified role or function within the organism other than providing a source of new cells.

meristem—undifferentiated plant cells and tissue from which new cells are produced.

stem cell—a growing, dividing, undifferentiated cell within animal embryos or adults that eventually differentiates into a variety of types of cells found in the animal's body.

apical meristem—a zone of rapidly dividing, undifferentiated plant cells near the tip or apex of a shoot, stem, or root.

lateral meristem—within a stem or root, a layer of undifferentiated plant cells whose division adds to the diameter of the stem or root.

stem. Once meristematic tissue generates new cells, it is the response of these cells to plant hormones that unfolds the differentiation and morphogenesis processes.

Morphogenesis: Organ Formation

Origin of Roots
After a period of dormancy, a seed responds to temperature and moisture levels appropriate for growth. For example, the seed absorbs available moisture and its coat cracks open. Germination follows immediately. Differentiation within the young seedling continues as it emerges from the soil (see Figure 9.13a). The primary root is the first structure to emerge from the seed. It thickens as it grows downward. The meristem near the tip generates many cellular descendants behind it that divide, enlarge, and elongate. The meristem also produces cells in the forward direction (down) to form a dome-shaped mass of expendable cells called a **root cap** that protects the root as it pushes through the soil (see Figure 9.13b). From the cellular descendants trailing behind the meristem, auxin-driven differentiation gives rise to the ground tissue for nutrient storage and a **vascular cylinder** consisting of **xylem** and **phloem** tissues that will conduct water and nutrients respectively throughout the plant. The rate at which cell division occurs in the root meristem is under the control of a class of plant hormones called **cytokinins**. These hormones are synthesized near the tips of the roots.

root cap—on the very tip of a root, a layer of cells that generates a mucoid secretion easing the root further into the soil.

vascular cylinder—also called the *stele;* within a root, a central collection of xylem and phloem tissue including internal meristematic and surface dermal tissues.

xylem—a transport tissue in plants; in trees it comprises much of the wood of the trunk; transports water upward within a plant.

phloem—a transport tissue in plants; carries nutrients, sucrose in particular, to all parts of the plant.

cytokinins—plant hormones that promote cell division in roots and shoots; contribute to dominance of growth of the central stem of a plant.

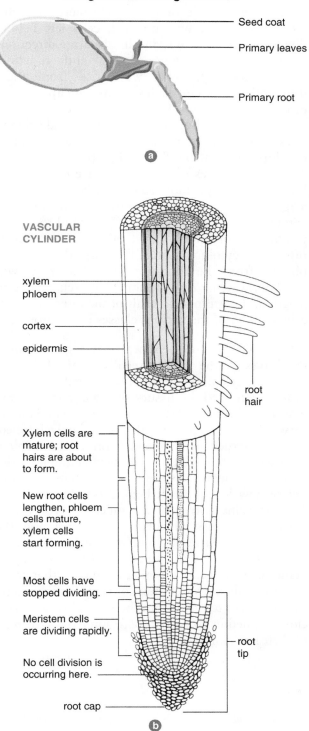

***Ginkgo biloba* seed germination**

- Seed coat
- Primary leaves
- Primary root

a

VASCULAR CYLINDER

xylem
phloem

cortex

epidermis

root hair

Xylem cells are mature; root hairs are about to form.

New root cells lengthen, phloem cells mature, xylem cells start forming.

Most cells have stopped dividing.

Meristem cells are dividing rapidly.

No cell division is occurring here.

root tip

root cap

b

Figure 9.13 Root Development. **(a)** The primary root is the first structure to emerge from the cracked seed coat. The cotyledons remain within the seed contributing their nutrients to the emerging seedling. **(b)** Zones of growth and differentiation found within a typical primary root.

Origin of Stems

In the embryo's shoot tip is another small collection of apical meristem cells. As it divides its way upward, cells left behind divide at different rates and in disparate directions differentiating in size, shape, and function. **Lateral** (axillary) **buds** will arise from these differentiated tissues, each with its own apical zone of meristematic cells. From these will come lateral stems, leaves, and eventually, in half of all gingko trees, ovule-containing stalks (see Figure 9.14). Stem development is also influenced by plant hormones. The young tissues of shoots produce **gibberellins**, hormones that promote stem lengthening. Auxins, a group of hormones mentioned above, also stimulate lengthening growth. They tend to inhibit production of lateral buds, but this tendency is offset by cytokinins travelling up through the phloem from the root tips. Apical stem growth and lateral stem grow are skillfully orchestrated in length and pattern as a result of the interactions of cells with all of the various classes of hormones.

Origin of Leaves

Shortly after germination, the leaves of the gingko seedling unfold. Within each leaf, cell populations have already begun to differentiate into the tissues that will compose the mature leaf. As the meristem in the apical bud moves forward, the immature leaf has a deeply bilobed, wing-like structure to either side on the stem. Below each wing is a bulge that will become the next tier of immature leaves. As the stem lengthens, tier after tier of new leaves is left behind (see Figure 9.15). The emerging leaves come under the control of the cytokinin class of hormones that promote the expansion of leaves to their full size and inhibit their aging. As the growing season progresses, the plant begins to generate other hormones that cause leaves to wilt and sever their connection to the stem, causing them to drop from the tree. This process is closely timed in *Gingko biloba*; some trees drop all of their leaves in a single day!

lateral bud—forming at the base (axil) of a leaf, embryonic tissue that will give rise to an axillary shoot from the surface of an existing stem.

gibberellins—plant hormones that regulate growth and differentiation particularly with respect to stem elongation, germination and flowering.

Ginkgo biloba stem development

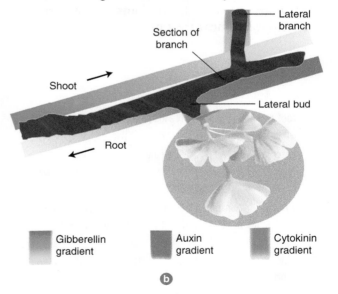

| Gibberellin gradient | Auxin gradient | Cytokinin gradient |

Figure 9.14 Stem Development. **(a)** On the top surface of the branch, a lateral bud has given rise to a long shoot (a new branch). On the lower surface, the lateral bud has generated one of the more numerous spur shoots that form leaves. **(b)** Whether a lateral bud becomes a long shoot or a spur shoot is dependent on the interactions between hormonal gradients within the branch.

Figure 9.15 Leaf Development. Hormonal signals in concert prompt the genetic programs within differentiated stem cells to give rise to new tiers of leaves.

As gingko leaves mature, their cells develop a surface, thickness, and shape that perfectly fit them to temperate climates. They are not designed for the sweeping winds of the tundra or the desiccating conditions of the desert. The ginkgo leaf develops a robust defensive chemistry that makes the trees resistant to a wide variety of insect pests. This chemistry may help explain their wide distribution within temperate regions of the planet.

Generally speaking, plant leaves vary widely across habitats in both their structure and chemical composition. These variations neatly adapt each type of plant to both the physical characteristics and the principle predators in their range of habitat (see Figure 9.16). Desert leaves are thick with heavy cuticles to prevent water loss. Aquatic plants have very thin leaves by comparison.

This habitat-constrained logic in the design of leaves has resulted in an almost limitless variety in leaf structure and chemistry that man has exploited for food (lettuce, cabbage, onion, rhubarb, spinach, etc.), spices (mint, bay, thyme, etc.), medicines (garlic, mint, belladonna, digitalis, teas), fumigants, construction materials (thatch, roofs, walls), waxes, abrasives, hair dyes, ropes, burlap, and for decorative purposes. Did we think that their only value was the oxygen they generated?

Origin of Reproductive Structures

The ginkgo tree's reproduction is unique in the plant world. Ginkgos develop according to a visually pleasing pattern in which long branches send out short branches via an attachment that is at almost a right angle with the parent branch. It is off of these short branches that the reproductive structures develop. While male trees have cone-like structures that generate pollen, female trees do not

(a)   (b)   (c)

Figure 9.16 Leaf Variation. **(a)** In this dessert cactus *Mammilaria*, leaves are reduced to mere spines. These minimize water loss and deter predators. **(b)** Another approach to minimizing water loss when sunlight is ample: spherical leaves of the *Senecio* plant. **(c)** When water is plentiful and sunlight more limiting, leaves approach two dimensionality and can become 11 inches in diameter as in this water lily (*Nymphae odorata*)

have either a **flower** (like in flowering plants) or a **cone** (as in conifers). Rather, under hormonal control, the short branches of the female tree send out 1.5-cm-long stalks on the end of which are ovules preparing for pollination (see Figure 9.8). But ovules and cones do not appear for the first 20 to 35 seasons of growth! Wind carries pollen from the male trees to the female ovules. The fleshy ovule becomes a yellow fruit the size of a cherry. The odor of this fruit is distinctly unpleasant, but the nuts inside are quite edible (see Figure 9.9).

Gingko's unique mode of reproduction confounds conventional classification schemes. But then, classification schemes are the products of mere men. The ginkgo is so adapted, yet graceful, in leaf morphology and so glorious in fall color that one looks for a gifted Artist behind such majesty.

> **flower**—a plant reproductive structure in angiosperms (flowering plants) that serves to bring ova and sperm nuclei together to form embryos within seeds.
>
> **cone (or *strobilus*)**—reproductive structure in conifers that generates pollen or ova, and following fertilization, seeds; often woody in structure.

IN OTHER WORDS

1. Ginkgo trees are unique in their leaf structure, reproductive processes, and natural history—a fascinating plant for study.
2. The life, the separate identity, of a ginkgo tree begins within the ovule of the maternal parent tree where fertilization takes place.
3. The maternal tissues, and specifically seed structures, protect and nutritionally support the developing embryo.
4. A multicellular gradient of auxin hormone within maternal tissues sets up a polar axis along which the embryo's root and shoot will develop.
5. Development in plants, especially in temperate climates, is often halted within the seed during winter months until acceptable growth temperatures resume in the spring.
6. Three basic types of plant tissue are the dermal tissues that protect plant surfaces, the ground tissues that support essential plant functions, and vascular tissues that transport substances from place to place in the plant.
7. Meristematic tissue in plants is a place of growth and division of undifferentiated cells. It supports development of the plant throughout the plant's entire life span, which may be thousands of years in length.
8. The plant root is the product of cell division in root tip meristem, cell elongation, and hormone-driven cell differentiation into the basic tissue types.
9. The shoot of the embryo becomes the trunk of the ginkgo tree; hormonal levels in cells all along the shoot control sites where lateral buds will form to become branches on the tree.
10. Leaf cells elongate and leaves expand in size under the influence of the cytokinin hormones.
11. Leaves have had a wide variety of uses by man, including food, shelter, and medicines.
12. The ginkgo tree's uniqueness among plants is shown by its lack of either flowers or cones in the production of female reproductive tissues; male cones have a very loose, open structure.

Early Events

Just as a glorious ginkgo tree results from the expression of a carefully crafted program of growth, cell division, differentiation, and morphogenesis, so does an adult human. Both the tree and the person who studies it begin as a humble microscopic zygote. Both begin life ensconced within maternal tissues. Let's wander inside the uterine tube of your mother (some years back) and discover what was happening to you. Once a human egg is fertilized by a sperm cell, within four days' journey along the uterine tube, it undergoes a sequence of initial cell divisions that leads to a tiny ball of 16 superficially similar cells called a **morula** (Lt. *morul* = a little mulberry; see Figure 9.17). It is the size of the period at the end of this sentence. Can we just stop here and be amazed at that? Sixteen complete copies of instructions to make "you" hide in a sphere 1/8 of a millimeter in diameter. If a miracle is something that defies both senses and rational explanation, then the morula closely approaches that definition.

Initially, there is very little growth; only a carving up of the available cytoplasm and placement of separate sets of genetic information (nuclei) into each portion (see Figure 9.17). But along with these cell divisions a subtle change is occurring. The cytoplasm of the original egg cell was regionally differentiated (see Figure 9.18). This geometric (or spatial) differentiation was created within the egg cytoplasm as *it* matured within the ovary. (Mom may not successfully orient the life of her teenager right now, but there was a time . . . !) During cell division within what was the egg cytoplasm, this spatially nonrandom distribution of molecules results in a population of cells that are cytoplasmically differentiated from each other, even though their appearance is quite similar. So if we observe cells in different locations within the embryo beginning to behave in different ways and appear different in structure, these distinctions can be traced back to differentiation of concentrations of cytoplasmic molecules (perhaps stable mRNAs?) within the first cell.

Soon, growth rate in the morula does increase and it becomes a hollow, fluid-filled ball of cells called a **blastocyst** (see Figure 9.17). Notice that the cells are now differentially arranged. Part of the hollow sphere of cells is a thicker inner cell mass. It's from this inner mass that the embryo will develop. The rest of the cells of the hollow sphere (the trophoblast) will contribute to the **placenta**: a baby organ perfectly adept at extracting nutrients from the mother's uterine lining. (The process of extracting maternal resources may continue in one form or another until the individual is 40 years old or older. . . .)

As development proceeds, the inner cell mass pulls away from the trophoblast resulting in a fluid-filled space on both sides of the embryo that will have a nice cushioning effect. The inner cell mass has now become organized into a flat disc, the blastodisc, which initially consists of two cell layers (see Figure 9.17). On the surface of the thicker of the two cell layers, a specific region near the center line of the disc begins to form a slight depression called the **primitive streak**. It's a zone where rapid cell division is coupled with an inward migration of daughter cells into a space that opens up between the two original cell layers. The name for this process is **gastrulation**. The result of all this rearrangement is three cell layers that are referred to

morula—a very early embryonic stage of development in mammals in which initial cleavage divisions have given rise to a ball of cells.

blastocyst—an early developmental stage in the human embryo in which further cell divisions in the morula have generated a hollow ball of cells with a central, fluid-filled cavity; implantation in the uterus occurs in this stage.

placenta—an organ that connects the developing embryo to the uterine wall of the mother for the exchange of nutrients and wastes.

primitive streak—a line bisecting the middle of the embryonic disc; from this area cells divide and migrate into the interior of the embryonic disc forming a mesodermal layer of cells.

gastrulation—a process occurring in a blastula or blastocyst in which cell movements on the surface of the embryo and into its interior result in the formation of the three primary tissue layers on which further differentiation will be based.

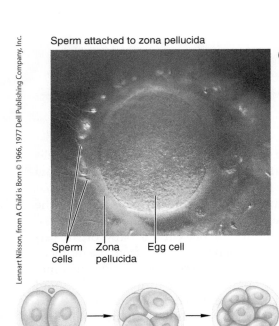

Sperm attached to zona pellucida

a **Day 0.** Sperm cells penetrate a clear area (zona pellucida) around the waiting egg as they "compete" to fertilize it.

Sperm cells Zona pellucida Egg cell

Figure 9.17 Early Human Development. The process begins after fertilization, is first dominated by cell division, then, about day five, growth and differentiation become apparent. By days 10 – 11 morphogenetic (organizational) processes begin shaping what will be the embryo itself.

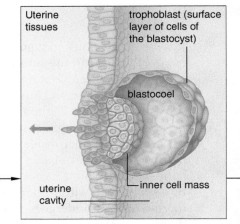

Uterine tissues

trophoblast (surface layer of cells of the blastocyst)

blastocoel

inner cell mass

uterine cavity

inner cell mass

actual size

b **Days 1–2.** The first cleavage furrow creates the two-cell stage. Tiny spheres within the zona are "polar bodies" that contain excess chromosomes.

c **Day 3.** Cleavage division continue allowing the now smaller cells to form a sphere and to communicate more efficiently with each other.

d **Day 4.** Sixteen to thirty two cells are present in this morula, a solid sphere of cells, most of which will give rise to cells involved in implantation and nutrient absorption.

e **Day 5.** The ball of cells is now a hollow blastocyst. Growth and differentiation have become part of the process now. The inner cell mass will generate the actual embryo. The inner cavity is fluid-filled.

f **Days 6–7.** The inner cell mass is differentiating into two separate cell layers at about the time the blastocyst begins to implant in the uterine wall.

unfertilized egg

cytoplasm regionally differentiated

multiple cleavage divisions

morula

cells become differentiated

as the **ectoderm, endoderm,** and the newly created **mesoderm** (because it lies in between the two original cell layers).

These three cell layers are referred to as *primary germ layers*. They represent the first three cell

ectoderm—a primary tissue layer in the embryo whose further differentiation gives rise to nervous system and integumentary surface tissues.

endoderm—a primary tissue layer in the embryo whose further differentiation gives rise to the internal lining of the digestive, respiratory, and urinary systems.

mesoderm—a primary tissue layer in the embryo whose further differentiation gives rise to digestive, circulatory, muscular, and other internal systems of the embryo.

Figure 9.18 Regional Differentiation. Color gradients in this diagram represent the concentration of some differentiating signal molecule. As cell division progresses, the cytoplasm of individual cells become differentiated. Signal molecules in the cells at the top of the morula will call for gene activity not called for in the cells further down.

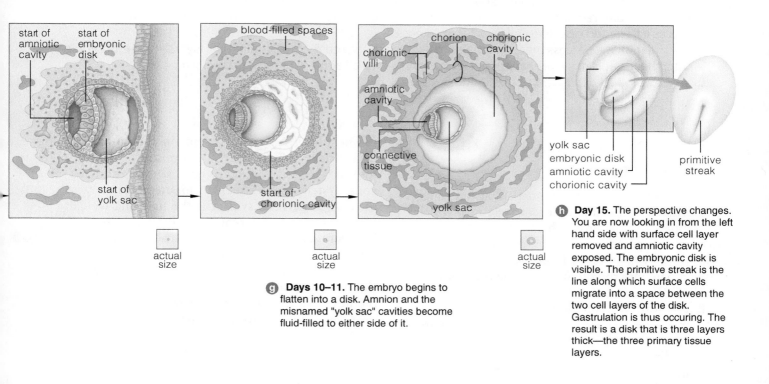

start of amniotic cavity **start of embryonic disk**

start of yolk sac

actual size

blood-filled spaces

start of chorionic cavity

actual size

g **Days 10–11.** The embryo begins to flatten into a disk. Amnion and the misnamed "yolk sac" cavities become fluid-filled to either side of it.

chorionic villi **chorion** **chorionic cavity**

amniotic cavity

connective tissue

yolk sac

actual size

yolk sac
embryonic disk
amniotic cavity
chorionic cavity

primitive streak

h **Day 15.** The perspective changes. You are now looking in from the left hand side with surface cell layer removed and amniotic cavity exposed. The embryonic disk is visible. The primitive streak is the line along which surface cells migrate into a space between the two cell layers of the disk. Gastrulation is thus occuring. The result is a disk that is three layers thick—the three primary tissue layers.

populations or tissues of the embryo. You, then, were once organized into just three different tissues: ectoderm, endoderm, and mesoderm. The origin of all the parts of your body can be traced from these three primary tissue layers (see Table 9.3). Thus by 14 to 15 days, you have a tissue level of organization.

Table 9.3 Primary tissue layers and structures derived from them.

Endoderm Derivatives	Epithelium of GI tract and its associated glands as well as glandular cells of the liver and pancreas Epithelium of the urinary bladder Epithelium of respiratory passages; the pharynx, trachea, bronchi, and alveoli. Epithelial parts of the tonsils, thyroid, parathyroids, tympanic cavity, thymus Epithelial parts of anterior pituitary
Mesoderm Derivatives	Cardiovascular system Cells of lymphatic system, spleen, adrenal cortex Skeleton, Striated muscles and smooth muscle coats Dermis of skin Connective tissue and vessels associated with organs Urogenital system (gonads, ducts and accessory glands)
Ectoderm Derivatives	Epidermis of skin, nails, hair, sweat, mammary and, sebaceous glands Central Nervous System, Peripheral Nervous System Retina and lens of eye Pupillary muscle of the iris (this is the only muscle of ectodermal origin) Pineal body, anterior and posterior pituitary, adrenal medulla, melanocytes, Schwann cells.

1. In four days' time, development converts a fertilized human egg cell into a ball of 16 cells called a *morula*. The morula is about the same size as the original egg cell.
2. Differentiation of molecular content of the egg cytoplasm thus becomes 16 differentiated cells that have identical genomes, which receive different signals from their respective cytoplasms.
3. Continued differentiation generates a hollow ball of cells, the blastocyst, within which the embryo develops as a flattened disc, two cell layers in thickness.
4. Gastrulation is a process that creates a third cell layer between the two original cell layers in the embryonic disc; the result is three primary tissue layers from which all adult structures finally form.

Embryonic Differentiation of Organ Systems

This two-week-old program of meticulously arranged and ordered differentiation events will now deepen in complexity. Numerous chemical signal gradients from precise points in the embryo will cause each of your three primary tissue layers to further grow and differentiate into the rudiments of the organ systems that will later form your adult structures.

But before we can describe this development efficiently, we require some unifying and simplifying terms for referring to the various aspects of a three-dimensional adult form (see Figure 9.19). Learning just four of them will greatly enhance our communication and your understanding. For a typical animal walking, crawling, or gliding forward, the front end is the *anterior* aspect and the hind end is the *posterior* aspect; the back or upper side is the *dorsal* surface, and the belly or underside is the *ventral* surface. We will use these terms freely in this and the next chapter as we refer to the various aspects of the form of an organism. Now, we are prepared to trace out just a few major patterns in the development of the form of the embryo.

The primitive streak region on the embryonic disc surface defines your anteroposterior (head to toe) axis and is the site where your central nervous system begins its development. Time wise then, your nervous system is the first one we can observe to begin differentiation. By day 18 the surface ectodermal layer ahead of the streak pushes forward and thickens to form a plate-like structure that then develops into **neural folds** to either side of a **neural groove** (see Figure 9.20a). Over the next five days the folds grow dorsally up and over the groove to form a **neural tube,** which will

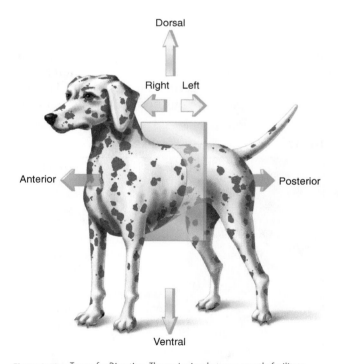

Figure 9.19 Terms for Direction. These six simple terms greatly facilitate discussion of the parts of an organism.

neural fold—paired thickened regions of ectodermal cells moving forward toward either side of the primitive streak; becoming ridge-like in shape with time.

neural groove—a shallow medial depression between the neural folds of the developing embryo.

neural tube—the result of the coalescing of the ridges of the neural folds above the neural groove; the precursor of the brain and spinal cord.

paired neural folds

neural groove

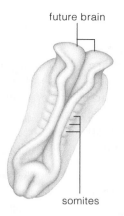

future brain

somites

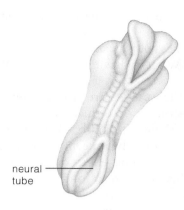

neural tube

a **Days 18–19.** Rudiments of the nervous system are first to be observed. The thickening ectoderm generates neural folds and the resulting groove between them. These folds will further thicken, grow toward each other and fuse to become the neural tube.

b **Days 20–21.** Further thickening at the head end of the embryo will become the brain. Mesodermal "blocks" of tissue called somites become visible beneath the ectodermal surface layer. They will become skeletal and muscular parts of the embryo's torso as well as the dermal layer of the skin.

c **Days 22–23.** The neural tube will become the spinal cord of the fetus; note the increased level of differentiation at the head end of the embryo.

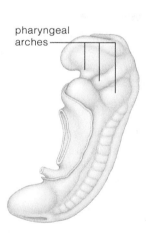

pharyngeal arches

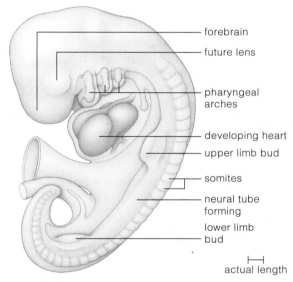

forebrain

future lens

pharyngeal arches

developing heart

upper limb bud

somites

neural tube forming

lower limb bud

actual length

d **Days 24–25.** Pharyngeal arches have begun to appear. Their differentiation will contribute to structures in the mouth, nasal cavity, middle ear and larynx.

e **Days 26–36.** Ectodermal and mesodermal thickening reveals early eye and lens formation; endocardial tubes have flexed and bent into the chambers of a heart, apical ridges are beginning to form limb buds; the yellow tube passing between the pharyngeal arches is the primordial digestive system.

Figure 9.20 Early Organogenesis. Following gastrulation, visible structural regions like the neural groove, somites and pharyngeal arches begin to appear. This sequence of figures directly follows those in Figure 9.17. A remnant of the primitive streak is visible at the base of the first drawing. Drawings **(a – c)** shown the embryo from its back. Drawings **(d)** and **(e)** are side views of the embryo. Corresponding differentiation events are occuring inside the embryo as indicated in drawing **(e)**.

differentiate further to become your spinal cord. The anterior end of the tube expands to become what will be your brain (see Figure 9.20b, Section 9.3c). What is driving all of this? We'll return to this question.

Meanwhile, the entire embryonic disc—once quite flat—continues to thicken and becomes more tube-like (see Figure 9.20b, c). Its edges begin to fold in and around the innermost endodermal layer of tissue. The folding edges coming in from each side soon fuse to form a long endoderm-lined sac that becomes your primitive gut (see Figure 9.20e). The gut lengthens as you grow and develops into three sequential regions: the foregut, midgut, and hindgut. As your endodermal and mesodermal layers expand and grow next to each other, they cooperate to both differentiate (many!) new cell types and organize them into new structures. The foregut will give rise to your **pharynx, esophagus,** stomach, upper portion of the **duodenum,** the respiratory tract and lungs, the liver, **gallbladder,** and the **pancreas** (see Figure 9.21; also Section 10.6). The midgut region will likewise differentiate into the lower portion of your duodenum, **jejunum** and **ileum,** the **appendix,** the ascending **colon,** and the first two-thirds of the transverse colon. The hindgut generates the last third of your transverse colon, your descending colon, **rectum,** and the upper part of the **anal canal.** These structures, while having mesodermally derived parts, are all lined with endodermally derived tissue.

pharynx—the part of the throat situated immediately below the mouth and nasal cavity and just above the esophagus, larynx, and trachea.

esophagus—an internal tube that connects the mouth and pharynx with the stomach; a passage for food from the site of initial ingestion to the site of storage and initial digestion.

duodenum—the first section of the small intestine in most higher vertebrates where most of chemical digestion occurs.

gallbladder—a small organ near the duodenum that stores bile secreted by the liver; the bile aids in digestion of fats.

pancreas—an organ located beneath the stomach that manufactures and secretes several important hormones such as insulin and digestive juices that follow a duct to the duodenum, where it degrades ingested food.

jejunum—the middle region of the small intestine accounting for almost half its length; large profuse projections (villi) within the jejunum absorb nutrients from digested food.

ileum—the final section of the small intestine, about one-third of its total length; absorbs vitamin B$_{12}$, bile salts, and residual nutrients not absorbed in the jejunum.

appendix—a small, narrow blind sac feeding into the upper end of the large intestine; appears to have fetal immune function and serves as a reservoir for maintenance of bacterial populations associated with the large intestine.

colon (large intestine)—the last portion of the vertebrate digestive system; absorbs water, salts, and compacts and eliminates unabsorbed indigestible remains of food.

rectum—final, straight portion of the colon that functions in the elimination of indigestible residue of food—the feces.

Differentiation in the primitive gut of the embryo

Figure 9.21   Early Gut Differentiation. The foregut, midgut and hindgut of the 4 week embryo give rise by differentiation to the indicated structures.

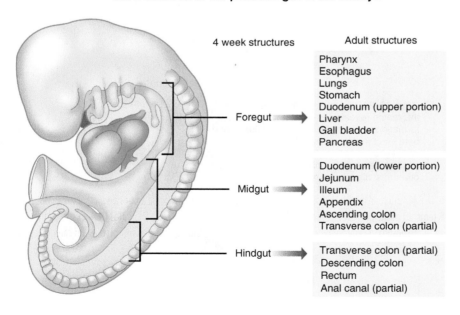

4 week structures

Adult structures

Foregut →
Pharynx
Esophagus
Lungs
Stomach
Duodenum (upper portion)
Liver
Gall bladder
Pancreas

Midgut →
Duodenum (lower portion)
Jejunum
Illeum
Appendix
Ascending colon
Transverse colon (partial)

Hindgut →
Transverse colon (partial)
Descending colon
Rectum
Anal canal (partial)

What becomes of that new internal mesodermal layer generated during your gastrulation? Initially, along your length it thickens and divides into several zones. Near your midline it differentiates into the **notochord,** a solid rod of tissue just beneath the ectodermal layer on the dorsal surface of the embryo (see Figure 9.22a). A diffusible signal molecule from notochord cells is what causes your surface ectodermal tissue to differentiate to form the neural folds and later the neural tube. Eventually, the notochord, having served this critical developmental role, recedes in significance and forms the jelly-like interior of the flexible discs between each **vertebra** in your vertebral column. These discs help to distribute weight loads when you are carrying things.

Just to either side of the notochord, a head-to-tail sequence of blocks of mesodermal tissue called the **somites** emerges (see Figure 9.22a). These will differentiate into all of the bones and skeletal muscles of your head and trunk as well as dermal cells that will form the basal layer of your skin. Finally, to either side of this central region beyond the somites, the **lateral** sheet of mesoderm divides into two separate layers known as **splanchnic** and **somatic mesoderm** (see Figure 9.22a). A space gradually forms between these layers, which will become the body cavity that houses your internal organs.

Let's follow the splanchnic layer a bit. Toward its anterior edge the primordial structure of the heart begins to form in a plate-like region of cells located at your cranial (anterior) end. Within this plate, a long, horseshoe-shaped zone of cell clusters begins to differentiate from the surrounding cells (see Figure 9.23). During week three of development, these cell clusters begin to coalesce to form two **endocardial tubes** to either side of your midline. The anterior and lateral folding of embryonic tissues mentioned earlier forces these tubes (medially) toward each other into the center of the **thoracic** region, where they fuse together forming a single, central endocardial tube—the primordial heart. In subsequent days, this tube subdivides into primordial heart chambers. Growth of the tube outstrips your overall growth in length during week four of development, so the tube bends back on itself! This will ultimately result in a circulation wherein the blood returns from the posterior end of the embryo to chambers high on the dorsal surface of the heart and flows out of the heart from chambers that are lower

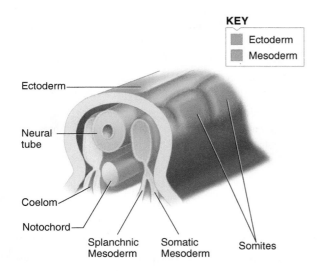

KEY
☐ Ectoderm
☐ Mesoderm

Ectoderm

Neural tube

Coelom

Notochord

Splanchnic Mesoderm

Somatic Mesoderm

Somites

Figure 9.22 Mesoderm Differentiation. A slice through the 4 week old vertebrate embryo (about half way between the head and tail) reveals surface ectoderm, a complete neural tube derrived from ectoderm, and elaborate differentiation of the mesoderm into somites, notocord, and splanchnic and somatic sheets of lateral mesoderm.

anal canal—terminal portion of the colon; its internal surface is ectodermal, not endodermal as in the rectum; lined with muscle tissue that controls defecation.

notochord—a flexible shaft of mesodermally derived cells found in the embryos of all vertebrate animals; influences formation of the nervous system.

vertebra—a single bone with many extension-like processes; a somewhat linear series of these bones surrounds and protects the spinal cord in vertebrates.

somite—one of numerous blocks of mesodermal tissue distributed along the side of the neural tube; gives rise to vertebrae, the dermal layer of skin, and skeletal muscle.

lateral mesoderm—tissue composed of cells descending from cells that migrated internally during gastrulation; arranged to either side of the midline tissues in the embryo.

splanchnic mesoderm—the inner layer of lateral mesodermal tissue that will contribute to development of the circulatory system and the digestive system of the fetus.

somatic mesoderm—the outer layer of lateral mesodermal tissue that contributes to the structure of the body wall.

endocardial tube—an embryonic structure differentiated from specialized cells in the splanchnic mesoderm; two such tubes coalesce to form the rudimentary heart.

thoracic—refers in humans to the region between the neck and the diaphragm containing the heart and lungs.

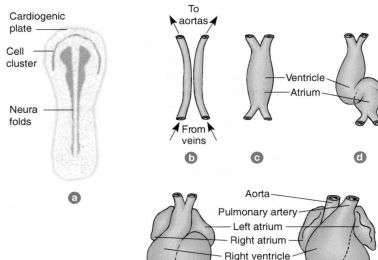

Heart development in humans

Cardiogenic plate

Cell cluster

Neura folds

To aortas

From veins

Ventricle
Atrium

Aorta
Pulmonary artery
Left atrium
Right atrium
Right ventricle
Left ventricle

a **b** **c** **d** **e** **f**

Figure 9.23 Heart Development. **(a)** Dorsal view of 18 day old embryo with dorsal surface ectoderm largely removed to make mesoderm visible. Near the front edge of the splanchnic mesodermal layer, cells that will become heart tissue begin to differentiate; **(b)** through **(f)** are ventral views of successive stages in heart formation. Notice the folding process that drives the atrium anteriorly to the ventricle.

and on the ventral face of the heart (see Figure 9.23). By the end of the eighth week your essentially "adult" heart chambers are intact. The original splanchnic layer of mesoderm that generates these heart structures will also surround the endodermal layer of the gut and generate the muscle and connective tissues that are part of your gastrointestinal tract.

Late in the third week of development, a series of prominent, largely mesodermal bulges begins to appear on the lateral surface of your head just posterior and to either side of the developing brain region. These **pharyngeal arches,** lined internally with endoderm and externally with ectoderm, will give rise to various portions of your mouth, inner ear, and **laryngeal** structures. Also during weeks three and four, mesoderm and ectodermal tissues are cooperating with each other to form **apical ridges,** which will further develop into limb buds that will eventually give rise to your arms and legs (see Figure 9.20).

This brief description of your early development is a wonderful mystery to which we have simply attached a collection of labels. But scientists love to search out mysteries like this. To explore a bit of the complexity they've unraveled, let's focus more specifically on one aspect of human development.

pharyngeal arch—mesodermal outpocket from the pharynx formed both to the right and left side of the four-week-old embryo; gives rise to structures within the mouth, ear, and larynx.

laryngeal—of or referring to the larynx, a cartilaginous structure in the throat that forms the voice box and protects the trachea.

apical ridge—region of thickened ectodermal cells that, with the underlying mesoderm, participate in formation of embryonic limbs: future arms and legs.

IN OTHER WORDS

1. Chemical signals emerging from precise points in the embryo cause each of the three primary tissue layers to continue differentiating into more and more diverse structures.
2. We use the terms *dorsal, ventral, anterior, posterior, lateral,* and *medial* to speak about aspects of the architecture of the three-dimensional biological organism.
3. The nervous system of humans begins development as a pair of thickened neural plates that fold into a neural tube destined to become the brain and spinal cord.

4. The primary endodermal tissue contributes the inner lining of the primitive gut and all structures derived from it, including lungs, liver, stomach, and large and small intestines.
5. The notochord, a mesodermal derivative, emits signal molecules to cause early differentiation of surface ectodermal tissue into elements of the neural tube.
6. The anterior portion of the inner layer of lateral mesoderm gives rise to the endocardial tubes that will become the adult heart.
7. Pharyngeal arches and apical ridges are sites where mesoderm, endoderm, and ectoderm interact with each other to differentiate structures of the mouth, nose, throat, forelimbs, and hind limbs.

Organogenesis of the Brain

Lacking space to focus in detail on all of your development, let's pick a modestly useful organ for further study: How about the brain? We start with the primary germ layer ectoderm and somehow we develop an organ—the brain. What an amazing project the Designer gives to every new conceptus that begins life! Charles Noback, a former professor of anatomy at Columbia University College of Physicians and Surgeons, has stated:

"To generate the estimated 100 billion neurons of the adult brain requires the production and differentiation of an average of 250,000 neurons per minute throughout the entire length of prenatal life."

How does that happen? We've described how the notochord, a mesodermal structure, induces the formation of the primitive neural tube. We then said that the anterior end of the tube/groove begins to thicken into what will become your brain with the spinal cord developing posteriorly (see Figure 9.20).

The anterior thickened end of the neural tube first expands, then differentiates and organizes into three separate regions: the forebrain, the midbrain (or mesencephalon), and the hindbrain (see Figure 9.24a). With time, your forebrain and hindbrain each further differentiate into two discernible regions yielding a total of five embryonic brain regions: the **telencephalon** and **diencephalon** from the forebrain, the **mesencephalon**, and from the hindbrain, the **metencephalon**, and **myelencephalon**. In Figure 9.24a and b, notice how the higher growth rate of cells on the dorsal surface of the neural tube causes the tube to curve following the curvature of the developing embryo. What causes cells at various points along the tube to differentiate into discrete and separate structures? Again, the process of embryonic induction is involved (see Figure 9.28). For example, cells in the very most dorsal peak of the neural tube secrete a signal protein called **Wnt** (see Figure 9.25a). Cells in the notochord ventral to the neural tube secrete a different signal protein called **SHH** (which stands for sonic hedgehog; developmental biologists have fun too...). All the cells along the lateral aspect (sides) of the neural tube have surface receptors for both of these

telencephalon—that forward region of the forebrain that gives rise to the cerebrum, the site of thought and volitional action.

diencephalon—that region of the forebrain that gives rise to thalamic structures such as the thalamus, which relays signals to and from the cerebrum and the hypothalamus, which regulates pituitary gland function.

mesencephalon—the midbrain; controls visual and auditory functions as well as moderating certain involuntary reactions.

metencephalon—that region of the hindbrain that gives rise to the cerebellum and pons, which function in integrating signals for muscle movement and information flow between the cerebellum and the telencephalon.

myelencephalon—that region of the hindbrain that gives rise to the medulla oblongata; a brain region associated with a variety of basic involuntary functions such as breathing rate.

Wnt—a widely distributed class of signal proteins in animals that are generated in one cell type and induce differentiation in nearby cells that specifically bind them.

SHH (sonic hedgehog)—one of three signaling proteins in the mammalian "hedgehog" signalling pathway; involved in brain organization, digit formation.

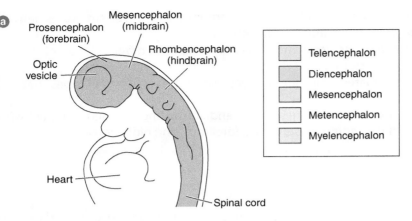

(a) Prosencephalon (forebrain), Mesencephalon (midbrain), Optic vesicle, Rhombencephalon (hindbrain), Heart, Spinal cord

Telencephalon
Diencephalon
Mesencephalon
Metencephalon
Myelencephalon

Figure 9.24 Brain Development. Shown are three separate stages of human brain development. **(a)** at about 3 weeks **(b)** at about 7 weeks, **(c)** at about 3 months *in utero*. Terms defining the differentiating regions of the brain are described in the text.

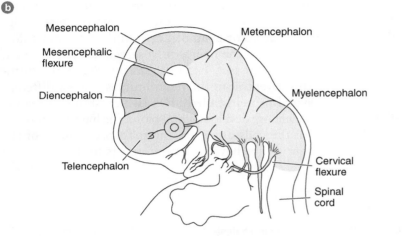

(b) Mesencephalon, Mesencephalic flexure, Diencephalon, Telencephalon, Metencephalon, Myelencephalon, Cervical flexure, Spinal cord

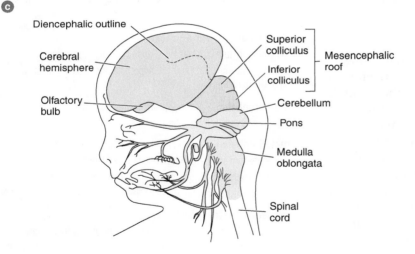

(c) Diencephalic outline, Cerebral hemisphere, Olfactory bulb, Superior colliculus, Inferior colliculus, Mesencephalic roof, Cerebellum, Pons, Medulla oblongata, Spinal cord

signal proteins (see Figure 9.25b); they therefore experience a crisscrossing gradient of these two signals (see Figure 9.25a). The amount of SHH experienced by a cell influences how it will respond to the Wnt signal it receives. Cells in the ventral portion of the neural tube, for example, sense almost no Wnt protein at all. Varying relative concentrations of these two signal substances results in differences in the genes activated within individual cells along the gradients. Activation of different genes is the essential source of differentiation patterns in cells.

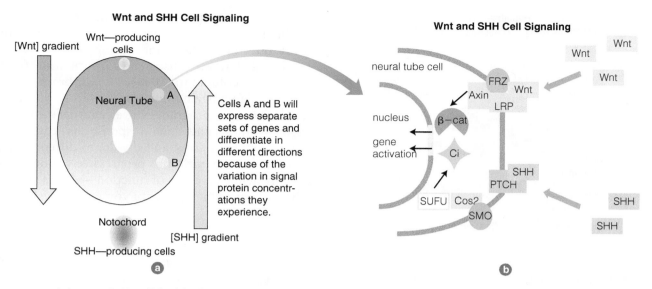

Figure 9.25 Induction in the Neural Tube. **(a)** Cells in the most dorsal part of the neural tube make and secrete the signal protein Wnt. **(b)** Cells throughout the neural tube have surface receptors for this protein. Cells closest to the dorsal surface of the neural tube will "sense" more of it than cells in the ventral parts of the tube. The notochord generates the signal protein SHH. Ventral neural tube cells sense more SHH than Wnt. These signal concentration differences result in different patterns of *intracellular* signalling via β- catenin or Ci protein pathways. These proteins interact to control which genes are expressed in the cell. Different gene expression patterns drive dorsal and ventral tube cells into separate differentiation pathways.

Obeying induction signals and gradients such as these, each of your five brain regions mentioned above goes on to differentiate the adult structures

cerebrum—a large, bi-hemispheric region of the vertebrate brain that in humans functions in learning, voluntary movement, and sensory interpretation.

thalamus—a coordinating center of the brain that routes sensory inputs to areas of the cerebrum devoted to generating motor responses.

hypothalamus—control center in forebrain that regulates body temperature and responses to hunger and thirst; generates pituitary hormones.

pituitary gland—an endocrine gland at the base of the brain that produces, stores, and secretes hormones controlling growth and sexual processes as well as secretions of other glands.

pineal gland—an endocrine gland in the thalamic region of the brain; secretes the hormone melatonin, which controls sleep/wake cycles in mammals.

cerebellum—a derivative of the metencephalic region of the embryonic brain; functions in muscle coordination, tone, and balance.

pons—a derivative structure of the metencephalon; appears as a swelling of the brainstem; relays signals from the cerebrum to the cerebellum relating to sleep, respiration, swallowing, hearing, equilibrium, posture, and other functions.

of the brain. The telencephalon, for example, expands to create the **cerebrum,** which controls all of your sensory and motor functions and is the locus of your thought and memory. The diencephalon differentiates into the brain regions known as the **thalamus,** the **hypothalamus** (with its **pituitary gland**), and the **pineal gland** (see Figure 9.26). The thalamus will coordinate sensory inputs to your cerebrum. The more ventral hypothalamus and pituitary gland will exert a dominant control over your endocrine system. The pineal gland will influence your sexual maturation and daily patterns of sleeping and wakefulness (more on that in Chapter 11).

The mesencephalon further differentiates into a series of structures called *colliculi* and *peduncles* (fancy Latin terms for protuberances or mounds; see Figure 9.24c). These brain regions are involved in such processes as the integration and relay of visual and auditory inputs coming from your sensory organs, the control of muscle tone, and the processing of incoming and outgoing information to and from the forebrain regions.

The metencephalon differentiates into two major brain regions. Dorsally, the **cerebellum** is involved in maintaining spatial balance and coordination (see Figure 9.26). Ventrally, the **pons** mediates information flow between your cerebellum and cerebrum (among other things).

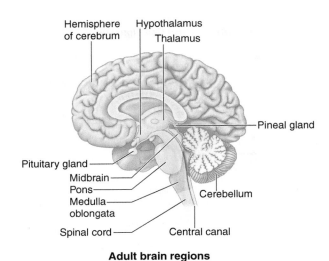

Hemisphere of cerebrum
Hypothalamus
Thalamus
Pineal gland
Pituitary gland
Midbrain
Pons
Medulla oblongata
Spinal cord
Cerebellum
Central canal

Adult brain regions

Figure 9.26 Adult Brain Regions. By induction of differentiation and subsequent morphogenetic changes, the structurally simpler embryonic brain attains the complexity of the adult brain. It is a miracle of organizational wisdom we wish we could fully understand.

The myelencephalon differentiates into the **medulla oblongata,** which helps regulate your heart rate, blood flow, the pacing of your respiratory inhalation. It also relays information from your spinal column to the rest of your brain.

And so an amazing organ results from the careful design of a program—an elegant sequence of signal synthesis and signal response that causes legions of cells to grow and divide, to differentiate, and then to organize into progressively more specifically defined regions of function—all at a rate of 250,000 per minute . . . until you are born.

medulla oblongata—portion of the brain closest to the spinal cord; functions in control of involuntary processes such as heart rate and breathing intensity.

IN OTHER WORDS

1. The anterior end of the neural tube becomes the five regions of the embryonic brain while the posterior end becomes the spinal cord.
2. The signal protein molecules Wnt and SHH interact across the dorsoventral axis of the neural tube to facilitate differentiation of specific structures in the developing brain.
3. Each of the five primary brain regions of the embryo contributes critical structures to the adult organ even though the cerebrum, derived from the telencephalon, appears to dominate the structure of the mammalian brain.

Cooperation of Organs in Organ Systems

But the brain, as an organ, is part of an **organ system** (see Figures 9.6, 9.27; see also Section 1.2). Therefore human development involves organizing into communicative, cooperative arrangements, sets of organs that together serve a more general function. (Life Is Complex.) The brain, **spinal cord,** and the **peripheral nerves** are an organ system—the nervous system. The system's function is tightly integrated. The organism is far better served by systems than by individual organs serving separately on their own. For example, many individual parts of the brain are committed to monitoring,

routing, and organizing the **afferent** signals coming in from the sensory system via the peripheral

organ system—an integrated selection of multi-tissue structures within the organism that cooperate in serving a common function.

spinal cord—an organ within the central nervous system that moderates the interaction of the peripheral nervous system with the brain that controls it.

peripheral nerves—all nerves throughout the body that lie outside the central nervous system—both those emanating from and returning to the central nervous system.

afferent—of or referring to signals generated from within the sensory systems of the body that then travel to the central nervous system.

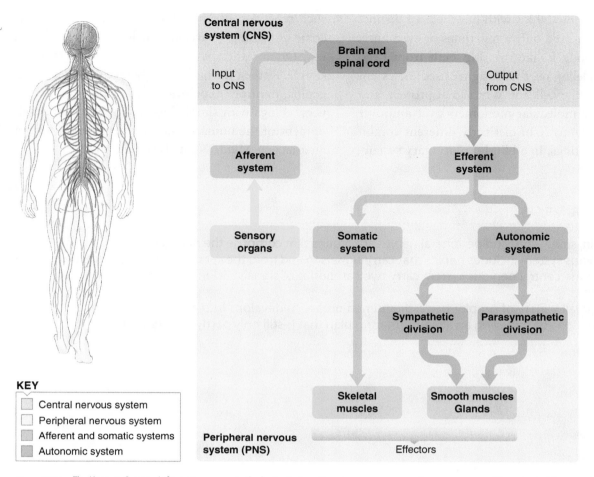

Figure 9.27 The Nervous System. Information comes to the brain via the afferent or sensory nerves from sense organs. The output of the central nervous system is of two sorts: one, somatic, carries signals that prompt the conscious use of muscles. The other—autonomic signals—take care of responses you do not consciously make. It uses two branches, the sympathetic and parasympathetic to control and coordinate opposite effects on each organ serviced. Generally the sympathetic system activates functions and the parasympathetic system relaxes them.

nerves. **Efferent** peripheral nerves, by contrast, connect the volitional parts of the brain with the muscles that carry out the brain's demands. The central nervous system also uses efferent nerves to drive glandular processes that are **autonomic**—you aren't even conscious of them. This degree of organization requires an even higher level of integration, control, and design. In terms of the level of integration of parts within the whole, we are here far beyond the functional versatility of any computing device ever invented by man. To quote the Psalmist of ancient Israel, "We are fearfully and wonderfully made . . ."

A great human seagoing invention was the fast-sailing clipper ship that plied the oceans of the nineteenth century. There are two ways to imagine building a detailed model of such a wonderful ship. It could be built with a few basic kinds of Lego-like blocks that are used repetitively but fashioned very, very artfully into the final product. Or the ship could

efferent—of or referring to signals generated from within the central nervous system of the body that then travel to the effector organs of the body such as muscles or glands.

autonomic—that part of the nervous system that exerts control over involuntary bodily functions such as blood circulation and digestion.

be built from a model kit with hundreds of distinct parts, each part used only a few times or even once. The human body is like the ship built from Lego pieces. In modeling us, the Designer used the essential pattern of the cell, the Wnt signal protein, and the same basic molecular monomers over and over again in a wide array of distinctly different combinations and settings. In a blind evolutionary system, such repetitive use of a few basic parts would become confusing—parts would interact that should not. Organization would have to remain painfully simple. Rather, the human body reveals a Designer's genius, multiply expressed in His ability to do diverse things with simple bits. The self-driven development of the human body is an entire triumph of an amazing Mind. What else could it be?

IN OTHER WORDS

1. The brain, spinal cord and peripheral nerves are organs that comprise the nervous system.
2. The nervous system includes nerves that carry signals to and from the central nervous system; those coming from the central nervous system carry two categories of signals: voluntary responses and involuntary responses.
3. From a small variety of simpler parts, the human organism develops into a vast variety of structures and their functions by following an already amazing plan that is still only partly understood.

9.4 ASKING AND ANSWERING QUESTIONS

In the discipline of developmental biology, singular elegant experiments have often been the basis for major generalizations that gave insight into the way forward. The following two figures can both help us review how scientific methodology works and exemplify two great generalizations that moved the discipline forward.

Elegant Experiment #1 — Induction

A Existing Knowledge

The Genus *Triturus*, poorly understood taxonomically, contains several species of newts: amphibians whose early development had been carefully observed.

The bottom of the egg, called the vegetal pole was more yolky than the top or "animal" pole. After fertilization of the egg, the pigmented animal pole shifts somewhat leaving behind a region called the "gray crescent".

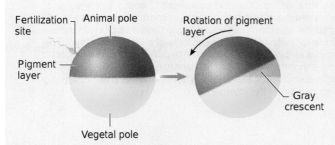

Later in development, a hollow ball of cells, the blastula develops with an internal fluid-filled space called the blastocoel. The grey crescent of the egg becomes the "blastopore" of the blastula, the spot where gastrulation begins with the inward migration of cells that become mesoderm.

Subsequent interactions between ectoderm, mesoderm and endoderm in the top half of the "gastrula" eventually gives rise to the embryo proper.

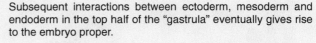

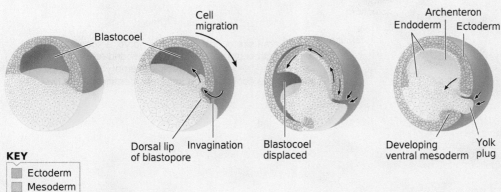

KEY
- Ectoderm
- Mesoderm
- Endoderm

B The Inquirer

Getty Images

Hans Spemann (1869–1941) was born in Stuttgart, Germany and in the 1890's began his study of embryology at the Universities of Heidelberg and Wurtzburg under the guidance of Gustav Wolff and Theodore Boveri. He worked with a variety of organisms but when contemplating his induction experiments he began working with the common newt, Genus *Triturus*.

C Question

Can one group of cells tell another group of cells what to do? That is, can the differentiation of a cell be induced to occur by a signal from another cell?

D Hypothesis

Dramatic changes in cell behavior occur at the blastopore. If the blastopore is surgically placed elsewhere on an embryo, gastrulation will occur at that novel site.

E Materials and Methods

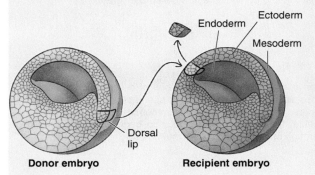

Donor embryo **Recipient embryo**

Endoderm, Ectoderm, Mesoderm, Dorsal lip

Spemann and his student, Hilde Mangold worked with two species of newt that had distinctly different surface pigmentation patterns. They performed a series of transplantation experiments involving the critical gray crescent area of the embryo surface. They waited until the gray crescent gave rise to the blastopore and gastrulation was about to begin. Since surgical work is traumatic to an embryo, the experiment was designed so that the blastopore lip was cut from one embryo and transplanted to a site on the opposite side of a second embryo. The recipient embryo thus has two blastopores spaced well apart from each other with one in its normal location. The donor embryo is discarded. Differences in donor and recipient tissue pigments facilitated the interpretation of the results.

F Results

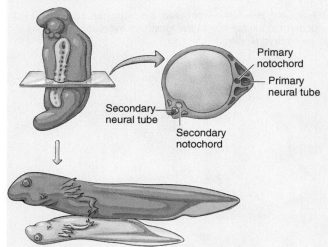

Primary notochord, Primary neural tube, Secondary neural tube, Secondary notochord

At the graft site on the recipient embryo, a second gastrulation event occurred. As a result, a second embryo began to develop on the side of the recipient embryo. Pigmentation differences confirmed the separate identities of the two embryos.

G Interpretation	It would be impossible for the few cells of the transplanted blastopore to themselves give rise to an entirely new embryo. Rather, the second blastopore at a novel site on a newt gastrula altered the course of development of cells in that area of the embryo. Instead of contributing to the development of the primary recipient, they were induced to contribute to the development of a new embryo.

H New Questions!	1. Do most of the cells in the second embryo come from the graft recipient embryo, or do they result from very rapid divisions within the graft itself? Is induction really happening? 2. Is induction the result of one set of cells "touching" another set of cells or is there a diffusible chemical that flows from one cell to cells around it? 3. Your question! :

Elegant Experiment #2 — Genomic Potency

A Existing Knowledge

Tom McHugh / Photo Researchers, Inc.

The Genus Xenop*us*, containing the African clawed toad, has been widely used in developmental biology studies.

The toad, like the newt *Triturus*, is an amphibian. Both produce eggs which hatch into larvae. The larval forms then undergo metamorphosis to the adult form.

The toad egg, has similar features to the newt egg and undergoes gastrulation in essential the same way. (See the diagrams in "Existing Knowledge" box of previous experiment.)

Irradiation with UV light inactivates DNA

Unfertilized egg

It was further known that ultraviolet (UV) light is highly destructive of DNA molecules. UV irradiated *Xenopus* eggs contain nuclei that will not support development.

B The Inquirer

John Gurdon (1933 –) was born in England and began working with *Xenopus* during his graduate studies at Oxford University. His initial studies with nuclear transplantation were carried out there. Much of his career has been spent at the Medical Research Council labs and in the Department of Zoology at Cambridge University. He has received the Lasker award for his seminal studies in the totipotency of the amphibian nucleus.

C Question

Could the nucleus of a fully differentiated cell still run the entire process of development? (Is a differentiated nucleus still "totipotent"?)

D Hypothesis

The nucleus in a highly differentiated cell still contains all of the DNA that was present in the zygote nucleus from which it ultimately derives. It can therefore still direct the process of development.

E Materials and Methods

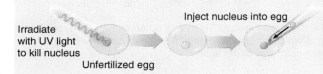

Irradiate with UV light to kill nucleus
Unfertilized egg
Inject nucleus into egg

Gurdon began by irradiating unfertilized *Xenopus* eggs, irreversibly mutating the DNA in their nuclei to the point that none would develop if fertilized. He then used a very fine needle to withdraw a single nucleus from a differentiated tadpole intestinal cell. The nucleus was then injected immediately into one of his irradiated egg cells. This procedure was carried hundreds of times.

F Results

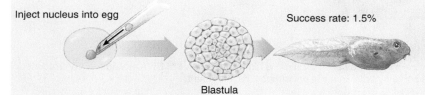

Inject nucleus into egg
Blastula
Success rate: 1.5%

Injecting a differentiated nucleus into an unfertilized egg cell caused the egg to develop all the way to the tadpole stage in 1.5% of the transplantations performed.

G Interpretation

The genes necessary to direct the earliest stages of development and all succeeding stages of development up to the tadpole stage were present in the tadpole intestinal cell nuclei. Further the egg cytoplasm was capable of activating those genes and causing them to be expressed.

H New Questions!

1. We said that a morula contains 16 complete copies of instructions to make you. How do we know that? How do we know that total genomic information is retained through life?
2. Could nuclei from an albino (no pigmentation) strain of toad be placed into irradiated eggs from a normal strain of toad? Would albino toads develop?
3. Your question!

QUESTIONS FOR REVIEW

1. Compose a sentence that describes the process of development. Be certain to use the phrase *information expression* in your sentence.
2. List four component processes that comprise development of the organism.
3. Consider the size of an unfertilized hen's egg and the size of a baby chick. When does most of growth occur during the embryonic development of a chicken?
4. Compare the diagrams of the stomach and the leaf. What kinds of tissues do they have in common? Which are unique?
5. What is induction? How does it work (in a general sense)?
6. Make a list of 11 human organ systems and for each list as many component organs as come to mind.
7. What biological event signals the origin of the life of an individual ginkgo tree? Where does it take place?
8. In the development of a ginkgo tree, are mitosis and cytokinesis always coordinated so that one occurs just before the other? Explain.
9. How are the root end and the shoot end of a ginkgo embryo determined?
10. List and describe the three basic types of tissue found in all parts of all plants.
11. What are the respective functions of xylem and phloem tissue within the root of a ginkgo seedling?
12. What common effect do both gibberellins and auxins have on the stem of a ginkgo seedling?
13. Explain why the range of growth of ginkgo trees is so much broader than for many other trees.
14. Higher plants are generally found in one of two large groups: either the angiosperms (flowering plants) or the gymnosperms (conifers, cone-bearers). The group, *Gingkophyta*, is outside of both these groups. Why is that?
15. Consider the fertilized human egg cell. Of the four component processes of development, which one dominates initial development? Which one dominates gastrulation?
16. What will be the function of the cells that develop from most of the 16 cells of the morula?
17. Construct your own chart of the three primary tissue layers and list under each layer the adult structures that will develop from that layer. Put initials after each structure indicating the organ system it is part of.
18. Draw a likeness of a dog. Label its aspects using the terms *dorsal, ventral, anterior, posterior, lateral,* and *medial*. Do the same thing for a human being; be careful here; biologists assign those words to humans while "standing" on all fours as a dog would.
19. Name two systems of the body that are closely related based on their embryonic pattern of formation.
20. Is the notochord found in adult humans? Explain your answer.
21. What two tissue layers give rise to your body cavity? Your body cavity is entirely the product of which primary tissue layer?
22. Select some terms from this chapter to briefly trace the development of your right arm.
23. List five embryonic brain regions; after each one list the major functions that structural derivatives of that region will carry out in the adult human.
24. List two intercellular signal molecules that influence cell differentiation in human development. List two *intra*cellular signal molecules that function in a similar way.

QUESTIONS FOR THOUGHT

1. In a quiet, friendly discussion with a pro-choice individual, you hear the rejoinder, "It's my body. Don't I have a constitutional right to decide what happens to my body?" How could you use the terms *zygote* and *fertilization* to respond to that statement?
2. In the differentiation of a zygotic cell into a red blood cell, turning on specific genes is involved. Would certain genes also be turned off? Explain your thoughts here.
3. Auxin gradients extend over very large numbers of cells. Auxins do not simply diffuse through

plant cell membranes. How then are these gradients set up?

4. Is seed formation more critically important in a tropical climate or a temperate climate? Explain your choice.

5. Predict what would happen to a small piece of meristematic tissue that is grown apart from a plant on a nutrient medium in a culture dish in the absence of any hormones.

6. In order to understand how differentiation and morphogenesis contribute to human development, with what population of cells should our study begin?

7. Which of the organ systems begins its development first? Speculate as to why that might be.

8. Why might the heart form from two separate lateral tubes instead of one medial one? Think "differentiative" thoughts!

9. Brain development gives rise to the pituitary gland, which enables the nervous system to interact in a variety of ways with which other body system(s)?

10. Differentiation of the cerebellum is most critical to what particular Olympic event?

11. Explain how all three primary germ layers are involved in the final development of your stomach.

GLOSSARY

afferent—of or referring to signals generated from within the sensory systems of the body that then travel to the central nervous system.

anal canal—terminal portion of the colon; its internal surface is ectodermal, not endodermal as in the rectum; lined with muscle tissue that controls defecation.

apical meristem—a zone of rapidly dividing, undifferentiated plant cells near the tip or apex of a shoot, stem, or root.

apical ridge—region of thickened ectodermal cells that, with the underlying mesoderm, participate in formation of embryonic limbs: future arms and legs.

appendix—a small, narrow blind sac feeding into the upper end of the large intestine; appears to have fetal immune function and serves as a reservoir for maintenance of bacterial populations associated with the large intestine.

autonomic—that part of the nervous system that exerts control over involuntary bodily functions such as blood circulation and digestion.

auxin—a class of plant hormones that tends to promote cell elongation leading to stem elongation and root initiation.

blastocyst—an early developmental stage in the human embryo in which further cell divisions in the morula have generated a hollow ball of cells with a central, fluid-filled cavity; implantation in the uterus occurs in this stage.

cerebellum—a derivative of the metencephalic region of the embryonic brain; functions in muscle coordination, tone, and balance.

cerebrum—a large, bi-hemispheric region of the vertebrate brain that in humans functions in learning, voluntary movement, and sensory interpretation.

colon (large intestine)—the last portion of the vertebrate digestive system; absorbs water, salts, and compacts and eliminates unabsorbed indigestible remains of food.

cone (or *strobilus*)—reproductive structure in conifers that generates pollen or ova, and following fertilization, seeds; often woody in structure.

connective tissue—a collection of cells in an extracellular matrix of supportive material that adds structural strength to other nearby collections of cells.

cytokinins—plant hormones that promote cell division in roots and shoots; contribute to dominance of growth of the central stem of a plant.

dermal tissue—those cellular layers that serve a protective function on the surface of the plant body; protection from desiccation and parasitic pests.

diencephalon—that region of the forebrain that gives rise to thalamic structures such as the thalamus, which relays signals to and from the cerebrum and the hypothalamus, which regulates pituitary gland function.

differentiation—a process by which a generalized cell or tissue matures into a specialized cell or tissue.

digestive system—that organ system in the animal body that takes in, breaks down, and absorbs the components of food.

dioecious (Gk. *di-* = two, *oikos-* = house)—a species of plant in which the reproductive organs of the two sexes are found on separate individuals.

duodenum—the first section of the small intestine in most higher vertebrates where most of chemical digestion occurs.

ectoderm—a primary tissue layer in the embryo whose further differentiation gives rise to nervous system and integumentary surface tissues.

efferent—of or referring to signals generated from within the central nervous system of the body that then travel to the effector organs of the body such as muscles or glands.

embryo—an organism in its early stages of developing toward maturity; immediately following fertilization, the cell has commenced this development.

endocardial tube—an embryonic structure differentiated from specialized cells in the splanchnic mesoderm; two such tubes coalesce to form the rudimentary heart.

endoderm—a primary tissue layer in the embryo whose further differentiation gives rise to the internal lining of the digestive, respiratory, and urinary systems.

endosperm—a plant tissue within a seed that contains stored nutrients for a developing embryo. It forms from fertilization of nuclei in the ovule by a nucleus in the pollen grain.

epithelial tissue—layers or groups of animal cells that cover body surfaces, line body cavities, and give rise to certain glands.

esophagus—an internal tube that connects the mouth and pharynx with the stomach; a passage for food from the site of initial ingestion to the site of storage and initial digestion.

fertilization—process by which a male sex cell and a female sex cell fuse to form a diploid first cell (zygote) of a new individual.

flower—a plant reproductive structure in angiosperms (flowering plants) that serves to bring ova and sperm nuclei together to form embryos within seeds.

gallbladder—a small organ near the duodenum that stores bile secreted by the liver; the bile aids in digestion of fats.

gastrulation—a process occurring in a blastula or blastocyst in which cell movements on the surface of the embryo and into its interior result in the formation of the three primary tissue layers on which further differentiation will be based.

germination—the beginning or resumption of growth in a seed, spore, or bud structure.

gibberellins—plant hormones that regulate growth and differentiation particularly with respect to stem elongation, germination and flowering.

ground tissue—the fundamental tissue system of a plant excluding its epidermal and vascular tissues.

growth—accumulation of biomass in either a cell, a tissue, an organ or an individual.

hormone—within an organism, a (usually small) molecule generated in one kind of tissue that becomes a signal or message causing cells elsewhere in the organism to alter their behavior in response.

hypothalamus—control center in forebrain that regulates body temperature and responses to hunger and thirst; generates pituitary hormones.

ileum—the final section of the small intestine, about one-third of its total length; absorbs vitamin B_{12}, bile salts, and residual nutrients not absorbed in the jejunum.

induction—that chemical process by which one cell or tissue produces a change in behavior or structure in a second cell or tissue.

jejunum—the middle region of the small intestine accounting for almost half its length; large profuse projections (villi) within the jejunum absorb nutrients from digested food.

laryngeal—of or referring to the larynx, a cartilaginous structure in the throat that forms the voice box and protects the trachea.

lateral bud—forming at the base (axil) of a leaf, embryonic tissue that will give rise to an axillary shoot from the surface of an existing stem.

lateral meristem—within a stem or root, a layer of undifferentiated plant cells whose division adds to the diameter of the stem or root.

lateral mesoderm—tissue composed of cells descending from cells that migrated internally during gastrulation; arranged to either side of the midline tissues in the embryo.

medulla oblongata—portion of the brain closest to the spinal cord; functions in control of involuntary processes such as heart rate and breathing intensity.

meristem—undifferentiated plant cells and tissue from which new cells are produced.

mesencephalon—the midbrain; controls visual and auditory functions as well as moderating certain involuntary reactions.

mesoderm—a primary tissue layer in the embryo whose further differentiation gives rise to digestive, circulatory, muscular, and other internal systems of the embryo.

mesophyll tissue—interior photosynthetic cells in a leaf.

metencephalon—that region of the hindbrain that gives rise to the cerebellum and pons, which function in integrating signals for muscle movement and information flow between the cerebellum and the telencephalon.

morphogenesis—the development of the form of the organism; involves getting and keeping differentiated cells and tissues organized into productive groupings.

morula—a very early embryonic stage of development in mammals in which initial cleavage divisions have given rise to a ball of cells.

myelencephalon—that region of the hindbrain that gives rise to the medulla oblongata; a brain region associated with a variety of basic involuntary functions such as breathing rate.

neural fold—paired thickened regions of ectodermal cells moving forward toward either side of the primitive streak; becoming ridge-like in shape with time.

neural groove—a shallow medial depression between the neural folds of the developing embryo.

neural tube—the result of the coalescing of the ridges of the neural folds above the neural groove; the precursor of the brain and spinal cord.

notochord—a flexible shaft of mesodermally derived cells found in the embryos of all vertebrate animals; influences formation of the nervous system.

organ system—an integrated selection of multi-tissue structures within the organism that cooperate in serving a common function.

ovule—a female reproductive structure in plants in which the haploid egg cell has matured. The mature ovule contains the new individual and is called a *seed*.

pancreas—an organ located beneath the stomach that manufactures and secretes several important hormones such as insulin and digestive juices that follow a duct to the duodenum, where it degrades ingested food.

peripheral nerves—all nerves throughout the body that lie outside the central nervous system—both those emanating from and returning to the central nervous system.

pharyngeal arch—mesodermal outpocket from the pharynx formed both to the right and left side of the four-week-old embryo; gives rise to structures within the mouth, ear, and larynx.

pharynx—the part of the throat situated immediately below the mouth and nasal cavity and just above the esophagus, larynx, and trachea.

phloem—a transport tissue in plants; carries nutrients, sucrose in particular, to all parts of the plant.

pineal gland—an endocrine gland in the thalamic region of the brain; secretes the hormone melatonin, which controls sleep/wake cycles in mammals.

pituitary gland—an endocrine gland at the base of the brain that produces, stores, and secretes hormones controlling growth and sexual processes as well as secretions of other glands.

placenta—an organ that connects the developing embryo to the uterine wall of the mother for the exchange of nutrients and wastes.

pollen grain—a spore-like structure in plants containing the haploid nucleus that will fertilize the female ovum to produce a zygote. It is carried from the male reproductive structure to the female one by wind, water, or other organisms.

pons—a derivative structure of the metencephalon; appears as a swelling of the brainstem; relays signals from the cerebrum to the cerebellum relating to sleep, respiration, swallowing, hearing, equilibrium, posture, and other functions.

primitive streak—a line bisecting the middle of the embryonic disc; from this area cells divide and migrate into the interior of the embryonic disc forming a mesodermal layer of cells.

rectum—final, straight portion of the colon that functions in the elimination of indigestible residue of food—the feces.

root—the portion of embryonic tissue that will give rise to underground parts of the plant designed for absorption and anchoring of the plant.

root cap—on the very tip of a root, a layer of cells that generates a mucoid secretion easing the root further into the soil.

seed—an embryonic plant together with its nutrient source enclosed within a protective coat of external tissue.

SHH (sonic hedgehog)—one of three signaling proteins in the mammalian "hedgehog" signalling pathway; involved in brain organization, digit formation.

shoot—the portion of embryonic tissue that will give rise to aerial parts of the plant: the stems, leaves, and flowers.

somatic mesoderm—the outer layer of lateral mesodermal tissue that contributes to the structure of the body wall.

somite—one of numerous blocks of mesodermal tissue distributed along the side of the neural tube; gives rise to vertebrae, the dermal layer of skin, and skeletal muscle.

spinal cord—an organ within the central nervous system that moderates the interaction of the peripheral nervous system with the brain that controls it.

splanchnic mesoderm—the inner layer of lateral mesodermal tissue that will contribute to development of the circulatory system and the digestive system of the fetus.

stem cell—a growing, dividing, undifferentiated cell within animal embryos or adults that eventually differentiates into a variety of types of cells found in the animal's body.

telencephalon—that forward region of the forebrain that gives rise to the cerebrum, the site of thought and volitional action.

thalamus—a coordinating center of the brain that routes sensory inputs to areas of the cerebrum devoted to generating motor responses.

thoracic—refers in humans to the region between the neck and the diaphragm containing the heart and lungs.

undifferentiated—referring to a cell or tissue that is committed to no specified role or function within the organism other than providing a source of new cells.

vascular cylinder—also called the *stele;* within a root, a central collection of xylem and phloem tissue including internal meristematic and surface dermal tissues.

vascular tissue—those structures both cellular and cellular products that conduct fluids from one place to another in the plant body.

vertebra—a single bone with many extension-like processes; a somewhat linear series of these bones surrounds and protects the spinal cord in vertebrates.

Wnt—a widely distributed class of signal proteins in animals that are generated in one cell type and induce differentiation in nearby cells that specifically bind them.

xylem—a transport tissue in plants; in trees it comprises much of the wood of the trunk; transports water upward within a plant.

zygote—a single diploid cell resulting from the fertilization of a haploid egg cell by a haploid sperm cell.

10

The Internally Integrated Human Animal

Survey Questions

10.1 **The Integrated Human**
  - At what structural level(s) does the human organism exhibit integration?
  - What is the level or degree of this integration? How many systems are involved?
  - When or at what times does the integration of parts become important?

10.2 **The Muscular System**
  - How widespread is the muscular system in the human body?
  - How is a muscle structured? How many levels of organization are there in the structure of a muscle?
  - What enables a muscle to shorten its own length—to contract?
  - How is a contraction event initiated? From where does the stimulus to contract come?
  - What is the nature of the signal that causes muscle contraction?
  - Does the signal occur at the level of the entire muscle (organ) or at the cellular level?
  - Are all muscles internally structured in the same basic way, or are there different classes or kinds of muscles?

10.3 **The Cardiovascular System**
  - How do nutrients and oxygen arrive at the muscle to enable it to contract repeatedly?
  - What is the role of blood in this process?

10.1 THE INTEGRATED HUMAN

Imagine you are visiting Washington, DC, the capital of the United States of America. You've ridden a subway into a huge underground station and have come up onto the Mall — a vast grassy area, America's "front yard" surrounded by many monuments and museums. The most prominent structure on the Mall is the towering Washington Monument (See Figure 10.1). As you walk toward it, it just gets larger and larger! Rather than taking the elevator to the top, you decide to climb its 896 steps. By the 150th step, a tiny hint of boredom begins to set in. You begin to wonder—just a fleeting thought—if this whole climb is just a matter of your muscles driving mindlessly forward. This thought is born of a secret inner inclination of yours that life should be simple, but the biology text you've been reading argues that it is complex. Hmm. Is it really? How complex could this "just climbing stairs" be? Let's dissect that question a bit.

Actually, several systems in your body ramp up to get you from the bottom to the top of the Monument (see Figure 10.2). Yes, your **muscular system** does the work, but muscles need something on

muscular system—a collection of organs (muscles) that facilitate movement of the body and movement within the body.

- How is the system that brings blood to the muscles structured?
- If more oxygen is needed in one area of the body than another, can this system respond differentially to that need?
- What happens to the waste products of muscle contraction? Is the blood involved in removing them?
- How does the human heart relate structurally to the system of vessels that carry the blood?
- How does the heart connect the system to the lungs—the source of oxygen?
- How do the fluids throughout the body relate to the blood in the blood vessels?
- The heart is quite dynamic. Is its muscle structured specifically for the process of repeated, coordinated contraction?
- How is the rate of a person's heartbeat controlled?

10.4 Basic Concepts of Immunity

- To what substances or foreign agents do humans become immune?
- How are these agents encountered?
- What is the nature of the immune response?
- What organs of the body are involved in responding to foreign agents?
- Are there specialized cells within these organs that are committed to the immune response? If so, what are they?
- Is there more than one way in which we respond to foreign pathogens?
- Are our responses learned? Can we improve our response to the same pathogen?
- How specific are our responses? Do we respond to all foreign pathogens in essentially the same way?
- What is the first step in our response to a particular pathogen? Where does it occur?
- How does our immune response finally destroy the pathogen invading our tissues?

Figure 10.1 The Washington Monument.

which to pull. That something is provided by the <u>skeletal system.</u> As your muscles start using up the oxygen and nutrients they had when you started, your heart rate (within your **cardiovascular system**) and breathing rate (in your **respiratory system**) both increase. You start to sweat (from your **integumentary system**) to remove the heat your muscles are generating. In addition, part of your **nervous system** (the sympathetic part) responds to the physical stress you are putting on your body by calling for hormones from the **endocrine system.** The wastes being produced

skeletal system—a collection of organs (bones) that gives support and form to the body and that assists the muscular system during movement.

cardiovascular system—a collection of organs that facilitate the movement of cells and soluble materials to and from all parts of the body.

respiratory system—a collection of organs that enables critical gaseous reactants and products to be added to and removed from blood.

integumentary system—a collection of organs (largely skin) that insulates the organism while protecting it from desiccation and invasion by foreign pathogens.

nervous system—a collection of organs composed of neurons that coordinates the activities of the organism while transmitting signals from one location to another.

endocrine system—a collection of organs (glands) that secrete hormones into the bloodstream; the hormones in turn control many aspects of the body's form and function.

- What are some strategies that pathogens use to invade our bodies? Do they ever successfully evade our immune response?
- What can we do to enhance our response to pathogens?

10.5 The Human Digestive System

- What function does this system serve?
- What are the major organs of this system?
- What substances are digested and what are the products?
- What happens to the products of digestion?
- How is the process of digestion controlled?
- Are other systems of the body involved in this control?

10.6 The Human Urinary System

- Why does the human body need a urinary system?
- What organs participate in the urinary system? What is the role of each?
- How do these excretory organs process waste at the cellular level?
- How is the urinary system related to the other systems of the body?

10.7 Neurons at Work

- How does the nervous system relate to all the other systems of the body?
- What is a neuron, and how does it relate to the rest of the nervous system?
- How is a neuron structured?
- What is the difference between a neuron and a nerve?
- How does a neuron transmit a signal to another neuron?
- Does a signal in one neuron always become a signal in any neuron it synapses with?
- Does a neuron receive signals from only one other neuron or from multiple neurons?
- How does a signal move along the length of a neuron?
- Are there different types of neurons or only one essential type?
- What is a reflex?
- How many neurons are involved in a simple reflex arc?

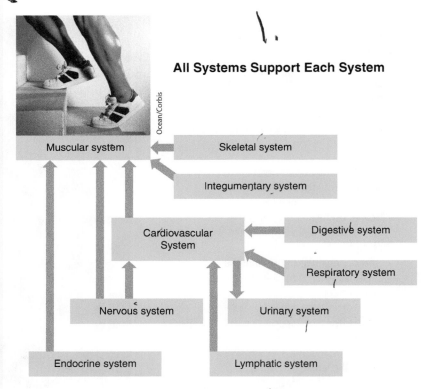

Figure 10.2 Life is Internally Integrated. Every system in the body serves and is served by every other system. The level of integration is staggering.

by the muscles' metabolism will be removed by the **urinary system.** On the way up, you grab the rail for support and then rub your eye to remove the sweat forming on your face. Now, your immune response, produced by the **lymphatic system,** will be stimulated to prevent you from getting sick due to viruses that were on the rail. Once you get to the top, you pull out a snack and activate your **digestive system.** All the systems in your body have worked together to get you to this point. Haven't we seen this sort of cooperation somewhere before?

In Chapter 5 we peered into a cell and saw that its organelles worked together, sometimes through each other to perform tasks that supported the common welfare—the good of the entire cell. Then our study of development in Chapter 9 showed us that cells divide, differentiate, and begin to communicate and cooperate

urinary system—a collection of organs that filters the blood, creating, collecting, and storing the resulting urine for excretion.

lymphatic system—a collection of organs that facilitates the surveillance of tissue fluids and their movement back to the bloodstream.

digestive system—a collection of organs that facilitates the intake and mechanical and enzymatic degradation of foods, followed by absorption of nutrients and elimination of wastes.

10.8 The Human Nervous System

- What are the component parts of the human nervous system?
- How do they work together to serve the entire organism?
- How is the brain organized, and what does it control?
- How is this important system protected from physical, chemical, and biological harm?
- How does the rest of the nervous system relate to the brain and spinal cord?
- What are the major nerves in the nervous system? What are their roles?
- How is the nervous system interrelated with the other major systems of the human body?

10.9 Drugs and the Nervous System

- How many drugs are available that affect the human nervous system? How widely are they used?
- What are some examples of widely used drugs?
- How and where does alcohol have its effects on the CNS?
- What is caffeine, and how does it affect our nervous systems? Is this drug dangerous?
- What is fluoxetine hydrochloride, and what effect does it have on the brain? When should this drug be used?

10.10 Life Is Internally Integrated: The Amazing ATP Molecule

- How does the ATP molecule illustrate the internal integration of structure?
- Where in the body does ATP function and in what ways?
- Besides being incorporated into DNA and functioning as an energy source, what other role does ATP serve?
- How can one molecule have such varied roles in a single organism? How could such versatility come to exist in one structural arrangement of atoms?

with each other to generate an entire multicellular organism. Here, however, the principle that the parts of a life-form support and function with and through each other is visible on a grander, macroscopic scale—the level of the entire organism. These cooperative activities are so dramatically displayed in your own body that we've decided to devote this entire chapter to a principle of life that embodies this concept: **Life Is Internally Integrated.** Entire multivolume works are devoted to an exploration of this principle. Our suspicion is that the integration between body systems is far more complex than research has yet revealed.

Let's return to our vertical hike inside the Washington Monument and look at each of these body systems in detail. Since the muscles appear to be doing all the work, let's start with them.

Life Is Internally Integrated—one of 12 principles of life on which this book is based.

IN OTHER WORDS

1. Climbing stairs requires the obvious activity of the muscular system, but it involves the cooperation of a variety of other systems as well.
2. The skeletal system provides leverage for the muscular system to get you up the stairs.
3. The cardiovascular system services your muscles with nutrients and oxygen, while removing carbon dioxide and other molecular wastes from them.
4. The respiratory system supplies oxygen and removes carbon dioxide from the body as a whole; the digestive system supplies the nutrients to be brought to the muscle tissues.
5. The kidneys remove cellular waste to the urinary system for excretion.
6. The immune response protects you from potential pathogens encountered in your environment.
7. Such cooperation between systems of organs in the body mirrors the cooperativity of organelles within a living cell.

10.2 THE MUSCULAR SYSTEM

As you climb the stairs of the Monument, the muscles in your legs and lower trunk propel you from one step to the next while the muscles in your arms and upper trunk allow you to use the stair railing as an external support. Muscles are amazingly built for one precise purpose: movement. Yet what a range of motion that includes! Think of the constriction of the pupil of the eye when you reach the observation level of the Monument and step into the bright sunlight streaming through one of the windows. The same kind of tissue can move on a much larger scale as your legs move your whole body up to the next step. Within this broad range of motion, muscle control is finely tuned to allow minute variations across this large range of movement. Muscles are structured at various levels of complexity (Life is Complex). These will be explored in the next section.

IN OTHER WORDS

1. Muscles are body organs that carry out a wide variety of movement from limb extension to pupil diameter adjustment.

Muscle Structural Organization

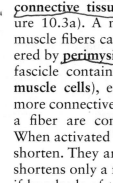

The whole muscle is surrounded by a sheath of connective tissue called the epimysium (see Figure 10.3a). A muscle is made up of bundles of muscle fibers called fascicles. Each fascicle is covered by perimysium (more connective tissue). Each fascicle contains many muscle fibers (individual muscle cells), each of which is covered by still more connective tissue called endomysium. Within a fiber are contractile units called sarcomeres. When activated by the nervous system, sarcomeres shorten. They are microscopic in size, so each one shortens only a fraction of a micrometer; however, if hundreds of these are lined up end to end in a cell and if they all shorten, the entire muscle cell can shorten quite a bit! Bundle many of these cells into fascicles, bundle the fascicles into a muscle, and shorten many of them at once, and a lot of tension and force can be developed—enough to propel your whole body up the Washington Monument steps!

connective tissue—generally fibrous collections of cells throughout the body that add support and structure to the organs they are within; collagen fibers comprise 25% of the body's connective tissues.

epimysium—a sheet or layer of connective tissue that envelopes an entire muscle.

fascicle—a bundle of skeletal muscle fibers surrounded by a perimysium.

perimysium—a layer of fibrous connective tissue that envelopes a fascicle or bundle of skeletal muscle fibers.

muscle fiber/muscle cell—elongated, cylindrical, multinucleated cells packed with contractile fibrils of actin and myosin proteins.

endomysium—a sheath of connective tissue that surrounds and carries capillaries and nerves to individual muscle fibers/cells.

sarcomere—the structural and functional unit within a muscle cell; intertwined protein fibrils of actin and myosin that pull against each other in the contraction process.

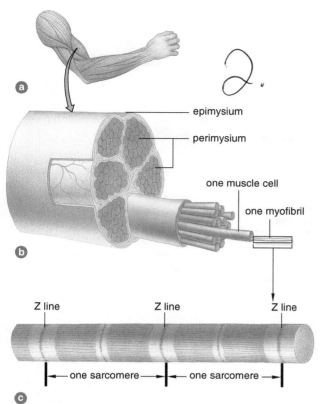

Figure 10.3 Levels of Organization in a Muscle. **(a)** Arrangement of muscles (organs) in the human forelimb. **(b)** a cross-section through a single muscle showing a bundle of muscle cells—a fasicle—drawn out. Within this tissue level of organization, single, elongated muscle cells are shown. **(c)** Within a muscle cell are elongated myofibrils (supra-molecular structures) that represent a linear array of sarcomere units (see text). Each sarcomere is bound to the next one by a complex of strong structural proteins called a "Z line". Contraction occurs within the structure of the sarcomere.

epimysium

perimysium

one muscle cell

one myofibril

Z line   Z line   Z line

——— one sarcomere ———   ——— one sarcomere ———

IN OTHER WORDS

1. A typical skeletal muscle is composed of many bundles or fascicles, each of which is in turn composed of many individual cells called *muscle fibers*.

Muscle Contraction

At the most basic level, muscle shortening is produced by many **myofilaments** sliding past each other. To understand how sliding filaments lead to contraction, we first need to understand the structure of the contractile unit, or sarcomere (see Figure 10.4). Each sarcomere has two types of filaments: thick **myosin** filaments that are anchored together across the center of the sarcomere and thinner **actin** filaments anchored to each other and to the sarcomere ends (see Figure 10.2d). During muscle contraction, protein heads on the myosin filaments attach to the actin filaments and pull on them (see Figure 10.4). This slides the actin filaments toward the middle of the myosin filaments, shortening the entire sarcomere. As

mentioned earlier, one sarcomere shortens just a fraction of a micrometer, but many sarcomeres lined up end to end and all shortening at the same time can lead to an amount of muscular shortening that is many millimeters in length.

myofilament—a protein strand within a muscle cell; composed of myosin, actin, or elastic proteins.

myosin—a class of proteins that uses ATP energy and a flexible head domain for movement along a protein strand of actin.

actin—a monomeric protein that makes up the structure of filaments—the scaffolding against which myosin proteins carry out linear movement by successive binding events between myosin head domains and the filament's own scaffolding.

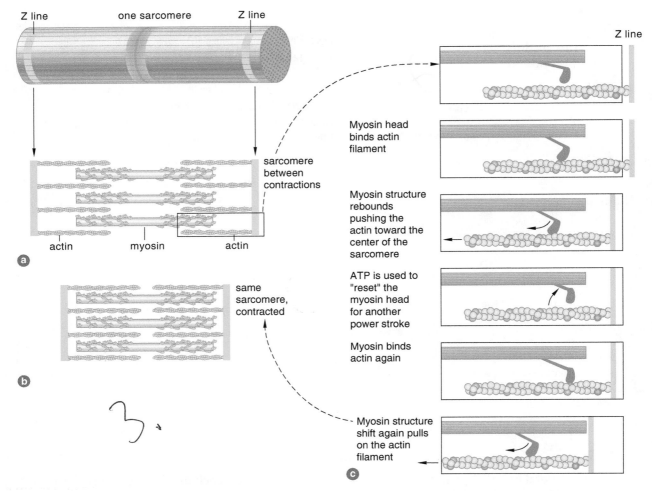

Figure 10.4 Internal Structure of the Sarcomere. **(a)** Actin and myosin fibers are interspersed within the sarcomere. Extensions of myosin protein called "heads" have binding sites on actin polymers to either side. **(b)** Successive binding and releasing of myosin heads causes them to crawl along the actin fibers resulting in a contracted state. **(c)** Each myosin head goes through succesive power strokes as it pulls on the actin fiber it binds to.

IN OTHER WORDS

1. Each muscle fiber contains a long series of functional contractile units called *sarcomeres*; these in turn contain interwoven filaments of actin and myosin proteins.
2. The binding of protein extensions of myosin filaments to actin filaments and the subsequent pulling on these filaments is what enables sarcomeres and the muscles they comprise to contract.

Control of Contraction: Ions, Gradients, and Membrane Potentials

What tells the muscle when to contract and how strongly to do so? Here is a primary example of how two different systems in the body are integrated with each other: The nervous system controls the activities of the muscular system. The muscular system cooperates with still other body systems to nutritionally support the nervous system. The nervous system's control of the muscular system is mediated by **ion gradients** and

ion gradient—a spatial variation from one point to another in the concentration of ions in solution, often over a short distance across a membrane.

Figure 10.5 Diffusion. The red dye molecules exhibit a gradient in the middle bowl: a higher concentration near where they were introduced, a lower concentration further away. Ordinary thermal energy will distribute them evenly within the bowl.

membrane potentials. All cells in your body have a **resting** membrane **potential**. This is the difference in the electrical charge from one side of the cell membrane to the other. This difference is called a *potential* because it represents a source of energy that can *potentially* do work. To see how this potential is formed, we first need to understand gradients. Examine the bowls in Figure 10.5. In the first bowl, there are more red dots in the left-hand portion of the bowl than in the right because that's where the dye (red dots) is being added. In other words, a gradient has been set up. Ordinary thermal energy allows the dots to move. In order for the red dots to reach equilibrium, some of them would have to move from the left to the right, so there would be an equal distribution of dots all through the bowl. (If thermal energy throws the dots around in random directions, a net dot movement from left to right will occur naturally.) Ions that are in different concentrations on either side of a cell's outer membrane are like the red dots. They tend to move toward an equilibrium distribution on either side of a membrane. There are actually two gradients of ions that cause them to move toward equilibrium: a concentration gradient and an electrical gradient. Like the red dots, ions will move back and forth so as to end up in equal numbers (concentrations) on either side of the plasma membrane. If there is a larger number of ions on the outside of the cell, there will be a net movement down the concentration gradient from the outside to the inside until their concentrations become equal on both sides. This occurs passively; no cellular energy input is required. To move them against the concentration gradient would require energy because they naturally tend to go to equilibrium.

The other type of gradient is an **electrical gradient.** Recall that ions are atoms that have lost or gained an electron(s). Because of this, they have a charge (either positive or negative). If there are more positive ions on the outside of the cell, then some of them will be *repelled* toward the inside of the membrane while any negative charges will be *attracted* toward the outside of the membrane until the ionic charge distribution is equal on both sides.

If more positive ions accumulate on the outside of the cell membrane and more negative ones are on the inside of the cell membrane, the inside of the membrane gains a net negative charge compared to the outside (see Figure 10.6a). This is the case in our cells. Each cell membrane contains special proteins called *sodium-potassium ATPase pumps,* or **Na-K-ATPase pumps** (see Figure 10.6b). These pumps use energy from ATP to push ions "uphill" against their concentration gradients. For each cycle of the pump, three sodium ions (Na^+) are pumped outside the cell and two potassium ions (K^+) into the cell, resulting in more positive ions outside the cell than in it.

In the cell membrane, along with these pumps, there are also **ion channels**—gates—that allow ions to pass from one side of the membrane to the other. They allow potassium ions to leave the cell again, returning down their chemical/electrical gradient. The overall result is a slightly higher concentration of positive (Na^+) ions outside. The muscle cell's measured (resting) membrane potential is normally −95mV, with the inside somewhat more negative than the outside.

membrane potential—the difference of voltage (or potential energy) between the inside and the outside of a cell.

resting potential—the relatively stable electrical charge difference across a cell membrane in an excitable cell not presently transmitting a signal; contrasts with action potential.

electrical gradient—a spatial variation from one point to another in the concentration of charged substances in solution, often over a short distance across a membrane.

Na-K-ATPase pump—a transmembrane protein complex using ATP energy to move sodium and potassium ions against their concentration gradients; the result is a membrane potential from the inside of the cell to the outside.

ion channel—a protein complex within a cell membrane that allows ions to flow down their electrical/chemical gradient across the membrane, influencing the membrane potential.

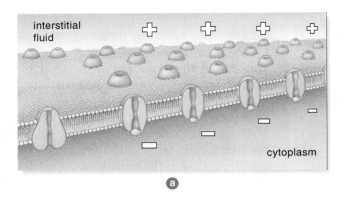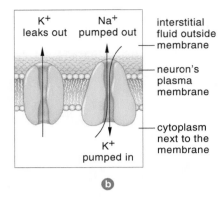

Figure 10.6 *Cell Membrane at Resting Potential.* **(a)** Due to differential pumping of 3 sodium ions out for every 2 potassium ions in, there's a slight charge differential across the cell membrane. **(b)** The sodium-potassium pump on the right requires ATP to drive sodium out and potassium in. If the gate (channel) on the left opens, it can relieve the gradient created by the pump by allowing any positive ions in.

IN OTHER WORDS

1. The nervous system uses changes in electrical potential differences across cell membranes to communicate the need for contraction to muscle cells.
2. Electrical charge differences across a membrane (electrical potential) are chemical and electrical gradients that are established by pumping ions from where they are in lower concentration to where they are already in higher concentration.
3. Pumping of ions is accomplished by the Na-K-ATPase protein complex found in the membranes of neurons and muscle cells.
4. The membrane potential is achieved by pumping Na$^+$ ions out of the cell, pumping K$^+$ ions into the cell, and allowing a fraction of these K$^+$ ions to leak out of the cell through K$^+$-specific ion channels.
5. The result is a continuous membrane potential that is slightly more negative to the inside of the membrane; momentary change in this potential will initiate the signal for the muscle cell to contract.

Control of Contraction: The Nervous System

When they are at rest, the myosin fibers in the sarcomeres of the muscle cell cannot bind to the actin fibers. The binding sites on the actin fibers are covered with a protein called **tropomyosin** that must shift its position in order for actin and myosin fibers to interact, thereby causing sarcomere contraction (see Figure 10.7). How does this shift take place?

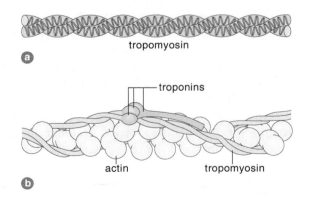

Figure 10.7 *Regulation of Sarcomere Contraction.* Strands of the tropomyosin protein **(a)** are wound around the actin strands **(b)** in a sarcomere such that their troponin proteins conceal the sites where myosin heads bind. Increased calcium levels shift the troponin proteins laterally exposing the head binding sites allowing the sarcomere to contract.

> **tropomyosin**—a long protein-containing fiber that binds to actin filaments within the sarcomere; helps control actin-myosin binding and therefore muscle contraction.

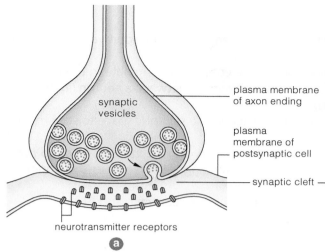

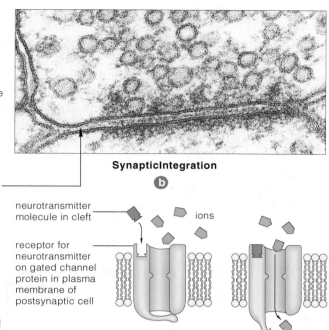

SynapticIntegration

(b)

neurotransmitter
molecule in cleft

ions

receptor for
neurotransmitter
on gated channel
protein in plasma
membrane of
postsynaptic cell

(c)

Figure 10.8 The Synapse. The nervous impulse travels down a nerve cell's axon till it reaches an end bulb **(a)** which lies very close to the membrane of the muscle cell. The impulse causes the release of neurotransmitter substances (like acetylcholine) from vessiles in the end bulb. **(b)** An electron micrograph showing vesicles ready to fuse with the end bulb membrane dumping their contents into the synaptic space (cleft). **(c)** Binding of acetylcholine opens ion channels starting an action potential (impulse) in the membrane of the muscle cell.

When the central nervous system (CNS) determines that a muscle needs to move, it sends a signal down a nerve cell to the place the cellmeets the muscle fiber, a narrow space or gap about 0.02 micrometers across called a **synapse** (see Figure 10.8). The nerve cell signal arriving at this synapse is actually an electrical signal. When it reaches the synapse, it causes calcium channels in the membrane to open and calcium (which is at a higher level outside the cell than inside) rushes down its concentration gradient into the synaptic terminal of the nerve cell. That rush of calcium causes vesicles to open up into the synaptic gap. The content of these vesicles is a chemical **neurotransmitter** substance called **acetylcholine**. The acetylcholine quickly crosses the narrow space in the synapse to the muscle cell surface. Located on the muscle cell membrane are receptor proteins that have a special binding site for acetylcholine. These receptors are actually ion channels! When acetylcholine binds to the receptors, they open, allowing sodium ions (Na^+) to rush into the muscle cell. This ionic movement changes the membrane potential of the muscle cell, which is its way of initiating a new electrical signal. This new signal spreads along the muscle cell and is called an **action potential**. The signal is nothing more than a temporary, positive shift in the membrane potential across the membrane as positive charges enter the cell. This spreading action potential causes the calcium storage tanks (vesicles) in the muscle cell to release their calcium ions (Ca^{2+}).

Along the tropomyosin fibers are proteins called **troponins.** When calcium ions bind to troponins s, they shift the tropomyosin fibers, exposing the myosin-binding sites on the actin (see Figure 10.7). With tropomyosin removed from the binding sites, the myosin heads can bind to the actin and pull on it. Muscle contraction is in this way enabled.

Of course, for the pulling action to occur, the myosin must have ATP to do the mechanical work of pulling. ATP production will require the activity of still other body systems, as we will see. Therefore both calcium and ATP are required for controlled contraction of the sarcomere.

synapse—a narrow gap or space between two excitable cells; a signal reaching the end of the first cell must become chemical in nature to cross the space and initiate a signal in the other cell.

neurotransmitter—a chemical substance that by rapid diffusion carries a signal across a synaptic cleft to the membrane of an excitable cell, where it may initiate a new action potential.

acetylcholine—a neurotransmitter chemical that is secreted into a synapse by the transmitting cell and that initiates a new signal in the receiving cell.

action potential—a momentary steep electrical charge difference across a membrane; the physical basis for a nerve impulse.

troponin—a protein along the tropomyosin fiber that specifically locks onto actin at the site at which myosin heads would otherwise bind; involved in control of muscle contraction.

1. The calcium mediates a shift in the physical relationship between actin and tropomyosin proteins such that myosin-actin pulling can occur.
2. Electrical signals—action potentials—initiating skeletal muscle contraction originate in the nervous system and become chemical in nature when they cross the synaptic space between a neuron (in the nervous system) and a muscle cell (in the muscular system).
3. A neurotransmitting chemical such as acetylcholine diffuses across the synaptic space to start the action potential in the membrane of the muscle cell.
4. When the action potential causes calcium release within the muscle cell, the calcium binds to proteins called *troponins* along the tropomyosin filaments. This calcium binding is what causes the tropomyosin configuration to alter, allowing myosin-actin pulling.
5. Both calcium release and ATP energy release are required for a muscle to contract.

Contraction of Cardiac and Smooth Muscle

We've just seen how skeletal muscle works. **Skeletal muscle** is considered voluntary muscle as we can choose whether or not to contract it. We also have two other types of muscle in our bodies: **cardiac muscle** and **smooth muscle,** both of which carry out involuntary contractions. The nervous and endocrine systems control these muscles without our conscious thought or voluntary desire. Cardiac muscle will be discussed in Section 10.3. Smooth muscle forms part of the digestive, urinary, respiratory, reproductive, and circulatory systems (see Table 10.1). Smooth muscle is similar to skeletal muscle in that contraction in both is generated by nervous stimulation involving an action potential, calcium signaling, and ATP energy. However, the calcium in smooth muscle binds to a different component—**calmodulin** instead of troponin—to uncover myosin-actin binding sites on their respective filaments. Smooth muscle serves many critical organismal functions (see Table 10.1); it helps keep our blood pressure regulated and our digestive processes effective. Each system of our body, though complex, is integrated with all of the others demonstrating a frighteningly high level of competence in design.

Table 10.1 Role of smooth muscle in body systems.

System	Functions
circulatory	(in walls of arteries) maintenance of blood pressure
lymphatic	maintenance of lymph vessel structure; movement of lymph fluid
excretory	contraction of the urinary bladder during voiding of urine
reproductive	(female) contraction of uterus; (male) propulsion of sperm
digestive	peristaltic waves moving food through the intestines
respiratory	function not yet understood
integumentary	pilo-erection (added insulation at low temperatures)
sensory	alteration in size of the iris of the eye

skeletal muscle—striated muscle generally attached to bones by tendons; under voluntary control of the peripheral nervous system.

cardiac muscle—striated muscle that comprises the walls of the heart; generally involuntary in its control.

smooth muscle—nonstriated muscle under involuntary control; forms much of the structure of the digestive and vascular systems.

calmodulin—a protein whose action is controlled by calcium ion influx; controls contraction of smooth muscle.

1. On the basis of control and structural differences, muscles are classified into three categories: skeletal muscle, smooth muscle, and cardiac muscle.
2. In smooth muscle, a distinct controlling component, calmodulin, determines the level of myosin-actin pulling instead of the tropomyosin used in skeletal muscle.

10.3 THE CARDIOVASCULAR SYSTEM

As you continue climbing the stairs of the Washington Monument, your muscles are using a lot of oxygen and other nutrients while producing metabolic wastes and giving off carbon dioxide. This would be a problem—you would quickly run out of needed substances and have a toxic buildup of wastes—if you did not have a way of replacing nutrients and removing wastes. Thankfully, you do! A brilliant Designer gave you a cardiovascular system! This system consists of blood that carries the nutrients and wastes, vessels for the blood to flow through, and a heart to pump the blood through the vessels! Let's examine each of these components of the cardiovascular system in more detail.

IN OTHER WORDS

1. The cardiovascular system supplies its own tissues and all other organ systems of the body with nutrients, oxygen, and hormonal signals. It removes waste products from these systems as well.

Blood: A Medium of Exchange

Did you know that blood is a tissue? It is a fluid type of connective tissue that functions to carry nutrients, oxygen, wastes, and hormones throughout the body while helping your **immune system** and forming clots to prevent excessive bleeding. Blood is made up of **plasma** and formed elements that are cells or parts of cells (see Figure 10.9). In the plasma (which is mostly water) are proteins, hormones, nutrients and wastes, oxygen and carbon dioxide. Each of the formed elements in the blood has a specific function: red blood cells (**erythrocytes**) carry oxygen through the blood to supply tissues with it. White blood cells (**leukocytes**) help us fight infection (see Section 10.4). **Platelets** are actually small fragments of cells that help form clots to prevent you from bleeding to death when blood vessels are traumatically opened.

immune system—a collection of organs that surveys blood and tissue fluids, detects and labels foreign particles or cells, and works to degrade and destroy those particles or cells.

plasma—the fluid component of blood that includes those factors that cause clotting of blood; it contains nutrients, hormones, and molecule wastes and is a vehicle for movement of the cellular components of blood.

erythrocyte—red blood cell whose hemoglobin-laden cytoplasm is a reservoir for oxygen being carried from the lungs to the body's tissues.

leukocytes—white blood cells that, as part of the body's immune system, help detect and destroy foreign cells and particles such as viruses.

platelet—fragment of a megakaryocyte cell that floats in the circulatory system helping to clot blood at sites of trauma and secreting growth hormone.

IN OTHER WORDS

1. Blood, composed of plasma fluid, cells, and cellular fragments, is a tissue that carries nutrients, oxygen, wastes, and hormones throughout the body.
2. Erythrocytes are cells designed to carry oxygen to the tissues while leukocytes are cells designed to detect and respond to infectious agents.

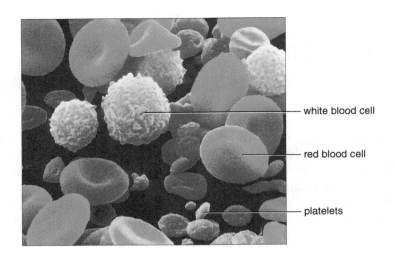

white blood cell

red blood cell

platelets

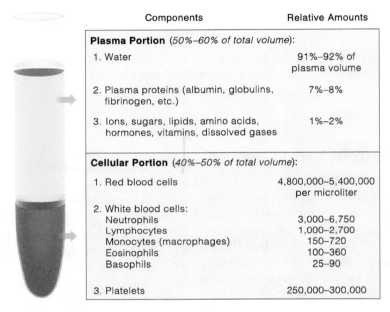

Components	Relative Amounts
Plasma Portion (*50%–60% of total volume*):	
1. Water	91%–92% of plasma volume
2. Plasma proteins (albumin, globulins, fibrinogen, etc.)	7%–8%
3. Ions, sugars, lipids, amino acids, hormones, vitamins, dissolved gases	1%–2%
Cellular Portion (*40%–50% of total volume*):	
1. Red blood cells	4,800,000–5,400,000 per microliter
2. White blood cells:	
Neutrophils	3,000–6,750
Lymphocytes	1,000–2,700
Monocytes (macrophages)	150–720
Eosinophils	100–360
Basophils	25–90
3. Platelets	250,000–300,000

Figure 10.9   The Composition of Blood. At the top is an electron micrograph of the cellular parts of blood. The sample in the centrifuge tube results from putting whole blood in a tube, separating it from attachment to the tube wall, and simply waiting. Clotting factors pull the formed elements together into the bottom of the tube leaving clear plasma behind. Since the clotting factors are employed in the bottom of the tube, the plasma above (without these factors) is called serum.

Blood Vessels: The Body's Avenue of Life

Blood is distributed throughout the body by a system of tubes or blood vessels—**veins, arteries,** and **capillaries.** Arteries carry blood away from the heart and to the body's tissues. They are muscular tubes that can change their diameter based on the body's needs at a given time. While you are climbing the stairs of the Monument, the arteries supplying your skeletal muscles will **dilate** (or open), allowing more blood—more oxygen

vein—a blood vessel that conducts blood away from the lung or tissues and toward the heart.

artery—a blood vessel that conducts blood toward the lung or tissues and away from the heart.

capillaries—small blood vessels extending between arteries and veins; blood flow is slowed within these vessels and nutrient, waste, and gas exchange occurs between them and the surrounding tissues.

dilate—to enlarge or expand.

and nutrients—to reach the muscles while carrying away more wastes and more carbon dioxide. At the same time, blood vessels supplying the gut/digestive system will **constrict** (or narrow), as your body has less need to supply them with blood while you are climbing the stairs. Once you reach the top of the Monument and grab a snack while enjoying the view, however, the blood flow will change. Your muscles, now at rest, will not need as much blood, so the arteries supplying them will constrict while the arteries supplying the digestive system will dilate; this allows the digestive organs to process the snack you are eating.

How do arteries deliver these nutrients to your tissues? They branch into progressively smaller arteries that eventually lead to capillaries (see Figures 9.2, 10.10). These very small, very thin vessels are where the exchange between blood and tissues takes place. Oxygen and nutrients go through the walls of the blood vessels into the tissues, whereas carbon dioxide and waste leave the tissues and enter the blood to be carried away. After leaving the capillaries, blood—now having higher carbon dioxide levels and lower oxygen levels—runs through progressively larger veins until the largest veins head back to the heart, where blood is then pumped to the lungs to get rid of the excess carbon dioxide and pick up more oxygen (the pulmonary circuit). The metabolic wastes will be filtered out of the blood by the kidneys and leave the body as part of the urine.

constrict—to narrow or shrink.

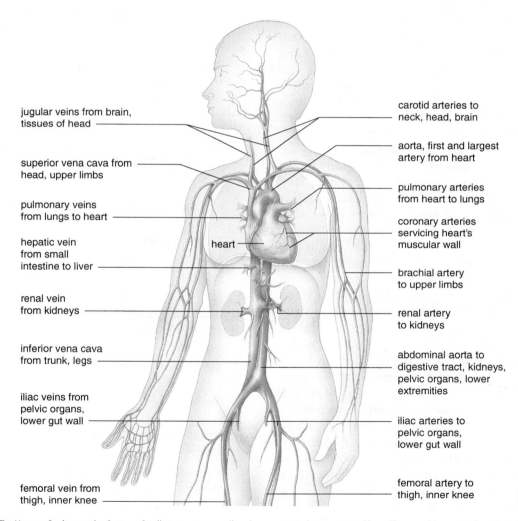

jugular veins from brain, tissues of head

superior vena cava from head, upper limbs

pulmonary veins from lungs to heart

hepatic vein from small intestine to liver

renal vein from kidneys

inferior vena cava from trunk, legs

iliac veins from pelvic organs, lower gut wall

femoral vein from thigh, inner knee

heart

carotid arteries to neck, head, brain

aorta, first and largest artery from heart

pulmonary arteries from heart to lungs

coronary arteries servicing heart's muscular wall

brachial artery to upper limbs

renal artery to kidneys

abdominal aorta to digestive tract, kidneys, pelvic organs, lower extremities

iliac arteries to pelvic organs, lower gut wall

femoral artery to thigh, inner knee

Figure 10.10 The Human Cardiovascular System. Capillaries are too small and numerous to be represented here. They would connect the extremities of the red and blue vessels together. Notice where main arteries lead to in the body and how they are named.

1. Generally speaking, arteries carry blood away from the heart toward the lungs and body systems; veins carry blood back from these extremities.
2. Capillaries are tiny vessels within the tissues themselves that connect arteries to veins; they are sites where gas and nutrient exchange take place.
3. The diameter of arteries is flexible—blood flow can be regulated such that at any given time, tissues most needing it can receive a larger share of blood.
4. Blood also flows through the kidneys, where potentially toxic waste products are removed and targeted for excretion from the body in urine.

The Heart: The Dynamo of Human Life

The heart is the engine that keeps your body heading toward the top of the Monument. It is actually two pumps in one! There are two circulatory systems in your body: the **pulmonary circulation** and the **systemic circulation** (see Figure 10.11). Blood from the body enters the right side of the heart and is then pumped out of the right side into the lungs, where gas exchange occurs. The blood then returns to the left side of heart via the veins of the pulmonary circuit, and from there it's pumped to the rest of the body over the systemic circuit.

What happens within the systemic circuit as the blood arrives at the tissues? There is a steady movement of plasma into the tissues. The residual fluid in the tissues (**interstitial fluid**) is collected by tiny ducts of the lymphatic system, where it is called lymph, and returned to the major veins carrying blood to the heart (see Figure 10.12a,b). There it reenters the circulatory system. Hormones control this balance so as to maintain a fairly constant blood volume. On its way back to the heart, lymph is filtered by lima bean–sized **lymph nodes** distributed throughout the body (see Figure 10.12c). In these nodes, an immune response can be triggered if a foreign pathogen is detected (see Section 10.4).

Most of the mass of the heart itself is made of cardiac muscle. It is similar to skeletal muscle except that cardiac muscle cells are connected by **gap junctions,** which unite the cells electrically, allowing the whole heart to contract together. This means an action potential in the heart will cause the heart as a whole to contract, squeezing blood out of both sides of the heart and into both the pulmonary and systemic circuits.

Blood enters the heart through the two **atria** (see Figure 10.13). Blood from the systemic circuit empties into the right atrium and then goes to the right ventricle from which it is pumped into the pulmonary circuit to the lungs. Blood from the lungs enters the left atrium of the heart, goes to the left ventricle, and then is pumped to the systemic circuit to supply oxygen and nutrients to the rest of the body.

Between the atria and ventricles and between the ventricles and the outside of the heart are **valves** (see Figure 10.13). The closing of these valves is what produces the sounds of the heartbeat. These valves prevent the backflow of blood so that it has to go in one direction through the circulatory system. Imagine trying to design a heart valve using only mutations in a system with no valves. The

pulmonary circulation—those blood vessels that carry deoxygenated blood from the heart to the lungs and reoxygenated blood from the lungs to the heart.

systemic circulation—those blood vessels that carry blood from the heart to the tissues (other than the lungs) and from those tissues back to the heart.

interstitial fluid (lymph)—that aqueous solution of biomolecules that exists between cells within tissues; it becomes lymph when transported in lymph capillaries back toward the heart.

lymph node—organ of the lymphatic system in which antigen-lymphocyte encounters occur; sites of tissue fluid filtration and surveillance.

gap junctions—small connections between animal cells that allow direct contact between the cytoplasms of those cells; in cardiac muscle, sites of rapid propagation of impulses calling for muscle contraction.

atrium—one of two chambers in the mammalian heart that receives blood from either the lungs or the tissues.

ventricle—one of two highly muscular chambers in the mammalian heart that pumps blood to either the lungs or the tissues.

valve—folds of tissue within the major arteries that allow blood to pass during ventricular contraction but that then seat against each other to prevent backflow of blood during ventricular relaxation.

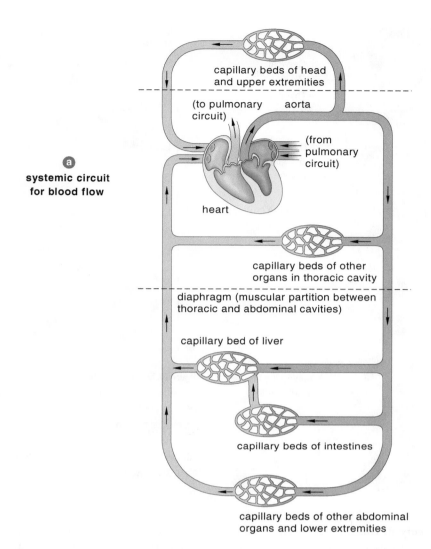

a

**systemic circuit
for blood flow**

capillary beds of head
and upper extremities

(to pulmonary
circuit)   aorta

(from
pulmonary
circuit)

heart

capillary beds of other
organs in thoracic cavity

diaphragm (muscular partition between
thoracic and abdominal cavities)

capillary bed of liver

capillary beds of intestines

capillary beds of other abdominal
organs and lower extremities

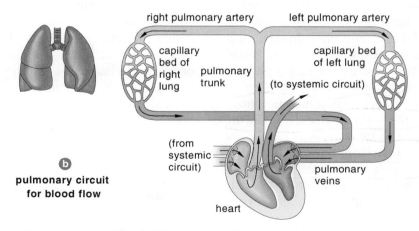

right pulmonary artery   left pulmonary artery

capillary
bed of
right
lung

pulmonary
trunk

capillary bed
of left lung

(to systemic circuit)

(from
systemic
circuit)

pulmonary
veins

b

**pulmonary circuit
for blood flow**

heart

Figure 10.11 The Human Circulatory System is Two Systems! **(a)** The systemic circuit. **(b)** The
pulmonary circuit.

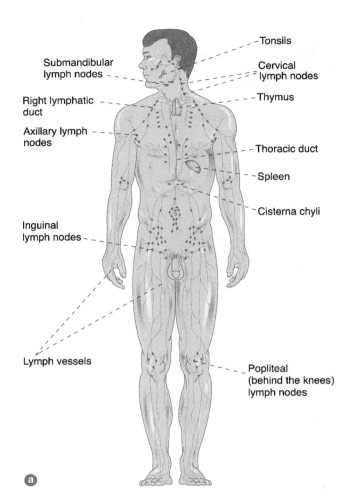

Tonsils
Submandibular lymph nodes
Cervical lymph nodes
Right lymphatic duct
Thymus
Axillary lymph nodes
Thoracic duct
Spleen
Cisterna chyli
Inguinal lymph nodes
Lymph vessels
Popliteal (behind the knees) lymph nodes

(a)

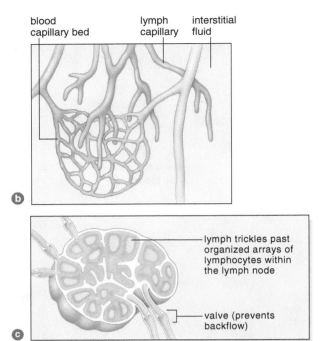

blood capillary bed   lymph capillary   interstitial fluid

(b)

lymph trickles past organized arrays of lymphocytes within the lymph node

valve (prevents backflow)

(c)

Figure 10.12 The Lymphatic System. **(a)** Lymph vessels drain circulating interstitial fluid from all parts of the body back through ducts to the systemic circulatory system near the heart. Many more lymph nodes exist than those represented here. **(b)** Lymph capillaries are close to circulatory system capillaries so that fluid can efficiently percolate through the tissues and then into the lymphatic system. **(c)** A cross section through a lymph node that lies along the network of lymph ducts.

blood must flow freely in the direction away from the heart and not at all in the opposite direction. The tissue composition and structure of valves is brilliantly crafted to achieve this purpose.

When the powerful left ventricle conracts, pressure in the arteries increases temporarily. Blood pressure is literally the pressure the blood puts on the blood vessel walls. You can feel that sudden increase in pressure—or **pulse**—in some superficial arteries (such as on the wrist or neck). When the heart contracts, the pulse pressure is at its highest value; we call that the **systolic pressure**—the higher number of your blood pressure reading. When the heart relaxes, pressure drops a bit and that is the **diastolic pressure**—the lower number of your blood pressure reading.

Your heart rate is controlled by the **parasympathetic** and **sympathetic** nervous systems (see Section 10.8). Climbing stairs is a form of physical stress on the body. As you begin, the sympathetic nervous system, which is activated under stressful conditions, will increase your heart

rate to ensure adequate oxygen delivery to your skeletal muscles. So here are six body systems immediately involved in obvious cooperation to convey you up the Monument stairs. The muscular system moves you there. The nervous system informs its activity. The cardiovascular system conveys the resources for climbing. The digestive and respiratory systems supply the resources, and the excretory and respiratory systems remove the waste products of the activity. No one system of the body can function without the others!

pulse—the sudden dilation of arterial vessels caused by ventricular contraction within the heart.

systolic pressure—the outward pressure of blood on arterial walls under the full force of a ventricular contraction.

diastolic pressure—the outward pressure of blood on arterial walls during the period of ventricular relaxation between contractions.

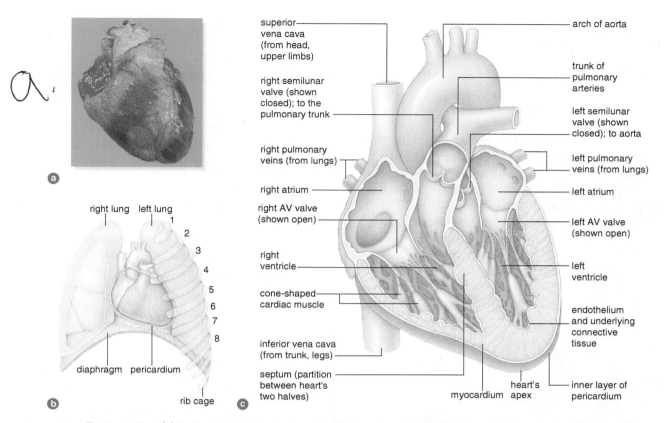

Figure 10.13 The Human Heart. **(a)** Your heart is about the size of your fist. **(b)** It's position within the thoracic cavity. **(c)** A section through the major heart chambers. The major vessels flowing into and out of the heart are here named.

IN OTHER WORDS

1. The heart is a dynamic organ that pushes blood toward the tissues in general and the lungs in particular.
2. It is a double pump; the larger chamber, the left ventricle, pumps blood to the tissues of the body for nutrient distribution.
3. In a separate system—the pulmonary circulation—the right ventricle pumps deoxygenated blood returning from the tissues to the lungs for dumping of carbon dioxide and resupply of oxygen.
4. Blood plasma that has crossed through capillaries and out into the tissues is called *interstitial fluid*.
5. Interstitial fluid gradually finds its way back to the blood from the tissues through lymph ducts, which converge and empty into the major veins returning to the heart, where it is reunited with the blood plasma.
6. On its journey through the lymphatic system, the lymph passes through lymph nodes, where it is assayed for the presence of any foreign objects that may be pathogenic.
7. Cardiac muscle has a unique arrangement of gap junction connections so that millions of individual cardiac cells can contract in synchrony, which gives rise to the heartbeat.
8. The human heart has four chambers. Two atria receive blood returning from major veins. Two ventricles pump blood out to major arteries.
9. Blood flow through the entire cardiovascular system is unidirectional because valves between the atria and the ventricles and between the ventricles and major arteries prevent its backflow.
10. When the ventricles contract, the pressure of the blood in the arterial system is at its highest value, termed systolic pressure; between these contractions, it reaches its lowest arterial pressure, termed diastolic pressure.
11. The rate at which your heart beats is modulated by two opposing branches of the nervous system: the sympathetic and parasympathetic systems. The parasympathetic branch controls the heart under normal circumstances, while the sympathetic branch increases the heart rate in times of stress.
12. The various systems of the body are meticulously and substantially interconnected with each other so as to deliver the life-giving flow of blood to those various systems.

10.4 BASIC CONCEPTS OF IMMUNITY

While you climb the stairs of the Monument, you need some external support, so you grab the handrail. What you do not think about is that hundreds of other people h ave touched that rail in the last hour, perhaps thousands since this morning! Those peoples' hands had germs on them—the ones they normally carry around, plus some **pathogens** too! Many handrail users have respiratory infections. One or two harbor HIV viruses and don't know it yet. Thankfully, most human pathogens die quickly with exposure to air. For example, HIV in the low

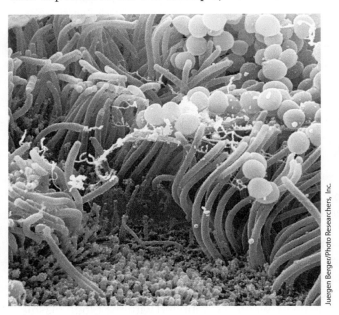

Juergen Berger/Photo Researchers, Inc.

Figure 10.14 *Staphylococcus aureus*. This opportunistic pathogen is shown here entrained in mucous secretions of nasal epithelial cells. It's on its way to the stomach where acids will recycle it's biomolecules for absorption and use to make "our" biomolecules instead.

Table 10.2 Three lines of defense in the human immune system.

BARRIERS AT BODY SURFACES (*nonspecific* targets)
Intact skin; mucous membranes at other body surfaces
Infection-fighting chemicals in tears, saliva, etc.
Normally harmless bacterial inhabitants of skin and other body surfaces that can outcompete pathogenic visitors
Flushing effect of tears, saliva, urination, and diarrhea

NONSPECIFIC RESPONSES (*nonspecific* targets)
Inflammation:
1. Fast-acting white blood cells (neutrophils, eosinophils, and basophils)
2. Macrophages (also take part in immune responses)
Organs with pathogen-killing functions (such as lymph nodes)
Some cytotoxic cells (e.g., NK cells) with a range of targets

IMMUNE RESPONSES (*specific* targets only)
T cells and B cells; macrophages interact with them
Communication signals and chemical weapons (e.g., antibodies)

concentrations found on a handrail would be inactivated within a few minutes' time. However, some microbes, like the bacterium *Staphylococcus aureus,* are quite resistant to dry environments and can live for a long time within the pitted surface of the rail inside the Monument (see Figure 10.14). Thankfully, your body has several lines of defense to protect you from these germs (see Table 10.2).

pathogen—any microorganism, viral, bacterial, or eukaryotic, that by its presence or growth in host tissues causes or contributes to a disease state.

IN OTHER WORDS

1. Our body's surfaces are constantly being exposed to a variety of foreign substances and pathogens.

Your First Line of Defense

The first line of defense is our integumentary system that provides a surface barrier. Your skin and mucous membranes form this barrier and prevent most things from the external environment from getting inside our bodies. Many pathogenic bacteria and viruses attach themselves to the surface of an epidermal skin cell that is already dead and will be sloughed off the next time you clap your hands or wash them. You just heard a climber, two flights up inside the Monument cough violently, spilling untold numbers of her respiratory microbes into the air. But as you inhale these microbes, they get entrained in the mucous secretions in your bronchial passages and slowly the **cilia** on the cells lining your **bronchi** carry those microbes and their mucus vehicle to your pharynx, where you swallow them (see Figure 10.14). The next stop—your acid-laden stomach—is death to the vast majority of such microbes.

IN OTHER WORDS

1. The most widespread and pervasive first line of defense against pathogens is the epidermal surface of our integumentary system.
2. We constantly slough off dead skin cells to which potential pathogens have witlessly attached themselves.
3. Pathogens that enter our respiratory, digestive, or genital tracts become entrained in mucous secretions; these secretions are removed by the movement of cilia on our cell surfaces.

Your Second Line of Defense

A few germs manage to get past your surface barriers via cuts, surgery, or perhaps smoking-induced defects in your respiratory ciliary "escalator." These microbes, now in your interstitial fluids or bloodstream, cause you to mobilize a second line of defense (see Table 10.2). This line includes **natural killer cells** that attach to your viral-infected cells or tumor cells and cause them to die. You also have a complete lineup of different types of white blood cells—leukocytes—each of which boasts a different strategy for doing warfare against foreign invaders (see Figure 10.15). These include the widespread **neutrophils** in the blood and **macrophages** in the tissues. Both of these ingest and digest foreign cells and particles. **Eosinophils** are leukocytes that attack invading parasites. **Basophils** in the bloodstream and **mast cells** in the tissues release **histamine** to support the inflammation process. So in both the bloodstream and the tissues, you have this second line of defense that detects and destroys foreign cells or inanimate particles that threaten your well-being. How does this second line of defense do its job?

One result of activating this second line of defense is the process of **inflammation** (see Figure 10.16a). In an area of the body where an infection is beginning, chemical signals from various leukocytes cause local capillaries to become dilated and more leaky. Increased release of fluid and cells into this area of tissue causes the redness, swelling, heat, and pain associated with inflammation. If the area is a joint, it may become immobilized or have reduced mobility due to the swelling. All of these symptoms of inflammation, although uncomfortable for us, are designed to promote healing by recognition and destruction of foreign bodies. Dilated,

cilia—organelles; projections from a cell's surface that oscillate in a whip-like fashion to generate movement of medium past a cell or movement of the cell within the medium.

bronchi (bronchus, sing.)—elongated, tube-like organs in the respiratory system that conduct air from the tracheal passage down into the lungs.

natural killer cell—a type of lymphocyte within the innate branch of the immune system that attacks tumor cells and virally infected cells using generalized markers on the surfaces of these cells.

neutrophil—a leukocyte within the innate branch of the immune system that patrols the bloodstream for foreign cells or objects; has phagocytic activity.

macrophage—a large, wandering cell that engulfs and degrades foreign particles and cells in the tissues of vertebrates; functions in both the innate and adaptive immune responses.

eosinophil—a leukocyte within the innate branch of the immune system that recognizes and attacks multicelled parasites.

basophil—a leukocyte within the innate branch of the immune system that functions within the bloodstream by participating in various aspects of the inflammation response; releases histamines.

mast cell—a leukocyte within the innate branch of the immune system that functions within the body's tissues by participating in various aspects of the inflammation response; releases histamines.

histamine—an organic nitrogen-containing compound released by basophils and mast cells; triggers the inflammation response by increasing permeability of capillary walls to cells and signals involved in inflammation.

inflammation—a chemically complex process in the tissues that results in pain, redness, swelling and localized fever; facilitates response to invading microorganisms.

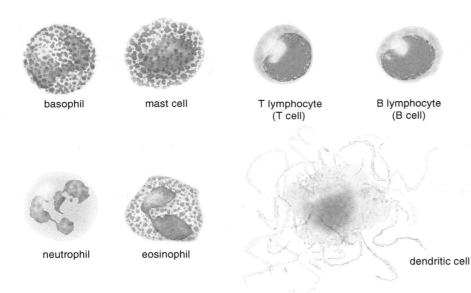

basophil   mast cell   T lymphocyte   B lymphocyte
                                      (T cell)   (B cell)

neutrophil   eosinophil   dendritic cell

Figure 10.15 Cells of the Human Immune System. Nuclei are stained purple, cytoplasms are light blue in most cases. The large granules in eosinophils, basophils and mast cells are actually vesicles full of destructive enzymes, toxins, or signalling molecules.

a Bacteria (purple) have invaded the tissues and are enzymatically degrading host cells as a nutrient source.

b Histamines (red) are released by mast cells in surrounding tissues causing local dilation of capillaries generating warmth and redness.

c The capillaries also become leaky and defensive proteins and signaling substance along with

d neutrophils leave the capillary and head out into the tissues.

e Phagocytosis of antibody-coated bacteria begins amidst tissue swelling and some pain.

Figure 10.16 Inflammation in Response to Infection.

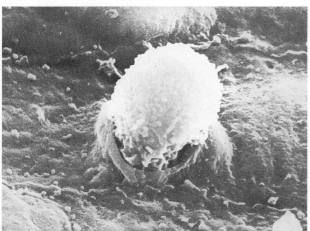

f An electron micrograph of a neutrophil escaping a capillary to seek out a pathogen in nearby tissue.

leaky capillaries allow tissue fluids to wash bacteria or viruses into the nearest lymph node, where they can be more completely recognized and responded to. Phagocytic leukocytes also leak into the area to engulf and degrade pathogens (see Figure 10.16b). Meanwhile, immobilization of an injured joint prevents further damage while it heals.

Another common result of the innate immune response is local or whole body temperature elevation. A fever is designed to help fight off foreign invaders. Again, although uncomfortable for us, the fever is actually a good thing as long as it does not get so high that it causes brain damage. The increase in body temperature helps the immune system components work better while inhibiting the growth of foreign invaders. For example, when your temperature is elevated, your own body's cells sequester iron. Iron is an important cofactor that many bacteria need for growth. So under feverish conditions, bacterial growth is slowed!

IN OTHER WORDS

1. Pathogens that breach our primary defenses gain entry to our internal tissues, where they encounter an array of defensive cells designed to engulf or destroy them.
2. Natural killer cells attach to tumor cells or virus-infected cells and use toxic chemicals to kill them.
3. Neutrophils and macrophages engulf foreign cells and particles and then enzymatically degrade them. Eosinophils respond to multicellular parasites in a similar way.
4. Basophil and mast cells chemically support the inflammation process that helps get immune cells out of the circulatory system and into effective contact with pathogenic cells in the tissues.
5. Fever, an elevation of body temperature caused by microbial invasion, alters our physiology such that our defensive cells have functional and nutritional advantages over the invading microorganisms.

Your Third Line of Defense

The first and second lines of defense are part of our **innate immunity**. They attack anything foreign in a nonspecific manner. Sly pathogens or rapidly multiplying agents that overwhelm that second line of defense trigger a third line of defense: **adaptive immunity**. The adaptive immune system develops an attack that is unique for each type of foreign substance or cell or virus we are presented with (see Table 10.3). It adapts to the needs of the moment.

In order for our immune system to protect us from anything foreign, the body must be able to distinguish between cells and substances that are our own (or "self") and ones that are *not* our own (or "non-self"). This is done by sensing the shapes of exterior molecules on cell or viral surfaces. All human cells, foreign cells, and viruses have a variety of proteins and carbohydrate groups on their surfaces that enable them to interact effectively with their environments. We have a class of defensive cells called **lymphocytes** that are designed in such a way that, as thousands of them mature, each one has a uniquely shaped surface receptor

ß.

Table 10.3 Characteristics of the adaptive immune response.

1. Requires exposure to foreign agent; non-innate
2. Is specific for the particular foreign agent
3. Is transferable from one host to another
4. Is remembered when foreign agent returns a second time.

protein that recognizes the shape of surface molecules on other cells. As they mature, those that would recognize and prepare to attack our own cell's surfaces are carefully destroyed. In addition, all of our body's cells have a particular class of molecules on them that signal to our immune system that they are "self." So the lymphocytes that survive maturation thus leave our cells alone (unless you have an autoimmune disorder). This maturation process then leaves us with an ever-changing population of lymphocytes well prepared to see and react to a wide variety of different foreign (bacterial, viral, parasitic) invaders. Any foreign object our lymphocytes react to is called an **antigen** because it is going to generate an antiforeign immune response.

innate immunity—those generalized aspects of the immune response that are not pathogen-specific; they require no previous exposure to the pathogen.

adaptive immunity—those pathogen-specific aspects of the immune response that involve antibodies and cells directed against the particular sort of pathogen that has bypassed initial, more generalized host defenses.

lymphocyte—a class of leukocytes that form the third line of defense against pathogens; B lymphocytes make antibodies; T lymphocytes generate signal substances or kill self cells infected with pathogens.

antigen—any foreign molecule or cell that generates an adaptive immune response.

Our lymphocytes thus recognize cells both because they are foreign and because they are not "self." This third line of defense will then specifically tag foreign cells and particles with a signal that attracts immune cells such as macrophages and neutrophils that will either engulf or kill the foreign invaders (see Figure 10.15).

Virtually all interstitial fluid circulates through the lymphatic system on its way back to the heart. The lymph nodes stationed carefully along this system are perfect areas for surveillance of what is currently in our tissues (see Figure 10.12). This is where the third line of defense does its "detective work." Immune cells congregate in the lymph nodes, monitoring the lymph searching for anything foreign. If something foreign is detected, the cells can mount an immune response specifically against that foreign object. If the foreign object enters the bloodstream instead of the tissues, the blood eventually flows through an immune system organ called the **spleen**. Lymphocyte detective work takes place there as well! Do lymphocytes have eyes and brains? How does this happen?

The cells in the lymph nodes and spleen need no eyes and brains; rather, they are well designed. Two groups of defensive cells—the macrophages and the **dendritic cells**—also have surface receptor molecules that can distinguish self surfaces from non-self surfaces on the basis of surface shape (see Figures 10.15, 10.17b). This is all based on the same sort of molecular fit that enables an enzyme to distinguish its own substrate from other substrates. When a macrophage's receptors bump into a cell with only self surface markers, they ignore it. But when foreign-shaped surfaces are present (as in bacteria, viruses, or cells infected with these microbes), these foreign entities are engulfed, partially degraded and their foreign parts are "presented" to the lymphocytes standing sentinel in the lymph node (see Figure 10.17c)! The macrophage is now an *APC*, or *antigen-presenting cell*.

Among the lymphocytes that cruise around within the node, some did their maturation in the thymus gland and are called T **lymphocytes**, or *T cells*. Others that will serve a different role, matured in the bone marrow and are called **B lymphocytes**, or *B cells*. Now, among many thousands of B and T lymphocytes, a few happen to have surface receptor shapes specific to the foreign surfaces of the pathogen (see Figure 10.17a, c). The T cells

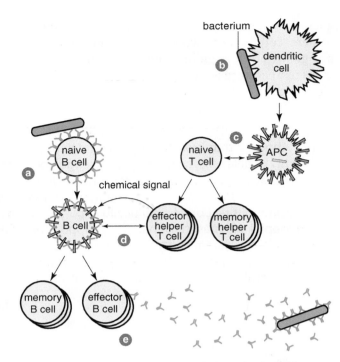

Figure 10.17 "Pathogen Wars Part I." An antibody-mediated adaptive immune response that occurs in lymph nodes or the spleen. See text for details.

sense these foreign molecular surfaces as displayed on the antigen-presenting cells. The B cells recognize those same foreign surfaces directly on the foreign cell itself. One group of T cells called **helper T cells**

spleen—organ of the lymphatic system in which antigen-lymphocyte encounters occur; sites of blood filtration and surveillance.

dendritic cell—part of mammalian immune system; engulfs foreign particles and cells, degrades them, and presents parts of the foreign entity on its surface for detection and binding by pathogen-specific lymphocytes of the adaptive immune system.

T lymphocyte—any lymphocyte that matures to competence in the thymus gland; several classes exist of which helpers and killers are most prominent.

B lymphocyte—a type of lymphocyte that detects foreign molecular surfaces on molecules or cells and generates soluble antibodies that will bind to those surfaces labeling them as foreign.

helper T cell—a type of lymphocyte that detects foreign molecular surfaces on molecules or cells and assists specific B or T lymphocytes to divide and become numerous for defense against the foreign entities.

responds to foreign surfaces by dividing many times to form a population of cells that start putting out a "hey, there's something foreign here!" chemical signal (see Figure 10.17d). The B cells receive this signal: it releases them to undergo many divisions to become a much larger population of effector B cells. This new population begins to produce soluble **antibody** molecules, proteins with shapes identical in structure to the receptor proteins on the progenitor cells that first saw the foreign surfaces (see Figure 10.17e). These antibodies will now begin to bind to and tag this sort of foreign cell surface wherever it might be they are found in the body. Anything in your body that gets coated with antibodies is destined for destruction—macrophages see to that! So here is a critically important branch of your third line of defense: an antibody-mediated response. It finds pathogens, uses surface-specific antibodies to tag the pathogen, and then it destroys the coated pathogen.

If a pathogen that's "at large" in your tissues gets promptly recognized, coated with antibodies and destroyed, then what's the safest place for that pathogen to set up shop and grow in your body? Probably that would be somewhere inside your own cells. The immune system has been trained to ignore your own cells, correct? In fact, some of the most successful human pathogens like viruses and the eukaryotic malarial parasite *Plasmodium falciparum* take just that approach. It's a tricky strategy, however. They can't get very far growing in just one body cell. So they need to hop from cell to cell and that often means putting some kind of marker or protein on the surface of your cells to assist in leaving one cell and entering the next one. And that marker is foreign! So a whole branch of your third line of defense has been designed for the fallen world of *intracellular* pathogens. It's called the *cell-mediated immune response,* and it's pictured in Figure 10.18.

The cell-mediated response begins in essentially the same way as the antibody-mediated response. In a lymph node, dendritic cells or macrophages feel a non-self surface and promptly engulf the sample. Soon, foreign surface molecules are presented on the surface of the cell (see Figure 10.18a). Two classes of T lymphocytes begin feeling the presented antigen in case their surface receptors are specific for it (see Figure 10.18b, c). Again, helper T cells with receptors specific for the foreign surface begin to divide to form a population. Another class of

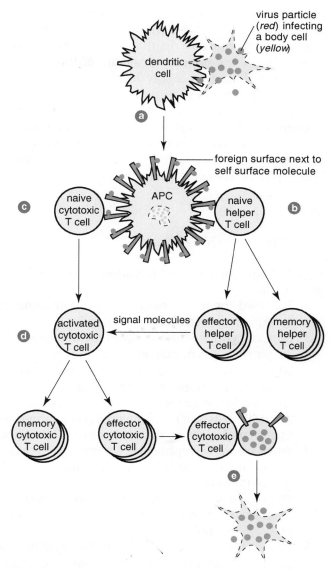

Figure 10.18 "Pathogen Wars Part II". A cell-mediated adaptive immune response that occurs in lymph nodes or the spleen. See text for details.

T cells, **cytotoxic T lymphocytes** (killer T cells), whose receptors are specific to the foreignness, also become activated. The green rectangles in the diagram indicate that these T cells are seeing antigens

antibody—a soluble multimeric protein produced by descendants of B cells; it recognizes and binds to a specific antigenic (foreign) surface, molecule, or cell.

cytotoxic T lymphocyte—a lymphocyte that matures in the thymus gland and recognizes and destroys host (self) cells that are infected by an intracellular parasite (i.e., a virus or bacterium).

(red circles) presented right next to other surface molecules that define the cell as "self". This recognition will be critical to their later roles. The stimulated helper T cell population again puts out signal molecules. These induce any local activated cytotoxic T cells to begin to proliferate in response (see Figure 10.18 d). These T cells now begin a recognition process throughout your body. Any time they find one of your body's cells that has surface foreignness right next to *normal self markers*, they secrete horribly toxic chemicals that punch large holes in the surface of these (infected) body cells and they soon die (see Figure 10.18e). In this way any of your body's cells that have "joined the other side" and are harboring or making pathogenic cells will be terminated by the cell-mediated portion of your third line of defense. Yes, a fallen world is jam-packed with pathogens that would sneak their foreignness past your sensory system's eyes. But whether they attempt either an intercellular or intracellular attack, your elegant immune system is designed to discover them, label them, and destroy them.

IN OTHER WORDS

1. The immune response has a third line of defense that is specific for any given pathogen that invades our tissues.
2. The third line of defense requires our immune system to distinguish between self cells or molecules and foreign or "non-self" cells or molecules.
3. Lymphocytes are the principle type of leukocyte involved in the third line of defense.
4. As lymphocytes mature in the thymus gland or bone marrow, those with receptors that would recognize and destroy self surfaces are eliminated leaving only those that seek out foreign surfaces.
5. Encounters between lymphocytes and foreign agents occur in lymph nodes that drain and filter our tissues and in the spleen that monitors foreignness in the bloodstream.
6. Dendritic cells and macrophages engulf non-self cells, degrade their structures, and present parts of their foreign molecules on their surfaces for T lymphocytes to detect.
7. When helper T lymphocytes are stimulated to divide in response to a foreign antigen, the resulting population functions by chemically signaling other classes of lymphocytes to divide in response to a foreign antigen they have detected.
8. When B lymphocytes are stimulated to divide in response to a foreign antigen, the resulting population functions by secreting antibodies that bind specifically to antigenic sites on the kind of foreign cell or molecule that stimulated B cell division in the first place.
9. Many pathogens avoid initial contact with host lymphocytes by quickly invading host cells and thus multiplying within a cell whose membrane surfaces are seen as self by the immune system.
10. When cytotoxic T lymphocytes are stimulated to divide in response to a foreign antigen, the resulting population functions by chemically attacking self cells whose surfaces also exhibit the foreign antigen that stimulated cytotoxic T cell division in the first place.
11. T cells differ from B cells in how they see antigen. B cells sense antigen on the surface of foreign cells. T cells sense it on the surfaces of your own infected cells because the antigen is right next to self surface marker proteins.

Preparing Your Immune System: The Preemptive Strike

Once exposed to something foreign, our adaptive immune system keeps a population of **memory lymphocytes** around that remember—and have receptors specific for—that nasty foreign object (see

memory lymphocyte—a class of B or T cell that does not differentiate immediately into antibody secretion or killing activity; it divides to form a population of cells specific for an antigen just encountered and waits for a second encounter to differentiate.

Figures 10.17, 10.18d). If we are ever re-infected with that same foreign entity, we can respond faster to the threat the second time! This wonderful immunologic memory is the basis for the valuable process called **vaccination.** When you receive a vaccine, you are receiving a dead or severely weakened form of the pathogen that would otherwise make you sick. Sometimes, the vaccine contains only certain molecular surface portions of the pathogen. Since these vaccine components are either: (1) dead pathogens, (2) weakened pathogens, or (3) only portions of the pathogen surface, they can't infect you. But their presence in your tissues allows your immune defenses to recognize that something foreign is present and to mount an immune response. That is why you sometimes feel a bit sick after being vaccinated. Later on, if you are exposed to a virulent form of that pathogen, your body already has immunologic memory built up and can mount an immune response much faster and more effectively than if you had not been vaccinated against that foreign invader.

Unfortunately, people with **HIV virus** infections do not respond well to vaccination. The virus invades and destroys their helper T lymphocytes (see Figure 10.19). Review the role of helper T cells in Figure 10.17 and 10.18. When helper T cell populations are depleted, your immune response isn't able to mount either a strong B cell or a strong killer T cell response to the vaccine. The HIV-positive individual just doesn't have much of a third-line of defense against pathogens anymore.

So as you are climbing stairs and touching handrails, your skin—your first line of defense—will prevent most germs from entering your body. If you have an open cut on your hand or forget to wash or sanitize your hands before grabbing that snack and eating, a second line of defense will turn on. Any pathogen resourceful enough to evade your macrophages or natural killer cells will generate a specific third-line attack by means of your adaptive immune system. If this third line of defense gets

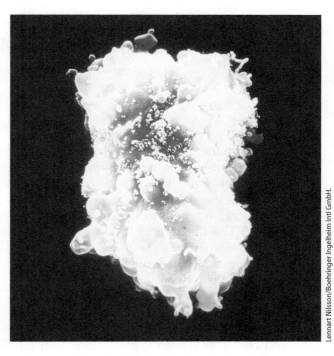

Figure 10.19 HIV Invasion. This color-modified scanning electron micrograph shows a helper T lymphocyte with a collection of HIV virus particles (blue) adsorbed to its surfaces. The viruses may hide inside this cell in a dormant state for several years, or they may begin to destroy the cell if it becomes sensitized to some foreign antigen.

Lennart Nilsson/Boehringer Ingelheim Intl GmbH.

involved, you may get sick while it is revving up, but you will generally conquer the pathogen and get better in a few days. Isn't it magnificent that we are able to defend ourselves against organisms our sensory systems are totally incapable of detecting?

vaccination—administering a preparation of killed microorganisms, living attenuated organisms, or parts of virulent organisms to produce or artificially increase immunity to a particular disease agent.

HIV virus—a noncellular pathogenic molecular machine composed of proteins and an RNA genome; causes human immunodeficiency or AIDS (acquired immune deficiency syndrome).

IN OTHER WORDS

1. Whenever B or T cell populations expand by cell division, one subpopulation of cells becomes a set of memory cells instead of secreting antibodies or attacking infected cells.
2. These memory cell populations can more quickly expand and attack a pathogen the second time it invades the host's tissues.
3. Vaccination generates these memory populations by using harmless vaccines to force B and T cells to respond to foreign antigen. When the real virulent pathogen arrives, the memory populations are present to attack it.

Standing at the top of the Washington Monument after climbing hundreds of stairs, you may notice a profound sense of hunger. While taking in the view, you grab a snack. Even before the food enters your mouth the digestion process starts. Your **salivary glands** are already producing saliva in anticipation of food. The function of the digestive system is to break down the foodstuffs we eat into small fragments that can be absorbed and then used for biosynthesis of the polymers our cells are made of. The food we eat is first broken down into monomers of the biomolecules covered in Chapter 4. Food is digested (or broken down) both mechanically and chemically. Both types of digestion take place in the **mouth** (see Figure 10.20); jaw muscles move the teeth and (aided by the tongue muscles) they break up the food mechanically while enzymes in **saliva** start chemical digestion. From the mouth,

food moves (via smooth muscle) down the esophagus into the **stomach**, where more chemical and much more mechanical digestion take place as the stomach muscles churn the food. After being mixed in the stomach, the food (now called **chyme**) is deposited into the **small intestine**, where most of the chemical digestion and **absorption** of nutrients into the bloodstream takes place (see Figure 10.21). Many enzymes from the **pancreas** along with **bile** that was generated in the **liver** and stored in the

salivary gland—an organ of the digestive system whose tissues synthesize digestive enzymes like amylase that degrade starch to simple sugars.

mouth—the entrance to the digestive system where both mechanical and chemical degradation of food begins.

saliva—a fluid produced by salivary glands that lubricates food and begins the digestion of starch polymer within the food.

esophagus—a muscular tube that carries food from the mouth to the stomach for further mechanical and chemical digestion.

stomach—a muscular organ that receives, temporarily stores, and digests food. Hydrochloric acid and the enzyme pepsin work to degrade protein structure here.

chyme—partially digested food that exits the stomach and proceeds through the small intestine by means of waves of smooth muscle contraction.

small intestine—a 21-foot-long tubular organ of the digestive system where mechanical digestion, chemical digestion, and nutrient absorption occur.

absorption—the transfer of digested food (nutrients) across the epithelial lining of the digestive tract and into surrounding capillary beds or lymphatic vessels for distribution to the body.

pancreas—an organ of the digestive system generating degradative enzymes; it is also glandular, secreting the hormones insulin and glucagon.

bile—a dark-green bitter fluid product of the liver that aids in the emulsification of fat globules into smaller fat droplets facilitating the digestion of fat molecules.

liver—an accessory organ of the digestive system; it processes and stores glycogen, decomposes old red blood cells, synthesizes blood plasma proteins, and hormones; it also detoxifies many toxins and drugs.

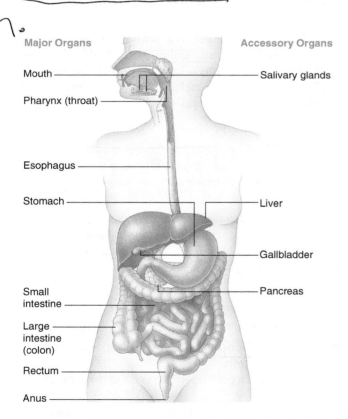

Major Organs   Accessory Organs

Mouth

Pharynx (throat)

Esophagus

Stomach

Small intestine

Large intestine (colon)

Rectum

Anus

Salivary glands

Liver

Gallbladder

Pancreas

Figure 10.20 The Human Digestive System. The major and accessory organs are described in the text.

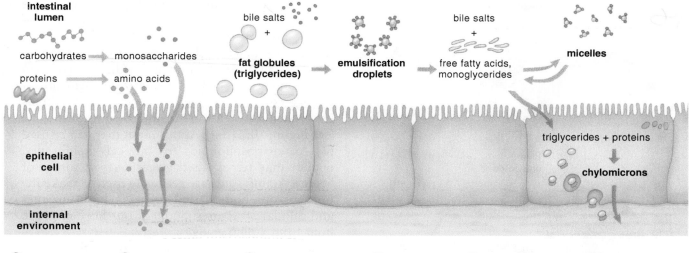

intestinal lumen

carbohydrates → monosaccharides

proteins → amino acids

bile salts +

fat globules (triglycerides)

emulsification droplets

bile salts +

free fatty acids, monoglycerides

micelles

triglycerides + proteins

chylomicrons

epithelial cell

internal environment

ⓐ Enzymes from the pancreas and epithelial cells degrade proteins and polysaccharides to amino acids and simple sugars.

ⓑ Active transport pulls amino acids and simple sugars first into the intestinal epithelium, then into blood capillaries.

ⓒ Muscular contractions in the small intestine mechanically break fat globules into smaller droplets. Bile salts from the liver keep the droplets separate.

ⓓ Enzymes from pancreas digest fat droplets down to fatty acids and glycerol.

ⓔ High concentrations of fatty acids and glycerol form tiny droplets called micelles. These difuse into the epithelial cell layer.

ⓕ New triglycerides (fats) form in the epithelial lining cells; combined with specific proteins they form chylomicrons--fat transporting particles bound for the lymphatic system.

Figure 10.21 Absorption in the Small Intestine.

gallbladder are emptied into the small intestine to help break down proteins, carbohydrates, and fats into monomers that can be absorbed into the bloodstream. The final stop of food's journey is the **large intestine**, where most of the remaining water and some **vitamins** are absorbed before any indigestible material and wastes finally exit the body as **feces.**

Our bodies break down carbohydrates such as starches into simple sugars like glucose, while proteins are broken down into single amino acids, and triglycerides (fats) are broken down into smaller monomers such as fatty acids and glycerol. These nutrients need to be absorbed into the bloodstream, but homeostasis must also be maintained. If the nutrients were absorbed directly into our systemic circulation, homeostasis would be badly disrupted every time we ate! To prevent this, we were designed with a **hepatic portal system** (see Figure 10.22).

In most tissues, arteries lead to capillaries, where exchange between blood and tissues takes place, and then the blood flows into veins and back to the heart. In other words, from the time blood leaves the heart, it flows through only one capillary bed before it is returned to the heart. The hepatic portal system is different in that it contains two capillary beds. The first is in the intestines, where digested

nutrients are absorbed. These capillaries coalesce to form a large **portal vein** that carries blood not back to the heart but to a second capillary bed in the liver, the largest organ in your body. There, enzymes process the absorbed nutrients and then release them

gallbladder—a small accessory organ that stores bile produced in the liver until needed for the digestion process.

large intestine—a 5-foot-long tubular organ of the digestive system that receives indigestible chyme residues from the small intestine; water reabsorption and some vitamin absorption occur here.

vitamin—an organic compound that is required in very small amounts as a cofactor or coenzyme for many vital metabolic processes.

feces—the relatively dry, compacted product of the large intestine consisting of indigestible wastes from digestion and large numbers of bacteria that use the waste as nutrients.

hepatic portal system—those capillaries and vessels that carry nutrient-laden blood from the small intestinal epithelium to the liver for processing and control of nutrient levels.

portal vein—the vessel that carries blood between the capillary beds of the small intestine and those of the liver.

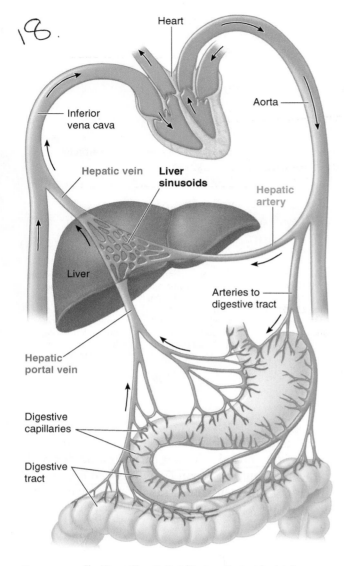

Figure 10.22 The Human Hepatic Portal System. See text for details.

Source: P. L. Senger, 2003, Pathways to Pregnancy and Parturition, 2nd ed., Current Conceptions Inc., Washington State University Research & Technology Park, pp. 16, 17

The carbohydrate monomers we absorb in the intestine—mainly glucose, fructose, and galactose—can be immediately distributed by the liver to the rest of the body's cells to be used as energy to generate ATP (see Section 6.7). Or the liver can store simple sugars by polymerizing them into a storage compound called glycogen. Dietary lipids get broken down, absorbed, and then reconstituted (see Figure 10.21d–f). At this point they can be used to create phospholipids for our cell membranes, or they may remain as triglycerides for storage of energy. Amino acids are generally used to make the proteins our bodies need to make both enzymes and cellular structures. Some of our hormones are built from amino acids.

So, that snack you eat at the top of the Monument will be broken down into monomers of glucose, amino acids, and small lipids. The food is moved along the digestive tract by the action of the muscular system; the nutrients are absorbed and carried through the body by the cardiovascular system, and the sense of hunger before your meal and the sense of satisfaction after it are much influenced by hormones of the endocrine system. Control over the entire digestion process is carried out by the parasympathetic nervous system, which will be discussed in Section 10.8. Consider again the design of the digestive system. Absence of the muscular, nervous, and cardiovascular systems would render it useless. The Designer—whether Father God or Mother Nature—had to see the entire picture before designing the individual pieces because Life Is Internally (Highly) Integrated.

into the **hepatic vein** of the systemic bloodstream. After returning to the heart, the nutrients are then spread throughout the body and used as needed.

hepatic vein—the vessel that carries blood between the capillary beds of the liver and the systemic circulation returning to the heart.

IN OTHER WORDS

1. The nervous system must in some way control digestion because anticipation of food initiates secretion of digestive enzymes.
2. Digestion begins in the mouth, where food is mechanically broken up by teeth and chemically broken up by enzymes that begin starch degradation.
3. Swallowed food travels the esophagus to the stomach, where mechanical and chemical degradation continue. Here in an acidic environment, enzymes degrade protein.

4. The resulting chyme is mechanically pushed in discrete quantities into the small intestine, where all major biopolymers are degraded and their monomers are absorbed.
5. The pancreas supplies some of the digestive enzymes used in the small intestine; the liver supplies bile salts for degradation of lipids (fats) in the small intestine.
6. In the large intestine, water used in digestion is reabsorbed and the indigestible material is compacted to form the fecal mass to be eliminated.
7. Complex carbohydrates are degraded to simple sugars, proteins to amino acids, and lipids to fatty acids and glycerol.
8. The concentrations of the resulting nutrients are adjusted and controlled by the liver. A portal vein leads from the intestine to the liver carrying blood whose nutrient levels need adjustment.
9. The hepatic vein carries blood with optimal nutrient levels back to the systemic circulation for use by the entire body.
10. Nutrients from the bloodstream are then used to replace worn structures and to produce new macromolecular structures and organelles as cells divide and grow.

THE HUMAN URINARY SYSTEM

As you climb those Monument stairs, your body produces a lot of molecular waste. For example, during every second of your climb, 2 million red blood cells wear out and are degraded. (No wonder you feel tired.) All that spent hemoglobin from those cells has to be degraded somewhere, somehow. The heme groups from each hemoglobin molecule (see Section 4.6) are one of those degradation products. They too need to be degraded, otherwise heme groups would just accumulate in the body. Heme's breakdown is a complicated story but one of the products is urobilinogen, which the liver simply releases into the blood. It's yellow in color. How might it finally leave the body? Hmm.

Urobilinogen, like so many other waste products, is eventually filtered out in the urinary system. (It's what makes the urine yellow.) The urinary system is critically important to us. It is designed to rid our bodies of excess fluids and soluble wastes. Its centerpiece is a truly amazing machine: the human **kidney**. Within it, the blood goes through an elegant filtration, reabsorption, and secretion system with the result that the composition and volume of your blood and tissue fluids are kept within narrow limits, and yet somehow, important nutrients are preserved while wastes like urea and the products of metabolized drugs are neatly eliminated. Incredible!

What does the kidney do with what's to be discarded? From the kidneys, the waste from your blood and tissues—now in the form of **urine**—goes through ducts called **ureters** to the urinary **bladder,** where it is stored until a convenient time for voiding (see Figure 10.23). When we choose to void (or the bladder chooses for us because it is so full), urine leaves the bladder via the **urethra** and exits the body.

Let's look more closely at this system. How do kidneys perform their amazing role? Generally speaking, they (1) filter the blood, (2) reabsorb what the body needs to keep, and (3) secrete things the body definitely needs to be rid of. (Just imagine that your name is "Natural Selection" and you are tasked with designing a filtration system that will manage those three challenges exquisitely!)

The unit of function in the kidney is called a **nephron.** It's a blood filtration unit followed by a

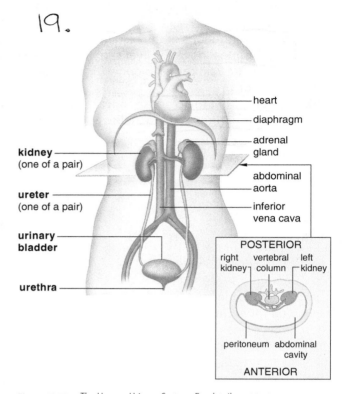

Figure 10.23   The Human Urinary System. For details, see text.

kidney— an organ of the urinary system that filters waste from the blood, controls water and ion content in the blood, and returns useful substances to the blood.

urine—the fluid that results from filtration of the blood and selective secretion activities of the kidney; the resultant fluid is voided from the bladder.

ureter—a duct within the urinary system that carries urine from its formation site in the kidney to its storage site in the urinary bladder.

bladder—an organ of the urinary system that stores urine prior to voiding.

urethra—a duct that extends from the base of the bladder to the exterior of the body; urine is excreted through this duct.

nephron—a multicellular filtration and reabsorption unit of the kidney; consists of a Bowman's capsule (filtration), distal and proximal tubules (reabsorption and secretion), and a loop of Henle.

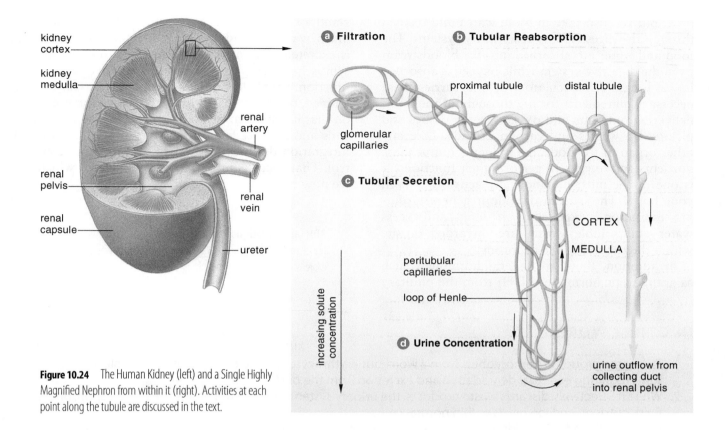

Figure 10.24 The Human Kidney (left) and a Single Highly Magnified Nephron from within it (right). Activities at each point along the tubule are discussed in the text.

series of three consecutive tubules that form urine (see Figure 10.24). Each kidney has about a million of these nephrons, and they are very effective machines! As the blood passes into the filtration unit of the nephron, very leaky capillaries allow water and small molecules to exit the blood and enter the front end of the kidney tubule as filtrate. Cells, plasma proteins, and some drugs are too large to pass through the holes in the capillaries, so they stay in the blood. The nephron now begins to reabsorb useful nutrients. Most of the water, ions, and small nutrients that escaped through the filter are now reabsorbed into capillaries that are wrapped around the nephron tubules. This works well because the nephron was designed so that a narrow portion of it—the loop of Henle—goes through a kidney region where salt concentration is higher. This means the water concentration in the region is lower. Water diffuses out of the tubule, leaving the developing urine more concentrated. All of this water and nutrient reabsorption is finely tuned in order to maintain proper blood volume and ion concentrations. The kidney has sensors that control how much water is removed from the body and how much is retained in the blood. So the nephrons

are really serving the circulatory system by avoiding low or high extremes of blood pressure. If a lot of water is reabsorbed, the urine produced will be concentrated; however, if more water is left in the filtrate, the urine will be dilute and have more volume. Finally, beginning within the proximal tubule, waste molecules are secreted from the capillaries into the nephron to be excreted. About half of the urea in the blood leaves the capillaries for the tubule as the filtrate moves along. At various regions along the distal tubule, specific, unneeded substances are selectively bound to capillary walls and transported out of the bloodstream and into the maturing filtrate. This is the point at which—arriving from the liver—caffeine's breakdown products leave your bloodstream. Then, happily, you can go to sleep!

This elegant system does not simply sit by itself monitoring blood levels of water and various substances. It is highly integrated into other body systems. Besides its obvious relationship to the circulatory system, the urinary system is closely tied to both the respiratory and digestive systems. We have already seen how the digestive system's liver prepares waste amino groups to be excreted as urea. But we also take in food, water, and oxygen through the digestive and respiratory systems. The food and water are absorbed into the bloodstream from the digestive system while oxygen is absorbed in the lungs. The circulatory system carries these necessary ingredients for life throughout the body, delivering nutrients and oxygen to the tissues and picking up wastes and carbon dioxide. Like any other organ of the body, the kidney requires these nutrients and oxygen to perform their functions. It is one of the most metabolically active organs in your body! The carbon dioxide it generates during respiration is expelled by the lungs, and excess water and soluble wastes are discarded on-site within the tubules of the nephrons.

In addition, there are several hormones, such as antidiuretic hormone (**ADH**) from the pituitary gland of the endocrine system, that affect how much water the kidneys reabsorb and how much is excreted in urine. Under stressful situations the sympathetic nervous system will also affect kidney function. So, like the other systems we've so far examined, there is so much internal integration going on that it is hard to state strictly where one system ends and another begins. Yet somehow, all of this integration does seem to relate to a focus of control. That focus is in the nervous system to which we now turn.

ADH (antidiuretic hormone)—secreted by the hypothalamus gland; makes kidney tubule walls more permeable to water so that more water returns to the blood.

IN OTHER WORDS

1. The heme groups in hemoglobins from a worn-out erythrocyte are one example of many molecular structures requiring eventual degradation and excretion from the body.
2. While it selectively discards waste products, the urinary system carefully maintains the body's appropriate fluid, nutrient, and ion levels within normal limits.
3. Urine, produced in the kidneys, is transported through the ureters to the bladder, where it is stored until it is voided from the body through the urethra.
4. Nephrons are multicellular units of function within the kidneys. They first filter the blood; they then reabsorb all valuable water ions and nutrients and finally collect and discard all molecular wastes in the urine.
5. Reabsorption of water depends on the nephron's tubule passing through kidney tissues with a higher salt content such that the water diffuses out of the tubule and back into the bloodstream.
6. Along the capillary walls that surround the nephron's tubule are a variety of receptors that selectively bind and transfer a variety of waste molecules from the blood into the tubule to be excreted.
7. The urinary system is intimately interfunctional with the circulatory, respiratory, digestive, and endocrine systems.

What commands the muscles in your legs to move as you walk up the steps to the top of the Washington Monument? What signals your heart to beat faster and your respiratory rate to increase so your muscles get more oxygen? What causes the blood vessels supplying blood to your muscles to dilate and the vessels supplying your digestive system to constrict until you have reached the top and started eating your snack? It is your nervous system! The nervous system is one of the control centers of your body; the other is the endocrine system. In general, the nervous system controls your responses to the external environment while the endocrine system maintains homeostasis of the internal environment. The most common cell in the nervous system is the **neuron.**

Neuron Structure and Function

Neurons are specialized cells that deliver electrical and chemical signals throughout the body. Their impressive length in one dimension admirably supports their signal-carrying role. They consist of **cell bodies** from which long slender projections called **dendrites** and **axons** extend (see Figure 10.25). Dendrites bring nervous signals toward the cell _21._

_22._

neuron—within the nervous system, a cell designed to transmit a nerve impulse from one location within the body to another.

cell body—that part of a neuron that contains the cell nucleus and other major organelles; the focus of information expression within the neuron.

dendrite—a process extending away from the cell body of a neuron; carries a nerve impulse from some other excitable cell toward the cell body of the neuron.

axon—a process extending away from the cell body of a neuron; carries a nerve impulse toward some other excitable cell and away from the cell body of the neuron.

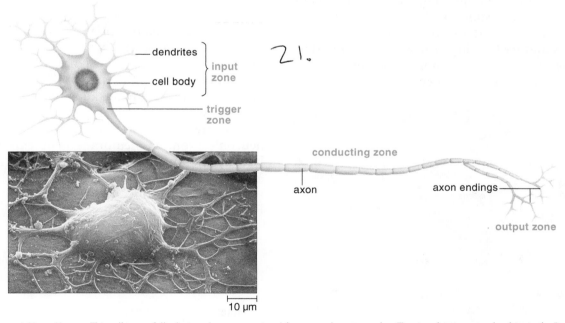

_21._

Figure 10.25   A Motor Neuron. This cell is carefully designed to move a signal from one place to another. The signal arrives at a dendrite in the "input zone", gets repropagated at the "trigger zone", gets transmitted over a considerable distance called the "conducting zone" and gets delivered at the "output zone". The signal travels in one direction only, in a motor neuron, from the central nervous system to an effector organ such as a muscle.

body, whereas axons carry them away. A **nerve** is a bundle of axons from functionally related neurons traveling through the body together.

Neurons, like all our excitable cells, have a resting membrane potential. While skeletal muscle cells have a resting membrane potential of -95 mV (see Section 10.2), neurons have one of -70 mV, again with the inside of the cell membrane more negative than the outside. When one neuron communicates with another neuron, it is similar in many ways to a neuron signaling a skeletal muscle to contract (see Section 10.2). When an impulse traveling down one neuron arrives at the end of its axon, it causes the release of a neurotransmitter that binds to receptors on the next (second) neuron. This signal binding in turn opens ion channels on the second neuron's membrane (see Figures 10.8, 10.26). If these open channels allow positive ions to enter the cell and negative ions to leave the cell, the membrane potential will be reduced (there will be less of a gradient of electrical charge). If the potential is reduced enough—to a certain **threshold** level—an action potential (an electrical signal) will be generated in the second neuron. Action potentials are the long-distance communication that neurons use. An action potential arriving at the end of an axon will cause neurotransmitters to be released. In neural communication with skeletal muscle, the neurotransmitter is always acetylcholine, but in signals between one neuron and another, there are many sorts of neurotransmitters. The binding of these chemical signals to the second neuron's receptors can be excitatory (leading to an action potential) or inhibitory (making the membrane potential of the second neuron even more negative and less likely

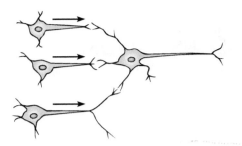

Figure 10.27 Neural Inputs Converge. Sometimes several neurons can input information to one neuron.

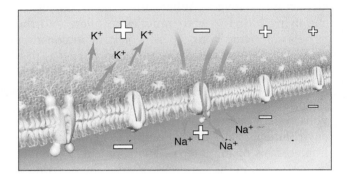

Figure 10.28 Membrane Repolarization. A signal (action potential) is moving along an axon from left to right in this diagram. As soon as an action potential has run by (middle), potassium ion channels open (left) allowing potassium ions out of the cell to restore a membrane potential similar to the original resting potential. This sudden reversal reveals the wisdom of the Designer in using a pump to produce opposing gradients of different but similarly charged ions.

to initiate an action potential signal). But—again—life is (even more) complex than this. The axons of multiple neurons can send signals to a single neuron cell body (see Figure 10.27). That neuron then filters those signals to make sure an appropriate response is sent as necessary.

Just after an action potential moves down the neuron's axon, its membrane is quickly repolarized by the opening of potassium ion channels. These allow potassium to leave the cell, quickly restoring the resting membrane potential (see Figure 10.28).

nerve—a collection of neuronal processes, usually axons from multiple neurons, travelling together inside a protective myelin sheath.

threshold—(in a neuron) the membrane potential difference that must be reached before an action potential can begin initiated and a fresh impulse sent along the neuronal membrane.

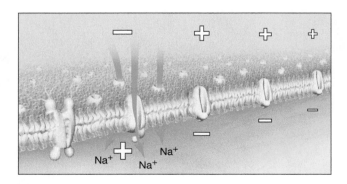

Figure 10.26 Signal Conversion at the Synapse. When a neurotransmitter causes local ion channels to open, sodium ions, which were being slowly pumped out are suddenly allowed to rush in, reversing the membrane polarity. If the voltage change is steep enough, an action potential begins propagating along the neuronal membrane.

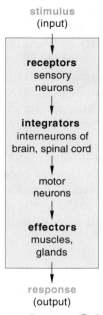

stimulus
(input)

↓

receptors
sensory
neurons

↓

integrators
interneurons of
brain, spinal cord

↓

motor
neurons

↓

effectors
muscles,
glands

↓

response
(output)

Figure 10.29 The Role of the Nervous System. Three classes of neurons are here used to illustrate how we respond to changes in our circumstances. This pattern can be as simple as a reflex arc or as complicated as solving a calculus problem.

brain or spinal cord to the proper area of the body to carry out that response. In this way the nervous system controls our bodies' responses to the external environment or carries out our decisions, such as stopping on the Monument steps to catch our breath.

sensory neuron—a cell that conducts action potentials (signals) away from stimulus receptors in the body and toward the central nervous system.

brain—an organ of the central nervous system; the coordinating center of the entire nervous system; all voluntary actions and many involuntary ones are responses that originate there.

spinal cord—an elongated tubular bundle of nerves and supportive tissues extending from the brain; supports transmission of signals between the brain and the rest of the body.

central nervous system—that portion of the nervous system that includes the brain and spinal cord; functions to integrate the signals it receives from the peripheral nervous system and coordinates responses to those signals.

motor neuron—a cell that conducts action potentials (signals) away from the central nervous system to an effector organ such as a muscle or a gland; part of the nervous systems' response machinery.

22. 23.

Sensory neurons carry signals toward the brain and spinal cord that will make us aware of conditions that we may need to respond to (see Figure 10.29). Once the **central nervous system**—the brain and spinal cord—determines a suitable response, **motor neurons** carry the signal from the

IN OTHER WORDS

1. The nervous system has control over every other system of the human body.
2. The unit of function of the nervous system is the nerve cell, or neuron.
3. The neuron has three structural elements to it: the cell body, where most of metabolism occurs; the dendrites, which are processes from the cell body that receive signals; and the axons, which are processes from the cell body that transmit signals to the next excitable cell.
4. A nerve is a bundle of axonal processes from multiple neurons. The processes are all going to a similar area or organ of the body.
5. A nerve impulse traveling along a neuron is nothing more than a rapid depolarization across the neuronal membrane achieved by the sudden opening of sodium ion channels.
6. When the depolarization reaches the end of the neuronal membrane, it must become a chemical signal to cross the synapse to the next neuron.
7. In the synapse, the neurotransmitter must produce a sufficiently strong (threshold) depolarization in order for the signal to continue along the next neuron.
8. A neuron often synapses with multiple other neurons; some have neurotransmitters that are excitatory, others are inhibitory.
9. The summation of neurotransmitter inputs will determine whether a threshold depolarization is reached causing the neuron to further propagate the signal.
10. Once an inrush of sodium ions causes a depolarization to occur, an immediate outrush of potassium ions restores membrane polarization so that the depolarization acts as a wave passing quickly over the length of the neuron.
11. Sensory neurons carry impulses away from receptors and toward the brain and spinal cord; motor neurons carry impulses away from the brain and spinal cord toward effector organs such as muscles and glands.

Nervous Reflexes

Some actions require a lot of combined neural signals and involve conscious thought. However, other actions involve no thought at all. Such automatic and predictable responses to certain stimuli are called **reflexes**. The simplest of these is the spinal reflex in which the signaling does not even involve the brain, but is operated on entirely by the spinal cord. The most familiar of these is the patellar reflex. When the ligament below the knee is tapped suddenly, as in a medical examination (see Figure 10.30), it stretches the muscles on the front of the thigh, which triggers a preprogrammed response to prevent overstretching the muscles. The body protects the muscle from being overly stretched by contracting the front thigh muscles while at the same time relaxing the back thigh muscles to allow the front ones to contract. The result is that your knee is straightened and you give the doctor a little kick. By tapping on the tendon, the doctor is testing the ability of a nervous signal to travel to the CNS and back to your leg.

What an elegant if unconscious reflex: A stretch **receptor** in the muscle detects the stretch and starts an action potential (see Figure 10.30). There are sensory neurons that then carry the signal that the receptor triggered to the spinal cord, which is an **integration center**. In the spinal cord, the sensory neuron may synapse with an integrating neuron which synapses directly with a motor neuron that will carry the message to the **effector** organ (in this case the muscles). In some cases the sensory neuron synapses directly with a motor neuron. These five components, the receptor, sensory neuron, the integration center, the motor neuron, and the effector, make up a **reflex arc**. The integration center is so called because multiple inputs can be integrated there. The CNS processes or integrates all the incoming information and then generates the appropriate response.

As you are climbing the stairs of the Washington Monument, several receptors in your legs are constantly sending signals to your brain to ensure that your muscles are not overstretched to the point of damage and that you remain upright as you climb (posture adjustment).

reflex—a suddenly, involuntary response to a stimulus.

receptor—a cell, part of a cell, or a tissue that converts a stimulus from the external or internal environment into a signal (action potential) that can travel sensory neurons to the central nervous system for interpretation and response.

integration center—a single interneuron or a collection of neurons that connects sensory and motor neurons to each other such that stimuli result in an appropriate response.

effector—a muscle or gland that can carry out a response to a stimulus that has been received and interpreted by the central nervous system.

reflex arc—a neural pathway that controls a reflexive response; sometimes only five elements in length: the receptor, a sensory neuron, an interneuron, a motor neuron, and an effector.

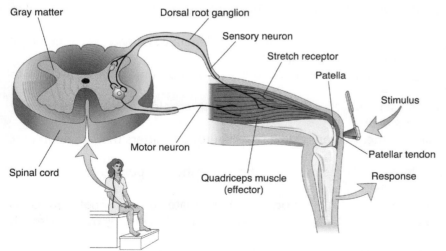

Figure 10.30 The Reflex Arc. When the doctor strikes your patelar tendon, stretch receptors in the thigh muscle initiate an action potential that travels over a sensory neuron to the spinal cord. There it synapses with a variety of neurons in the integration center. Some will take the signal to the brain that "you've been hit!" But before you are aware of the fact, the signal has crossed a synapse between the sensory neuron and a motor neuron and has already caused the thigh muscle to contract, raising your lower leg.

Gray matter
Dorsal root ganglion
Sensory neuron
Stretch receptor
Patella
Stimulus
Motor neuron
Patellar tendon
Spinal cord
Quadriceps muscle (effector)
Response

1. Reflexes are rapid responses to stimuli that require no conscious thought and minimal integrative activity in the CNS.
2. In the patellar reflex arc, the stimulus is a tap with a rubber hammer; receptors in the thigh muscle initiate an action potential in sensory neuron dendrites in the thigh.
3. Action potentials in sensory neurons cause threshold depolarizations within dendrites of neurons in the spinal cord.
4. The dendrites of a motor neuron lie in the spinal cord even though its cell body lies outside; threshold-level signals from its dendrites can cause it to depolarize and signal the thigh muscle to contract.

The nervous system controls much of what your body does. It can be divided into two main sections: the CNS and the **peripheral nervous system** (PNS; see Figure 10.31a). The CNS consists of the

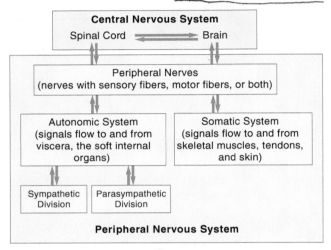

Central Nervous System

Spinal Cord ⟷ Brain

Peripheral Nerves
(nerves with sensory fibers, motor fibers, or both)

Autonomic System
(signals flow to and from viscera, the soft internal organs)

Somatic System
(signals flow to and from skeletal muscles, tendons, and skin)

Sympathetic Division | **Parasympathetic Division**

Peripheral Nervous System

a

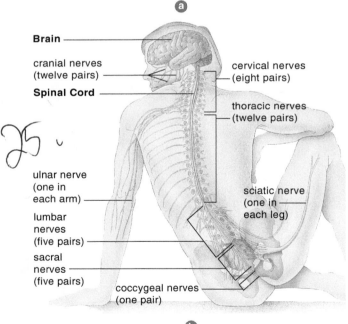

Brain

cranial nerves
(twelve pairs)

Spinal Cord

cervical nerves
(eight pairs)

thoracic nerves
(twelve pairs)

ulnar nerve
(one in
each arm)

sciatic nerve
(one in
each leg)

lumbar
nerves
(five pairs)

sacral
nerves
(five pairs)

coccygeal nerves
(one pair)

b

Figure 10.31 The Human Nervous System. **(a)** a diagram of the major divisions of the nervous system and their functional relationships to each other. **(b)** The structural arrangement of the major, visible parts of the nervous system. The brain and spinal cord constitute the Central Nervous System. All other named nerves are part of the Peripheral Nervous System.

brain and spinal cord. The rest of the nervous tissue in the body belongs to the PNS (see Figure 10.31b). The PNS is functionally divided into sensory and motor branches. The sensory branch—also called the *afferent branch*—carries signals on their way to the CNS; the motor branch—also called the *efferent branch*—carries signals traveling away from the CNS. This motor branch of the PNS is further subdivided into the **somatic** (voluntary) and **autonomic** (involuntary) nervous systems. Signals traveling out over the somatic system go to effectors you are consciously controlling, like your skeletal muscles. The autonomic nervous system (ANS) on the other hand, carries signals to effectors you do not consciously control such as your smooth muscles or glands. Stomach or bladder activities are examples of these.

And finally (for our purposes), this autonomic portion of the efferent system can be divided into **parasympathetic** and **sympathetic** nervous systems. The parasympathetic system keeps your involuntary body functions quietly operant while you are essentially at rest while the sympathetic system depresses those same functions and activates others that are appropriate to stressful situations. Let's examine the parts of the nervous system more closely.

peripheral nervous system—the collection of all nerves and ganglia that lies outside of the brain and spinal cord.

somatic system—that portion of the peripheral nervous system associated with voluntary control of skeletal muscles and with sensory reception of stimuli such as hearing or touch.

autonomic system (ANS)—that portion of the peripheral nervous system that acts to control involuntary functions such as visceral activity, perspiration, or heart rate.

parasympathetic system—the branch of the autonomic nervous system that stimulates resting state activities such as digestion, urination, or sexual arousal.

sympathetic system—the branch of the autonomic nervous system that stimulates the fight-or-flight activities associated with stressful situations.

1. The human nervous system is highly organized; its parts reflect separate aspects of its role in receiving, interpreting, and acting upon information from the environment and the human will.

The Central Nervous System *Xe.*

Structurally, the CNS consists of the brain and spinal cord. Functionally, it has a variety of separate regions (see Figure 10.32) whose development was outlined in Section 9.3c. The large part of the brain that occupies most of the space within the cranial bones is the cerebrum. It has several lobes, or areas that handle different sensory and motor functions (see Figure 10.33a). Conscious thought, problem-solving skills (understanding biology textbooks), speech production, voluntary movement and other complicated processes occur in the cerebral cortex—the thin outermost layer of the cerebrum.

At the base of the brain is the cerebellum (see Figure 10.32), which controls coordination of our motor movements. Its capabilities are beautifully demonstrated in gymnastic exercises such as competitive routines on the balance beam. Under the cerebrum, almost in the center of the brain, the embryonic region known as the *diencephalon* has differentiated to form the thalamus and hypothalamus (see Figure 10.32) along with ventricles (see Figure 10.33b) or cavities that produce and contain the **cerebral-spinal fluid** (CSF) that cushions

and protects the brain and spinal cord. The thalamus sorts incoming information from the PNS and sends it to the proper place in the cerebrum. The hypothalamus controls the ANS and much of the endocrine system; it also regulates food and water intake, sleep and wake cycles, and body temperature (see Section 11.5). In addition, the hypothalamus is part of the **limbic system**—the emotional area of the CNS (see Figure 10.33c).

Extending posteriorly from the diencephalon is the brainstem that contains the midbrain, pons, and medulla oblongata (see Figure 10.32). When you step into the bright sunlight at the top of the Monument, the midbrain controls the constriction of the pupils of your eyes. It handles other visual and auditory reflex reactions as well. The pons controls still other

cerebrospinal fluid—a clear, colorless body fluid internal to the meninges of the brain; the brain and spinal cord float in this medium.

limbic system—a set of brain regions such as the hippocampus and amygdala that are broadly involved in emotions, behavior, long-term memory, and olfaction.

Figure 10.32 The Human Brain. A photo of a section right through the middle of the brain; the right hemisphere is shown. See text for descriptions.

The Human Brain and Associated Structures

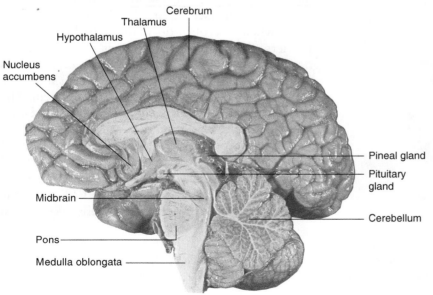

Cerebrum
Thalamus
Hypothalamus
Nucleus accumbens
Midbrain
Pons
Medulla oblongata
Pineal gland
Pituitary gland
Cerebellum

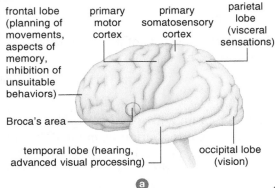

frontal lobe (planning of movements, aspects of memory, inhibition of unsuitable behaviors)

primary motor cortex

primary somatosensory cortex

parietal lobe (visceral sensations)

Broca's area

temporal lobe (hearing, advanced visual processing)

occipital lobe (vision)

a

Figure 10.33 Regional Diagrams of the Human Brain. **(a)** major sensory and integrating centers of the human cerebrum. Broca's region controls speech functions. **(b)** diagram showing spaces within the brain (in blue) where cerebrospinal fluid is produced and collects. **(c)** regions of the brain that together comprise the limbic system—the emotional center of the brain. The amygdala region converts cognitive inputs into a stimulus for the sympathetic division of the ANS to become more active.

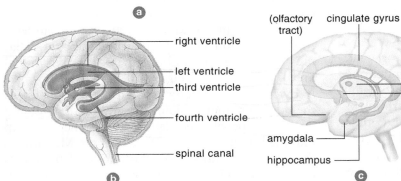

right ventricle

left ventricle

third ventricle

fourth ventricle

spinal canal

b

(olfactory tract)   cingulate gyrus   thalamus

amygdala

hippocampus

hypothalamus

c

automatic functions such as swallowing, and the medulla oblongata controls heart and breathing rates.

Directly beneath and continuous with the medulla oblongata is the spinal cord that connects nerves from the peripheral nervous system to the brain (see Figure 10.34). It contains both sensory and motor neurons and also handles some simple reflexes that do not require conscious thought, such as the patellar reflex discussed in Section 10.7.

Just one element of the wisdom of the CNS is the sophistication of the structures that protect it despite its physical prominence. Significant protection against physical trauma is afforded by the skeletal system, specifically the cranial bones and the spinal vertebrae. But beneath this mineral-laden superstructure and surrounding both the brain and spinal cord are three connective tissue layers called **meninges** that help prevent infection in this critical control system (see Figure 10.34). On rare occasions when microbes do manage to breech these barriers, the resulting infection is called *meningitis*. Within this protective series of membranes is an additional cushion formed by the CSF in the ventricles of the diencephalon and brainstem. The brain and spinal cord thus float in a shock-resistant environment behind three separate tissue layers.

Protection occurs at the chemical level as well! The CSF is a filtrate produced from the blood, but it is not continuous with the blood (see Figure 10.35). Cells lining the ventricles filter the CSF from the capillaries in the ventricles. These cells take needed

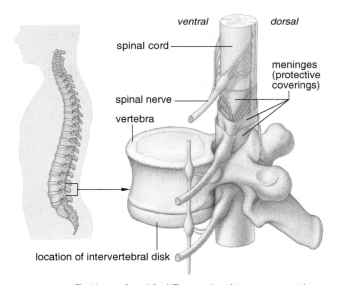

ventral

dorsal

spinal cord

meninges (protective coverings)

spinal nerve

vertebra

location of intervertebral disk

Figure 10.34 The Human Spinal Cord. The spinal cord is continuous with the brain stem. Here it's shown in relationship to the vertebrae of the spinal column that protects it. Notice the three layers of tough connective tissue (the meninges) that surround and protect both the brain and spinal cord.

meninges—a system of multiple membrane layers that surround the parts of the central nervous system.

The Blood Brain Barrier

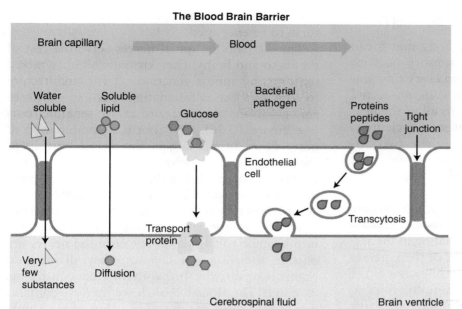

Figure 10.35 The Blood Brain Barrier. The endothelial layer of cells lining brain capillaries are highly selective and have tight junctions between them. The majority of water-soluble compounds and proteins are excluded. No foreign cells can cross the barrier. Only solutes useful for brain protection and nutrition are brought across either by diffusion (of lipids), transport (of glucose) or vesicles (for certain proteins). The latter process is called transcytosis.

substances such as glucose from the blood to the filtrate. They are carried right through the cells by transport proteins or inside of vesicles and are then emptied into the ventricles to the inside of the cellular lining. This carefully monitored separation of the CSF and blood is called the **blood-brain barrier,** and it helps keeps potential pathogens in our blood from infecting our brains. The only things that can diffuse from the blood to the CSF are substances that are either lipid-soluble (because they can cross the plasma membrane of the cells lining the ventricles), or very small molecules (such as oxygen, carbon dioxide, and hormones). All other substances require selective transport by proteins or in vesicles, and these are easily controlled.

Human designers have carefully arranged protective systems and structures around buildings—buildings critical to the welfare of our nation—such as the Central Intelligence Agency. Clearly, a high-profile system that closely controls all the other activities of our bodies is protected quite well by an elegantly conceived system of bone, membranes, cells, and fluids.

blood-brain barrier—the separation of blood from cerebrospinal and brain fluids that is maintained by tight junctions between endothelial cells that surround the blood capillaries that enter brain tissue.

IN OTHER WORDS

1. The CNS consists of the brain and spinal cord.
2. The cerebrum functions in event interpretation, conscious thought, problem solving, and voluntary actions; the cerebellum functions in the coordination of complex muscular actions involved in movement.
3. Beneath the cerebrum, the diencephalon region of the embryonic brain differentiates into the thalamus and hypothalamus regions; the thalamus coordinates signals from the PNS to the CNS, and the hypothalamus coordinates activities in the endocrine system.
4. The midbrain, pons, and medulla regions of the brain receive input from and control a variety of involuntary functions ranging from pupillary size in the eye to the heart rate.
5. The spinal cord receives the spinal nerves of the PNS and coordinates sensory and motor responses to both voluntary and involuntary functions throughout the body.
6. The CNS is protected by the cranial bones, spinal vertebrae, three meningeal layers of connective tissue, and the cushioning effect of cerebrospinal fluid.
7. At the chemical level, the blood-brain barrier carefully sorts substances for transport into brain tissues; most of the blood content remains behind in the capillary beds.

The Peripheral Nervous System

The PNS is so widespread in the body that it can hardly be described! All of the sensory neurons coming back toward the CNS from every tiny sensory receptor in your skin, eyes, ears, nose, and muscles are included, in addition to all of the neurons that run from the CNS to every muscle mass and gland in your body. Together, these two categories comprise a large number of neurons that no one has ever precisely counted. Where can we begin to appreciate this complexity?

The parts of the PNS that are most obvious are 12 pairs of **cranial nerves** originating from the brain and 31 pairs of **spinal nerves** originating in the spinal cord (see Figure 10.31b). Most of these nerves serve both the afferent and efferent branches of the PNS: They have both sensory and motor roles to play. Among the motor functions, they are most heavily involved in the somatic or voluntary functions involving skeletal muscles. The functions of the cranial nerves are listed in Table 10.4. Included in the table is a new, 13th pair of nerves recently studied (and numbered the "0th" pair) that may be involved in detecting chemical signals emanating from other members of our species! Notice also that a cranial nerve can have either purely sensory neurons, purely motor neurons, or a mixture of both sorts. The functions they serve are all localized in the head and upper torso. In each case, the cranial nerve appears to leave the brain at an optimum position given the centers within the brain

that it originates from and the part of the head or torso to be enervated.

The 31 pairs of spinal nerves serve the rest of the torso and limbs. They virtually all have mixed sensory and motor functions. Their architecture for this purpose is fascinating. Each spinal nerve emerges from the spinal cord as two separate roots (see Figure 10.36). One root is a combination of nerve fibers originating in the dorsal portion of the spinal cord; the other root is from the ventral portion of the cord. The dorsal root of each spinal nerve carries axons from afferent sensory nerves. The ventral root of each spinal nerve carries axons of efferent motor neurons. These two roots merge into a single spinal nerve, but once the nerves are outside the vertebral column, they divide into branches again, this time with different constraints in mind! The dorsal branch, or **ramus**, contains nerves that serve the dorsal portions of the trunk. It carries some autonomic motor, some somatic motor, and all sensory information to and from the

cranial nerve—a multicellular bundle of neural processes that extends away from the surface of the brain and enervates a particular region of the body.

spinal nerve—a multicellular bundle of neural processes that extends away from the surface of the spinal cord and enervates a particular region of the body.

ramus—a major branch of a nerve such as the dorsal branch of a spinal nerve.

Table 10.4 The cranial nerves.

#	Name	Sensory or Motor?	Function
0	Nerve "0"	S	Detection of pheromones
I	Olfactory	S	Transmits smells
II	Optic	S	Transmits visual information
III	Oculomotor	M	Enervates eye muscles, incl. cilliary body
IV	Trochlear	M	Enervates oblique eye muscle
V	Trigeminal	S,M	Transmits facial sensation, controls chewing
VI	Abduscens	M	Enervate lateral eye muscle
VII	Facial	S,M	Facial expression, some taste info, salivary glnds
VIII	Vestibulocochlear	S	Senses sound, rotation, gravity
IX	Glossopharyngeal	S,M	Senses taste, salivary gland control
X	Vagus	S,M	Voice muscles, parasymp to visceral organs
XI	Accessory	M	Shoulder and head movement
XII	Hypoglossal	M	Swallowing, speech articulation

Spinal Nerve Structure

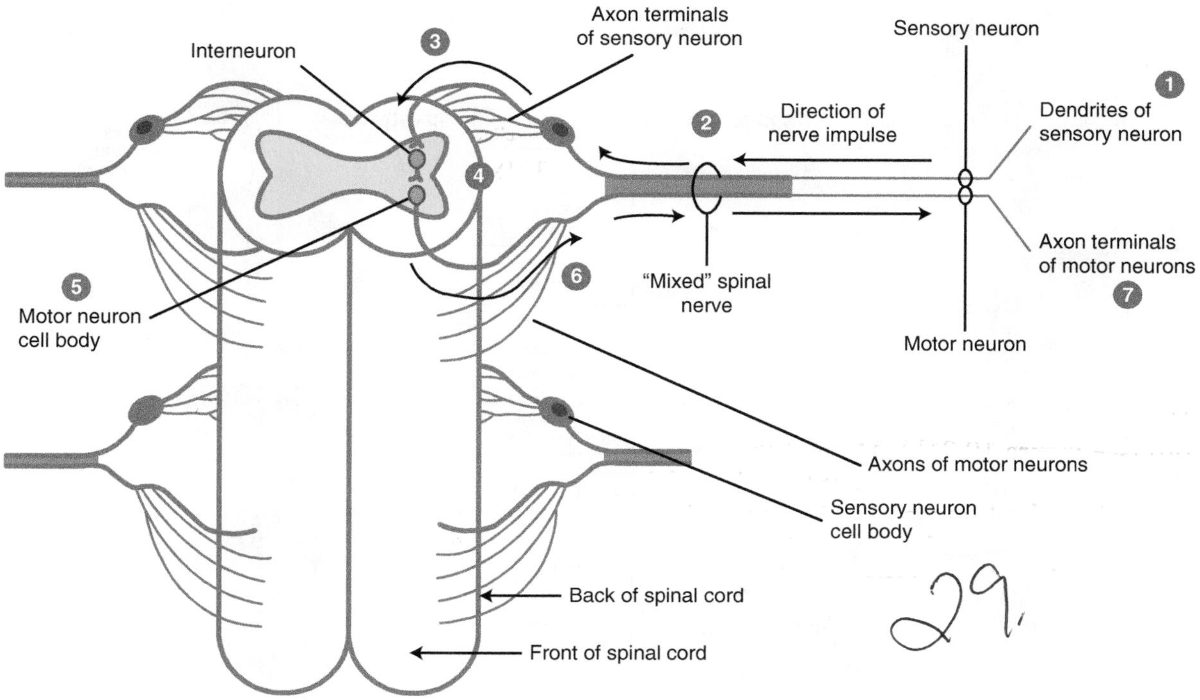

Interneuron

Axon terminals of sensory neuron

3

Sensory neuron

1

2 Direction of nerve impulse

Dendrites of sensory neuron

4

5

Motor neuron cell body

6

"Mixed" spinal nerve

Axon terminals of motor neurons

7

Motor neuron

Axons of motor neurons

Sensory neuron cell body

29.

Back of spinal cord

Front of spinal cord

Figure 10.36 Anatomy of a Spinal Nerve. A touch from a special person is **(1)** sensed by receptors in the skin of the hand and becomes an action potential travelling sensory neuron dendrites **(2)** to the sensory neuron cell body within a ganglion of such bodies. The cell body triggers a new action potential **(3)** that travels axons within the nerve to the spinal cord where integration **(4)** occurs. In this case cognitive areas of the brain get involved! Signals are transmitted to motor neurons **(5)** from which they follow motor neuron axons **(6)** back to neuro-muscular junctions **(7)** in the hand, which, of course, takes the initiating hand.

29.

skin and muscles of the back. The ventral branch of each nerve serves the remaining ventral parts of the trunk and the upper and lower limbs. It carries autonomic motor, somatic motor, and sensory information to and from these areas. Together the spinal nerves form a highly sophisticated communication network. Its sensory and motor functions are neatly partitioned within the spinal cord but distributed to the body regions in a coordinated fashion.

While the somatic portion of your PNS is under voluntary control, the ANS works for your welfare day and night, selflessly, dispassionately, without a thought! In both its parasympathetic and sympathetic divisions it contains neurons that enable the CNS to control all of the involuntary functions required in the body. Both divisions

innervate both the glands and the smooth muscle of all major organs. They receive information from these structures and carry impulses back to them, but the two divisions have opposite effects (see Figure 10.37). The parasympathetic division mediates control of processes operating within its organs when the body is essentially at rest. The sympathetic division mediates the control of these same organic processes when the body is under stress. For example, the sympathetic division produces the fight-or-flight response that increases heart and respiratory rates, causes sweaty palms and dry mouth—all things you feel when you are nervous or scared. The parasympathetic division is what stimulates your digestive processes while you restfully listen to a quiet recording of nature sounds with your stereo ear buds.

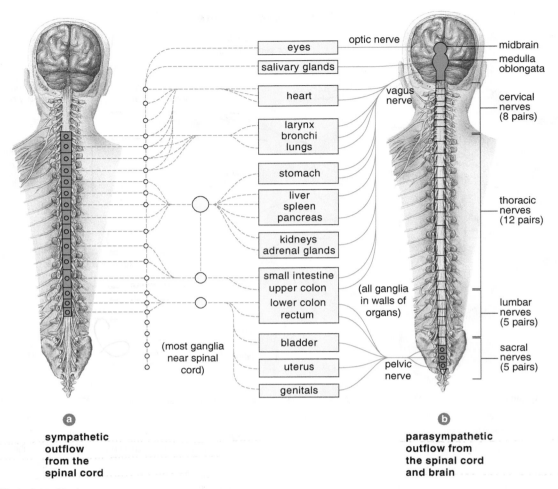

eyes

salivary glands

heart

larynx
bronchi
lungs

stomach

liver
spleen
pancreas

kidneys
adrenal glands

small intestine
upper colon

lower colon
rectum

bladder

uterus

genitals

optic nerve

vagus
nerve

(all ganglia
in walls of
organs)

(most ganglia
near spinal
cord)

pelvic
nerve

midbrain

medulla
oblongata

cervical
nerves
(8 pairs)

thoracic
nerves
(12 pairs)

lumbar
nerves
(5 pairs)

sacral
nerves
(5 pairs)

a

sympathetic
outflow
from the
spinal cord

b

parasympathetic
outflow from
the spinal cord
and brain

Figure 10.37   The Autonomic Nervous System. The nerves are represented by red lines. Each pathway is two neurons in length. The cell body of the first neuron lies in the CNS. The second neuron's cell body lies within a collection of such cell bodies called a ganglion. Ganglia for the parasympathetic division lie in or near their respective organs and are not shown.

IN OTHER WORDS

1. The peripheral nervous system (PNS) includes all nerves and their component neurons and processes that lie outside of the brain and spinal cord.
2. The most obvious components of the PNS are the 12 pairs of cranial nerves emanating from the brain and the 13 pairs of spinal nerves extending laterally from the spinal cord.
3. As the spinal nerves leave the CNS, they are divided into sensory and motor branches; these cross justoutside the CNS so that nerves branching dorsally or ventrally carry both sensory and motor components within them.
4. The autonomic nervous system (ANS) is the part of the PNS that serves involuntary functions that we are not consciously aware of, such as circulatory and digestive functions.
5. The ANS has two divisions, each of which enervates the same organs; the sympathetic division activates a stress-oriented set of responses while the parasympathetic division maintains a more relaxed set of responses.

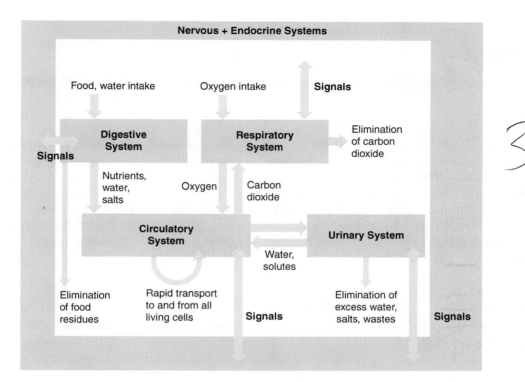

Figure 10.38 Life is Internally Integrated. The systems shown here are integrated in many ways other than those represented by arrows. The muscular system could not be accurately placed within the diagram because it is so intimately associated with all of the others systems. Design overwhelms us at this point.

The Nervous System Is Internally Integrated

The nervous system together with the endocrine glands coordinates the internal integration of all the other body systems together. It controls aspects of every one of them (see Figure 10.38). Within the climber of the Washington Monument, the CNS is receiving afferent sensory input from both the external environment and internal sensors and sending efferent motor signals to all parts of the PNS to keep everything functioning within normal limits. The somatic system controls your skeletal muscles while the ANS controls the processes that will keep your body in homeostasis in spite of the changing demands being placed upon it. If you start sweating, it can compensate with decreased urine production. If your muscle and liver glycogen levels fall, the nervous system interprets your fatigue and causes you to decide to slow your pace. Only internal integration of all the systems conveys the climber to the top. The nervous system coordinates this integration as the climb begins, when the climb is most stressful, and after the stress of the climb is past. It is a truly amazing invention.

IN OTHER WORDS

1. Together, the nervous system and the endocrine system control the activities of all the other systems of the human body.
2. This control is not generalized or superficial; rather, these two systems intimately interconnect with all parts of all other systems so that the human organism is truly internally integrated.

10.9 DRUGS AND THE NERVOUS SYSTEM

Drugs were a $307 billion part of the American economy in 2010. Besides this fiscal impact, where do drugs have their effect in the body, and why would we consider them in a chapter on internal integration of biological function? The answer is amazing. A major part of the pharmaceutical industry is built around the tiny 30-nanometer-wide space (0.03 micron) that exists between communicating neurons: the synapse. Apart from invading pathogens targeted by antibiotics, the synapse is where the majority of drugs taken by humans have their effect. Of the thousands of drugs available over the counter and by prescription today, let's consider just three that are used quite commonly in society today: alcohol, caffeine, and fluoxetine.

IN OTHER WORDS

1. Psychoactive drugs are a major portion of the American economy; they have their effect in the synapses between nerve cells.

Alcohol: The Oldest Sedative

"Give strong drink to the one who is perishing . . ."

(PROVERBS 31)

When the comfort of a relationship to God is unexplored or marginalized, there exists a time-honored drug that many teenagers and tired, discouraged adults often turn to. Alcohol, specifically **ethanol** (C_2H_5OH), is that mysterious drug. Its effects are fascinating. In beverage form ethanol leaves the digestive system from the stomach and small intestine and enters the circulatory system, which carries it to the blood-brain barrier. In the capillaries there, blood alcohol concentrations of only 0.03% to 0.12% are sufficient to allow its lipid-like structure to carry it into brain tissues of the limbic system, where it promotes a sense of euphoria characterized by increased confidence and sociability. But as the level rises toward 0.2%, the broadly **sedative** nature of ethanol begins to manifest itself in a slowed reaction time, slurred speech, and a staggering gait. Between levels of 0.2% and 0.3%, loss of consciousness is possible, and between levels of 0.3% and 0.4% death becomes a possibility as breathing and heart rate are minimized. What's happening in the CNS that causes these responses?

Ethanol is a small biomolecule and is lipid-soluble. It spreads out within the cerebrospinal fluid and enters many areas of the brain, penetrating cell membranes and percolating through a variety of brain tissues. One particular area, the **nucleus accumbens** (see Figure 10.32) moderates feelings such as pleasure, a sense of reward, and such actions as laughter. It is also the site of virtually all chemical addictions. One prominent neurotransmitter that functions in this area of the brain is a chemical called **dopamine**. In a drug-free experience of pleasure (see Figure 10.39a, left-hand side), the sending neurons' signals cause vesicles

> **ethanol**—an organic compound composed of two carbon atoms bonded to each other, to five hydrogen atoms, and to one hydroxide (−OH) group; a small alcohol.
>
> **sedative**—a chemical that relaxes or tranquilizes the nervous system; usually functions within synapses.
>
> **nucleus accumbens**—a body of neurons within the striatum region of the brain that mediates feelings of pleasure or reward; drug addiction is centered in this region as well.
>
> **dopamine**—a neurotransmitter substance used in many parts of the brain to mediate (among other processes) cognition, motivation, voluntary movement, memory, learning, and sexual gratification.

Drug Action of Alcohol—Excitement, pleasure

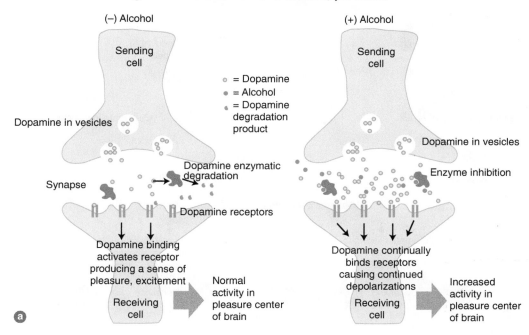

Drug Action of Alcohol—Sedative Effect

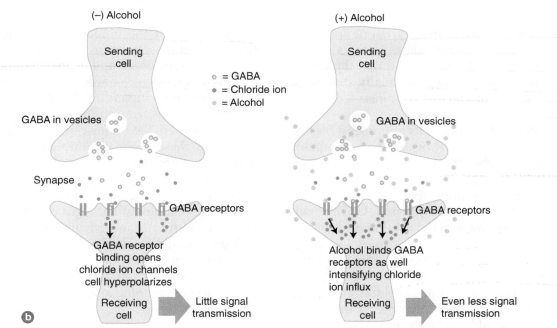

Figure 10.39 Alcohol Invades the Synapse. **(a)** Ethanol results in the unnatural accumulation of the neurotransmitter dopamine in synaptic spaces of the brain's pleasure center—the result is euphoria. **(b)** Ethanol binds strongly to GABA receptors slowing impulse transmission and thus sedating the individual. **(c)** Ethanol disrupts glumate reception on receiving neurons decreasing the general excitability of the CNS.

containing dopamine to empty into local synaptic spaces. The dopamine quickly crosses by diffusion and initiate depolarizations in the membranes of neurons within the nucleus accumbens. It is believed that an enzyme within the synaptic space quickly degrades the dopamine so that the receiving neuron experiences additional depolarizations only if additional dopamine is secreted by the sending neuron. Alcohol changes all this (see Figure 10.39a, right-hand side). We suspect it inhibits

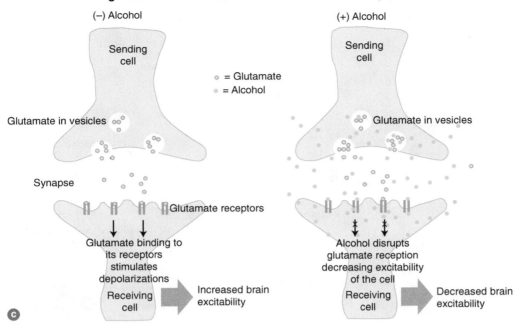

Drug Action of Alcohol–lost coordination, slurred speech

(–) Alcohol

Sending cell

○ = Glutamate
● = Alcohol

Glutamate in vesicles

Synapse

Glutamate receptors

Glutamate binding to its receptors stimulates depolarizations

Receiving cell

Increased brain excitability

(+) Alcohol

Sending cell

Glutamate in vesicles

Alcohol disrupts glutamate reception decreasing excitability of the cell

Receiving cell

Decreased brain excitability

c

Figure 10.39 *(Continued)*

31. the activity of the enzyme in the synaptic space. We know that dopamine accumulates in the synapses of the affected neural pathways so that the receiving nerve is repeatedly and continually stimulated causing a prolonged sense of happiness—the basis of the proverbial happy hour.

But as the alcohol concentration rises a bit, the sedative effects of alcohol begin to predominate. In cerebral or cerebellar parts of the brain that affect speech or coordination, other neurotransmitters such as gamma amino butyric acid (**GABA**) and **glutamate** are commonly found. GABA tends to quiet the brain by actually inhibiting depolarization in receiving neurons. It causes ion channels to open up that allow chloride ions (Cl⁻) into the cell interior making it even harder for other neurons to start an action potential there (see Figure 10.39b). The receptor proteins on receiving cells that would normally bind GABA bind to alcohol strongly as well. So alcohol intensifies the quieting or sedative effect of GABA, slowing speech and perceptions.

About 40% of neurons in the brain respond to the neurotransmitter glutamate by depolarizing and in this way contributing to the general attentive, coordinated responsiveness of the individual. When alcohol is present in the synaptic spaces, it tends to disrupt the binding of glutamate to its receptors on these neurons. Typical results of this include slurred speech and an uncertain gait, both the result of impaired coordination of muscle activity. In extreme dysfunction of glutamate receptors, breathing is affected and the life of the organism is compromised. Yet because of alcohol's addictive effects on the nucleus accumbens, the consumer will ingest more and more of it. Alcohol, like other recreational drugs, is a way in which humans have discovered how to abuse the pleasure center of the brain. Physical pleasure is a gift our physical body grants us naturally in response to life's ordinary and unexpected sources of joy. How frightening that deliberate manipulation of it can result in worship of a sensation that, in the extreme, denies life its deeper meaning and even its continuity.

gamma amino butyric acid (GABA)—a neurotransmitter substance that plays a major role in inhibition of a wide variety of activities within the central nervous system.

glutamate—one of 20 different amino acids used to build proteins; in the central nervous system and throughout the body it is a major neurotransmitter with an excitatory role.

IN OTHER WORDS

1. Ethanol in beverage form is first ingested through the mouth, absorbed in the stomach and small intestine, circulated throughout the bloodstream, crosses the blood-brain barrier, and diffuses through the tissues of the brain.
2. The presence of ethanol in the nucleus accumbens of the brain causes the neurotransmitter dopamine to generate pleasurable and addictive effects there.
3. Ethanol intensifies the quieting effects of the neurotransmitter GABA; this is part of the basis for its sedative effects.
4. Ethanol's disruptive effect on the binding of neurotransmitter glutamate to its receptors is another basis for its sedative effects.

Caffeine: Catalyst of the Technological Revolution

America runs on **caffeine**. It is an entirely legal and widely consumed **psychoactive** drug. About 90% of American adults consume it daily. It is also the most widely studied drug. Thousands of studies have searched for serious side effects of this substance, and no conclusively negative results have emerged except those related to overdosage. Some of us with tendencies toward anxiety or excitability are urged to limit our use of it. Why is that? And how does it cause the added alertness and wakefulness we use it for?

Brain chemistry again explains part of this activity. One by-product of ATP breakdown is the nucleotide fragment **adenosine** (see Figure 10.40). Adenosine is generally an inhibitory chemical in brain tissues. It binds specifically to membrane

caffeine—an alkaloid chemical isolated from various plant tissues that is a psychoactive drug in humans; a strong stimulant of activity in the central nervous system.

psychoactive—descriptive of a drug that affects the brain and its behavior.

adenosine—the five-carbon sugar ribose attached to the purine base adenine; a building block for production of adenosine triphosphate, a major energy source and subunit in RNA synthesis; a calming neurotransmitter in the central nervous system.

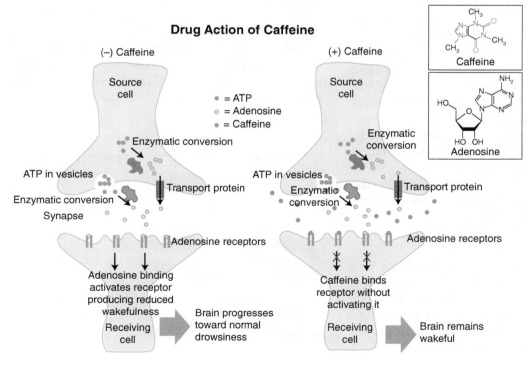

Drug Action of Caffeine

Figure 10.40 Caffeine Invades the Synapse. The normal binding of the neurotransmitter adenosine to its receptor has the effect of slowly quieting the central nervous system. Caffeine inhibits this effect by binding to adenosine's receptors but failing to activate them. The result is an abnormal state of wakefulness.

receptors on CNS neurons, thereby decreasing their excitability. Caffeine, being lipid-soluble, easily crosses the blood-brain barrier and, in brain tissue, appears to sufficiently mimic the structure of adenosine such that it binds successfully to adenosine receptors. But this binding does not result in the reduced excitability like adenosine binding does. So by displacing adenosine from its own receptors, caffeine subverts the normal process of a reduction in CNS excitability. You remain alert, attentive, and even a bit tense. About 200 to 300 milligrams of caffeine per day is found in 2 to 3 cups of home-brewed coffee. This amount can have a positive impact on recurring headaches or even on some types of diabetes. But 2 to 3 cups of coffee from the best-known coffee shops often supply 400 to 600 milligrams per day—a definite threat to anyone struggling with high blood pressure, insomnia, stomach ulcers, or calcium absorption issues. So is a caffeine-laced drink an occasional treat for you or is it your sleep substitute? (Scientists enjoy asking good questions.)

IN OTHER WORDS

1. Caffeine is the most widely used drug in America; it is disruptive of adenosine's normal quieting effect on the CNS.
2. In the human brain, serotonin is a neurotransmitter that, by stimulating appropriate neurons, causes a general feeling of well-being in the organism.

32. Fluoxetine Hydrochloride: Chemical Joy

Are you discouraged, depressed, anxious? Your psychiatrist can change that perception at the chemical level. In 1935, Vittorio Erspamer, an Italian neurochemist, discovered the neurotransmitter **serotonin**. Subsequent studies revealed that serotonin is a normal chemical signal in the CNS that communicates a feeling of well-being. It originates from collections of neuron clusters located throughout the posterior part of the brain (the brainstem) and becomes a neurotransmitter to receiving cells throughout the rest of the brain. As with various other neurotransmitters, serotonin is sequestered into vesicles, which, upon signaling, open into synaptic spaces between the sending and receiving cells (see Figure 10.41, left-hand side.) They start a new (happy) action potential in the receiving cells, but this happens quite quickly because **transporter proteins** in the sending cell membrane quickly reabsorb the serotonin from the synapse so that further uncontrolled depolarizations do not occur in the receiving cells.

Individuals who are clinically depressed or unusually anxious appear to have abnormally low levels of serotonin in their brains. Researchers like David Wong of Eli Lilly believed that these individuals could experience the apparent presence of more serotonin in their brains if they could find some organic chemical that would jam the transporter protein (see Figure 10.41, right-hand side). Once that chemical was in the synapse, any serotonin secreted there would tend to remain there elevating the frequency of (happy) depolarizations in the receiving cells. The chemical **fluoxetine hydrochloride was the first chemical to have the highly specific jamming effect that Wong was looking for.** It was later marketed by Eli Lilly under the trade name Prozac. The class of about 10 such transporter-jamming chemicals has become known as **SSRI** compounds (selective serotonin reuptake inhibitors). About 10% of Americans used antidepressant medication in 2005, and fluoxetine was the most frequently prescribed drug in that category.

serotonin—a neurotransmitter in certain synaptic spaces within the brain that signals action potentials in cells resulting in a feeling of well-being.

transporter protein—a membrane protein that binds a substance on one side of the membrane and transports it back to the opposite side of the same membrane.

fluoxetine—chemical name for the first SSRI to be synthesized and marketed successfully.

SSRI (serotonin-specific reuptake inhibitor)—a chemical that inhibits the activity of serotonin transport proteins such that high concentrations of serotonin remain in the synaptic space.

Drug Action of an SSRI

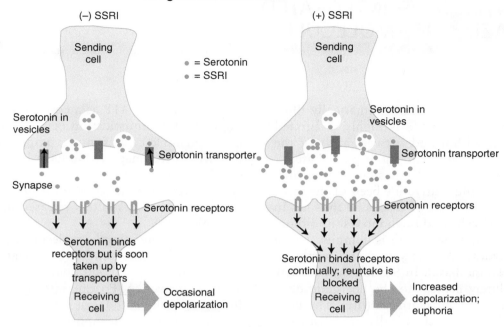

Figure 10.41 A Serotonin-Specific Reuptake Inhibitor Invades the Synapse. By binding to a transport protein, the SSRI causes released serotonin to remain in the synaptic space for longer amounts of time. This causes the receiving cell that communicates the experience of well-being to continue depolarizing.

SSRIs have raised many fascinating social and medical issues. Some have been blamed for suicides among teenagers. They also focus attention on the broader question of whether the degree of happiness in a person's life is significantly affected by the phenotype of how much serotonin they naturally produce. Phenotypes result—at least in part—from genotypes (see Chapter 12). Do a person's genes influence their susceptibility to depression or anxiety? As drugs become physiologically safer and more specific in their effects on human synapses, questions such as these will beg for clear answers.

IN OTHER WORDS

1. In the human brain, serotonin is a neurotransmitter that, by stimulating appropriate neurons, causes a general feeling of well-being in the organism.
2. Serotonin's effect on receiving neurons can be intensified by preventing its reuptake from synaptic spaces.
3. Many antidepressant drugs work by inhibiting the activity of transport proteins that remove serotonin from the synaptic space after it has been released there.
4. Fluoxetine hydrochloride was the first SSRI marketed and is widely prescribed today for clinically depressed and even mildly depressed individuals.

LIFE IS INTERNALLY INTEGRATED: THE AMAZING ATP MOLECULE

There is one biomolecule that dramatically illustrates the principle that life is highly integrated internally, both within and between cells of the body. That molecule is adenosine triphosphate, or ATP. Consider how central it has been to our discussion and how illustrative it's been of the most basic principles of life we've discussed thus far. In Section 4.7 we saw how, though modest as biological molecules go, its structure is complex, being partly carbohydrate (ribose sugar) and partly nitrogenous (adenine base). In Section 6.6, we saw ATP as absolutely central to the energetic driving force of cellular biosynthesis (life). The need for and use of energy is chemically the most basic concept of how living systems function. Then, in Section 7.2, we saw that ATP is one of only four critical building blocks of the informational molecule RNA. (By removing just one oxygen atom from it, it becomes a building block of DNA as well.) So here is ATP participating prominently in the other critical component of what it means to be alive: information expression. These two fundamental roles for ATP are both intracellular and could be viewed as sufficient to make it the most critical of all biological molecules, but research has continued to amaze us. ATP not only participates in energy transduction and information expression, but it is also a key player in the internal integration of the multicellular organism: it is a neurotransmitter as well!

This amazing discovery has taken years to find acceptance among those who study neuron function (neurophysiologists). Slowly, the data has emerged: ATP can be found in vesicles as adrenaline or acetylcholine can. It is often shed as a **cotransmitter** into synaptic spaces all over the body, and receiving cells have a variety of receptors for it so that it can open ion channels and start responses in excitable cells. In humans, it's involved in controlling the dilation and constriction of blood vessels; in slime molds it influences **turgidity** by controlling water uptake by cells. It functions in transmission of signals from the **rod** and **cone** receptor **cells** in your eye to sensory neurons in the optic nerve. Mice that lack receptors for ATP on their excitable cells have

no sense of taste! ATP as a cotransmitter is teaching us that communication between neurons and other excitable cells is more complicated than we had wished to imagine. We have begun to understand that much of the fine-tuning of our nervous system's responses is based on relative amounts of differing neurotransmitters released into the same synaptic space.

How can one simple molecule be used in so many crucial yet seemingly unrelated ways in the human body? Evolutionary materialists have a ready answer: ATP came into use early in evolutionary history and just got tapped repeatedly for these diverse but important roles. This notion sounds elegantly simple, but complex issues lurk behind it. How does a primitive system that has evolved one use for ATP favor a mutation that will begin to sequester it in an uncontrolled way for a new purpose (see Figure 10.42)? This would introduce competition for ATP molecules within the same organism. Imagine a different organism in which mutation favored the use of ATP for storing energy and some other available molecule for building RNA. This latter individual would have a more efficient metabolism unless the supply of ATP was unlimited. But in a simple **unbuffered** aqueous

cotransmitter—a molecule that, when found in a synaptic space along with some other neurotransmitter, influences the probability that the receiving cell will start an action potential.

turgid—to be filled with solvent, usually water, to the point of structural rigidity.

rod cell—a receptor cell in the retina of the eye that is responsive to differing degrees of light intensity distinguishing light from darkness.

cone cell—a receptor cell in the retina of the eye that is particularly responsive to wavelengths of light in the visible region; detects color.

buffer—a collection of (usually complex) ions in solution that keeps the concentration of hydrogen ions within close limits by combining with them when they're in excess and generating more of them when they are scarce.

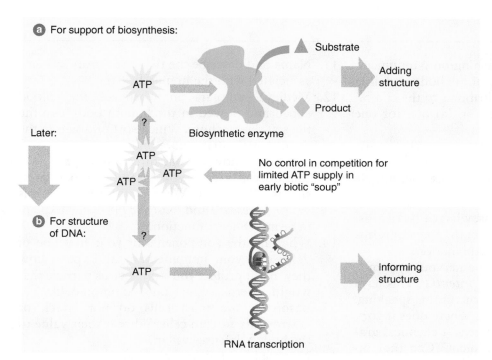

(a) For support of biosynthesis:

ATP

Substrate

Biosynthetic enzyme

Product

Adding structure

Later:

ATP

ATP ATP

ATP

No control in competition for limited ATP supply in early biotic "soup"

(b) For structure of DNA:

ATP

RNA transcription

Informing structure

Figure 10.42 Evolutionary Origin of ATP Use. If use of ATP in widely differing ways evolved sequentially, then there would be long periods of time during which the apportioning of ATP to two different processes would be a matter of competition rather than control. This would not bode well for the evolving cell.

system, ATP is highly unstable. Try to imagine that early cell in which ATP would be needed for RNA and DNA structure, biosynthetic enzyme use, and cell-to-cell communication. That primitive cell could hardly be expected to be able to effectively coordinate its use in these three significant respects. A gifted Designer would be needed to (1) see the possibilities for its use in these three areas, (2) prepare three molecular contexts in which its multiple uses would have biological meaning, and (3) coordinate controlled production and distribution of it so that appropriate amounts would be available for each process. Life Is Internally Integrated. Every molecule that exemplifies this integration whispers the word *design* to us. ATP shouts the word unapologetically.

IN OTHER WORDS

1. The biomolecule ATP illustrates how completely a single biomolecule can be integrated into three different spheres of life processes.
2. ATP functions in energy storage, information storage, and information transmission to various parts of the body.
3. In this last role, ATP is often a cotransmitter in the synaptic space along with other neurotransmitters such as acetylcholine.
4. Since free ATP in solution is relatively short-lived, its concentrations and distribution must be carefully controlled so that it's available for use in each of its functional roles.

QUESTIONS FOR REVIEW

1. You are climbing the Washington Monument. List vertically the systems of the body and, in a phrase, how each one contributes to the climb.
2. Match the following terms in (a) one for one with the terms in (b):
   a. Organ, tissue, cell, macromolecular structure, biomolecule
   b. Sarcomere, muscle, myosin, fascicle, muscle fiber
3. Explain, in molecular terms, what causes a muscle to contract along its length. Use the terms *actin* and *myosin* in your explanation.
4. A signal traveling within the nervous system is sometimes called an *action potential*. This term is functional in nature. Structurally speaking, what is an action potential? Where does it go?
5. What is the difference between a chemical gradient and an electrical gradient? Can they involve the same particles? Explain.
6. Ion pumps and ion gates both take ions across a membrane. What is the functional difference between a pump and a gate? Why does one of the two require ATP energy to work while the other does not?
7. Where is tropomyosin found? Select the best choice. Its role in muscle contraction is to:
   a. Contract structurally
   b. Energize the contraction
   c. Control the contraction
   d. House the contraction
8. List three broad classes of muscle tissue and examples of the organs in which they are found.
9. Classify the components of blood. Using correct terminology, begin by dividing blood into its fluid and cellular components. Under each of these two headings, list appropriate components.
10. Fill in six blanks below using the names of body system:

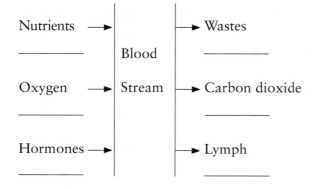

11. Name and describe the two circulatory systems associated with the human heart.
12. Medieval scholars once believed that blood ebbed and flowed in the human body like the tides at the seashore. Which sort of organ in the circulatory system, more than any other, argues that blood moves in one direction only?
13. The doctor advises you that your blood pressure is 140 over 80. What is meant by the terms *systolic pressure* and *diastolic pressure?* Explain in terms of heart function.
14. What are the components of your first line of defense in your immune system? Explain how they might protect you from a virus particle that would otherwise give you a common cold.
15. Basophils and mast cells do not attack or destroy any foreign cells. What is their value to the body's defense system?
16. Neutrophils and macrophages respond similarly to foreign cells or particles. What is the major functional difference between them?
17. List the four characteristics of inflammation and the cause of each characteristic.
18. List four characteristics that distinguish the adaptive immune response from the innate immune response.
19. What is the minimum number of kinds of immune system cells found inside a lymph node? Name these different classes of cells.
20. How do helper T cells "help"? What functional role do they play in the immune response?
21. What is the functional role of an antibody? It doesn't kill anything. How is it of use to the immune system?
22. What is the difference between the way a B cell sees antigen and the way a T cell sees antigen?
23. Describe the role of a memory B cell.
24. What makes the HIV virus so debilitating to the human immune response?
25. Select five terms from Section 10.5 and, using arrows between them, arrange them into a sequence that indicates how food passes through the body.
26. Explain why the hepatic portal system is needed as part of the digestive system.
27. Make a list of structures that describe the route that a urobilinogen molecule would take from its formation in the liver to its appearance in the urine leaving the body.
28. List, in order, three interdependent processes that go on as body fluid passes through a nephron.

29. List three ways in which the circulatory system serves the kidney. List three ways in which the kidney serves the circulatory system.
30. Distinguish between the role of the nervous system and the role of the endocrine system in the control of other body systems.
31. Redraw a typical motor neuron on a piece of paper and label both its structural parts and its functional zones.
32. Will any shift in membrane potential result in the initiation of a depolarization event? Explain your answer.
33. Using a sequence of phrases, trace the path of the simplest possible reflex arc that occurs when you accidently touch an extremely hot object. Use the following terms: *motor neuron, sensory neuron, synapse, receptor, effector muscle, neurotransmitter, action potential*.
34. List the organs that are components of the CNS. List those of the peripheral nervous system. (Recall that an organ is a collection of cofunctional tissues and that large nerves have blood vessels within them.)
35. List the regions of the brain and the principle function(s) carried out by each region.
36. Which feature(s) of the central nervous system would best protect it from:
    a. Being hit by a falling rock _____
    b. Being infected by a pathogenic bacterium _____
    c. Being punched by a heavy-weight boxer _____
    d. Being poisoned by an herbicide _____
    e. Being attacked with a sharp object _____
37. Which sort of drug would be more likely to be effective in the brain, one that is water-soluble or one that is lipid-soluble? Why?
38. What sort of cellular processes (extensions of neurons) would be found inside the trigeminal nerve (see Table 10.4)?
39. List three known ways that ethanol alters brain function and the mechanism of each.
40. Describe how ATP is both produced and used in the human body. (*Hint:* Revisit Section 6.7.)

QUESTIONS FOR THOUGHT

1. Getting more blood to flow to a new area of the body and less to a previous area is formally somewhat similar to getting transport proteins for indole acetic acid to move from one side of a cell to another (see Section 11.4). Recall your study of the cell in Chapters 5 and 7. What organ system controls relative levels of blood distribution in the body? What organelles are (or may be) involved in moving IAA transport proteins to where they are needed?
2. Trace the journey of an erythrocyte that has just been oxygenated in the lungs until it returns to the lungs depleted of oxygen.
3. Many biologists argue that, quite apart from the lungs and pulmonary vessels, the human body has two complete and somewhat separate circulatory systems. Explain what they mean by this.
4. Which of the two ventricles of the human heart is larger and more muscular? Explain why this is so.
5. Pathogens can get to humans by means of wounding, food, water, sexual transmission, or respiratory inhalation. Construct a chart with four rows and two columns in it. In the first column list these four portals of entry to the human body. Then use an online encyclopedia to find three to four common examples of pathogens that enter at each of the four portals of entry. Which one of these four categories would you suppose is the source of the preponderance of all human infections?
6. Natural killer cells and cytotoxic T cells both kill cells using toxic chemicals. What is the fundamental difference between these two classes of cells? (*Hint:* Consider when they are described within Section 10.4.)
7. Recall what you have learned about cell surface receptor proteins from your study of cancer in Chapter 8. The receptor proteins in the surface membranes of B and T cells are referred to as *bifunctional* proteins. What are the two functions of such a receptor protein?
8. The food-borne pathogenic bacterium *Salmonella* multiplies in the gastrointestinal tract and, in so doing, often invades the epithelial

cells that line the digestive tract. What separate defense systems will the immune response employ to rid the digestive system of this pathogen?

9. You are charged with developing a new vaccine for a bacterial pathogen. No one has found a way to kill or weaken this bacterium without ruining its ability to stimulate the human immune system. You decide to try molecular parts of the bacterial cell as antigens to stimulate an immune response. What part or parts of the cell would you try to use first?

10. Review Section 4.2 in your text. Two broad classes of reactions were described there. Which class would be critical to the digestion process? Which class would best reflect what the body does with absorbed nutrients?

11. As food moves through the small intestine, it exists as spherical masses a few centimeters in diameter called *boli*. These are pushed through the small intestine by waves of muscular contractions called *peristalsis*. How might such rolling and pushing of food contribute to the process of digestion? Could you classify this contribution as either mechanical or chemical? Explain why or why not?

12. In one carefully constructed sentence, describe the purpose and the role of the nephron in the kidney.

13. About 99% of the water that is lost during filtration is reabsorbed. If the amount of urine produced in one day equals about 1.5 liters, calculate how many liters of filtrate pass through the kidneys each day. Your blood is filtered and refiltered many times in a day!

14. Listed below are the steps that precede and follow an action potential passing along a membrane. Fill in the second and third steps that represent the action potential itself.
    a. sodium-potassium pump: steadily pumps sodium ions out, potassium ions in
    b. sodium ion channels?
    c. potassium ion channels?
    d. sodium-potassium pump: resumes pumping sodium ions out, potassium ions in

15. Use an example from the patellar reflex arc to illustrate a neuron that synapses with at least two other neurons. Explain where the action potential comes from and where the action potentials go to.

16. Circle the actions that are generally involuntary:
    a. Flexing your arm muscle
    b. Blinking your eyelid
    c. Sweating
    d. Swallowing
    e. Moving food into your stomach
    f. Urinating
    g. Sneezing
    h. Shuddering

17. What might be the value of having a mixed-function spinal nerve divide into separate motor and sensory roots just before it enters the spinal cord? (*Hint:* Think carefully about the role of the CNS in nervous system function.)

18. Identify which division of the autonomic nervous system might be causing the following:
    a. The pupils of your eyes to widen _____
    b. A decrease in your heart rate _____
    c. Increased stomach secretions _____
    d. Increased adrenal gland secretion _____
    e. The slowing of food movement in the small intestine _____
    f. The stimulation of urination _____

19. Go ahead, try it! Redraw Figure 10.38 on a sheet of paper, including the arrows and substances as shown. Now, add the muscular system. Pick the best location for it within the diagram and link it to as many other systems as your diagram allows without extending arrows into or out of the page or crossing other arrows.

20. Which process would need to evolve first in the earliest cell: the production of ATP or the use of ATP? Explain the difficulties inherent in either answer.

21. A discouraged, perpetually sad individual visits both a minister and a physician. The minister explores with the individual behaviors that are wrong—damaging to the individual's relationship with others and to his faith. The physician listens to the individual's complaints and prescribes an SSRI. Eventually, the individual's symptoms resolve. Who is most helpful to the individual? Explain.

GLOSSARY

absorption—the transfer of digested food (nutrients) across the epithelial lining of the digestive tract and into surrounding capillary beds or lymphatic vessels for distribution to the body.

acetylcholine—a neurotransmitter chemical that is secreted into a synapse by the transmitting cell and that initiates a new signal in the receiving cell.

actin—a monomeric protein that makes up the structure of filaments—the scaffolding against which myosin proteins carry out linear movement by successive binding events between myosin head domains and the filament's own scaffolding.

action potential—a momentary steep electrical charge difference across a membrane; the physical basis for a nerve impulse.

adaptive immunity—those pathogen-specific aspects of the immune response that involve antibodies and cells directed against the particular sort of pathogen that has bypassed initial, more generalized host defenses.

adenosine—the five-carbon sugar ribose attached to the purine base adenine; a building block for production of adenosine triphosphate, a major energy source and subunit in RNA synthesis; a calming neurotransmitter in the central nervous system.

ADH (antidiuretic hormone)—secreted by the hypothalamus gland; makes kidney tubule walls more permeable to water so that more water returns to the blood.

antibody—a soluble multimeric protein produced by descendants of B cells; it recognizes and binds to a specific antigenic (foreign) surface, molecule, or cell.

antigen—any foreign molecule or cell that generates an adaptive immune response.

artery—a blood vessel that conducts blood toward the lung or tissues and away from the heart.

atrium—one of two chambers in the mammalian heart that receives blood from either the lungs or the tissues.

autonomic system (ANS)—that portion of the peripheral nervous system that acts to control involuntary functions such as visceral activity, perspiration, or heart rate.

axon—a process extending away from the cell body of a neuron; carries a nerve impulse toward some other excitable cell and away from the cell body of the neuron.

B lymphocyte—a type of lymphocyte that detects foreign molecular surfaces on molecules or cells and generates soluble antibodies that will bind to those surfaces labeling them as foreign.

basophil—a leukocyte within the innate branch of the immune system that functions within the bloodstream by participating in various aspects of the inflammation response; releases histamines.

bile—a dark-green bitter fluid product of the liver that aids in the emulsification of fat globules into smaller fat droplets facilitating the digestion of fat molecules.

bladder—an organ of the urinary system that stores urine prior to voiding.

blood-brain barrier—the separation of blood from cerebrospinal and brain fluids that is maintained by tight junctions between endothelial cells that surround the blood capillaries that enter brain tissue.

brain—an organ of the central nervous system; the coordinating center of the entire nervous system; all voluntary actions and many involuntary ones are responses that originate there.

bronchi (bronchus, sing.)—elongated, tube-like organs in the respiratory system that conduct air from the tracheal passage down into the lungs.

buffer—a collection of (usually complex) ions in solution that keeps the concentration of hydrogen ions within close limits by combining with them when they're in excess and generating more of them when they are scarce.

caffeine—an alkaloid chemical isolated from various plant tissues that is a psychoactive drug in humans; a strong stimulant of activity in the central nervous system.

calmodulin—a protein whose action is controlled by calcium ion influx; controls contraction of smooth muscle.

capillaries—small blood vessels extending between arteries and veins; blood flow is slowed within these vessels and nutrient, waste, and gas exchange occurs between them and the surrounding tissues.

cardiac muscle—striated muscle that comprises the walls of the heart; generally involuntary in its control.

cardiovascular system—a collection of organs that facilitate the movement of cells and soluble materials to and from all parts of the body.

cell body—that part of a neuron that contains the cell nucleus and other major organelles; the focus of information expression within the neuron.

central nervous system—that portion of the nervous system that includes the brain and spinal cord; functions to integrate the signals it receives from the peripheral nervous system and coordinates responses to those signals.

cerebrospinal fluid—a clear, colorless body fluid internal to the meninges of the brain; the brain and spinal cord float in this medium.

chyme—partially digested food that exits the stomach and proceeds through the small intestine by means of waves of smooth muscle contraction.

cilia—organelles; projections from a cell's surface that oscillate in a whip-like fashion to generate movement of medium past a cell or movement of the cell within the medium.

cone cell—a receptor cell in the retina of the eye that is particularly responsive to wavelengths of light in the visible region; detects color.

connective tissue—generally fibrous collections of cells throughout the body that add support and structure to the organs they are within; collagen fibers comprise 25% of the body's connective tissues.

constrict—to narrow or shrink.

cotransmitter—a molecule that, when found in a synaptic space along with some other neurotransmitter, influences the probability that the receiving cell will start an action potential.

cranial nerve—a multicellular bundle of neural processes that extends away from the surface of the brain and enervates a particular region of the body.

cytotoxic T lymphocyte—a lymphocyte that matures in the thymus gland and recognizes and destroys host (self) cells that are infected by an intracellular parasite (i.e., a virus or bacterium).

dendrite—a process extending away from the cell body of a neuron; carries a nerve impulse from some other excitable cell toward the cell body of the neuron.

dendritic cell—part of mammalian immune system; engulfs foreign particles and cells, degrades them, and presents parts of the foreign entity on its surface for detection and binding by pathogen-specific lymphocytes of the adaptive immune system.

diastolic pressure—the outward pressure of blood on arterial walls during the period of ventricular relaxation between contractions.

digestive system—a collection of organs that facilitates the intake and mechanical and enzymatic degradation of foods, followed by absorption of nutrients and elimination of wastes.

dilate—to enlarge or expand.

dopamine—a neurotransmitter substance used in many parts of the brain to mediate (among other processes) cognition, motivation, voluntary movement, memory, learning, and sexual gratification.

effector—a muscle or gland that can carry out a response to a stimulus that has been received and interpreted by the central nervous system.

electrical gradient—a spatial variation from one point to another in the concentration of charged substances in solution, often over a short distance across a membrane.

endocrine system—a collection of organs (glands) that secrete hormones into the bloodstream; the hormones in turn control many aspects of the body's form and function.

endomysium—a sheath of connective tissue that surrounds and carries capillaries and nerves to individual muscle fibers/cells.

eosinophil—a leukocyte within the innate branch of the immune system that recognizes and attacks multicelled parasites.

epimysium—a sheet or layer of connective tissue that envelopes an entire muscle.

erythrocyte—red blood cell whose hemoglobin-laden cytoplasm is a reservoir for oxygen being carried from the lungs to the body's tissues.

esophagus—a muscular tube that carries food from the mouth to the stomach for further mechanical and chemical digestion.

ethanol—an organic compound composed of two carbon atoms bonded to each other, to five hydrogen atoms, and to one hydroxide (–OH) group; a small alcohol.

fascicle—a bundle of skeletal muscle fibers surrounded by a perimysium.

feces—the relatively dry, compacted product of the large intestine consisting of indigestible wastes from digestion and large numbers of bacteria that use the waste as nutrients.

fluoxetine—chemical name for the first SSRI to be synthesized and marketed successfully.

gallbladder—a small accessory organ that stores bile produced in the liver until needed for the digestion process.

gamma amino butyric acid (GABA)—a neurotransmitter substance that plays a major role in inhibition of a wide variety of activities within the central nervous system.

gap junctions—small connections between animal cells that allow direct contact between the cytoplasms of those cells; in cardiac muscle, sites of rapid propagation of impulses calling for muscle contraction.

glutamate—one of 20 different amino acids used to build proteins; in the central nervous system and throughout the body it is a major neurotransmitter with an excitatory role.

helper T cell—a type of lymphocyte that detects foreign molecular surfaces on molecules or cells and assists specific B or T lymphocytes to divide and become numerous for defense against the foreign entities.

hepatic portal system—those capillaries and vessels that carry nutrient-laden blood from the small intestinal epithelium to the liver for processing and control of nutrient levels.

hepatic vein—the vessel that carries blood between the capillary beds of the liver and the systemic circulation returning to the heart.

histamine—an organic nitrogen-containing compound released by basophils and mast cells; triggers the inflammation response by increasing permeability of capillary walls to cells and signals involved in inflammation.

HIV virus—a noncellular pathogenic molecular machine composed of proteins and an RNA genome; causes human immunodeficiency or AIDS (acquired immune deficiency syndrome).

immune system—a collection of organs that surveys blood and tissue fluids, detects and labels foreign particles or cells, and works to degrade and destroy those particles or cells.

inflammation—a chemically complex process in the tissues that results in pain, redness, swelling and localized fever; facilitates response to invading microorganisms.

innate immunity—those generalized aspects of the immune response that are not pathogen-specific; they require no previous exposure to the pathogen.

integration center—a single interneuron or a collection of neurons that connects sensory and motor neurons to each other such that stimuli result in an appropriate response.

integumentary system—a collection of organs (largely skin) that insulates the organism while protecting it from desiccation and invasion by foreign pathogens.

interstitial fluid (lymph)—that aqueous solution of biomolecules that exists between cells within tissues; it becomes lymph when transported in lymph capillaries back toward the heart.

ion channel—a protein complex within a cell membrane that allows ions to flow down their electrical/chemical gradient across the membrane, influencing the membrane potential.

ion gradient—a spatial variation from one point to another in the concentration of ions in solution, often over a short distance across a membrane.

kidney—an organ of the urinary system that filters waste from the blood, controls water and ion content in the blood, and returns useful substances to the blood.

large intestine—a 5-foot-long tubular organ of the digestive system that receives indigestible chyme residues from the small intestine; water reabsorption and some vitamin absorption occur here.

leukocytes—white blood cells that, as part of the body's immune system, help detect and destroy foreign cells and particles such as viruses.

Life Is Internally Integrated—one of 12 principles of life on which this book is based.

limbic system—a set of brain regions such as the hippocampus and amygdala that are broadly involved in emotions, behavior, long-term memory, and olfaction.

liver—an accessory organ of the digestive system; it processes and stores glycogen, decomposes old red blood cells, synthesizes blood plasma proteins, and hormones; it also detoxifies many toxins and drugs.

lymph node—organ of the lymphatic system in which antigen-lymphocyte encounters occur; sites of tissue fluid filtration and surveillance.

lymphatic system—a collection of organs that facilitates the surveillance of tissue fluids and their movement back to the bloodstream.

lymphocyte—a class of leukocytes that form the third line of defense against pathogens; B lymphocytes make antibodies; T lymphocytes generate signal substances or kill self cells infected with pathogens.

macrophage—a large, wandering cell that engulfs and degrades foreign particles and cells in the tissues of vertebrates; functions in both the innate and adaptive immune responses.

mast cell—a leukocyte within the innate branch of the immune system that functions within the body's tissues by participating in various aspects of the inflammation response; releases histamines.

membrane potential—the difference of voltage (or potential energy) between the inside and the outside of a cell.

memory lymphocyte—a class of B or T cell that does not differentiate immediately into antibody secretion or killing activity; it divides to form a population of cells specific for an antigen just encountered and waits for a second encounter to differentiate.

meninges—a system of multiple membrane layers that surround the parts of the central nervous system.

motor neuron—a cell that conducts action potentials (signals) away from the central nervous system to an effector organ such as a muscle or a gland; part of the nervous systems' response machinery.

mouth—the entrance to the digestive system where both mechanical and chemical degradation of food begins.

muscle fiber/muscle cell—elongated, cylindrical, multinucleated cells packed with contractile fibrils of actin and myosin proteins.

muscular system—a collection of organs (muscles) that facilitate movement of the body and movement within the body.

myofilament—a protein strand within a muscle cell; composed of myosin, actin, or elastic proteins.

myosin—a class of proteins that uses ATP energy and a flexible head domain for movement along a protein strand of actin.

Na-K-ATPase pump—a transmembrane protein complex using ATP energy to move sodium and potassium ions against their concentration gradients; the result is a membrane potential from the inside of the cell to the outside.

natural killer cell—a type of lymphocyte within the innate branch of the immune system that attacks tumor cells and virally infected cells using generalized markers on the surfaces of these cells.

nephron—a multicellular filtration and reabsorption unit of the kidney; consists of a Bowman's capsule (filtration), distal and proximal tubules (reabsorption and secretion), and a loop of Henle.

nerve—a collection of neuronal processes, usually axons from multiple neurons, travelling together inside a protective myelin sheath.

nervous system—a collection of organs composed of neurons that coordinates the activities of the organism while transmitting signals from one location to another.

neuron—within the nervous system, a cell designed to transmit a nerve impulse from one location within the body to another.

neurotransmitter—a chemical substance that by rapid diffusion carries a signal across a synaptic cleft to the membrane of an excitable cell, where it may initiate a new action potential.

neutrophil—a leukocyte within the innate branch of the immune system that patrols the bloodstream for foreign cells or objects; has phagocytic activity.

nucleus accumbens—a body of neurons within the striatum region of the brain that mediates feelings of pleasure or reward; drug addiction is centered in this region as well.

pancreas—an organ of the digestive system generating degradative enzymes; it is also glandular, secreting the hormones insulin and glucagon.

parasympathetic system—the branch of the autonomic nervous system that stimulates resting state activities such as digestion, urination, or sexual arousal.

pathogen—any microorganism, viral, bacterial, or eukaryotic, that by its presence or growth in host tissues causes or contributes to a disease state.

perimysium—a layer of fibrous connective tissue that envelopes a fascicle or bundle of skeletal muscle fibers.

peripheral nervous system—the collection of all nerves and ganglia that lies outside of the brain and spinal cord.

plasma—the fluid component of blood that includes those factors that cause clotting of blood; it contains nutrients, hormones, and molecule wastes and is a vehicle for movement of the cellular components of blood.

platelet—fragment of a megakaryocyte cell that floats in the circulatory system helping to clot blood at sites of trauma and secreting growth hormone.

portal vein—the vessel that carries blood between the capillary beds of the small intestine and those of the liver.

psychoactive—descriptive of a drug that affects the brain and its behavior.

pulmonary circulation—those blood vessels that carry deoxygenated blood from the heart to the lungs and reoxygenated blood from the lungs to the heart.

pulse—the sudden dilation of arterial vessels caused by ventricular contraction within the heart.

ramus—a major branch of a nerve such as the dorsal branch of a spinal nerve.

receptor—a cell, part of a cell, or a tissue that converts a stimulus from the external or internal environment into a signal (action potential) that can travel sensory neurons to the central nervous system for interpretation and response.

reflex—a suddenly, involuntary response to a stimulus.

reflex arc—a neural pathway that controls a reflexive response; sometimes only five elements in length: the receptor, a sensory neuron, an interneuron, a motor neuron, and an effector.

respiratory system—a collection of organs that enables critical gaseous reactants and products to be added to and removed from blood.

resting potential—the relatively stable electrical charge difference across a cell membrane in an excitable cell not presently transmitting a signal; contrasts with action potential.

rod cell—a receptor cell in the retina of the eye that is responsive to differing degrees of light intensity distinguishing light from darkness.

saliva—a fluid produced by salivary glands that lubricates food and begins the digestion of starch polymer within the food.

salivary gland—an organ of the digestive system whose tissues synthesize digestive enzymes like amylase that degrade starch to simple sugars.

sarcomere—the structural and functional unit within a muscle cell; intertwined protein fibrils of actin and myosin that pull against each other in the contraction process.

sedative—a chemical that relaxes or tranquilizes the nervous system; usually functions within synapses.

sensory neuron—a cell that conducts action potentials (signals) away from stimulus receptors in the body and toward the central nervous system.

serotonin—a neurotransmitter in certain synaptic spaces within the brain that signals action potentials in cells resulting in a feeling of well-being.

skeletal muscle—striated muscle generally attached to bones by tendons; under voluntary control of the peripheral nervous system.

skeletal system—a collection of organs (bones) that gives support and form to the body and that assists the muscular system during movement.

small intestine—a 21-foot-long tubular organ of the digestive system where mechanical digestion, chemical digestion, and nutrient absorption occur.

smooth muscle—nonstriated muscle under involuntary control; forms much of the structure of the digestive and vascular systems.

somatic system—that portion of the peripheral nervous system associated with voluntary control of skeletal muscles and with sensory reception of stimuli such as hearing or touch.

spinal cord—an elongated tubular bundle of nerves and supportive tissues extending from the brain; supports transmission of signals between the brain and the rest of the body.

spinal nerve—a multicellular bundle of neural processes that extends away from the surface of the spinal cord and enervates a particular region of the body.

spleen—organ of the lymphatic system in which antigen-lymphocyte encounters occur; sites of blood filtration and surveillance.

SSRI (serotonin-specific reuptake inhibitor)—a chemical that inhibits the activity of serotonin transport proteins such that high concentrations of serotonin remain in the synaptic space.

stomach—a muscular organ that receives, temporarily stores, and digests food. Hydrochloric acid and the enzyme pepsin work to degrade protein structure here.

sympathetic system—the branch of the autonomic nervous system that stimulates the fight-or-flight activities associated with stressful situations.

synapse—a narrow gap or space between two excitable cells; a signal reaching the end of the first cell must become chemical in nature to cross the space and initiate a signal in the other cell.

systemic circulation—those blood vessels that carry blood from the heart to the tissues (other than the lungs) and from those tissues back to the heart.

systolic pressure—the outward pressure of blood on arterial walls under the full force of a ventricular contraction.

threshold—(in a neuron) the membrane potential difference that must be reached before an action potential can begin initiated and a fresh impulse sent along the neuronal membrane.

T lymphocyte—any lymphocyte that matures to competence in the thymus gland; several classes exist of which helpers and killers are most prominent.

transporter protein—a membrane protein that binds a substance on one side of the membrane and transports it back to the opposite side of the same membrane.

tropomyosin—a long protein-containing fiber that binds to actin filaments within the sarcomere; helps control actin-myosin binding and therefore muscle contraction.

troponin—a protein along the tropomyosin fiber that specifically locks onto actin at the site at which myosin heads would otherwise bind; involved in control of muscle contraction.

turgid—to be filled with solvent, usually water, to the point of structural rigidity.

urea—a waste substance formed in the liver by attaching two amine groups to one carbon dioxide molecule; forms a major component of urine.

ureter—a duct within the urinary system that carries urine from its formation site in the kidney to its storage site in the urinary bladder.

urethra—a duct that extends from the base of the bladder to the exterior of the body; urine is excreted through this duct.

urinary system—a collection of organs that filters the blood, creating, collecting, and storing the resulting urine for excretion.

urine—the fluid that results from filtration of the blood and selective secretion activities of the kidney; the resultant fluid is voided from the bladder.

vaccination—administering a preparation of killed microorganisms, living attenuated organisms, or parts of virulent organisms to produce or artificially increase immunity to a particular disease agent.

valve—folds of tissue within the major arteries that allow blood to pass during ventricular contraction but that then seat against each other to prevent backflow of blood during ventricular relaxation.

vein—a blood vessel that conducts blood away from the lung or tissues and toward the heart.

ventricle—one of two highly muscular chambers in the mammalian heart that pumps blood to either the lungs or the tissues.

vitamin—an organic compound that is required in very small amounts as a cofactor or coenzyme for many vital metabolic processes.

Elegant Responsiveness

Survey Questions

11.1 Life's Responsiveness
- To what sort of things is life responsive?
- Are all life-forms, including bacteria, responsive?
- What is the result of a life form being unresponsive?
- In general, what does responsiveness accomplish for the organism?
- Do all responses made by living things occur only at the cellular level?

11.2 **Responsiveness at the Transcriptional Level**
- What kind of things would a simple bacterium need to be responsive to?
- How might a bacterial cell respond to a new food source in its environment?

Herbie loves computer games. He got a highly engaging one at Christmas (see Section 2.1) that caused him to sit around all through January. Since he's easily 60 lbs overweight, his trim and lovely sister Harassa has pestered him about his appearance using words like "gluttony" and "couch potato." Herbie is sick of it. He sells his old bicycle and buys an attachment for his Mom's treadmill. Now, he plays his game while walking uphill all evening long. He quickly loses about 10 lbs and then starts maintaining. This is frustrating. He's still being called "fat boy." Herbie's Mom takes him to a medical specialist who (is overweight but) has studied obesity. The result is much dialog, many questions, and a test or two. Soon, the doctor has some good/bad news for poor Herbie.

He suggests that Herbie's fatty adipose tissue is putting out elevated levels of signal molecules—**hormones** called **leptins** (see Figure 11.2). These reach his brain where they bind to **hormone receptor** proteins. These receptors are designed to help generate signals that dampen Herbie's appetite so that he'll eat less. But his brain receptors vary genetically from normal ones. They aren't as sensitive to the signal molecules as they would be in thin people. So Herbie's set point is higher; he isn't gaining weight, but he will have a very hard time losing what he's gained. The good news is that he is *genetically* obese. The bad news is he's still obese.

Herbie's hormone receptors are part of a system designed to help control weight. It is supposed to sense the excess calories he ingests and stores and respond by dampening his appetite. The result is supposed to be a constant, desirable weight level. This system contributes to what is called **homeostasis**—a broad pattern of regulatory relationships that sense disruptive changes and responds to those changes so as to keep body chemistry constant. And it works!

hormone—a chemical substance released by a cell or gland that signals another cell or organ of the body to respond in some way.

leptin—a protein hormone that helps to control energy intake into the body by regulating the appetite for food.

hormone receptor—usually a membrane-bound protein whose surface conformation enables it to both bind to and respond to a hormonal signal molecule.

homeostasis—maintenance of stable conditions chemically and physically within the body; the result of highly regulated and coordinated activities of the body's systems.

- By what molecules would that response be mediated, and how would it work?
- How would this molecular system sense that a new food source is available?

11.3 Responsiveness at the Cellular Level

- How does a system of cells recognize a change in its environment?
- How does such recognition result in a signal? What is the nature of the signal?
- How does the signal move from cell to cell?
- What is the response to the signal?
- How does such a response serve the organism?

11.4 Responsiveness at the Hormonal Level

- What is a hormone?
- How is a hormonal signal an improvement over direct cell-to-cell signaling?
- Do plants have hormones? What sort of changes do plants need to respond to?
- What are some plant hormones, and where do they produce their effects?
- How might a plant sense that the amount of sunlight it is receiving has changed?
- How might a plant respond to changes in the amount of sunlight it receives?
- How would such changes serve the plant (or its species)?

11.5 Responsiveness at the Organ System Level

- Can human beings also respond to changes in daylight levels?
- How are daylight levels sensed in humans (in vertebrates, generally)?
- What are some responses we make to daylight levels?
- What organs/cells sense the light levels, and what organs/cells respond to these sensations?
- Are hormones involved? If so, which hormone(s)?
- How broad are the effects of such hormones?

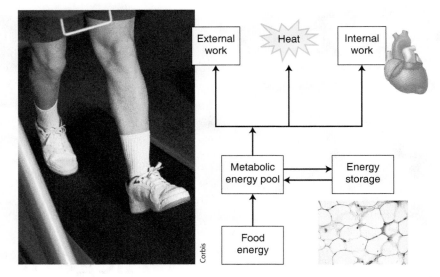

Figure 11.1   Life is Responsive. Signals within the organism control the energy flow represented by the arrows in the diagram. The body responds appropriately both to the exercise and to the food intake and coordinates the two processes.

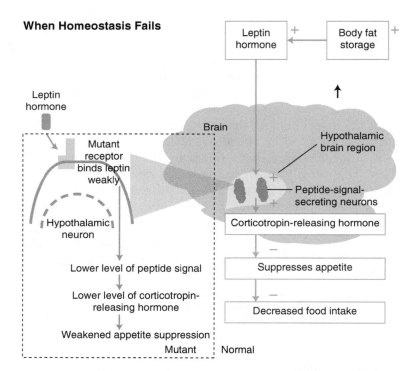

Figure 11.2   When Homeostasis Fails.   The normal result of fat accumulation is a signalling process that results in a decrease in appetite for food.   However, mutant cell surface receptors for leptin molecules may result in weak leptin binding, weakened subsequent hormonal signalling and weakened appetite suppression.

11.6 Responsiveness at the Behavioral Level

- How does behavior compare with our other examples of responsiveness in complexity and structural basis within the organism?
- How are behavioral responses classified?
- Can all behaviors be neatly categorized as instinctive or learned?
- Are bird songs learned or instinctive?
- What is the value of a learned response to the organism? to the species?

It's just like a thermostat, but in Herbie's case it's set too high. And that's a genetic problem that would be impossible for Herbie to fix. Because there are other variables he can control—like caloric intake—he will fight with his weight for the rest of his life. And his trim sister, who is largely ignorant of biology, will verbally abuse him for the duration.

IN OTHER WORDS

1. In a complex organism like *Homo sapiens,* hormonal signals secreted at one site in the body can travel the bloodstream and generate responses in distant, less related parts of the body.
2. When environmental or physiological changes threaten the chemical stability of the human body, those changes are sensed and responded to homeostatically so as to maintain the stability that is otherwise threatened.

The environment is constantly changing. Weather changes occur. Seasons change. Biological communities change as different species interact over time. More rarely, catastrophes occur. These sorts of changes impact each kind of organism in the biological community (see Figure 11.3). They do so by altering specific individual conditions such as temperature, humidity, light levels, altitude, the presence or absence of specific predators or parasites, new inorganic chemicals, or biomolecular

**The Environment:
Constantly Changing**

**Environmental
Changes**

- Weather changes
- Seasonal changes
- Community changes
- Catastrophes

Resulting Alterations

- Temperature
- Humidity
- Light levels
- Altitude
- Predators, parasites
- Inorganic chemicals
- Biomolecules

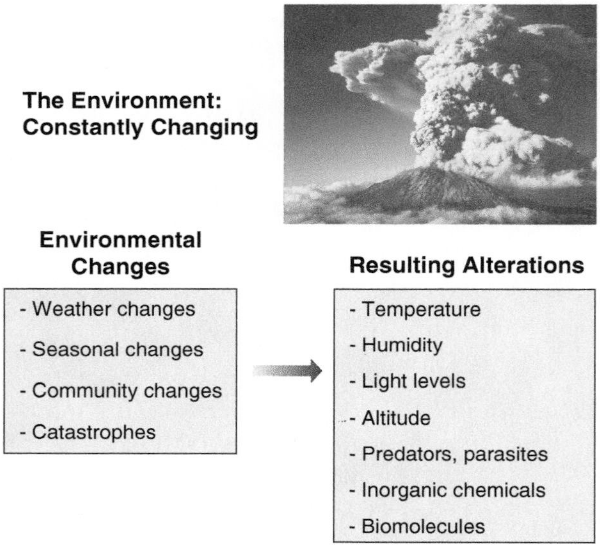

Figure 11.3 The Environment: Constantly Changing. The eruption of Mt. St. Helens in 1980 radically altered the surrounding landscape for decades. Recovery is occurring naturally.

signal molecules. There are far too many examples of changes to list here. Instead, in this chapter, we will consider some specific examples. For comparison's sake we'll introduce them all right now (see Table 11.1). Then, in subsequent sections of the chapter, we'll return to each example and peer more closely at how homeostatic responses are made.

Suppose you were a bacterial cell living in Herbie's bowel (nice thought . . .). Today, Herbie eats a pack of Oreo cookies and a half gallon of vanilla ice cream. Tomorrow, he feels guilty and does spinach and bottled water. A bacterium "doing life" in the bowel of an American teenager has got to be ready for anything! Or let's go to a bog. The environment of a humble bog plant is acidic water that's rarely recirculated. Lots of plant tissue degradation has provided plenty of carbon, hydrogen, and oxygen available in the form of energy sources. But nitrogen is the big challenge. The bog water is low in nitrogen. All the other plants need it too. Could you, as an enterprising plant, try getting nitrogen from insects? You can give them cheap sugar to attract them. But also like junior high kids, insects move fast! And you're just a dumb plant. Insects don't stay long and they leave quickly when threatened. You have to respond quickly—even if you are a plant—when your opportunity comes!

What if you were a mustard plant, *Arabidopsis thaliana?* A huge old tree has just fallen next to you, and every morning it blocks the sunlight that you desperately need to generate your own stem, leaves, flowers, and the seeds of the next generation. How can you get more sunlight now that

Table 11.1 Examples of environmental change to which organisms respond

Organism	Initial State	Altered State	Nature of Response
Coliform bacterium	high-lactose nutrients	nutrients lacking lactose	transcriptional
Venus fly trap	no insect food source	insect on plant leaf	electrical, biochemical, mechanical
Mustard plant	no lack of sunlight	shaded for much of day	hormonal, transcriptional
Human being	bright incident light	darkness	hormonal, biochemical
White-crowned sparrow	inborn song expressed	hears nearby male song	behavioral

you're suddenly in the shade? You can't move like an animal. You'll have to grow toward the sunlight and out of the shade. But how do you do that?

Or consider yourself. You are highly responsive to many stimuli. You are very conscious of the differences mentioned in Genesis 1 that relate to light and darkness, day and night. During the day, bright sunlight makes it easy to read books, see blackboards, go to class, or find the library. During the night, the darkness represents an opportunity to rest the mind, the eyes, the limbs, the soul. "Say, we actually do feel more like sleeping at night and more wakeful during daylight hours. Is this an actual physiological response to the light changes in a solar day?"

Finally, consider humble sparrows. As a male sparrow grows, it hears older sparrows of its species sing bird songs. But which older sparrows? It depends on the older individuals that happen to be in the immature bird's environment. And environments change. If you change which birds the immature bird listens to, you can impact the details of the song it learns, and hence it's reproductive success in its immediate environment.

What happens if these organisms we've observed are unresponsive to the kinds of environmental changes we have talked about here? A bacterium that is unprepared to digest a certain type of nutrient will suffer if that nutrient is what's available (see Figure 11.4). If a Venus fly trap can't tell when a fly is sitting on its leaf surface, the plant may starve for nitrogen. If a plant is unable to reach sunlight, its ability to photosynthesize its own carbohydrate energy is sorely limited. If a human being ignores environmental changes by sleeping in during the day (i.e., in class) and playing all night, or if he's a pilot and he keeps flying from continent to continent and therefore never sees night, all sorts of strange things begin happening to his physiology.

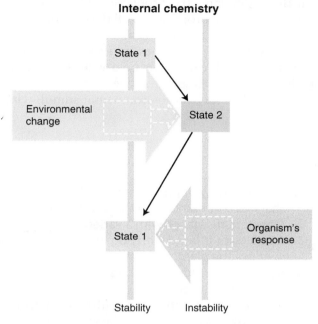

The Organism's Response - Homeostasis

Internal chemistry

Figure 11.5 The Organism's Response: Homeostasis.

Perhaps the Designer of life-forms assumed that the environment around them would be changing. Those changes might even have been part of an overall scheme for this planet. He simply designed life-forms to respond. Happily, **Life Is Responsive.** Life-forms respond in such a way as to stably maintain their internal chemistry. Any molecular machinery that responds to external changes (or other system changes) and helps retain internal chemical stability is said to be *homeostatic* (see Figure 11.5). In this chapter, the homeostatic mechanisms we'll examine work at several discrete levels to stabilize the internal chemistry of a bacterium, a plant, a songbird, and in us. We will see that as the complexity of an organism increases, the variety of homeostatic strategies available to that organism increases as well.

A simple bacterium senses biochemical changes in its environment and responds by altering its pattern of mRNA transcription (see Table 11.1). In a multicellular plant, a variety of distinct cell types participate in the physiology of its response. Multicellular plants and animals can sense an

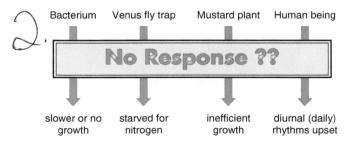

Organisms Must Respond to Environmental Change

Figure 11.4 Organisms Must Respond to Environmental Change.

Life Is Responsive—the eighth principle of life elaborated in this textbook.

environmental change with one kind of cell. This cell then stimulates the production of a hormone signal that can be broadcast to all the cells throughout the body of the organism. The hormone can cause a variety of cell types in a variety of locations to respond, each in its own way! Finally, organisms complex enough to have a nervous system can respond to specific environmental stimuli with very sophisticated behavioral patterns that maintain the organism's favorable position within the biological community in which it lives. Learned behaviors are not necessarily homeostatic: They don't always impact internal chemistry directly. But if the learned behavior has survival value, it is, in effect, preserving the organism's internal chemistry in a stable state.

IN OTHER WORDS

1. A wide variety of physical and chemical changes in the environment impose a wide variety of biological changes on organisms in that environment.
2. A bacterium is faced with a variety of differing nutritional sources in its environment.
3. A bog plant is faced with bog water that is unusually low in nitrogen content compared to the nutritional needs of the plant.
4. A plant in a meadow may be suddenly challenged with an environmental limitation regarding the amount of sunlight it receives.
5. A human being, confronted with daylight followed by darkness every 24 hours, needs to be optimally able to use these time periods in healthful patterns.
6. A male sparrow needs to be able to hear the song dialect of its local population and learn to sing it in order to attract females and perpetuate the local population of sparrows.
7. Organisms unable to respond appropriately to significant environmental changes will either be disadvantaged compared to other population members, or will die.

Let's get a bit closer to the systems we've introduced. Consider the bacterium *E. coli*. In the human bowel, the disaccharide sugar **lactose** would be a wonderful microbial energy source, but it is seldom available to that humble microbe (see Figure 11.6). It's generally absorbed by the host's small intestine (unless the host is **lactase** insufficient). It would be wasteful for *E. coli* to make an enzyme to degrade lactose if the sugar isn't present in significant quantities. But sometimes dairy items are the major part of a human host's meal! Then, it would be nice if the microbe could signal its genetic machinery to (1) generate the degradative enzyme for the lactose that's present and (2) stop producing the enzyme when the lactose is used up.

How is the production of lactose-degrading enzymes controlled? For the sake of efficiency, the three genes whose protein products control lactose use are all found next to each other in the DNA of *E. coli*. These genes are referred to collectively as **structural genes** and together with the controlling sequence next to them, they are called the lactose **operon** (see Figure 11.7a). When RNA polymerase

transcribes these three structural genes, the protein products needed to transport in and degrade lactose will be present and active with the bacterial cell. But when are these genes transcribed?

Along the DNA molecule, just upstream from the structural genes (see Figure 11.7a, b) is a region called the **promoter** site. This site is a sequence of bases in DNA that preferentially binds the enzyme RNA polymerase. By the molecular surfaces it exposes to the polymerase's surface shape, the promoter DNA sequence stimulates serious binding of the polymerase so that it can glide along the DNA and begin its work of transcribing the structural genes into messenger RNA. Along the DNA strand, near this promoter region and just upstream from the beginning of the first structural gene, is another short sequence of DNA bases called the **operator** region. The sequences of bases in this region of DNA are designed to bind specifically to a regulatory protein called a **repressor** protein (see Figure 11.7a). Here is where we begin to see the cell's responsiveness come into play.

lactose—a disaccharide sugar found in milk and milk products, degraded to the monosaccharides glucose and galactose before being catabolized for energy generation.

lactase—a protein enzyme capable of degrading the sugar lactose into its monosaccharide products.

structural gene—a gene that codes for a protein product that contributes directly to the functional activities of the cell; a gene whose product has no regulatory role.

operon—in DNA, a sequence of adjacent structural genes whose products are usually functionally related together with an upstream operator region of DNA to which regulatory proteins specifically bind.

promoter—a sequence of DNA base pairs just upstream from a gene or set of genes to be transcribed; RNA polymerase selectively binds to this sequence.

operator—a segment of DNA at the front end of an operon; regulatory proteins conditionally bind the operator influencing whether or not transcription of the operon occurs.

repressor—a regulatory protein that by binding to the operator sequence of DNA within an operon prohibits transcription of the genes within the operon.

Responsive at the Level of Transcription

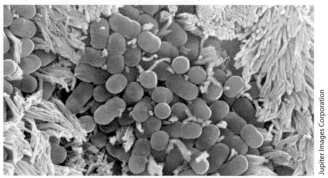

Jupiter Images Corporation

E. coli bacteria (red) clustered on the surface villi of intestinal endothelial cells in a small child. Breast-fed infants have a high lactose diet.

In adults:
- Lactose seldom available in large amounts in the bowel
- Making its degradative enzymes continuously would be foolish
- Smarter: transcribe genes for these enzymes only when lactose is present

Figure 11.6 Responsive at the Level of Transcription.

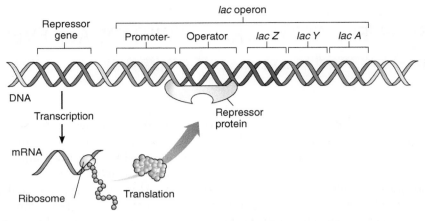

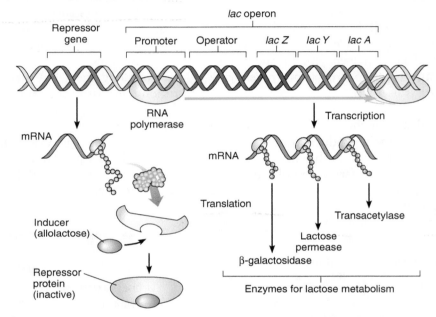

(a) When allolactose is absent, a repressor protein binds the lactose operon and inhibits binding of RNA polymerase to the lactose operon's upstream promoter.

(b) When allolactose (and therefore lactose) is present, it deforms the repressor protein allowing transcription of the genes whose products break down lactose.

Figure 11.7   The Lactose Operon.

The repressor protein is the product of the repressor gene found elsewhere in the DNA. The repressor protein for the lactose operon is always present but always in low concentrations. It's really a neat protein! It has two separate binding sites on its surface. At one site it can bind to DNA that has the base sequence of the operator region of the lactose operon. At a different site on its surface, it can bind to an intracellular form of lactose called **allo-lactose** (see Figure 11.7b). The responsiveness of the whole system we're describing is based on the fact that when the repressor protein binds to an

allo-lactose molecule, its operator DNA binding site is changed so that it can no longer bind to operator DNA. So it becomes a homeostatic on-off switch. Isn't that neat? A regulatory protein that changes what it does based on whether or not allo-lactose

allo-lactose—a chemically altered form of lactose often present intracellularly where it can bind to the lac operon repressor protein turning on synthesis of its structural genes.

(lactose) is present! Consider now how this protein works. If lactose is absent (Figure 11.7a), the repressor protein binds to the operator sequence lying between the promoter site and the structural genes. In this situation, it's a molecular roadblock to the RNA polymerase enzyme. Since RNA polymerase can't get by it, transcription of the lactose-degrading enzyme genes will not happen, which is good. If lactose isn't there, its degradative enzyme isn't needed.

But if lactose is present (Figure 11.7b), soon a bit of its allo-lactose form will be present within the cell. This form will bind the repressor protein, reducing the protein's ability to bind operator DNA. The repressor protein then falls off the DNA. But that means that RNA polymerase is then free to transcribe the DNA and the products of the lactose operon become available to break down the lactose that is present! Is that elegant?! That is truly elegant! That is designed! So even at the basic level of transcription, Life Is Responsive to changes in environmental conditions. "So Herbie, drink your low-fat milk. Bacterial lactase will degrade the lactose you don't absorb and grant you some wonderful flatulence as a by-product."

IN OTHER WORDS

1. A bacterium living in the human bowel will experiment with temporal changes in available amounts of the sugar lactose to burn for energy.
2. When lactose is present, the bacterium synthesizes the proteins needed to transport it into the cell and degrade it; when lactose is absent, the bacterium no longer makes these proteins.
3. The structural genes coding for the transport protein and the degradative enzyme sit together along the DNA in a sequence called the *operon*.
4. The operon is controlled from two upstream sequences in the DNA, the promoter and the operator.
5. The promoter is an RNA polymerase binding site that prepares polymerase to transcribe the operon; the operator can bind a repressor protein that blocks polymerase's transcription activity.
6. Whether or not the repressor protein binds to the operator depends on the presence or absence of lactose in the cell's environment.
7. Lactose in its allo-lactose form can bind to the repressor protein causing it to fall off of operator DNA. In this way, allo-lactose controls whether the genes to process it are transcribed or not.

Our previous example was a response to change by a molecule binding directly to DNA and influencing transcription processes. Now we'll consider an example one step removed from the basic level of gene expression (transcription and translation). In this next system, all the components necessary for a homeostatic response are already synthesized and in place. We consider now the fringed trapping leaves of the Venus fly trap. We mentioned their value in the nutritionally spare environment of the bog habitat (see Figure 11.8). Water is quite low in nitrogen content. But nitrogen is all around. Seasonally, in spring and summer, it's imported into the habitat in the form of insects—flies—if you can just catch them!

When you are as slow as a plant, how do you respond by trapping a nitrogen source that moves as quickly as a fly? Each of the paired, lobe-like leaves that comprise the trap has a set of three sensory hairs and a thin film of luscious, high-carb **nectar** on its

(a)

(b)

Jim Zipp/ Photo Researchers, Inc.

Dan Suzio/Photo Researchers, Inc.

Figure 11.8 Life at the Bog. **(a)** A typical bog in northern Maine in May. **(b)** A Venus Fly Trap, *Dionaea muscipula*, shown with its traps open.

inner surface (see Figure 11.9). Doesn't that sound diabolical? The system gets activated when one sensory hair is touched twice in rapid succession or if two hairs are touched simultaneously. This arrangement keeps the system from responding too quickly to unprofitable stimuli—like a wind-blown piece of leaf litter! What a beautiful design: Only a walking insect is likely to trip the hairs in just the right way to start things off. This appropriate combination of hair touches starts a small **electrical potential** change across the leaf cell membranes—a rush of ions across the membrane that is similar to the depolarizations that occur in animal nerve cells (see Figure 11.10). Wow—a plant with elements of an animal nervous system! Clearly the war for speed is on!

This sudden redistribution of ions across a cell membrane leads rapidly to the next step: It causes the cells of the outer layer of the leaf blade to pump protons into the structure of the cell walls. The resulting higher concentration of protons activates **expansin** enzymes within the wall that loosen cellulose fibers in the structure of the cell walls (see Section 11.4). Since the cells maintain much higher concentrations of dissolved substances than the fluids around them, this structural loosening allows water to rush into these cells. The result is cell expansion. This expansion of the outer cells causes the leaves to pop shut, which coerces the fly to "stay for dinner." Isn't that charming? What a sequence of events! Homeostasis, in this situation, appears to be carefully arranged into an elegant series of responses that are first mechanical, then electrical, then enzymatic, then osmotic, and finally mechanical again. No single response by itself achieves the required effect. What a challenge it would be to describe how that sequence of responses could have evolved using randomly derived mutations!

> **nectar**—a sweet liquid secreted by specialized cells of a plant; used to attract insects; a major source of honey.
>
> **electric potential**—the inherent energy in positively charged particles; equal to the work it would take to push the particles there from a position with zero potential.
>
> **expansin**—a category of enzymes that break cross-linking covalent bonds between cellulose fibers, weakening the overall structure of which they are a part.

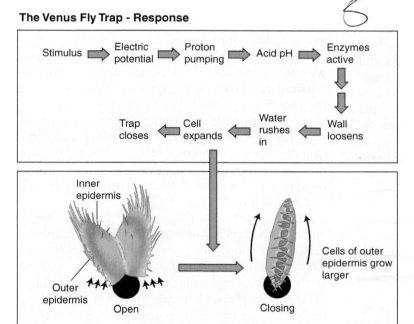

Figure 11.9 Venus Fly Trap Stimulus and Response. A couple of sequential touches of the **(a)** sensory hair on the inner face of the highly modified leaf results **(b)** in the rapid closure of the trap.

David M. Dennis/Tom Stack and Associates

David M. Dennis/Tom Stack and Associates

a

b

The Venus Fly Trap - Response

Stimulus ⇒ Electric potential ⇒ Proton pumping ⇒ Acid pH ⇒ Enzymes active

Trap closes ⇐ Cell expands ⇐ Water rushes in ⇐ Wall loosens

Inner epidermis

Outer epidermis

Open

Closing

Cells of outer epidermis grow larger

Figure 11.10 The Venus Fly Trap — Response. The stimulus is the tripping of a sensory hair by the insect. The response is the opening of channels—gates—that allow ions across the cell membranes in cells on the outer leaf surface. The result is the pumping of hydrogen ions (protons), and a resultant change in pH. This alters enzyme activities which result in loosened cell walls, water influx and a resultant expanding of cells on the outer side of the leaf. Later, hydrolytic enzymes will enter the leaf and digest the nitrogenous fly.

IN OTHER WORDS

1. The fringed leaves of the Venus fly trap are capable of trapping insects within their structure and subsequently digesting them as a protein (nitrogen) source.
2. On the leaf surface are both nectar, which attracts the fly, and tiny projections that, when tripped by the fly's movement, signal the leaf to rapidly close.
3. The signal causes outer leaf cell surface ion depolarizations and proton pumping, which enhance the activities of cell wall degrading enzymes called *expansins*.
4. As expansins weaken the walls of outer leaf cells, they expand by taking in water; this swelling on the outside of the leaf snaps the leaf halves shut on the hapless insect.

In the previous response to environmental change, we saw a series of cell membrane and wall changes involving cells communicating directly and sequentially with each other. Now we'll see an example of a plant homeostatic response that is hormonally mediated. The stimulus is, again, an environmental change. But in this case the initial response to the change occurs within a single type of cell whose response is to produce a hormone (see Figure 11.11). The hormone becomes a signal moving throughout the organism's body. Responses to the hormone will occur in *any* cell type that has a surface receptor that specifically binds that hormone. In this way, the system can be designed so that a diversified set of responses can be made to a single environmental change.

There is a small but significant variety of plant hormones. Table 11.2 summarizes the major ones and their roles in plant development. Notice the kinds of processes that plant hormones govern. Some of these processes are cued to systematic changes in the environment. Hormones make these connections between environmental stimuli and appropriate plant responses. Our particular focus in this example will be on a class of hormones called **auxins**.

Table 11.2 Plant Hormones

Gibberellins	promote stem elongation, help end dormancy, contribute to flowering
Auxins	promote cell elongation in stems, role in gravitropism, phototropism
Cytokinins	promote cell division, leaf expansion, retard leaf aging
Abscisic Acid	promotes stomatal closure, promotes bud and seed dormancy
Ethylene Gas	promotes fruit ripening, flower senescence, abscission of leaves, flowers

How does an ordinary weed in a meadow respond to the sudden, long-term intrusion of a large object casting a shadow, such as a fallen tree that lands within 2 feet of it? *Arabidopsis*, a member of the mustard family of plants, typically flowers early in the growing season. It grows optimally with long sunny days powering its photosynthesis. The plant's response to changes in the availability and direction of solar radiation occurs in the context of plant growth. Growth normally involves cell division to form new cells followed by elongation of those cells (see Figure 11.12a).

In the mid-1800s, the work of Charles Darwin and his son Francis with excised plant shoot tips suggested that control of growth appeared to emanate from the tip of the plant shoot. Later, in an ingenious study in the early twentieth century, a tiny block of agar was placed beneath a cut tip from an actively growing shoot. What sort of substances might wander out of the tip and into the agar (see Figure 11.12b)? Later, in a dark environment, the tip was cut from another actively growing shoot. The agar block was placed on the cut surface, but off-center (see Figure 11.12c). In the shoot newly exposed to the agar block, only the cells under the block elongated.

Responsive at the Hormonal Level

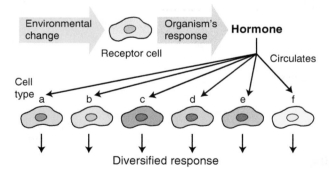

Figure 11.11   Life is Responsive at the Hormonal Level. One stimulus, generating a single hormonal response, can result in a wide array of cellular responses throughout the organism. Each of the responding cell types need only present an appropriate receptor for the hormone on its cell surface. Seemingly unrelated multifaceted responses to a single external stimulus is just one context in which the Designer illustrates His great prowess.

auxin—a class of plant hormones, particular members of which are involved in stimulation of growth as in stem elongation or giving dominance to the apical bud on a stem.

Shoot apical meristem
Dividing cells near all shoot tips are responsible for a shoot's primary tissues and growth.

Cell divisions in shoot apical meristem

New cells elongate and start to differentiate into primary tissues.

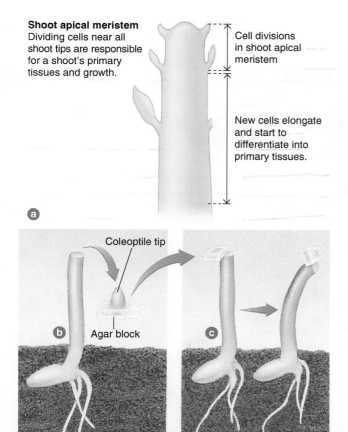

Coleoptile tip

Agar block

Figure 11.12 Auxins Behavior in Plant Shoot Tips. **(a)** The structure of a typical plant apical shoot. Zones of cell division and elongation are indicated. **(b)** Placement of a cut shoot tip on an agar block to allow growth controlling substances to enter the agar. **(c)** Use of the primed agar block to influence growth in a shoot that lacks it's own tip. (See text for details.)

Runk/Schoenberger/Grant Heilman

Figure 11.13 Phototropism. Shoots of corn plants, *Zea mays*, have the ability to grow toward a directional light source. How does the stem do this? See text for details.

Those on the other side of the shoot did not. The result was a bent shoot! Apparently, growth by cell elongation was mediated by a diffusible substance. They gave it the name *auxin*. It appeared that this diffusible substance travelled downward from the growing tip of the plant, encouraging cell elongation in the region of the shoot just below the tip. Once the particular auxin in question, **indole-3-acetic acid (IAA)**, was isolated, it was discovered to be absent from fluids within the plant's vascular system (the xylem and phloem). How then did it travel down through the plant body? It had to be moving from cell to adjacent cell. But its rate and pattern of movement has revealed a carefully crafted asymmetry that caused it to be called **polar transport.**

The rate of hormone movement is slightly faster than can be explained by diffusion alone. Active transport must also be involved. The pattern of movement can be best explained if the auxin diffuses into the upper end of a cell but through **active transport** is quickly carried out of the lower end of that cell in preparation for diffusion into the *next* cell. This provides a pre-determined directionality to the flow of the auxin from the shoot tip to the region of elongation immediately behind it.

Now, let's add another variable to environment. Suppose a new shadow blocks solar rays coming to a plant. *Arabidopsis*, like most plants, will respond by growing out of the shadowy area toward a spot where it obtains the needed sunlight (see Figure 11.13). For that strategy to work, the plant must be able to monitor the direction from which its light source is shining, and then grow in that direction by a process called **phototropism.** How does this positive tropic (growth) response to sunlight work?

indole-3-acetic acid (IAA)—a particular auxin that causes plant cells to elongate as part of the general growth process of the plant.

polar transport—the unidirectional transport of a substance through a series of cells such as from the apex of a plant shoot to its root system.

active transport—the movement of dissolved substances across a membrane with or against a concentration gradient; utilizes cellular energy to insure transport.

phototropism—the tendency of a plant to grow toward a light source such as the sun.

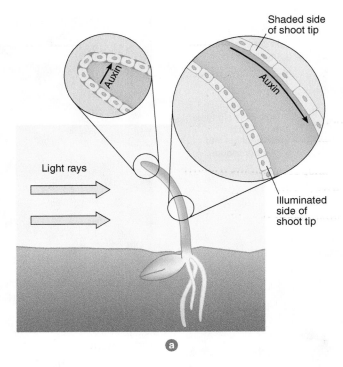

Shaded side
of shoot tip

Auxin

Auxin

Light rays

Illuminated
side of
shoot tip

(a)

Phototropic Response

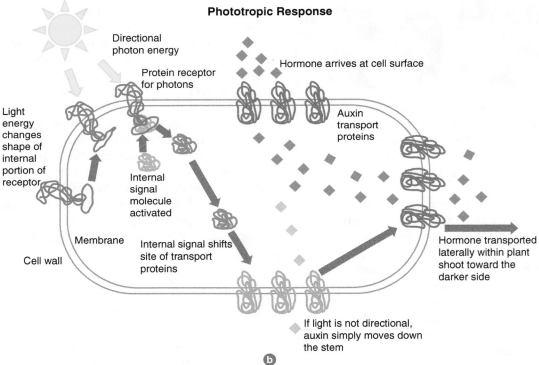

Directional
photon energy

Hormone arrives at cell surface

Protein receptor
for photons

Light
energy
changes
shape of
internal
portion of
receptor

Auxin
transport
proteins

Internal
signal
molecule
activated

Membrane

Internal signal shifts
site of transport
proteins

Cell wall

Hormone transported
laterally within plant
shoot toward the
darker side

If light is not directional,
auxin simply moves down
the stem

(b)

Figure 11.14 Phototropic Response. **(a)** Directional light intensity causes auxin to flow across the shoot tip to the darker side of the plant before it begins its downward transport. **(b)** One current theory is that the photoreceptor protein on the cell surface (in response to high light intensity) sets up an internal molecular signal that causes bits of cell membrane containing auxin transport proteins to shift from the ventral side of the cell to the side of the cell facing away from the light. This channels auxin hormone toward the darker side of the plant instead of simply downward within the stem.

Formally there are two possibilities. If light hits the surface of a plant differentially, then the plant might either sense a greater amount of light on one side or a greater amount of darkness on the other. Study has revealed the presence of **photoreceptor** proteins in the surface membrane of many plant cells (see Figure 11.14). Increased light intensity results in molecular shape changes in these proteins. Such changes activate an internal signal that results in the movement of auxin transport proteins toward the side of the cell facing away from the light! This causes the auxin hormone IAA to be transported from cell to cell laterally *away from* the side of the plant stem that is getting the most light. On the darker side of the shoot, it then continues its migration down the stem (by polar transport), generating cell elongation as it goes. Since most of the elongation is now on the darker side of the stem, the result is the bending of the entire stem toward the light!

A wonderful elegance is revealed here that uses a plant's biochemical response to light to shift the position of auxin transport proteins directionally within a single plant cell. Shuttling transport proteins from one side of the cell to another is an elaborate process in which vesicles carry transport proteins within their membranes from one internal face of the cell membrane to another. A new position for the auxin transport proteins on the cell's darker side then results in selective channeling of the plant hormone to the side of the stem where its effect is needed. This design could not be used in an animal system; it only works in plants because cell orientation within a plant is fixed by its growth from the soil toward the light.

But control is still more elaborate than this. Once the auxin IAA arrives at the cell where elongation is required, it appears to effect this change in two complementary ways. First, IAA within a cell's cytoplasm stimulates proton pumps in the cell membrane to shunt protons (H$^+$ ions) out of the cell interior and into the structure of the wall that surrounds the cell (see Figure 11.15). This higher H$^+$ion concentration

photoreceptor—a large organic molecule, usually a protein, whose structure is altered by the influx of photons. The altered structure results in a signal used by a cell or organ to respond properly to the presence of light.

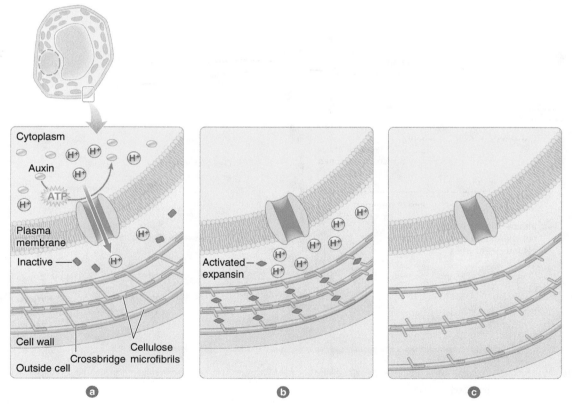

Figure 11.15 Auxin-Induced Cell Elongation. The most immediate action of the auxin IAA in shoot tip cells is to disrupt the cellulosic structures in the cell wall allowing the cell to absorb more water and elongate rappidly. **(a)** The presence of the auxin induces proton pumping. **(b)** The resulting increased hydrogen ion concentration activates the enzyme expansin. **(c)** Expansin degrades crossbridges in cellulose microfibrils, weakening the cell wall's resistance to water uptake.

activates the same collection of expansin enzymes we noted previously (see Section 11.3). Expansins then begin breaking covalent bonds that cross-link cellulose **fibril**s in the wall. What does this accomplish? Well, the concentration of water molecules is higher in fluids surrounding the cell than within it. The law of diffusion reminds us that water will then tend to flow from the region of higher concentration outside the cell to the region of lower concentration within the cell. This water flow is normally resisted by a strong cell wall that simply will not expand. Expansin-driven weakening of the wall allows additional water to enter. This dramatically expands (elongates) the cell.

But IAA not only has its effect inside the cell. Amazingly, this same IAA hormone binds to a particular receptor molecule on the *outer* surface of the same cell (see Figure 11.16). This binding sets up a new intracellular signal that calls for the synthesis of enzymes that *build* the cell wall. How cleverly devised is this system? The IAA quickly enters the cell causing the immediate proton pumping that will weaken the walls. The surrounding fluids are always ready to expand the cell if a wall is weak. Then, the more slowly, transcriptionally induced IAA signaling system sets up the cell to repair what it just disassembled, but only after the cell has elongated. The hormone is a small, witless molecular message in an elegantly fashioned photon-searching system that grows *Arabidopsis* toward the light. Here is a plant that is prepared to respond to a sudden loss of solar radiation by growing toward the greatest amount of light available to it. Fascinating!

fibril—a strand of several cellulose polymer molecules interwoven around each other for added strength.

Wall Synthesis Response to IAA Hormone

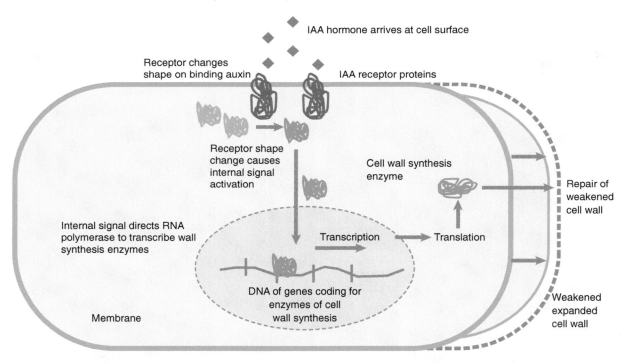

Figure 11.16 Wall Synthesis Response to IAA Hormone. The extracellular signal IAA is converted by its surface receptor to an intracellular signal that initiates the synthesis of enzymes that function in cell wall synthesis and repair.

IN OTHER WORDS

1. The concept of the hormone is elegant; a hormone molecule is secreted by one cell type, travels throughout the vascular system of the organism, and can generate a response in any cell that has a specific receptor for that hormone.

2. One class of plant hormones, the auxins, signal plant cells to grow, elongate, and form the mature structures of the plant.

3. One auxin, indole-acetic acid (IAA) stimulates plant growth toward the source of light waves, a response called *phototropism*.

4. Auxins are elaborated in plant shoot tips and are transported downward toward the root stimulating cell growth and elongation as they arrive.

5. Differential amounts of light on two sides of a shoot tip can cause auxins to be transported laterally with the tip so that more auxin is transported down the darker side of the plant shoot.

6. The resulting differential elongation of the stem causes it to bend toward the light such that growth occurs in that direction.

7. IAA has two effects on the plant cell. The immediate effect is to loosen cell walls so that water uptake elongates them. The second effect is to stimulate transcription of the genes that code for cell wall construction enzymes that restore wall strength following elongation.

Animals make significant use of hormones as well in responding to environmental changes. Consider the normal human tendency to remain awake midmorning versus wanting to fall asleep later at night. It all seems so natural, doesn't it: this pattern that we so glibly violate by burning lights all night and sleeping late into the day (see Figure 11.17)? Normal daytime wakefulness is really a highly adaptive response to environmental change. What is the change and how do we respond to it?

We live in an environment that alternates between light and dark every 24 hours. Many of our bodily functions vary rhythmically in response to this periodicity (Life Is Responsive!). Our body's **core temperature** falls at night and rises in the day (see Figure 11.18). We become less aroused, more lethargic as night comes on. On the anterior aspect of our brain, just above the **optic chiasm** and within the **hypothalamus** region of the brain, lies a pair of cone-shaped structures called the **suprachiasmatic nuclei** (see Figure 11.18). (The term *nuclei* here refers to visible structures, each of which is composed of 20,000 neurons or nerve cells that, together, are about the size of a rice grain.) The suprachiasmatic nuclei exert their control over wakefulness and body temperature with a period of roughly 25 hours, independent of the daily

cycling of light! But light influences these nuclei. It entrains them into a rhythmicity that precisely correlates with the solar day. How does this happen? How does our body actually respond to changes in light and darkness?

The suprachiasmatic nuclei are connected through the optic chiasm to the **optic nerves** coming from the **retina** of your eye. The rhythmic influx of light and darkness over a 24-hour period entrains or controls the periodicity of the chemical output of these nuclei. Periodically, they send impulses over nerve pathways to a small gland at the juncture of your two **cerebral hemispheres** in the geometric center of your head—a gland called the **pineal gland** (see Figure 11.18). The pineal gland is the only gland of the body that gets a direct "read" on daylight or darkness surrounding the human body (see Figure 11.19). When darkness begins to dominate and light levels fall, the pineal gland responds

Figure 11.17 "It's still daytime isn't it? Why am I so tired?" Very few light sources match the sun's ability to decrease the concentration of the hormone melatonin in our bloodstreams.

core temperature—the operating temperature of structures deep within the body of the organism.

optic chiasm—a structure behind the eyes in a vertebrate in which the nerve tracts from the eyes meet and interweave before entering the brain.

hypothalamus—a ventral brain region containing the suprachiasmatic nuclei; it helps to regulate many aspects of the internal fluid environment of the body as well as core temperature and wakefulness.

suprachiasmatic nuclei—small portions of brain tissue just above the optic chiasma that transmit signals associated with the maintenance of circadian rhythms.

optic nerve—a set of neurons that carry form, color, motion, and light intensity information from the retina of the eye to the brain.

retina—the sensory surface within the back of the eye where light waves initiate sensory nerve impulses.

cerebral hemisphere—right and left halves of the cerebrum, the largest portion of the mammalian brain.

pineal gland—an endocrine gland at the center of the brain; secretes the hormone melatonin.

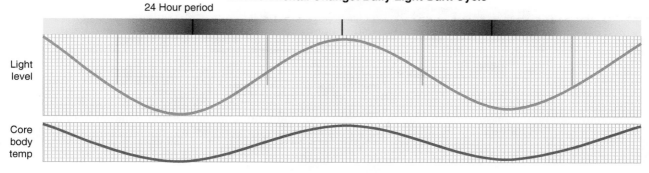

Environmental Change: Daily Light-Dark Cycle

24 Hour period

Light level

Core body temp

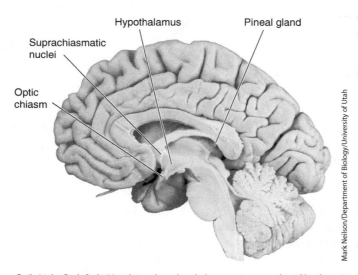

Hypothalamus Pineal gland

Suprachiasmatic nuclei

Optic chiasm

Mark Neilson/Department of Biology/University of Utah

Figure 11.18 Environmental Change: Daily Light-Dark Cycle. Visual signals such as light intensity are gathered by the retina of the eye and transmitted via optic nerves to the optic chiasma where signals are interwoven and passed along optic tracts to the brain. Some of the neurons in these tracts enter and inform the suprachiasmatic nuclei which are in turn connected neuronally to the pineal gland.

to its retinal signals by secreting the hormone **melatonin**. Melatonin, a derivative of the amino acid tryptophan, enters the bloodstream and heads out toward its receptors all over the body. Many of these receptors are right in the suprachiasmatic nuclei of the brain, where the body's temperature and sense of wakefulness are controlled. Thus the increased melatonin concentration in the blood informs the suprachiasmatic nuclei within the hypothalamus that it's nighttime. The nuclei then allow the melatonin levels to inform or correct the periodicity of their day-night signaling system. Soon, signals from these nuclei cause you to feel drowsy. The hypothalamus, in which the nuclei are found, sends its own hormonal signals out to other glands of the body, such as the **thyroid gland**, where decreased output of **thyroxin** can lower your basal metabolism rate and start the cooling down process that prepares you for your long evening's nap.

The behavior of modern Western society amply illustrates that human beings all too willingly throw off the basic pattern of sleeping at night and working during the day with little regard to its impact on their health. Isn't it wonderful that the Designer of the human species anticipated our ignorance of

melatonin—a hormone secreted by the pineal gland in response to darkness; helps entrain the body's biological rhythms to a light-dark cycle.

thyroid gland—an endocrine gland in the cervical region of the body whose hormones regulate basal metabolism rate and calcium balance within the body's tissues.

thyroxin—a hormonal product of the thyroid gland that regulates metabolic rate in the tissues.

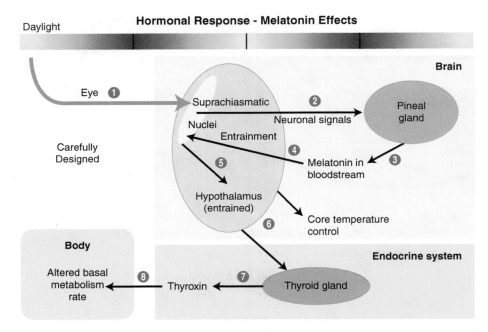

Hormonal Response - Melatonin Effects

Figure 11.19 Hormonal Response – Melatonin Effects. Alterations in the daily influx of light on a person's retinas influence the secretion levels of melatonin by the pineal gland. Melatonin levels in the bloodstream that services the suprachiasmatic nuclei help to entrain these nuclei and the entire hypothalamic machinery of the brain to the current increases and decreases in light levels in a given solar day. They control the organism's circadian rhythms. See text for details relating to numerical sequence in the diagram.

our own **circadian** physiology? He built into us a hormonal response to the 24-hour cycle that would predispose us to sleep when it is dark and be wakeful when it is light. How wonderfully practical is this propensity! We're designed to thrive within the changing environment He created for us!

Melatonin's widespread distribution within the body has led to a recent fascination with its multiple and varied effects (see Table 11.3). It is known to influence rates of bone growth. It controls the onset of human sexual maturation, and it's involved in scavenging **hydroxyl radicals** within the tissues of the body, particularly within the brain. Since melatonin production is dependent on a lack of light, the short days of winter mean that in winter, the amount of melatonin in your body will be greater than in the longer days of summer. In some individuals, the longer periods of drowsiness and lethargy can actually result in a depressive state known as **seasonal affective disorder,** or SAD. Melatonin

may have many other far-reaching effects on our physiology and metabolism. Based on its photoperiodic effects, melatonin is now being used by some individuals as an alternative to traditional sleep-inducing medications. Look forward to many new discoveries surrounding this amazing hormone that helps you to wake up gently in the morning.

For individuals who are having trouble waking up on winter mornings, some have suggested light therapy: crawling to the bathroom which you have painted bright titanium white and loaded up with bright fluorescent lights. You just manage to get the switch on, and the lights so stimulate the optic nerve tracts that melatonin dries up faster and you wake up faster. Sounds painful. Is this approach really the best for your overall physiology? On the other hand,

Table 11.3 Melatonin: Widespread Distribution and Effects

- bone growth rates
- human sexual maturation
- scavenging hydroxyl radicals within body
- core temperature control
- seasonal affective disorder

circadian—refers to any process or characteristic that respects a 24-hour cycle or period.

hydroxyl radical—the neutral form of the hydroxide ion (^-OH); highly reactive and destructive of the chemical integrity of reduced biological molecules.

seasonal affective disorder—a mood alteration in wintertime characterized by a depressive state; reduced amounts of daylight may be causative.

Table 11.4 Melatonin: Two Views

Traditional Medicine	Alternative Medicine
Melatonin Supplements: • have some positive effects • do induce sleep in some subjects	**Melatonin Supplements cure:** • insomnia • jet lag • six types of cancer • depression, anxiety • high cholesterol levels
Melatonin Supplements: • lack sufficient testing to substantiate cure claims made by many • contain a powerful hormone whose total high dosage effect on humans is unknown	**Melatonin Supplements slow:** • multiple sclerosis • heart disease • epilepsy • osteoporosis

for individuals suffering from insomnia, a warning may be appropriate. The alternative medicine community has quickly advocated the use of melatonin supplements (see Table 11.4). The assertion is that melatonin cures insomnia, jet lag, six types of cancer, depression, and anxiety. There are good things to say about it. Melatonin is a free radical scavenger; it also lowers cholesterol levels. Some studies suggest that at appropriate levels it inhibits processes contributing to multiple sclerosis, coronary heart disease, epilepsy, and postmenopausal osteoporosis. So millions of users are consuming melatonin at oral doses of about 10 times the normal body concentrations! Traditional reductionist scientists argue that many positive assertions regarding melatonin are based on suggestive evidence or circumstantial arguments that are not well documented. These scientists remind us that melatonin is a hormone. We don't even know all the cell types that have receptors for it. So users are participating in a dangerous long-term experiment with unpredictable consequences. Which medical community is correct? This is an issue that science will someday be able to use experimental data to decide.

IN OTHER WORDS

1. The hormone melatonin is used by the hypothalamus in the human brain to slow the body's metabolism and to decrease wakefulness as light levels decrease toward the end of the solar day.
2. The retina of the eye, the optic nerves and tracts, and the suprachiasmatic nuclei of the hypothalamus are used to sense the daily pattern of light intensity.
3. Secretion levels of melatonin by the pineal gland are an initial response to this pattern of light intensity.
4. Melatonin circulates throughout the body and helps control core temperature, basal metabolism rates, and wakefulness, as well as some features of sexual maturation and bone growth.
5. Melatonin's ability to decrease wakefulness has become the basis for its use as a dietary supplement. Its tendency to scavenge hydroxyl radicals in the brain is another desirable feature of the hormone.
6. The medical community continues to discuss the virtues and risks of the regular use of melatonin as a nutritional supplement.

11.6 RESPONSIVENESS AT THE BEHAVIORAL LEVEL

We have saved for last the most complex sort of response that an animal can make to changes in its environment: those that are sensed, interpreted, and responded to within the structure of the nervous system. There are two broad classes of such adaptive behaviors: <u>instinctive</u> behaviors and learned behaviors. Simple organismal behaviors like the suckling of milk by mammalian infants appear to arise directly as genetically programmed responses to environmental stimuli (see Figure 11.20). These are instinctive responses: the responses of a preprogrammed nervous system.

<u>Learned behaviors</u> tend to utilize higher-order capabilities of the nervous system. Animals continually process and integrate information that has been gained from experiences in responding to environmental change. The information and experience gained is then used to vary or change subsequent responses that will be made to future environmental stimuli. Learned behaviors are responses that may, in part, arise directly from the products of gene expression. But always in addition to any preprogrammed contribution, the response also arises from the effects of experience in the life of the animal. Consider the next example.

How and where does a bird get the ability to sing its songs? We assume that there is a genetic basis for the wiring of the bird's nervous system—the wiring that enables it to hear sounds, to distinguish its own sounds, and to generate certain basic aspects of the song it will eventually sing. This explains the fact that bird songs can be recognized by human listeners—they appear to be species specific. But there is growing evidence, at least in the development of *Zonotrichia leucophrys*, the white-crowned sparrow, that the songs that a particular sparrow hears as he matures, affect the song that he finally sings (see Figure 11.21).

White-crowned sparrows from different habitats use slightly different but distinct variations (**dialects**) of their species' songs. An individual male sparrow's song matures during a critical period of between 10 and 50 days after it hatches (see Figure 11.22). The mature song results partly from genetic parameters built into its nervous system. But many of the details in the song result from a response—the response of listening to other male sparrows in its habitat singing the local dialect!

Responses at the Behavioral Level: Instinctive

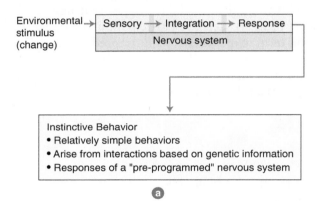

(a)

Responses at the Behavioral Level: Learned

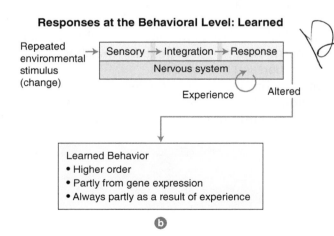

(b)

Figure 11.20 Responses at the Behavioral Level. **(a)** Instinctive Behaviors are pre-programmed into the cell or organism. **(b)** Learned Behaviors are those that are modifiable by the organism in response to environmental change.

instinctive (of behavior)—inborn tendency to behave in a manner that is genetically informed for a given species.

learned behavior—those responses that are conditioned by experience or in some cases by study.

dialect—a form of a language that has its own variations of sounds and terms not found in other forms of the same language.

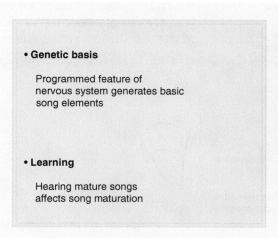

- **Genetic basis**

  Programmed feature of nervous system generates basic song elements

- **Learning**

  Hearing mature songs affects song maturation

Zonotrichia leucophrys
white-crowned sparrow

Arthur Morris/Corbis

Figure 11.21 Bird Songs—Composite Response. The White-crowned Sparrow. This humble but beautiful species, *Zonotrichia leucophrys*, turns seeds and insect prey into wonderful song patterns. It can stay awake for up to two weeks at a time during its migrations.

And these details are sensed very selectively and responded to in the fledgling bird's song maturation.

Ornithologist Peter Marler raised fledgling male sparrows in soundproof chambers so they couldn't hear adult males singing (see Figure 11.23). When the fledglings reached adulthood, their songs had none of the detailed structure heard in a typical adult male's song. Marler then started to add recordings of adult songs to the experience of the sound-isolated juvenile males. The results were fascinating! If he exposed the baby birds to a mixture of songs of adult male white-crowned sparrows and adult male song sparrows *(Melospiza melodia)*, then when the baby birds became adults, they sang only the white-crowned songs. And their dialect was that of the white-crowned males whose songs were recorded for use in the experiment. So while the predisposition to select the correct species song is strongly genetic, the dialect of the song is learned.

What is the survival value of learning to pattern your own song after that of a specific dialect of your local area? The male bird's basic song that isolates it within a given species is genetically determined. But the tendency of males to learn by experience

ornithologist—a scientist who studies birds.

Bird Songs—Variations within a Species

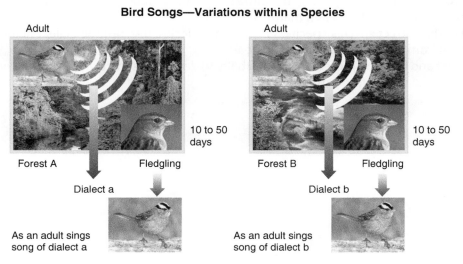

Adult

Forest A

10 to 50 days

Fledgling

Dialect a

As an adult sings song of dialect a

Adult

Forest B

10 to 50 days

Fledgling

Dialect b

As an adult sings song of dialect b

Figure 11.22 Bird Songs – Variations Within a Species. Unlike in human beings, in birds all members of a given species sing the same basic song (language). But regional dialects of these songs do exist.

Environmental Change: Alteration in Song Heard

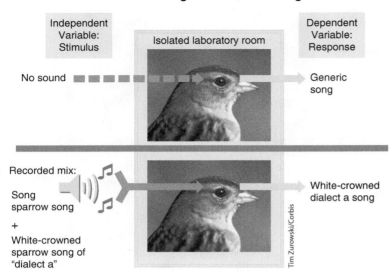

Independent Variable: Stimulus

Isolated laboratory room

Dependent Variable: Response

No sound ▪ ▪ ▪ ▪ ▪ ➔ Generic song

Recorded mix:

Song sparrow song

+

White-crowned sparrow song of "dialect a"

➔ White-crowned dialect a song

Tim Zurowski/Corbis

Figure 11.23 Environmental Change: Alteration in Song Heard. A fledgling sparrow can pick it's own dialect of song out of a mixture of two different bird species songs and incorporate that dialect into its own song.

the songs of adult males closest to them spatially will enable them to communicate most effectively with the sparrows that are immediately around them. Establishing a male's territory and attracting females to it will be more efficient processes because the level of communication through song is probably higher. So here we see an instance where the responsive ability of a life-form helps to effectively perpetuate and extend the territory of that life-form.

IN OTHER WORDS

1. Behaviors rooted in the animal nervous system are among the most complex responses an organism can make.
2. Instinctive behaviors are preprogrammed responses to stimuli that are informed principally by the genetic information the organism brings to the situation.
3. Learned behaviors are responses to stimuli that are informed by the genetic resources of the organism as modified by a sequence of experiences the organism brings to the current stimulus.
4. Birds' songs are largely the result of instinctive activity that is species specific. They can be generated in crude form in an environment containing no auditory stimuli whatever.
5. In male white-crowned sparrows, the final, mature form the bird's song takes is conditioned by the white-crowned male songs that the fledgling bird hears as it matures.
6. In a fledgling bird, selection of the correct species-specific song to sing is instinctive, but the dialect of the species-specific song is learned from bird songs the fledgling hears.
7. The combined effects of instinct and learning protect the bird's ability to develop a song that will optimally aid it in establishing its territory and in securing a mate.

11.7 A REALITY BEHIND RESPONSIVENESS

Responsiveness in living systems might be better understood by an analogy from a simpler context: the responsiveness of tools (see Figure 11.24). One of the simplest tools we know of is a rock. An otter uses a rock to crack its way into a mussel shell in search of a tasty lunch. A camper who's forgotten a hammer uses a rock to put tent pegs into the ground. Rocks are unresponsive tools. There is no way to adjust them to their tasks unless you manually—with great effort and at some risk—try to change their shape. Most users struggle along with them as they are. It is fairly easy to assume that a rock has no design to it. Some glacier randomly cracked it off of a larger rock, and it rolled to its current size and shape.

But as tools become more responsive, we begin to assume that they were designed for a purpose. The tent peg can be sent into a hole in the ground using a small pile driver (admittedly a bit of over-kill . . .). The pile driver has a carefully milled cylindrical hammer that fits precisely within a cylindrical chamber in a steel block. There is a steel housing, with molded hand grips, and controls to set how high the hammer rises and the rapidity with which it falls. There is no doubt in anyone's mind that this tool was carefully designed for a specific purpose.

The responsiveness of the human nervous system—to daylight, to temperature, to noise, to a thousand odors, to chili peppers, to crises, to a proposal of marriage, to the concept of the Divine—all teach that it is elegantly designed for some purpose. And in the case of the human nervous system, the tool itself has the ability to discover that purpose. Amazing, the responsiveness of life!

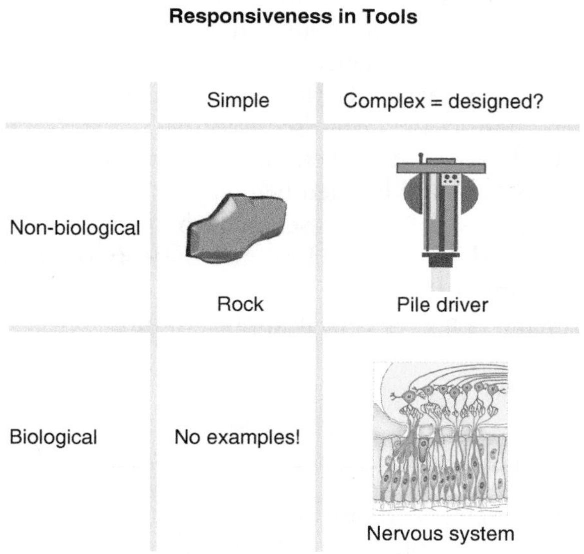

Responsiveness in Tools

	Simple	Complex = designed?
Non-biological	Rock	Pile driver
Biological	No examples!	Nervous system

Figure 11.24 Adjustability in tools is evidence of their intelligent design. Nervous system activity is far more adjustable than a pile driver.

IN OTHER WORDS

1. The simplest tools are normally used in the form in which they are found. No design is apparent in their structure.
2. Sophisticated tools are evidently designed and intentionally fabricated for the purposes for which they'll be used.
3. No existing tools rival the complexity of the eye-brain-hand machine.

QUESTIONS FOR REVIEW

1. Define the term *homeostasis*.
2. What is a hormone? Where is it generated? Where does it act? How does it arrive at its site of activity?
3. Describe a specific example of how failure to respond to an environmental change results in a harmful loss of homeostasis.
4. In the structure of an operon, distinguish between a promoter site and an operator site. What is each site responsible for in operon function?
5. Draw a diagram of the lactose operon in a situation where it is shut down.
6. Draw a diagram of the lactose operon in a situation where it is functioning.
7. When a fly trips a sensory hair on the modified leaf of a Venus fly trap, describe the very next event that occurs in that leaf?
8. What is an expansin? What does it do?
9. Using arrows horizontally between phrases, arrange in sequence the signals that intervene between a fly tripping a sensory hair on a Venus fly trap's leaf and the closure of the leaf.
10. Explain how an organism can make a variety of different, more or less simultaneous, responses to a single environmental stimulus.
11. What does the term *phototropism* mean?
12. What is the general role of auxins within a plant?
13. Review the definition of the term *active transport*. How is active transport different from the simple diffusion of substances?
14. Using arrows horizontally between phrases, arrange in sequence the signals that intervene between the stimulus of the decline of light intensity in your window and the responding decline of your basal metabolism rate. Be sure to include the terms *pineal gland* and *suprachiasmatic nuclei* in your sequence.
15. What is seasonal affective disorder? How is it related to melatonin secretion?
16. Distinguish between innate (or instinctive) behavior and learned behavior.
17. A bird's song represents both instinctive and learned behavior. How are these two aspects distinguished?
18. What is a dialect as it applies to bird songs?

QUESTIONS FOR THOUGHT

1. The repressor protein for the lactose operon is an allosteric protein: It has two distinct binding sites for two different kinds of molecules. What are these two molecules? How does binding at each site affect the activity of the lactose operon?
2. Can flowing water trap a fly? If so, where, precisely, is the water flowing?
3. Auxins generally get transported from a shoot tip vertically down the shoot toward the root of the plant. What process might cause them to flow laterally across the shoot from one side to the other?
4. List two separate ways in which indole-acetic acid (an auxin) supports plant cell elongation.
5. Section 11.5 states, "The suprachiasmatic nuclei exert their control over wakefulness and body temperature with a periodicity of roughly 25 hours, independent of the daily cycling of light." How could you test the validity of this statement with only a cave, a clock, a clipboard, a lamp, a cot, and a substantial food supply?
6. Why is the traditional/conventional medical community hesitant to endorse widespread use of melatonin as a dietary supplement? What is your own position on this issue and why?
7. Predict what might happen to the adult song of a white-crowned sparrow if, as a fledgling, it was secluded in a soundproof chamber where it was continuously exposed to the songs of white-crowned sparrow from two widely distant populations of its own species. Would such a bird fare better or worse in the wild than a normal sparrow?
8. Suppose that while walking along a beach you observed, partially buried in the sand, a solid red latex ball about 3 inches in diameter. What features of it would lead you to assume it lacked a designer? What features would lead you to assume it had a designer?

GLOSSARY

active transport—the movement of dissolved substances across a membrane with or against a concentration gradient; utilizes cellular energy to insure transport.

allo-lactose—a chemically altered form of lactose often present intracellularly where it can bind to the lac operon repressor protein turning on synthesis of its structural genes.

auxin—a class of plant hormones, particular members of which are involved in stimulation of growth as in stem elongation or giving dominance to the apical bud on a stem.

cerebral hemisphere—right and left halves of the cerebrum, the largest portion of the mammalian brain.

circadian—refers to any process or characteristic that respects a 24-hour cycle or period.

core temperature—the operating temperature of structures deep within the body of the organism.

dialect—a form of a language that has its own variations of sounds and terms not found in other forms of the same language.

electric potential—the inherent energy in positively charged particles; equal to the work it would take to push the particles there from a position with zero potential.

expansin—a category of enzymes that break cross-linking covalent bonds between cellulose fibers, weakening the overall structure of which they are a part.

fibril—a strand of several cellulose polymer molecules interwoven around each other for added strength.

homeostasis—maintenance of stable conditions chemically and physically within the body; the result of highly regulated and coordinated activities of the body's systems.

hormone—a chemical substance released by a cell or gland that signals another cell or organ of the body to respond in some way.

hormone receptor—usually a membrane-bound protein whose surface conformation enables it to both bind to and respond to a hormonal signal molecule.

hydroxyl radical—the neutral form of the hydroxide ion ($^-$OH); highly reactive and destructive of the chemical integrity of reduced biological molecules.

hypothalamus—a ventral brain region containing the suprachiasmatic nuclei; it helps to regulate many aspects of the internal fluid environment of the body as well as core temperature and wakefulness.

indole-3-acetic acid (IAA)—a particular auxin that causes plant cells to elongate as part of the general growth process of the plant.

instinctive (of behavior)—inborn tendency to behave in a manner that is genetically informed for a given species.

lactase—a protein enzyme capable of degrading the sugar lactose into its monosaccharide products.

lactose—a disaccharide sugar found in milk and milk products, degraded to the monosaccharides glucose and galactose before being catabolized for energy generation.

learned behavior—those responses that are conditioned by experience or in some cases by study.

leptin—a protein hormone that helps to control energy intake into the body by regulating the appetite for food.

Life Is Responsive—the eighth principle of life elaborated in this textbook.

melatonin—a hormone secreted by the pineal gland in response to darkness; helps entrain the body's biological rhythms to a light-dark cycle.

nectar—a sweet liquid secreted by specialized cells of a plant; used to attract insects; a major source of honey.

operator—a segment of DNA at the front end of an operon; regulatory proteins conditionally bind the operator influencing whether or not transcription of the operon occurs.

operon—in DNA, a sequence of adjacent structural genes whose products are usually functionally related together with an upstream operator region of DNA to which regulatory proteins specifically bind.

optic chiasm—a structure behind the eyes in a vertebrate in which the nerve tracts from the eyes meet and interweave before entering the brain.

optic nerve—a set of neurons that carry form, color, motion, and light intensity information from the retina of the eye to the brain.

ornithologist—a scientist who studies birds.

photoreceptor—a large organic molecule, usually a protein, whose structure is altered by the influx of photons. The altered structure results in a signal used by a cell or organ to respond properly to the presence of light.

phototropism—the tendency of a plant to grow toward a light source such as the sun.

pineal gland—an endocrine gland at the center of the brain; secretes the hormone melatonin.

polar transport—the unidirectional transport of a substance through a series of cells such as from the apex of a plant shoot to its root system.

promoter—a sequence of DNA base pairs just upstream from a gene or set of genes to be transcribed; RNA polymerase selectively binds to this sequence.

repressor—a regulatory protein that by binding to the operator sequence of DNA within an operon prohibits transcription of the genes within the operon.

retina—the sensory surface within the back of the eye where light waves initiate sensory nerve impulses.

seasonal affective disorder—a mood alteration in wintertime characterized by a depressive state; reduced amounts of daylight may be causative.

structural gene—a gene that codes for a protein product that contributes directly to the functional activities of the cell; a gene whose product has no regulatory role.

suprachiasmatic nuclei—small portions of brain issue just above the optic chiasma that transmit signals associated with the maintenance of circadian rhythms.

thyroid gland—an endocrine gland in the cervical region of the body whose hormones regulate basal metabolism rate and calcium balance within the body's tissues.

thyroxin—a hormonal product of the thyroid gland that regulates metabolic rate in the tissues.

Informational Continuity in Organisms

Let us make man in our image, after our likeness . . .
—GENESIS 1:26, *KJV, BIBLE*

And Adam knew Eve his wife; and she conceived, and bare Cain. . . .
—GENESIS 4:1, *KJV, BIBLE*

Information is ubiquitous. Most of it is trivial. Much is erroneous. But some is highly precious. Precious information gets preserved—often at considerable expense.

In the National Archives in Washington, DC, American taxpayers preserve a 235-year-old document entitled the Declaration of Independence (see illustration, next page.) Its information is precious; it describes the origin of a great nation. The medium in which the information is preserved is essentially a collection of xylem tissue (parchment) and iron salts in oak gall acid (ink)—all of it dead. It is preserved under conditions that will keep any bacteria or mold from degrading it as a carbon source. When humans preserve hand-written information for a long period of time, they use a dead medium (parchment), retained in an environment that fosters death.

Designed life-forms also preserve precious information at considerable expense—strands of DNA—some of which are hundreds, even thousands of years old! But the Designer's approach to information preservation is more dynamic, more functional than man's. In life-forms, the information is preserved in a viable medium: the cell. The cell uses its own energy to actively protect

Survey Questions

12.1 Reproduction: Sexual and Asexual

- What is asexual reproduction?
- What are the values of sexual and asexual reproduction?
- What are some organisms that reproduce asexually?
- Why does sexual reproduction exist at all?
- How might sexual reproduction have originated in a species that did not possess it?
- What happens to genetic information during sexual reproduction?

12.2 Preparing Reproductive Cells for Multicellular Organisms

- If sperm and egg cells must combine in sexual reproduction, what happens to the genome in this process?
- How are chromosomes organized in a typical body cell?
- What is meiosis and why is it necessary?
- How does meiosis prepare a cell to become either a sperm or an egg cell?
- How do reproductive cells contribute to the genetic variability of the offspring they generate?
- Where do egg and sperm cells ultimately originate in the developing organism?
- How do egg and sperm cells become so structurally different from each other?

12.3 Reproduction in Humans

- How is the subject of human reproduction treated in this text?
- How and where are ova produced in the human female? How is this process controlled?
- How and where are sperm cells produced in the human male? How is this process controlled?
- How many body systems are involved in the process of reproduction?
- Where does fertilization occur along with zygote formation?

12.4 Reproduction Constrained, Part I: Control of Birth

- What does the term *birth control* actually mean? Why are such methods used?
- What means are available for controlling birth?
- How safe is the life of a conceptus in these methods?
- How safe is the health of the female partner in these methods?
- How effective are the methods in preventing pregnancy?

12.5 Reproduction Constrained, Part II: Destruction of Life

- Why would human beings destroy embryonic human life?
- When have scholars argued that human life begins?
- Does biology contribute to this dialog?
- How is human life destroyed during its early stages?

12.6 Reproduction Constrained, Part III: Mendel and His Laws

- Who was Gregor Mendel? Where did he study and work?
- What system did he study that led him to his laws?
- What terms or concepts are needed to understand Mendel's laws?
- What is Mendel's first law? What does it control the behavior of?

Life Is Informational Continuity—the sixth principle of life on which this text is based.

Brooks Kraft/Corbis

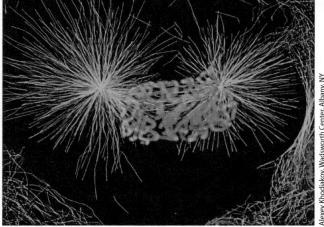

Alexey Khodjakov, Wadsworth Center, Albany, NY

Two radically different ways in which highly precious information is preserved.

and preserve the information making high-fidelity copies of it without ever destroying the originals.

Our sixth principle of life captures this concept of prolonged information preservation: **Life Is Informational Continuity.** In this chapter we will watch biological information flow down through time. We've already seen this principle at work when a single cell preserves and extends its identity by doubling itself in the process of mitosis and cytokinesis (see Chapter 8). Now we'll focus on information flow in multicellular organisms. As we transition from cell division to organismal reproduction, the glory inherent in our sixth principle only grows greater (see Figure 12.1). Consider the quotes at the head of this chapter. God cooperates with Himself to create man in His own image. So, man, in God's image, desires to create as well. He cooperates with other humans to create masterpieces just as God has. Man creates the computer. But notice how the first Creator's glory clearly excels. Eve is designed in such a way as to entirely reproduce herself using just a single cell of her own and the cooperation of Adam. Cain, her son, contains exactly as much genomic information and functionality as his father! That is amazing. Now, computers can design, but they cannot cooperate to produce new versions of themselves, which will, in turn, generate new versions of *them*selves, hardware and all. How humans and

- What is the best way to illustrate the law?
- What is independent assortment? What is being sorted?
- How universal is independent assortment? Does it explain the relationship between any two genes in any genome?
- How is independent assortment of alleles tested for?
- Are there exceptions to Mendel's laws that were subsequently discovered?
- What would such exceptions reveal about the nature of gene control in higher organisms?

12.7 Reproduction Explained: The Chromosomal Basis of Heredity

- How are chromosomes involved in the mechanism of heredity?
- What is the relationship between meiosis and Mendel's laws?
- What is the evidence that Mendel's factors (genes) really are on chromosomes?
- If genes are on chromosomes, do they all completely obey Mendel's laws?

Wim van Egmond

(a)

Dr. Stanley Flegler/ Visuals Unlimited

(b)

Hans Pfletschinger

(c)

Figure 12.1 Genetic Information Flow. **(a)** Mitotic division of a single-celled alga *Micrasterias*, **(b)** Asexual budding in a 5 mm tall multicellular animal—a freshwater *Hydra*, **(c)** Sexual reproduction in the common leopard frog *Rana pipiens*. In each case reproduction is an amazingly complex and integrated expression of genetic information, all for the purpose of transmitting that information to the next generation.

computers create is totally understood by each of their separate Designers. Prepare, then, to enjoy the mystery that surrounds this wonderful principle of life as expressed in multicellular organisms.

Asexual Reproduction

Let's root our discussion in some review. We saw informational continuity operating in mitosis. For a single-celled organism like *Paramecium bursaria,* mitosis *is* reproduction (see Figure 12.2). Mitosis is the way information is passed on from one generation of cells to the next. What three things must a parent cell provide each daughter cell with so that it can eventually become a parent cell? The parent must provide:

1. Information
2. The machinery to use it
3. A supply of monomers and energy for the machinery to work with

Therefore it is critical that the information be equally represented in each daughter cell. We saw that this is accomplished by replicating DNA during premitotic S phase to form chromosomes composed of duplicate sister chromatids (see Figure 8.11). The cell then splits apart the chromatids of each chromosome to form equal daughter chromosomes. The cell then sent each daughter chromosome into one of the two daughter cells.

The daughter cells will not be able to add to the cell machinery and materials they received from the parent cell unless adequate information is there to guide production of more cell "stuff."

If a multicellular organism arises from one cell by mitosis and cell division (see Chapter 9), then an organism is, bio-logically, just a huge collection of genetically identical cells. To reproduce itself, it might commit a certain subset of its cells to differentiate into spores that will float away, germinate, and become new individuals. Organisms like lichens or sea stars may simply fragment to form multiple new individuals. By continued cell division and differentiation, these new individuals can generate brand new copies of the original multicellular organism (see Figure 12.1b). Since only a single organism is involved in this process it is termed **asexual reproduction.**

asexual reproduction—generation of offspring without the production by meiosis of haploid sex cells and thus without fertilization.

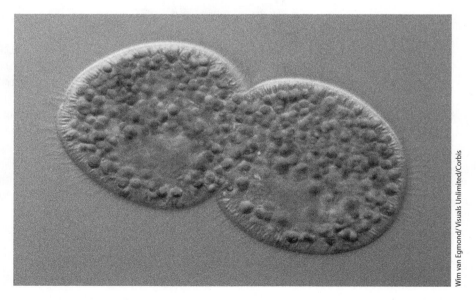

Figure 12.2 *Paramecium bursaria* dividing. Mitosis has already occurred, the separate nuclei are the large hazy intracellular areas. Cytokinesis is almost complete.

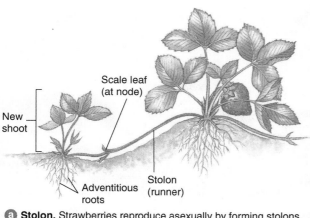

New shoot

Scale leaf (at node)

Adventitious roots

Stolon (runner)

a **Stolon.** Strawberries reproduce asexually by forming stolons, or runners. New plants (shoots and roots) are produced at every other node.

Rhizome

Adventitious roots

b **Rhizome.** Irises have horizontal underground stems called rhizomes. New aerial shoots arise from buds that develop on the rhizome.

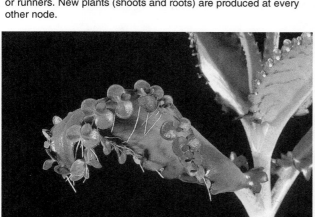

Jerome Wexler/ PhotoResearchers, Inc.

c

Figure 12.3 Asexual Reproduction in Plants. **(a)** A runner extends from a mature strawberry plant to available space in soil and a new plant begins there. **(b)** Iris flowers spread by means of underground "rhizomes" which are modified stems. Buds generate new aerial shoots which later flower. **(c)** The *Kalanchoe* producing plantlets along its leaves.

Plants are notorious for this amazing approach to self-propagation (see Figure 12.3). Strawberry bushes send out horizontal stems called *runners* that take root and start new daughter plants that are genetically identical to the mother plant. Iris plants can grow up from extensive underground stems. New *Kalanchoe* plants start as marginal projections of the plant's leaves! They simply break off of an existing plant, primary roots already intact, fall to the ground, and take root to become new individuals—again—genetically identical to the parent plant. We call them **clones** of their parent; they will rehearse the same developmental pattern as their parent and eventually appear identical to their parent in its adult state.

Sometimes this asexual reproduction in plants can seem almost out of hand. In Utah, there are 262 acres of quaking aspen trees that are reproductively related and genetically identical! That's right! They all appear to have derived from the same original

male parent tree forming from **adventitious** shoots coming off of the parent plant's root system (see Figure 12.4). Called "Pando the Trembling Giant," they are really an individual organism that probably weighs about 6600 tons.

Sexual Reproduction

An obvious question arises here: If asexual reproduction occurs in many organisms (and it does), and if it is so efficient (only one parent required), then why

clone—any DNA molecule, cell, or organism that is identical genetically to some precursor DNA molecule, cell, or organism from which it arises.

adventitious—in plants, a structure that arises from an unusual place such as roots growing out of stems or leaves.

Figure 12.4 Extreme Asexual Reproduction. This photo shows only a portion of a single, asexually reproducing male quaking aspen "individual" tree. The collective adventitious root system from that tree has slowly come to cover an area of 262 acres. Shoots from these roots gave rise to the forest. Thus all the trees here are genetically identical!

does **sexual reproduction** exist at all? Why are there many higher organisms that can reproduce *only* sexually (like us)? Indeed, sexuality has many disadvantages. For example, only 50% of a parent's genes are passed on to an offspring. This means that there is a 50% chance of losing a rare, beneficial mutation that might occur. Sex also means that no selectively optimal combination of genes can ever be passed on in its entirety. Superman has no super-children (just some really rather strong kids). It is also biologically costly in genome space to maintain information for making sex organs and to maintain mechanisms to stop the female's immune system from destroying incoming sperm or the offspring she carries. On the behavioral side, sometimes sexual displays can be cumbersome and make the organism more vulnerable (see Figure 12.5). Also, it takes energy to find a mate. The organism must expend that energy; otherwise, it will die without passing on its genes. That's a lot of investment in time and materials considering that asexual organisms such as bacteria reproduce very quickly.

Yet most higher organisms (like starfish, for example), even if capable of asexual reproduction, are also capable of sexual reproduction. The evolutionary explanation for this is that asexual reproduction of vast numbers of offspring generates a population of organisms with very little genetic variation present. Except for new mutations, the population members are genetically identical! If the environment varies from time to time, sometimes in odd ways (and many environments do this), then a population with **genetic variability** will be better adapted to surviving in such dynamic surroundings (see Chapter 13). **Natural selection** will have a robust variety of individuals from which to select the most

Figure 12.5 Costly Sexual Display. The male most successful in mating is the one displaying the largest number of "eyespot" feathers on his tail. This success selects in favor of males with enormous tail plummage. This complicates the male's escape from predators.

sexual reproduction—generating offspring from the union of gametes from two parents, by way of meiosis, gamete formation, and fertilization.

genetic variability—quality of a population in which members possess a variety of different forms of a given gene or genes.

natural selection—the driving force of evolution; environmental characteristics happen to favor the survival of population members having certain desirable and heritable traits.

Figure 12.6 Plant Tissue Culture. Cost reduction has caused many plants like these orchids to be cloned in the laboratory. All plantlets in this dish are genetically identical. Hence their susceptibility to viruses and fungal diseases is identical. Manipulation under carefully controlled conditions is required. Wild varieties are generally more "robust" in their resistance to disease than domesticated varieties.

adapted individuals! Most biologists who espouse a Biblical view of creation also accept this view of genetic variability. In a fallen world, catastrophes occur. Predation and parasitism constantly put pressure on a population to be genetically adept or to become extinct (see Figure 12.6). So although gene mutation is costly to the individual organism (most mutations are harmful), in a large population, the rare mutation may actually help a population to survive if an abrupt change occurs in environmental conditions (see Chapter 13).

But a critical distinction must be made here. Yes, there are advantages to sexual reproduction; a population that loses this reproductive mode will surely be outcompeted by a corresponding population that retains it. But this does not mean that sexual reproduction's potential benefit to a population is somehow able to generate within the genome the new information needed to *create* and support sexuality within a population. It is virtually impossible to get at the origins of sexuality. The fossil record contains early algal fossils that show sexuality. But is their sexuality primitive or elegant like that of modern red algae? Rocks can't answer that question for you. Did sexuality exist before that point in the record and is simply yet to be discovered? What would the first sexual organism have been? Perhaps some single-celled microbe? The first sexual population would require at the very least a set of complementary surface receptor molecules, sexual structures to function in gene exchange, and cellular behaviors to support the process (see Figure 12.7). From a

basic system like this, sexuality in higher forms would have to become thoroughly enmeshed into nervous, endocrine, and other body systems—quite a complicated and tortuous design process! How tortuous? The modern geneticist doesn't really know what portion of the vertebrate genome is needed to generate sexuality in the individual. So it's impossible to intelligently calculate how many mutations would have to occur in the genome of some supposedly "primitive" sexual species in order to generate sexual systems like our own. By analogy then, from our experience with other highly complex phenomena, it appears—at least for now—that sexuality exists because a Designer informed the process.

If natural selection's work is limited to *maintenance* of sexuality, why then, might a Designer have wanted it to exist in the first place? The Biblical creation account hints at a plausible answer. The Designer described in Biblical texts has three personalities who appear to have mutual joy and delight in the process of creating life in general and mankind in particular (see the first quote at the head of the chapter). Sexuality in their human creatures may be a way in which their overt ecstasy can be relived when pairs of humans set about to create something so mysterious and sacred as life.

But the nature of sexuality reminds us that, just as at the beginning, more than one source of information is used to generate a human being. That has not changed. For each trait you possess—say for example the color of your

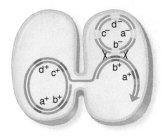

Figure 12.7 Sex is Expensive. Conjugation between two bacterial cells (sexual exchange) allows for the transfer of bacterial genes (blue DNA strands) from one cell to another. Just the red DNA sequence shown here contains about 20 separate genes needed to make DNA transfer from one cell to the other possible. Protein products of these genes, such as those that form the bridge between the two cells mesh seamlessly with all the surrounding gene products they are required to interact with.

hair—information to generate that trait exists in *two* complete sets (see Figure 12.8)! One came from your mother, the other from your father. Since both parents supply the same general sort of information controlling hair color, we call the information from the two sources **homologous** information. Units of genetic information are called **genes.** You thus have two homologous sets of genes influencing hair color. Two homologous sets of genes for all of your traits are arranged on two homologous sets of chromosomes, one from each of your parents. The 46 chromosomes found in each of your cells are really two homologous sets of 23 chromosomes—one set from each parent. In the set of 23 chromosomes, for example, chromosome 19 contains a gene, *HCL1,* that influences hair color. The form—the information content—of that gene may be somewhat different in the two chromosomes 19 that you inherited from your parents. Your parents both had hair color, but it may have been quite different! The two homologous *HCL1* genes that influence hair color

Figure 12.9   Genetic Variation within species *Homo sapiens*. Because of sexual reproduction, genes for hair color, skin color, eye color, or any other trait can float around between races within our species. Culture and geography have minimized such gene flow in the past but that is changing.

Peter Bowater/Photo Researchers, Inc.; Sam Kleinman/Corbis; Owen Franken/Corbis

are called **alleles** of each other. One allele is on the chromosome 19 that you got from your mother; the other allele is at the corresponding position on chromosome 19 that you got from your father. The terms *homologous chromosomes* and *alleles* are very useful in understanding how your (duplex) genome is organized. Perhaps you feel somehow more secure in the knowledge that you face life with two copies of all the information needed for effective functioning as a human! But think further. The variation generated by sexual reproduction glorifies a brilliant Designer,: it means that He can fashion interbreeding populations that, of *themselves* create their own novelties, yet within the context of His predesigned, generic categories (see Figure 12.9). The result is a perfect combination of creativity within thematic limits: a truly high form of art!

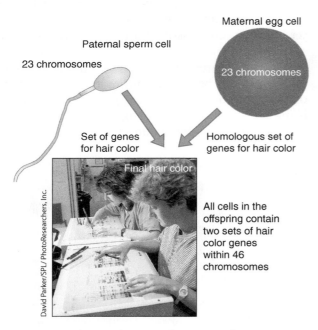

Maternal egg cell

Paternal sperm cell

23 chromosomes

23 chromosomes

Set of genes for hair color

Homologous set of genes for hair color

Final hair color

David Parker/SPL/ PhotoResearchers, Inc.

All cells in the offspring contain two sets of hair color genes within 46 chromosomes

Figure 12.8   Homologous Information. All genes controlling hair color are represented twice in the individual's genome because two complete sets of information in each body cell nucleus come ultimately from two different parents.

homologous—refers to a correspondence; a fundamental similarity between two items. In heredity, two information sources that have the same role but do not carry it out identically.

gene—a sequence of bases within the structure of a nucleic acid, usually DNA, that code for a protein or an RNA that has a biological function.

allele—a specific form of a gene; it occupies a defined position on a particular chromosome within an individual. Other individuals may have other forms of the gene at that location.

1. For a single-celled organism, cell division is equivalent to reproduction.
2. In asexual reproduction, a multicellular organism simply sets aside a subpopulation of its cells to give rise to a new individual organism or organisms.
3. Most plants (like strawberries) and many animals (like starfish) exist that are capable of asexual reproduction.
4. Sexual reproduction is biologically expensive. Much energy and many materials are consumed in the process.
5. The advantage of sexual reproduction lies in the genomic variability it introduces into a population of organisms—variability that is useful for thriving in a changing environment.
6. This value of sexuality doesn't explain its origin, however. Sexual processes are intricate enough to require considerable new information for their construction and maintenance.
7. The genetic information, the chromosomes, in each cell's nucleus are organized into two homologous sets, one from the maternal parent and one from the paternal parent.

PREPARING REPRODUCTIVE CELLS FOR MULTICELLULAR ORGANISMS

The Challenge of Making a Reproductive Cell

Clearly, then, sexual reproduction implies wonderful, new possibilities for individual human variation. But it also means putting together genes—indeed putting together whole cells—from two different sources in one individual. What does this fusion of two cells require genetically?

Let's reason numerically a bit. There are 46 chromosomes present in a normal human cell. Suppose, then, that any one cell divides mitotically into two daughter cells. How many chromosomes would each of them have? Forty-six, correct? They would now be unreplicated chromosomes because centromeres split during mitosis. But each daughter cell has the same 46 chromosomes its maternal parent began her existence with.

Now let's imagine a Designer of human beings who wasn't quite as talented as ours. He designs humans such that *every* body cell has 46 chromosomes in it. We can further imagine that your own parents were part of this simpler creation. Suppose they meet, marry, and decide to procreate. We fuse one of your dad's sperm cells with one of your mother's egg cells to form a conceptus—a zygote, you! You then develop by mitotic divisions to your current size (see Figure 12.10). How many chromosomes will be present in each of your cells? Ninety-two, correct?

Let's suppose further that your own adulthood brings the desire to marry and procreate as well, again by means of mitotic cell divisions. Your spouse, a fine product of the same process in the paragraph above will have—yes—92 chromosomes in every cell of his/her body? If your first child is again the result of egg and sperm cell fusion following only mitotic events, that poor child will have how many chromosomes in each of its cells (see Figure 12.10)? One hundred eighty-four, correct? Clearly this transgenerational accumulation of chromosomes cannot go on! We call this a **ploidy** problem. The term *ploidy* refers to the number of sets of chromosomes a cell possesses. Normal human cells

Life Without Meiosis

	Generation	Chromosome Number/Cell
	1	46
	Sex cell formation	46 + 46
	2	92
	Sex cell formation	92 + 92
	3	184
		etc.

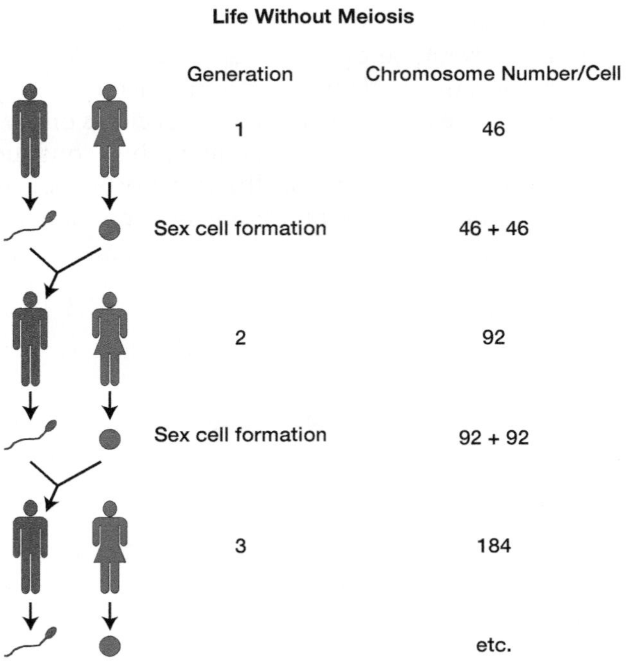

Figure 12.10 Life Without Meiosis. Combining egg and sperm cells requires the doubling of the chromosome number. The only way this can be compensated for is by halfing the number of chromosomes in both cells before fertilization happens.

are diploid—they possess two homologous sets of genetic information. But here we are generating offspring that are now octaploid. Each generation doubles the ploidy number!

How Can This Ploidy Problem Be Solved?

So here is the first problem we must solve in generating egg and sperm cells. We need a special type of cell division that cuts the diploid number

ploidy—refers to the number of complete sets of chromosomes in the nuclei of an individual's cells. Most higher animals are diploid (two sets) except in their sex cells.

of chromosomes by half—down to 23—or what is called the **haploid** number. Then, when mature haploid egg and sperm cells fuse in the process of fertilization, the normal diploid number of chromosomes (46) is restored! Happily, the real Designer fashioned this special type of preparatory division. We call it **meiosis** (Gk. *meioun* = to diminish). But there is another problem that the Designer of meiosis must solve. If we randomly discard half the chromosomes from a sperm cell and half from an egg cell, how can we be sure we'll get two complete sets when the two cells fuse? For example, if you randomly discarded half the cards from one card deck and half from another and then tried to assemble a whole deck, your approach would virtually never work!

The solution to this second problem lies in recalling that your 46 chromosomes are actually two complete homologous *sets* of 23 chromosomes (see Figure 12.11). For meiosis, then, the challenge is to initially sort 46 chromosomes into 23 pairs of similar (homologous) chromosomes. Once that's done, we can send one chromosome from each pair into each daughter cell so that each egg or sperm cell ends up with a single complete set of genomic information. Once they fuse in fertilization, the zygote will have a restored diploid number of chromosomes with one chromosome in each pair coming from the egg cell and one from the sperm cell. Aren't you glad you didn't have to invent this process in order to profit from it? It's already been designed (masterfully) and you're an elegant product of it!

haploid—refers to a cell or an organism whose cells contain a single copy of the genome of the organism; sex cells are typically in this category.

meiosis—a sequence of two cell division events that halves the number of chromosomes in the nucleus and supplies them to the sex cell in their unreplicated state.

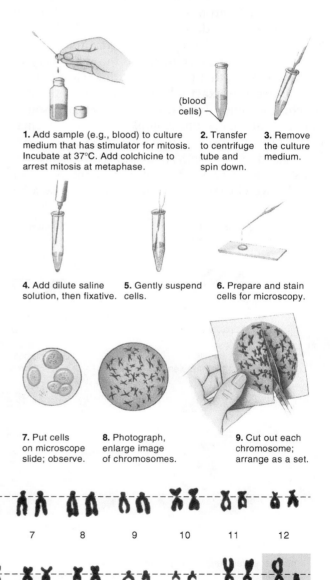

1. Add sample (e.g., blood) to culture medium that has stimulator for mitosis. Incubate at 37°C. Add colchicine to arrest mitosis at metaphase.

2. Transfer to centrifuge tube and spin down.

3. Remove the culture medium.

4. Add dilute saline solution, then fixative.

5. Gently suspend cells.

6. Prepare and stain cells for microscopy.

7. Put cells on microscope slide; observe.

8. Photograph, enlarge image of chromosomes.

9. Cut out each chromosome; arrange as a set.

Figure 12.11 A Human Karyotype. The chromosomes in the human white blood cell nucleus can be chemically induced to condense. They can then be photographed through a microscope. The chromosomes are then cut from the photo and arranged into obvious pairs as shown here. There are 23 pairs of chromosomes in a normal individual. Forty eight chromosomes are shown here to illustrate the difference in sex chromosomes between an X and a Y chromosome in males. Females have two Xs as shown.

1 2 3 4 5 6 7 8 9 10 11 12

13 14 15 16 17 18 19 20 21 22 XX (or XY)

Meiosis: A Triumph of Genome Reduction and Genetic Variability

Let's observe the elegance with which meiosis solves the problems we've raised while increasing a population's genetic variability along the way. Consider a diagram of the overall process of meiosis (see Figure 12.12). At first glance, meiosis looks a lot like two mitosis events in sequence (see Chapter 8). But if we look closely, there are some critical differences. In mitosis, homologous chromosomes "ignored" each other since 46 chromosomes simply replicated and split. But in meiosis, similar (homologous) chromosomes must find each other and pair up. How do they do this? We don't know yet. But we're glad they do! The members of the homologous pair must then use the machinery of metaphase such that (1) not only does each daughter cell get 23—exactly half—of the total number of chromosomes but, (2) the 23 chromosomes obtained all make one complete set of information (one chromosome from each of 23 pairs going into each daughter cell). Amazing! As we follow the steps in Figure 12.12, we will follow the behavior of only two chromosome pairs—23 would be a bit much! The two pairs of chromosomes differ from each other in size:

1. Notice that as meiosis begins, the cell has already been through a premeiotic S phase. The DNA of all four chromosomes has been replicated. Look carefully at the centromere of each chromosome: It is attached to two sister chromatids—the products of DNA replication. Also notice that somehow (!) homologous chromosomes have already found and paired with each other. Notice that they have different colors in the diagram: pink for the homolog of maternal origin, blue for the paternal homolog. Follow a romantic analogy here for a moment: The homologous chromosomes pair so intimately with each other that in the lower-left corner the one pair is actually exchanging arms with each other in a process called **genetic recombination**. Information that

genetic recombination—an enzyme-driven process in which DNA strands in two homologous chromosomes are broken and rejoined so that segments of the two chromosomes are physically switched.

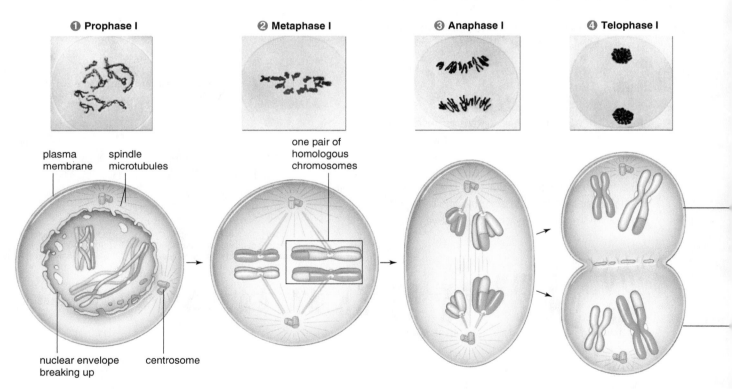

Figure 12.12 The Stages of Meiosis. Meiosis is here diagrammed along with photographs of actually chromosomes in meiosis in lily plant cells (*Lilium regale*). Human cells contain 23 pairs of chromosomes. In these diagrams, for simplicity' sake, only two pairs of homologous chromosomes are shown. Details of the process are discussed in the text.

is maternal in origin will now be on a chromosome of paternal origin and vice versa. We'll say more about that below.

2. The chromosomes have now completed their condensation process and by means of microtubule orientation now lie on a metaphase plate. But look closely at the centromeres. Each centromere is attached to only *one* microtubule, not two as in mitosis. Unlike in mitosis, no centromeres are going to split at the end of this metaphase. And some still mysterious process has caused one homologous chromosome in each pair to be on alternate sides of the midline of the cell. We are thus prepared to divide each homologous pair of chromosomes into sister cells. Watch!

3. Anaphase is now separating whole replicated homologous chromosomes from each other. This is what we call a *reduction division*. The parent cell (in meiotic metaphase I) had four replicated chromosomes. Each daughter cell will

have only two. The reduction we required of meiosis is here completed in a very orderly way.

4. Cytokinesis now generates two haploid daughter cells. But we have a residual problem: Because no centromeres have split, the chromosomes are still in their replicated states. Each daughter cell has two replicated chromosomes. Watch how this problem is neatly solved.

5. Without going through another cell cycle—another S phase—the daughter cells move directly into a second division, which is actually a mitosis event. Keep your eyes on the centromeres as prophase moves into metaphase.

6. Notice how, just as in a normal mitosis, the chromosomes are on the metaphase plate with each centromere attached to both poles of the mitotic spindle. Centromeres will split here and replicated chromosomes will be returned to the unreplicated state. That is, sister chromatids will become chromosomes. Each maternal cell

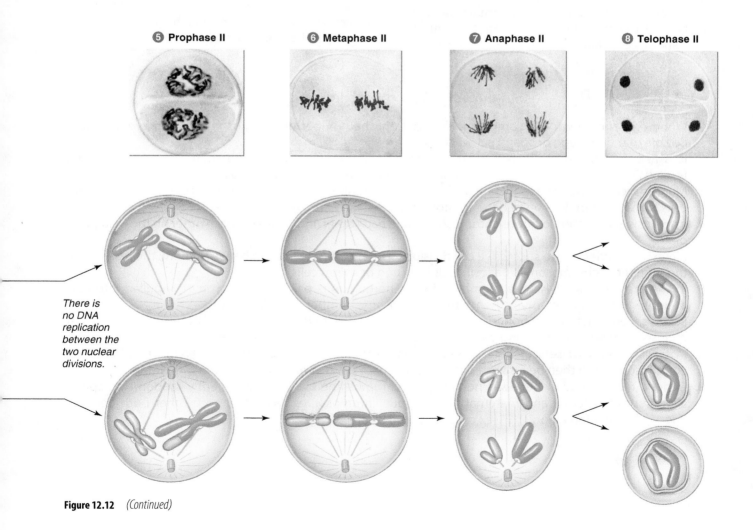

⑤ **Prophase II** ⑥ **Metaphase II** ⑦ **Anaphase II** ⑧ **Telophase II**

There is no DNA replication between the two nuclear divisions.

Figure 12.12 *(Continued)*

in step (5) had two replicated chromosomes (the haploid number); each daughter cell in step (8) will have two unreplicated chromosomes. (7–8). Meiosis comes to a conclusion with a final anaphase and telophase, which, in our drawing includes the cytokinesis that follows.

Look across the figure again to review what has happened. In the first division of meiosis, the *number* of chromosomes is cut in half. In the second division of meiosis, the *state* of the chromosomes is altered from replicated to unreplicated. Our final product, stage 8, is haploid with unreplicated chromosomes and, genetically, is ready to participate in fertilization.

Before we structurally convert these haploid cells into sperm or egg cells, let's notice how, right in the midst of reducing the number of chromosomes, we are actually increasing the variability of our population of organisms. Returning to step (1) in our diagram, think about the enzyme-driven breaking and rejoining of chromatid strands represented there. Such recombination events are really a shuffling of maternal and paternal genes that greatly increases the potential for variability in the egg or sperm cells that will result from this process.

Only two pairs of homologous chromosomes are shown in our diagram. If 23 pairs are involved in human sex cell formation, you may be certain that virtually no egg or sperm cell will ever contain entirely maternal or paternal chromosomes. Since there are two to three recombination events per chromosome (on average), each haploid cell will be a thoroughly recombined mixture of chromatid arms from the two sources.

But a glance at step (2) reveals another source of variation. We are ignorant of why this is so, but in our diagram the left-hand set of homologous chromosomes could just as easily have lined up in the opposite orientation (with blue on top) relative to the right-hand pair of chromosomes. For each of 23 pairs of chromosomes, the haploid egg cell will have either the maternal or the paternal chromosome, but it can be different for each pair of chromosomes! This also adds enormously to the variation in genetic information present in each of your sperm or egg cells. And which of these variant egg and sperm cells will be the one that participates in fertilization is still another huge variable over which you have no control whatever (at present).

IN OTHER WORDS

1. When egg and sperm cell combine in fertilization, the number of chromosomes in the zygote will be double that of the egg or sperm cell nucleus.
2. It is therefore necessary to halve the number of chromosomes in either a sperm or egg cell so that fertilization will restore the normal number of chromosomes instead of doubling it.
3. Meiosis accomplishes the reduction of chromosome number in a systematic way that leaves egg or sperm cells with one complete set of genetic information instead of the normal two sets.
4. In meiosis, pairs of homologous chromosomes find each other and lie next to each other on the metaphase plate.
5. Meiosis is a series of two successive cell divisions with no DNA replication between them; the result is half the number of chromosomes per cell nucleus in egg or sperm cells.
6. In the first meiotic division, a member of each homologous pair of chromosomes is pulled into each daughter cell during anaphase, hence the chromosome number per cell is halved.
7. In the second meiotic division, sister chromatids—the products of the original DNA replication prior to meiosis—are separated leaving daughter cells with unreplicated chromosomes.
8. In fertilization, two sets of unreplicated chromosomes combine to form the diploid number; these chromosomes will then be replicated in preparation for the first mitosis to occur in the zygote.
9. Genetic recombination between homologous chromosome arms and apparently random metaphase alignment of paternal and maternal homologous chromosomes relative to each other both generate enormous variation among the sex cells produced by an individual.

Differentiation of Reproductive Cells: A Biological Context

We've been focusing attention on biological information in chromosomes. Let's revisit sex cell production now and seek a structural context in which to place these meiotic events (Figure 12.13). Early in your own development, a subset of diploid cells called **primary germ cells** (PGCs) began to develop within your pre-ectodermal tissue. During the third week of development, about 50 of these cells rambled about near the posterior end of your yolk sac coming to lodge in the endodermal and mesodermal tissues of the yolk sac wall (see Figure 12.14a). Was induction of future differentiative events occurring at this time? Eventually, they moved across the wall of the future rectum and travelled two separate paths through mesodermal tissues till they took up residence in one of two **gonadal ridge** regions to either side of your midline (see Figure 12.14b). Later, these ridges would differentiate into your sex organs, either **ovaries** or **testes**. By the time they reached the future gonadal tissues, they had increased in number to about 5000.

As the gonadal ridges in females mature into ovaries, immigrant PGCs mature within them into **oogonia,** pre-ova cells that are preparing for meiosis to occur. This maturation process begins in prenatal life! The last DNA replication before meiosis yields the last diploid cell in the developmental pathway

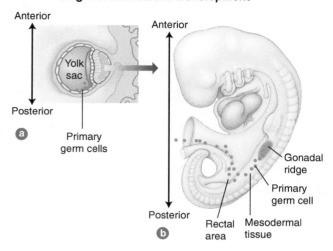

Origin of Gametes in Development

Figure 12.14 Origin of Gametes in Development. **(a)** This diagram is pre-gastrulation; mesodermal cells are not yet defined, but this is the precise place within a slightly later embryo where the primary germ cells lodge temporarily. **(b)** This diagram traces out the route that germ cells take in order to reach and invade the gonadal tissue where their own maturation will continue.

of a primary germ cell. It's a large cell with a well-stocked cytoplasm called the **primary oocyte** (see Figure 12.15a). This cell will not complete meiosis until the time of fertilization! Primary oocytes stop maturing at the end of prophase of the first meiotic division within a few weeks after a baby girl is born. They remain in prophase I until the child matures sexually. Then, at a rate of one to several per month, the primary oocytes complete the first meiotic division, becoming haploid

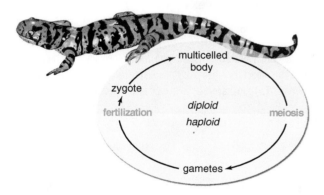

Figure 12.13 Animal Life Cycle. We have defined the progression from zygote to a multi-celled body as *development*. During this time frame the organisms's gonadal tissues and sex cells mature. Once meiosis is complete, the haploid portion of the life cycle commences. In higher animals this portion is only one cell in length. Gametes have but one purpose, to fertilize each other or die.

primary germ cell—those cells in the early embryo whose daughter cells will ultimately differentiate into sex cells, that is, sperm and ova.

gonadal ridge—mesodermal tissue between the somites and lateral mesoderm that develops into gonadal tissue, either ovaries or testes.

ovary—a female reproductive organ whose tissues secrete hormonal signals and both house and mature developing ova.

testis—a male reproductive organ whose tissues secrete hormonal signals and mature developing sperm cells.

oogonium—an immature, diploid, pre–ovum cell that arises from primary germ cells by mitosis.

primary oocyte—an immature, diploid pre–ovum cell that is genetically and structurally prepared to undergo meiotic divisions.

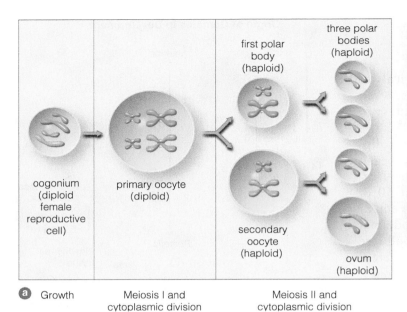

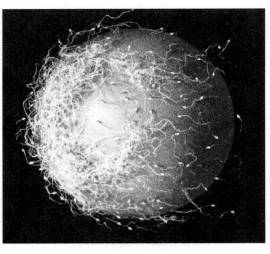

a Growth   Meiosis I and cytoplasmic division   Meiosis II and cytoplasmic division

oogonium (diploid female reproductive cell)

primary oocyte (diploid)

first polar body (haploid)

three polar bodies (haploid)

secondary oocyte (haploid)

ovum (haploid)

b Growth   Meiosis I and cytoplasmic division   Meiosis II and cytoplasmic division

spermatogonium (diploid male germ cell)

primary spermatocyte (diploid)

secondary spermatocytes (haploid)

spermatids (haploid)

cell differentiation, sperm formation (mature, haploid male gametes)

midpiece

Figure 12.15 Gamete Formation. Primary germ cells divide for many generation while the organism housing them is maturing developmentally. Once they approach maturity and begin the process of meiosis we use a specialized terminology to refer to the stages they then pass through. The painting of the human egg surrounded by sperm cells gives an accurate sense of the size difference of these two gametic types. **(a)** gamete formation in human females; **(b)** gamete formation in human males.

secondary oocytes. They stop development again at metaphase of the second meiotic division until they are fertilized—then they complete meiosis. The meiotic cell divisions during oogenesis are very highly unequal in their division of the cytoplasm of the primary oocyte. At each division, one cell keeps virtually all of the cytoplasm and the other set of chromosomes is shunted into a tiny nucleus within a fragment of cytoplasm called a **polar body.** These

secondary oocyte—an immature, haploid pre–ovum cell that has undergone a single meiotic division and is preparing for a second such division.

polar body—the remnant of a nucleus containing a complete set of replicated or unreplicated chromosomes; found within the periphery of an ovum; it deteriorates with time.

polar bodies eventually deteriorate. This leaves the mature egg with the correct level of ploidy and replicative state of its chromosomes contained within a robust amount of cytoplasm to support future embryonic development. In fact, the egg is the largest of any cell in the human female's body. Mature sex cells, ready to participate in fertilization are called **gametes.** Eggs (or ova) and sperm both fit this category.

The gonadal ridges in males mature into testes, and male primary germ cells mature within them into **spermatogonia,** cells that are preparing for meiosis to occur (see Figure 12.15b). Maturation from PGCs into spermatogonia begins during puberty in males. Again, the last DNA replication before meiosis yields the last diploid cell in the developmental pathway toward mature sperm: a large cell called the **primary spermatocyte.** Once sperm production has begun, millions of these cells enter meiosis each day. The first division of a primary spermatocyte generates two haploid **secondary spermatocytes.** These daughter cells go on directly to complete meiosis forming four **spermatids,** which are essentially spherical, haploid cells, now with unreplicated chromosomes. All four products then undergo a radical morphological transformation. They shed much of the remaining one-fourth of the cytoplasm they inherit from the primary spermatocyte. Their mitochondria are retained and highly concentrated in a midpiece section of the maturing sperm cell (see Figure 12.15b). These organelles will generate the ATP that powers the sperm cell toward the waiting egg. Extending posterior to the midpiece, human sperm cells develop a single flagellum built around a circular array of microtubules whose mutual sliding adjacent to each other causes the flagellum to whip around and the sperm cell to swim forward. While the posterior end of a spermatid is differentiating for the purpose of swimming, the anterior end accumulates hydrolytic (digestive) enzymes in an **acrosome** cap. These enzymes will be used as the sperm digests its way into the surface structures of the mature egg. From start to finish, sperm maturation takes about 63 days. The final product, about 1/20 of a millimeter in length, is a triumph of efficiency in space utilization, energy transduction, and swimming agility. It appears perfectly constructed for its singular task in life. No human mind has arrived at a superior design for it given the organismal constrains upon it.

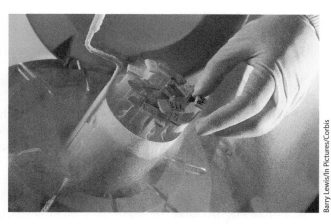

Figure 12.16 Human Sperm Banks. The holder contains "straws" of human sperm quick frozen in liquid nitrogen to protect cell viability. The sperm will be used for *in vitro* (in a test tube) fertilization.

Sperm cells reveal fascinating features of the human psyche. We know we can't live without them. Yet we can't begin to explain their origin without reference to a Designer who crafted them before our species even existed. When Anton van Leeuwenhoek, the great Dutch lens grinder and early microscopist, first observed human sperm cells in 1677, he hesitated to have his work published because of the indelicacy of the subject. Three and a half centuries later, they are being sold on the open market to couples wanting to control the features of their offspring (see Figure 12.16). The sperm of Danish men seem to bring the highest price.

gamete—a sex cell; a cell that has both completed meiosis and differentiated morphologically such that it can participate in the process of fertilization.

spermatogonia—an immature, diploid, pre–sperm cell that arises from primary germ cells by mitosis.

primary spermatocyte—an immature, diploid pre–sperm cell that is genetically and structurally prepared to undergo meiotic divisions.

secondary spermatocyte—an immature, haploid pre–sperm cell that has undergone a single meiotic division and is preparing for a second such division.

spermatid—a pre–sperm cell that has completed meiosis and is about to differentiate structurally to possess a midpiece, flagellar tail, and acrosome.

acrosome—an organelle that covers the anterior portion of a sperm cell; contains hydrolytic enzymes capable of digesting an opening into the surface layers of a mature ovum.

1. Egg and sperm are derived from earlier generations of primary germ cells that arise by differentiation of early ectodermal cells.
2. Primary germ cells divide and migrate to gonadal tissues, where the final stages of their differentiation will be supported and directed.
3. When a primary germ cell differentiates into either a primary spermatocyte in a male or a primary oocyte in a female, it is prepared to undergo two meiotic divisions.
4. As a primary oocyte divides in meiosis, one daughter set of chromosomes is shunted into a polar body leaving the other daughter set of chromosomes with most of the cytoplasm; this later cell will become the egg.
5. Mature eggs or sperm ready for fertilization are termed *gametes*.
6. Primary germ cells in males begin their final stages of differentiation during puberty; in females this process begins before birth.
7. When meiosis is completed in males, extensive differentiation of the haploid spermatid occurs to produce a sperm cell complete with an acrosomal head, haploid nucleus, mitochondrial midpiece, and flagellum.

12.3 REPRODUCTION IN HUMANS

Moment/cultura/Corbis

Dr. Adler here, enters a dimension of human reproduction carefully avoided in most biological writing. He is "standing on the shoulders" of biology seeking to describe a higher aspect of humanity where, once again, a clear flavor of design is present. This higher aspect frustrates scientists because its analysis is refractory to our methods. We can follow information flow from generation to generation, but we cannot define love or explain its relationship to the neurology and endocrinology of reproduction. Must our physical-biological discussion, therefore, cast this higher realm of study aside? How valuable is the potential gain in trying to see as much of the whole picture of human reproduction as its particulars will allow or

even suggest? Thoughtful designs have something of their Designer lodged within them. Surely, we want to know as much about *this* Designer as His designs will allow us to discover.

So, if you have never been primed with basic information about the human sexual act, this discussion will give you at least some of the graphic, biologic details. But we are here exploring one of the most amazing human activities that exists! It appears to figure deeply in the high purposes of its Designer. So expect us to digress into analogies where there may be potential to discover more of the nature of the Designer of this incredible act and its supportive processes.

The earliest written record we have of a human being resulting from sexual reproduction was the birth of Cain, a man described in Genesis 4. The historical record begins its account of Cain's tragic life by saying, "Adam knew Eve his wife; and she conceived." This "knowing" the record speaks of, is an Old English term for the most intimate physical, emotional, and spiritual relationship that is possible between a man and a woman. The physical part of the "knowing" is the sexual process that results in human reproduction.

Annie Engel/Corbis

Let's review a bit. What happens in sexual reproduction? Most of the time in the world of biology, reproduction is the result of one cell dividing to become two (see Figure 12.17a).

Cell Division and Cell Fusion (Fertilization)

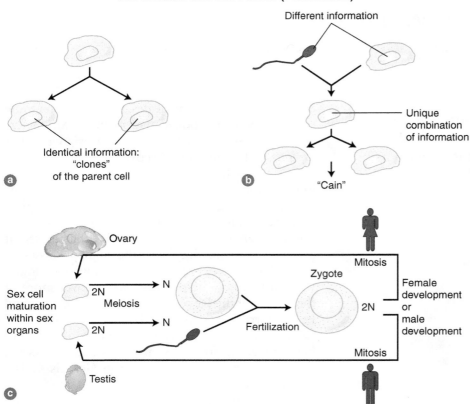

a Identical information: "clones" of the parent cell

b Different information / Unique combination of information / "Cain"

c Ovary / Sex cell maturation within sex organs / 2N / Meiosis / N / 2N / N / Fertilization / Zygote / Mitosis / 2N / Female development or male development / Mitosis / Testis

Figure 12.17 Cellular Relationships. **(a)** Cell division is the most common intercellular event in biology. Daughter cells are clones of the parent cell. **(b)** Cell fusion in fertilization brings divergent sources of information together into one cell generating a unique cellular genome. If the cell is a zygote, then a unique individual will result. **(c)** The human life cycle alternates between diploid body cells and haploid gametes that fuse in fertilization.

But in sexual reproduction we have that rarer situation where cell division is preceded by a unique event in which two cells fuse to become one (see Figure 12.17b). It is from that resulting cell that Cain emerged. When two cells result from one, their information can *only* reflect what was in the parental cell—the two daughter cells must be clones. They are identical replicas of the parental cell. But in sexual reproduction, each sex cell supplies a separate, unique set of information for making a human being (see Figure 12.17c). Barring abnormalities, any human egg cell could, in principle, be fertilized by any human sperm cell. That's a major way that genetic variety increases within a species.

If there are lots of traits to being human—and there are—then a new individual will be a unique blend of those traits that were present in the two parents from which he arose. How do we arrive at that unique blend? Is the union of a particular sperm and egg cell an essentially random event? Biologists can discover factors that might cause a sperm cell to swim faster or an egg cell to mature more quickly. But amazingly, the Biblical text argues that the Creator-Designer, at some level at which He operates, determines which sex cells will unite to form human beings. Here is an initial example then, of how the Hand of the Designer respects, yet intervenes, in the will of man in designing and producing a new human being! With this mystery as a context, let's consider the two cells from which Cain arose.

Oogenesis in Humans

Inside of Eve there was a collection of tissues committed to the function of reproduction. That group of tissues, or organ, is called an *ovary*. Eve had two of them. Inside a woman's ovary (see Figure 12.18) are thousands of individual egg cells or ova in various stages of their maturation process; some haven't begun meiosis, others are beginning the process, and the most mature one is arrested in between the two meiotic divisions. The larger oocytes are encased in an even larger spherical cluster of

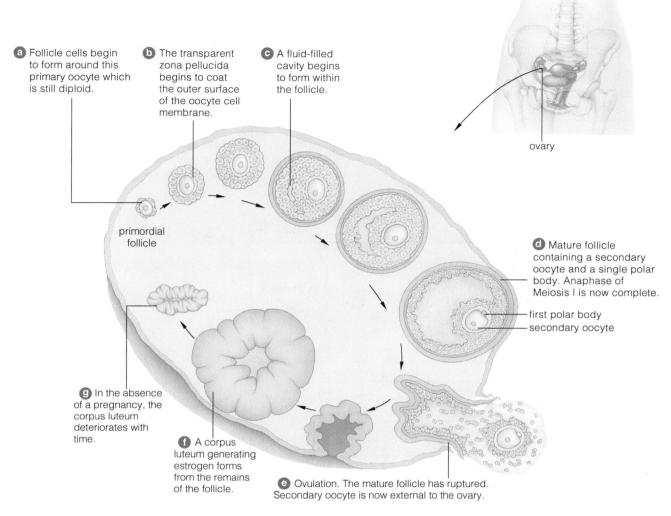

a Follicle cells begin to form around this primary oocyte which is still diploid.

b The transparent zona pellucida begins to coat the outer surface of the oocyte cell membrane.

c A fluid-filled cavity begins to form within the follicle.

ovary

primordial follicle

d Mature follicle containing a secondary oocyte and a single polar body. Anaphase of Meiosis I is now complete.

first polar body
secondary oocyte

g In the absence of a pregnancy, the corpus luteum deteriorates with time.

f A corpus luteum generating estrogen forms from the remains of the follicle.

e Ovulation. The mature follicle has ruptured. Secondary oocyte is now external to the ovary.

Figure 12.18 The Human Ovary. Inside the ovary a sequence of stages in the maturation of a follicle and its internal oocyte is shown. This does not involve internal movements as suggested by the arrows, rather each follicle matures in place. There are three essential stages in maturation: the first stage is follicular growth, the second stage is ovulation, the third stage is formation of the corpus luteum from the ruptured follicle.

cells called a **follicle.** The follicle cells nutritionally support the developing oocyte until it reaches a size appropriate for leaving the ovary. Follicle cells are a physical example of a generality we see repeatedly in the biological world. These cells have no value whatever to the individual that generates them. Their only value is their support of the ovum that will on fertilization become a separate embryonic individual draining resources from the parent organism. The Designer appears quite content to arrange cellular relationships such that one group of cells is totally dependent on the selfless energy expenditure of another group of cells: fundamental dependence based on selfless giving. We must learn to expect this principle at work elsewhere among the Designer's creations.

Dependence operates at the system level as well. (Life Is Internally Integrated.) A woman's endocrine system interacts intimately with her reproductive system organizing the reproductive system's work into a carefully controlled 28-day cycle—the **menstrual cycle** (see Figure 12.19).

follicle—a spherical collection of cells that develops within the ovary of a female animal; it houses and nutritionally supports a developing ovum.

menstrual cycle—a sequence of structural and hormonal changes within the uterus of the female that prepare the uterus for a potential pregnancy; it sheds its lining if the pregnancy fails to occur.

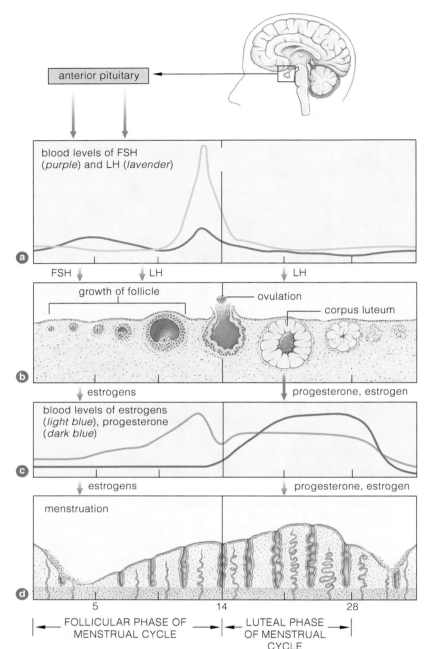

Figure 12.19 The Menstrual Cycle. Monthly uterine and ovarian changes are controlled by hormonal inputs from the pituitary gland and from the ovaries and uterus themselves. This diagram represents the cycle as 28 days with mentruation beginning on day 1. Green arrows indicate where in the cycle the hormones have their effects. **(a)** the blood levels of FSH and LH from the pituitary gland. **(b)** The dramatic surge in LH mid-cycle prompts ovulation. **(c)** The blood levels of estrogen and progesterone emanating from the ovaries. **(d)** The thickness of the uterine wall at various points in the cycle is shown. Estrogens prompt the increase in wall thickness.

For example, her **pituitary gland** uses follicle-stimulating hormone (**FSH**) and luteinizing hormone (**LH**) to order the activities of her ovaries. For about half of her monthly cycle, FSH leaves the pituitary gland and upon arriving at the ovary, signals it to bring one of its more advanced follicles (containing a primary oocyte) to complete maturity. This maturation involves bringing the oocyte further along in meiosis I, furthering the maturation of its surface layers. As a closely orchestrated process continues, the cells of the maturing follicle now begin to secrete the hormone

pituitary gland—a 0.5-g lobe-like extension from the hypothalamic region of the brain; has endocrine function secreting hormones that control a variety of developmental functions often via control of other endocrine glands; the master gland.

FSH (follicle stimulating hormone)—synthesized and secreted by the pituitary gland; it regulates critical aspects of the maturation of sex cells.

LH (luteinizing hormone)—synthesized in the anterior portion of the pituitary gland; causes ovulation in females; stimulates testosterone production in males.

estrogen which in turn causes the entire follicle to more closely approach the marginal surface of the ovary. Meanwhile, the increase in levels of follicle-derived estrogen in the bloodstream is signaling the pituitary gland that follicular development is proceeding normally in the ovary. Once the follicle is the correct size, the estrogen level in the blood is sufficient to cause the pituitary gland to suddenly secrete high levels of the hormone LH (see Figure 12.19a, b). Its level peaks fairly suddenly but precisely in the middle of the calendar month. This sudden elevation of LH levels in the bloodstream causes the most mature follicle in the ovary to rupture at its surface. This rupturing is called **ovulation.**

The mature egg, freed of its follicle, is now momentarily loose in the abdominal cavity of the female (see Figure 12.20). But very close beside the ovary lie the finger-like fringes or **fimbriae** of the cilia-lined **fallopian tubes.** The fimbriae capture the ovum and sweep it into the fallopian tube, where it begins a passive, cilia-powered journey down the tube that will result in its fertilization and eventual **implantation** in the nutrient-rich lining of the woman's **uterus.**

The uterus is a muscular organ that opens to the exterior through a narrowed orifice termed the **cervix.** The cervix secretes a mucous that enhances

estrogen—a class of hormones controlling various aspects of sexual reproduction in females.

ovulation—a process in which a mature ovum or egg cell ruptures from a follicle next to the surface of the ovary such that the ovum leaves the ovary and enters the fallopian tube.

fimbriae—a highly articulated fringe of tissue around the opening of the fallopian tube closest to the ovary; these sweep the ovulated egg into the fallopian tube.

fallopian tubes (uterine tube, oviduct)—a cilia-lined passage that extends from the ovary to the uterus; carries mature or fertilized ovum to the uterus for implantation.

implantation—the process by which an embryo about six days postfertilization burrows into the endometrial lining of the uterus to continue growth using maternally derived nutrients from the uterine lining and eventually the placenta.

uterus—female organ in which a fertilized egg implants and matures as an embryo to the point of birth.

cervix—the posterior, narrow neck of the uterus that connects it to the vaginal canal; stretches minimally for endometrial shedding and maximally during birthing. progesterone—a progestogen steroid hormone in females that supports embryonic development and participates in the control of the female menstrual cycle.

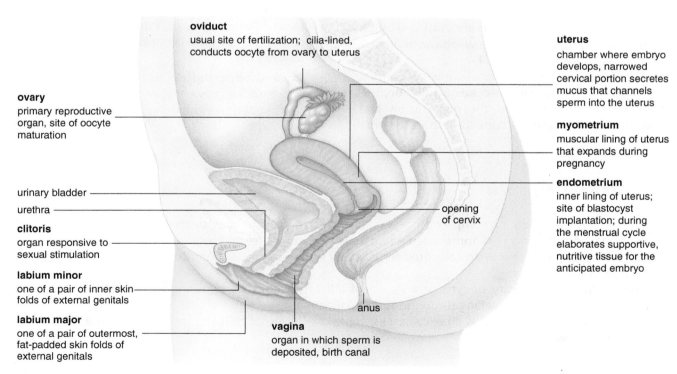

oviduct
usual site of fertilization; cilia-lined, conducts oocyte from ovary to uterus

uterus
chamber where embryo develops, narrowed cervical portion secretes mucus that channels sperm into the uterus

myometrium
muscular lining of uterus that expands during pregnancy

endometrium
inner lining of uterus; site of blastocyst implantation; during the menstrual cycle elaborates supportive, nutritive tissue for the anticipated embryo

ovary
primary reproductive organ, site of oocyte maturation

urinary bladder

urethra

clitoris
organ responsive to sexual stimulation

labium minor
one of a pair of inner skin folds of external genitals

labium major
one of a pair of outermost, fat-padded skin folds of external genitals

opening of cervix

anus

vagina
organ in which sperm is deposited, birth canal

Figure 12.20   The Female Reproductive System.

the movement of sperm into the uterus while blocking the entrance of many (much smaller) bacterial cells. The inner lining of the uterus, the **endometrium,** contains nutritive connective tissues, blood vessels, and glands all designed to support the growth of an embryo.

The reproductive system uses hormones to "think ahead"—to anticipate pregnancy. The ovarian hormones estrogen and (later on) **progesterone** guide the preparation of the uterus for its role in supporting a possible pregnancy. They cause a thickening in the nutritive lining of the uterus that prepares it for the arrival of a fertilized oocyte (see Figure 12.19c, d). Once ovulation has occurred, the follicle from which the egg ruptures continues to secrete the hormones estrogen and progesterone to cause the uterus to maintain its rich, vascularized lining for several days should a cadre of sperm cells arrive in the vicinity! This spent follicle—called the **corpus luteum**—eventually deteriorates. If the ovulated egg is not fertilized by the time of its deterioration, the hormonal maintenance of the uterus ceases and the extra uterine endometrial tissue and some blood leave the uterus and the **vagina** over a period of three to six days during the process of menstruation.

This menstrual cycle—its uterine and follicular preparation, ovulation, and endometrial maintenance followed by endometrial deterioration—begins in females aged 10 to 16 and repeats itself at approximately 28-day intervals until a woman reaches her late 40s or early 50s when she no longer hormonally supports the cycle. For this entire 30- to 40-year interval, her sensory, endocrine, circulatory, and reproductive systems are beautifully orchestrated to work together in the preparation and protection of the woman's contribution to the next generation. There is a humbling selflessness to this design. The average pregnant human female gains 12.5 kilograms of weight by her third trimester and has a basal metabolism rate 25% greater than prepregnancy levels. She faces possible calcium deficiencies, back pains, gestational diabetes, varicose veins, months of diminished sleep quality, all for the well-being of another individual. All of this energy expenditure offers no significant enhancement of her physical well-being whatever. The result contributes to a higher purpose—the perpetuation of her species—a purpose she may not emotionally embrace. Apparently, the Designer of informational continuity cherishes a vision of life that is higher than the individuals that comprise it. His designs are characterized by calling for sacrifice in one part of His living world entirely for the good of another part. If this is a reflection of the Designer's own character, then that is an encouraging thought indeed (or challenging when our own propensities are considered).

> **endometrium**—the inner lining of the mammalian uterus.
>
> **progesterone**—a progestogen steroid hormone in females that supports embryonic development and participates in the control of the female menstrual cycle.
>
> **corpus luteum**—the yellow (luteal) remains of a ruptured ovarian follicle after ovulation; secretes estrogen and progesterone for maintaining the uterine lining for a possible pregnancy.
>
> **vagina**—a tubular canal leading from the uterus to the exterior of the female body; receives the penis during sexual intercourse and is the birth canal during parturition.

IN OTHER WORDS

1. Human reproduction is a complex process involving biological changes, deep emotional expression, and spiritual bonding. It is best appreciated when these aspects are treated together.
2. In theory, any human sperm cell could fertilize any human egg; the potential genetic variation among gametes is enormous.
3. Within the human ovary, oocytes at a variety of different stages are maturing within follicles under the control of hormones travelling throughout the bloodstream.
4. The human ovarian follicle is an excellent example of a group of cells that exist only for the sake of the oocyte cell within them.

5. The human menstrual cycle is guided over a 28-day period by the hormones FSH and LH released from the pituitary gland and estrogen and progesterone generated by the follicle.
6. The ovulated ovum is caught by fimbriae extensions of the fallopian tubes, which carry it toward swimming sperm cells and then toward the uterus, where it implants.
7. The uterus generates a thick, nutrient-rich inner lining, or endometrium, within which a fertilized conceptus can develop.
8. Once a follicle ruptures, it converts into a yellow conglomeration of cells called a *corpus luteum;* this begins to secrete the hormones estrogen and progesterone, which help maintain the uterus in a receptive state for implantation of a conceptus.
9. The menstrual cycle functions repeatedly over a period of from 30 to 40 years in a normal human female, during which time her body systems cooperate in the selfless venture of generating mature oocytes.

Spermatogenesis and Fertilization

But the organ systems that comprised Cain, though fashioned within Eve, were also informed by Adam. Inside Adam's **scrotal sac** lay two testes in which haploid sperm cells were forming (see Figure 12.21). In human males, the testes begin their formation on the wall of the abdominal cavity and descend into the scrotal sac shortly before birth. There, outside the abdominal cavity, the lower optimal temperatures for sperm formation can be more conveniently maintained and adjusted.

Inside the testis are the tightly coiled **seminiferous tubules** (see Figure 12.21). There is over one complete football field's length of tubule in each testis. (Happily the tubule is less than 60 μm in

scrotal sac—an enclosure composed of skin and muscle that houses the male testes at a temperature suitable for sperm production.

seminiferous tubules—long, narrow ducts within the testis of the male; site of meiosis followed by sperm production.

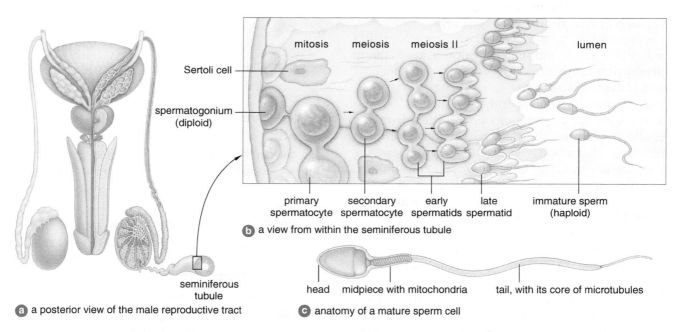

Figure 12.21   Sperm Formation. **(a)** Sperm form within the two testicles lodged in the human scrotal sac (not shown here). One testicle is shown in cross-section. The seminiferous tubule is extracted from one testicle and **(b)** a cross-sectional view of the tubule is shown. The Sertoli cell is specifically crafted to provide nutrients to differentiating spermatocytes. Small tendrils (not shown) connect spermatocytes to the nearest Sertoli cell. **(c)** The anatomical parts of a sperm cell are diagrammed.

diameter.) Adam used these tubules to generate possibly a trillion sperm cells in his lifetime! One of them would initiate and help guide the development of Cain. Inside the tubule, we observe the spatial architecture in which meiosis is halving the informational content of the developing sex cells. Immature sex cells are being constantly generated around the periphery of the tubule. As they progress through meiosis, they are also progressing toward the center of the tubule, called here the **lumen.** Once they arrive in the lumen of the tubule, they are mature sperm cells and are carried along to a nearby region of long, coiling ducts called the **epididymis.** They are stored there. Natural selection might have been content with perfecting a one-dimensional assembly line for sperm beginning at the far end of the seminiferous tubule and ending at the epididymis. But a Designer saw ahead. A two-dimensional system in which maturation occurs laterally all along the tubule is capable of efficiently generating a much higher number of sperm in a short time period. High sperm loads would suit a more complex and defensively structured female reproductive system in which many sperm cells die before a few reach the waiting egg.

Sperm production in the seminiferous tubule is not an autonomous process. It is closely controlled. Adjacent to the tubules are **Leydig cells** that produce and secrete the hormone **testosterone,** which is critical for maintaining sperm production. Leydig cells in turn are under the control of LH and FSH. These pituitary hormones keep sperm production firmly under the control of the nervous and endocrine systems.

How and when do sperm leave the epididymis? Smooth muscle contractions propel them from the epididymis during the climax of sexual arousal in the man. Somehow, Adam and Eve knew the appropriate and bio-"logical" way to consummate this sexually aroused state. God had said, "Be fruitful and multiply . . ." Perhaps at some later point He revealed to them that when the **penis** of the male physically deposits sperm within the vagina of the female, other wonderful things are accomplished: Adam and Eve become mysteriously united emotionally and spiritually as well. In this high context of creating new life, they would become one being, even though they were two persons. So this process would both accomplish the Designer's command to be fruitful and multiply and would also make them more in His image. All this creating and uniting in one pleasurable act!

On the other hand, it does say in Proverbs Chapter 25 that it is the glory of God to conceal a matter and the glory of kings to search it out. Adam and Eve were designed with rational minds: Surely they appreciated the complementarity of their sexual anatomy! Observations of reproductive behaviors in animals with the resulting production of like offspring would have quickly confirmed their happiest suspicion that this activity was the way to obey the commands to "become one flesh" and also to "be fruitful and multiply." In any case, transfer of sperm to Eve and all her daughters is perhaps the most universally pleasant task in human society.

The male nervous system carries off a sequential work of art here. Adam's richly endowed sensory system combined with his love for his mate to heighten his sexual arousal. In humans, as this sequence progresses, arteriolar relaxation in the penis is called for. This causes blood flow into its **erectile tissue** to exceed its efflux. The penis then enlarges and stiffens. As this preparation is completed, muscular contractions along the length of the reproductive system quickly collect sperm cells from the epididymis at the top of each testis. The sperm are swept along a duct called the **vas deferens** (see Figure 12.22). They glide rapidly past glands like the **seminal vesicles,** which

---

lumen—the interior channel of any duct or tubule.

epididymis—a lobe on the surface of the male testis housing a highly coiled tubule in which mature sperm are stored prior to ejaculation.

Leydig cells—within the male testis, cells that are primary sites of production of the hormone testosterone.

testosterone—a steroid hormone that in males regulates production of sperm and secondary sexual characteristics; in females it influences the desire for sexual activity.

penis—an external sexual organ in males that, in placental mammals, also serves as an organ of urination.

erectile tissue—a collection of cells within the male penis that becomes engorged with blood during sexual arousal preparing the penis for sperm deposition in the female vaginal canal.

vas deferens—a duct leading from the epididymis to the ejaculatory duct within the prostate gland; carries mature sperm toward the urethra of the male during sexual arousal.

seminal vesicle—a tubular gland in males that secretes a nutritive fluid comprising part of semen.

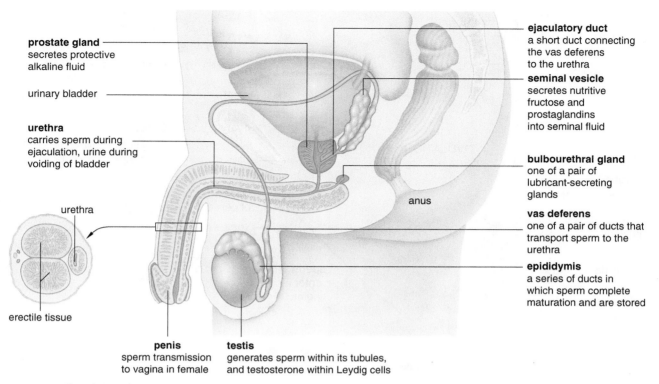

prostate gland
secretes protective
alkaline fluid

urinary bladder

urethra
carries sperm during
ejaculation, urine during
voiding of bladder

urethra

erectile tissue

penis
sperm transmission
to vagina in female

testis
generates sperm within its tubules,
and testosterone within Leydig cells

anus

ejaculatory duct
a short duct connecting
the vas deferens
to the urethra

seminal vesicle
secretes nutritive
fructose and
prostaglandins
into seminal fluid

bulbourethral gland
one of a pair of
lubricant-secreting
glands

vas deferens
one of a pair of ducts that
transport sperm to the
urethra

epididymis
a series of ducts in
which sperm complete
maturation and are stored

Figure 12.22   The Male Reproductive System.

perfectly time their secretions to infuse the sperm load with a sugar-rich solution to nourish them. Along the way, they pass a contracted sphincter muscle that prevents urine from the bladder from mixing with them. Their path leads next through the **prostate gland,** which adds fluid that protects sperm viability in the female reproductive track! Finally, a **bulbourethral gland** secretes a carefully timed mucoid secretion just ahead of the sperm load to lubricate their passage along the urethra. The resulting seminal fluid is quickly propelled out of the urethra in the man's penis and into the anterior cervical area of the vagina at the climactic moment of sexual activity. Neurotransmitters flood synapses in the brain. The moments during which informational continuity is most highly cooperative are those most overwhelmed by joy.

In the meantime, sexual arousal in the female is also a highly complex and neurologically controlled process. It is maximized in the warm, trusting context of a covenantal bond (or naïve anticipation of one). One result of sexual arousal is mucous secretion from glands in the vagina that lubricate the entrance of the penis prior to ejaculation of sperm there. Following the male's sexual climax, a population of sperm cells roughly equivalent in number to the entire population of the United

States now begins its journey to the anterior. A large fraction of the sperm die almost immediately when exposed to the hostile (protective) acidity of the vagina. More will fail to properly negotiate the mucous barrier in the cervix. During the fertile days of her cycle, a woman's mucus usually thins and becomes more supportive of sperm movement. Nonetheless, only about 1% of the viable sperm will negotiate the cervix and move on to the uterus. From there, approximately half of the remaining number will swim toward the fallopian tube that contains no fertile oocyte.

But some of these barriers are systematically overcome. For example, chemicals called **prostaglandins**

prostate gland—an accessory sexual gland in males whose secretion buffers the environment of the sperm against vaginal acidity and induces muscular contractions in the female reproductive system.

bulbourethral gland—a lobular exocrine gland that secretes a pre-sperm lubricant into the urethra that also neutralizes the acidity of any residual urine.

prostaglandin—any of a class of lipid molecules that contains 20 carbon atoms, including a five-carbon ring; often influencing the contraction and relaxation of smooth muscle local to the site of their secretion.

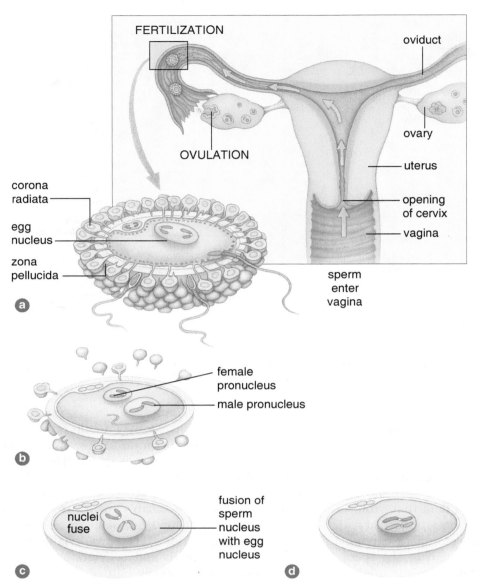

Figure 12.23 Fertilization. **(a)** A sperm cell has digested its way through the corona radiata and the zona pellucida. The surface of the zona no longer binds any other sperm cells. Meiosis II division now goes to completion leaving behind three polar bodies and an ovum nucleus **(b)** The sperm nucleus swells in size, leaving midpiece and flagellum behind; the two nuclei are now called pronuclei. **(c)** the precise moment of fertilization—when the two pronuclei fuse **(d)** the mature diploid zygote

are secreted by the seminal vesicles (see Figure 12.22) of the male into semen. Once semen is deposited in the cervical region, they promote and intensify smooth muscle contractions all along the cervix and uterine lining. The female promotes her own smooth muscle contractions by secreting oxytocin, a brain hormone, during sexual stimulation of her vaginal canal. Contractions resulting from both these stimuli rapidly carry seminal fluid with its precious cargo of sperm toward the fallopian tubes, where fertilization normally takes place.

The swimming ability of the sperm is useful at various points during the fertilization process. But it is not efficient in getting the sperm up into the woman's fallopian tubes. Swimming the distance would take about an hour against the downward beat of the cilia that line the tube. But the woman's muscular contractions can get the sperm the whole distance from the vagina to the end of the fallopian tube in three to five minutes (see Figure 12.23)! So here again is an example of a process whose design involves selflessness. True, the success of the process (fertilization) results from features unique to the (sperm) cells participating in it. But the efficiency of that same process depends much more heavily on the selfless cooperation of powerful forces inherent in the sympathetic design of another organism (the female). That other organism derives no direct benefit from the expression of those forces. The design involves giving for the sake of the species, not the individual.

The final destination is the waiting egg. It is halted at a point early in the second meiotic division. Genetically, it is haploid but with chromosomes still in their replicated state. It is surrounded by the **corona radiata**: a layer of cells it took with it from inside the follicle. Hydrolytic enzymes in the seminal fluid and in the acrosomal region on the sperm's head digest a path through the corona radiata and the **zona pellucida**—the outer membrane of the egg cell proper (see Figure 12.23).

Soon, one solitary sperm cell—probably the strongest and fastest one—penetrates the zona pellucida. Immediately, a rapid, oocyte-initiated, enzymatic digestion occurs within the outer surface of the zona pellucida. It removes surface recognition sites that sperm cells normally bind to. This renders the egg impenetrable by any other sperm cells. Imagine the triploid confusion that would result if an egg were fertilized by two different sperm cells! The sperm cell's head and midpiece leave the flagellar tail behind once they're inside the egg cell. This entry signals the egg cell to complete its second meiotic division, which may have begun months or even years ago! Consider the amazing interlocking of chemical signals and biological processes in both the egg and sperm nuclei, two structures that must soon fuse and that have never contacted each other before! Their behavior is a high tribute to an amazing Designer who likes His machines a whole lot more complicated than we can afford ours to be.

The head of the sperm now swells to become the male **pronucleus.** The nucleus of the egg is the female pronucleus (see Figure 12.23). The fusing of these two pronuclei—the intermeshing of two separate genomes—is the actual, quintessential moment of fertilization, although to the parental participants it could hardly compare with the excitement of an hour ago! Pronuclear fusion forms the diploid nucleus of the fertilized egg or zygote. Those trained in genetics look at this historic moment in the fallopian tubes of Eve as the instant in which Cain became a living being. The zygote has a complete genetic independence to it. All "he" now needs is nourishment and time in order to become, physically, a completely independent human life.

Cain now began a multi-day roller coaster ride down the fallopian tube in which his origin occurred (see Figure 12.24). His own genetic program was fully operational. He began to enzymatically digest away his zona pellucida so critical to the success of the fertilization that generated him. By the time he reached the uterus, he hatched from within the zona to reveal a whole new surface layer of **trophoblastic** cells perfectly designed for his next task: the attachment to and invasion of his mother's uterus. Its lining was hormonally well prepared to receive and support the totally dependent young life she and Adam had conceived. Cain's trophoblast cells now began to generate a whole battery of enzymes to digest its way into the uterine capillary beds, causing blood to pool in tiny sinuses that would now feed the growing embryo. His cells also elaborated

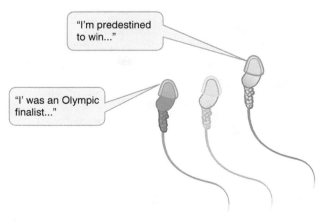

Sperm Cell Repartee.

corona radiata—two or three layers of cells, residual from the follicle, that surround an ovulated egg; they supply nutritive protein to the egg cell.

zona pellucida—a protective layer of an ovulated egg external to the cell membrane; docking site for sperm; its presence is required to initiate the sperm's acrosomal hydrolytic enzyme activities.

pronucleus—the nucleus of either the egg cell or the sperm cell during the process of fertilization; used to refer to both nuclei after the sperm nucleus has entered the egg cytoplasm.

trophoblastic—of or pertaining to a layer of cells that surrounds the early embryo; this layer is adapted to deriving nutrition from maternal tissues.

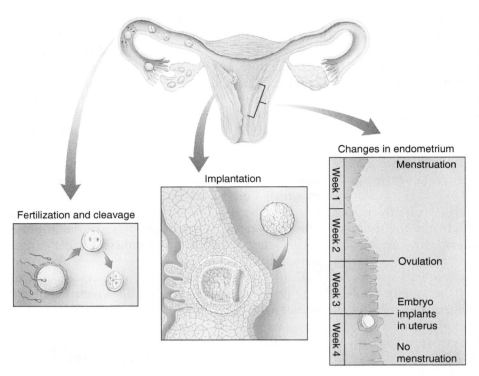

Figure 12.24   The Anatomy of Early Development. Fertilization occurs far up in the Fallopian tube; implantation occurs in the uterine wall. The corpus luteum and eventually the blastocyst itself hormonally maintain the thickness of the uterus; no menstruation takes place.

Fertilization and cleavage

Implantation

Changes in endometrium

Menstruation

Week 1

Week 2

Ovulation

Week 3

Embryo implants in uterus

Week 4

No menstruation

immunosuppressing substances to keep his mother's immune cells from attacking him. Eve is totally unaware of these processes. Yet their origin in her son's genome is part of an elegant design that perfectly guides Cain's early maturation.

After about 270 days, Cain was born. His total dependence on his parents for life was eventually his downfall. He became an agent of death. That's really what his parents were too, although they hardly wished to believe it. The Genesis record describes a deliberate moral and spiritual failure in the lives of the first two parents prior to their conception of Cain. Human physical and spiritual death was the eventual results of their choices. How symbolic that the first human being produced totally by human beings was both a most miserable source of his brother's death and finally a sorrowful example of death himself.

Our physical heritage from our first parents is death-riddled (see Chapter 16). Because of Adam's moral choice, we all die. But the sexual character of human reproduction supplies us with a most pleasing metaphor. The human egg, apart from a sperm cell is destined for death as well. It's a miniscule speck of tragedy in a sea of discarded uterine tissue and blood. But a sperm cell changes

everything. The egg is rescued to a physical life that is primed with spiritual potential. That egg is a precise picture of the mortal human condition: life preparatory for death. But rescue is possible. It too follows a conjugal event—two parties are the critical requirement (see Figure 12.25). A human being made receptive to the Designer's Spirit of grace is necessary, but a human being alone is not sufficient to achieve this new life! The Designer must come alongside to gently enter that human's

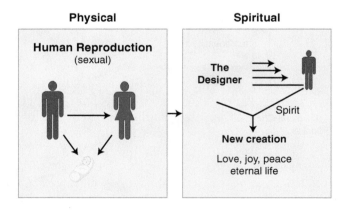

Figure 12.25   The Physical and the Spiritual. It is reasonable to suspect that biological relationships may be a picture of spiritual ones if both realms have the same Designer.

life. Eventually, at a climactic moment of surrender in the human, the Designer joyfully implants the seed of His life-giving Spirit deep within its spiritual womb: the human soul. The new human spirit conceived there issues in selfless love, responsive joy, and a quiet peace. Eternal union with the family and person of the Designer result. Biologists cannot explain this spiritual conception and birth. But biological process analogizes it beautifully and some biologists . . . have experienced it.

IN OTHER WORDS

1. Within the testes of the male lie the seminiferous tubules, the site of sperm production in the male.
2. Sperm cell maturation involves meiosis and differentiation that occurs as the cells move from the periphery of the tubule to the lumen from which they are transported to the epididymis for storage.
3. Sperm cell formation is controlled by local levels of the hormone testosterone produced in the Leydig cells between the tubules in the testis.
4. The first humans understood their own sexuality either as a result of revelation from a Designer or by rational analysis of animal behavior.
5. The preparation for ejaculation of sperm from the urethra of the male is a carefully sequenced series of events governed by the brain.
6. The seminal vesicles, prostate, and bulbourethral glands each contribute their own critical components to seminal fluid as the sperm are propelled through or past them on their way to the urethra.
7. Only about 1% of the sperm deposited in the vagina will reach the entrance to the fallopian tubes.
8. Prostaglandins in the seminal fluid of the male and oxytocin in the bloodstream of the sexually aroused female promote muscular contractions within the uterus that move sperm along more rapidly toward their destination.
9. When sperm meets egg, the sperm cell must digest its way through the remaining follicular cells and the zona pellucida to reach the egg cell membrane.
10. Entry of a single sperm cell causes a sudden enzymatic alteration of the zona pellucida surface, keeping other sperm cells from effectively entering and fertilizing the egg.
11. When the sperm penetrates the egg, the flagellum and midpiece deteriorate, the nucleus swells to pronuclear size, the female nucleus completes meiosis, and the two pronuclei fuse to complete the fertilization.
12. Seven to ten days after fertilization, the conceptus will implant in the endometrial lining of the uterus. Another 270 days or so will be required before birth.

12.4 REPRODUCTION CONSTRAINED, PART I: CONTROL OF BIRTH

Given the sheer elegance of oogenesis, spermatogenesis, sperm migration, fertilization, and implantation, one might wonder (for at least a minute?) why any couple would want to limit or place constraints on such a highly integrated and exalted process! Imagine, creating another human life—what a miracle—what a high privilege! And if the Designer of human development is also the source of the Genesis record—another wonderfully designed piece of work—then along with the honor of creating life came His first ever imperative for mankind: "Be fruitful, multiply, fill the earth . . ." In regard to sexual reproduction, then, we are given both the privilege and a command. In the twenty-first century in Western technological societies, this command has been particularly difficult to receive. New human life is equated with an enormous amount of time and money as well as pain and some degree of female physical deformation. As a result, many couples (unimpressed with the privilege or its inherent wisdom) simply ignore the command. Other couples respect the command, yet seek to postpone obedience to it. Since hormonal and neurological drives are not altered by such postponement, most couples seek ways to engage in the high pleasure of the creative experience while avoiding its natural product—the child. The free market has responded with a variety of methods collectively referred to as *birth control*, a euphemism for birth avoidance. These birth control methods vary widely in their mode of intervention, the point at which birth is obviated, the degree of parental safety, the expense, and the ease of use. We classify them here on the basis of their mode of intervention: How does the birth control method work?

1. Sperm Blockage

These methods are either mechanical or chemical but are conservative in the degree to which they require invasion or alteration of internal tissues and associated functions. They are all **contraceptive** rather than **abortive** in their mode of intervention.

Spermicides, whether foams, creams, or gels, are inserted vaginally prior to sexual contact and are reasonably effective (see Table 12.1). However, some of the chemicals used have been shown to cause vaginal or penile irritation and, in rare cases, urinary tract or vaginal infections. Mechanical,

> **contraceptive**—any substance or method that prevents sperm from uniting with the egg.
>
> **abortive**—any substance or method that prevents a zygote or subsequent stages in human development from proceeding further; terminating of an individual organism's life.
>
> **spermicide**—any substance or drug that is lethal to sperm cells.

Table 12.1 Pregnancy Rates for Birth Control Methods

Method	Lowest Possible Rate of Pregnancy	Typical-Use Rate of Pregnancy
Spermicide + Diaphragm	6%	20%
Condoms	3%	14%
Withdrawal	4%	19%
Oral Contraceptive	0.1%	5%
IUD (copper based)	0.6%	0.8%
Vaginal Ring	1–2%*	8%**
Rhythm Method	1–9%	25%
Tubal Ligation	0.5%	0.5%
Vasectomy	<1%	<1%

Data (except where noted below) from US Food and Drug Administration, 1997.
*American Pregnancy Association
**Contracept.org

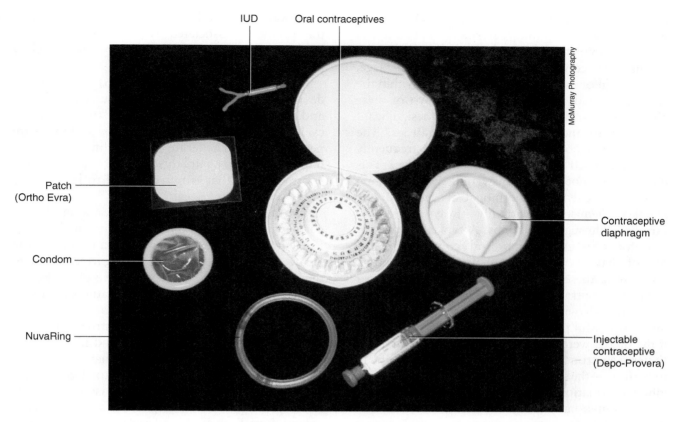

Figure 12.26 Examples of Commonly Used Birth Control Methods. Hormonal alteration of the female can be accomplished by a pill, a skin patch, a vaginal ring, injection, or IUD. All of these use fundamentally the same approach to contraception. None can be categorically ruled out as a possible abortifacient (cause of abortion).

flexible devices like **diaphragms** (see Figure 12.26) are inserted prior to sexual contact and cover the cervical opening. Diaphragms are most effective when fitted to the cervix following measurement by a physician.

Flexible **condoms** cover the penis prior to sexual contact and prevent sperm entry into the vagina. Condoms occasionally break, and they prohibitively reduce the level of pleasure for some men. The use of condoms is a widespread and conservative approach to birth control. In 1844, the Good Year Tire Company introduced the first latex condom! But the concept dates back to ancient Egypt (1000 BC) when linen was used (albeit considerably less effectively) to make the same appliance. By 1040 AD, Celtic England was generating condoms from animal intestines. For those with immune systems hyper responsive to latex, animal intestinal condoms are still sold. Condoms protect the user from a variety of sexually transmitted bacterial infections and somewhat reduce the risk of most virally transmitted infections as well.

Withdrawal of the penis before climax is reached is a very old method of trying to separate the fun from the conception eventuality. Since the climax of the sexual intercourse represents the maximal amount of pleasure, this method proves less effective than is initially desired.

2. Altering Body Function

Here we begin to manipulate the systemic (whole body) hormonal chemistry of the female partner.

Oral contraceptives come in two basic varieties. The most common is the pill, which utilizes a combination

---

diaphragm—a flexible latex or silicone shield placed in front of or over the cervix that prevents sperm from entering the uterus.

condom—a flexible barrier placed over the male penis to keep sperm from passing into the vagina of the sexual partner; constructed of latex or lamb intestine.

withdrawal method—the removal of the penis from the vagina of the female just prior to ejaculation of sperm; used as a method of birth control.

oral contraceptive—the pill; hormonal supplements taken by mouth to prevent ovulation in the female; usually containing estrogen and/or progestogen.

of an estrogen and a progestogen to (1) inhibit a woman's release of pituitary hormones FSH and LH governing ovulation, (2) cause a thickening of the mucus of the cervical plug inhibiting sperm passage, and (3) thin or inhibit tissue development within the endometrium of the uterus. The first two of these effects are contraceptive and result in a significant reduction in the frequency of pregnancies. The third effect is potentially abortive. How frequently might this third effect result in an abortion? This question is not easily answered. Contraception based on conservative hormonal alteration of the female's chemistry is virtually always subject to rare breakthrough ovulations. A typical pregnancy rate for a woman using oral contraceptives is 5% of that of a woman not using contraception. Sometimes, these pregnancies are due to improper use of the contraceptive. But some are the result of breakthrough ovulation and fertilization. How many more successful pregnancies would occur on the pill if the uterus were more hospitable to implantation? Experiments to answer this question would be difficult to perform—the same combination of hormones that inhibits ovulation also alters endometrial quality. Every woman has the right to know, however, that the possibility of aborting an early embryonic person by the use of the combination oral contraceptive pill is a realistic one that has not been disproved.

The **intrauterine device (IUD)** has been used since the 1970s. It must be inserted into the uterus by a qualified physician. Over the years, they have decreased in size and are now constructed of plastic and copper metal, or of plastic that releases a **progestogen** hormone, which inhibits ovulation. Originally, IUDs functioned solely in the uterus. They prevented implantation of the conceptus and were thus entirely abortive of new life. Since copper is spermicidal and ovulation rarely occurs during use of the progestogen type of IUD, these devices are now designed to be contraceptive, not abortive. However, as mentioned above, contraception based on chemical alteration of the female parent is virtually always subject to rare breakthrough ovulations. In the presence of the IUD, the resulting fertilized ovum, which is now a new individual (see Section 12.5), will probably fail to implant due to induced uterine inflammation. Thus by a combination of contraception and abortion, any breakthrough ovulation is "taken care of" and avoidance of pregnancy reaches 99%. There are still problems for the user: Occasional increased bleeding accompanies the copper IUD. The progestogen-based IUD, while causing a beneficially lower systemic hormone level

than oral contraceptives, may still result in some of the problems associated with altered hormonal levels. The insertion process always increases slightly the risk of intrauterine infection.

Vaginal rings (see Figure 12.26) are a newer device that can be inserted without clinical help and slowly add hormones that can stop a woman's cycle (ovulation), thicken her mucous to slow sperm penetration, and generate a uterine lining hostile to implantation; so again, this is one of those dilemma contraceptives that is not designed to be abortive but is possibly so.

The methods reviewed here involve asking a female partner to voluntarily alter her hormonal chemistry in the interest of failing to conceive a new life-form. An evolutionary view of human origins leads one to the assumption that our reproductive physiology is hardly more complex than those features of it that we've already discovered. Thus what could be the danger in increasing a woman's estrogen level by a mere 50 µg at a time? Animal and human trials with oral contraceptives suggest that there is no danger apart from some well-understood side effects. But the history of birth control measures is replete with available warnings regarding scientists' naïve assumptions. Early IUDs and oral contraceptives alike prompted lawsuits and were withdrawn from the market for the variety of pathologies they enhanced.

A view of human origins based on design cautions us that our reproductive machinery may interrelate to our general physiology in much more complex ways than we've yet envisioned. Sudden or prolonged arbitrary increases in hormonal levels will probably have unforeseen physiological and neurological effects. Life Is Complex.

3. Avoiding Intercourse

By charting her body temperature every morning and following changes in her cervical mucus secretions, a woman can accurately chart the **rhythm** of her

---

intrauterine device—a plastic, T-shaped frame either wound with copper wire or containing the hormone progestogen; inserted into the uterus to prevent ovulation, conception, or implantation of the egg cell.

progestogen—a class of similarly structured steroid hormones of which progesterone is an example.

vaginal ring—a flexible drug delivery appliance made of polyethylene and vinyl acetate that delivers progesterone and an estrogen to the female tissues inhibiting ovulation.

rhythm method—the monitoring of temperature and mucus viscosity to chart a woman's monthly cycle; used as a means of birth control.

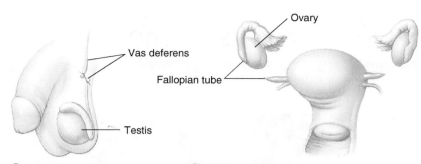

Ovary

Vas deferens

Fallopian tube

Testis

Figure 12.27 Sterilization. **(a)** Vasectomy. The vas deferens extending from both testicles are cut and then cauterized or tied off. **(b)** Tubal Ligation. Each Fallopian tube is cut and pinched off or cauterized. Sperm can no longer reach the egg.

ⓐ **Vasectomy.** The vas deferens (sperm duct) on each side is cut and cauterized.

ⓑ **Tubal sterilization.** Each Fallopian tube is cut and cauterized so that ovum and sperm can no longer meet.

monthly cycle. This **method** determines the three days of the cycle surrounding ovulation when her temperature rises slightly and conception is most likely to occur. If she avoids sexual relations on the days surrounding her ovulation date, she can, by noninvasive means, avoid conception with a high degree of probability. Software and literature are readily available from advocates of this approach. While this approach by itself requires abstention from sexual relations over a period of several days, the method is often supplemented with the use of condoms during the fertile period of the month.

4. Permanent Surgical Methods

"That's it; two screaming kids are enough! Find me a surgeon; I'm having my tubes tied!" The medical community has developed two elegant, surgical procedures that semipermanently sterilize either the female or male partner in the relationship. Both **tubal ligation** (cutting and pinching off the fallopian tubes in the female) and **vasectomy** (cutting and tying off of the vas deferentia in the male) have become reversible processes (see Figure 12.27). But there are a variety of secondary effects to be tolerated. Tubal

ligation is a serious, expensive surgical procedure with potential for postoperative complications. Vasectomies have fewer potential side effects, although studies are emerging suggesting a decreased sexual desire in perhaps 10% of vasectomized males. For either of these surgeries, later deliberate reversal of sterilization is a more complicated procedure; restoration of fertility is definitely *not* guaranteed. So if an only daughter is tragically killed while her parents are still of childbearing age, having had these surgeries could seriously complicate their attempts at a future pregnancy.

A chart (see Table 12.1) of birth control methods reveals that, generally speaking, the less invasive approaches are the least effective ones. Radical intervention tends to achieve higher rates of effectiveness. However, the higher the effectiveness, the higher the potential cost.

tubal ligation—a surgical method of female sterilization in which the fallopian tubes are severed and then pinched or sewed shut.

vasectomy—a minor surgical method of severing the vas deferentia of a male so as to render him sterile.

IN OTHER WORDS

1. Since the rise of civilization, attempts have been made to separate sexual intercourse from conception. A variety of birth control methods exist today.

2. Methods that keep sperm from reaching the egg include the use of condoms, diaphragms, spermicidal foams and gels, and the preclimax withdrawal method.

3. Methods that inhibit ovulation with the possibility of also being abortive include oral contraceptives, the intrauterine device, and vaginal rings.

4. A method that avoids sexual intercourse at the time of the month when a female is fertile is termed the *rhythm* or *symptothermal method.*

5. Methods considered semipermanent or permanent—tubal ligation in the female or vasectomy in the male—involve sterilization of the person having the procedure.

6. Generally, the most invasive methods of controlling birth are the most effective ones and the most productive of side effects.

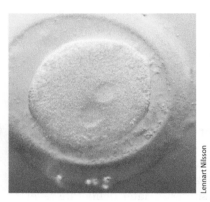

REPRODUCTION CONSTRAINED, PART II: DESTRUCTION OF LIFE

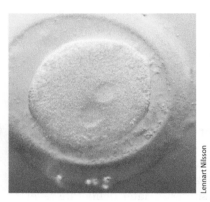

Male and female pronuclei about to fuse to produce a zygote.......a human?

Plato (427–348 BC)

Thomas Aquinus (1225–1274)

There is evidence that the Designer of life is also the source of 10 laws on which Western civilization is based (see Section 2.3). Civilization is at its best when it reacts faithfully to the law that says, "You shall not kill." In its original language this command refers to murder—the taking of human life. In Section 12.4, birth control methods were described that terminate the life of the blastocyst at or prior to its implantation. This raises a critical societal question, one for which biologists are being asked to supply an answer. That question is: When does human life begin? We know it begins within the maternal parent. But when does the life of a new human individual become separate from the mother who conceived it? Many thoughtful scholars have proffered tentative answers along with rational arguments to support them.

Philosophers and Theologians Attempt to Define Personhood

Sometimes scientists take off their white jackets and muse a bit in the world of philosophy. Both James D. Watson and Francis Crick, the co-discoverers of the structure of DNA, did this in the 1970s. They used their notoriety to publically speculate that the best time to grant an infant the status of human being would be several days after its birth. This view, championed more recently by ethicist Peter Singer of Princeton University, arises more from a self-oriented societal pragmatism than a rational consideration of principle. Waiting several days after delivery allows time for genetic screening and gives parents

Figure 12.28 Ancient philosophers and church fathers alike have tried with little success to use rational thought to determine when human life begins.

opportunity to decide if they wish to raise a child with severe disabilities or even substandard intelligence or appearance. If not, the life could be terminated by a morphine overdose in a baby bottle—the potential human being would not realize the miserable existence it was "rescued from." Most scholars have not taken this extreme position seriously.

The ancient Greek philosopher Plato (427–348 BC) suggested that the life of the human individual begins at "ensoulment" which appeared to him to be at birth (see Figure 12.28). Twenty-three hundred years later, philosopher Ayn Rand (1905–1982) proclaimed the same notion: An embryo is only a potential life. It has no rights till birth. A modern variant of this view is that human life begins at that point in development where, if pregnancy ends prematurely, the result is a live birth. Since medical technology has pushed that time point back from 34 weeks to around 22 to 24 weeks after fertilization, defining personhood in this way appears somewhat arbitrary.

The Greek philosopher Aristotle (384–322 BC) wanted the physical embryo to be "animated" in order to consider it ensouled, or truly human. In his understanding, this was a three-stage process that resulted in **quickening** or movement within the womb.

quickening—the first physical movements made by a fetus *in utero* that the mother is able to sense.

While this is generally first observed at about 126 days of pregnancy, he believed it began 40 days after conception of a male or 80 days after conception of a female! Sixteen hundred years later, Catholic theologian Thomas Aquinas (1225–1274) continued to argue that after conception, 40 days were required to mature a human to the point of having a soul (see Figure 12.28). Although the Catholic Church has much valued the teachings of Aquinas, they've long argued that human life should be protected from the point of conception onward. While not denying Aquinas's concept of ensoulment, their Declaration issued in 1974 based its belief on the premise that "he who *will* be a human being is already a human being." It was out of an essential reverence for the creation of human life that the church argued against aborting either the process (birth control) or the product at any point. Since scholars have long been ignorant of the molecular biology of human development, the safest view in church thinking has been to assume human life begins at conception, the moment after which all that is required is time and nutrition to produce a complete human being.

While conception is a very objective point at which to place body and soul together, Scripture passages such as Genesis 46:26 and Hebrews 7: 9-10 might be suggesting that souls pre-exists conception, in some way associated with the sperm cell of the male. In this way, the soul is inherited from the male parent in much the same way that the origin of the body's developmental program is inherited via the egg cytoplasm.

One practical problem with this sort of reasoning is that personhood is at least partially a theological concept. Eastern religions, Western religions, and agnostic individuals all differ in how they define personhood. Thus a free society has difficulty legislating the protection of early human life. Can biological research support a more humble but potentially more universal concept of personhood that would support legislators in the difficulties they face?

Biologists Work to Define the Human Individual

The U.S. Supreme Court decision in *Roe v. Wade* in 1973 used the **trimester** concept to grant women the right to abort their own embryos early in the pregnancy (see Figure 12.29). Since then, much heated debate has placed social pressure on the biological community to come up with a time point at which

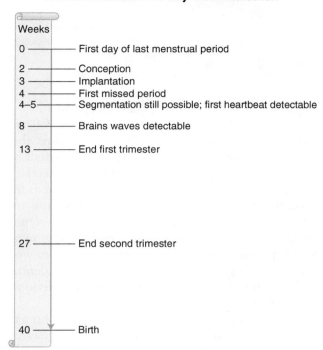

Human Gestation–A Forty-Week Marathon

Weeks	
0	First day of last menstrual period
2	Conception
3	Implantation
4	First missed period
4–5	Segmentation still possible; first heartbeat detectable
8	Brains waves detectable
13	End first trimester
27	End second trimester
40	Birth

Figure 12.29 Human Gestation—The 40 Week Pregnancy. For purposes of reference to different times during pregnancy, the concept of three trimesters was developed.

a human person begins to exist. Biologists' methodology (see Chapter 2) cannot define *personhood*. A more fruitful question for biologists is: When does a human organism become a *biologically separate individual* from its maternal parent? Various scientific perspectives on this issue have been derived from observation and research.

Studies of **fetuses** *in utero* (in the uterus) have revealed much that is human in appearance and behavior. Data from fetal viability and sensory perceptions teach us that birth is just a transition that a human being makes from placental sustenance to mammary gland/ lung sustenance. **Fetology** is thus sending us further back in developmental time in search of the individual's origin.

trimester—one of three consecutive time periods comprising a typical pregnancy.

fetus—a developing mammal in between its embryonic stage and birth; in humans it extends from nine weeks post-conception until birth.

fetology—the study of developing humans between the ages of nine weeks post-conception and birth.

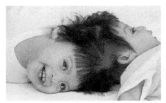

Figure 12.30 Conjoined Twins. These twins arose from a single blastocyst by incomplete segmentation occurring sometime before day 21 of the pregnancy. Have these two human beings arisen from a single human being?

Could eight weeks post-conception be a more realistic juncture for the genesis of the individual (see Figure 12.29)? At about that time, according to neurologist JM Goldenring (1951–), the fetus is eliciting brain waves detectable by **electroencephalography.** If death is defined as the cessation of brain waves, perhaps that's how the initiation of life should be defined. Brain waves may be an indication that the growing embryo is gaining a consciousness of self. One must struggle here with the issue of whether consciousness of self defines individuality. It does not for an adult individual who is in a comatose state, for example.

Some biologists have pushed the origin of human life back to 21 days post-conception and argue that an embryo cannot be a person before that time. During days 14 to 21, **segmentation,** the splitting of embryonic cells to produce twins and triplets, is still possible (see Figure 12.30). How can a single human asexually become two humans? Is the self divisible like the cells it inhabits? Becoming a separate individual must therefore occur once this window of time has passed and twin formation is no longer possible. Others respond that the ability to form two persons simply means that the embryo at this point is capable of being at least one individual.

It would be convenient for those fearing pregnancy to define life as beginning at or just after implantation of the embryo. Most birth control methods exert their effects by or before that point. Even post-intercourse drugs, like mifepristone (RU-486) or ulipristal acetate (Ella), appear to limit endometrial production thus discouraging development at the implantation stage if not before.

Many contemporary scientists and physicians, such as Bernard Nathanson (1926–), argue that a human embryo becomes a person at implantation—the commencement of pregnancy (see Figure 12.29). It is now known that many embryos are **spontaneously aborted** or miscarried at or just prior to this stage. They certainly don't exist long enough to give us any evidence of personhood. But more importantly from a biological perspective, it is not until about the time of implantation that the male genetic information from the sperm nucleus begins to be translated into protein products (see Figure 12.31). The embryo now begins to take on a molecular character of its own.

electroencephalograph—a mechanical device that senses, measures, and records electrical activity resulting from depolarizations (firing) of neurons, usually in the brain.

segmentation (in embryology)—a radical division of early cleavage-stage blastomeres (cells in blastocyst) such that two or more embryos are generated from one blastocyst.

spontaneous abortion—loss of a developing blastocyst, embryo, or fetus due to natural, often unpredictable causes; most occur because of failure to implant properly.

Early Cellular Events in Human Development

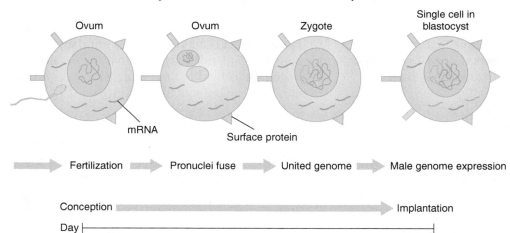

Figure 12.31 Early Cellular Events in Human Development. Pink lines refer to DNA or RNA of maternal origin. Blue lines and shading refer to paternal contributions. Foreign surface molecules, especially proteins are antigenic—they stimulate the immune system to attack the cell displaying them. The paternally encoded proteins would appear foreign to maternal immune cells.

Surface proteins coded by the sperm's genome now make embryonic cells immunologically distinct from maternal cells. That is why the blastocyst secretes immunosuppressive molecules into endometrial tissues (see Section 12.3b). They serve to inhibit the maternal immune system from attacking the antigenically foreign embryo/individual.

There are two problems with defining the individual's origin at implantation: First, if initiation of male gene expression is chosen as the origin of individuality, then we have the entire process of gene expression to dissect. Where in the expression process does the individual begin? Before male genes can be expressed, regulatory proteins calling for their transcription must themselves be transcribed and then translated (see Section 7.3) When in development does this regulatory process commence?

Second, male genome-encoded proteins on cell surfaces grant the embryo individuality because they are an integral part of embryonic structure that could not have been supplied by the maternal genome. But the male genome itself, composed of DNA—while informational in role—is also *structural* in nature. It is intricately unfolded and arranged on protein scaffolding (see Section 5.2c), within the nucleoplasm of the cell and not condensed like some foreign chromosome to be consulted in a distant future. Some process, still mysterious to us, begins preparing this exquisite network of male information to be selectively accessible to early RNA polymerases. Thus the genetic information itself renders the cells holding it a separate individual.

Possessing genetic information from another source is a property of a zygote immediately following fertilization. It is a product of conception. Yet it clearly sets the zygote apart, structurally, from all other cells within the female's body. Conception, therefore, remains a highly objective juncture at which to confer the status of individual on the diploid cell whose genome is informationally and structurally distinct from all others around it. What features must one have to be human? Independent viability? A beating heart? Pity the gentlemen temporarily on a heart-lung machine. Would the achievement of a certain developmental stage qualify? Stages are arbitrary and flow into each other. For example, single neurons can transmit nervous impulses well before highly coordinated brain waves are detectable.

Life Is Informational Continuity. If a zygote has paternal information—if in that genetic sense it is clearly distinct from a maternal cell, then a biologist is ready to call it a separate individual—an individual cell that may very well be an individual human.

Destruction of Human Life Takes Various Forms

A pregnancy can be ended using a combination of drugs. Mifepristone will cause the pregnancy to be terminated and prostaglandin will help to expel it. Alternatively, surgical procedures exist that dilate the cervix and either suck or scrape the developing human embryo from the surface of the uterine wall. The surgical procedures last about 15 minutes. But in the process, the life of a separate human individual has ended, and in the survivor of the procedure, subsequent depressive and suicidal thoughts typically require prolonged counseling and drug intervention.

IN OTHER WORDS
....

1. Since one of society's fundamental laws prohibits the taking of human life, it has become critical to determine exactly when human life begins.
2. Various views have been expressed regarding the time of initiation of human life: several days after birth, the time of birth, the time of quickening with the womb, the time of conception, or even earlier in the life of the sperm.
3. Biologists, attempting to define the genesis of human individuality, have suggested life begins when brain waves can be detected, after segmentation is possible, at the time of implantation, or at the time of conception.
4. Implantation is often chosen as the time of initiation of individuality both because pregnancy starts then and because the male genome begins its expression then.
5. Conception is a more rational time of initiation because after this point, the ovum contains and services male genome-encoded structures.
6. Human embryonic life can be terminated using either abortifacient chemicals or surgical procedures

....

The theme of this text has consistently been that of a great Designer's genius at work in living systems. Now we'll see how Mendel's laws brilliantly praise that Artisan. They'll take patience to understand. Why not pause here and have another look at the Survey Questions for this section. Glance down through the subsection headings below so you can see how we're going to treat Mendel and his observations. This first subsection introduces you to Mendel and his perspectives. The next two subsections cover the laws he derived.

A Brilliant Empiricist

Gregor Mendel was an **empiricist;** his questions led to observations and experiments. But his experiments then led to great generalizations that explain how you inherited your mother's freckles or your father's blond hair. Who was Gregor Mendel, and how did he interpret the processes that grant informational continuity to life? Mendel was born on a farm in 1822 near Brno in the Czech Republic (see Figure 12.32). He failed his high school science classes but later took a liking to math and physics. Eventually he became a monk, taking vows of poverty, chastity, and obedience or as they say on the inside, "No money, no honey, and a boss." But as with most other monks, this great lifestyle change did nothing to quell his innate fascination with reproduction!

Simply put, however, Mendel's interests in reproduction were more broadly biological than for most men! He began studying *Pisum sativum*—the common garden pea. He was taken with the way in which pea plants pass along genetic information to the next generation. He was interested in informational continuity!

Many people in Mendel's day didn't believe that information flow was confined to organisms of the same species. There were many early myths. One was that an ostrich could be the result of a llama mating with a gnat! Such fanciful ideas were not good science—they led to few predictions—and an ostrich was never observed being born to a llama. Various ideas of this sort came and went. Serious plant breeders also practiced their craft in Mendel's day. But most of them, like the ones studying peas, were all simply trying to breed a more robust, higher-yielding pea plant.

Mendel circumvented both of these shortsighted approaches. What was so productive in his approach? First, he was a monk who had studied the Biblical text. What he saw in nature was best described by the dictum in Genesis 1: "like begets like." He stayed with that framework for his analysis of the flow of genetic information. This conviction opened to him what has turned out to be an amazing reality. You have millions of species on the planet, yet when two individuals of the *same* species procreate, you get another individual clearly of the same species (unless you take cheap tabloid stories seriously). However, the new individual is not precisely like either parent— it's a blend of parental traits. The plant breeders knew this was true, but their economic motivation colored what they saw.

So second, and by contrast, Mendel chose to focus on discrete characteristics of his pea plants, following them through his crosses. The seven traits

Figure 12.32 Gregor Mendel (1822-1884) Born in what is now the Czech Republic, he developed the early generalizations that unified the discipline of genetics.

Moravian Museum, Brno

empiricist—one who reaches conclusions as a result of evidence gathered by sensory experience that frequently involves experimentation.

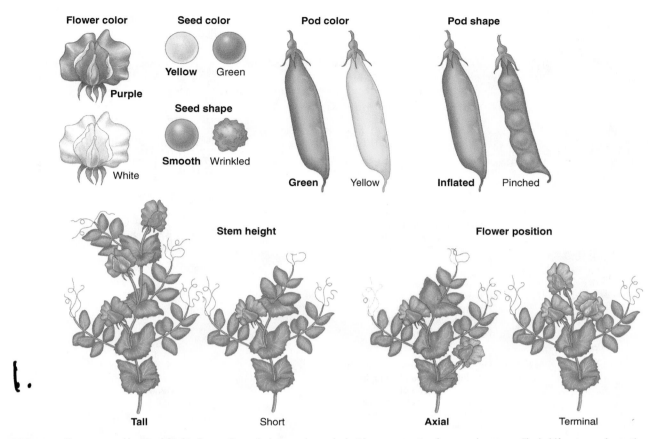

Flower color — Purple / White
Seed color — Yellow / Green
Seed shape — Smooth / Wrinkled
Pod color — Green / Yellow
Pod shape — Inflated / Pinched
Stem height — Tall / Short
Flower position — Axial / Terminal

Figure 12.33   Characters used by Mendel in his Crosses. For each character, he worked with two contrasting forms or phenotypes. The boldface term refers to the more dominant form of the character.

he studied most carefully are listed in Figure 12.33. The blending of parental characteristics that plant breeders observed was being dissected by Mendel, who followed the inheritance patterns of very specific characters instead of general appearance. As a result, Mendel's crosses brought him beautifully to two great laws that describe the inheritance of traits in all higher organisms.

Third, he developed **pure-breeding** strains for the individual characters he studied. This took some effort. He did this by inbreeding his strains of plants over several generations. In peas, this is accomplished by allowing flowers on plants to self-fertilize. (Peas have "perfect" flowers possessing both sexes on the same flower; see Figure 12.34a.) Small paper sacs can be placed over individual flowers so that pollen from pea plants of other strains cannot get to the female parts of the flower. Mendel kept mating individuals plants of his tall strain of plants to each other over several generations until its peas would *always* produce only tall plants.

Finally, Mendel counted offspring from his crosses; his work was quantitative. This enabled him to discover ratios among the traits of the offspring and move toward powerful generalizations about how the traits were being inherited.

A Brilliant Law: Segregation of Alleles

How did Mendel arrive at his first law of inheritance? He carried out a series of crosses between pea plants using the process illustrated in Figure 12.34, steps a and b. He began by crossing a

pure-breeding—a strain or population of a species that possesses a specific characteristic and gives rise only to individuals possessing that characteristic; only alleles supporting that characteristic are present in the strain.

Pea plant

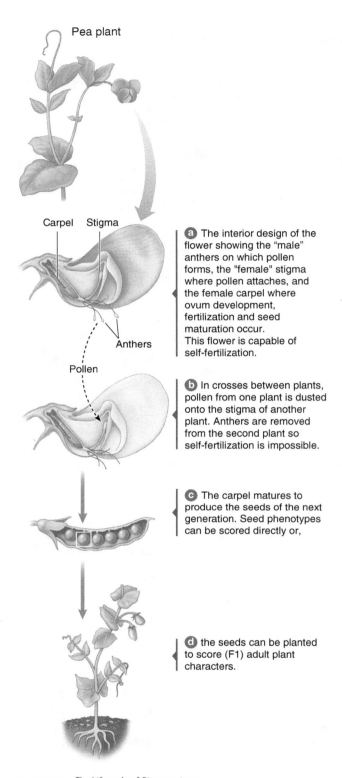

Carpel Stigma

a The interior design of the flower showing the "male" anthers on which pollen forms, the "female" stigma where pollen attaches, and the female carpel where ovum development, fertilization and seed maturation occur.
This flower is capable of self-fertilization.

Anthers

Pollen

b In crosses between plants, pollen from one plant is dusted onto the stigma of another plant. Anthers are removed from the second plant so self-fertilization is impossible.

c The carpel matures to produce the seeds of the next generation. Seed phenotypes can be scored directly or,

d the seeds can be planted to score (F1) adult plant characters.

Figure 12.34 The Life cycle of *Pisum sativum*.

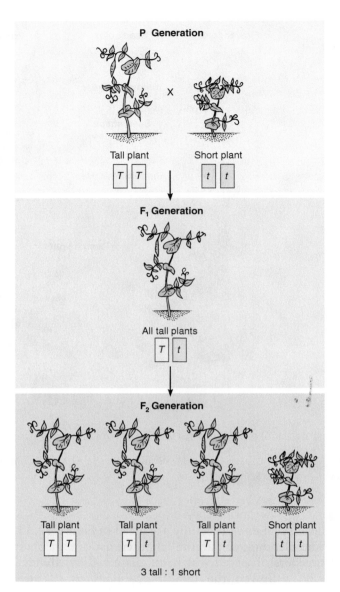

Figure 12.35 Tall Pea Plants crossed to Short Ones. Mendel observed that the "short" trait was hidden in the first generation of offspring but reappeared as a minority of individuals in the second (F_2) generation. The phenotypes of pea plants are drawn. The genotypes in the yellow and orange boxes were inferred by Mendel from the results of the crosses themselves.

pure-breeding tall strain of plant to a pure-breeding short strain of plant (see Figure 12.35). These were his parent (P) plants. In their first generation of offspring, the F_1 generation, all the pea plants were tall. It was as if the short trait had entirely disappeared! If he tried crossing two of the tall plants of the F_1 generation to each other, the short trait reappeared in the next, or F_2, generation. When he

F_1—a symbol referring to the first filial generation; the immediate offspring of the original parents of a cross.

F_2—a symbol referring to the second filial generation; the second-generation offspring of the original parents of a cross.

counted offspring, he saw about 75% tall plants and 25% short ones.

How were these results to be interpreted? Mendel referred to the tall trait as being **dominant** not because of its size but because it was the only one of the two traits that appeared in the F_1 generation. The short trait was considered to be **recessive** because it disappeared at that time. If a trait could be present, disappear, and then reappear a generation later, Mendel inferred that each visible trait must be controlled by invisible *factors* (Mendel's term). And there must be two factors for each trait! As we will see, that is the only way to explain how the short trait could survive, even though it wasn't expressed, and then reappear in a future generation.

Geneticists have come to refer to the appearance of a trait as the **phenotype** (tallness is a phenotype). The factors (or genes) that control the expression of that trait are called the **genotype** (see Figure 12.36a). Individual factors can take various forms and later geneticists called them *alleles*. We'll use a capital T to represent an allele that generates the tall phenotype, and a lowercase t to represent the allele that generates the short phenotype.

Mendel went on to infer that his pure-breeding short parent plants, for example, had only one kind of allele to place into their sex cells since all of their offspring bred short. Pure-breeding plants must be **homozygous** for the short trait (see Figure 12.36b). The F_1 plants that gave off both tall and short individuals must have had both kinds of alleles in their cells and should therefore be termed **heterozygous.**

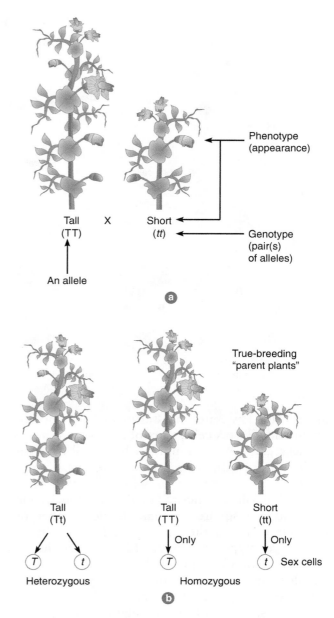

a

b

Figure 12.36 Terms Geneticists Use. **(a)** The alleles of a genotype control what the phenotype of the organism will look like. **(b)** If an organism has only one kind of allele to send into sex cells, it is homozygous. If it has two kinds of allele for a given trait, it is heterozygous.

2.

dominant—when two or more alleles of a gene are present in a cell, the allele whose phenotype is expressed.

recessive—when two or more alleles of a gene are present in a cell, the allele whose phenotype is hidden or masked.

phenotype—a specific aspect of the appearance of an organism, such as "tall" in pea plants.

genotype—a combination of alleles that control or influence some specific aspect of the appearance of an organism, such as T/t in pea plants.

homozygous—a genotype for a single gene locus in which both alleles are identical; example YY in the cells of a yellow pea seed coat color.

heterozygous—a genotype for a single gene locus in which the two alleles are nonidentical; example Yy in the cells of a yellow pea seed coat color.

Finally, Mendel saw that pairs of alleles must come apart during the formation of sex cells (see Figure 12.37). Sex cells are the ova or pollen nuclei of the pea plant. This separation of alleles is the only way he could see of getting F_2 short plants from F_1 tall parents. Mendel summarized this inference as a law he termed the *law of segregation* of factors or

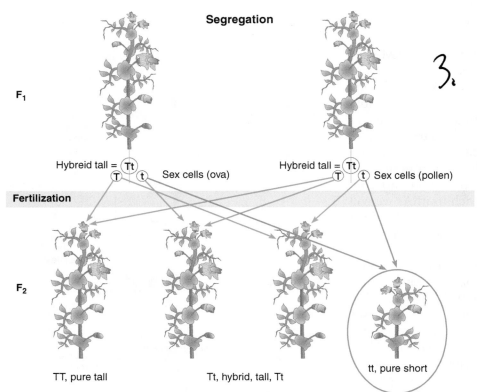

Segregation

F₁

Hybreid tall = (Tt)   (T) (t)   Sex cells (ova)

Hybreid tall = (Tt)   (T) (t)   Sex cells (pollen)

Fertilization

F₂

TT, pure tall   Tt, hybrid, tall, Tt   tt, pure short

Figure 12.37 The Principle of Segregation Illustrated. In the formation of sex cells (ova or pollen nuclei) pairs of alleles segregate—come apart—so that only a single allele for each trait goes into a sex cell. Random combinations of sex cells during fertilization produce the progeny shown at the bottom of the figure.

alleles. That law states that during the formation of an individual's sex cells, pairs of alleles come apart (or **segregate**). While a normal body cell has two alleles for any trait, a sex cell only has one.

The law of segregation was illustrated later by an English geneticist, Dr. R. C. **Punnett**. He subdivided a **square** by making the number of columns equal to the number of kinds of male gamete genotypes (see Figure 12.38). Then, he set the number of rows equal to the number of kinds of female gamete genotypes. In the cross you see here, if factors in F₁ plants come apart in the formation of gametes, then half of each plant's gametes will carry a big *T* and the other half will carry a little *t*. We combine these gametes probabilistically. That means that we perform all possible fertilization events by filling in the boxes of the Punnett square. Each square represents one possible combination of ovum genotype and pollen genotype. Each square becomes a kind of offspring in the next generation. In this cross, three-fourths of the offspring will be tall. Half of the offspring will have the heterozygous genotype *T/t*. These observed ratios are possible only if pairs of alleles segregate during the formation of sex cells. Segregation of alleles is Mendel's first generalization. All humans, dandelions, and earthworms obey this law! So do most other higher life-forms.

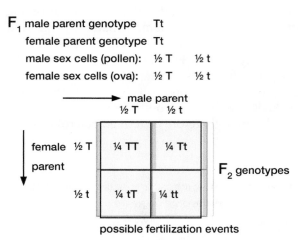

F₁ male parent genotype   Tt
    female parent genotype   Tt
    male sex cells (pollen):   ½ T   ½ t
    female sex cells (ova):   ½ T   ½ t

	male parent ½ T	½ t
female ½ T	¼ TT	¼ Tt
parent ½ t	¼ tT	¼ tt

F₂ genotypes

possible fertilization events

Ratios: 1:2:1   (genotypes)
          3:1   (phenotypes)

Figure 12.38 Punnett Square Representation of Mendel's First Law. See the text for details.

segregate—the behavior of alleles of a pair during sex cell formation; during meiosis, that separation of alleles, which yields haploid sex cells from diploid gametocytes.

Punnett square—a diagram in which known genotypes of sex cells are arranged along two axes of a rectangle and used to predict the genotypes of offspring resulting from random fertilization events between the sex cells.

1. Gregor Mendel was born in 1822, enjoyed quantitative reasoning, became a monk, and experimented with garden peas in plots beside the monastery.
2. Mendel's study led to his great generalizations because he examined individual traits in his plants, developed pure-breeding lines of plants, and in his crosses, he counted offspring having each type of trait.
3. When Mendel crossed tall and short pea plants, all the offspring were tall. Thus the short trait was recessive to the tall one.
4. In a second-generation cross, short plants reappeared indicating that controlling factors (alleles) form an underlying genotype that controls the phenotypic appearance of the plants.
5. The only way for short plants to be offspring of tall ones is for short alleles to be hiding in the genotype of tall plants.
6. Further, pairs of alleles must come apart in sex cell formation for short plants to reappear. This is Mendel's first law.

Mendel's Laws as Therapy

In this section we explore Mendel's Laws (that are actually a Designer's Laws). It's so amazing: You have many, many species all passing on traits using many, many different structures. Yet trait transmission follows the *same* basic pattern—so simple, yet so magnificent!! Mendel's Laws weld a powerful message into the inquiring mind!! That message? Behind gene flow there is *another* mind—bigger than Mendel's—or any other human mind: one of infinite power and genius. And that mind loves order. It enjoys regularity and repeatability. And what does that awareness do for the thoughtful, searching mind?? Two things. First it points us toward peace. This biosphere probably isn't going to suddenly self-destruct or morph into some kind of deadly planet, because that doesn't fit the orderliness that is evident in the Designer's mind.

Secondly, the glory of Mendel's Laws encourages us to do something quite difficult. You see, the Designer of Mendel's laws has also crafted some moral laws, all of which are very difficult to obey. Most university students simply don't find the spiritual energy within themselves to respond to moral law the way a pea plant responds to Mendel's laws. But look again! What we see here is a Designer's natural Laws resulting in unity within complexity, freedom within structure, and the power to really live! You know, this should give us courage—on the moral side of our lives—to go looking for the ability we lack!

Mendel discovered two huge laws of nature! May their ingenuity give us a high regard for their Designer—and, for His moral laws that we find impossible to consistently obey. If you go in search of the power to obey them, you will eventually discover a wonderful gift that Designer has prepared for you, if you have the humility to accept it.

A Brilliant Law: Independent Assortment

Mendel's law of segregation can be illustrated using only a single pair of alleles, like T and t. His second law results from observing the behavior of two entirely separate traits in the same cross, what we call a **dihybrid cross**. This required him to assume that he was following two separate pairs of alleles in each of his plant plants! He selected a parent plant whose seeds had a yellow seed coat and were round in shape and crossed it to a plant whose seeds were green with a wrinkled shape (see Figure 12.39a). The offspring in the F_1 generation were all round, and none were wrinkled. They were all yellow; none were green. So clearly the round trait was dominant to wrinkled, and the yellow trait was dominant to green. Mendel then crossed two plants each resulting from these F_1 seeds. And the results would have put a smile on any mathematician's face (see Figure 12.39b).

Looking at these F_2 ratios among the offspring, Mendel must have had an "aha!" moment. There were four phenotypic classes of F_2 offspring. The two parental types were round yellow and wrinkled green, but there were also two recombinant kinds of seeds: round green and wrinkled yellow! And the genes for the two separate traits had to be behaving independently of each other because the four classes appeared in a 9:3:3:1 ratio, which is

dihybrid—descriptive of a cross between two individuals in which two separate traits or characters are being followed in the offspring.

Cross:

P   Round yellow   X   Wrinkled green

Results:

F_1 All round yellow seeds

(Dominant traits)

Cross:

Two F_1's: Round yellow   X   Round yellow

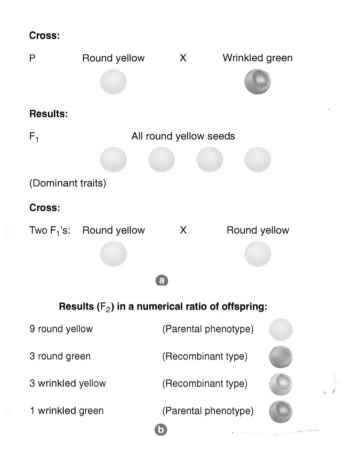

a

Results (F_2) in a numerical ratio of offspring:

9 round yellow	(Parental phenotype)	
3 round green	(Recombinant type)	
3 wrinkled yellow	(Recombinant type)	
1 wrinkled green	(Parental phenotype)	

b

Figure 12.39   Mendelian Dihybrid Cross – Phenotypes. **(a)** Parental and F_1 phenotypes are shown. **(b)** F_2 phenotypes and their frequencies are shown.

Genotypic Interpretation:

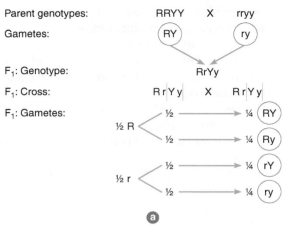

Parent genotypes: RRYY   X   rryy

Gametes: RY   ry

F_1: Genotype: RrYy

F_1: Cross: R r Y y   X   R r Y y

F_1: Gametes:

½ R → ½ → ¼ RY
       ½ → ¼ Ry
½ r → ½ → ¼ rY
       ½ → ¼ ry

a

Cross: *Rr Yy × Rr Yy*

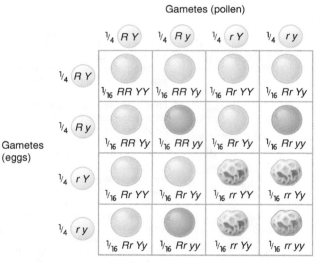

Gametes (pollen)

Phenotypic ratio: 9 round yellow : 3 round green : 3 wrinkled yellow : 1 wrinkled green

b

Figure 12.40   Mendel's Dihybrid Cross – Genotypes. **(a)** The genotypes of the parents, their sex cells, the F_1 individuals and their sex cells are given. **(b)** The genotypes and phenotypes of the F_2 individuals are shown within a Punnett square.

really two separate 3:1 ratios superimposed on top of each other! (Can *you* see that?) In Figure 12.39, what's the ratio of round to wrinkled in these offspring? And what's the ratio of yellow to green? That's right! Each pair of alleles is showing us a 3:1 ratio. But they are doing so independently of each other. If they were totally dependent on each other, the ratio would be three round yellow to one wrinkled green. But the two new classes of offspring show us that color and seed shape are inherited independently of each other!

Let's do the cross again, this time using alleles in genotypes (see Figure 12.40a). Capital letters go to alleles whose trait appears dominant in the F_1 generation. So big *R* generates round seeds; little *r*, wrinkled. Big *Y* generates yellow seed color; little *y*, green. An F_1 gamete can have either a big *R* or a little *r* but not both. (That's Mendel's first law.) The same is true of the *Y*s but (!) each *R* gamete could contain either a big *Y* or a little *y*. Either possibility is

equally likely. —and that is the essence of Mendel's second law. To state the law of **independent assortment**: "The way *R* alleles are sorted into sex

independent assortment—a Mendelian relationship between alleles at two different genetic loci; the sorting into sex cells of alleles at one locus has no effect on the sorting of alleles at the second locus.

cells (that's the first law) is *independent* (that's the second law) of how the Y alleles are sorted. To see how these gametes from each F_1 parent contribute to the F_2 generation, consider Figure 12.40b.

Here, inside of a four-by-four Punnett square, are the phenotypes and ratios of the four different kinds of offspring. Go ahead and count up the number of each kind of pea seed.

Wow! Doesn't this square beautifully explain Mendel's 9:3:3:1 ratios? Now, look even more closely. If you can see that there are four large squares here, showing a 3:1 ratio of round to wrinkled and that within each large square are four smaller ones each showing a 3:1 ratio of yellow to green, then you are visualizing Mendel's second law! Now try to imagine this relationship holding true for millions of kinds of organisms and that their Designer saw this all clearly one morning before breakfast . . . (and without the help of Punnett's square!). You

have just moved a bit closer to reality in your new perception of the Designer's greater Glory!

To finish our discussion of Mendel's work, let's review his two broad generalizations one more time: His first law, the law of segregation argues that in the formation of gametes, pairs of factors or alleles segregate into separate gametes. That is, they get separated from each other. So normal body cells have two copies of an allele. Sex cells have only one. When you write the genotypes of gametes, they will always have only half the number of alleles that would be written for an individual's genotype.

Mendel's second law states that the way one pair of alleles segregates is independent of the way a second pair of alleles segregates. Many exceptions to this second law have been discovered with time. We'll see why when we start looking at the relationship of alleles to chromosomes in the next section.

IN OTHER WORDS

1. Mendel's second law is illustrated using alleles at two separate genetic loci in the context of a dihybrid cross.
2. In a dihybrid cross between two individuals, where each individual is homozygous for contrasting alleles at two different loci, all offspring will be heterozygous for all alleles at both loci.
3. In a dihybrid cross, where both gene loci are heterozygous in both parents, four kinds of offspring are observed in a phenotypic ratio of 9:3:3:1.
4. A 9:3:3:1 ratio is really two separate 3:1 ratios superimposed on each other and represents a mathematical demonstration of independent assortment.
5. In the cross between double heterozygotes, the 9:3:3:1 phenotypic ratio in the offspring conceals a 1:2:1 : 2:4:2 : 1:2:1 genotypic ratio among the nine possible genotypic classes of offspring.
6. Mendel's first law states that in the formation of gametes, pairs of factors or alleles segregate into separate gametes.
7. Mendel's second law states that the way one pair of alleles segregates is independent of the way a second pair of alleles segregates.

Brilliant Laws: Variations on the Theme

Mendel's laws were derived using genes whose alleles followed a clear "pecking order." Each allele was clearly either dominant (*T*) or recessive (*t*) to the alternate allele. As geneticists continued their studies, new relationships—ones that Mendel had not anticipated—were soon discovered between alleles at a given locus and between separate gene loci. Life's picture always has unanticipated subtleties.

Codominance In 1900, a gifted Jewish biologist and physician, Dr. Karl Landsteiner, discovered and correctly interpreted the four major blood groupings in humans: the AB, A, B, and O blood types. These types are based on the interactions of three different known alleles that exist for the *ABO* gene (see Figure 12.41). This DNA sequence codes for an enzyme that does the final processing on a carbohydrate that forms part of the membrane surface of human red blood cells. One allele, *A*, processes the carbohydrate in one

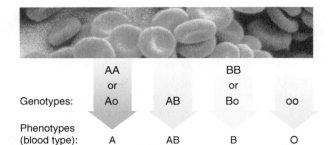

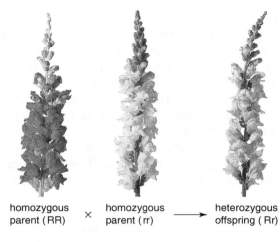

	Ⓡ	Ⓡ
Ⓡ	RR	Rr
Ⓡ	Rr	rr

Genotypes: AA   BB
              or   or
              Ao   AB Bo   oo

Phenotypes
(blood type): A   AB   B   O

Figure 12.41 The *ABO* Gene in Humans. The three known alleles of this gene combine pairwise at the *ABO* locus to give the indicated phenotypes: the four possible blood types.

homozygous   ×   homozygous   ⟶   heterozygous
parent (RR)   parent (rr)   offspring (Rr)

ⓐ The cross of two pure-breeding plants with red and white flowers.

ⓑ A Punnett square diagram showing sex cell genotypes in a cross between two heterozygous pink individuals. Expected flower color of offspring are shown in the boxes of the square. Genotypic and phenotypic ratios are the same: 1:2:1

Figure 12.42 Snapdragon Flower Color. Flower color exhibits an inheritance known as incomplete dominance.

way, causing it to become an A antigen. A second allele, *B*, processes the carbohydrate in a different way, yielding a B antigen. The *o* allele (note its recessive, lower case letter) codes for a dysfunctional enzyme that leaves the carbohydrate unprocessed and virtually nonantigenic. This means the immune system fails to recognize the surface carbohydrate's existence. Alleles *A* and *B* are <u>codominant</u>. An *A/B* heterozygous individual will have both forms of the enzyme at work on her red cell surface carbohydrates. Thus both the A and B antigens will appear on her cells; her blood type will be AB. The *o* allele is recessive; heterozygotes who are *A/o* will show only the A antigen; the product of the *o* allele does nothing. Hence, their blood type is A. If you are homozygous *o/o*, then your surface carbohydrates are completely unmodified and your blood type is O. What two ABO genotypes would cause a person to have type B blood?

These blood type phenotypes become important when receiving blood transfusions. (In 1930, Landsteiner won a Nobel Prize for his work. Think for a moment. If you have type O blood, then your immune system has never seen either an A or a B antigen. If you receive any type of blood other than type O, your lymphocytes will attack, clump, and destroy any cells with A or B antigens. A serious illness results. Happily, if you have type AB blood then your system considers both A and B antigens to be "self" molecular surfaces and thus ignores them. You can receive any type of human blood (in the ABO system) without consequence.

Incomplete Dominance Snapdragons are beautiful works of art with a species-defined flower shape. But strains within the species differ in petal

color (see Figure 12.42). When you cross a pure-breeding red variety with a pure-breeding white one, you are in for a post-Mendelian surprise. The heterozygotes are not red nor are they white. They are pink! So neither allele is completely dominant. Think about how easy Mendel's task might have been. Every genotype resulting from any cross is immediately revealed. Thus red alleles are represented with a capital *R* and white alleles with a small *r* simply because *R*-containing cells make a red pigment and *r/r* containing cells make none. What must the genotype of a red-flowered plant be?

Epistasis In our study of Mendel we examined traits that each appeared to be controlled by a set of alleles working at a single genetic locus. Height

codominant—an allele whose phenotypic effect is visible regardless of what other allele happens to be opposite it.

in peas depended on *T*'s and *t*'s at a single locus. Even codominance and incomplete dominance involve allelic relationships at a single locus. Years of subsequent genetic analysis have shown that organismal traits controlled by only a single gene locus are rare. It is far more common to have a single trait controlled or at least influenced by more than one genetic locus. When the phenotypic expression of one gene is modified by the product of a second independent gene, we refer to the second gene's effect as *epistatic* (Gk. = standing on top of) with regard to the first gene. A beautiful example of <u>epistasis</u> is the production of coat color in Labrador retrievers.

In these noble animals, at least two genetic loci affect coat color (see Figure 12.43). One determines the level of pigment production and a second locus controls the deposition of the pigment. For pigment production the mere presence of the dominant *B* allele produces enough pigment to generate the black coat color seen in black animals. The homozygous recessive individual, *b/b*, lacks this allele and produces only enough pigment to give a chocolate brown color. However, another locus controls the efficiency of deposition of these pigments in the hair follicles. As long as an *E* allele is present at this second locus, normal deposition will yield either the black or brown color depending on the genotype at the B/b locus. But if the animal is homozygous recessive *e/e*, pigment deposition is severely limited giving rise to the yellow phenotype some owners prefer. The *e* allele is thus epistatic, controlling the expression of the *B/b* locus.

Pleiotropy

Epistatic relationships occur when two or more genes influence a single phenotypic trait. But consider the alternative situation. Does a single gene's product ever affect more than one phenotypic trait? Yes, and again, this is a frequent occurrence. In those systems where it can be documented, it is given the name **pleiotropy** (Gk. *pleio* = more or full). In many genetic diseases of humans, this "fuller" effect of a single gene product on phenotype can be readily seen. Consider sickle cell anemia. The defective allele generates a hemoglobin molecule with a *single* amino acid substitution in its sequence. That is all. But oh the differences that follow from that tiny design alteration! Truly, many aspects of the individual's phenotype are altered by that one small change (see Figure 12.44). In an evolving system where each cell slowly accumulates separate, new facilities and functions, one might not expect many instances of pleiotropy. But in a highly integrated set of predesigned functions, pleiotropy is a common and expected effect.

> **epistasis**—a form of gene expression in which two or more gene loci affect the same phenotypic trait.
>
> **pleiotropy**—a form of gene expression in which one genetic locus has multiple phenotypic effects on the organism.

| Black BBEE, BbEE, BBEe or BbEe | Yellow BBee, Bbee or bbee | Chocolate bbEE or bbEe |

Renee Stockdale/Animals Animals

Figure 12.43 Epistatic Control of Coat Color. Hair pigmentation is the result of both pigment production and pigment deposition, processes controlled by two different gene loci. The B locus controls production and the E locus, deposition. The result is wonderful.

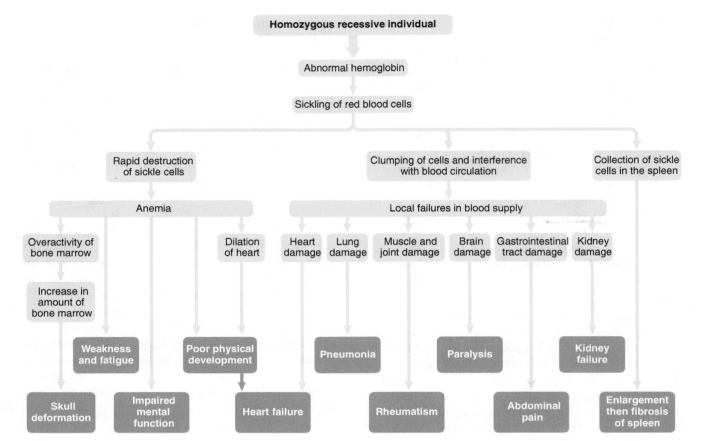

Figure 12.44 Pleiotropic Effects of Abnormal Hemoglobin. A single amino acid substitution near the front end of a single hemoglobin polypeptide radically affects the solubility of the molecule within the cell. Crystallization of the hemoglobin results in a wide variety of phenotypic effects.

IN OTHER WORDS

1. The human gene *ABO* has three allelic forms, two of which, *A* and *B*, are fully expressed whenever either one is present. These alleles are codominant.
2. Snapdragon plants have two alleles for flower color, *R* and *r*. The presence of the *r* allele can be detected because two copies of *R* generate more pigment than one copy alone.
3. In Labrador retrievers, coat color depends on two gene loci. One locus controls production of pigment, the second locus controls its deposition in the hair follicles.
4. As in the case of the genetic disease sickle cell anemia, most gene loci have pleiotropic effects because most gene products interact with other gene products and so have a ripple effect throughout the organism.

12.7
REPRODUCTION EXPLAINED:
THE CHROMOSOMAL BASIS OF HEREDITY

Section 12.6 treated Mendel's fundamental laws for how genes behave as they move from one generation into the next. We'll review those concepts yet again. But now we want to see how the inheritance of invisible genes relates to the inheritance of visible bodies in the cell nucleus called *chromosomes*. A wonderful correlation is waiting for us!

Let's review gene transmission one last time. How do genes move in sex cell formation? When a pea plant or a human being sets about to form ova or sperm nuclei, what happens to the pairs of alleles Mendel discovered?

Mendel's first law says that paired alleles separate or *segregate* from each other, i.e., they come apart in sex cell formation. Mendel's second law says that they separate independently of other such pairs. Observe Figure 12.40 again. The parent plant genotypes have four symbols in them. But because of segregation, the gamete genotypes arranged along the sides of the square have only two. That's Mendel's first law. Mendel's second law

is also shown there. Just because a gamete picks up a big *R* from the maternal plant does *not* tell you whether it will get a big *Y* or a little *y*. Either event is equally likely. So we must show a big *R* gamete with both a big *Y* and one with a little *y*—that's what the second law is all about.

Let's leave Mendel's alleles alone for a bit. Let's explore some marvelous, tightly coiled, visible bodies in the cell nucleus, first seen in the 1900s about four decades after Mendel discovered alleles. These bodies stained easily, so they were called *chromosomes*. How do chromosomes behave during sex cell formation? Well, we know that meiosis occurs then. What happens in meiosis? Chromosome numbers are halved (review Figure 12.12). But *how* does that reduction in numbers happen? Well, pairs of chromosomes separate. Wow! So we have both alleles and chromosomes in pairs! And both alleles and chromosomes are behaving the same way at meiosis!

In Figure 12.45, consider the cell at the top left that's going to form the sex cells at the bottom. How

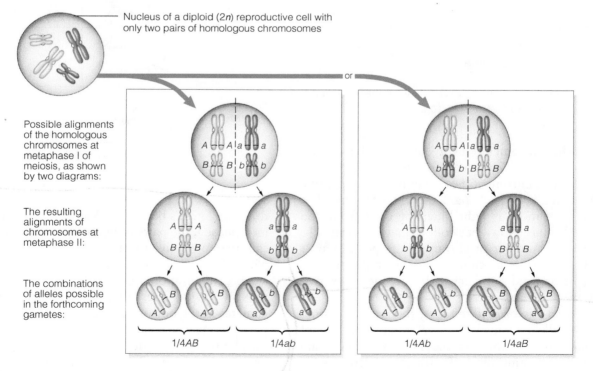

Nucleus of a diploid (2n) reproductive cell with only two pairs of homologous chromosomes

or

Possible alignments of the homologous chromosomes at metaphase I of meiosis, as shown by two diagrams:

The resulting alignments of chromosomes at metaphase II:

The combinations of alleles possible in the forthcoming gametes:

1/4AB   1/4ab   1/4Ab   1/4aB

Figure 12.45 Independent Assortment with Chromosomes. This figure uses only two pairs of homologous chromosomes to illustrate the mechanism behind Mendel's Laws. This individual's cells happen to be heterozygous at both the *A* and *B* loci. Notice the orientation of *A* alleles relative to *B* alleles in the two equally likely panels of the figure. These two options illustrate Mendel's second law.

Chapter 12 Informational Continuity in Organisms   423

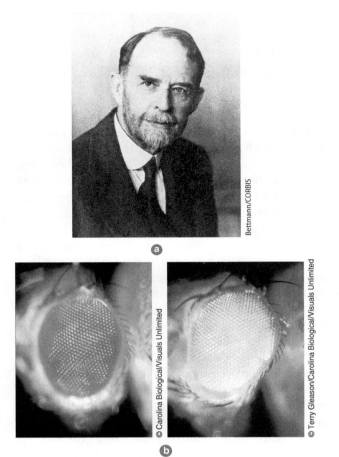

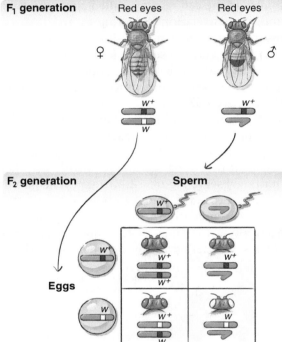

Pure breeding red-eyed female X white-eyed male

P generation

Red eyes (wild type) ♀ × White eyes ♂

X w^+
X w^+

X w
Y

F₁ generation

Red eyes ♀   Red eyes ♂

w^+
w

w^+

F₂ generation   **Sperm**

w^+ (empty)

Eggs

w^+ w^+ / w^+ w^+ (male)

w w^+ / w w (male)

All red-eyed females | ½ red-eyed, ½ white-eyed males

¾ red eyes : ¼ white eyes

Figure 12.46 The Work of Thomas Hunt Morgan. **(a)** These studies were performed by Morgan in the "Fly Room" at Columbia University. **(b)** The eye color on the left is the normal or "wild type" version of a fly eye. The "white" eye on the right is a mutant phenotype discovered by Morgan. **(c)** The cross scheme that convinced Morgan that genes are located on chromosomes. The fly cartoons give you the phenotypes. Morgan had to figure out the genotypes and draw them on the chromosomes on his own!!

many chromosomes does it contain? The diploid number is four: That means there are two pairs of homologous chromosomes. One pair is large; one pair is small. In each pair, the chromosome that came from mom is light blue; the ones from dad are dark blue. Now, let's follow meiosis vertically. What's the number of chromosomes per cell after the first meiotic division? There are now two per cell (the haploid number) with just one set of two chromosomes per cell.

Now, let's go back to thinking about alleles. Could the two allelic forms of a gene reside *on* a pair of chromosomes? Notice that the chromosomes contain letters representing alleles. Try tracing the letters—the alleles—through meiosis. Why are there two sides to

the diagram? It's because of Mendel's second law. At metaphase I, the pairs of homologous chromosomes can line up relative to each other on the metaphase plate in either of two different configurations. And either configuration is equally likely.

Now review the distribution of alleles in the gametes at the bottom of each side of this diagram. Contrasting genotypes are observed. The point is simple: If we put genes on chromosomes, they end up obeying Mendel's laws! The top cell in each panel is *AaBb* but the gametes have only one of

Bettmann/CORBIS

© Carolina Biological/Visuals Unlimited

© Terry Gleason/Carolina Biological/Visuals Unlimited

each letter; they are haploid. That illustrates his first law. The fact that we can get all four possible types involving big and little *A*s and *B*s illustrates Mendel's second law. To review again, a big *B* in a gamete is no predictor of which sort of *A* allele one will get; it could be either big *A* or little *a*. That's Mendel's second law. So we have here a truly elegant correlation between the behavior of alleles and the behavior of chromosomes. This strongly suggests that the alleles of genes are *on* chromosomes.

But are they? What's the hard evidence that genes are really on chromosomes? In 1910, one of America's really great early biologists, Dr. T. H. Morgan of Columbia University was working with the common vinegar fly *Drosophila melanogaster.* These flies normally have lovely red eyes (see Figure 12.46b). But eventually Morgan discovered a white-eyed fly. He sensed immediately that white eyes versus red eyes gave him the opportunity to repeat Mendel's work in a different organism. Could Mendel's laws be generalized to insects?

Morgan took the white-eyed fly (a male) and mated it to a virgin female fly with red eyes. All flies in the F$_1$ generation were red-eyed, making red dominant. That seemed Mendelian enough. The cross of the F$_1$ flies to each other yielded flies in a ratio of 3:1 red eyes to white eyes—again just what was expected. Then, he checked the sex of each F$_2$ fly. Amazing! All the white-eyed flies were males. So Mendel's first law had been exhibited. But eye color and sex were definitely not assorting independently! In independent assortment, there should have been white-eyed flies of both sexes, right?

Hmm. Morgan knew something about the flies' chromosomes by that time. Workers in other labs had begun to stain favorable types of cells, rupture their nuclei and take pictures of their chromosomes (see Figure 12.11). Then they would cut the chromosomes out of the photograph with scissors and arrange them into an orderly array as shown below, a **karyotype**. In *Drosophila*, there were eight chromosomes per cell nucleus instead of the 46 chromosomes found in human cell nuclei (see Figure 12.47). When matched for size and shape, all the chromosomes paired nicely in females, but there was an odd couple in male cells. Morgan inferred correctly that the odd couple must in some way influence or control the sexuality of the fly since their shapes varied with sex. All flies, then, had three pairs of homologous chromosomes, which we now call **autosomes**. The fourth pair, the **sex chromosomes**, differed in size and in function in males and females. As in humans, the two sex chromosomes in females were called **X chromosomes**, and the stubby odd partner in the male was called the **Y**. Females pass an X chromosome to every gamete they produce.

karyotype—an orderly arrangement of figures of chromosomes from a cell nucleus; homologous chromosomes are shown in pairs.

autosome—any chromosome that does not, by its presence, determine the sex of the organism.

sex chromosome—by its presence along with its homolog it determines the sex of the organism that bears it.

X chromosome—in humans and various other animals, the sex chromosome that in two copies predisposes the individual bearing it to be female.

Drosophila melanogaster–Karyotype Diagram

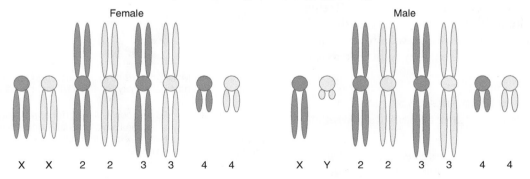

Figure 12.47   Drosophila Karyotype Diagram. Chromosomes are represented in their duplicated state as long arms attached to centromeres (circles). The sex chromosomes are by convention given the number #1. The autosomes are numbers 2–4. In males and females karyotypes differ only by their sex chromosomes.

Males determine the sex of their offspring because about 50% of their gametes contain an X chromosome just as do the female gametes, but the other 50% contain the Y and will generate males.

Morgan speculated that if genes were on chromosomes, the eye color gene could be *on* the sex chromosome (the X, that is). Clearly, the **Y chromosome** could not carry as much genetic material as the X, so Morgan assumed that it had *no gene* for eye color. Morgan started drawing chromosomes and imagining genes on them (see Figure 12.46c). He assumed that the male mutant he found was recessive. So he drew an X chromosome with a little *r* on it (for white eyes) and put it opposite a Y chromosome with no eye color gene on it. Mutations like white eyes would be rare. So Morgan assumed that the female he mated his mutant fly to was homozygous for the normal red eye allele, *R/R*. Figure 12.46 diagrams the cross and illustrates how only white-eyed males can appear in the F_2 generation. First, the parental genotypes are listed. Their gametes are then used to construct a Punnett square that shows us the possible genotypes of the F_1 generation. When an F_1 heterozygous red female is crossed with the F_1 red-eyed male (having just one copy of the gene), look what shows up in the F_2 generation! The phenotypic ratio is three red-eyed flies for each white-eyed fly. But all the white-eyed flies are males! Isn't that neat! Do you know what that says? It says that genes are found on chromosomes. That is the big message of this section of the chapter.

So then, genes on different chromosomes obey Mendel's law of independent assortment. But chromosomes are very large by comparison with single gene sequences. Many genes are on any given chromosome. How can genes that are linked closely to each other on a chromosome obey Mendel's second law? They don't. *Drosophila* eye color genes and sex genes didn't, did they? Rather they exhibit **linkage.** Two alleles linked closely with each on the same chromosome will follow each other into the same gamete; they will not assort

into gametes independently of each other, unless a recombination event occurs between them. Recall our discussion in Section 12.2c. In a recombination event, crossing over of maternally and paternally derived homologous chromosome arms causes a mixing of alleles on the two chromosomes (see Figure 12.48). But the closer together two genes are on a chromosome, the less likely they are to be separated by a recombination event—and therefore the less likely they are to obey Mendel's law. Genes controlling freckles and red hair tend to stay together because they are tightly linked on a chromosome. Genes that are at extreme ends of long chromosomes tend to obey Mendel's law because there are so many recombination events between them that their passage into gametes is independent of each other.

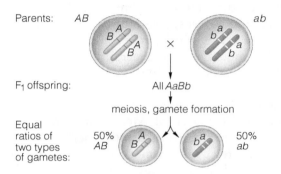

a If two genes A and B are tightly linked (close together) along a chromosome, very few recombination events will occur between them. They will assort into sex cells together or dependently yielding fewer types of sex cells.

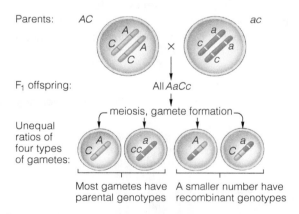

Most gametes have parental genotypes   A smaller number have recombinant genotypes

b two genes A and C are loosely linked (far apart) along a chromosome, many recombination events will occur between them. They will assort into sex cells independently as if they were on separate, non-homologous chromosomes. They thus appear to obey Mendel's second law.

Figure 12.48 Behavior of Linked Genes. **(a)** tightly linked genes. **(b)** loosely linked genes.

Y chromosome—in humans and various other animals, the sex chromosome that by its presence predisposes the individual bearing it to be male.

linkage—the close attachment of two genes on the same chromosome; as a result, in crosses, the two genes do not obey the law of independent assortment

Well then, how did Mendel arrive at his law while studying seven different traits in peas? It just happened (!) that the traits he selected for study were either on separate, nonhomologous chromosomes, or they were on the same homologous chromosome but so far apart that recombination enabled them to behave independently. Had Mendel chosen two tightly linked genes to study, his conclusions may have been more tentative or never reached. The history of science is always available to humble us when necessary.

Life on planet Earth is a long-term transmission and expression of information—informational continuity. Think of all the things your fingers have done for you in your lifetime. Mine are generating this sentence right now! The information that uses cell death to carve your fingers out of a lump of limb bud has been passed on to you from countless generations in the past. We have explored in this chapter how that information moves from one generation to the next. But where did that information originate? Who first used it? That question takes us to a new principle of life and the next chapter in this text.

IN OTHER WORDS

1. Mendel's laws state that pairs of alleles come apart during sex cell formation and they assort into sex cells independently of the way in which other pairs of alleles assort.
2. In the early 1900s it was eventually discovered that chromosomes exist in pairs that also disjoin during meiosis and that do so independently of other pairs of chromosomes.
3. Mendel's laws are easily illustrated by drawing pairs of alleles on separate pairs of nonhomologous chromosomes and then following both alleles and chromosomes through meiosis.
4. Thomas Hunt Morgan demonstrated the genetic quality of chromosomes by proposing that eye color genes in the vinegar fly, *Drosophila melanogaster,* are located on their sex chromosomes. The linkage of eye color to sex is precisely rationalized in this way.
5. Genes that are closely linked to each other on the same homologous chromosome do not assort independently of each other as Mendel's second law predicts.

QUESTIONS FOR REVIEW

1. Make a list of the classes of components a daughter cell must receive from a parental cell in order for the daughter cell to survive and reproduce itself.
2. Make a list of the ways in which various plants reproduce themselves asexually. If you have time, go outside of your textbook in search of examples.
3. Sexual reproduction has numerous disadvantages when compared with asexual reproduction. What is its greatest apparent advantage?
4. What force or process adequately explains (a) how sexuality is maintained in a population of organisms and (b) how sexuality originates in a population?
5. If two genes are homologous to each other, what are three things that you immediately know about them?
6. Describe the ploidy problem that meiosis solves.
7. What process must occur in meiosis in order for each daughter cell to get one complete set of genetic information?
8. DNA replication occurs during S phase just before the two divisions of meiosis. When is the next time that DNA replication will occur?
9. Describe three processes or aspects of meiosis and fertilization that will keep any of your children from looking exactly like one of their grandparents.
10. Which cell division in meiosis is most like mitosis? Why?
11. Which cell division in meiosis is termed the *reduction division*? Why?
12. List the tissues that primary germ cells are exposed to in sequence. How many opportunities for induction of fresh gene expression are there in that sequence?
13. How does a primary spermatocyte differ from a primary germ cell?

14. In a sperm cell, what is the function of the acrosome? the "head"? the midpiece? the flagellum?
15. What quality of the human species does cell fusion (fertilization) contribute to (a quality that cell division cannot contribute to)?
16. Describe two ways in which a follicle supports the production of a new human being.
17. What is the role of luteinizing hormone in human reproduction? How are its levels in the bloodstream controlled?
18. Using anatomical (structural) terms, trace the path the oocyte takes until the moment it is born as a child.
19. What is the role of a corpus luteum following ovulation? What happens to the reproductive system as its function ceases?
20. Using arrows and terms for male and female organs, trace the flow of a sperm cell from its site of maturation to the egg it fertilizes.
21. List the hormones mentioned in this chapter, and after each one, list its role in the control of human reproduction.
22. List the three accessory glands in the male reproductive system, and after each one, list its value to the reproductive process.
23. If 100 sperm cells reach an egg, how does the egg respond such that only one sperm cell effectively fertilizes it?
24. Draw a two-part timeline. On it chart the time of fertilization as 0 days. On the line, plot the average time of implantation (in days) and gestation (the time till birth, in days).
25. List the methods of birth control described in this chapter. After each method list its chief advantage and its chief disadvantage in your eyes.
26. How does a progestogen-based, intrauterine device (IUD) limit pregnancy?
27. What is a philosophical, nonscientific argument for saying that human life begins at conception? What is a scientific argument for asserting the same position?
28. What features of Mendel's crosses made his experiments productive fodder for good generalizations?
29. Explain the difference between a dominant and a recessive trait. Use the term *allele(s)* in your explanation.
30. In blood transfusion, persons with which *ABO* genotype are capable of giving blood to anyone? Which individuals would be capable of receiving blood from anyone?
31. A child presents to a physician with a swollen abdomen, underweight, fatigued, and complaining of abdominal pain and joint pain. Why does the doctor order a blood test for the child?
32. Which specific part of meiosis are Mendel's two laws most closely associated with?
33. In human beings, it is much more common for a male to be a hemophiliac (congenital bleeding with delayed clotting time) than for a female. What does this suggest about the location of the gene for hemophilia?

QUESTIONS FOR THOUGHT

1. Using simple anatomical terms, explain how the principle Life Is Informational Continuity is exemplified in your grandparent, your parent, and in you.
2. Name an enzyme that is right at the very heart of informational continuity.
3. Developing sexuality in a species of organism was described as an insurmountable problem. Of the obstacles listed in our discussion (or any other challenges that occur to you), which one appears the greatest to you? Explain your reasoning.
4. For sexuality in microbes to originate, we said three things were needed: complementary surface receptor molecules, sexual structures to function in gene exchange, and cellular behaviors to support the process. Which of these three should evolve first in order to get the pathway to sexuality started? Which should evolve first in order for the system to have any value to the population?
5. What is the biological advantage to having two sets of information to support your form and function instead of just one?
6. The sperm has a long distance to go and an important function to perform. Observe Figure 12.15 again. How can a sperm cell afford to get by with so little cytoplasm as compared with a human ovum?
7. At one time in the history of biology, scholars believed that an entire human being, perfectly formed but far smaller, could almost be seen within the confines of the sperm cell. Which of the four aspects of development are ignored or minimized by such a view?

8. Human love cannot be defined scientifically. Is it possible to study it scientifically in the context of human reproduction?

9. Are your features the result of a random combination of an egg cell with a sperm cell? Explain.

10. Consider Figure 9.6. Can you think of any system of the body that is not involved in the reproduction of another human being?

11. Suppose this chapter had limited itself to a purely biological-physical treatment of human reproduction. Describe how your view of reproduction would be different from what it now is.

12. Prostaglandins are not hormones. Visit an online encyclopedia or search engine to discover ways in which a prostaglandin differs from a hormone.

13. Is the use of birth control immoral for a youthful, healthy couple? Explain your position.

14. Do an online search/study using the key term *symptothermal method*. Discover its effectiveness at preventing pregnancy. What are its advantages and disadvantages?

15. Are the arguments about the origin of human life more fruitful within the theological/philosophical community or within the scientific community? Explain.

16. Fashion a concise, four-sentence argument to refute the position that human life begins two weeks after the infant is born.

17. How would you criticize the symmetrical view that human life begins when brain waves are first detectable and ends when they are no longer detectable?

18. Studies suggest that 50% of fertilized embryos contain genetic abnormalities that cause them to abort spontaneously. Should this affect a woman's decision to use chemical birth control if the result is the possible abortion of a very rare breakthrough ovulation? Explain.

19. Reductionism in science isn't always a blessing! What major assumption is made about the human female in the design of most oral contraceptives? Is that assumption justified?

20. Four crosses between pea plants are represented below. The genotypes of the parents involved in each cross are given. For each cross, list the genotypes of the sex cells that can be formed by each parent and use a Punnett square to combine the sex cells to form individuals of the next generation (pencil and paper fertilization). Each box in the Punnett square should show the diploid genotype of the zygote cell. Finish by giving frequencies of the possible phenotypes and genotypes in the F_1 generation.
   a. $TT \times tt$
   b. $Tt \times tt$
   c. $Tt \times Tt$
   d. $Tt \times TT$

21. We have a tall pea plant. But what is its genotype, TT or Tt? How can we find out? What kind of pea plant can we cross our tall plant to in order to discover its genotype? Use a Punnett square to explain how your cross gives the answer.

22. In question 20b, is it possible to recover any homozygous tall pea plants among the offspring? Explain.

23. In the cross between individuals of genotypes $AAbbCCdd \times aaBBccDD$, how many kinds of sex cells can be formed by each individual parent? Therefore, how many kinds of offspring can emerge from this cross? Yes, this is a trick question. Do you really understand homozygosity?

24. A $TtYy$ individual is crossed to one that is $ttyy$. List the types of gametes produced by each parent. Form a Punnett "square" (rectangle) and derive the genotypes of the offspring. How many phenotypic classes will you have in the offspring? How many genotypic classes?

25. Red snapdragons are crossed to white ones. Using R for the red allele and r for the white allele, what are the genotypes of these parents? What are the genotypic and phenotypic ratios among the F_1 offspring? If the F_1 individuals are crossed to each other, what are the F_2 phenotypic and genotypic ratios?

26. A male Labrador retriever with the genotype $BB\ Ee$ is crossed to a female with genotype $bb\ ee$. Assume that B controls pigment production and that E controls pigment deposition. What phenotypes will result from this cross and in what frequencies?

27. Suppose Morgan had found a white-eyed female fly and crossed her to a pure-breeding red-eyed male. What would be the eye color phenotypes in the F_1 generation? Would they be correlated to the sex of the fly? Suppose the F_1 individuals were mated to each other. What would be the phenotypic ratios for sex and eye color in the F_2 generation?

28. Genes on the same homologous chromosome are either close to each other or far apart. How could recombination events between them be used to decide which of the two possibilities is the case?

GLOSSARY

abortive—any substance or method that prevents a zygote or subsequent stages in human development from proceeding further; terminating of an individual organism's life.

acrosome—an organelle that covers the anterior portion of a sperm cell; contains hydrolytic enzymes capable of digesting an opening into the surface layers of a mature ovum.

adventitious—in plants, a structure that arises from an unusual place such as roots growing out of stems or leaves.

allele—a specific form of a gene; it occupies a defined position on a particular chromosome within an individual. Other individuals may have other forms of the gene at that location.

asexual reproduction—generation of offspring without the production by meiosis of haploid sex cells and thus without fertilization.

autosome—any chromosome that does not, by its presence, determine the sex of the organism.

bulbourethral gland—a lobular exocrine gland that secretes a pre-sperm lubricant into the urethra that also neutralizes the acidity of any residual urine.

cervix—the posterior, narrow neck of the uterus that connects it to the vaginal canal; stretches minimally for endometrial shedding and maximally during birthing.

clone—any DNA molecule, cell, or organism that is identical genetically to some precursor DNA molecule, cell, or organism from which it arises.

codominant—an allele whose phenotypic effect is visible regardless of what other allele happens to be opposite it.

condom—a flexible barrier placed over the male penis to keep sperm from passing into the vagina of the sexual partner; constructed of latex or lamb intestine.

contraceptive—any substance or method that prevents sperm from uniting with the egg.

corona radiata—two or three layers of cells, residual from the follicle, that surround an ovulated egg; they supply nutritive protein to the egg cell.

corpus luteum—the yellow (luteal) remains of a ruptured ovarian follicle after ovulation; secretes estrogen and progesterone for maintaining the uterine lining for a possible pregnancy.

diaphragm—a flexible latex or silicone shield placed in front of or over the cervix that prevents sperm from entering the uterus.

dihybrid—descriptive of a cross between two individuals in which two separate traits or characters are being followed in the offspring.

dominant—when two or more alleles of a gene are present in a cell, the allele whose phenotype is expressed.

electroencephalograph—a mechanical device that senses, measures, and records electrical activity resulting from depolarizations (firing) of neurons, usually in the brain.

empiricist—one who reaches conclusions as a result of evidence gathered by sensory experience that frequently involves experimentation.

endometrium—the inner lining of the mammalian uterus.

epididymis—a lobe on the surface of the male testis housing a highly coiled tubule in which mature sperm are stored prior to ejaculation.

epistasis—a form of gene expression in which two or more gene loci affect the same phenotypic trait.

erectile tissue—a collection of cells within the male penis that becomes engorged with blood during sexual arousal preparing the penis for sperm deposition in the female vaginal canal.

estrogen—a class of hormones controlling various aspects of sexual reproduction in females.

F_1—a symbol referring to the first filial generation; the immediate offspring of the original parents of a cross.

F_2—a symbol referring to the second filial generation; the second-generation offspring of the original parents of a cross.

fallopian tubes (uterine tube, oviduct)—a cilia-lined passage that extends from the ovary to the uterus; carries mature or fertilized ovum to the uterus for implantation.

fetology—the study of developing humans between the ages of nine weeks post-conception and birth.

fetus—a developing mammal in between its embryonic stage and birth; in humans it extends from nine weeks post-conception until birth.

fimbriae—a highly articulated fringe of tissue around the opening of the fallopian tube closest to the ovary; these sweep the ovulated egg into the fallopian tube.

follicle—a spherical collection of cells that develops within the ovary of a female animal; it houses and nutritionally supports a developing ovum.

FSH (follicle stimulating hormone)—synthesized and secreted by the pituitary gland; it regulates critical aspects of the maturation of sex cells.

gamete—a sex cell; a cell that has both completed meiosis and differentiated morphologically such that it can participate in the process of fertilization.

gene—a sequence of bases within the structure of a nucleic acid, usually DNA, that code for a protein or an RNA that has a biological function.

genetic recombination—an enzyme-driven process in which DNA strands in two homologous chromosomes are broken and rejoined so that segments of the two chromosomes are physically switched.

genetic variability—quality of a population in which members possess a variety of different forms of a given gene or genes.

genotype—a combination of alleles that control or influence some specific aspect of the appearance of an organism, such as *T/t* in pea plants.

gonadal ridge—mesodermal tissue between the somites and lateral mesoderm that develops into gonadal tissue, either ovaries or testes.

haploid—refers to a cell or an organism whose cells contain a single copy of the genome of the organism; sex cells are typically in this category.

heterozygous—a genotype for a single gene locus in which the two alleles are nonidentical; example *Yy* in the cells of a yellow pea seed coat color.

homologous—refers to a correspondence; a fundamental similarity between two items. In heredity, two information sources that have the same role but do not carry it out identically.

homozygous—a genotype for a single gene locus in which both alleles are identical; example *YY* in the cells of a yellow pea seed coat color.

implantation—the process by which an embryo about six days postfertilization burrows into the endometrial lining of the uterus to continue growth using maternally derived nutrients from the uterine lining and eventually the placenta.

independent assortment—a Mendelian relationship between alleles at two different genetic loci; the sorting into sex cells of alleles at one locus has no effect on the sorting of alleles at the second locus.

intrauterine device—a plastic, T-shaped frame either wound with copper wire or containing the hormone progestogen; inserted into the uterus to prevent ovulation, conception, or implantation of the egg cell.

karyotype—an orderly arrangement of figures of chromosomes from a cell nucleus; homologous chromosomes are shown in pairs.

Leydig cells—within the male testis, cells that are primary sites of production of the hormone testosterone.

LH (luteinizing hormone)—synthesized in the anterior portion of the pituitary gland; causes ovulation in females; stimulates testosterone production in males.

Life Is Informational Continuity—the sixth principle of life on which this text is based.

linkage—the close attachment of two genes on the same chromosome; as a result, in crosses, the two genes do not obey the law of independent assortment.

lumen—the interior channel of any duct or tubule.

meiosis—a sequence of two cell division events that halves the number of chromosomes in the nucleus and supplies them to the sex cell in their unreplicated state.

menstrual cycle—a sequence of structural and hormonal changes within the uterus of the female that prepare the uterus for a potential pregnancy; it sheds its lining if the pregnancy fails to occur.

natural selection—the driving force of evolution; environmental characteristics happen to favor the survival of population members having certain desirable and heritable traits.

oogonium—an immature, diploid, pre–ovum cell that arises from primary germ cells by mitosis.

oral contraceptive—the pill; hormonal supplements taken by mouth to prevent ovulation in the female; usually containing estrogen and/or progestogen.

ovary—a female reproductive organ whose tissues secrete hormonal signals and both house and mature developing ova.

ovulation—a process in which a mature ovum or egg cell ruptures from a follicle next to the surface of the ovary such that the ovum leaves the ovary and enters the fallopian tube.

penis—an external sexual organ in males that, in placental mammals, also serves as an organ of urination.

phenotype—a specific aspect of the appearance of an organism, such as "tall" in pea plants.

pituitary gland—a 0.5-g lobe-like extension from the hypothalamic region of the brain; has endocrine function secreting hormones that control a variety of developmental functions often via control of other endocrine glands; the master gland.

pleiotropy—a form of gene expression in which one genetic locus has multiple phenotypic effects on the organism.

ploidy—refers to the number of complete sets of chromosomes in the nuclei of an individual's cells. Most higher animals are diploid (two sets) except in their sex cells.

polar body—the remnant of a nucleus containing a complete set of replicated or unreplicated chromosomes; found within the periphery of an ovum; it deteriorates with time.

primary germ cell—those cells in the early embryo whose daughter cells will ultimately differentiate into sex cells, that is, sperm and ova.

primary oocyte—an immature, diploid pre–ovum cell that is genetically and structurally prepared to undergo meiotic divisions.

primary spermatocyte—an immature, diploid pre–sperm cell that is genetically and structurally prepared to undergo meiotic divisions.

progesterone—a progestogen steroid hormone in females that supports embryonic development and participates in the control of the female menstrual cycle.

progestogen—a class of similarly structured steroid hormones of which progesterone is an example.

pronucleus—the nucleus of either the egg cell or the sperm cell during the process of fertilization; used to refer to both nuclei after the sperm nucleus has entered the egg cytoplasm.

prostaglandin—any of a class of lipid molecules that contains 20 carbon atoms, including a five-carbon ring; often influencing the contraction and relaxation of smooth muscle local to the site of their secretion.

prostate gland—an accessory sexual gland in males whose secretion buffers the environment of the sperm against vaginal acidity and induces muscular contractions in the female reproductive system.

Punnett square—a diagram in which known genotypes of sex cells are arranged along two axes of a rectangle and used to predict the genotypes of offspring resulting from random fertilization events between the sex cells.

pure-breeding—a strain or population of a species that possesses a specific characteristic and gives rise only to individuals possessing that characteristic; only alleles supporting that characteristic are present in the strain.

quickening—the first physical movements made by a fetus *in utero* that the mother is able to sense.

recessive—when two or more alleles of a gene are present in a cell, the allele whose phenotype is hidden or masked.

rhythm method—the monitoring of temperature and mucus viscosity to chart a woman's monthly cycle; used as a means of birth control.

scrotal sac—an enclosure composed of skin and muscle that houses the male testes at a temperature suitable for sperm production.

secondary oocyte—an immature, haploid pre–ovum cell that has undergone a single meiotic division and is preparing for a second such division.

secondary spermatocyte—an immature, haploid pre–sperm cell that has undergone a single meiotic division and is preparing for a second such division.

segmentation (in embryology)—a radical division of early cleavage-stage blastomeres (cells in blastocyst) such that two or more embryos are generated from one blastocyst.

segregate—the behavior of alleles of a pair during sex cell formation; during meiosis, that separation of alleles, which yields haploid sex cells from diploid gametocytes.

seminal vesicle—a tubular gland in males that secretes a nutritive fluid comprising part of semen.

seminiferous tubules—long, narrow ducts within the testis of the male; site of meiosis followed by sperm production.

sex chromosome—by its presence along with its homolog it determines the sex of the organism that bears it.

sexual reproduction—generating offspring from the union of gametes from two parents, by way of meiosis, gamete formation, and fertilization.

spermatid—a pre–sperm cell that has completed meiosis and is about to differentiate structurally to possess a midpiece, flagellar tail, and acrosome.

spermatogonia—an immature, diploid, pre–sperm cell that arises from primary germ cells by mitosis.

spermicide—any substance or drug that is lethal to sperm cells.

spontaneous abortion—loss of a developing blastocyst, embryo, or fetus due to natural, often unpredictable causes; most occur because of failure to implant properly.

testis—a male reproductive organ whose tissues secrete hormonal signals and mature developing sperm cells.

testosterone—a steroid hormone that in males regulates production of sperm and secondary sexual characteristics; in females it influences the desire for sexual activity.

trimester—one of three consecutive time periods comprising a typical pregnancy.

trophoblastic—of or pertaining to a layer of cells that surrounds the early embryo; this layer is adapted to deriving nutrition from maternal tissues.

tubal ligation—a surgical method of female sterilization in which the fallopian tubes are severed and then pinched or sewed shut.

uterus—female organ in which a fertilized egg implants and matures as an embryo to the point of birth.

vagina—a tubular canal leading from the uterus to the exterior of the female body; receives the penis during sexual intercourse and is the birth canal during parturition.

vaginal ring—a flexible drug delivery appliance made of polyethylene and vinyl acetate that delivers progesterone and an estrogen to the female tissues inhibiting ovulation.

vas deferens—a duct leading from the epididymis to the ejaculatory duct within the prostate gland; carries mature sperm toward the urethra of the male during sexual arousal.

vasectomy—a minor surgical method of severing the vas deferentia of a male so as to render him sterile.

withdrawal method—the removal of the penis from the vagina of the female just prior to ejaculation of sperm; used as a method of birth control.

X chromosome—in humans and various other animals, the sex chromosome that in two copies predisposes the individual bearing it to be female.

Y chromosome—in humans and various other animals, the sex chromosome that by its presence predisposes the individual bearing it to be male.

zona pellucida—a protective layer of an ovulated egg external to the cell membrane; docking site for sperm; its presence is required to initiate the sperm's acrosomal hydrolytic enzyme activities.

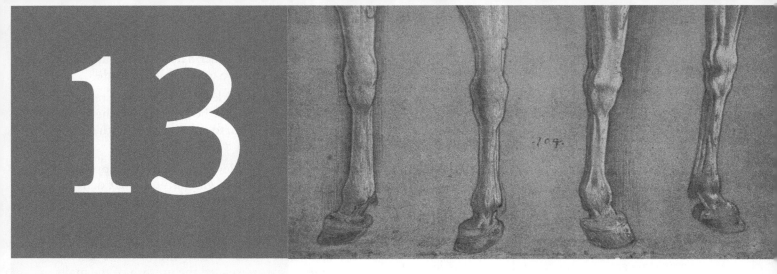

13

Life Is Ultimate Art

Survey Questions

13.1 Life and Its Diversity: Ultimate Art or Ultimate Accident?

- Is life the work of an Artist or the result of accidental hereditary changes?
- Which students of nature have held each of these views?
- How did they arrive at their conclusions?
- Will this question be answered in this chapter to the readers' satisfaction?

13.2 Can Life Originate Without Artistry?

- How complex is the simplest living cell?
- How much information is used to code for that cell?
- What starting materials are available for evolving a cell?
- What might these starting materials combine spontaneously to form?
- How would the information that codes for a cell originate?
- Is information needed simply to generate cell parts, or is it required for their spatial placement as well?

13.3 Can Life's Diversity Increase without Artistry?

- Can Darwinian evolution create new structures if living organisms with information-bearing genomes are already in place?
- Specifically, can Darwinian evolution create a flight feather on a dinosaur or a bird?

Science commits suicide when it adopts a creed.
—THOMAS HUXLEY, A NINETEENTH CENTURY POPULARIZER OF DARWINIAN EVOLUTION

Scientific thinking is usually bullied by the scientist's own desires. He begins by operating on reasonable working assumptions about experiments and their reproducibility. But his inner demand for **autonomy** slowly converts these assumptions into a life philosophy that says that nature alone is real. This creed then turns round and imprisons the methods of science (see Chapter 2) within its conceptual walls. Nowhere is this problem more poignantly felt than in our exploration of the origin of life and its diversity. This chapter is an attempt to take science's methods outside the wall of **naturalism.** Can we reexamine the origin and diversity of life leaving more than one philosophical option open? Let's begin by journeying back to fifteenth century Florentine Italy to the Tuscan hillside town of Vinci.

autonomy—having complete personal freedom in moral behavior and in self governance.

naturalism—the philosophy or world-and-life view that declares nature, its forms, and its rules to be all that exists; any evidences of the supernatural are illusory.

- What features of a bird's wing suggest that feather evolution may or may not be possible?
- Does the microstructure of a feather suggest to us that it could have evolved?
- What is the molecular material from which the structure of a feather is made?
- How does a flight feather develop? What skin structures generate it?
- How do the barbs and barbules of a feather get cut out and arranged?
- What simpler sort of feather might the flight feather have evolved from?
- Is a feather irreducibly complex?
- What directs where mutations will occur in the avian genome?
- What does the term *random* mean in the neo-Darwinian synthesis?
- What are the effects on the organism of random mutations?
- Can random mutations create new genetic information?
- What is natural selection and how does it work?
- At what level does natural selection work: genes, cells, organisms, or populations?
- What factors affect natural selection's power within a population?
- Are natural selection's changes in a population permanent?
- Can natural selection anticipate future needed changes?
- Are mutation and natural selection adequate to generate a flight feather from a down feather?

13.4 Did Life's Diversity Increase without Artistry?

- Apart from the issue of the adequacy of natural selection, is there any evidence that life has evolved from a common ancestor?
- What is the role of fossils in providing evidence that life may have evolved?
- What was the Cambrian explosion? Does this phenomenon support evolutionary theory?

Renaissance—a period of European history, commencing in the 1400s, in which a renewed interest in classical literature and ancient Biblical texts arose.

13.1 LIFE AND ITS DIVERSITY: ULTIMATE ART OR ULTIMATE ACCIDENT?

Life as Ultimate Art

In 1452, on an April evening, a peasant woman in Vinci gave birth to a son who would become arguably the greatest artist-scientist-engineer the world has ever seen. At the age of 14 he found himself in Florence, the cultural center of the **Renaissance,** where he became apprenticed to Verrocchio, one of the greatest of Florentine artists. Leonardo da Vinci's training there in chemistry, metallurgy, leatherwork, drafting, carpentry, drawing, painting, modeling, and sculpting granted him a broad base of knowledge. His subsequent contributions to the world of art and science would one day cause him to be viewed as the consummate Renaissance man. Within a few years he excelled his master and as his skill matured, he went on to paint the *Mona Lisa, The Last Supper,* and other glorious and enduring works of art.

Leonardo's sketchbooks ran to thousands of pages. He loved to draw animals, particularly horses. His artwork graces the beginning of this chapter. With time, he had his own studio and pupils to whom his advice was, "Study nature, observe life in all its moods, and paint what you see . . ." Centuries later, Webster's dictionary would define *art* as the conscious use of *skill* and creative *imagination* in the production of aesthetic objects. Yet in Leonardo's

Figure 13.1 Leonardo da Vinci, self portrait done in 1512.

Bettmann/Corbis

- How do Darwinists attempt to explain the Cambrian explosion?
- What is *homology?* What does it mean to say that two structures are homologous?
- How do homologous structures support the theory of evolution?
- At what level is homology thought to exist? Can molecules or cells be homologous?
- Is homology dependent only on structural features of an organism, or can the mere location of the structural features also be homologous?
- Can genes be homologous? Does a common sequence indicate homology? Why?
- Is the concept of homology ruined by assuming a common Designer instead of a common ancestor?

13.5 What Is the Product and Value of Evolution?

- If mutation and selection are not capable of creating new structures, do they have any value in the biological world?
- Can either harmful or neutral mutations contribute to the evolutionary process in any way?
- Do beneficial mutations exist? What is their nature? Is a beneficial mutation always, categorically beneficial?
- Is natural selection itself an accident or might it be a designed feature of nature?
- Does natural selection have just one way of working, or does it have different roles in the natural world?
- Can natural selection consistently move a population in a whole new direction over time?
- Do records containing revealed truth place any constraints on how evolution might be seen to be working?
- Are organisms becoming more advanced and more fit today? Is evolution currently creating anything new?
- Are new species currently resulting from the creation of new structures or more sophisticated mating behaviors?

sketches, there is far more of skill than creative imagination. Long before photography was invented, he was rendering legs, arms, faces, and torsos with breathtaking realism of form, proportion, and detail. Where then is the art in the sketch of a horse's leg? Leonardo supplied his inimitable representational skill. What is the source of the creative imagination?

Could the glory of the horse's leg result from an extrinsic source of design? Might the leg *itself* be art if conscious use of skill and creative imagination were to explain its combination of beautiful form and superior engineering? Perhaps in this drawing at least, Leonardo is creating art by representing existing art. In his Renaissance culture, this suspicion would not have been seriously doubted. Leonardo wrote in one of his manuscripts, "O you, who look on this our machine, do not be sad that with others you are fated to die, but rejoice that our Creator has endowed us with such an excellent instrument as the intellect."

1. art & Creator

> *art: the conscious use of skill and creative imagination in the production of aesthetic objects*

Life as Ultimate Accident

On February 12, 1809, a wealthy Wedgewood family daughter in Shrewsbury, England, gave birth to a son who would write a revolutionary treatise on natural history. It would initiate a new paradigm that was to set all future biological discoveries in an entirely new context. By the age of eight, Charles Darwin was already a collector of wildlife, and like Leonardo, he became a keen observer of a wide variety of life-forms. Although he was eventually sent off to medical school, he continued to show more interest in natural history, joining the Plinian Society, a student group of natural history lovers.

Distaste for medicine soon found him enrolled as an undergraduate in Christ College, Cambridge, where he again found more fascination in beetle collection and hunting than in his formal preparation for the pastorate. His friendship with botany professor John Henslow eventually resulted in his signing on board the HMS *Beagle* as a naturalist and collector on a two-year expedition commissioned to chart the coastline of South America.

2. During the voyage, which ran to five years (1831–1836), Darwin studied the geology and natural history of the South American continent, islands, and seas. He studied marine invertebrates, **plankton**, fossilized seashells and mammalian remains, the

plankton—microscopic life-forms found in the oceans of the world.

Figure 13.2 Charles Darwin **(a)** His portrait early in his career. **(b)** The five-year voyage of the *HMS Beagle* that granted Darwin the opportunity to discover the breadth of intraspecific variation for many traits.

anthropology of the natives on Tierra del Fuego, the finches and tortoises of the Galapagos Islands (see Figure 13.3a), and the mockingbirds of Chile and the associated islands. Evenings he was reading the geological writings of Charles Lyell, whose **uniformitarian** view of geological history was consistent with the eighteenth century **Enlightenment**'s emphasis on natural law and the constancy of physical relationships.

Darwin's extended forays into natural history taught him that populations of organisms were comprised of individuals who, although of the same species, had generous amounts of variation for most individual traits studied. Ranges in the size of finch beaks (see Figure 13.3b–e) or tortoises' shells, for example, could easily be demonstrated. Darwin's observations were informed by his

reading of Thomas Malthus's work on the dynamics of human populations. What Malthus saw in human populations, Darwin began to see in natural populations: For most species, a robust **reproductive potential** generated far more individuals than the environment could possibly support (see Table 13.1). Malthus went on to argue that such reproductive potential threw members of a population into competition with each other for resources. But, as Darwin had noted, the competitors vary from each other across many traits. Darwin brilliantly took the next step and argued that due to the constraints the environment places on a population, nature selects the variations in the population best suited to survive and reproduce. Weaker individuals don't compete well. They live shorter lives and leave fewer young.

With the passage of time, then, the environment selects among whatever new variations are available to it, altering the character of the population by leaving it with whatever are the fittest structures and processes. Hence, the environment automatically improves the species. Next, Darwin saw how populations of the same species, reproducing in two distinct environments, might slowly respond to their respective environments in divergent ways, structurally or behaviorally, to the point where they were no longer capable of interbreeding and thus were separate species. As its title suggests, his book *The Origin of Species* gave an entirely reasonable explanation for how two new species could arise from one parental species. But of itself, this explanation was not the source of the power of the book. To understand the revolution ignited by *The Origin,* we must appreciate its historic context.

uniformitarianism—a geological concept that operant natural forces in the present are identical to natural forces in the past and are responsible for all of the landforms and patterns of strata currently observed on Earth.

Enlightenment—a period of European history commencing in the 1700s in which Divine authority was exchanged for human reason, the new measure of all things.

reproductive potential—the ability of the members of a species to maintain or expand population size by reproducing themselves.

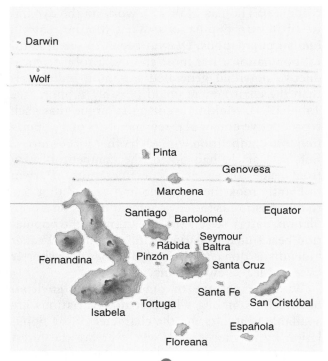

Figure 13.3 Galapagos Islands and their Finches. These are examples of the 13 finch species, some of which Darwin observed, on the Galapagos Islands. Note the variability in the shapes of their bills. They are thought to have a single common ancestor having come from the South American mainland. **(a)** The Galapagos Islands are the result of a volcanic eruption 1000 km west of Ecuador. **(b)** *Certhidea olivacea* has a slender bill to extract insects from vegetation. **(c)** *Geospiza scandens* bill suitable for eating cactus fruit and flowers. **(d)** *Geospiza magnirostris* has a bill strong enough to crush cactus seeds. **(e)** *Camarhynchus pallidus* with a bill adapted to extracting insects from bark or as shown here using a cactus spine to probe for termites.

(b) *Certhidea olivacea* **(c)** *Geospiza scandens* **(d)** *Geospiza magnirostris* **(e)** *Camarhynchus pallidus*

4. **Table 13.1** The Darwinian Model of Evolution.

Observations ⟶	Interpretations ⟶	Theory/Definition
Most organisms produce large numbers of offspring	Individuals within populations of these species are thrown into competition with each other for the limited resources	Evolution is a process in which better adapted traits accumulate among individuals within a population through time, changing the characteristics of the individuals and ultimately the species.
Species of these organisms do not displace other species and "take over" the earth.		
Resources for each species of organism are limited compared to their numbers.		
The individuals within a population vary from each other in many of their traits.	Some traits enable their bearers to survive better and produce more offspring than others.	
Many of these traits appear to be successfully passed on to subsequent generations (How?)		

Table 13.2 Some Features of Enlightenment Thinking. **6.**

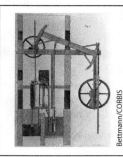

1.	Human reason is the primary source of authority.
2.	Traditions are to be questioned in light of human reason.
3.	Science and the experimental methods flourish.
4.	Strong spirit of individualism
5.	Strong desire to accumulate and systematize knowledge
6.	Natural causation is sought for every effect.
7.	Society progresses toward utopia if individuals are free to follow reason.

Bettmann/CORBIS

While the Renaissance and Reformation periods were characterized by widespread acceptance of a Divine intelligence that created all things, the "Enlightened" thinkers of the late 1700s began to provide a contrasting, practically **atheistic** context for viewing life (see Table 13.2). Some Deity may have been the prime mover, but nature's inviolable laws were now in charge and miraculous intervention in natural process was not observed. As long as natural law was predictable, man could base his efforts on it and biological and social *progress* would be possible. During the Enlightenment, the concept of a slow, evolutionary progress replaced the Christian concept in which God would suddenly usher in a huge quantum of progress at some past or future time. Darwin's intellectual life was saturated in the Enlightenment sentiments of the university. In the Plinian Society at Edinburgh, natural history was often approached from a framework of philosophical **materialism.** His reading of Lyell on geology moved Darwin to view the history of life as Lyell did the Earth: a long, plodding but predictable pathway leading from relative simplicity of land (or life) forms in the past to the vast variety of intricately composed strata (or species) observable today. In short, his data took him to a predictive theory of how species might change with time: what later thinkers have called **microevolution** (see Figure 13.4). But his philosophical worldview took him beyond his evidence to a conviction that environmental constraints could create whole new structures and organisms. His theory of **macroevolution** replaced the Renaissance Creator with an environment that could create solely by constraint. It allowed Darwin and his ideological posterity to lose sight of the miraculous and hence the theism of their

3.

3.

5.

youth. It bullied them into a comfortable **agnosticism** that has characterized much of academia since the 1800s.

In Darwin's new view, biology is still seen loosely as art. But to do so, our definition must have the term *conscious* struck from it. Art is now the stumbling of Mother Nature upon patterns of structure and function that happened to grant superior reproductive ability to the organism in which they arose. Thus since Darwin's day, society has faced two competing philosophies regarding the origin of nature's complexity. Naturalism seeks this origin within the machinery of nature. **Theism** seeks it within the conscious Mind of God (see Figure 13.5). In the scientific community, naturalism has largely won the day.

5.

atheism—belief in the nonexistence of God.

materialism—the notion that physical matter is the only form of reality and all metaphysical phenomenon can be explained in terms of physical interactions between materials.

microevolution—the process by which mutations and recombination between alleles generate new individuals in a population that slowly change its genetic and structural character with time.

macroevolution—the process by which chemicals slowly give rise to cells that then diverge to form many cell types and eventually many types of organisms representing all the diversity of life on Earth.

agnosticism—(a) the belief that a God may or may not exist; (b) the belief that it is not possible to know if a God exists.

theism—belief in the existence of God.

3.

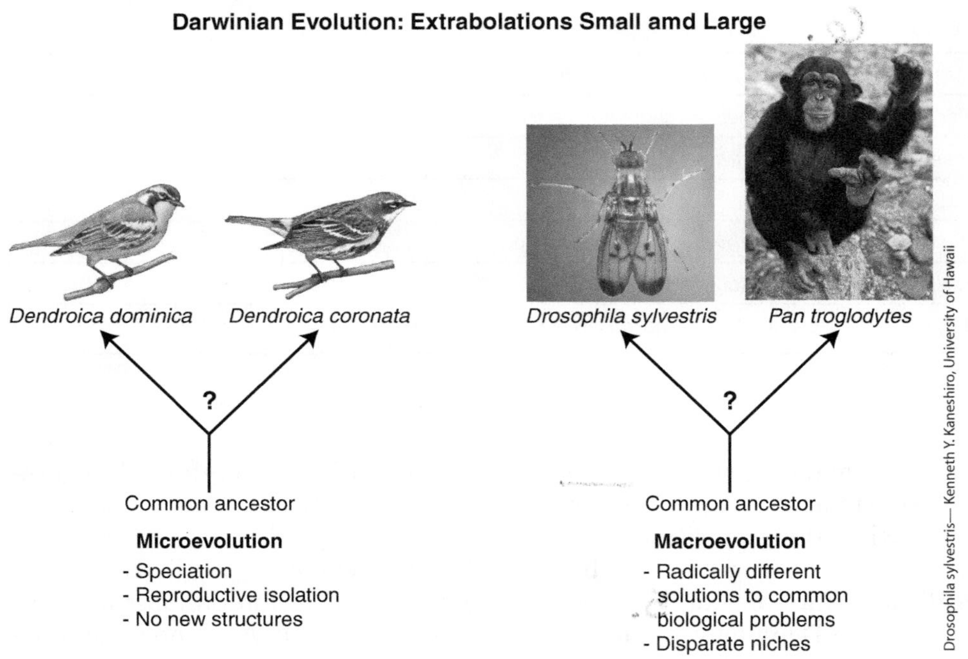

Darwinian Evolution: Extrabolations Small amd Large

Dendroica dominica   *Dendroica coronata*

?

Common ancestor

Microevolution

- Speciation
- Reproductive isolation
- No new structures

Drosophila sylvestris   *Pan troglodytes*

?

Common ancestor

Macroevolution

- Radically different
  solutions to common
  biological problems
- Disparate niches

Drosophila sylvestris— Kenneth Y. Kaneshiro, University of Hawaii

Figure 13.4   Microevolution and Macroevolution. Darwin's observations of the effects of the environment on existing organisms explains how one species can deteriorate into two separate species that no longer reproduce with each other. Does it have the same predictive power when it is required to create entirely new ways of handling common biological problems? The fly's skeleton is external, the chimp's is internal. Did the common ancestor of these two forms have no skeleton at all?

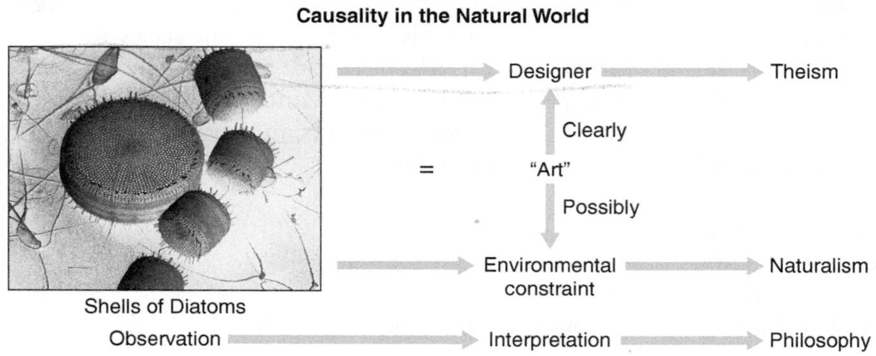

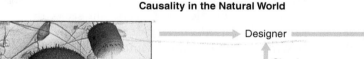

Causality in the Natural World

Designer ➡ Theism

Clearly

= "Art"

Possibly

Environmental
constraint ➡ Naturalism

Shells of Diatoms

Observation ➡ Interpretation ➡ Philosophy

Figure 13.5   Causality in Nature.

Who or what is the source of all the art within the nature around us that Leonardo asks us to study and that Darwin so meticulously did? In the chapter sections that follow, our approach will be to start with the hypothesis that biological art emanates from nature itself quite apart from a conscious Designer. There are two reasons for this. First, it is the simpler hypothesis. Why drag all the complications of an omnipotent Deity into our study if forces operating entirely within nature can explain its complexity? Secondly, for good or ill, the concept that unaided nature has generated her own life-forms is the prevailing **paradigm** in the contemporary university. Therefore our critical evaluation of the naturalistic hypothesis will contribute to a broader understanding of the academic community that has made this hypothesis its creed.

paradigm—a broadly based intellectual framework for thinking; a philosophical context in which to interpret experimental results and develop new theories.

1. Born in 1452, Leonardo da Vinci became a great artist, scientist, and engineer during the Italian Renaissance centered in Florence, Italy.
2. Leonardo's sketchbook was filled with examples of his abilities as an artist.
3. Part of the greatness of his work is the subjects from the living world that he chose to draw.
4. Born in England in 1809, Charles Darwin grew up following the eighteenth century Enlightenment's cultural and ideological features that infused contemporary thought.
5. Darwin's personal study and reading made him one of the greatest naturalists of his day; he became intimately acquainted with the widespread variations between individuals within the species he studied.
6. Darwin's reading of the works of Thomas Malthus and Charles Lyell caused him to see life-forms as having been in competition with each other for millions and millions of years.
7. Yet because of their immense reproductive potential, only the fittest individuals of a population would be able to survive; nature, by its constraints, selects the fittest to survive.
8. The survival of the fittest in a given species has the potential to change features of that species over time; it can cause a single species to diverge into two new species.
9. Darwin's worldview led him to the further belief that the process of natural selection could actually create whole new structures and organisms by slowly varying the simpler structures and organisms available to natural selection to work with.
10. Since Darwin's day, society has struggled with two contrasting views of the natural world: one that calls it art and attributes it to God and one that considers it a glorious accident attributable to the constraints of natural selection.

In a letter to a friend, Charles Darwin imagines a small, warm pool somewhere in which inanimate matter would arrange itself into "evolutionary matter," aided by chemical components and sufficient sources of energy (see Figure 13.6). He freely admitted in his writing that current ignorance of molecular details reduced him to this sort of speculation. Sixteen intervening decades have given us both a somewhat clearer notion of the sorts of molecules available in nature as a starting material for evolution and the sort of minimal life-form that might emerge at the end. Were Darwin alive today, he could easily appreciate the small but significant variety of molecules available to contribute to life's origin. What would be far less easy for him to imagine is how nature would constrain those molecules to develop lifelike structures initially and then a viable cell as a final product. How likely is the primordial process that Darwin imagined? Let's begin by considering the simplest independent form of life we know of.

Evolution's First Goal: The Smallest Cell

Right from the start we have an issue. How much precellular evolution we require depends on how much independence we demand of a cell to consider it viable. All the smallest cells we know of are **parasitic** to other larger cells. They can afford to be small since the large **host cell** supplies molecules and energy that other cells have to generate from scratch. We will select as our smallest cell, the bacterium *Mycoplasma genitalium* (see Figure 13.7).

Smaller "cells" have been found, but they tend to remain completely within their host cells. At least **mycoplasmas** have an **extracellular** phase of life that grants a small measure of independence. We have been able to grow some species of this bacterium in **broth culture** without giving them host cells to infect. Somehow, then, the molecules of life must be carefully selected by nature and must self-assemble to produce a mycoplasma. What is a mycoplasma?

Mycoplasma genitalium was first discovered in 1981 in the inflamed urethras of two male patients. It is one of over 100 species in the genus

parasite—a microscopic organism living on or in another organism from which it gains nutrients and/or energy at the expense of the other organism.

host cell—a cell that supports the growth or reproduction of a virus, bacterium, or larger microbial form that has either entered it or is in close association with it.

mycoplasma—a very small bacterium that lacks a cell wall; appears genetically related to genera *Lactobacillus* and *Clostridium*, much larger gram-positive bacteria having cell walls.

extracellular—a structure or process that is found or takes place outside of a living cell.

broth culture—usually an aqueous solution containing sufficient nutrients to allow for the growth or maintenance of a particular kind of microorganism or a collection of related microorganisms.

Figure 13.6 Pre-life Earth. Since Darwin's day geologists have inferred from their data that earth's surface conditions were controlled by volcanic eruption of gases, high temperatures, torrential rainfall and lightening, and meteoric collisions. As an historic science, geology's conclusions are tentative and continue to evolve.

Courtesy Reader's Digest Books. Drawing by H.K. Wimmer

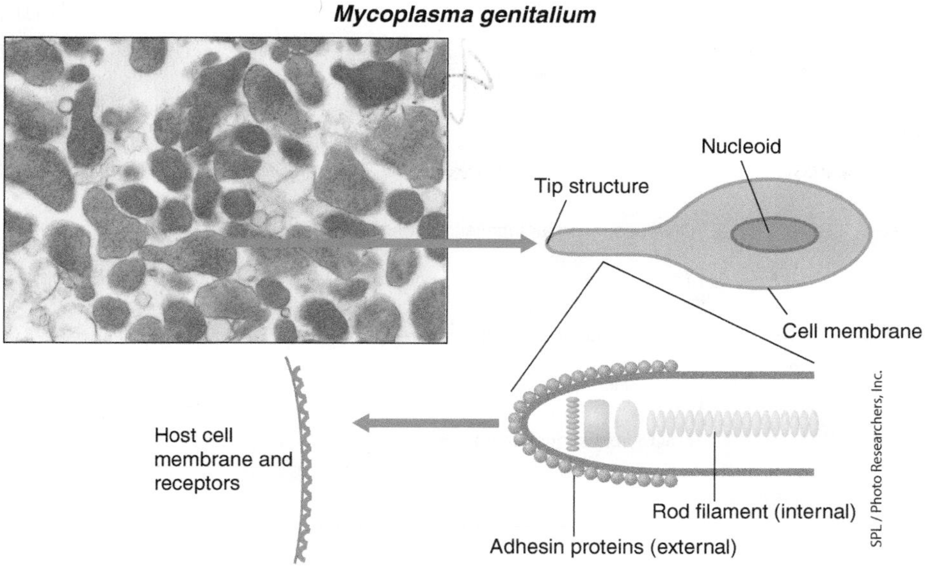

Mycoplasma genitalium

Tip structure

Nucleoid

Cell membrane

Host cell membrane and receptors

Rod filament (internal)

Adhesin proteins (external)

SPL / Photo Researchers, Inc.

Figure 13.7 *Mycoplasma genitalium.* A false-colored electron micrograph of an unusually small bacterium illustrating the flexibility of its shape due in part to the lack of a cell wall. Genetic information is stored in the nucleoid region of the cell. The tip structure and internal filament are discussed in the text. Length of a typical cell is 0.4 micrometers or 0.0004 millimeters.

Mycoplasma. Since its discovery, strains of this species have been implicated in various genital tract and lung infections in both men and women. Mycoplasmas are also found in the tissues of patients with rheumatoid arthritis, chronic fatigue, and Gulf War syndromes. What enables mycoplasmas to be so small as bacterial cells go?

At first blush, they are pathetic little slackers. They lack the cell walls of most bacteria making them so osmotically fragile that they're forced to travel directly from one moist surface to another. In other words, they require intimate contact with another person or their fluids in order to effect transmission from one person to another. Their entire genome contains only about 470 genes—about 1/10 the number found in a more typical bacterial cell such as *E. coli* (see Figure 13.8). Their energy metabolism is largely limited to glycolysis (see Chapter 6), and they are deficient in enzymes for amino acid biosynthesis because they just sop up the amino acids they need from a nearby host cell. At first, like most naturalistic thinkers, we are tempted to assume that they are a result of nature's witless attempts to simply ditch redundant genes in a nutrient-rich host cell milieu. That way, their own reproduction goes faster because they have fewer genes to duplicate and express.

Though small in size, information content, and metabolic ability, they use their DNA molecules very efficiently. Of the 470 gene sequences they possess, 126 of them exhibit regions of **overlap**. Gene sequence overlap is highly efficient space-wise, but it greatly complicates genome design. It means that you must generate regions of DNA sequence that can be read either backward or forward or in different **reading**

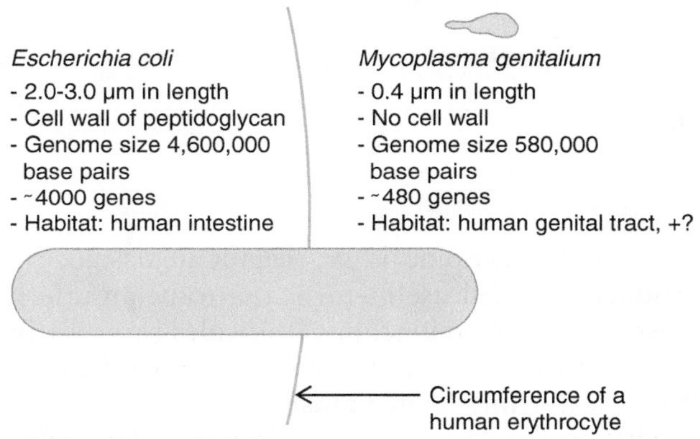

A Comparison of two Bacteria

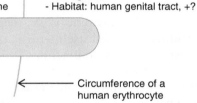

Escherichia coli
- 2.0-3.0 µm in length
- Cell wall of peptidoglycan
- Genome size 4,600,000 base pairs
- ~4000 genes
- Habitat: human intestine

Mycoplasma genitalium
- 0.4 µm in length
- No cell wall
- Genome size 580,000 base pairs
- ~480 genes
- Habitat: human genital tract, +?

Circumference of a human erythrocyte

Figure 13.8 A Comparison of Two Bacteria. *Mycoplasma* species are all quite small having limited genome size and metabolic capabilities compared to the typical colon bacillus *E. coli.*

frames to generate parts of two different proteins—all from the same sequence (see Figure 13.9)! So there are 126 segments of the *M. genitalium* genome that can tolerate virtually no mutational changes because any change is highly likely to ruin either one protein or the other coded by that sequence. This genome is a highly engineered and highly efficient information storage device.

overlap—in genetics, a single sequence of DNA or RNA that contains information for two or more coding sequences or genes.

reading frame—a way of commencing the transcribing of a DNA sequence; since a sequence of mRNA is read in codons of three bases each, there are three possible starting points and three reading frames for the same sequence of bases.

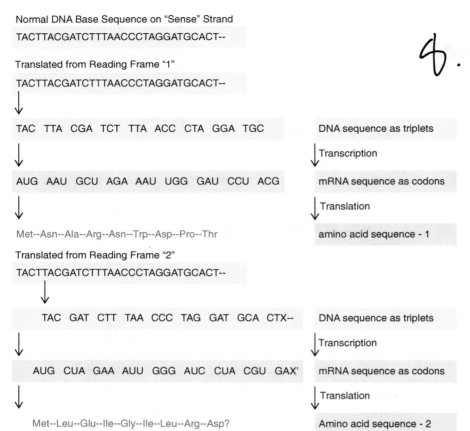

Normal DNA Base Sequence on "Sense" Strand

TACTTACGATCTTTAACCCTAGGATGCACT--

Translated from Reading Frame "1"

TACTTACGATCTTTAACCCTAGGATGCACT--

↓

| TAC | TTA | CGA | TCT | TTA | ACC | CTA | GGA | TGC | DNA sequence as triplets |

↓ Transcription

| AUG | AAU | GCU | AGA | AAU | UGG | GAU | CCU | ACG | mRNA sequence as codons |

↓ Translation

Met--Asn--Ala--Arg--Asn--Trp--Asp--Pro--Thr   amino acid sequence - 1

Translated from Reading Frame "2"

TACTTACGATCTTTAACCCTAGGATGCACT--

↓

| TAC | GAT | CTT | TAA | CCC | TAG | GAT | GCA | CTX-- | DNA sequence as triplets |

↓ Transcription

| AUG | CUA | GAA | AUU | GGG | AUC | CUA | CGU | GAX' | mRNA sequence as codons |

↓ Translation

Met--Leu--Glu--Ile--Gly--Ile--Leu--Arg--Asp?   Amino acid sequence - 2

Figure 13.9 Translation from Different Reading Frames. When a base sequence in mRNA is read as codons, a place along the mRNA must be chosen as the starting codon. This choice establishes a "reading frame". As can be seen from the sequences of amino acids, different start points can generate two different protein products from the same DNA sequence.

But if the genome is so elegant in design, the product—the cell itself—turns out to be an utterly masterful invasion machine. It invades carefully by means of **chronic** infection without killing its host. It is a powerfully facile parasite.

The species *M. genitalium,* in particular, sports a highly adapted **tip structure** that always points forward (see Figure 13.7). The tip's precise arrangement of external **adhesin** proteins and internal filament enables the cell to glide swiftly forward, attach firmly to the surface of human **epithelial** cells, and on occasion, to burrow inside host cells, thus evading the host immune system that is searching for them. The recognition abilities of the host's immune system, however, have been anticipated through an entirely different strategy. External tip structure proteins as well as other surface proteins in *M. genitalium* come in a variety of surface shapes! A total of 5% of its tiny genome is committed to coding for different versions of external tip structure proteins (see Figure 13.10). This wardrobe of tip protein genes is coupled to an ingenious switching mechanism that allows any of the variant adhesion gene copies to be expressed in any individual cell. In this way, a fairly small population of invading *M. genitalium*

cells can deftly evade much of the immunological weaponry of the host organism. But the variation is not limited to this one species of mycoplasma. Different, less related species of *Mycoplasma* have tip structures with adhesin surface proteins specific for other species of organisms from man to flies to flowers. It appears that different species of genus *Mycoplasma* exist that recognize and infect widely differing species of host organisms. Early workers in the 1980s described this organism as **degenerate** because of its small genome size and

chronic—a condition or disease that recurs through time; usually of less severity than a sudden, acute condition or disease.

tip structure—a morphologic region on the anterior region of some mycoplasmas; used to adhere to host cells and for motility.

adhesin—a biomolecule, usually a protein on the surface of a cell or structure that enables it to fix itself firmly to the surface of some other structure or host cell.

epithelial—of or referring to a cell or group of cells (tissue) that covers either an interior or exterior surface of an organ or individual.

degenerate—in reference to a cell, a biological structure or individual organism whose supposed evolutionary ancestors were larger, more complex or more well adapted.

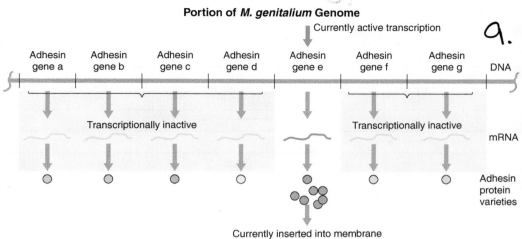

Portion of *M. genitalium* Genome

Currently active transcription

| Adhesin gene a | Adhesin gene b | Adhesin gene c | Adhesin gene d | Adhesin gene e | Adhesin gene f | Adhesin gene g | DNA |

Transcriptionally inactive   Transcriptionally inactive

mRNA

Adhesin protein varieties

Currently inserted into membrane

Figure 13.10 Adhesin Gene Expression. The genome of *M. genitalium* has a variety of adhesin protein genes each of which binds selectively to human epithelial tissue. The adhesin protein surfaces are distinct enough immunologically so that the host responds to only the one currently being placed in the mycoplasma membrane. If a cell switches to a different adhesion protein, then the host immune response is temporarily evaded.

its apparent genetic relatedness to cells with larger genomes. Subsequent discoveries are rendering the degeneracy concept an evolutionary simplism. It would help our hypothesis if the smallest independent cell we could find also happened to be, functionally, the most crude. Yet those larger bacterial cells to which *M. genitalium* seems genetically related lack the elegantly crafted tip structure with its interchangeable surface proteins—a marvelous combination of movement, attachment, and invasion functions.

We have examined the mycoplasmas in some detail here for a singular reason. Although we can guess that natural selection might have attempted to generate life using fewer, less elegant genetic sequences, we have no right to expect that a *free-living* cell can operate on fewer than the 470 highly functional and meticulously interrelated genes of *M. genitalium*. Somehow, natural selection must fashion existing, available molecules into a life-form of comparable integrity. Our hypothesis is beginning to sweat a bit.

IN OTHER WORDS

1. Charles Darwin and his contemporaries were significantly ignorant of the challenges their theory faced at the level of organic molecules in the production of the first cell.
2. The smallest functional cell we are aware of that has some degree of independence from its host cell is *Mycoplasma genitalium*.
3. Members of genus *Mycoplasma* are parasites that have been found to live on the surface of, and in some cases within, host cells.
4. In humans, the parasites are associated with such diseases as walking pneumonia, genital tract infections, chronic fatigue syndrome, and arthritis.
5. They are osmotically fragile having no cell wall and have unusually small genomes compared to most other bacterial species.
6. High levels of design are observed in the efficiency of their overlapping genes and the elegant specificity of their tip structures with which they adhere to their host cell surfaces.
7. The structure of its rRNA suggests an ancestral relationship to much larger cells that lack its elegant tip structure.

Evolution's Starting Materials: Small Geochemicals

In an evolutionary model of origins, what molecules in an **abiotic** environment are available for such a daunting project? Geologists surmise that molecules such as CO_2, H_2O, CH_3, and NH_3 might have

been available to varying degrees (see Table 13.3). In these compounds, you may recognize that life's most important atoms are all present! That is a start.

abiotic—of or referring to anything that is nonliving; usually in reference to physical aspects of an ecosystem.

Table 13.3 Compound Availability in Conjectured Early Atmospheres.

Compounds Present	Miller-Urey-Oparin Atmosphere	Earth/Venus' Original Atmosphere*	Venus' Atmosphere Today
methane (CH_3)	high	low	none
ammonia (NH_3)	high	low	none
hydrogen (H_2)	high	low	very low
nitrogen (N_2)	none	moderately high	low
water (H_2O)	high	high	none
carbon dioxide (CO_2)	none	high	very high
oxygen (O_2)	none	very low	none

*the first stable atmosphere after initial hydrogen gas is lost by escape.

But these molecules are not all equally valuable in life's production. Many of life's most important molecules—larger by comparison than those just listed—are chemically **reduced;** that is, they have lots of loosely held electrons, which are critical to their biological role. So those small molecules above that contain oxygen are going to be less useful in constructing the biological monomers we need. The hydrogen in H_2O and the carbon in CO_2 are both highly **oxidized,** and due to oxygen's tight hold on its electrons, they just aren't going to be very reactive for the purpose of building biological things. In summary, like a building project waiting on materials, the available molecular "girders" will be too rusty to do anything constructive with them.

In the face of this potential problem, a Russian biochemist, Dr. A. I. Oparin (1894–1980) noted that **methane** (CH_3) was present in the atmospheres of some of the larger planets of our solar system (see Table 13.3). He then speculated that perhaps the early Earth's oceans and atmosphere were amply supplied with highly reduced compounds such as methane, ammonia, and hydrogen, but low in oxygen and oxides. His hypothesis led Miller and Urey to carry out their "Mars Jars" experiments—the ones described in Section 4.8. These highly touted studies made it clear that by adding continuous electrical energy to a collection of simple, reduced compounds like methane, ammonia, and hydrogen (in water), all sorts of interesting (larger) biological molecules emerged, among them amino acids, some simple sugars, and organic compounds used to build nucleotides.

But within the design of these experiments is a troubling flaw. Geochemical models of planet formation have not been able to clearly confirm that the Earth's early atmosphere was highly reducing in nature (see Table 13.3). Considerable amounts of carbon dioxide and water vapor emerge from volcanoes. Small amounts of free oxygen are generated from CO_2 by solar UV radiation. So how reducing was the early atmosphere? If workers disagree on this issue, is it good science to *assume* certain conditions were present because a particular desired result is *needed* for life to have emerged? Suppose we wished to repeat the Miller-Urey experiments, making them even more like early Earth conditions? What amounts of CH_4, NH_3, and H_2 should be present in our simulations of the early atmosphere? Less than Miller and Urey used? Then, very few organic molecules would result from our improved experiments. But if the oceans were fairly dense with these molecules our simulation would yield a mixture of organic compounds as complex as asphalt! There would be so many different kinds of organic molecules present that the few monomers that life now uses (see Figure 4.3) would never find each other.

In an effort to move away from the ambiguity surrounding early atmospheric conditions, numerous workers have suggested that life could begin under the *known* conditions surrounding deep ocean **geothermal vents** (see Figure 13.11). Reduced molecules such as CH_4 and NH_3 are abundant in the vent's environment and the high temperatures can promote

reduced—an atom whose oxidation number has been decreased (by the addition of an electron).

oxidize—to attract electrons away from; in biological systems this is often carried out by oxygen.

methane—an organic compound whose molecules are composed of one carbon atom covalently bonded to four hydrogen atoms; a fuel for cooking.

geothermal vent—a break in the deep ocean floor from which superheated water emerges; the water often contains reduced inorganic compounds.

Figure 13.11   Deep Sea Hydrothermal Vent. The superheated water emerging from these vents contains reduced compounds such as sulfides. There is a temperature gradient from the core of the black plume (60 to 460 degrees Celcius) to the surrounding ocean water (2 degrees Celcius).

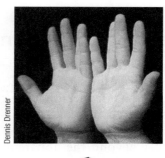

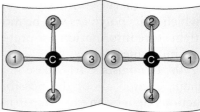

Figure 13.12   D and L Forms of Amino Acids. Recall the structure of an amino acid (Figure 4.23) Imagine the following functional groups on each molecule in this diagram: 1= a hydrogen, 2= a carboxyl group (−COOH), 3= an amine group (NH_2) and 4= an "R" group (a larger functional group unique to that amino acid). The two molecules will have the same number of atoms and the same sequence of functional groups around the central carbon atom. But the sequences are mirror images of each other and the cell's enzymes only work with amino acids whose sequence is shown to the right (the L form). D forms are useless. Yet when amino acids are synthesized in a test tube, equal proportions of these two forms are generated and compete with each other to enter a polymeric structure.

reactions resulting in amino acid formation. Even short peptide sequences of amino acids can form if reaction products diffuse between hot and colder water in a cycle. Yet the challenges cited earlier dog this theory as well. There is still nothing present in the environment to constrain the variety of monomers synthesized to the few forms found in living things. In the particular case of amino acids, each sort of amino acid can exist in two alternating arrangements of side groups. These are termed the L **forms** and the D **forms** (see Figure 13.12). Life seems to have utilized exclusively L forms. Yet both the Miller-Urey experiments and the geothermal vent simulation systems generate both L and D forms of amino acids in approximately equal amounts. Nothing in the system or its environment limits polymerization of amino

acids to only L forms, so our chosen hypothesis lacks useful constraints. It allows for the formation of everything on the shelves of our chemical stockroom and has no way of drawing together the minority of monomers used to generate a mycoplasma.

> L **and** D **forms**—two nonidentical, mirror-image forms of a molecule built around an asymmetric central carbon atom.

IN OTHER WORDS

1. The evolutionary model postulates that molecules on an early Earth such as CO_2, H_2O, CH_3, and NH_3 would have been available to form biological monomers like amino acids and simple sugars.
2. A. I. Oparin, a Russian biochemist, postulated that the Earth's early atmosphere was highly reducing in nature; this quickly led to experimental systems that successfully generated biological monomers like amino acids.
3. But the open question of how oxidizing or reducing the early Earth atmosphere and oceans were is a fundamental variable in attempting to model the origin of biological monomers and the polymers they would need to give rise to.
4. Geothermal vents are postulated to have been sites of early molecular evolution; models of this process generate biologically useful monomers as a minority proportion of a vast array of different organic products.

Evolution's Highest Hurdle: Creating and Storing Information

Let's grant our hypothesis a bit of wiggle room. We will posit a nice collection of biologically useful monomers and a few polymers that have somehow become enclosed within a concentrating boundary, like a bilayer of lipids (see Figure 13.13). How does this protocell get beyond the apparent biological randomness of its otherwise orderly chemistry to determine which of its polymers will be most useful to life and then store information for preferentially making those molecules?

In the 1990s, biologists Carl Woese and Walter Gilbert became excited about the possibility that RNA production might be an early step in molecular evolution toward life. Even small RNA molecules have a base sequence that can carry information, and some of the larger ones have catalytic properties as well: They can accelerate the rates of certain reactions much as protein-based enzymes do in modern cells. So here were two very important cell activities: both information content and catalysis bound up in a single sort of molecule! Could early protocells have started with RNA information and catalysis and later (slowly?) shifted to the current DNA-to-RNA-to-protein system of information expression (see Figure 13.14)? As the modeling of an **RNA world** progressed, new difficulties emerged. It was soon discovered that no imaginable set of conditions would favor the production and maintenance of both the ribose sugar and the nitrogen base components needed for assembling the nucleotide monomers (see Figure 13.15). But one can't generate an RNA polymer without constituent monomers. In our cells, such monomers are made in highly coordinated, enzyme-driven metabolic pathways. So although it could be theorized that a world existed in which RNA was *the* molecule of life, it is not clear how these molecules would have been generated.

12.

RNA world—a prebiotic/protobiotic cellular environment in which RNA molecules serve both informational and catalytic roles.

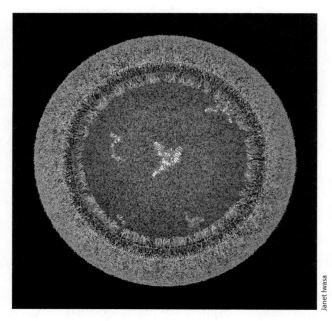

Figure 13.13 A Real Protocell. Evolving a small modern cell directly from molecules has long been thought impossible. Intermediate primitive forms called protocells "must" have existed first. The one shown here has a fatty acid membrane and RNA molecules enclosed inside. It was intelligently designed in a laboratory using presynthesized fatty acid and RNA molecules. But is nature as calculating or constraining as our protocell designers?

Janet Iwasa

Scheme for the Evolution of Information Flow in an "RNA World"

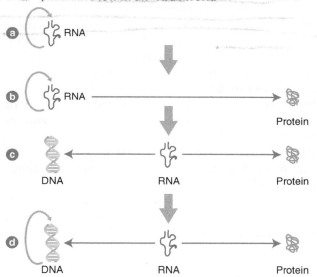

Figure 13.14 Evolution of Information Flow. We here imagine an RNA polymer that has somehow reached a size such that **(a)** it can replicate itself given enough properly structured monomers to do so! **(b)** After thousands of generations of replication, the RNA sequence begins to be utilized to also code for the amino acid sequence of some accidentally useful protein. **(c)** Eventually RNA becomes double-stranded and begins to code for DNA versions of its base sequence. **(d)** Finally, DNA becomes the archival molecule and RNA after years of successful selection for its former role is now relegated to information carrying in current information flow systems. Precious few geochemical or biochemical constraints guide speculation in this area of research.

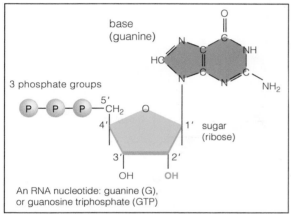

A modern ribozyme, an RNA with a catalytic,
enzyme-like activity

Laguna Design / Photo Researchers, Inc.

base
(guanine)

3 phosphate groups

P — P — P — 5'
CH₂   O

4'   1' sugar
         (ribose)

3'   2'

OH   OH

An RNA nucleotide: guanine (G),
or guanosine triphosphate (GTP)

The nucleotide: a monomeric subunit of RNA

Figure 13.15   RNA World Difficulties.

"RNA World" Difficulties

1. Imagining chemical conditions allowing complete monomer (nucleotide) formation

2. Imagining a selective force that incorporates only "good" monomers into the growing RNA chain

3. Covering all the catalytic needs of a proto-cell with the limited capabilities of RNA catalysis

4. Increasing RNA polymer length to a points where catalytic activity is even possible

5. Generating a coding role for the nucleotide sequence in RNA

6. Generating a de-coding system that allows RNA base sequence to yield amino acid sequence in proto-proteins.

7. Coupling coding and decoding to an energy source that drives synthesis forwards instead of simply destroying the whole system.

Then, as the catalytic functions of RNA came to be better understood, scientists began to realize that the handful of kinds of reactions RNAs catalyze is sorely limited compared to the thousands of reactions catalyzed by the protein-based enzymes of even the simplest cells. Worse still, little if any catalytic activity is possible in an RNA polymer until it approaches the size of 100 nucleotides in length. Since high-energy sources would threaten to degrade such polymers with time, it is difficult to imagine what forces in the environment or in the protocell would protect long RNAs from degradation until (years later) a biological function could be found for them. In many modern cells, mRNAs carry out their functions in only a matter of minutes before their purposeful degradation.

Let's grant our hypothesis more grace and imagine the prolonged existence of a large stable RNA molecule. Let's further assume that its base sequence allowed it, if given a nice supply of

nucleotides, to catalytically make new copies of itself. Let's further assume that variations on the RNA sequence would begin arising by chance or by an imperfect replication process. Even though somewhat stable, this system will need to move toward a more modern cell in which proteins begin taking over catalysis of the cell's chemical reactions—particularly those not involving the RNA itself. How could such a transition begin? How could new variant RNAs begin coding directly for amino acid sequences of proteins? In Section 7.3c, we discovered the critical role that transfer RNAs play in bringing amino acids to a ribosome so that they can be sequentially incorporated into a growing peptide chain. This is done following the sequence of codons in the mRNA. In the years since the description of the translation process, molecular biologists have been unable to discover any fruitful way in which mRNA codons could directly specify a sequence of amino acids without the intervening help of the anticodons on tRNA molecules. And the correct bonding of amino acids to tRNAs requires the specific catalytic activity of **tRNA synthetases** (see Figure 13.16). But these are proteins! Alas, we require mature proteins to begin to generate an RNA world system that will code .... for proteins. Our hypothesis requires the product of a process in order to generate the process itself.

Superimposing biological information on the base sequence of any nucleic acid, whether RNA or DNA, is a challenge that no current hypothesis successfully grapples with. So in summary, although the properties of atoms can somewhat direct the formation of organic molecules, the properties of the monomers thus formed do not suggest biologically meaningful ways to generate polymers. The modern cellular mRNA-to-protein coding system appears too complex to develop gradually. Its individual components have no selective value without the rest of the system. And apart from preexisting, encoded information in our short RNA polymers, there is no ordering principle within the developing protocellular system to give a few new peptides we generate any biologically meaningful utility.

tRNA synthetase—a protein enzyme that binds a specific class of transfer RNA molecules and binds a specific kind of amino acid to them.

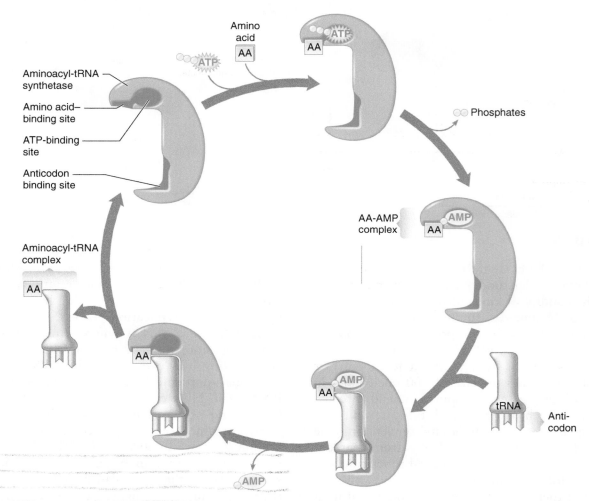

Figure 13.16 Getting tRNAs Bonded to Their Correct Amino Acid. Effective decoding of mRNA sequence into amino acid sequence requires that tRNAs carry the correct amino acid to the site of protein synthesis. Here the correct amino acid (out of 20 alternatives) is represented by a blue box. It's correct tRNA is represented by a golden icon. For precise binding to occur, a large (green, here) synthetase protein must supply an active site that precisely fits just one kind of amino acid and only its respective tRNA. RNA world models do not explain how the synthetase function is carried out apart from such complex structuring. Notice that the synthetase also nicely harvests ATP energy to drive the bonding process forward.

1. Modern RNA molecules exist that are capable of both information storage and catalytic activity; as such they have been attractive to evolutionary thinkers as a basis on which to build cellular life.
2. RNA molecule production is difficult to model in the early oceans; a variety of conditions are needed to generate the separate parts of the monomeric units.
3. RNA molecules would not be catalytic until they approach 100 nucleotides in length, a size that may have been geochemically unachievable.
4. No model exists for how RNA molecules could begin to code for simple protein molecules, yet protein catalysis is critical to the survival of modern cells.

Evolution's Final Challenge: Spatial Ordering of Biological Activity

In the 1980s and 1990s, tremendous progress was made in our understanding of the **ultrastructure** of cells. It became apparent that above the complexity level of proteins and nucleic acids, there are additional levels of functional organization to be reckoned with in structuring a cell. Let's grant still more grace to our hypothesis by assuming that the monomers Miller and Urey created are polymerized into biologically useful polymers. These polymers still need to be built into larger macromolecular structures (see Figure 1.17) that will operate within either the membranes or the

A Few Regions of *Mycoplasma* Ultrastructure

Ribosomes

1 Cell membrane
2 Cytoplasm
3 Nucleoid
4 Tip protein macro-molecular structure
5 "Bowl" or "ring" structure
6 Core filament structure

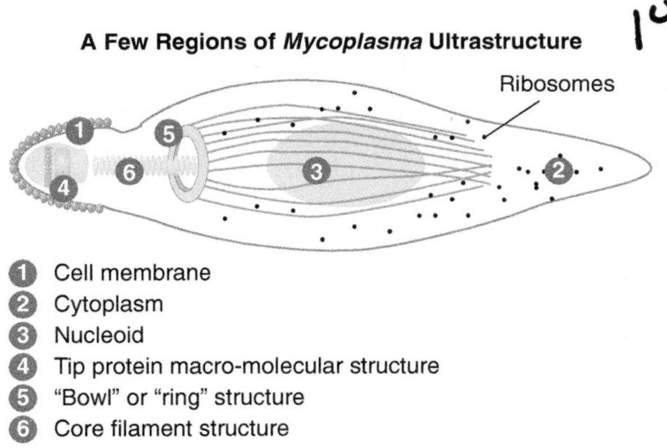

Figure 13.17 A Few Regions of *Mycoplasma* Ultrastructure. When a new protein is synthesized on a ribosome, information must be included that controls the final cellular location of the protein. For example, adhesin proteins must reach the surface of the cell membrane. Apart from such positional information, the protein is of no use to the cell. There must be simultaneous evolution both of the structure and of the spatial location and orientation of the final product. This must be accomplished using randomly introduced changes in an early, error-fraught coding system.

cytoplasm of the evolving protocell. In our "simple" *M. genitalium,* the tip structure confronts us with this sort of challenge (see Figure 13.17). The adhesin proteins translated from mRNA in the cell cytoplasm have at least three functional constraints on them. First, as indicated previously, they must be biologically useful; they must have a tertiary structure that attaches neatly to surface molecules on host cells. But second, they must find their way to the cell surface, where they must congregate (or co-assemble?) not just anywhere but at the leading end of the tip structure itself. Third, they must associate properly with other surface lipids and proteins adjacent to them. If any one of these constraints is not satisfied, for example, if the adhesin protein simply floats around in the cytoplasm, it is worthless to the cell.

Similarly, the proteins that compose the dense rod in the core of the tip structure have no value whatever to the cell by themselves. They must have a tertiary structure (see Section 4.5) that attracts them into (and stabilizes them within) a macromolecular rod-like filament. It is the filament that contributes to the shape of the tip structure and the motility of the entire cell. In this case, the cell has to position its translational machinery to generate rod proteins internally and near the site where the rod is being built.

Is it possible that a single polypeptide chain with some future potential use within the tip's core filament may have initially evolved to serve some other unrelated, simpler function (see Figure 13.18)? Then, at a later time, its structure evolves further and accidentally becomes a nicely fitting, repeat component of the core filament's repeating structure? This is

ultrastructure—biological structures within a cell that are larger than polymeric molecules but too small to be seen with bright-field (light) microscopes.

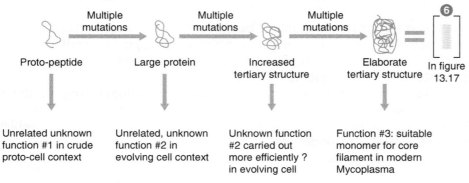

Suggested Evolution of a Core Filament Monomeric Protein

Proto-peptide → Multiple mutations → Large protein → Multiple mutations → Increased tertiary structure → Multiple mutations → Elaborate tertiary structure = In figure 13.17 ⑥

Unrelated unknown function #1 in crude proto-cell context

Unrelated, unknown function #2 in evolving cell context

Unknown function #2 carried out more efficiently ? in evolving cell

Function #3: suitable monomer for core filament in modern Mycoplasma

Figure 13.18 Suggested Evolution of a Core Filament Monomeric Protein. A primitive sequence of amino acids is conjectured to yield a crude peptide of modest selective value to a proto-cell. Over the course of multiple random mutations, the peptide evolves into a larger protein whose structure happens to fit it better for some new function that our hypothesis is unable to predict. Eventually accumulation of size and alteration results in a protein that happens to serve elegantly as a monomer in the structuring of the core filament labelled in Figure 13.17.

possible to imagine, but if our hypothesis is unable to predict what that prior, simpler unrelated function might have been, then it is disappointingly weakened.

As early as 1973 the sort of informational obstacles discussed so far began to appear overwhelming to the noted DNA biochemist Francis Crick. In the journal *Icarus,* he encouraged protocell modelers to just give up. He argued that the informational content of life was too high to expect such random processes to succeed. Later in 1993, he argued from **microfossils** that cellular life had existed intact for

far too high a proportion of Earth's history (by then current geological calculations; see Figure 13.19). There simply wasn't enough time for life to evolve from nonlife on this planet in the early proportion of time that was left! Also, it was just too improbable that good nucleotide polymerizing would occur

microfossil—within sedimentary rock, fossil forms of prokaryotic cells that are detectable only by microscopy.

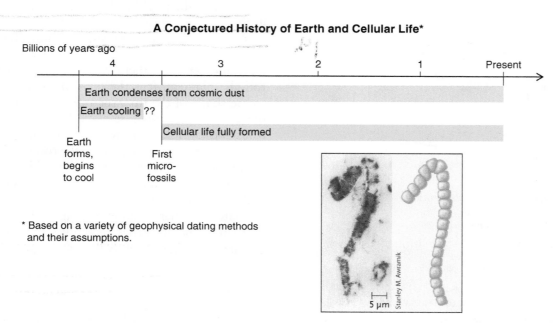

A Conjectured History of Earth and Cellular Life*

Billions of years ago

4   3   2   1   Present

Earth condenses from cosmic dust

Earth cooling ??

Cellular life fully formed

Earth forms, begins to cool

First micro-fossils

* Based on a variety of geophysical dating methods and their assumptions.

5 µm

Stanley M. Awramik

Figure 13.19 A Conjectured History of Earth and Cellular Life. Most geologists have argued that the earth is about 4.4 billion years old. Most paleontologists who study fossil forms of life argue that cellular life was intact and functioning 3.5 billion years ago. This would leave at the most 1 billion years for life to form from biomonomers if very little time is allowed for earth's surface to cool. Francis Crick argued that this time frame remaining for life's spontaneous formation on earth was overwhelmingly insufficient.

with any oxygen around. What was Dr. Crick's conclusion regarding the origin of life? He had none. Instead, he argued that life was seeded on this planet as a small variety of cellular forms by a civilization of life-forms apparently superior to us. He and his associate, Leslie Orgel, gave this concept the romantic name **directed panspermia**. It attempts to grant legitimacy to evolution of multicellular life-forms on planet Earth while throwing the more challenging *cellular* design problems back onto a remote society of designers we have not yet otherwise encountered. (We might hope that this advanced society would also understand our biological and social dilemmas without placing moral constraints on the ultimate products of their cellular designs!)

In conclusion, our hypothesis that cellular life could arise from standard chemical reactions between geologically available molecules appears adequate to generate an enormous variety—indeed an excessive variety—of potential chemical monomers of life. And it is certainly simpler than bringing in a supreme Designer. But it is too simple. It lacks a fundamental ordering principle that could (1) select appropriate monomers from an ultracomplex organic slime, (2) drive and protect polymer formation without simultaneous polymer degradation occurring, and (3) give biological meaning to the random polymers thus generated. It cannot take us to the complexity required for a simple, independent, cellular life-form. Too much art is present in a mycoplasma. To return to our art analogy, nature has the ability to generate a vast variety of colored pigments, graphite, silver, and chalks. And at one

Figure 13.20 Ascribing equine nobility to an omnipotent Designer seemed reasonable to Leonardo. By Darwin's day, the mood had changed.

level, that is all that Leonardo's famous horse drawings were: simple pigments. But the glory of the art comes from the minds of the Designer of the subject and the renderer of the work (see Figure 13.20).

directed panspermia—the concept that generative life-forms have been seeded on this (or another) planet by the purposeful actions of intelligent beings.

IN OTHER WORDS

1. Cells do not survive simply by making proteins. They must get these proteins to their proper location within the ultrastructures of the cell. This requires additional information.
2. An adhesin protein in *Mycoplasma genitalium* must be successfully transcribed and positioned in a specific portion of the cell membrane in order for it to have any functional value at all to the cell.
3. It is possible to imagine that a primitive form of the adhesin molecule had some other, unrelated, simpler function in an earlier cell, but our hypothesis is incapable of suggesting what that function might have been.
4. In order to sidestep the difficulties inherent in showing how cellular life evolved, Crick and Orgel postulated that directed panspermia had occurred—primitive but functional cells were seeded on this planet by superior beings capable of such behavior.
5. The hypothesis that random generation and assembly of biological molecules could produce a functioning cell is simplistic; it does not account for the information required to structure a cell.

The naturalistic hypothesis for the origin of life is clearly preferable scientifically because it is so elegantly simple and unifying. The geophysical world just naturally yields useful organic molecules, which then assemble into the polymers and higher structures that form a living cell. We have appreciated the simplicity of the hypothesis but have struggled much with its adequacy. We now bring it to a new arena of the biological world. Suppose that information-rich genomes already exist within communities of living, reproducing cells (see Figure 13.21). This would grant us a context in which new mutations could alter genetic information reproducibly and cause predictable changes in protein structure. Natural selection could then operate on these novel products. Our question now becomes: Can our hypothesis explain the creation of structural novelty at the level of the multicellular organism?

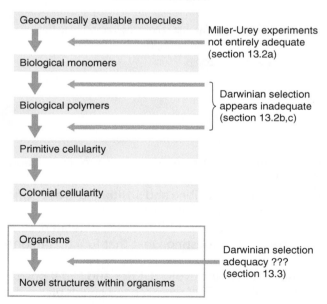

Complexity Levels at which Natural Selection can be Evaluated

Geochemically available molecules

Miller-Urey experiments not entirely adequate (section 13.2a)

Biological monomers

Biological polymers

Darwinian selection appears inadequate (section 13.2b,c)

Primitive cellularity

Colonial cellularity

Organisms

Darwinian selection adequacy ??? (section 13.3)

Novel structures within organisms

Figure 13.21 Complexity Levels at which Natural Selection can be Evaluated. We have evaluated the ability of Darwinian selection to generate biological molecules and cells. If entire organisms already exist, is Darwinian selection able to generate novel structures within these organisms as they change through time?

The Gap to Be Bridged: Invention of Novel Complex Structures

A critical role of macroevolution by natural selection is the development of new biological structures that solve problems for the evolving organism. This is a critical requirement for the generation of life's diversity. Legions of such structures—legs, kidneys, antlers, acorns, feathers, roots, eyes—adorn the living world. Macroevolution must generate all of them. Let's select as our example one specific structure that supports the function of flying in birds: the **primary flight feather.**

Modern **vertebrate** organisms can be divided into two groups: those that fly, or at least glide, and those that do not. Our hypothesis presumes that since most vertebrates do not fly, and since flying appears to be a highly specialized activity, the fliers must have evolved from nonflying ancestors, probably from animals that climbed and then glided down from trees (see Figure 13.22). Could active, flapping flight evolve in a population of dinosaurs or birds that were simply gliders?

While gliders may have profited from primary flight feathers, such feathers are absolutely essential to active flight. Therefore evolutionary change must produce them. The challenges of producing a flight feather are daunting at a variety of structural levels.

The primary flight feather contributes, along with secondary, tertiary and **covert feathers,** to an aerodynamically superior flapping wing (see Figure 13.23). The resulting **airfoil** shape handles

primary flight feather—those large feathers on the distal portions of the avian wing principally supportive of flight.

vertebrate—any animal that possesses a dorsal, medial sequence of inter-articulating bone segments; commonly referred to as a *backbone*.

covert feather—feathers that cover over other feathers smoothing the contour of the body surface for more efficient air flow.

airfoil—a three-dimensional shape designed to cause a desired response in a moving current of air, for example, an airplane wing.

Figure 13.22 An Artist's Conception of *Microrapter gui*. Found as a fossil in China, this therapod dinosaur was less than 1 meter in length and appears to have used its flight feathers to glide down from trees. Evolutionary thinkers believe that some common ancestor of this organism and of modern birds made the first use of flight feathers for gliding.

Portia Sloan

structures that appear optimized for flying (see Figure 13.24d). Both the macroscopic shape of the feather and its microstructure contribute independently to its powerful ability to bear aerodynamic load. The **proximal** part of the feather's shaft, the **calamus**, is circular, reflecting the **sheath** in which the feather developed. But the **distal** part of shaft, the **rachis**, has a curved and ribbed rectangular cross-sectional shape that's better able to bear the stress of the bird's mass (see Figure 13.25). The central shaft of the feather has a lengthy, uniform array of **barbs** distributed to either side. But a microscopic look reveals more intricate patterns.

air flow so elegantly that critical aspects of it are copied by aircraft designers. For example, engineers use carefully crafted slots within their wing designs to improve stability during flight through zones of high air turbulence. In such turbulence, the bird's wing and tail feathers elegantly create corresponding air channels by slightly pivoting critical feathers using tendons to which the feathers are attached.

A cursory observation of feather anatomy reveals a complex arrangement of **keratin**-based

keratin—light, fibrous, sulfur-containing proteins contributing most of the structure of hair, nails, and feathers.

proximal— in anatomy, located close to the central, internal surfaces of a body.

calamus—the rounded, proximal (lower) portion of the shaft of a feather, usually containing no barbs.

sheath—in living systems, a thin layer of cells or tissues, or that which covers or protects an underlying structure.

distal—far from; in anatomy, characterizing structures that are far removed from the central, medial portion of a body or form.

rachis—in compound leaves or feathers, a central shaft that supports leaflets or barbs extending laterally from its surfaces.

barb—a branch that extends laterally from the rachis or shaft of a feather; a shaft in its own right that supports smaller extensions called *barbules*.

Figure 13.23 Feathers on the Whimbrel (Numenius phaeopus). This is a shore wader bird that searches in mud and sand for tasty invertebrates. Their flight feathers are critical to their seasonal long distance migrations.

Feathers on the Whimbrel (*Numenius phaeopus*)

Arthur Morris/Corbis

Covert feathers

Primary flight feathers

Secondary feathers

Tertiary feathers

Down feathers

Tail feathers

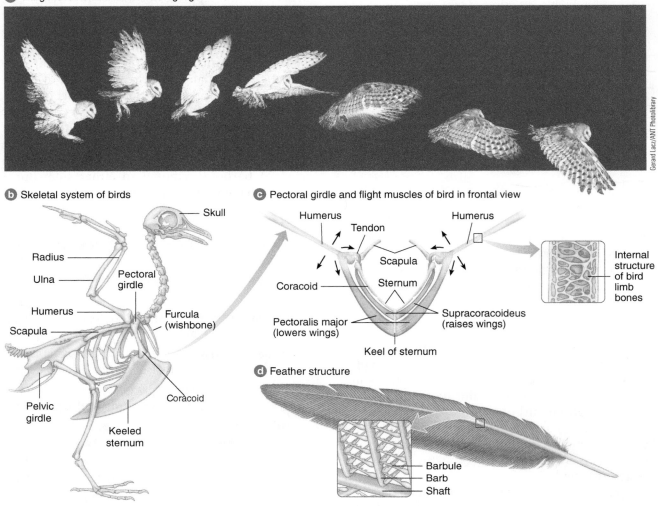

a Wing movements of an owl during flight

Gerard Lacz/ANT Photolibrary

b Skeletal system of birds

- Skull
- Radius
- Ulna
- Pectoral girdle
- Humerus
- Scapula
- Furcula (wishbone)
- Pelvic girdle
- Keeled sternum
- Coracoid

c Pectoral girdle and flight muscles of bird in frontal view

- Humerus
- Tendon
- Humerus
- Scapula
- Coracoid
- Sternum
- Pectoralis major (lowers wings)
- Supracoracoideus (raises wings)
- Keel of sternum
- Internal structure of bird limb bones

d Feather structure

- Barbule
- Barb
- Shaft

Figure 13.24 Elements of Flight Design in Birds. **(a)** time lapse still frames of a bird in flight, the flapping wing provides both lift and forward propulsion. **(b)** the skeletal system of a bird. Note the unusual depth and shape of the sternum. **(c)** flight muscle arrangement, the larger pectoralis muscles produce the downstroke (power stroke), the supracoracoideus returns the wing to the raised position. **(d)** feather flexibility and air resistance is based on an intricate interlocking of barbules by means of tiny hooklets just visible in this diagram as bumps along the (blue) barbules.

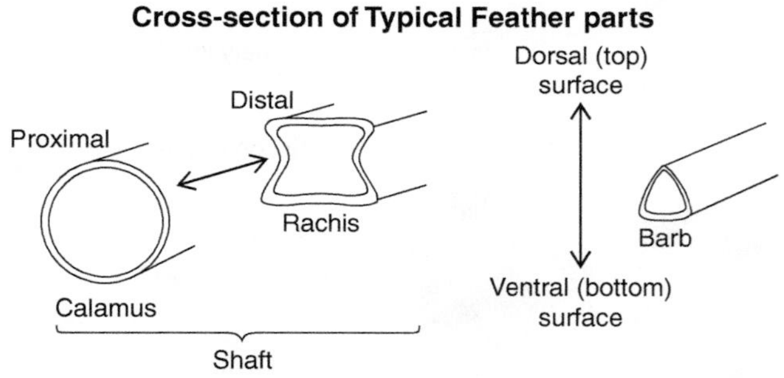

Cross-section of Typical Feather parts

- Proximal
- Distal
- Rachis
- Calamus
- Shaft
- Dorsal (top) surface
- Barb
- Ventral (bottom) surface

Figure 13.25 Typical Cross-sections of Feather parts. The calamus or shaft of the feather modifies its shape as it lengthens into the rachis during development.

Between the barbs, extending laterally from them, is a fine, double-layer meshwork of thousands of crisscrossing **barbules**. These are systematically and repeatedly attached to each other by uniformly structured **hooklets** that grab onto

barbule—small keratinous extensions from the lateral surfaces of barbs; structures that impede the flow of air through a flight feather.

hooklet (or barbicel)—a small curled projection from a barbule surface that latches into the groove or ridge on the surface of an adjacent barbule; holds the barbs of a feather into a closed planar structure.

Figure 13.26 Bird Preening. The point of the beak is run between barbs of a feather, re-aligning and re-attaching feather barbules to each other.

inversely shaped ridges on adjacent barbules (see Figure 13.24d). The barbule's shape in cross section contributes to a structure that limits airflow through the feather during the bird's powerful down stroke. Yet the same structure allows air through the feather in the upstroke, thus increasing lift. The activities of fliers frequently disrupt the integrity of the barbules' hooklet and ridge system, compromising the feather's ability to support flight. Such feather surface breaks are periodically repaired, however, by a combing action of the bird's bill during **preening** behavior (see Figure 13.26). This involves the use of oily secretions from the **uropygial gland,** which also contains bacterial waste products that antagonize the growth of other microbes that destroy feather microstructures. This preening activity can serve all flight feathers only if a bird's neck can rotate through 180 degrees. (Yours cannot!) So a variety of avian neurological, skeletal, and glandular features are critical to the maintenance of feather structural integrity during the bird's lifetime.

Of all the proteins that could be used to make a feather, keratin has a high specific strength for its mass. The secondary structure of keratin protein in feathers takes the form of β-pleated sheets (see Section 4.5), which contain many hydrogen bonds in their structure. In flight feathers, these proteins are further heavily cross-linked using **disulfide bonds.** The result is a protein-based infrastructure with a very low ratio of mass to tensile strength. Along the rachis of a flight feather, the midregion, which absorbs the most torsional stress, is where the alignment of keratin molecules is most systematic and disulfide bonding is most dense. So at the molecular level, a bird's feather is optimally arranged for flying.

Keratin proteins are organized at higher levels into fibrils and fibers (see Figure 13.27). The fibers that comprise the barbules appear very similar to the fibers that compose the walls of the rachis. There appears to be a unit structure in the feather that is combined in various ways to form all the higher-order morphological varieties of feathers. But how does this higher-order structuring happen?

To understand what natural selection must build for us here, flight feather structure is an important

preen—in birds, the activity of drawing the bill along the space between feather barbs reestablishing hooklet and ridge attachments and thus the integrity of the feather surface.

uropygial gland—structure in the base of the avian tail that secretes an oil used for preening and/or waterproofing the feathers.

disulfide bond—a covalent bond formed between two sulfur atoms that helps stabilize the secondary structure of a protein molecule.

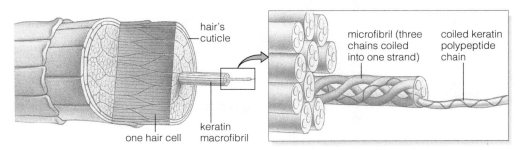

Figure 13.27 Keratin Fibers. This figure shows the multiple levels of organization of α – keratin in cells of a human hair. Notice how the cell's entire interior is consumed with keratin polymer. β- keratin in feather keratinocytes also fills feather cells at their point of "death" and has these multiple levels of organization. The polypeptide chain shown at the right is where millions of hydrogen bonds per macrofibril help to stabilize the protein's secondary structure.

but insufficient consideration. A sense of the breadth of the project is better understood by asking how a flight feather develops from the wing surface. How are the keratin fibers elaborated and how is a flight feather manufactured from it? It results from the activity of a variety of genes working within the context of a developing wing structure. Thickenings, or **plaques,** form on the wing **epidermis** at places where feather origins would be optimal for flight. These epidermal thickenings induce a response in the underlying **dermal** layer (see Figure 13.28a). A series of induction events (see Section 9.1b) result in the production of a tube-like **follicle** consisting

plaque—a localized thickened area or patch on a surface such as the skin.

epidermis—the outermost external layer of cells within the skin; many of the cells in this layer are already dead and soon to be sloughed off.

dermal—of or referring to the deeper, vascularized layer of the skin containing cells that divide to maintain the integrity of the skin as a surface barrier.

follicle—in avian anatomy, the skin-derived structure that gives rise to feathers.

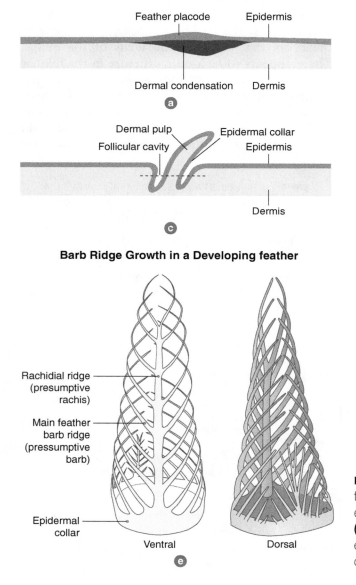

Barb Ridge Growth in a Developing feather

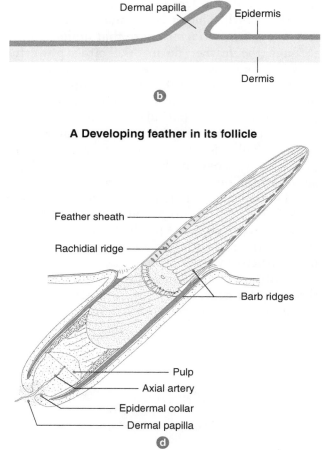

A Developing feather in its follicle

Figure 13.28 Development of a Bird Feather. **(a)** Initial plaque stage in the formation of a feather papilla. **(b)** emergence of a feather papilla from the epidermal surface **(c)** papilla in initial stage of follicle formation **(d)** a growing feather inside its follicle with the fusing of barb ridges not yet evident. **(e)** diagrams a helical pattern of barb ridge growth from the epidermal collar. Fusion sites of barbs to form the rachis are shown.

of two, now separate epidermal layers, the outer one of which will form a **socket wall** for containing and guiding the growing feather. The inner epidermal layer will form a **collar** that gives rise to the feather itself. The dermal **pulp** in between the two epidermal layers is nicely positioned to supply nutrients that will both support the cells generating the feather and supply the pigments that will color the feather (see Figure 13.28b).

Within the collar of the follicle, feather-generating cells, or **keratinocytes**, proliferate and are induced to begin generating massive quantities of the protein β-keratin. As successive keratinocytes develop, they push older layers of cells out of the follicle to begin further steps in development. There appears to be some prognostic wisdom in this process. As these cells differentiate further, they are moving further away from the dermal pulp at the follicular base (see Figure 13.28c). This isolation slowly causes the migrant cells (which are fluid-filled and heavier) to die out leaving the lighter deposited keratin in their place.

Growth from the upper edge of the collar is differential. It is limited to specific loci around the collar. From these loci, barbs extend, lengthen, and grow helically around in a circle until, at their bases, they fuse at the collar's midline to form the rachis or central shaft of the feather (see Figure 13.28d). As the barbs lengthen and thicken into multiple layers of cells, a highly intricate pattern of cell death and cell proliferation laterally along the barbs results in the cutting out and formation of hundreds of tiny barbules along each feather barb. These barbules form the precisely shaped hooklets that will grab onto the ridges of adjacent barbules. But that happens only after the feather, forming as a cylinder (!), emerges entirely from the follicle and converts to a **planar**, mature feather. The entire process would be akin to a laptop computer assembling itself as it rolled along a conveyor belt. . . .

Behind this intricate process of development lie two potential resources for guiding it: genes and a preexisting structure to guide the placement of gene products. Genetic information coding for the production and deposition of β-keratin must be present. Genes controlling the timing and pattern of cell death must function at just the right times. Genes determining structural-**topological** relationships between the rachis, barbs, barbules, and the hooklet and ridge system must exist if any of this detailed microstructure is going to happen.

Leaving aside the need for supportive tendons, wing bone architecture, glandular and neurological features, we can focus on flight feather

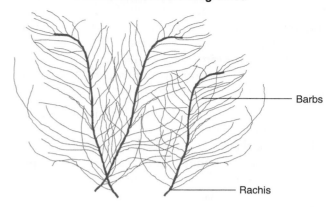

Barbs

Rachis

Figure 13.29 Fossilized Feathers Diagramed. A free-hand line drawing representation of fossilized feathers showing a rachis that is more developed than in standard down feathers. Barbs emanate from the rachis in alternating fashion. Barbules are small or absent. Evolutionary reasoning sees this as a functional intermediate between pre-down feathers and pre-flight feathers.

microstructure and ask, what did natural selection have available to it from which to fashion a flight feather? How great is the structural gap to be filled? Remnants of simpler feathers have been found in France preserved in amber, the fossilized remains of tree resin (see Figure 13.29). These feathers have a rudimentary central shaft with a plumy tuft of barbs emanating from it. Their lack of barbules and hooklets created an open structure more like modern **down feathers** that would possibly have trapped air and helped some primitive bird or small warm-blooded dinosaur to retain its body heat. The rudiments of a central shaft may have made the feather even more efficient at helping to create still air space against the body. In any case, they clearly would not support either flying or gliding behavior.

socket wall—the outer, epidermal surface of an avian follicle that contains and guides the growth of an internal prefeather structure.
collar—an inner epidermal surface within an avian follicle that divides off keratinocytes that form the body of a feather.

pulp—in avian anatomy, that internal dermal layer of cells within the follicle that is nutritive of the keratinocytes forming the feather.

keratinocyte—a cell that by its synthesis of the protein keratin contributes to the final form of the avian feather.

planar—of or referring to a flat, nearly two-dimensional surface.

topological—of or referring to the surface contour of a three-dimensional shape.

down feather—a class of avian feathers that aid homeothermic fowl to retain body heat.

Our hypothesis, then, must get the feather from this rudimentary state to a flight feather by gradually building the developmental program that generates one. Since we don't understand how genes run such a program, we can list here only a few basic advances that must occur essentially together in order to gain the flight feather:

1. The rachis must be greatly lengthened and reshaped to help support the organism's weight.
2. The barbs must now build the rachis in this way such that they themselves end up in a precise two-dimensional support grid once the feather unfolds.
3. Barbules must form with (a) the proper shape and (b) the alternating crisscross pattern that limits air flow through the feather in a perpendicular direction.
4. Hooklets and ridges that will lock barbules together will need to form with shapes sufficiently complementary to achieve that "purpose."
5. The system of hooklets and ridges must latch together in such a way that when shearing or mechanical forces pull the barbs apart, they can be counteracted by the simple preening behaviors of the bird.

The need for the simultaneous function of these elements creates a situation referred to by biochemist Michael Behe as an *irreducibly complex* system. For aerial support, a dense, uniform pattern of barbs emanating from a central rachis is worthless unless these barbs are closed into an impervious sheet by an interwoven pattern of barbules, hooklets, and ridges. What features of Darwinian evolution are available to support this multifaceted change?

IN OTHER WORDS

1. Mutation and natural selection might be expected to function more robustly in a system that already contains populations of reproducing organisms with archival genomic information.
2. Early dinosaurs may serve as an example. Can mutation and natural selection create flight feathers in a species of dinosaur?
3. Features of bird wing shape, feather distribution, and flight feather architecture suggest that this will be a major design challenge for mutation and selection.
4. Preening and flight behaviors must also be evolved simultaneously.
5. β-Keratin is elegantly arranged in higher-order polymers and fibers within feather structure.
6. Mutation and selection must generate the entire developmental process that gives rise to the flight feather in a modern bird.
7. Feather development involves changes to the skin layers, follicle production, selective growth and death of certain keratinocytes, and a whole series of induction events to generate the pattern of barbs and barbules on a feather.
8. The many concurrent structural and regulatory gene activities required to generate a feather form an irreducibly complex system.

Bridging the Gap I: Random Mutation in Primitive Feather Keratinocytes

Charles Darwin did not understand the sources of variation in the finches he observed on the Galapagos Islands. Some 80 years later, the **neo-Darwinian synthesis** rooted these variations in the allelic forms of genes discovered by Gregor Mendel (see Section 12.6). Had Mendel studied bird feathers instead of peas, he might have discovered rare variant birds having different alleles of a gene influencing barbule orientation. The different alleles might have caused barbules to project in a variety of directions. Each of these variant forms would

irreducible complexity—a level of orderliness in a system whereby the removal of one component renders the rest of the system inoperable.

neo-Darwinian synthesis—that version of Darwin's theory in which Mendelian genes are the informational basis for the variations observed between members of a population.

Hypothetical Evolution of Flight Feather Barbule Pattern

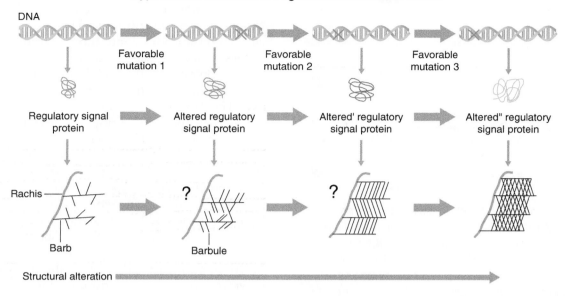

Figure 13.30 Hypothetical Evolution of Flight Feather Barbule Pattern. A sequence of mutations must occur in the gene or genes that control barbule formation sites and orientation. We don't know how many mutations or in what sequence. This figure makes the simplistic assumption that only one regulatory protein is involved. Several genes and several regulatory proteins may code for barbule orientation.

be the result of one or more mutational changes in the base sequence of the DNA in some ancestral form of the gene. In Darwinian thinking, the ancestral form of the gene may have served some other function in another organism. But in flight feather production, several new mutations are needed at specific sites in the gene so that it can begin to direct barbule projection in an alternating pattern that will support flight (see Figure 13.30). How are these mutations to be generated?

Our hypothesis lacks an ordering mechanism at this point! It asserts that mutations occur infrequently and randomly along the sequence of our gene in question. Randomness is a critical concept here. By it we mean that given the location of a single mutation along our gene sequence, there is no way known to science to predict where the *next* mutation will occur. Some hopeful evolutionary thinkers are quick to take advantage of science's limitations here. They argue that science cannot show mutations to be random in any ultimate sense. Some force or Being we haven't understood may actually be controlling when and where needed mutations are occurring. Such **theistic evolutionary** thoughts are an appeal to design that lies outside the scope of the neo-Darwinian synthesis;

it is an option Darwin would not have taken. He spoke of variations as entirely random because, for him and his modern proponents, design comes in at the level of natural selection—a later step in the process.

But how could random mutations be useful in generating a flight feather? Our hypothesis assumes that most mutations will be harmful; they will tend to degrade in some measure a system that has shown some degree of success in nature. Many mutational studies have taught us several features of the character of mutational change:

1. The vast majority of harmful mutations are only very slightly harmful, with many mutations having little or no effect at all (see Figure 13.31).
2. However, genes coding for enzymes have taught us that as the number of random mutations in *a single gene* increases from one to two in number; the result is virtually always a deterioration of function.

theistic evolution—the concept that the history of life is a long sequence of selection events operating on a corresponding sequence of Divinely chosen mutations in the genetic information.

Effect of Mutations on the Individuals of a Population

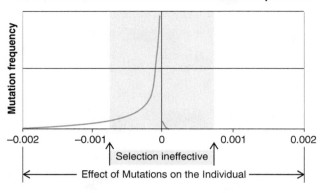

Figure 13.31 Effect of Mutations on the Individuals of a Population. On the X axis, a 0.00 means the mutation has no effect. A value of −1.0 would represent absolute lethality—death from the mutation. Notice that a very small proportion of mutations can be very harmful (off the graph to the left). Most mutations, however, have very slight harmful effects, not easily removed by selection. A very tiny fraction have a slightly beneficial effect on the population but selection is generally ineffective at "finding" these rare mutations. This graph assumes that no long term radical change is occurring in the environment.

3. It is clear that mutations do not, in one step, create whole new informational sequences that now perform a needed function. This is why our hypothesis conservatively defines a rare mutation as "good" if it just enables its possessor to survive and reproduce better than the nonmutated form.

For example, consider a population of bacteria that suddenly finds itself in the presence of a brand new "knock 'em dead" **antibiotic**. The antibiotic is (unwittingly) transported into the bacterial cell, where it does its killing (see Figure 13.32). Occasionally, a mutation event in the population generates an individual cell whose transport protein is now defective. The antibiotic can no longer be transported in! This cell and its offspring will be resistant to the antibiotic. Successful reproduction in the presence of the antibiotic causes this minor, new subpopulation of cells to almost entirely replace the original population of transport-enabled cells. No new favorable bacterial gene sequence has been created. Rather, a gene coding for a transport protein has been altered so that what it transports no longer includes the antibiotic. There has been a loss of function. If, as a result, the antibiotic is now no longer effective and therefore no longer used, the new nontransporting bacterial population will be disadvantaged in its normal transport functions compared to the original nonmutant competitors and will now become a minor subpopulation of the bacterial strain in question.

The same conclusion has been reached in the plant world (see Figure 13.33). After X-rays and

antibiotic—a chemical from a natural source or from a laboratory that limits the growth of or kills microbes, particularly bacteria.

Selective Effect of an Antibiotic

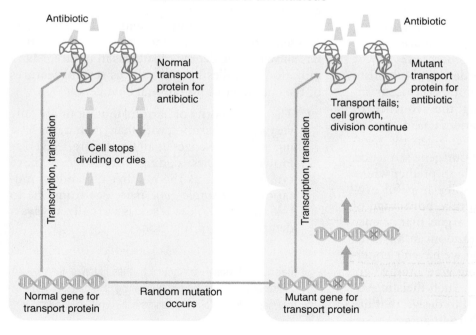

Figure 13.32 Selective Effect of an Antibiotic. An antibiotic in therapeutic concentrations within a microbes's environment generates a radical alteration in the effect of natural selection on that microbe. Such a change would be very rare in nature where antibiotics exist at much lower concentrations. The normal microbial genome is now deadly. Any mutation that interrupts or minimizes the effect of the antibiotic will confer survival value on its cell even if the mutation is somewhat harmful in the absence of the antibiotic.

Figure 13.33 Plant Breeding. Many mutagenesis experiments have been done on corn plants. X-rays and mutagenic chemicals are virtually always destructive of existing gene sequences. Sometimes a weaker expression of a gene is desirable for agricultural or nutritional purposes. For this purpose, a mutation can often be found. But such a mutation never results from the addition of new information.

mutagenic chemicals were discovered to greatly enhance mutation rates, huge experiments were run by plant breeders in an attempt to discover new favorable mutations that could be bred into existing strong stocks of plants. After decades of such efforts, not one mutation was recovered that represented an improvement by the addition of information. At one point, a mutation was discovered in corn plants that made the kernels more desirable for cattle feed. But this mutation ruined a biochemical process that occurs in natural corn strains.

The vinegar fly *Drosophila melanogaster* teaches us the same lesson. Flies from a population maintained at the University of California for over 600 generations were continually selected for decreased development time (from egg to adult stage). After a 20% decrease in development time was achieved, individual genomes were searched for new, mutated sequences that could have contributed to the decrease. Considerable recombination occurred between existing alleles of a number of genes, but it was difficult to demonstrate the production of any new information—new gene sequences—that contributed to decreased development time.

To create flight feathers from down feathers, a new process is needed to cut barbs and barbules from follicular collar cells like cookies from rolled-out dough. For this process, new segments of information are needed that will influence cell reproduction, movement, differentiation, and death. Since mutation alters only preexisting genetic sequences, it is necessary to imagine that the new set of information is hidden in a variety of more rudimentary sequences that code for other unknown and unrelated functions. A short random sequence of mutations must then convert each segment of information to a form that would help guide feather development (see Figure 13.34).

mutagenic—any process or substance that causes changes in informational molecules such as DNA or RNA.

Mutations Needed to Generate Flight Feathers

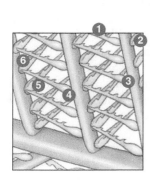

1. Gene sequence matching barbule length (given its orientation) to space between barbs

2. Gene sequence coordinated with gene sequence #1 above that controls orientation of the barbule as it grows from lateral aspect of barb; necessary for both sides of the barb.

3. Gene sequence(s) controlling the shapes of the barbule at base and at tip.

4. Gene sequence controlling repetitive frequency of barbules along barb length by governing the cell death events along barb surface.

5. Gene sequence(s) controlling hooklet shape and frequency along each barbule.

6. Gene sequence modifying barbule surface to generate ridges specific for anchoring hooklet structure.

Figure 13.34 Mutations Needed to Generate Flight Feathers.

Then these new sequences must become coordinately regulated in a new, developmental network that generates flight feathers! Our hypothesis cries out at this point for biological guidance in the production of potentially useful mutations, but randomness is the only response nature can provide.

IN OTHER WORDS

1. In the neo-Darwinian synthesis, the source of structural and functional variations in a population result from variant forms of alleles at specific genetic loci (genes).
2. The synthesis requires that these variations—or mutations—are entirely random; no outside intelligent force guides or directs their frequency or site of appearance.
3. The vast majority of mutations in a population of organisms are slightly harmful or of no effect whatever.
4. Mutations do not generate whole new elements of information; they simply alter existing elements of information.
5. Under rare environmental conditions, altered genetic elements may be of positive value to a population of organisms.

Bridging the Gap II: Natural Selection in Primitive Feather Keratinocytes

If random mutational events along a DNA sequence in a particular reptile or bird happen to generate novel information that improves the reproductive capabilities of an individual, then Darwin described a process that would find that individual and hyper-represent its genes in subsequent generations. That process is **natural selection**. Richard Dawkins, a noted neo-Darwinian, describes natural selection as a process in which genes that program embryos to develop successfully into adults are protected reproductively in the gene pool at the expense of genes that fail at this. This description places the onus for producing genes capable of developing an organism on the process of random mutation. It then depends on natural selection to find those rare genes among a multitude of trial mutation events. Natural selection has been studied in microbial cultures, fly population cages, and a variety of other settings both in the laboratory and, more realistically, in the field (see Figure 13.35). Certain characteristics have emerged that help us to better understand its capabilities and limitations. Let's consider its essential features.

First, natural selection is limited to operating on phenotypes of individuals. Much as the population geneticist would wish otherwise, natural selection has no way of operating on individual genes. A rare, truly excellent new mutation may be lost to the future of the species if it arises in an individual whose slightly weak variations in other genes offset the good effect of the new mutation (see Figure 13.36a). Recall that harmful mutations have a higher frequency than beneficial ones. The effects of a rare, high quality mutation combined with those of several slightly harmful gene mutations will tend to cancel each other out! This is particularly a problem if a new helpful mutation emerges that is linked genetically on a chromosome where several harmful genes happen to reside (see Figure 13.36b): Selection must act on the block of genetic information because a rare recombination event would be required to separate them (see Section 12.7) Thus natural selection is an averaging force operating on the entire genome of the individual whose overall fitness determines its reproductive potential. If, in the avian genome, a new gene evolves that might help differentiate barbules from the lateral surfaces of a barb, finding and keeping it would be somewhat like trying to select for and retain a highly effective soldier based on the performance of an army of a million men.

A related problem is that a barbule-generating gene's effect is contextualized within the effects of functionally related genes—the phenomenon of epistasis we've considered earlier (see Section 12.6d). By chance, a newly mutated gene may now code for a regulatory protein with superior functional potential

natural selection—that characteristic of the environment that favors the viability and reproductive activity of one individual in a population over another.

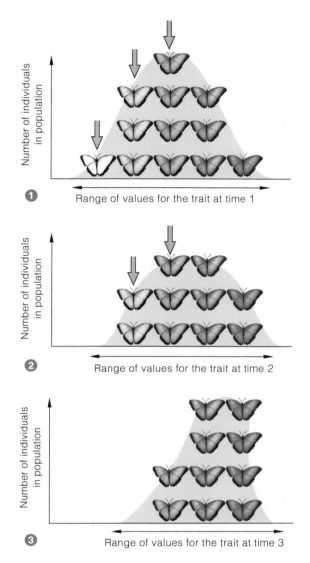

Figure 13.35 Example of Natural Selection. Suppose a new mutation occurs in a population of butterflies that results in increased pigment production in wings. Suppose also that the environment for this population contains an increasing number of shaded areas. Over a period of many seasons (times "1", "2", and "3" in the diagram, the predators will more easily locate light colored individuals for "lunch". Their effect is indicated by the orange arrows. The color distribution in the population will then shift in favor of the darker variety, causing a change in the appearance of the species: evolution has occurred. Micro-evolution to be precise.

Number of individuals in population — Range of values for the trait at time 1

Number of individuals in population — Range of values for the trait at time 2

Number of individuals in population — Range of values for the trait at time 3

of its own, but that protein may still function poorly when required to cooperate epistatically with other existing gene products (see Figure 13.36c). For example, our new barbule-differentiating gene may be exactly what we need to move toward flight, but its product may function poorly with a set of

proteins that currently "roll out" down-like feathers whose value is insulation, not flight.

A second major feature of natural selection is that its power varies enormously depending on the size of the population in which it works. A very rare beneficial mutation may never increase in frequency in a small population scattered over a wide area (see Figure 13.36d). Competition under these circumstances is relaxed and individuals with harmful or neutral mutations will survive essentially as well as the new "super-beast."

Small populations (like those of mammals or many mollusks) hamper natural selection in another way. Selection is expensive even in large microbial populations. It becomes prohibitively expensive in smaller ones. Consider the antibiotic experiment that goes on in hospitals across America. The antibiotic is the major selective force in the microbe's environment. Eventually, its use reveals a rare individual that is resistant to its effects. But in order to discover this individual, trillions and trillions of bacterial cells had to die! Of course, this is what was desired. Thousands of human hosts recover from their infections in the context of this experiment. But the majority of microbes must die (see Figure 13.36e)! The same is true of our bird population. When a new gene arises in one bird that generates crude hooklets on the ends of its barbules, vast numbers of birds lacking this new mutation must die within a limited number of generations in order for the new gene to become frequent enough to be found in a bird that will undergo the *next* favorable mutation. In many populations, a high proportion of individuals dies from environmental effects that take no account whatever of the relative "feather fitness" of the individuals. An avian virus, for example, kills individual birds whether they have crude hooklets or not. So in many populations, there are actually very few individuals left that can die out or reproduce poorly just because they lack hooklets on their barbules.

A third feature of natural selection is that its effectiveness is presumed to vary with the level of functional sophistication of the organism. Selection is more effective if the organism is structurally primitive or crude because a higher proportion of random mutations will be beneficial to a system where multiple options for improvement exist (see Figure 13.36f). Although this implies that natural selection was once far more effective in natural populations than it is now, this assumption cannot be tested because in all observable organisms

Limits to Natural Selection

Figure 13.36 Limits to Natural Selection.

a New beneficial mutation occurs in an individual with a variety of slightly weaker genes at other loci.

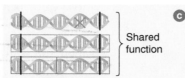

c New beneficial mutation occurs in a gene whose product interacts with two other gene products. The interaction is now poorer unless the other two genes also experience an unlikely beneficial mutation to support the improvement that is underway.

Shared function

b New beneficial mutation occurs in a chromosomal location in which it's closely linked to a somewhat harmful mutation.

d

Competition drives natural selection. The beneficial mutation in the right-hand panel will compete favorably with the weaker individuals around it. The low density population in the left-hand panel will relax selection; weaker forms will survive as well as the new mutant.

Limits to Natural Selection

Time 1   Time 2   **e**

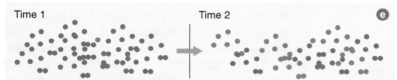

If the red individual carries a new beneficial mutation, it's increase in frequency by "time 2" will require the selective deaths of a vast number of individuals in intervening generations that are not shown here. But predation and disease also take many individuals.

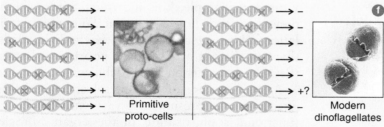

f

Primitive proto-cells

Modern dinoflagellates

New beneficial mutations are a higher proportion of total new mutations in a more primitive cell type in which more possibilities for improvement exist.

Limits to Natural Selection

Figure 13.36 (Continued)

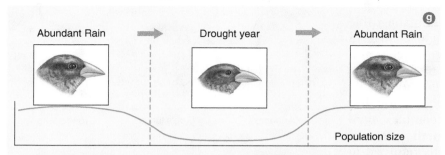

If environmental constraints (rainfall) change in a cyclic fashion, then natural selection reverses its direction and phenotypic traits simply oscillate between two extremes. The long-term result of such change is negligible.

Limits to Natural Selection

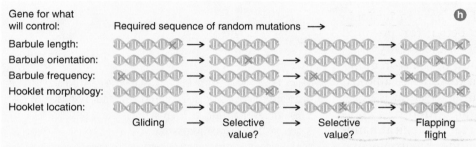

New beneficial mutations in individual gene components of a feather development system must in some way confer advantage to the individual even though other needed mutations in the system have not occurred yet.

today, elegance is so extreme and homeostasis so intrinsic that options for improvement of genetic instructions are wanting. Only a severe change in environmental conditions could favor an alteration in the modern development program that controls barb and barbule production in flight feathers. The program is so finely integrated into the bird's development and physiology that virtually any change in the genome is degradative.

A fourth feature of natural selection is its subjectivity to the complexity of the environment. Environmental complexity can neither be successfully modeled algorithmically nor sufficiently simulated in the laboratory. So virtually all selection studies are simplistic in the degree of the constancy they accord it. Selection's effects can change radically with altered weather patterns, global climatic changes, community structure (see Chapter 15), or now, human behavior. Consider the finches of the Galapagos Islands. Darwin's voyage made them famous although his interest in and understanding of

them was limited. Through the 1970s, their beak size became the subject of careful scrutiny by Peter and Rosemary Grant, a husband and wife research team from Princeton University. They happened to study the birds on Daphne Major Island during the 1977 season when a lack of rainfall there became a significant environmental stressor (see Figure 13.36g). As a result, a major food source for the finches—plant seeds—became limiting. This placed **selection pressure** on the birds. Competition for seeds was intense. The population declined to about 15% of its typical size! One result of this pressure appeared to be a slight increase in the body and beak size of an increased proportion of individuals in this smaller population.

selection pressure—any force within the environment that reduces the reproductive potential of one variety of individuals in a species over another variety.

The Grants inferred, probably correctly, that birds with thicker, larger beaks could crack open larger, tougher seed coats that were unmanageable for ordinary, smaller birds. This slight change in bird morphology came about rather quickly and encouraged the Grants to suspect that such change was indeed evolutionary and might, ultimately contribute to **speciation** within the population. But rainfall is a variable property of a complex environment. In subsequent years, rainfall increased on Daphne Major, small, fleshy seeds returned in abundance and so did the proportion of the finch population with smaller beak sizes. While natural selection undeniably brings change to populations, the complexities of the environment tend to rob it of a long-term directional quality. Selection pressure in a dinosaur population may, in a given decade, favor small mutational changes in its torso that would fit it somewhat better for powered flight. But a significant change in the variety of its prey species in a future decade may favor mutational changes that preserve a torso more adapted to climbing and gliding. Natural selection is not a constant, principled decision **algorithm** in a computer program. It is rather a real, biological handmaid of environmental vicissitude. Environmental alterations can be more easily explained than predicted, so they have a randomness to their sequence through time that saps predictive power from our attractive but simplistic hypothesis.

Finally, natural selection is **cybernetically blind.** It doesn't "see ahead" or comprehend the structural hierarchies it is required to construct. When it selects in favor of an individual whose feather barbs now have air-deflecting bumps that are the beginnings of barbules, it does not see flight as a future possibility (see Figure 13.36h). It must enable the individual with "bumpy barbs" to leave more offspring even though the bumps will not enable flight but will add mass to the bird and require more metabolic energy to synthesize. It must find a use for such projections.

This problem exists on a broader and more threatening scale because the active flier's body is adapted to flying in many other ways. Natural selection is tasked with simultaneously preparing the bone density, bone shape, musculature, respiratory, and behavioral systems for the activity of flight. Bone density must decrease radically and its internal architecture be revised to support the contrasting challenges of both flight and landing. The **keel** of the **sternum** must be deepened to support

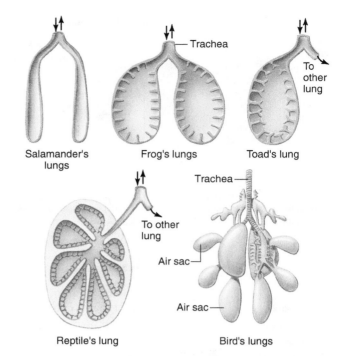

Figure 13.37   Some Vertebrate Lungs. Air flows into and out of amphibian and reptilian lungs in a reciprocal cycle of inhalation and exhalation as in humans. Avian and alligator lungs and associated air sacs allow for a sequential, "flow-through" process that avoids a large volume of residual air in the lungs and that extracts more oxygen from the ambient air. It is difficult to imagine how mutation would begin to alter the primitive reptilian lung in a dinosaur so as to produce the new more efficient air flow pattern.

stronger muscles that will flap the wings (see Figure 13.24b). The respiratory system must be reworked at its most basic structural levels because air must flow unidirectionally through it instead of cyclically as in most nonflying vertebrates (see Figure 13.37). Landing and taking-off behaviors

speciation—the formation of two new species from one by an isolating process that allows two populations of a species to become genetically distinct from each other to the point of intersterility.

algorithm—a defined sequence of steps, often repetitive that are used to solve a problem, often a mathematical one.

cybernetics—the theoretical study of how highly automatic and inter-articulated systems are controlled.

keel—in avian anatomy, the central (medial) pronounced ridge on the sternal bone of the bird where powerful flight muscles attach.

sternum—the breastbone; a compound, ventral bone to which ribs and skeletal musculature are attached.

must be integrated into the nervous system so that flight does not result in injury. Natural selection must modify all of these systems more or less simultaneously to achieve flight. Worse, our hypothesis is required to find selective value in each faltering step forward. (What is the first step in converting a cyclical respiratory process into a flow-through alternative?)

Consider again the amber-encased feathers recently discovered in France (see Section 13.3a above) that to some workers appear transitional between downy filaments and an aerodynamic, planar shape that enables flight. The feathers clearly would not themselves support flight in any way. Yet they had selective value or they wouldn't have survived. Was it improved insulation? If so, natural selection will blindly continue preserving variations that will improve the feathers' insulating role. The inability to see a radically new and useful biological function while protecting an existing one reveals a profound weakness in our chosen hypothesis.

IN OTHER WORDS

1. The process of natural selection works to increase the frequency of individuals in a population whose genetic makeup best suits them to leave the most offspring for the next generation.
2. Natural selection works at the level of the individual; it averages out the effects of harmful and rare beneficial mutations in determining which individuals survive.
3. Natural selection is more effective in large populations within small geographic areas, where competition is most intense; in sparse distributions of individuals, selection has little effect.
4. Natural selection is most effective in primitive, poorly adapted individuals in which many positive options for moving forward exist.
5. Natural selection's directional progress depends on the stability of environmental conditions; cyclical environmental changes result in cyclical directions of selection.
6. Natural selection is mindless; it does not build systems by coordinating multiple, simultaneous genetic changes. It only finds the individual that produces the most offspring under current environmental conditions.

Evaluation of the Naturalistic Hypothesis

A single, apparently simple, flight feather lying on the ground before us has confounded an hypothesis on which so much of Western thought is now based. The feather illustrates for us how Darwin's hypothesis has remained elegantly simple while the world of biology has stunned us with its emerging complexities. In regard to the vertebrate eye, biochemist Michael Behe has stated, "Although Darwin was able to persuade much of the world that a modern eye could be produced gradually from a much simpler structure, he did not even attempt to explain how the simple light sensitive spot that was his starting point actually worked." The feather constitutes a similar challenge. At the level of *gross* morphological structure it is not difficult to arrange modern feathers into a gradual series ranging from simple hair-like projections, to down feathers, to feathers with a central shaft, to fully functional flight feathers (see Figure 13.38). But as we begin to explore the developmental program that unfolds these feathers, new demands on our hypothesis emerge. What is more frightening is that behind the developmental program is a genetic regulatory network whose gene sequences and their regulated interrelationships require a vision of the flight feather that man's mind is only beginning to understand. If our hypothesis rests on two processes—mutation and selection—neither of which has a designer's mind, then, though elegant in its simplicity, Darwinism proves inadequate in its perceptivity.

Conjectured Feather Evolution

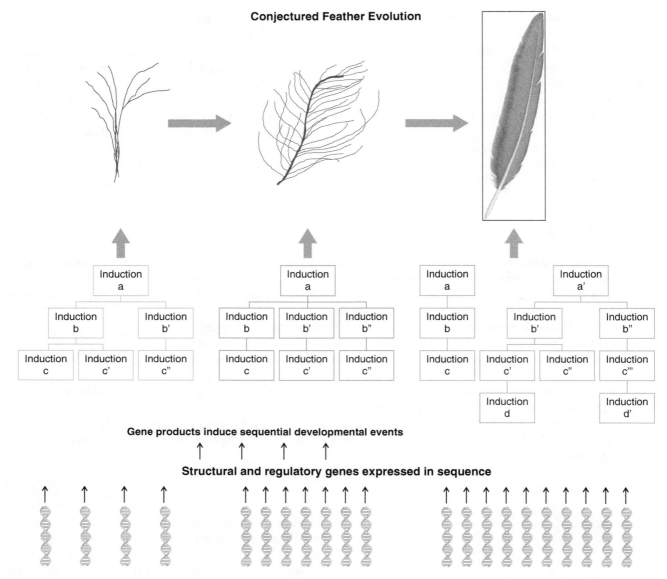

Figure 13.38 Conjectured Feather Evolution. Seemingly modest structural "advances" in feathers require corresponding advances in developmental pathways and the genetic information that supports them. Random mutation is saddled with the responsibility of generating the new information and its inter-relation to existing information.

IN OTHER WORDS

1. Nature shows us a variety of different forms of feathers. The neo-Darwinian synthesis cannot show how feathers built by a demanding developmental program can evolve from feathers built by a simpler program.

DID LIFE'S DIVERSITY INCREASE WITHOUT ARTISTRY?

We have discovered thus far that life's diversity cannot arise without deliberate forethought and design. Neo-Darwinian naturalism, in search of favorable accidents, treats morphogenesis simplistically. Yet here life is—complete with diversity! And considerable evidence exists that this diversity had a common origin. Could life have evolved this diversity by some means other than random mutation and selection? Impressive studies exist in the areas of life's history. Structural comparisons across many species of organisms fill the biological literature. Can we use either of these sets of data to establish that evolution on a grand scale *must* have occurred? In this section we will examine the fossil record and the concept of homology in order to see if they require an evolutionary origin of life.

The Cambrian Explosion

Neat phrase, isn't it? Most youthful scientists enjoy a good explosion. Explosions always have an adequate cause. Let's see if this early feature of the fossil record can talk to us about life's origins. In the eighteenth century before Darwin's synthesis began to canalize scientific thought, naturalists like William Smith and George Cuvier began to appreciate the worldwide distribution of piles of **sedimentary rock** layers and the fossils within them (see Figure 13.39a). As observations accumulated through the nineteenth century, it became clear that certain varieties of fossils tended to be associated with certain layers of rock. These were called *index fossils* and a picture of life began to emerge in which large numbers of unusual, **extinct** organisms were generally preserved in the lowest layers and more modern organisms, such as flowering plants and mammals, were found in the upper layers (see Figure 13.39b, c). These layers were gradually given names, and geologists began speculating about the amount of time required to deposit them all. Darwinists of the late nineteenth century soon made a critical assumption about life's history that the rocks themselves could never actually verify. A vertical succession of fossil forms in rocks might simply be an historically arranged deposition of separately designed organisms

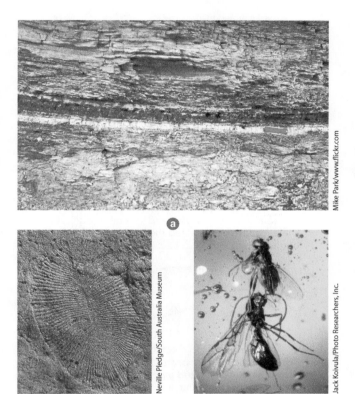

Figure 13.39 Fossils and their Milieu. **(a)** Layers of sediment under the influence of time and pressure form sedimentary rock strata such as these shown here. A red pocket knife shows us their scale of size. **(b)** A fossil of a now-extinct soft-bodied Ediacaran found in pre-Cambrian rock. **(c)** fossilized modern-looking insects trapped in coniferous resin which then hardened into amber. Fine details of the organisms's structure are captured in these rare amber specimens.

(see Figure 13.40). But Darwin's theory linked these organisms together into ancestral-descendant relationships. The older organisms gave rise to the

sedimentary—descriptive of a rock or layer of rock formed by compaction and conglomeration of sand, silt, or other particulates; often containing fossils.

index fossil—a kind of fossil form that is typically associated with a particular layer of sedimentary rock.

extinct—in reference to species of organisms, a species that no longer has living representatives.

a *Mesonychid*, an extinct terrestrial mammal, proposed to have been the ancestor of whales.

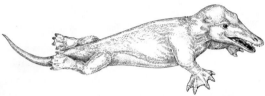

b *Ambulocetus natans*, a proposed transitional form between modern whale descendants and their terrestrial ancestors, possessed several recognizable whale features yet retained the hind limbs of its four-legged ancestors.

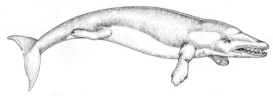

c The more recent *Rodhocetus* had flexible vertebrae that permitted a powerful dorsoventral movement during swimming.

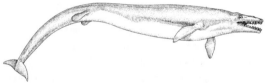

d *Basilosaurus* was more streamlined and possessed tiny nonfunctional hind limbs.

e *Balaenoptera*, the modern blue whale, contains vestiges of pelvis and leg bones embedded in its body.

D.J. Futuyma/Sinauer Associates

Figure 13.40 Origin of the Whale. A collection of fossil forms from various parts of Asia have been given their "soft parts" by artists and arranged in a single sequence as shown. Do they represent genetic continuity? Is the form at the top the ancestor of the modern whale? Or might various of them have been separately designed and then become extinct? (The figures are not drawn to a comparative scale.)

modern ones by means of mutation and selection over long periods of time.

For over 150 years now, design proponents and evolutionists have argued about the relationships of fossil organisms within this rock record. Critical to this debate is a serious deficiency of intermediate or *transitional forms* between well-characterized species. Such forms would allow evolutionists to trace out well-defined patterns along which organisms might have changed through time. But the historical nature of the science often leaves even Darwinists disagreeing with each other about whether a particular fossil form might be a transitional intermediate between two other well-studied forms or whether it is simply an evolutionary dead-end (see Figure 13.41). But in all of this debate, one feature of the fossil record places far more constraint on argumentation. It is the way in which the record begins.

Deep within the strata of sedimentary rocks is a layer of rocks and fossils that geologist Adam Sedgewick named the Cambrian formation (see Table 13.4). Cambria or Wales, in Great Britain, had many Cambrian rocks that were well exposed for study. Conventional geology concludes that they were laid down some 540 millions of years ago. Rocks *below* this layer contain a small variety of **microfossils** of bacterial and algal forms and a few soft-bodied invertebrate organisms called **Ediacarans**. But an amazing "explosion" of diversity occurs in these Cambrian rocks. Over what is assumed to be a (geologically) brief time period of 5 million years at the beginning of the Cambrian, about half of the 40 or so modern animal **phyla** just appear—Presto, Changeo—complete with **chordate** fish! Phyla are major groupings of animals

Cambrian—the name for a geological period represented by a well-characterized layer of rock that contains certain index fossils.

microfossils—shapes of microscopic size within rocks; the shapes are believed to be the remains of early bacterial or algal forms of life.

Ediacaran—an extinct group of marine invertebrate animals represented by fossils some of which are found in pre–Cambrian rocks.

phylum—one of the large major divisions of the animal kingdom; there are about 40 such divisions in the animal kingdom.

Chordate—a phylum of animals that, during some stage of their development, possess a dorsal, central cord of tissue that, in some representatives, is tough and fibrous and lends support to the organism.

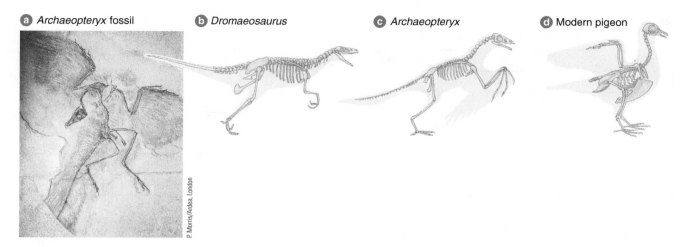

(a) *Archaeopteryx* fossil (b) *Dromaeosaurus* (c) *Archaeopteryx* (d) Modern pigeon

P. Morris/Ardea, London

Figure 13.41 "Evolution or stasis? In this figure, the fossil bird Archaeopteryx **(a)** (long viewed as a "transitional form") is pictured **(c)** between a modern bird **(d)** and Dromaeosaurus, **(b)** a small bipedal dinosaur whose forelimbs were somewhat free to evolve into wings. Did they? In this case the fossil record is of little help because both Archaeopteryx and Dromaeosauridae were present in late Jurassic rocks. So, is there genetic continuity leading from the dinosaurs through Archaeopteryx to modern birds? Or was Archaeopteryx a species that simply became extinct, with modern birds representing a separately designed group? Fossils do not decide such questions.

Table 13.4 The Conventional Geologic Time Scale as expressed in Sedimentary Rock Layers*

Eras	Periods	Time Frame	Representation organisms found
Cenozoic		66 mya – present	angiosperms, songbirds, grazing mammals, herbs, man
Mesozoic		200 mya	dinosaurs, gymnosperms, later angiosperms
Paleozoic	Permian	299 mya	many conifers, insects, mammal-like reptiles
	Carboniferous	359 mya	ferns, club mosses, amphibians, gymnosperms
	Devonian	416 mya	forests, trilobites, jawed-fishes, amphibians
	Silurian	444 mya	vascular plants, coral reefs, jawless fish, arthropods
	Ordovician	488 mya	spores of bryophytes (?), invertebrates, coral reefs, fish
	Cambrian	540 mya	worms, mollusks, arthropods, first fish, sponges, sea stars ("bang!")
Proterozoic	Ediacaran	600 mya	algae and soft-bodied invertebrates
	Early Proterozoic	2500 mya	eukaryotic (?) microfossils
Archaean		4.6–2.5 billion years ago	oldest rocks, some microfossils of prokaryotes

*mya = millions of years ago as based on radiometric dating techniques for each superimposed rock layer.

representing fundamentally distinct body plans. And this presumed sudden **radiation** of phyla occurs with no apparent transitional forms between them.

Could these observations be explained by a Darwinian model of a gradual generation of 20 new body plans from a universal common ancestor through mutation and selection? Darwin was aware of this sudden appearance of many diverse animal forms in one initial stratum of rock. He saw the potential problem for his theory. What he did not foresee was (1) that 150 years of additional fossil hunting would do little to indicate an earlier existence for any of these phyla and (2) how molecularly complex each of these body forms would turn out to be. For example, sponges—members of **phylum Porifera**—are present in Cambrian rock. Five new types of cells had to evolve just to support this simplest of animal body plans. But phylum **Arthropoda** (which includes insects) is also represented, requiring at least another 45 cell types. As we saw with feather structure,

radiation (in evolutionary theory)—a long-term process by which a single ancestral species gives rise to two or many daughter species as a result of mutation and natural selection.

Porifera—a phylum of animals consisting of sponges; the supporting skeleton is of calcium carbonate spicules or an organic material called *spongin*; the body is highly porous to currents of water.

Arthropoda—a large phylum of animals characterized by segmented bodies and appendages, an open circulatory system, and a chitinous exoskeleton; includes insects.

Table 13.5 Vertebrate Body Plans—Genome Differences. If vertebrate animals like the human and the zebrafish differ by as much as 92% of their DNA sequences, then it is unlikely that current mutation rates could generate 19 new animal phyla right at the beginning of the Cambrian Period.

Percent Differences between Genome Sequences					
genome comparison	zebrafish	frog	chicken	mouse	human
zebrafish					
frog	36				
chicken	67	62			
mouse	95	89	93		
human	92	87	91	43	

generating these cell types means evolving all of the proteins and genetic regulatory networks unique to the function of each of those cells. Let's assume for a moment the existence of just the sponges at the beginning of the Cambrian period. If we further assume a (modern) spontaneous mutation rate on the order of 1 in 1,000,000,000 base pairs of DNA per generation of cell, population geneticists tell us that DNA would experience a 1% base sequence change in 10 million years. It is very difficult to see how even a 5% change in sponge DNA could grant us 19 other body plans from a humble sponge genome in the time allowable (see Table 13.5). Where has all the new information come from?

For their part, some neo-Darwinists have argued that an explosion has not really occurred. Rather, many of these animal phyla are assumed to have existed before the Cambrian era began as soft-bodied animals whose remains could not fossilize. In this way, their evolution could have been progressing for millions and millions of years prior to the Cambrian period. For them, the Cambrian strata just reflect a sudden appearance of skeletalizing elements—hard parts—that suddenly made a wide variety of forms preservable and therefore evident in the rocks. But this reasoning, based on meager and disputable evidence, merely begs the question of how so many different animal forms all happened to acquire fossilizable hard parts at the same time. The suddenness just takes a new form. The problem with the data arises because of the required gradual plodding of random mutation accumulation. Design, on the other hand, is temporally limited only by the talent of the Designer. The Cambrian explosion can be a proliferation of designs from an explosively powerful Mind. Such an hypothesis is clearly more complicated than the Darwinian hypothesis, but it is considerably more adequate for explaining the product.

IN OTHER WORDS

1. The fossil record and the existence of homologous structures in living organisms have long been used to argue that all living things have evolved from a common ancestor.
2. Geologists in the seventeenth century described and began interpreting the origin of sedimentary rocks and the index fossils within them.
3. Darwin's followers have assumed that most fossils are related genetically to fossils above and below them in the sedimentary rock strata.
4. In evolutionary thinking, a fossil that is intermediate in structure between two other fossils is termed a *transitional form*.
5. The Cambrian formation of rocks begins with an explosive array of basic, new animal body plans that represent about half of all modern animal phyla.
6. Darwin and his followers have found the Cambrian explosion difficult to explain because of the high level of diversity that appears in a short period of time.
7. Currently, evolutionists argue that these diverse phyla existed in pre-Cambrian rocks but were not fossilizable at that point in time.
8. Current design theorists argue that it is highly improbable that 20 phyla of animals would all become fossilizable in the short time indicated.

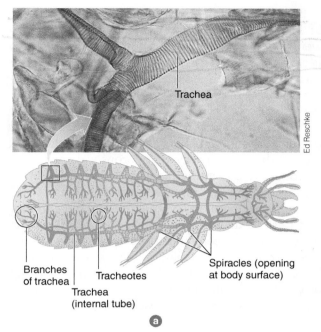

Trachea

Ed Reschke

Branches
of trachea

Trachea
(internal tube)

Tracheotes

Spiracles (opening
at body surface)

a

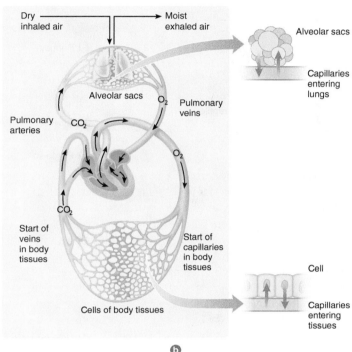

Dry
inhaled air

Moist
exhaled air

Alveolar sacs

O_2

Pulmonary
veins

Pulmonary
arteries

CO_2

O_2

Alveolar sacs

Capillaries
entering
lungs

Start of
veins
in body
tissues

CO_2

Start of
capillaries
in body
tissues

Cell

Cells of body tissues

Capillaries
entering
tissues

b

Figure 13.42 Oxygen Distribution in Animals. The trachea of insects and the capillaries of mammals are analogous structures. Though they arise quite differently embryologically, they perform the same function: moving oxygen to internal tissues. **(a)** the tracheal system in an insect **(b)** a representative capillary bed in mammalian tissue

The Evidence from Homology

Let's turn now to a set of observations that Darwin and his followers have considered the strongest support for the naturalistic hypothesis: the homologies between organisms at the molecular, cellular, and organismal levels.

Real biologists love to compare things. It's been done for centuries. For example, it was noted early on that a network of chitin-lined trachea carry oxygen to all parts of the insect body for use in cellular respiration. Blood vessels perform this function in your body (see Figure 13.42). The embryonic development of these structures in insects and mammals is radically different, yet trachea and arteries perform precisely the same function in both animals. In the 1840s, prior to Darwin's theorizing, the great British anatomist Richard Owen used the term analogous in reference to such structures. Trachea are analogous to arteries; they have different origins but obviously do the same job.

Soon, the forelimbs of vertebrates were compared with each other, and an entirely different situation

chitin—a polymer of glucose subunits that forms a tough exoskeleton for the outer surface of arthropods.

trachea—a single member of a complex system of branching, gas-filled channels in the body of an insect; the system of channels carries oxygen to the animal's tissues and waste carbon dioxide away from them.

analogous (in biology)—in reference to two structures, functions, or behaviors that are highly similar though their origins may be quite distinct.

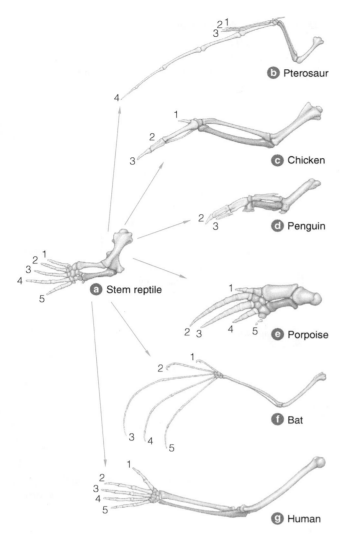

Figure 13.43 Comparison of Vertebrate Forelimbs. These forelimbs are homologous. But what does that mean about their origins? Is the reptilian limb really ancestral to all of the others? The digits in each diagram are numbered.

was observed (see Figure 13.43). Here it was discovered that despite the variety of functions these forelimbs performed—running in dogs, swimming in porpoises, or flying in birds—all vertebrate forelimbs appeared to have a common arrangement of bones within the limb. A pattern of 1 + 2 + many bones is repeated over and over again among vertebrates. Limbs possessing this common structural pattern were described by Owen as being **homologous**. To him, this meant that vertebrate forelimbs were built against a common "archetype" for the vertebrates. He did not discuss at length the origin or significance of this archetype. Perhaps he sensed that empirical science had no clear way of seeing a further significance to homology.

But Darwin's theory promptly gave the concept of homology a very specific meaning! Organisms were now believed to possess homologous structures because they derived from a common ancestor! Some early **tetrapod** vertebrate, perhaps a primitive reptile, walked on four limbs. The limbs had a 1 + 2 + many bone structure. All vertebrates descend from that common ancestor and thus retain that original combination of bones. Once again, as with the fossil record, there is no way to rigorously demonstrate reproductive continuity between modern vertebrate organisms and a common ancestor. Only fossil remains and homologous structures are there to suggest this. To design proponents, the common bone pattern reflects a common concept in the mind of the Designer. But at this point the Darwinist asks why limbs that perform such distinct functions as flying or climbing would not be constructed in discretely separate ways optimal for each task? Why is there commonality of structure? Again, the Darwinist's explanation of homology is clearly the simpler one. And in this case, it is also the more elegant one! But again, the Design theorist wonders if the explanation is *adequate*. Disputes such as these are mired in the limitations of historical science (see Section 2.3). But another problem plagues them as well—the same problem we encountered with feather evolution. It is superficial to evaluate the homology of highly complex organs—like forelimbs—when we don't understand their development or the genetic networks that interact to govern that development.

In the 1980s, DNA technology provided us with the option of exploring the sequences of just a few of the genes that lie behind and inform such processes as limb development. It is more profitable to evaluate the presumed homology between such genes than the more complex structures they inform. Consider a collection of genes called **homeobox** genes. These genes contain an internal sequence of 180 DNA base pairs that code for a 60-amino-acid-long

homologous (in biology)—in reference to two structures, functions, or behaviors that are believed to have a common origin in a common ancestral organism.

tetrapod—any organism that walks on four appendages; often used of an ancestral form from which many vertebrates radiated evolutionarily.

homeobox—a sequence of bases within a *Hox* gene that code for a protein domain that enables the Hox protein to bind a specific region of DNA sequence.

Homeobox Gene

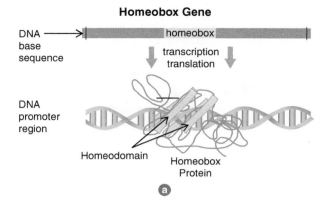

DNA base sequence

homeobox

transcription
translation

DNA promoter region

Homeodomain

Homeobox Protein

a

Figure 13.44 Homeobox Gene. **(a)** These genes code for proteins that regulate transcription of other genes. They switch on transcription by binding to the promoter region upstream in the DNA from the gene(s) to be actively transcribed. Thus each homeobox gene contains a sequence of nucleotide bases within its structure called the homeobox. When the homeobox gene is translated, this portion of the protein product is called the homeodomain and it enables the protein to bind the specific promoter regions of the genes needing activation (transcription). **(b)** The homeobox protein is only a part of the total regulatory complex that turns on a specific developmental pathway. Other accessory signals contribute to the specificity of switching genes on.

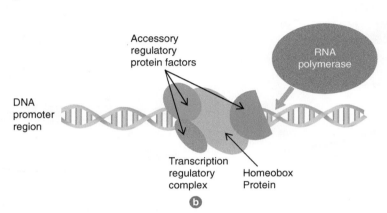

Accessory regulatory protein factors

RNA polymerase

DNA promoter region

Transcription regulatory complex

Homeobox Protein

b

internal portion, or **domain,** of a **homeoprotein** (see Figure 13.44a). The homeobox-encoded domain enables the homeoprotein to bind to specific base sequences along DNA. As suspected, these proteins turn out to be **transcription factors.** They form parts of multiprotein, regulatory aggregates that bind to specific DNA sequences that are parts of the promoter sequence of many genes (see Figure 13.44b). This DNA binding results in the switching on of cascades of these genes—genes that drive specific developmental pathways—like forelimb development.

An important distinction must be made here. Homeobox genes are not limb makers as such. They are rather limb *locators.* It's beautiful, really. We saw earlier (see Section 9.3) that the egg cytoplasm has a differential distribution of mRNAs in it so that at different ends of the embryo, a few basic genes are activated very, very, early in development (see Figure 13.45). Products of these genes diffuse across cell boundaries and set up a gradient of concentration throughout the entire embryo, front to back, side to side, top to bottom. Now this is neat: The transcription factors for activating homeobox genes "sense" those gradients. Just like flipping a light switch, the combination of chemical signals from interacting gradients turns on different homeobox genes in different

regions of the embryo. And somehow (by random mutation or design), the gradients in cells of the future eye region of the embryo activate the homeobox gene that turns on the eye development genes (see Figure 13.46). But in cells of the future forelimb region of the embryo, those same gradients (at different concentrations) activate homeobox genes, which turn on limb development genes. Amazing.

But hang onto your hats, folks. The *most* amazing feature of homeobox genes is how similar their sequence is even though widely distributed within the living world. They were originally found in the

domain—an obvious structural region within a protein molecule; composed of a specific amino acid sequence that confers on the protein a predictable functionality—like DNA binding or contributing to quaternary structure.

homeoprotein—a regulatory protein, part of whose internal structure is coded for by a sequence of bases called a *homeobox;* the internal structure allows it to regulate genes by binding to the DNA of their promoter sequences.

transcription factor—a class of regulatory protein molecules that bind promoter DNA and influence the frequency of transcription of the adjacent structural portion of a gene.

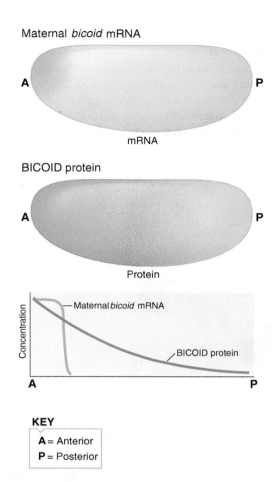

Maternal *bicoid* mRNA

A   P

mRNA

BICOID protein

A   P

Protein

Maternal*bicoid* mRNA

BICOID protein

A   P

KEY

A = Anterior
P = Posterior

Figure 13.45 Bicoid Gene Expression in *Drosophila*. This gene is active in the egg prior to fertilization. But all of it's mRNA gets concentrated at one end of the egg creating a steep concentration gradient. As the mRNA is translated into protein a more gentle gradient exists across the egg cytoplasm. When the egg gets cut up into separate cells, cells from one pole of the embryo to the other will have differing concentrations of this "bicoid" regulatory protein. Each concentration of protein along the curve will result in the activation of differing constellations of genes in these cells, thus setting up the embryo for different homeobox gene-driven differentiation in different regions of the embryo.

African clawed toad, *Xenopus laevis,* and in the common vinegar fly, *Drosophila melanogaster.* (Biologists do not usually select their organism of study because it is "pretty"). But homeobox genes with very similar homeobox sequences have since been identified in a wide assortment of invertebrates, reptiles, birds, and mammals and even in nematode worms, sponges, and yeast cells (of kingdom Fungi)! The same homeobox gene that controls the location of an eye in *Drosophila* also controls the location of the eye in a mouse or a human—they are virtually interchangeable (see Figure 13.46)! Of course, sponges and yeast cells do not have eyes; their homeobox proteins, by binding to DNA sequences, serve other regulatory roles.

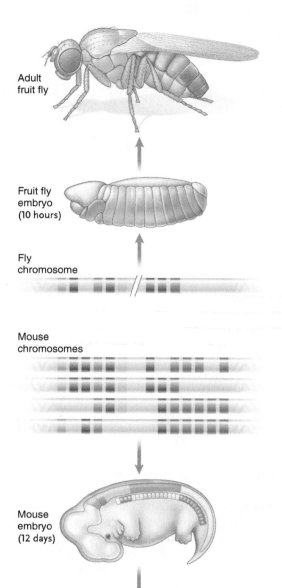

Adult fruit fly

Fruit fly embryo (10 hours)

Fly chromosome

Mouse chromosomes

Mouse embryo (12 days)

Adult mouse

Figure 13.46 Homeobox Genes in Insects and Mammals. These genes are distributed in clusters along the chromosome. These clusters are very similar across the Animal Kingdom. The order in which the genes of the cluster are arranged reflects the order of the segments or parts of the organism! The color of the homeobox gene is correlated by color with the segment of the embryo whose differentiation it calls for.

When we consider this vast distribution of common homeobox genes across the animal world, we are drawn back to our previous question: Are these genes homologous? They surely appear so! They appear to indicate that all animals possessing them have a common ancestor via evolution, don't they? Or did a Designer just use the DNA binding ability of their homeo-domain whenever He wanted to assign a spot in any embryo for the genesis of some new structure? Before choosing between these two notions, more implications of homeobox gene function must be considered.

First of all, the product of the homeobox gene is a control protein, not a structural protein. Its control function has to do with *where* to place a forelimb, not *how* to make one. This functional difference highlights a major problem faced by natural selection in developing limbs. It is forced to work on how to make a limb and where to put that limb at the same time (see Figure 13.47). As the program to *make* the limb is evolving, it must be integrated into a somewhat separate program to place it properly. But the mere existence of a particular homeobox gene does not mean a specific location within the developing organism has now been defined. For example, the homeobox gene *HoxC6* is involved in locating the forelimb of a mouse or a man in its correct location and orientation. But the homologous gene in nematode worms, *lin 39,* controls the positioning of cells that will form the vulva, a ventral reproductive structure in the worm. The homeobox gene must function within an irreducible *constellation* of regulatory genes before a limb location is specified. So natural selection faces a serious "chicken-and-egg" problem: A place chosen for a limb has no value without the limb. A limb in an unacceptable site can be useless or worse! Natural selection must develop both the structure of the limb and a system by which to place it.

Second, homeobox proteins do not generally turn on sets of genes by themselves. They are only one of a set of multiple factors that bond to each other and to a DNA promoter sequence telling RNA polymerase exactly where to begin transcribing (see Figure 13.44b). Apparently, there are too many undesirable sites along the DNA sequence that a single homeobox protein could bind to. Control of development is only effective when multiple regulatory factors bind together to specify a site currently requiring transcription. This further complicates natural selection's task. It must now develop or discover a homeobox protein useful in *helping* to turn on a development program for a limb while it recruits other regulatory genes to help refine the switching-on process. Let's contextualize this dilemma within natural history.

In conventional geological reasoning, what is the time frame for assembling these homeobox genes, connecting them with the development process they are supposed to turn on, and integrating their functions with other regulatory genes such that control is sufficiently specific? Returning to our discoveries in the Cambrian rocks will be a troubling experience.

Sponges are found in Cambrian and some pre-Cambrian rocks. Homeobox genes in sponges have only a few distinct cell types to arrange into an adult structure. Four to five homeobox genes seem to do the trick. But along with sponges in the Cambrian period, fish existed as well. So somewhere in the brief beginnings of the Cambrian period, the number of homeobox genes must have expanded from several up to the 230 or so found in modern fish (in order to have . . . . a fish!) (see Figure 13.48). All the connections of developmental pathways—for fins, eyes, mouth, internal organs—to the various homeobox genes and their interconnections to higher-order regulatory genes must have occurred in that short time period. And then, recalling the

Simultaneous Roles of Natural Selection in Forelimb Evolution

1) Perfect structural gene coding for proteins used in bone, muscle, epidermal, nerve cells

2) Construct gene cascade that will determine where within the limb cells of various types will migrate to and mature

3) Associate the proper homeobox gene with activation of correct cascade for a given body segment

4) Properly relate the homeobox gene in 3) above with other regulatory genes needed to get wing development going

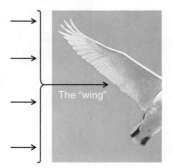

The "wing"

Figure 13.47 Simultaneous Roles of Natural Selection in Forelimb Evolution.

Role of Natural Selection as Cambrian Deposition Begins

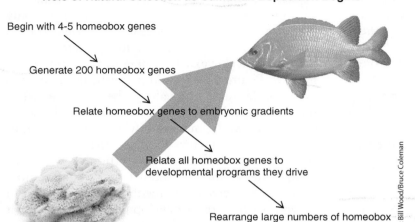

Begin with 4-5 homeobox genes

Generate 200 homeobox genes

Relate homeobox genes to embryonic gradients

Relate all homeobox genes to developmental programs they drive

Rearrange large numbers of homeobox genes for 20 distinct body plans

fish: Bill Wood/Bruce Coleman

Figure 13.48   Role of Natural Selection as Cambrian Deposition Begins.

nature of the Cambrian explosion, we are requiring homeobox genes to begin to support that wide variety of differentiative functions in a wide diversity of basic body plans that we discovered earlier.

So in trying to imagine several sequences of mutations that would develop, say, five anatomically discrete vertebrate limbs from one ancestral limb, the homeobox genes appear to compound the problem we face. We can't simply make 20 or so needed changes to the structural program of a basic walking limb to move toward a human forelimb or a fish's pectoral fin. We must also rearrange how its homeobox gene relates to other such genes along the anterior-posterior and dorso-ventral body axes so that our forelimb appears at the correct spot for optimal function—the arm in the human and the fin in the fish. An evolving homeobox gene must remain functional and responsive to embryonic axis gradients, all the while adjusting that responsiveness for optimal limb placement and orientation in the new organism. Currently, a homeobox gene mutation in insects can give the insect a leg where its antenna should be (see Figure 13.49)! Or, as is usually the case in

Figure 13.49   Homeobox Gene Mutation in the vinegar fly *Drosophila*. **(a)** In modern organisms, mutations in homeobox genes do not improve function. Vision will be a problem for the antennapedia mutant in which antennae are replaced by limbs. **(b)** a scanning electron micrograph of the anterior aspect of an antennapedia fly.

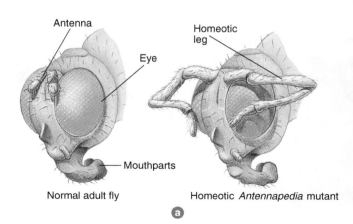

Antenna

Eye

Mouthparts

Normal adult fly

Homeotic leg

Homeotic *Antennapedia* mutant

a

Eye   Homeotic leg

Dr. Thomas Kaufman

b

250 µm

mammals, the result is just abortion of the developing individual. Natural selection in this context becomes more and more expensive: More animals have to die because of the many favorable mutations that are needed. Mutations to convert a structural program for a leg to one for a fin must be accompanied by new critical mutations in the regulatory parts of homeobox genes to get the fin in the right place. It must be in the right place both (1) for optimal function and (2) relative to other supportive structures.

Now we can return to our earlier question: Is the naturalistic hypothesis of origins sufficiently elaborate to explain the level of control of development observed here? Early Darwinists saw mainly morphology. It was therefore easy to wonder why a Designer would bother retaining a common pattern of bones in vertebrate forelimbs that would be required for such a variety of disparate functions. Surely such a common pattern argued more strongly for a single common ancestor. However, molecular biologists have thickened the plot. Evolving from leg to fin or leg to wing must occur on one structural front and at least two regulatory fronts at once.

The Design theorist, by contrast, could argue that a common bone pattern reflects a common Designer for each type of limb rather than a different Designer for each type (see Figure 13.50). This singular Designer would simply have to have

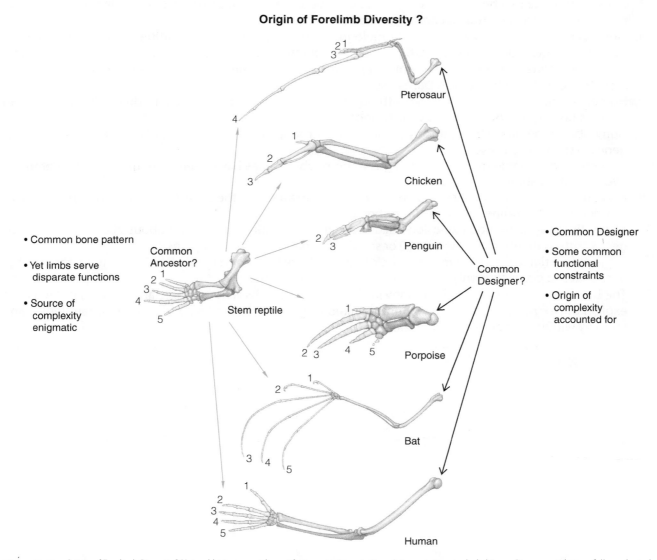

Origin of Forelimb Diversity ?

- Common bone pattern
- Yet limbs serve disparate functions
- Source of complexity enigmatic

Common Ancestor?

Stem reptile

Pterosaur

Chicken

Penguin

Porpoise

Bat

Human

Common Designer?

- Common Designer
- Some common functional constraints
- Origin of complexity accounted for

Figure 13.50   Origin of Forelimb Diversity? Natural history provides artifacts, not interpretations. Interpretations include biases. Biases must be carefully evaluated. Such evaluation is threatening.

greater design capabilities! The design theorist could also speculate that all forelimbs face common challenges: the stress of flexing at their base, rotational needs great or small, a variety of mediums to engage, and manipulative needs at the distal end. A 1 + 2 + many bone arrangement might uniformly suit those common needs. But where should the Darwinist begin his speculation about how random mutation is to build on such a common pattern? The result must be an elegant placement, orientation, development, final structure, and function of each separate vertebrate limb. A field of random mutations to select from begins to appear rather dry and dusty after 60 years with no new selective mechanisms to "water" the intellectual field.

IN OTHER WORDS

1. Structures in two different organisms that perform the same function but have disparate embryonic origins are termed *analogous structures*.
2. Structures in two different organisms that appear to have common component features and a common embryonic pattern of development are termed *homologous structures*.
3. Darwinists argue that homologous structures exist because the two organisms containing them derive by mutation and selection from a common ancestor.
4. Since some structures assumed to be homologous turn out not to be when studied in detail, it is safer to search for homology among genes, the actual sites of mutation.
5. Homeobox genes have sequence similarities across the entire animal kingdom and as such are widely assumed to be homologous in a Darwinist sense.
6. Homeobox gene products combine with regulatory proteins from other loci to determine where in an animal's body its various structures will be located spatially.
7. Homeobox gene products do this by sensing their location within chemical gradients set up by maternal genes in the early embryo.
8. At present, detectable mutational changes to homeobox genes have been without exception deteriorative of existing animal body plans.
9. Natural selection is required to fashion a forelimb for an animal at the same time that it is altering homeobox genes to determine where the limb should go.
10. At the time the Cambrian explosion occurred, natural selection had to find about 200 new homeobox genes and assign them roles within 20 or so different basic animal body plans.
11. Large proportions of early animal populations would have to die by natural selection for this large number of changes to occur suddenly within the early Cambrian period.
12. The Darwinian explanation of homology in vertebrate forelimbs is both simple and elegant, but it fails to explain the extreme information content required to generate a forelimb and position it temporally and spatially within the development of the animal.

WHAT IS THE PRODUCT AND VALUE OF EVOLUTION?

It appears that mutation and natural selection are incapable of generating either cellular life or the fundamental structures that grant vitality and variety to macroorganisms. Do they, therefore, have any consequential role in nature or should biologists simply ignore them? Let's consider these two processes more closely before trying to answer that question. We'll consider mutation first.

Mutations Harmful, Neutral, and Helpful

We stated earlier that most mutations are at least slightly harmful. To a Design theorist, the reason is simple. Any change made to something elegantly designed will deteriorate that design. To a Darwinist, there is also a plausible reason for this. Evolution has been designing new structures for so long that the population's **adaptation** to its environment is now quite advanced (see Figure 13.51). Since most organisms are now highly adapted to their environments, most random mutational changes would be expected to be harmful. Consider a tiny **deletion** of just three base pairs in the DNA of a particular gene

adaptation—a feature of an organism that allows it to reproduce more offspring under a given set of environmental conditions.

deletion—the mutational removal of one or more bases of DNA sequence or of a much larger visible portion of a cell's chromosome.

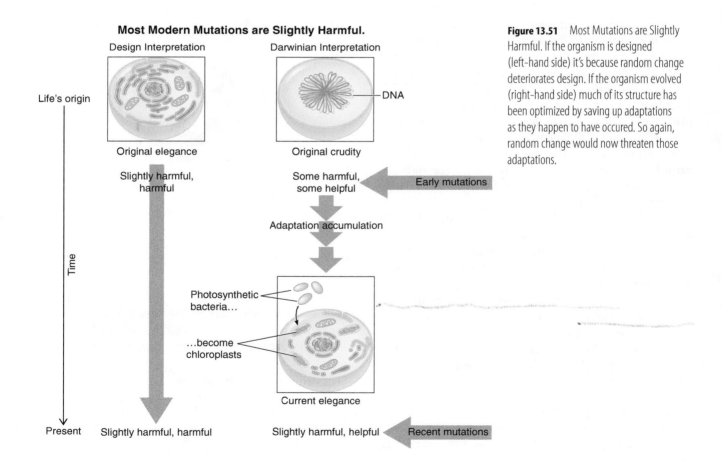

Figure 13.51 Most Mutations are Slightly Harmful. If the organism is designed (left-hand side) it's because random change deteriorates design. If the organism evolved (right-hand side) much of its structure has been optimized by saving up adaptations as they happen to have occured. So again, random change would now threaten those adaptations.

Most Modern Mutations are Slightly Harmful.

Design Interpretation — Original elegance
Darwinian Interpretation — DNA — Original crudity

Life's origin

Slightly harmful, harmful
Some harmful, some helpful ← Early mutations

Adaptation accumulation

Time

Photosynthetic bacteria... ...become chloroplasts

Current elegance

Present
Slightly harmful, harmful
Slightly harmful, helpful ← Recent mutations

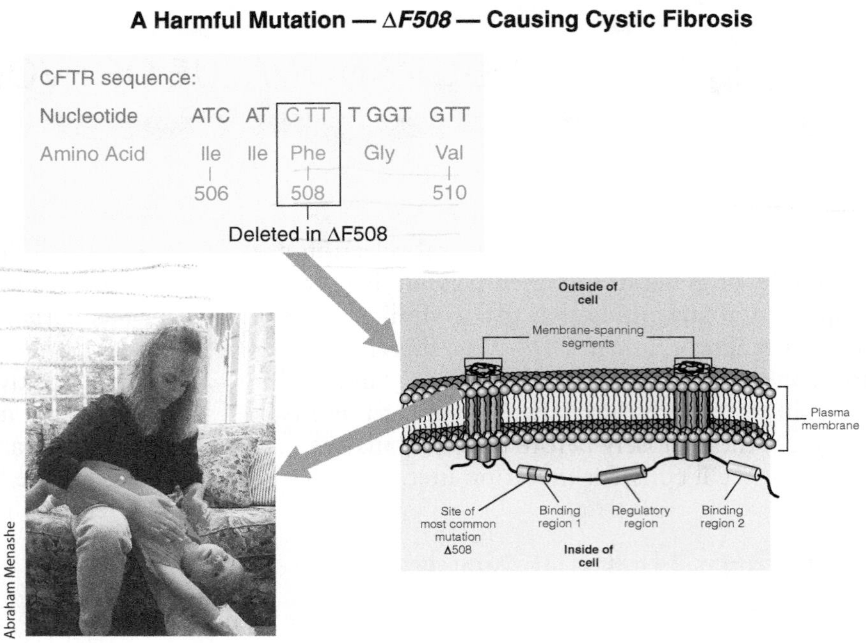

Figure 13.52 A Harmful Mutation – ΔF508 – Causing Cystic Fibrosis. In this mutation, a sequence of just three nucleotide bases in DNA—the length of one codon—is deleted. The result is the deletion of just one amino acid in the sequence found in the CFTR protein that controls ion flow across the cell membrane. This small aminao acid deletion in "binding region #1" makes the protein incapable of binding to the ATP molecules that drive ion transport. The result is a dramatic increase in the thickness of mucus produced by goblet cells in the lining of the lung. Physical thumping on the chest helps dislodge this mucus to keep airways open.

A Harmful Mutation — ΔF508 — Causing Cystic Fibrosis

CFTR sequence:

Nucleotide	ATC	AT	C TT	T GGT	GTT
Amino Acid	Ile	Ile	Phe	Gly	Val
			506	508	510

Deleted in ΔF508

(see Figure 13.52). This deletion results in the loss of a single amino acid out of 1480 amino acids in a protein coded for by that gene. That protein is a transmembrane transport protein, and the result is cystic fibrosis, a disease that greatly shortens a person's life. Or consider another dramatic variation like the pathetic featherless chicken shown in Figure 13.53. Extreme traits like this suit some animal breeder's purpose under a specific set of commercial growth conditions—like the heat of a henhouse in Israel. But a mutation like this typically does not suit the population well for survival in its native habitat. There is a whole gamut of harmful mutations ranging from very slightly disadvantageous all the way to lethality. None of these mutations contribute in any positive way to the process of evolution.

A major fraction of mutations consists of small neutral changes within genes—changes that do not improve or impair the function of the gene product coded for. Therefore natural selection has little or no effect on them. For an example, just review the genetic code (see Figure 7.22). Some amino acids are coded for by more than one different codon in their mRNA. A mutation from one codon (like CCU) to another codon (like CCC) will have no effect on an amino acid sequence because both of these codons call for the same amino acid: proline. Neutral mutations like this just accumulate silently in the DNA of the population (see Figure 13.54).

Figure 13.53 Feather-less Chickens. These birds can result from random mutations or genetic engineering efforts. In commercial maintenance these birds live well (for a time!) but in the wild, males would have difficulty mating and the animals would be more susceptible to mosquitos and parasites.

Still other mutations are like the one that changes the hairline on your forehead so that it comes to a peak instead of simply tracing a line across the forehead (see Figure 13.54). In this case, there is a pronounced physical change. But there is no indication

Neutral Mutations ?

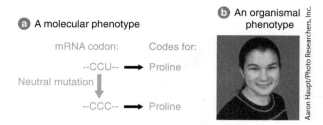

a A molecular phenotype

mRNA codon: Codes for:

--CCU-- ➡ Proline

Neutral mutation ⬇

--CCC-- ➡ Proline

b An organismal phenotype

Aaron Haupt/Photo Researchers, Inc.

Figure 13.54 Neutral Mutations ? **(a)** One genotypic change in DNA results in a new molecular phenotype: an altered codon in mRNA. But the genetic code makes this phenotype invisible during the translation process. **(b)** Another genotypic change in DNA results in a new (dominant) organismal phenotype: an altered hairline that now includes a widow's peak.

A "Good" Mutation ?

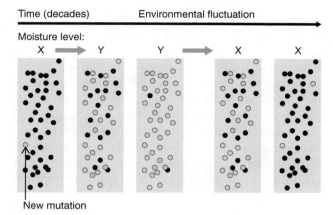

Time (decades)   Environmental fluctuation

Moisture level:

X ➡ Y   Y ➡ X   X

New mutation

Figure 13.55 A "Good" Mutation ? Is a mutation categorically good if it enables an individual to have more offspring under one set of conditions but not under a different set of conditions, particularly if, like environmental moisture levels, the condition tends to fluctuate?

that such a change has any negative effect on your ability to reproduce and leave offspring. With neutral mutations, then, the evolutionary process has no resources for taking the population in any new creative direction. Instead, such mutations create new alleles whose frequency in the population wanders up and down aimlessly with no significant effect on the vitality of the resulting population.

The big question (!) is whether or not beneficial mutations are occurring. Design theorists and Darwinists will differ somewhat on how to define a beneficial mutation. To the former, a beneficial mutation would improve on the quality of the organism's design—something very unlikely to occur! The Darwinist, on the other hand, broadly defines a good mutation as one that helps its host to compete favorably in a particular habitat. Any mutation that enables its bearer to leave more competitive

offspring will qualify. So if, in a present-day environment, a mutation causes a potato plant to reach reproductive age faster or generate more hardy potato seed, then that is defined, evolutionarily, as a good mutation. But nature then leaves us with a gnawing question (see Figure 13.55). Suppose a mutation is favorable in a specific, current environment but in a future potential set of environmental conditions the mutation is less useful? A thicker beak in a Galapagos finch is such an example. Shall we call this a beneficial mutation? If we do not, then the variety of mutations available to Darwinian selection is reduced—so therefore is its ability to create structural features of organisms over long periods of time.

IN OTHER WORDS

1. Mutation and natural selection do not appear to have the power to create new kinds of organisms or fundamentally new structures within organisms.
2. Most mutations are slightly harmful to modern organisms because they have a high level of either design or adaptation depending on your view of origins.
3. Very small changes in DNA sequences can cause profoundly detrimental effects in the organism in which they occur.
4. Some mutations are selectively neutral; they do not alter the phenotype of the organism, or they do so in a way that gives the resulting organism no selective advantage.
5. Neither harmful nor neutral mutations contribute positively to evolutionary change.
6. A helpful mutation is any change in the genome that allows its bearer to leave more healthy offspring for the next generation compared to rival organisms of the same population.
7. Such beneficial mutations depend on the environmental variables. What is optimal in one set of conditions may be harmful in a different set of conditions.

What Does Nature Select?

Let's now consider natural selection's work on these mutations. A population is a large collection of potentially interbreeding organisms in a given location. In a population, there is usually a diversity of genetic variations (see Figure 13.56). Mutations have accumulated in all of the genes of the population's gene pool over a period of many years. Is this long and tortuous history of accumulated mutations what distinguishes you from a mushroom or a sea anemone? That depends on the power of natural selection. If natural selection is an integral part of nature, then it also may be the work of a brilliant Designer. If so, it surely has a valuable purpose whether or not it is capable of the creative activity the Darwinist seeks to wring from it. How does natural selection operate on a population? What must be its function if all it ever gets to operate on are changes that depart from the elegance of design?

Let's consider a form of natural selection called stabilizing selection. This kind of selection eliminates individuals with extreme traits or phenotypes from the population (see Figure 13.57). The loss of such individuals means the loss of their genotypes—their portion of the gene pool. We said that most mutations produce phenotypes that are harmful. Here then, is a beautiful example of how the process of natural selection itself is a wonderful gift from the Designer—it helps protect a population from extreme forms of mutational departure from the elegance of its design. It tends to stabilize the population at the level of design degeneracy it currently has, inhibiting further deterioration through seriously harmful mutation. You might say, "Fine, but then stabilizing selection

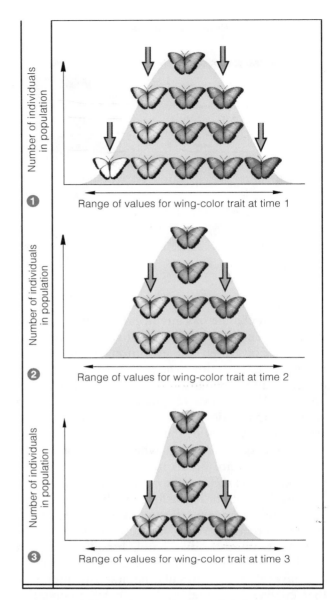

Figure 13.57 Stabilizing Selection. In this diagram lack of wing coloration or very deep coloration are mutational extremes that would be harmful to the individuals bearing them. Stabilizing selection (orange arrows) tends to eliminate such extremes, often by means of increased predation on these forms.

isn't 'taking the population anywhere' evolutionarily." That is correct. The simple fact that natural selection operates on existing mutations does not mean that evolution has the power to create new structures. In the case of stabilizing selection, it

stabilizing selection—that form of natural selection that removes extremes of phenotype (harmful mutations) from a population, causing it to maintain its phenotype without significant alteration.

Figure 13.56 Genetic Diversity in Snail Populations. Shell color and pattern are highly variable traits in these Carribean snail populations.

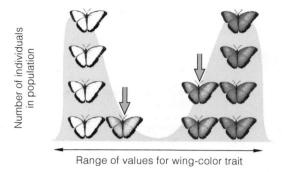

Range of values for wing-color trait

Figure 13.58 Disruptive Selection. Consider a species of butterfly in which the sexes have separate colors. If a mutation generates an intermediate phenotype, this would be potentially confusing to both sexes and mating behaviors would tend to exclude it from reproduction. Thus it would be eliminated from the population.

has the power only to destroy twisted alternatives to what a Designer made that was once very good.

But in some cases extremes of phenotype are a good thing. Think about sexual differences as an example. In a population of birds, it would be disastrous if the males and females of the species were slowly becoming more and more like each other until they could not clearly tell each other apart. Much population energy would be wasted on mating attempts that would fail. The second form of natural selection operates on mutations that would minimize or eliminate such differences. It's called disruptive selection. This selection helps maintain phenotypic extremes in the population (see Figure 13.58). It tends to eliminate the rare mouse, fly, or even human whose sexuality, for example, is intermediate between a distinct female or male.

Consider a population of birds in which two distinct beak sizes each have separate advantages at different times in the year. Perhaps the species consume seeds of two discrete sizes. Seeds of an intermediate size are not available to this species. One beak size is 12 mm across, and the other is 15 mm across. A beak size intermediate between these two values would be disadvantageous, and very few birds will have beaks intermediate in size. Disruptive selection favors birds whose beaks go to one extreme or the other and selects against birds with intermediate beak sizes by starving them. So, as in stabilizing selection, disruptive selection works not by creating new biological inventions but by eliminating mutant forms that threaten the stability of the gloriously designed species under observation.

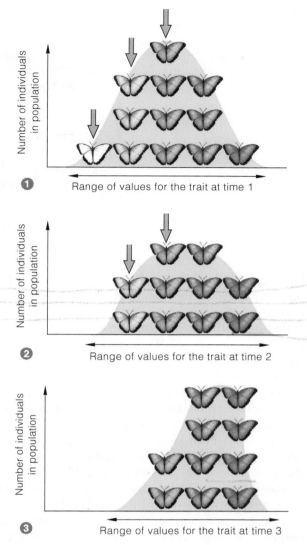

① Range of values for the trait at time 1

② Range of values for the trait at time 2

③ Range of values for the trait at time 3

Figure 13.59 Directional Selection. Imagine a population of butterflies in an environment with many dark-colored surfaces. The lightest colored variants are easily seen by predators against this background and are thus removed from the breeding population. This will tend to move the population indefinitely in the direction of darker pigmentation (unless environmental change later causes the lighter colored forms to be favored.

The third form of selection is more controversial because it has the potential to move the population, phenotypically, in a new direction. It does this by eliminating phenotypes at one end of a range of values, thus pushing the overall phenotype of the population in the opposite direction (see Figure 13.59).

disruptive selection—that form of natural selection that removes intermediate phenotypes from a population, causing it to maintain itself in a rigidly dimorphic state; sexuality is maintained in this way.

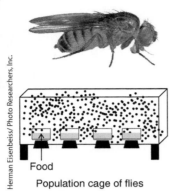

Figure 13.60 Directional Selection in *Drosophila melanogaster*. Notice the bristles on the dorsal surface of the adult. A adult fly is actually 1-2 mm in length.

Herman Eisenbeiss/ Photo Researchers, Inc.

Food

Population cage of flies

Steps in selection process:

1. Examine 100 flies from purchased sample, select 10 with largest number of bristles on thorax.

2. Introduce 10 flies to population cage, allow to populate cage for 2 generations. (about 22 days)

3. Remove all flies. Examine 1000 flies, select 10 with largest number of bristles on thorax. (directional selection)

4. Repopulate cage with these 10 flies. Add fresh food. Wait 22 days.

5. Repeat steps 3, 4 as often as funding allows!!

Directional selection is what the Darwinist relies upon to generate new body structures like wings and new behaviors like fight-or-flight responses in male lions. What demonstrative examples of directional selection exist? We want to see if, by shifting a phenotypic range, new structures or functions can be created.

Directional selection experiments have been tried many times in the laboratory with the common vinegar fly *Drosophila melanogaster*. One characteristic that has been studied is the number of large bristles growing on the dorsal (or upper) aspect of the fly's **thorax**, or midsection (see Figure 13.60). Normally, about 24 bristles are present, but there is some variation around this number. How would a typical experiment work? The researcher mates flies to each other over many, many generations. For each new generation, he selects for mating the flies that have a higher than normal number of bristles on their thoraxes. Remember, thousands of flies are examined and mutations are constantly occurring. Is it possible, over many generations of selection, to increase the number of bristles to 30 or 50 or even 100? This is directional selection because we are eliminating all the flies with the lowest number of bristles. We are shifting the population in the direction of greater bristle number. In these experiments, it is always possible, after 30 or 40 generations, to achieve a small increase in the average number of bristles per fly. But after a while, continued selection for an increase in bristle number leads to an accompanying weakness and loss of fertility in the flies.

How are such results to be interpreted? It seems as though the flies live in a deep developmental genetic "trough" or channel (see Figure 13.61).

Design theorists would call it an intricately designed, interwoven developmental pattern. Selecting for extreme traits is a way of pushing the flies out of that channel, or pattern. What you get is a small, positive response and then: sterility. The system—the fly genome—is genetically **canalized;** it resists extreme changes in structure and function. Apparently, bristle number is connected functionally to a variety of other fly traits. When you focus on changing a single trait, you are really stressing a highly integrated system. You are making one change that you have arbitrarily determined is "good." But along with that change, other hidden changes that are somehow "bad" for the fly must necessarily happen, and the result is reduced fertility.

These results mean that **directional selection** is real—to a point! And we would love to see if it could use such selection to move a population of simple, primitive organisms toward long-term change. The problem is that there are no simple, primitive organisms available to test the idea on! All living things are so internally integrated that

directional selection—that form of natural selection that removes one extreme of phenotype from a population causing it to shift its phenotypic character toward the opposite extreme; this often involves favoring of a new mutation.

thorax—the central section(s) of the animal body, located posterior to the head and anterior to the abdomen.

canalize—(in evolution) to channel, to cause certain time-honored, highly integrative gene sequences to be retained in a population in favor of new mutations whose instability would move the population in a new phenotypic direction.

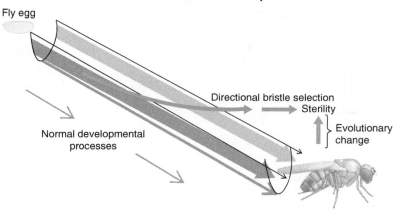

Canalization in Animal Development

Fly egg

Normal developmental
processes

Directional bristle selection
Sterility

Evolutionary
change

Figure 13.61 Canalization in Development. See text for details.

a seemingly good change in one direction for one trait means a bad change somewhere else in the form or function of the organism. In summary then, directional selection should be a powerful force in a simple primitive organism. But as soon as life is as complex as a bacterial cell, the internal integration of the organism causes long-term directional selection to lose its power.

Most Darwinists do not want this to be true. They desire to believe that natural selection is taking any population to a better, more fit state. But it is hard to say whether or not, over thousands of years, gene frequencies are really "going somewhere." What if they are simply oscillating around some ancient preferred values in response to oscillation of environmental conditions within fairly standard geoclimatic limits? In Figure 13.62, notice where the red lines end up. Everybody agrees that fitness levels are high now! The big question is: were they once much lower, or were they always high? The fossil record does not contain unequivocally primitive, "sloppy" life-forms.

Adding in Revealed Truth

The term **evolution** implies that nature is now actively progressing from simpler forms to more complex ones. A student of design who happens upon the Biblical documents discovers a picture of origins quite contradictory to this evolutionary picture (see Figure 13.63). They describe the designing of creation in the context of three specific events in sequence. First, the Designer calls forth or creates and then deems the results of His

work "very good." Second, on the seventh day, the Designer rests from His labors. And finally, in the very next section of text, the Earth is cursed because of man's sin. How might this sequence of events constrain our view of the evolutionary process?

First, when a powerful Designer views something as "very good," it's probably foolish to assume that mindless nature can improve on it using randomly generated mutations! The theistic evolutionist will say that a Designer used evolution to create. Interestingly, the Genesis account of God resting—ceasing from creating—may mean there was a fixed point in time when what was "very good" started to exist outside the Designer's mind and from then on, became no better. It was "finished." Then, there appears this curse of both nature and mankind. Could mutant phenotypes such as cystic fibrosis or cancer, be a result of this? Might the living world now be a shadow of what it once was? St. Paul, in his letter to the Romans, says in Chapter 8 that creation "is in bondage to decay." This does not sound as though things are getting better.

We must now draw some threads together. First, as naturalist and author, Steven J. Gould suggested, we must strip evolution of the notion of progress that it acquired in the Age of Enlightenment. This returns it to the status of a data-driven, scientific process that does not "see its way forward" to

evolution—directional changes in gene frequencies within a population's gene pool over time.

How Has Organismal Fitness Changed?

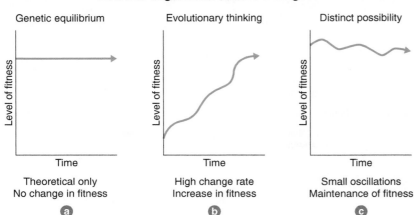

Genetic equilibrium

Level of fitness | Time

Theoretical only
No change in fitness

ⓐ

Evolutionary thinking

Level of fitness | Time

High change rate
Increase in fitness

ⓑ

Distinct possibility

Level of fitness | Time

Small oscillations
Maintenance of fitness

ⓒ

Figure 13.62 The History of Organismal Fitness. Has the fitness of species **(a)** always been uniformly high? Or **(b)** was it once quite low and is currently high as a result of Darwinian processes. Or **(c)** might fitness oscillate in response to cyclic environmental change? Might it even be decreasing if selection is unable to keep up with multitudes of mutations that are constantly occurring?

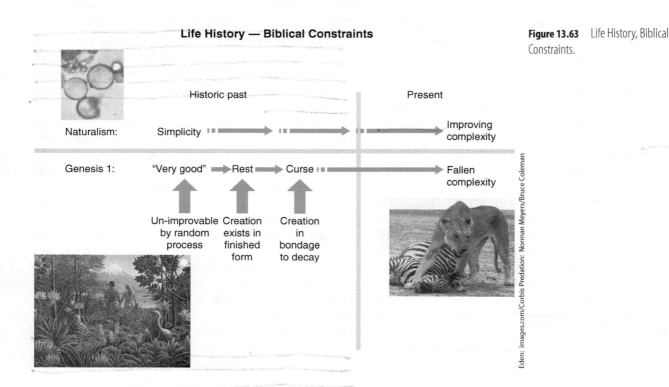

Life History — Biblical Constraints

Historic past — Present

Naturalism: Simplicity ➡ Improving complexity

Genesis 1: "Very good" ➡ Rest ➡ Curse ➡ Fallen complexity

Un-improvable by random process | Creation exists in finished form | Creation in bondage to decay

Figure 13.63 Life History, Biblical Constraints.

Eden: images.com/Corbis Predation: Norman Meyers/Bruce Coleman

anything. Evolution predictably presents us with hosts of new mutations, most of which are very slightly harmful (see Figure 13.64). When a few very harmful ones emerge, natural selection plays a homeostatic role of protectively removing them from the population. And that is what the fossil record shows us—stasis. So natural selection becomes a powerful process that helps cleanse the genome of harmful mutations and, in combination with mutations, it buffers the genome against environmental change. How effective is it at these tasks? Clearly, it removes the least fit organisms from the population. It cannot possibly remove all of the slightly harmful mutations that constantly enter the population anew. This would be too selectively expensive (see Section 13.3c). So one effect of this mutational curse is that populations everywhere are in genomic decline (see Figure 13.64). Ever since mutations first occurred, nature has been regressing, not progressing.

Darwinian Processes Revisited

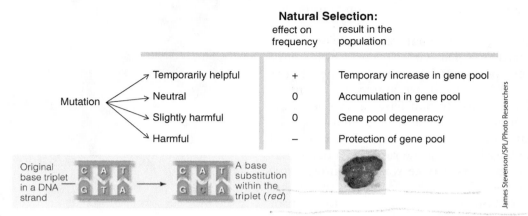

Natural Selection:

Mutation		effect on frequency	result in the population
	Temporarily helpful	+	Temporary increase in gene pool
	Neutral	0	Accumulation in gene pool
	Slightly harmful	0	Gene pool degeneracy
	Harmful	–	Protection of gene pool

Original base triplet in a DNA strand → A base substitution within the triplet (*red*)

James Stevenson/SPL/Photo Researchers

Figure 13.64 Darwinian Processes Revisited. Mutations can be as simple as a single substituted base along the DNA as a result of mis-replication or an environmental mutagen. The result could be a genetic predisposition to forming melanomas. Is this mutation slightly harmful or quite harmful? Will natural selection remove the person with a melanoma before their reproductive years are complete? Several variables complicate a neat answer to this question.

Speciation: Mere Loss of Reproductive Continuity

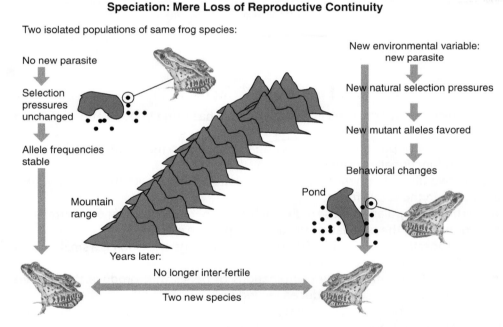

Two isolated populations of same frog species:

No new parasite

Selection pressures unchanged

Allele frequencies stable

Mountain range

Years later:

No longer inter-fertile

Two new species

New environmental variable: new parasite

New natural selection pressures

New mutant alleles favored

Behavioral changes

Pond

Figure 13.65 Speciation: mere loss of reproductive continuity. See text for details.

Suppose a new extreme environmental variable threatens a given population of a species. To counteract it, a new, otherwise deteriorative mutation, may suddenly become slightly advantageous for a time (see Figure 13.65). If enough of such mutations occur over time, our population of the species may become reproductively isolated from other populations of the species living elsewhere and not experiencing the environmental extreme. A new species might be the result. In this way, speciation may be creative of a new scientific category—a new species—while it is essentially deteriorative of the population sustaining it. Thus evolution is a real process—a valuable part of the overall design of nature. We just don't want to lean on it to design anything for us.

So what do you see in nature? Whose eyes have you, Leonardo's or Darwin's? If you see the glory of a flower opening at just the right time of year (see Figure 13.66), you are seeing an invention that St. Paul in his Roman letter asks you to attribute to a great Designer. If you see a lion tearing a beautiful impala to pieces on a grassland plain, you may be seeing the result of a curse: nature not as good as it once was. And now, natural selection—a Designer's gift, it appears—fights a war to contain the mutational deterioration of the corporate organismal genome. Reduced visual acuity and speed are in the future for both predator and prey. Stabilizing selection will slow this deteriorative process. But only a Designer's new Design could ever undo what a curse has done. *Creation. Curse. Deterioration.* These three words far surpass the concept of gradual evolution in accurately describing the current biosphere of which we are a part.

Ed Reschke

Figure 13.66 Design or Debris? Can we say with confidence that this glory is the result of random sequence alterations in DNA when we do not yet understand how its DNA sequences generate all of the inter-related symmetry we see here.

IN OTHER WORDS

1. If natural selection is itself the result of design, then it almost certainly has value in populations of living organisms.
2. Stabilizing selection removes from a population those individuals containing mutations that represent extreme departures from what is functionally normal.
3. Disruptive selection conserves two different phenotypes in a population but removes individuals whose phenotype is intermediate between those two forms.
4. Directional selection removes from a population those individuals containing variations at one extreme of a phenotypic distribution, thus pushing the population toward the opposite extreme.
5. When directional selection is purposefully practiced on *Drosophila* populations, the result is a small shift in the population's phenotype followed by increasing sterility.
6. The sterility is presumed to result from unfavorable combinations of genes that produce the desired extreme of phenotype but in so doing also result in reduced fecundity.
7. A major remaining question for biologists is the historic nature of population fitness. Has fitness increased significantly over long periods of time as Darwinian thinking assumes?
8. Biblical accounts of the origin of life portray a sequence of initial optimal fitness followed by a curse that implies mutational loss of fitness.
9. Despite the effects of stabilizing selection, the accumulation of large numbers of slightly harmful mutations suggests that genomes are in a slow state of decline in genetic quality.
10. Speciation may be an essentially deteriorative process in which reproductive isolation results from the accumulation of diverse mutations in different populations of a species.

QUESTIONS FOR REVIEW

1. Leonardo da Vinci and Charles Darwin were both careful and enthusiastic students of nature. What drew them to such contrasting views of the origin of living things?
2. How would Darwin explain the fact that finches on different islands of the Galapagos Archipelago have differently shaped beaks?
3. State, in order of presentation in your text, the elements of Darwin's theory of evolution by natural selection.
4. Explain the difference between microevolution and macroevolution.
5. Why does your text start observing data using Darwin's hypothesis that nature itself can create new life-forms?
6. Why would the simplest cell be parasitic? Why would a totally independent, free-living cell have to have a larger genome?
7. Explain how overlapping genes represent a difficulty for Darwin's model of slow accumulation of variations in a species over time.
8. What roles does the tip structure play in the life of *Mycoplasma genitalium*?
9. Explain why a host organism's immune response to the tip structure surface of a *Mycoplasma genitalium* cell population is not an insurmountable problem for that population.
10. Suppose the Miller-Urey early Earth simulation generates all the amino acids needed to make a fully functional protein. Name two of three problems that still remain in order to generate the functioning protein.
11. What features of modern geothermal vents have attracted the interests of molecular evolutionists who view them as sites where biomolecules could easily form?
12. What two properties of RNA molecules have made them attractive as a starting point for the evolution of life?
13. What problems inherent in RNA synthesis have made the molecule appear less attractive as a starting point for the evolution of life?
14. Match the following structural terms with their correct level of organization:
    a. Amino acid   i. Cellular
    b. tRNA synthetase   ii. Organellar
    c. Membrane surface   iii. Macromolecular structure
    d. *Mycoplasma genitalium*   iv. Biomolecule/polymer
    e. Tip structure   v. Biomolecule/monomer
15. In an online encyclopedia, look up the term *panspermia*. What is panspermia, and how is it different from directed panspermia?
16. "Coding is the central problem that molecular evolutionists face." Explain the meaning of this statement and evaluate its veracity.
17. Besides the details of flight feather anatomy, list some other aspects of a dinosaur that would need to evolve in the right direction if the dinosaur were to develop the flapping flight of a bird.
18. List five specific features of a primary flight feather that fit it for use in flying.
19. Could a bird that lacks preening behavior be able to fly? Explain your answer.
20. In Chapter 9 we examined the concept of induction during development. Give an example of an induction event in the formation of a bird's feather.
21. What is meant by the phrase *irreducible complexity*? How is flight feather development an example of this?
22. How would a theistic evolutionist's view of natural selection be different from a creationist's view? How would his view of mutation be different from a creationist's view? from an evolutionist's view?
23. How do biologists define a beneficial mutation?
24. Give an example of how a beneficial mutation could result from a loss of function.
25. If mutation is responsible for generating any new beneficial variations, then what is the value of natural selection?
26. Why are we unable to test the hypothesis that the frequency of beneficial mutations will be higher in a population of primitive organisms than in a population of advanced ones?
27. Why did we argue that natural selection might not be able to use a new barbule-producing mutation to move a down feather toward the formation of a flight feather?
28. What is an index fossil? How might it be used?
29. What is a Cambrian rock? What aspect of the Cambrian explosion is most difficult to explain in terms of mutation and natural selection?

30. What evolutionary explanation is given for the sudden radiation of animal phyla in the absence of any transitional forms between them?

31. Distinguish between the terms *analogous* and *homologous* as applied to living organisms.

32. Distinguish between Richard Owen's use of the term *homologous* and Charles Darwin's use of it.

33. What does a homeobox protein do physically in the cell in which it is formed?

34. How does a homeobox gene control where on an animal's body a given structure will develop?

35. List three features of forelimb development that natural selection must guide in order for the limb to have an appropriate structure and position for the function it is to perform.

36. How does a Design theorist explain the homology that appears to exist between the bone structures of a bird's wing and a man's arm?

37. Why are most mutations harmful to an organism from a design perspective? from an evolutionary perspective?

38. Explain how a substitution of one base (say, an A for a C) in a DNA molecule that codes for a protein might have absolutely no effect on the structure of that protein.

39. List three kinds of natural selection and how each kind serves the population in which it acts.

40. Would directional selection be a more powerful force for change in a population of primitive organisms or a population of highly advanced ones? Explain.

41. In a design-based model of the living world, what is the value of natural selection? What is the long-term result of mutation?

QUESTIONS FOR THOUGHT

1. Your author says that sometimes the principles of your discipline become the philosophy of your life. For example, not expecting miracles to influence the results of your experiments can become a belief that miracles cannot happen and have never happened. How could such a change occur in a person's thinking?

2. Is a woman's face art in and of itself? Explain your position on this.

3. Can the formation of two species from one be a deteriorative process instead of a progression toward further complexity of structure and function?

4. Consider the statement: "The diseases of mankind have controlled the biological science he has done." Is this statement accurate? If so, give an example of its validity.

5. Recall our treatment of molecules such as carbon dioxide and water in our discussion of respiration and photosynthesis back in Chapter 6. Why are molecular evolution simulation experiments not done using just these two substances and nitrogen?

6. What structures and/or functions must be in place in a cell in order for a polymer like RNA to contain useful information for generating the sequence of amino acids in a protein?

7. Suppose the gene coding for an adhesin protein molecule experienced a mutation such that it no longer recognizes or binds to host cell tissue. That seems like a harmful mutation. But an evolutionist would argue that it might just be a useful/good mutation. Why would he say this and what would be your response to his hypothesis?

8. We've found the Darwinian hypothesis to excel in simplicity and the Design hypothesis to excel in capability. Which of these two characteristics—simplicity and capability—seems more important to you? Which is more valuable to the immediate progress of science?

9. In trying to determine how a complex feather might have evolved from a simpler one, why are biologists interested in how both feathers develop during the embryonic life of the bird?

10. When an evolutionary biologist finds a fossil of a feather whose structure is intermediate between that of a modern down feather and a modern flight feather, he assumes that the fossil find is indeed one step through which the flight feather evolved. What is another formal possibility he must consider, however, even within an evolutionary model?

11. Mendel crossed two varieties of peas to each other, one with green pea seeds and one with yellow pea seeds. If you had to guess which

color existed first or which other form was a mutant, which form would you pick? Why?

12. Two new mutations occur by chance in a single individual: one is harmful, and the other is helpful. How can we know whether the value of the beneficial mutation outweighs the detriment of the harmful mutation?

13. What do we mean when we say that natural selection is very expensive to a population of organisms?

14. A population of gliding dinosaurs is evolving toward flapping flight. Suggest an example of an environmental change that might discourage the evolution of flapping flight. (Think, what would be the value of active flying over gliding? Under what conditions might that value be diminished?)

15. You discover a new fossil. It appears intermediate in structure between two existing, well-studied fossil types. It could be a transitional form between them or it could be a design novelty that is now extinct. What factor(s) in your thinking would influence your choice between these alternatives?

16. Give an example of two analogous structures other than the ones mentioned in the text.

17. Which is a better choice for the analysis of homology, a structural part of an organism or a gene? Why?

18. Which aspects of homeobox genes suggest that they might all have originated from a single original ancestral animal? Which aspects render that suspicion considerably less plausible?

19. Why is a homeobox gene by itself inadequate to determine the location of a forelimb on an animal body?

20. "No single mutation can be categorically beneficial to a species." Explain why your textbook author takes this position.

21. Some scientists argue that homosexuality in humans is the result of genetic variation—the appearance of new mutant forms of alleles. What evolutionary principle stands against this argument?

22. Of the three kinds of natural selection available to the evolutionary process, which kind would be most important in the development of flight feathers from simple plumes extending from the skin? Explain your choice.

23. Speculate about bristle numbers on the dorsal surface of the *Drosophila* thorax. Why might an extreme increase in bristle number lead a population toward sterility?

24. According to a Biblical model of origins, how would accounts of extreme longevity in early humans be explained?

SUGGESTED READING LIST

Since this principle of life is highly controversial within the community of biological scientists, a brief reading list is here included to give the reader a wide spectrum of authors who share a common sense that design is observed in nature.

Behe, Michael. *Darwin's Black Box.* New York: Simon and Schuster, 1996.

Burgess, Stuart. *Hallmarks of Design,* 2nd ed. Leominster, UK: Day One Publications, 2002.

Dewitt, David. *Unraveling the Origins Controversy.* Lynchburg: Creation Curriculum LLC, 2007.

Meyer, Stephen C. *Signature in the Cell, DNA and Evidence for Intelligent Design.* New York: HarperCollins, 2009.

Sanford, John. *Genetic Entropy & the Mystery of the Genome.* Waterloo, NY: FMS Publication, 2005.

Schaefer, Henry F. *Science and Christianity: Conflict or Coherence.* Watkinsville: The Apollo Trust, 2008.

GLOSSARY

abiotic—of or referring to anything that is nonliving; usually in reference to physical aspects of an ecosystem.

adaptation—a feature of an organism that allows it to reproduce more offspring under a given set of environmental conditions.

adhesin—a biomolecule, usually a protein on the surface of a cell or structure that enables it to fix itself firmly to the surface of some other structure or host cell.

agnosticism—(a) the belief that a God may or may not exist; (b) the belief that it is not possible to know if a God exists.

airfoil—a three-dimensional shape designed to cause a desired response in a moving current of air, for example, an airplane wing.

algorithm—a defined sequence of steps, often repetitive that are used to solve a problem, often a mathematical one.

analogous (in biology)—in reference to two structures, functions, or behaviors that are highly similar though their origins may be quite distinct.

antibiotic—a chemical from a natural source or from a laboratory that limits the growth of or kills microbes, particularly bacteria.

Arthropoda—a large phylum of animals characterized by segmented bodies and appendages, an open circulatory system, and a chitinous exoskeleton; includes insects.

atheism—belief in the nonexistence of God.

autonomy—having complete personal freedom in moral behavior and in self governance.

barb—a branch that extends laterally from the rachis or shaft of a feather; a shaft in its own right that supports smaller extensions called *barbules*.

barbule—small keratinous extensions from the lateral surfaces of barbs; structures that impede the flow of air through a flight feather.

broth culture—usually an aqueous solution containing sufficient nutrients to allow for the growth or maintenance of a particular kind of microorganism or a collection of related microorganisms.

calamus—the rounded, proximal (lower) portion of the shaft of a feather, usually containing no barbs.

Cambrian—the name for a geological period represented by a well-characterized layer of rock that contains certain index fossils.

canalize—(in evolution) to channel, to cause certain time-honored, highly integrative gene sequences to be retained in a population in favor of new mutations whose instability would move the population in a new phenotypic direction.

chitin—a polymer of glucose subunits that forms a tough exoskeleton for the outer surface of arthropods.

Chordate—a phylum of animals that, during some stage of their development, possess a dorsal, central cord of tissue that, in some representatives, is tough and fibrous and lends support to the organism.

chronic—a condition or disease that recurs through time; usually of less severity than a sudden, acute condition or disease.

collar—an inner epidermal surface within an avian follicle that divides off keratinocytes that form the body of a feather.

covert feather—feathers that cover over other feathers smoothing the contour of the body surface for more efficient air flow.

cybernetics—the theoretical study of how highly automatic and inter-articulated systems are controlled.

degenerate—in reference to a cell, a biological structure or individual organism whose supposed evolutionary ancestors were larger, more complex or more well adapted.

deletion—the mutational removal of one or more bases of DNA sequence or of a much larger visible portion of a cell's chromosome.

dermal—of or referring to the deeper, vascularized layer of the skin containing cells that divide to maintain the integrity of the skin as a surface barrier.

directed panspermia—the concept that generative life-forms have been seeded on this (or another) planet by the purposeful actions of intelligent beings.

directional selection—that form of natural selection that removes one extreme of phenotype from a population causing it to shift its phenotypic character toward the opposite extreme; this often involves favoring of a new mutation.

disruptive selection—that form of natural selection that removes intermediate phenotypes from a population, causing it to maintain itself in a rigidly dimorphic state; sexuality is maintained in this way.

distal—far from; in anatomy, characterizing structures that are far removed from the central, medial portion of a body or form.

disulfide bond—a covalent bond formed between two sulfur atoms that helps stabilize the secondary structure of a protein molecule.

domain—an obvious structural region within a protein molecule; composed of a specific amino acid sequence that confers on the protein a predictable functionality—like DNA binding or contributing to quaternary structure.

down feather—a class of avian feathers that aid homeothermic fowl to retain body heat.

Ediacaran—an extinct group of marine invertebrate animals represented by fossils some of which are found in pre–Cambrian rocks.

Enlightenment—a period of European history commencing in the 1700s in which Divine authority was exchanged for human reason, the new measure of all things.

epidermis—the outermost external layer of cells within the skin; many of the cells in this layer are already dead and soon to be sloughed off.

epithelial—of or referring to a cell or group of cells (tissue) that covers either an interior or exterior surface of an organ or individual.

evolution—directional changes in gene frequencies within a population's gene pool over time.

extinct—in reference to species of organisms, a species that no longer has living representatives.

extracellular—a structure or process that is found or takes place outside of a living cell.

follicle—in avian anatomy, the skin-derived structure that gives rise to feathers.

geothermal vent—a break in the deep ocean floor from which superheated water emerges; the water often contains reduced inorganic compounds.

homeobox—a sequence of bases within a *Hox* gene that code for a protein domain that enables the Hox protein to bind a specific region of DNA sequence.

homeoprotein—a regulatory protein, part of whose internal structure is coded for by a sequence of bases called a *homeobox*; the internal structure allows it to regulate genes by binding to the DNA of their promoter sequences.

homologous (in biology)—in reference to two structures, functions, or behaviors that are believed to have a common origin in a common ancestral organism.

hooklet (or barbicel)—a small curled projection from a barbule surface that latches into the groove or ridge on the surface of an adjacent barbule; holds the barbs of a feather into a closed planar structure.

host cell—a cell that supports the growth or reproduction of a virus, bacterium, or larger microbial form that has either entered it or is in close association with it.

index fossil—a kind of fossil form that is typically associated with a particular layer of sedimentary rock.

irreducible complexity—a level of orderliness in a system whereby the removal of one component renders the rest of the system inoperable.

keel—in avian anatomy, the central (medial) pronounced ridge on the sternal bone of the bird where powerful flight muscles attach.

keratin—light, fibrous, sulfur-containing proteins contributing most of the structure of hair, nails, and feathers.

keratinocyte—a cell that by its synthesis of the protein keratin contributes to the final form of the avian feather.

L and D forms—two nonidentical, mirror-image forms of a molecule built around an asymmetric central carbon atom.

macroevolution—the process by which chemicals slowly give rise to cells that then diverge to form many cell types and eventually many types of organisms representing all the diversity of life on Earth.

materialism—the notion that physical matter is the only form of reality and all metaphysical phenomenon can be explained in terms of physical interactions between materials.

methane—an organic compound whose molecules are composed of one carbon atom covalently bonded to four hydrogen atoms; a fuel for cooking.

microevolution—the process by which mutations and recombination between alleles generate new individuals in a population that slowly change its genetic and structural character with time.

microfossils—shapes of microscopic size within rocks; the shapes are believed to be the remains of early bacterial or algal forms of life.

microfossil—within sedimentary rock, fossil forms of prokaryotic cells that are detectable only by microscopy.

mutagenic—any process or substance that causes changes in informational molecules such as DNA or RNA.

mycoplasma—a very small bacterium that lacks a cell wall; appears genetically related to genera *Lactobacillus* and *Clostridium*, much larger gram-positive bacteria having cell walls.

natural selection—that characteristic of the environment that favors the viability and reproductive activity of one individual in a population over another.

naturalism—the philosophy or world-and-life view that declares nature, its forms, and its rules to be all that exists; any evidences of the supernatural are illusory.

neo-Darwinian synthesis—that version of Darwin's theory in which Mendelian genes are the informational basis for the variations observed between members of a population.

overlap—in genetics, a single sequence of DNA or RNA that contains information for two or more coding sequences or genes.

oxidize—to attract electrons away from; in biological systems this is often carried out by oxygen.

paradigm—a broadly based intellectual framework for thinking; a philosophical context in which to interpret experimental results and develop new theories.

parasite—a microscopic organism living on or in another organism from which it gains nutrients and/or energy at the expense of the other organism.

phylum—one of the large major divisions of the animal kingdom; there are about 40 such divisions in the animal kingdom

planar—of or referring to a flat, nearly two-dimensional surface.

plankton—microscopic life-forms found in the oceans of the world.

plaque—a localized thickened area or patch on a surface such as the skin.

Porifera—a phylum of animals consisting of sponges; the supporting skeleton is of calcium carbonate spicules or an organic material called *spongin*; the body is highly porous to currents of water.

preen—in birds, the activity of drawing the bill along the space between feather barbs reestablishing hooklet and ridge attachments and thus the integrity of the feather surface.

primary flight feather—those large feathers on the distal portions of the avian wing principally supportive of flight.

proximal—in anatomy, located close to the central, internal surfaces of a body.

pulp—in avian anatomy, that internal dermal layer of cells within the follicle that is nutritive of the keratinocytes forming the feather.

rachis—in compound leaves or feathers, a central shaft that supports leaflets or barbs extending laterally from its surfaces.

radiation (in evolutionary theory)—a long-term process by which a single ancestral species gives rise to two or many daughter species as a result of mutation and natural selection.

reading frame—a way of commencing the transcribing of a DNA sequence; since a sequence of mRNA is read in codons of three bases each, there are three possible starting points and three reading frames for the same sequence of bases.

reduced—an atom whose oxidation number has been decreased (by the addition of an electron).

Renaissance—a period of European history, commencing in the 1400s, in which a renewed interest in classical literature and ancient Biblical texts arose.

reproductive potential—the ability of the members of a species to maintain or expand population size by reproducing themselves.

RNA world—a prebiotic/protobiotic cellular environment in which RNA molecules serve both informational and catalytic roles.

sedimentary—descriptive of a rock or layer of rock formed by compaction and conglomeration of sand, silt, or other particulates; often containing fossils.

selection pressure—any force within the environment that reduces the reproductive potential of one variety of individuals in a species over another variety.

sheath—in living systems, a thin layer of cells or tissues, or that which covers or protects an underlying structure.

socket wall—the outer, epidermal surface of an avian follicle that contains and guides the growth of an internal prefeather structure.

speciation—the formation of two new species from one by an isolating process that allows two populations of a species to become genetically distinct from each other to the point of intersterility.

stabilizing selection—that form of natural selection that removes extremes of phenotype (harmful mutations) from a population, causing it to maintain its phenotype without significant alteration.

sternum—the breastbone; a compound, ventral bone to which ribs and skeletal musculature are attached.

tetrapod—any organism that walks on four appendages; often used of an ancestral form from which many vertebrates radiated evolutionarily.

theism—belief in the existence of God.

theistic evolution—the concept that the history of life is a long sequence of selection events operating on a corresponding sequence of Divinely chosen mutations in the genetic information.

thorax—the central section(s) of the animal body, located posterior to the head and anterior to the abdomen.

tip structure—a morphologic region on the anterior region of some mycoplasmas; used to adhere to host cells and for motility.

topological—of or referring to the surface contour of a three-dimensional shape.

trachea—a single member of a complex system of branching, gas-filled channels in the body of an insect; the system of channels carries oxygen to the animal's tissues and waste carbon dioxide away from them.

transcription factor—a class of regulatory protein molecules that bind promoter DNA and influence the frequency of transcription of the adjacent structural portion of a gene.

tRNA synthetase—a protein enzyme that binds a specific class of transfer RNA molecules and binds a specific kind of amino acid to them.

ultrastructure—biological structures within a cell that are larger than polymeric molecules but too small to be seen with bright-field (light) microscopes.

uniformitarianism—a geological concept that operant natural forces in the present are identical to natural forces in the past and are responsible for all of the landforms and patterns of strata currently observed on Earth.

uropygial gland—structure in the base of the avian tail that secretes an oil used for preening and/or waterproofing the feathers.

vertebrate—any animal that possesses a dorsal, medial sequence of inter-articulating bone segments; commonly referred to as a *backbone*.

14

An Infinity of Diversity

14.1 THE CHALLENGE OF CLASSIFYING LIFE'S DIVERSITY

Survey Questions

14.1 The Challenge of Classifying Life's Diversity

- How diverse is life? How many species are there?
- What are the primary challenges to classifying all the kinds of organisms in the living world?
- How does the complexity of the organism affect our ability to classify it?
- Should a system of classification take into account the origin of the species being classified?

14.2 Classification: Engaging the Challenge

- What processes or activities are involved in building a classification scheme for living organisms?
- How is the unit of the classification scheme defined? What items, exactly, are being classified?
- Does classifying living things involve any sort of hierarchical system of categories? If so, what are these?

14.3 Characteristics Used in Classification

- Which characteristics of living organisms are used for classifying them?
- How are these characteristics selected for this purpose?
- Are all of the characteristics visible? How are unicellular forms classified?

"Mooooooooooommmmmm . . . . where's my wallet?"
"Look where you left it, dear, that's where you'll find it."
"(Grrrrr . . . .) . . .If I knew where I left it, would I be asking you where it is?"
"Bertrand, when are you going to clean up your room?"
"Mom, why are we getting off the subject?!! Where's my wallet"
"It might be in your room. Why not start cleaning it and see what you find."
"I'll get to it tomorrow."
"Good! I'll put that on my calendar. It'll take you two days to do it right and don't just throw everything into the laundry. If you do, I'll probably wash your wallet."
"Mumble, mumble . . . . . ."

Organizing things is such an utterly provincial concept. Few care to do it anymore unless a computer forces their hand. Yet the admirable progress that's been made in the biological sciences has been supported by serious, protracted, competitive attempts to organize the biological world for study. Why is this necessary? Because the diversity of species on this planet is even greater than the number of tee-shirts on Bertrand's room floor.

- How can we know that the characteristics we've chosen are the best ones for the purpose of classifying?

14.4 Using Characters: Priorities and Presuppositions

- Do all scientists agree on which characteristics should be used for classification?
- Which characteristics are the most important ones? Are these used at the highest hierarchical levels of classifying?
- If there was a common Designer for all living things, how can we know that any classification scheme is valid?

14.5 Using Characters to Derive "Groups"

- What are some examples of the largest taxonomic groups that scientists have created?
- How many are there?
- Which characteristics distinguish them from each other?
- We wouldn't put a human being and a corn smut fungus into the same large group, would we? If so, why?

14.6 Classification: Persistent Problems

- What are the most persistent problems associated with classification?
- Do any of these problems arise from assumptions relating to the origins of the species?

14.7 Classifying Man

- How has *Homo sapiens* been classified relative to other organisms?
- What issues are unique to classifying humans within a taxonomic scheme?
- Should humans be related to other organisms systematically using only biological characteristics?

Life Is Diverse—the tenth principle of life on which this text is based.

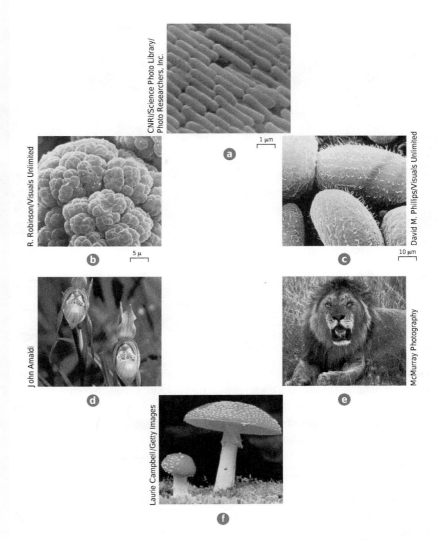

Figure 14.1 Life is Diverse. Just six of millions of species that populate our planet. **(a)** a bacterium, *Bacillus anthracis* that causes the disease anthrax in cattle and occasionally in humans **(b)** an Archean, *Methanosarcina mazei*, whose tiny prokaryotic cells generate a useful gas, methane, as a biproduct of their metabolism **(c)** large cells of the eukaryotic ciliate *Tetrahymena pyriformis;* these are fresh-water dwellers that have become highly useful in molecular genetic research **(d)** The fascinating flower of the lady slipper, *Phragmipedium caricinum* **(e)** *Panthera leo,* King of his pride **(f)** The beautiful and halucinogenic mushroom *Amanita muscaria.*

Life Is Diverse. How diverse? We don't even know (see Figure 14.1)! Our ignorance is going to surface rather early in our exploration of this Principle of Life. While we know of almost 2 million species on our planet (see Figure 14.2a), microbiologists are confronting us with soil and water samples containing possibly millions of distinct, yet novel, bacterial DNA sequences. Current surmise is that there are many more left to be discovered. Indeed we've found only the easiest ones to find! Even with just the species of life we know are here, what an overwhelming task we face in trying to examine them all and relate them to each other! Some of them, including many microbial

Classification Challenges

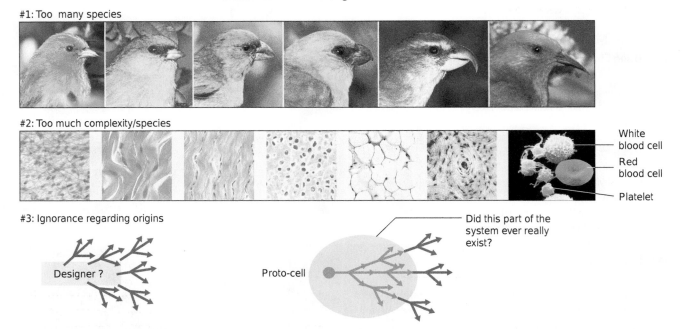

#1: Too many species

#2: Too much complexity/species

White blood cell

Red blood cell

Platelet

#3: Ignorance regarding origins

Designer ?

Proto-cell

Did this part of the system ever really exist?

Figure 14.2 Classification Challenges. #1. These birds are all closely related Genera that go by the name Hawaiian honeycreeper. The Hawaiian Islands alone contain over 500 of the 1500 species of the common vinegar fly, *Drosophila*. The tropical rain forests of Brazil have a species diversity that is too vast to begin to measure! #2 These photographs are stained sections of different connective tissues found in *Homo sapiens*. They are from left to right: Loose connective tissue, dense connective tissue, dense regular connective tissue, cartilage, adipose tissue, bone, blood. Each tissue contains a variety of specialized cell types. The complexity of man is almost infinite. #3 The origin of species is controversial; how that origin is described has a profound effect on schemes derived to classify those species.

1 Jack Jeffrey Photography, 2 John Cunningham/Visuals Unlimited; Ed Reschke; Science Photo Library/ Photo Researchers, Inc.; University of Cincinnati, Raymond Walters College, Biology; Michael Abbey/ PhotoResearchers, Inc.; Science Photo Library/ Photo Researchers, Inc.

species yet to be cultured or described, are entirely unrelated to any creatures we now know. Brave is the scientist who wants in on this project, who, in effect, says to God, "We can organize this!"

The diversity of life-forms is not the only problem the biologist faces. Just as daunting is a problem we've already wrestled with: the unfathomable complexity of each organism to be classified (see Figure 14.2b). Each kind of organism out there has a bewildering array of structural, functional, developmental, and molecular characteristics that are highly integrated. And these characteristics vary from beast to beast! If the Designer of each life-form is a genius, then He is a genius 10 million times over!

How does this complexity of organisms frustrate the student of diversity? Consider the boxes shown in Figure 14.3a. Each has just four letters inside of it. Let's allow each box to represent a species of organism and each letter to represent one characteristic of that organism. Each organism, then, has only four features or characteristics that are observable. Examine these boxes and classify the organisms into two groups on a piece of paper. Not too hard was it? You simply constructed one group

containing all the ABC boxes and one containing all the XYZ boxes. It's like being given four trees and four **mammals** to classify into two groups. Great! Now having developed a bit of expertise at this, let's consider Fig 14.3b.

Hmm, what's wrong here? Later on you'll see some actual examples of organisms that exemplify this problem. They're scattered all through nature! It's maddening. You select a small set of important characteristics and start grouping organisms according to the characteristics they have. Inevitably some organism will cross a criterion line and be found in both groups. There are just too many organisms with too much complexity to enable a simple means of classification to work well.

But a third problem faces us when we think about the origin of all of these organisms (see Figure 14.2c). If, like Carl Linnaeus, you assume that all modern life-forms are fairly similar to the original ones God

mammal—a group of vertebrate animals that possess hair and nourish their young with milk; includes humans.

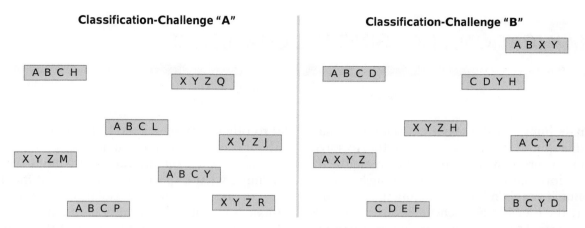

Figure 14.3 Classification – Challenge. **(a)** Classification as perceived by a young biology student working with a few trees and mammals. **(b)** Classification as an everyday challenge for a taxonomist.

created, then you just start looking for important and common characteristics across large collections of species. You hope that large groups can be formed reflecting broad patterns of thought that were in the mind of God. How many patterns might that be? There might be many, but you'd feel no need to draw these patterns together into just one or a few preliminary patterns based on even more widely shared characteristics.

Oh, but if you are an evolutionist who believes that life only started once, then your task of classification is to nest the many patterns of organisms you discover into still larger groups according to how they appeared in history. For example, if early on the first life-form evolved in seven different directions, you'd need to try to coax all life-forms into just seven large groups reflecting seven large family trees that were just emerging. This need to bring the entire diversity of living things back into just a few original groups and then ultimately one group has placed enormous burdens on our classification efforts—burdens that, from a design perspective, may not even represent historical reality.

IN OTHER WORDS

1. We are ignorant of how many species of life-forms exist on this planet because of our limited exploration and because we have trouble defining the word *species*.
2. We currently have described 1.7 million species of life-forms and we know other life-forms exist on the planet.
3. A major problem that frustrates classification schemes is the biological complexity of the organisms being classified.
4. Another problem facing taxonomists is disagreement regarding the importance of origins of species in fashioning hierarchical relationships within the classification scheme developed.

CLASSIFICATION: ENGAGING THE CHALLENGE

The innate hubris of the scientific community has resulted in quite a belabored human effort to solve problems a brilliant Designer has created! We could explore the intrinsic humor of such a situation. But if man's mind is a brilliant Designer's product, then let's take science seriously and see how we've tried to solve these enormous organizational problems.

Science has approached the diversity of organisms with two contrasting but closely related strategies. One strategy is to start collecting individual organisms into species and larger groupings. The other is to develop a general scheme for organizing large numbers of groups of organisms. We called these two approaches **taxonomy** and **systematics** (see Figure 14.4).

In the discipline of taxonomy, we seek to give a scientific label or name to each variety of life-form we find: a **species** name. We then seek to relate it to other similar species. If you're thinking now about honeybees and bumblebees, this sounds rather easy if a bit subjective. It is not easy. Even defining what a species *is* has proven difficult. We try to use reproductive isolation as a criterion (male honeybees don't mate with female bumblebees), but consistent application of this approach is laborious and not without its own problems. (Which varieties of dogs can and cannot interbreed, for example?)

Once we think we have species tentatively defined, we begin to group them. Usually, a newly defined species is closely related structurally or genetically to some previously discovered species or group of species. So we then collect these related species together with the new one and call them a **genus.** A genus is a more inclusive group whose structural and functional variations are broader than those found within a single species (see Figure 14.5). Using Latin root words, the new species is then named for its primary distinguishing features using two words (names) in accordance with standard rules: Its genus name is listed first and capitalized. The species name is listed second and is in lowercase letters (see Figure 14.6). The entire name is either underlined or placed in italics. So while your street name may be Homer Sapsucker, your scientific name is *Homo sapiens,*

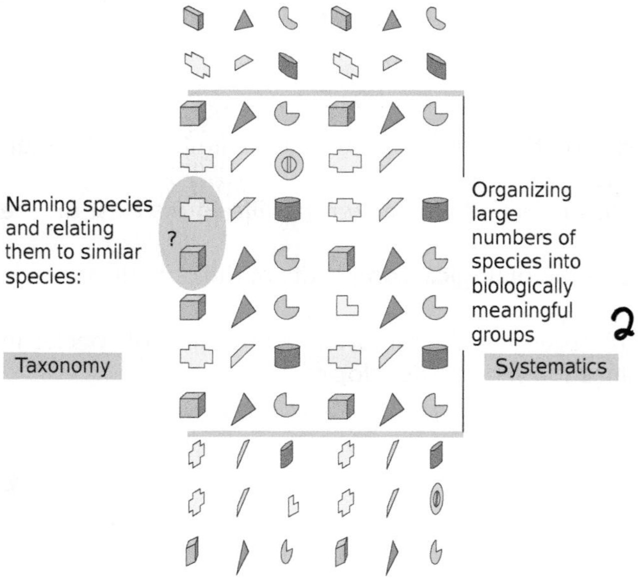

Naming species and relating them to similar species: ?

Taxonomy

Organizing large numbers of species into biologically meaningful groups

Systematics

2.

Figure 14.4 Classification: two related approaches to it. In taxonomy we build a classification system by comparing elements within the system to each other. In systematics we seek to form biologically meaningful groups within the system.

taxonomy—the science of classifying individual varieties of organisms into an orderly system.

systematics—the structuring and criticism of attempts at natural groupings of life-forms usually according to presumed evolutionary relationships.

species—a collection of populations of organisms that are similar enough to each other to be able to inter-mate to produce fertile offspring.

3.

genus—a collection of species that are structurally closely related to each other and distinct from other such collections.

Homo sapiens—the formal generic and specific name for human beings; the scientific name for mankind.

Figure 14.5   Male Cichlid Fish Species from Lake Victoria. These closely related species of fish have similar size and morphology differing largely in color patterns. But colors are visual cues to females who will mate with males of only their own species. These fish would probably fall into the same Genus, but generic relationships are not well worked out for this Family of fish.

meaning *man who is wise*. And apparently, sapiens is the only known species extant (alive today) in genus *Homo*. Your name can also be written in abbreviated form as *H. sapiens*.

In the discipline of systematics, we attempt to derive a unified and biologically meaningful filing system for dumping these many genera and species into. As the number and diversity of species

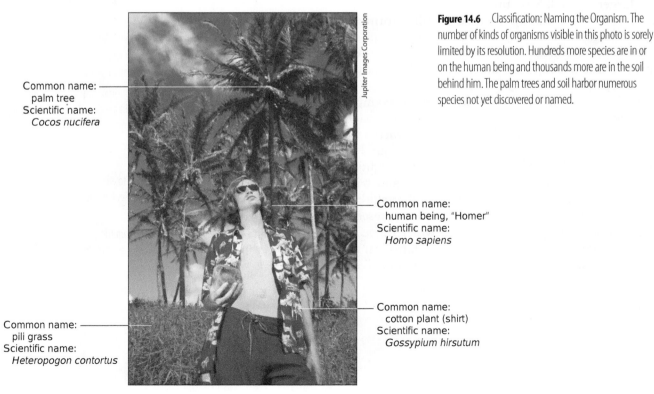

Common name:
   palm tree
Scientific name:
   Cocos nucifera

Common name:
   pili grass
Scientific name:
   Heteropogon contortus

Common name:
   human being, "Homer"
Scientific name:
   Homo sapiens

Common name:
   cotton plant (shirt)
Scientific name:
   Gossypium hirsutum

Figure 14.6   Classification: Naming the Organism. The number of kinds of organisms visible in this photo is sorely limited by its resolution. Hundreds more species are in or on the human being and thousands more are in the soil behind him. The palm trees and soil harbor numerous species not yet discovered or named.

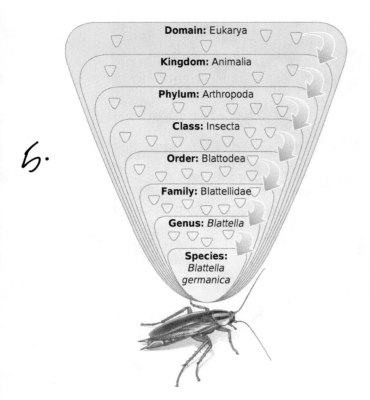

Figure 14.7 The Systematics of the German Cockroach. Systematics has developed a nested hierarchy in which to describe any particular species. Each taxonomic level contains far more species than the one shown within it.

beetles, bees, wasps, dragonflies, and other orders forms the immense class Insecta: all insects. Insects, along with spiders, centipedes, shrimp, scorpions, crabs, and barnacles form a much larger phylum called the *Arthropods*. The arthropods, along with thousands of kinds of starfish, clams, sponges, worms, and people, etc!, are collected in a vast kingdom called **Animalia**: the animals. Workers in the last century went on to group all animals, plants, fungi, and **protistan** forms into a still larger grouping called the **domain** of the Eukaryotes.

Our filing system has had difficulty keeping pace with the rate of discovery of new species. By the end of the 20th century, the number of kingdoms had gone from two (plant and animal) to six or more; at each taxonomic level such as class or order there were superclasses and subclasses, superorders and suborders, and so on. When you explore the inner reaches of the Designer's Mind, the vistas just get bigger and bigger.

cataloged has increased, the filing system has gotten larger as well. Structurally related genera were collected into a **family**. Related families form an **order**. Related orders were grouped into a **class**. Classes were collected into a **phylum** (or **division** in the plant world). And diverse but related phyla were organized into a **kingdom**.

Let's use a common household pest as an example of how this system works. The German cockroach has the scientific name *Blattella germanica* (see Figure 14.7). It is one of about 50 species found in the genus *Blattella*. This genus, along with eight to nine others forms a family of household and wild varieties of cockroaches called the Blattellidae. The family, along with about five others representing a broader geographic area and wider range of shapes and sizes, comprise the order Blattodea: all cockroaches. This order, along with the butterflies,

family (in systematics)—a formal grouping of structurally related genera that is distinct from other such groupings.

order (in systematics)—a formal grouping of structurally related families that is distinct from other such groupings.

class (in systematics)—a formal grouping of structurally related orders that is distinct from other such groupings.

phylum (in systematics)—a formal grouping of structurally related classes that is distinct from other such groupings.

kingdom (in systematics)—a formal grouping of structurally related phyla (in animals, or divisions, in plants) that is distinct from other such groupings.

Animalia—a taxonomic kingdom that includes all living and extinct animals.

protistan—an archaic term that refers to a broad, highly heterogeneous group of unicellular and colonial eukaryotes, once lumped together into kingdom Protista.

domain—an increasingly archaic term referring to a broad collection of organisms having a particular sequence of ribosomal RNA.

1. Classification involves two related and complementary processes: taxonomy and systematics.
2. The taxonomist is chiefly concerned with describing a new organism, naming it, and relating it to other organisms similar to it.
3. The systematist seeks to draw large groups of related organisms into an overall hierarchical scheme that becomes a mammoth filing system for all life-forms.
4. The rules for naming a new organism are well agreed upon; the name consists of two parts, the generic and the specific names for the organism in question.
5. Related genera of organisms have been grouped into families; related families into orders, related orders into classes, related classes into phyla, and related phyla into kingdoms.
6. In recent decades, kingdoms have been collected by some workers into large groups called *domains*, but this terminology is more tentative.
7. Each of these taxonomic levels can have both sub and supergroups. Subclasses and superorders exist, for example.

Classifying organisms into groups requires the choice and use of specific characteristics of living things as criteria for placing the organisms into these groups. Classifying organisms occurs at all levels within our filing system (see Figure 14.8). One sort of characteristic might be chosen for making distinctions at the genus level, say, between the domestic cat and the wild cat. A quite different set of characteristics would be used for making distinctions at the kingdom level, say between a domestic cat and a maple tree. To make our filing system biologically meaningful, we have to use characteristics appropriate to the filing level at which we are classifying things. Such choices really test our understanding of which biological characteristics are more or less fundamental. Only seasoned biologists are very good at this!

In this brief chapter, we have time to look at only the highest levels of organization that make up the entire array of life-forms. For major groupings of organisms, we use only very important characteristics of living things—those that allow comparisons across the entire biological world! These will be basic features of the organism's structure and role in nature. A design theorist would call them *fundamental features*—features that solve problems faced by virtually all organisms the Designer placed on this planet. An evolutionist would call these same features **primitive** because he assumes that they showed up very early as life diverged into its primary new directions.

What sorts of features meet this criterion? First, a good criterion will divide the living things before it into a small number of equally large groups. For example, were we to classify all motor vehicles into groups, which characteristic would be superior: a truck versus a car, or a blue vehicle versus a nonblue vehicle? Surely the former characteristic would give us two, more equally sized groups and therefore be more useful. The color of the vehicle is less fundamental structurally and would give two very unbalanced groups: all blue vehicles versus a huge majority of nonblue vehicles. In this latter characteristic choice, we'd have done far less classifying and have less information than with the former choice. In the living world, to divide all life-forms into those that make their own food and those that do not would be far more useful than to divide all forms into those with eyes and those without since the former distinction is so fundamental and since the vast majority of organisms do not have eyes!

Second, as you might guess, characteristics for placing organisms into very large groups are generally cellular and molecular features. An evolutionist would have it no other way, since it is assumed that organisms were cellular long before they had any higher levels of organization. Let's now list some of the basic features used for classifying living things (see Table 14.1).

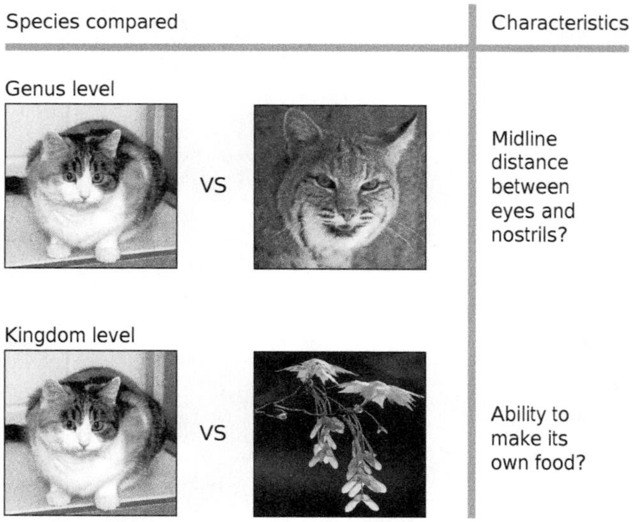

Species compared	Characteristics
Genus level	
VS	Midline distance between eyes and nostrils?
Kingdom level	
VS	Ability to make its own food?

Figure 14.8 Systematics: Building the Filing System. Items farther apart in a classification scheme differ from each other by more fundamental characteristics.
cat: College of Veterinary Medicine, Univ. of Texas, bobcat: William H. Mullins/ Photo Researchers, Inc., maple: R. Carr

primitive (in biology)—descriptive of a characteristic of an organism that is presumed to have great evolutionary age.

Table 14.1 Systematics: Fundamental Characteristics.

Character	Alternative states		
Photosynthesis ?	Yes: autotrophy *Euglena gracilis,* Euglena		No: heterotrophy *Saccharomyces cerevisiae,* brewer's yeast
Multicellularity ?	Yes: multicellular *Cyclommatus pulchellus,* staghorn beetle		No: unicellular *Paramecium aurelium,* Paramecium
Nucleus ?	Yes: eukaryotic *Dipodomys Dseserti,* desert rat cells		No: prokaryotic *Lactobacillus bulgaricus,* Bacterium in yogurt

(Continued)

7.
Characteristic #1: Does It Do Photosynthesis?

Can the cell utilize solar energy to make food, or must it get food from some other organism? Many biologists wouldn't care to admit this, but Moses tells us in Genesis 1 that this first distinction was important in God's eyes as well. Photosynthetic organisms were formed on day three of creation week while those that could not utilize solar energy show up later. In larger organisms, this distinction is so fundamental that Aristotle, the Father of Biology, saw it clearly. He said, "Of the psychic powers above enumerated (nutritive, appetitive, sensory, locomotive, thinking), some kinds of living things . . . possess all, some less, others one only. Plants have none but the first . . . ." And so **autotrophy**, the ability to make one's own food, became the basis for placement of an organism into either the plant or the animal kingdom.

autotroph—an organism (or cell) that is capable of producing its own food either via photosynthesis or geochemical exothermic reactions.

Table 14.1 *(Continued)*

Flagellae ?	Yes: one anterior	None

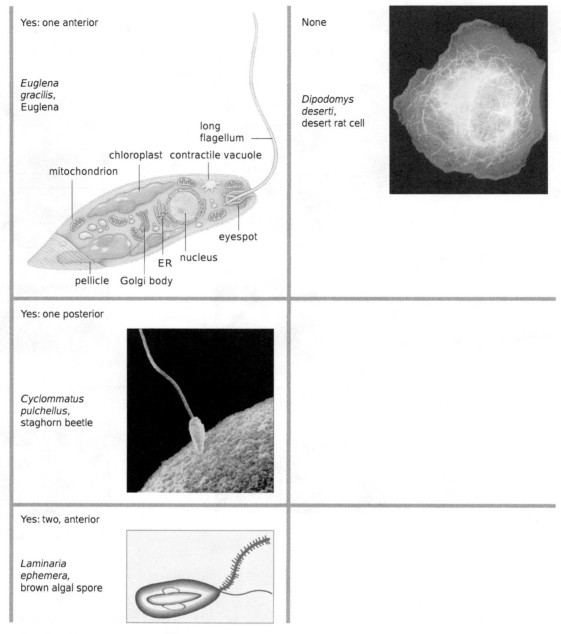

	Yes: one anterior	None
	Euglena gracilis, Euglena	*Dipodomys deserti,* desert rat cell

long flagellum

chloroplast contractile vacuole

mitochondrion

eyespot

pellicle Golgi body ER nucleus

	Yes: one posterior	
	Cyclommatus pulchellus, staghorn beetle	

	Yes: two, anterior	
	Laminaria ephemera, brown algal spore	

(Continued)

Characteristic #2: Is It Multicellular?

Aristotle had no microscope. But Ernst Haeckel, a German zoologist in the 1870s did. He discovered a whole world of microorganisms, some of which confounded the two-kingdom system—they were neither clearly plant nor animal. So whether or not an organism is **unicellular** or **multicellular** has become important for assigning it to life's largest groups. Some cells both swim like animals and do

unicellular—descriptive of a kind of organism that is composed of one cell.

multicellular—descriptive of a kind of organism that is composed of many cells.

Table 14.1 *(Continued)*

Mitochondria ?	Yes: cristae disc-like (tube-like in some forms) *Rattus norvegicus*, brown rat cell vcytoplasm	None: amitochondrial *Giardia lamblia*, Giardia	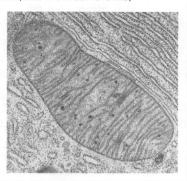 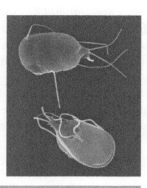
Amoeboid Movement ?	Yes: *Chaos carolinensis*, an Amoeba	No: *Pyrus communis*, European pear, stone cells (from fruit)	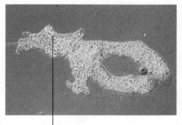 
Gene Sequences (examples)	Ribosomal RNA The 16S rRNA gene product is a structural part of the ribosome's small subunit	DNA polymerase Genes coding for DNA polymerase are compared across many species	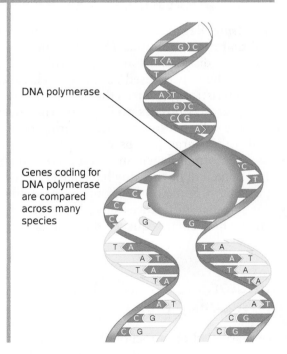

Pseudopodium

photosynthesis like plants. So this multicellularity criterion can relegate the issue of autotroph versus non-autotroph to the multicellular level, where differences are *somewhat* more clear cut.

If an organism is multicellular, we look more closely and ask: Is it, like an algal strand, merely a **colonial** association of relatively independent cells attached to each other, or are the cells (as in a moss plant) differentiated into separate types to form **tissues**? Tissues serve separate complementary roles within the life of the multicellular organism.

Characteristic #3: Has It Got a Nucleus?

Edouard Chatton, a French marine biologist in the 1930s, argued that an important biological characteristic of a cell is whether or not it possesses a visible, membrane-bound or true nucleus. He called cells that got by without a visible nucleus **prokaryotes**. Cells that had managed, with time, to evolve one he termed **eukaryotes**. At first, prokaryotes were described as being significantly smaller and simpler than eukaryotic cells, but those distinctions have begun to break down.

Characteristic #4: Has It Got Flagellae and Where?

Flagellae (*sing.* **flagellum**) are whip-like extensions of a cell that make it motile. They were once used as a basis for distinctions among microbes but in recent years have been used as a major classification characteristic right across the biological world. Some large groups possess no flagellae whatsoever. Others have cells with only one, pointing posteriorly. Still other large groups consist of cells that possess one normal flagellum and a second highly modified flagellum having tiny hair-like projections along its length. Some of the groups created on the basis of flagellar differences have been shown to have major molecular sequence differences as well (see below).

Characteristic #5: What Are Its Mitochondria Like?

You've learned that mitochondria are the powerhouses of the cell, generating large quantities of ATP from carbohydrate sources. Some groups of organisms however, do not have mitochondria even though they have a nucleus and other organelles. Still other groups have highly modified mitochondria. The internal structure of a mitochondrion includes inward extensions of the inner membrane called **cristae**. The structural shape of these cristal extensions—whether disc-like or tubular—has also been used to group organisms into large categories. This character choice is based on the assumption that mitochondria were once prokaryotic cells that invaded larger cells (eukaryotic ones) and began a cooperative existence there. Such events would have occurred early in life's evolution, hence the logic for giving differing cristae structure such importance.

Characteristic #6: Can It Flow (Go) Places?

Some cells have a novel form of motility called *amoeboid movement*. A forward projecting portion of the cell boundary expands suddenly. The cytoplasm in the vicinity becomes fluid and the cell flows into the extension. This allows them to project across surfaces by extending portions of their cytoplasm in a new direction. Other large assemblages of cells completely lack this ability.

colonial—descriptive of a multicellular aggregation (organism?) in which the relations between cells are superficial; basic cell functions are retained by each cell in the colony. Many algae fit this description.

tissue—a collection of highly similar cells and their intercellular materials that associate closely with each other and carry out a common function for a larger organism.

prokaryote—a type of cell whose genetic information is not organized within the confines of a nuclear membrane.

eukaryote—a type of cell or organism whose genetic information is highly organized within the confines of a membrane-bound nucleus.

flagellum—a whip-like shaft extending from the surface of a cell that by its own internal flexion is capable of propelling the cell through a liquid medium.

cristae—membranous internal folds of the inner mitochondrial membrane; these increase the surface area required for aerobic respiration reactions.

```
     honeycreeper ...CRDVQFGWLIRNLHANGASFFFICIYLHIGRGIYYGSYLNK--ETWNIGVILLLTLMATAFVGYVLPWGQMSFWG...
Gough Island finch ...CRDVQFGWLIRNIHANGASFFFICIYLHIGRGLYYGSYLYK--ETWNVGVILLLTLMATAFVGYVLPWGQMSFWG...
       song sparrow ...CRDVQFGWLIRNLHANGASFFFICIYLHIGRGIYYGSYLNK--ETWNVGIILLLALMATAFVGYVLPWGQMSFWG...
          deer mouse ...CRDVNYGWLIRYMHANGASMFFICLFLHVGRGMYYGSYTFT--ETWNIGIVLLFAVMATAFMGYVLPWGQMSFWG...
  Asiatic black bear ...CRDVHYGWIIRYMHANGASMFFICLFMHVGRGLYYGSYLLS--ETWNIGIILLFTVMATAFMGYVLPWGQMSFWG...
      bogue (a fish) ...CRDVNYGWLIRNLHANGASFFFICIYLHIGRGLYYGSYLYK--ETWNIGVVLLLVMGTAFVGYVLPWGQMSFWG...
               human ...TRDVNYGWIIRYLHANGASMFFICLFLHIGRGLYYGSFLYS--ETWNIGIILLLATMATAFMGYVLPWGQMSFWG...
thale cress (a plant) ...MRDVEGGWLLRYMHANGASMFLIVVYLHIFRGLYHASYSSPREFVWCLGVVIFLLMIVTAFIGYVLPWGQMSFWG...
       baboon louse ...ETDVMNGWMVRSIHANGASWFFIMLYSHIFRGLWVSSFTQP--LVWLSGVIILFLSMATAFLGYVLPWGQMSFWG...
        baker's yeast ...MRDVHNGYILRYLHANGASFFFMVMFMHMAKGLYYGSYRSPRVTLWNVGVIIFTLTIATAFLGYCCVYGQMSHWG...
```

Figure 14.9 Portion of the Amino Acid Sequence of the Respiratory Protein Cytochrome b. A wide variety of organisms is listed to the left. The individual letters in each row represent a specific kind of amino acid in the protein's primary structure in the cells of that organism. The Hawaiian honeycreeper (a bird) provides the reference sequence at the top. Notice that the finch sequence differs by only 4% while a mouse's sequence differs by 24%. The mouse is thus 20% less similar to the honeycreeper than is the finch. Makes sense. But this is only one small portion of the huge pool of sequences that could be compared. Could this one pool of protein sequences be used to realistically relate all known species to each other in a single large "diagram"? A naturalist hopes so.

Characteristic #7: What Are Some of the Cell's Gene Sequences?

Although they come last historically, molecular sequence comparisons have become the principle determinants in recent years in assigning organisms to broad groups. What makes these comparisons useful? Well, consider songbirds. They get classified into groups based on the colors of their feathers. But feathers are found only in birds. There are certain molecules however, that are in all living things!

- Virtually all living cells make proteins and thus have ribosomes. And there are certain molecules of RNA (rRNA) in these ribosomes that have a specific common role within the ribosome's structure.
- Or consider the respiratory protein cytochrome b. It is found in virtually any cell and in *every* cell it has exactly the same role: helping to transfer electrons to make ATP.
- Then there are DNA and RNA polymerases found in virtually all cells. They copy cellular genetic information. Both of these molecules do identical jobs in every cell where they are found and they are found in most cells!

This gives enormous value to sequence comparisons across large groupings of organisms (see Figure 14.9). Comparing the amino acid sequence of a cytochrome b protein from a honeycreeper and from a song sparrow is far more valuable than comparing the color of a blue jay and a bluebird because two sequences of amino acids can be compared objectively, numerically, and statistically. Differences can be quantified. You can say quantitatively how much more different a yeast cytochrome is from an oak tree cytochrome or a porcupine cytochrome. Great stuff!

IN OTHER WORDS

1. Characteristics used in classification vary widely in their biological significance. More important characteristics are used at higher taxonomic levels, such as kingdoms; less important ones distinguish genera or species from each other.
2. The ideal characteristic divides the organisms left to be classified into two large, practically equal groups.
3. Most of the important biological characteristics are cellular or molecular in nature; they tend to generate large, minimally overlapping groups.
4. Examples of important biological characteristics are the ability to generate carbohydrate energy, the number of cells per organism, the presence or absence of cell nuclei, flagellae, amoeboid movement, or mitochondria.

6. These seven sets of criteria have been used by various systematists to group all the kinds of organisms known to exist into a variety of conflicting kingdom or domain structures (see Figure 14.10). Due to constantly emerging data and arguments over its importance, these systematic groupings are always in a slow state of flux. It is therefore prudent to draw back from embracing a specific classification system. Rather, we'll simply recognize about 10 of the larger groups of organisms that appear to be informationally and structurally distinct from other such groups. We will use the term **group** rather than the terms *kingdom* or *domain*. Systematics is moving so quickly that the word *kingdom* is used for the last set of mistaken assemblages previously agreed upon. Newer, possibly better but more controversial assemblages get the less dignified term *group*.

group (in systematics)—a large, informal collection of life-forms physically distinct from other such collections.

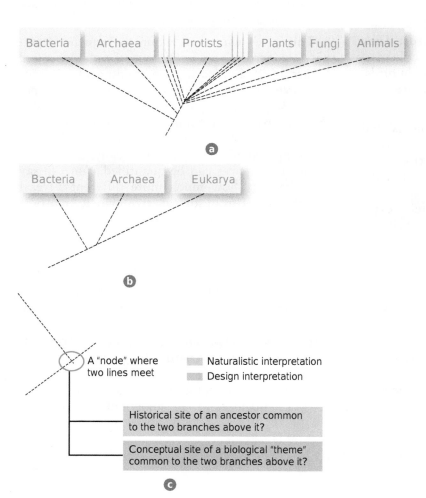

Figure 14.10 Two Conventional Classification Schemes. **(a)** Systematists here classify all organisms into 6 Kingdoms. The boxes to either side of Kingdom Protista are an admission of it's artificiality—it's members are fundamentally different from each other. In this text these members are distributed across 6 of 10 "Groups". **(b)** Here systematists, "leaning heavily" on a few molecular sequences, have organized all of life into just three large domains. Four Kingdoms in scheme a) are fit into Domain Eukarya.

(c) In either diagram, at each juncture where two lines meet, the naturalist must find a common ancestor microfossil. The Designer adherent sees at these points, diverging concepts in the mind of a Designer.

9. Evolutionary naturalists perch these large groups as branches on a huge tree of life and call them **clades.** All the members of a clade are thought to go back to a single common ancestor (see Figure 14.10c). These ancestors are then presumed to hark back to one single common ancestor—the "mother protocell" that gave rise to all of life! Today, the ancestor of each clade is thus thought to be a microfossil somewhere in the lowest rock layers that record life's history. The character of microfossils remains ambiguous almost whenever we find them! So these ancestral forms are almost purely hypothetical. Design theorists are not saddled with these historic assumptions. For good or ill, their assumptions are less accessible to science.

They see these large groups as concepts somewhere in the Mind of the Designer.

But in one very important sense, it doesn't matter whether our groups resulted from some fossil ancestor or from a sublime mental construct of an infinite Creator. These systematizing activities are quite legitimate (if tentative) and they add great efficiency to the work of science.

> **clade**—an evolutionary grouping of organisms that include a single ancestral species and all descendant species that have arisen from it.

IN OTHER WORDS

1. This text uses the simple term *group* to describe a large collection of organisms united by a common possession or absence of a small constellation of significant biological characteristics.
2. Evolutionary thinkers assume that all modern groups of organisms are related through time back to a single common biological ancestral cell type that once lived in the primordial seas.
3. Design proponents tend to see large groups of organisms as separate concepts in the mind of an original Designer who saw life in different modes and created it as such.

10

USING CHARACTERISTICS TO DERIVE GROUPS

Let's consider 10 different groups into which all life-forms could be distributed. You will be given a name for each group and an example of an organism from each group. You will then see a list of diagnostic characteristics that place our example organism in its appropriate group. Finally, you will see a list of a few additional examples of well-known organisms from each of the groups.

Group #1: The Bacteria

Escherichia coli

Dr. David M. Phillips/Visuals Unlimited

The first group, whose members are least complex in structure, is the **Bacteria.** An example of an organism from this group is the common colon bacillus, *Escherichia coli.* This bacterium is so widespread in your large intestine that there are probably as many *E. coli* cells in your bowel as there are human cells in the rest of your body! How can that be possible? They are tiny as cells go. Hundreds of them could adhere to the surface of just one of your intestinal epithelial cells. A single mitochondrion from one of your cell's cytoplasm is about the size of an *E. coli* cell.

> **Bacteria**—a large group of prokaryotic, mostly unicellular organisms; those with cell walls contain the polymer peptidoglycan in those walls.
>
> **cyanobacteria**—widely distributed prokaryotic unicellular and colonial life-forms that do photosynthesis, liberating oxygen to the atmosphere.
>
> **nitrogen cycle**—a global, bio-geo-chemical sequence of chemical reactions within and between life-forms that moves the world's nitrogen supply through a variety of compounds, including several important to living things.

Some bacteria are autotrophic and some are not. But *most* bacteria are unicellular and all of them are prokaryotic. The Bacteria group includes vast collections of autotrophic (blue-green) **cyanobacteria** that populate moist areas of the Earth. It also includes some nasty heterotrophs like the gonococcus that infects casual sexual partners, the salmonella that poisons some prepared foods, and wonderful microbes that keep the entire **nitrogen cycle** on planet Earth going.

Anabaena sp.

cyanobacteria: Dennis Drenner

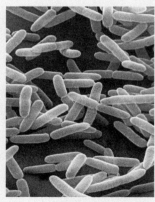

Salmonella sp.

Group #2: The Archaea

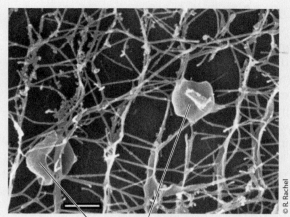

Pyrodictium occultum

A second group, whose members are of comparable complexity to bacteria, is the **Archaea**. An example of an organism from this group is the geothermal vent dweller, *Pyrodictium occultum*. This particular Archean exists near the ocean floor. At the edge of these amazing vents, pressure can be up to 250 atmospheres; temperatures at 220°F—well above the boiling temperature of water. Perhaps a gifted Designer created this microbe just to convince us that He can design life-forms for any environment you can think of! The Archaea are also unicellular forms that are prokaryotic. Again, they are tiny as cells go. They include many of the salt-loving bacteria that populate briny pools, lakes, and ponds. Archeans also include those colorful, sulfur-reducing microbes that thrive in ultra-hot water springs like those at Yellowstone National Park.

Archaea—a large group of prokaryotic, mostly unicellular organisms that tend to inhabit extremes of environment such as high-temperature, high-pressure, or high-salt environments.

Halophilic archaeans in commercial salt evaporation ponds

Sulfur-reducing archaeans generate the bright yellow sulfur deposits around this hot spring.

Group #3: The Excavata

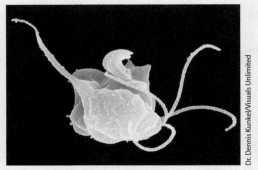

Trichomonas vaginalis

The third group, whose members are all heterotrophic and microscopic in size, is the Excavata. An example of an organism from this group is the trichomonad, *Trichomonas vaginalis.* These large flagellated cells swim about in the genital tracts of sexually active humans. There, they contribute to a nasty sexually transmitted infection characterized by a foul-smelling greenish purulence (that makes their host wish she had "just said, 'No.'"). The Excavata are composed entirely of unicellular forms that are eukaryotic in structure. They can be either parasitic or free-living in their habitat. Though microscopic, they get rather large as single cells go. The Excavata are defined as cells that have two to four or more flagella on the anterior surface of the cell near a ventral feeding groove supported by microtubules. Food passes down this groove. They also lack mitochondria. For energy, they get by with that portion of respiration that we called *glycolysis*. The Excavata includes both the **trichomonads** and the **diplomonads** like the nasty parasite *Giardia* that haunts public water supplies from which it infects and torments your digestive tract.

Excavata—a large group of unicellular eukaryotic organisms with mitochondria that are highly modified or absent; usually possessing two, four, or more flagellae.

trichomonad—an order of anaerobic, usually parasitic eukaryotic flagellated cells including parasites of humans and symbionts within termite guts.

diplomonad—an order of parasitic flagellates that includes members of genus *Giardia*, which causes dysentery in humans; each cell has two nuclei and no functional mitochondria.

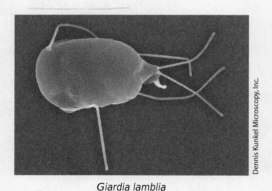

Giardia lamblia

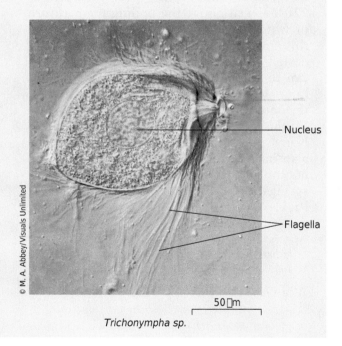

Nucleus

Flagella

50 μm

Trichonympha sp.

Group #4: The Rhizaria

Globigerina bulloides

The fourth group, whose members are also microscopic in size, is the **Rhizaria**. An example of an organism from this group is the **foraminiferan,** *Globigerina bulloides*. These Rhizarians live throughout the world's oceans as part of the surface plankton. Then they die to become part of the "ooze" on the ocean floor. Eventually, they become limestone. Their shells form most of the structure of the great pyramids of Egypt. Slaves provided the construction, but God provided the materials.

The foraminifera also tell the world's geologists where the oil deposits are. This group is entirely unicellular and eukaryotic in structure and marine in habitat. They get rather large as single cells go. Their mitochondria contain cristae that are tubular (tube-like) in structure. The Rhizaria also include the glorious **radiolarian** cells whose beautiful glass cytoskeletons are further exhibits of the exquisite art and architectural genius of their Designer.

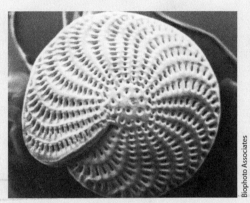

A foraminiferan shell showing holes through which slender cytoplasmic strands extend

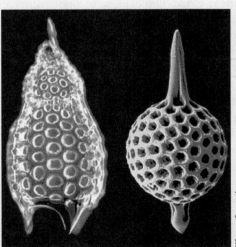

Internal skeletons of two Radiolarian species; cells built on "glass" (silicon dioxide)

Rhizaria—a large group of unicellular eukaryotes that includes ameboid cells as well as foraminerans and radiolarians; most have mitochondria with tubular cristae.

foraminiferan—a group of ameboid eukaryotes that possess strand-like pseudopodial (false feet) extensions of the cell's cytoplasm; found in marine plankton.

radiolarian—a group of amoeboid eukaryotes that produce intricate extracellular skeletons of silicates or strontium sulfates; possess needle-like pseudopodial extensions of their cells.

Group #5: The Discicristates

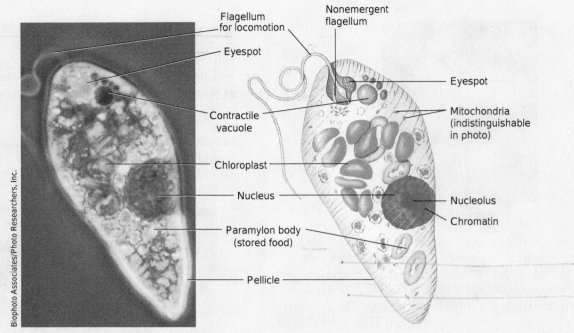

Flagellum for locomotion

Nonemergent flagellum

Eyespot

Contractile vacuole

Eyespot

Mitochondria (indistinguishable in photo)

Chloroplast

Nucleus

Nucleolus

Chromatin

Paramylon body (stored food)

Pellicle

Euglena gracilis

Biophoto Associates/Photo Researchers, Inc.

A fifth group, whose members range from microscopic to macroscopic in size, is the Discicristates. An example of an organism from this group is the protistan, *Euglena gracilis*. This microbe has a pivotal position in the history of systematics! Ernst Haeckel, a brilliant nineteenth century German zoologist, was stopped in his tracks by this microscopic jack-of-all-trades. Its animal-like flagellar swimming and green, plant-like chloroplasts just shouted, "Go ahead, try to classify me!" This was when Haeckel decided that two kingdoms weren't enough. So he added a third one: Protista. It's now obsolete. Since his day, the number of kingdoms has expanded to something like the 10 groups you see here. The Discicristates are composed entirely of unicellular and colonial forms that are eukaryotic in structure and diverse in habitat.

Like the Excavates, the Discicristates have two to four or more flagellae on the anterior surface of the cell near a ventral feeding groove. But the Discicristates all contain mitochondria whose cristae are disc-shaped. This group also includes the trypanosomes that cause sleeping sickness in Africa and the related leishmanias that cause a severe systemic disease that issues in large boil-like lesions.

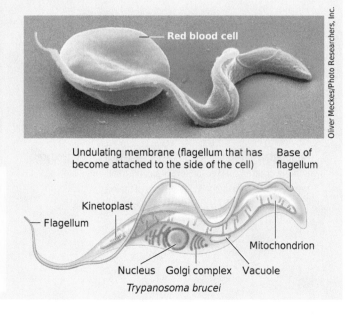

Red blood cell

Oliver Meckes/Photo Researchers, Inc.

Undulating membrane (flagellum that has become attached to the side of the cell)

Base of flagellum

Kinetoplast

Flagellum

Mitochondrion

Nucleus   Golgi complex   Vacuole

Trypanosoma brucei

Discicristate—a large group of unicellular eukaryotes whose mitochondrial cristae are disc-like in shape; includes many euglenoid forms such as genus *Euglena*.

trypanosomes—a genus of flagellated, single-celled parasites, many of which are transmitted to their host by blood-feeding invertebrates, including the agent that causes sleeping sickness in humans.

Group #6: The Alveolata

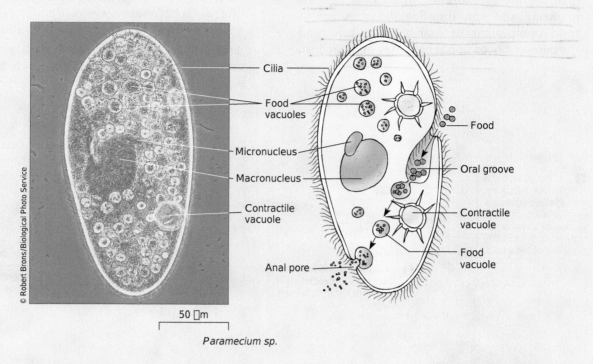

Cilia

Food vacuoles

Micronucleus

Macronucleus

Contractile vacuole

Food

Oral groove

Contractile vacuole

Food vacuole

Anal pore

© Robert Brons/Biological Photo Service

50 ☐m

Paramecium sp.

The sixth group, whose members are again microscopic in size, is the **Alveolata.** An example of an organism from this group is the ciliate, *Paramecium aurelium*. These animal-like Alveolates move around using cilia (*sing*. **cilium**): small, whip-like hairs that beat in synchrony. They have a ventral groove that terminates in a cellular "mouth" complete with its own cilia for food gathering. Many of these large, freshwater cells simply feed on smaller cells. Paramecium can divide two to three times a day. If a single one of them divided just once a day and all the offspring lived, in 113 days the mass of Paramecium would equal the mass of the Earth. (Something must be eating *them* or limiting their food supply!) This group is unicellular and eukaryotic in structure and diverse in habitat. Alveolate cells contain **alveoli**—flattened vesicles packed into a continuous layer just beneath the cell's membrane. Taken together, the alveoli form a flexible **pellicle** layer that

Alveolate—a large group of unicellular eukaryotic forms that includes those possessing cilia and the sporozoan cells that cause malaria; possess mitochondria with tubular cristae.

cilium—a narrow protuberant organelle found extending from the surface of certain eukaryotic cell types; they are usually present in large numbers on the cell surface.

alveoli—flattened vesicles just under the surface of the cell membrane in some unicelled eukaryotes; together the alveoli contribute to a sub-membrane layer called the *pellicle*.

pellicle—a thin layer of sacs beneath the cell membrane of Alveolates that, by its stiffness, helps support the membrane and retention of cell's shape.

helps maintain cell shape. The Alveolata also includes the **sporozoans** (that cause humans malaria) and the **dinoflagellates**, a major food component of marine plankton (and the cause of occasional red tides on beaches).

sporozoan—a group of Alveolates that possess a unique organelle called the *apicoplast* that supports penetration of the cell into a host cell during parasitic invasion; malarial parasites belong to this group.

dinoflagellate—a group of flagellated unicellular eukaryotes most of which are marine plankton; about half of them are photosynthetic.

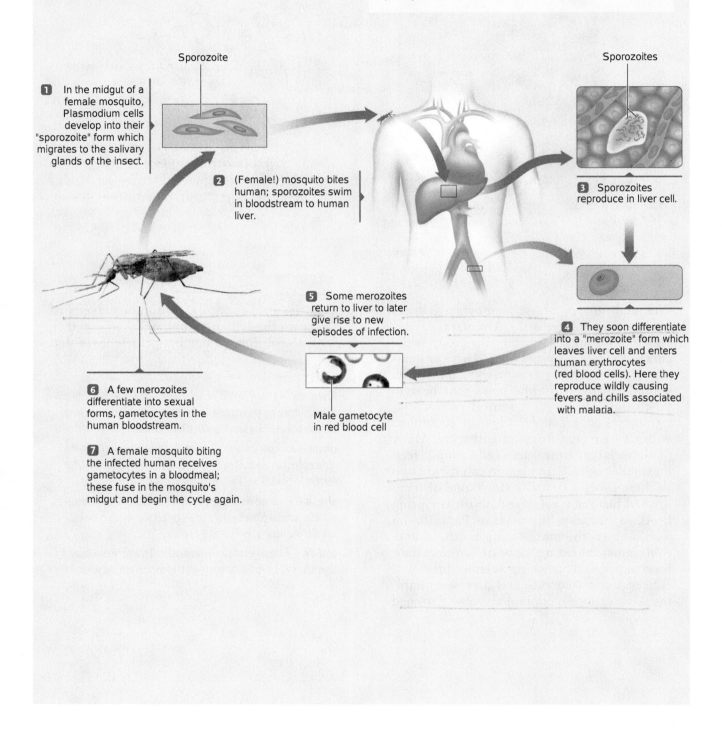

Sporozoite

1 In the midgut of a female mosquito, Plasmodium cells develop into their "sporozoite" form which migrates to the salivary glands of the insect.

2 (Female!) mosquito bites human; sporozoites swim in bloodstream to human liver.

Sporozoites

3 Sporozoites reproduce in liver cell.

4 They soon differentiate into a "merozoite" form which leaves liver cell and enters human erythrocytes (red blood cells). Here they reproduce wildly causing fevers and chills associated with malaria.

5 Some merozoites return to liver to later give rise to new episodes of infection.

Male gametocyte in red blood cell

6 A few merozoites differentiate into sexual forms, gametocytes in the human bloodstream.

7 A female mosquito biting the infected human receives gametocytes in a bloodmeal; these fuse in the mosquito's midgut and begin the cycle again.

Group #7: The Stramenopiles

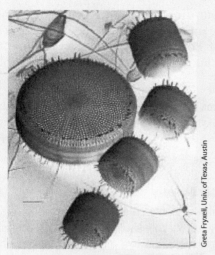

Stephanodiscus niagarae

The seventh group, whose members vary widely in size, is the **Stramenopiles**. An example of an organism from this group is the colonial **diatom**, *Ellerbeckia arenaria.* Diatoms show us how one Creator can be the ultimate biologist, material scientist, and artist, all at once. The artistic beauty of diatoms is unrivalled in the living world. Yet they are critically productive organisms. As autotrophs, they convert solar energy into food. And they are the major component of **plankton,** the nutritional base of the marine food chain.

Humans use diatoms too, in hundreds of applications like reflective paint on road signs and for texture in McDonald's milkshakes. Ultimately beautiful, ultimately supportive in the biosphere, amazingly useful in human technology—they're the perfect servant organism!

The Stramenopiles are largely unicellular and colonial multicellular forms that are eukaryotic in structure and diverse in habitat. The group name indicates that its cells have two unequal flagella. The anterior flagellum is covered with lateral bristles or *mastigonemes,* while the other flagellum is whip-like, smooth and usually shorter, or sometimes reduced to a basal body. The Stramenopiles include all of the diatoms, **water molds,** and the **brown algae** some of which, like the giant kelps, can have stalks (*blades*) that are over a football field in length!

Saprolegnia parasitica infecting the tail fin of a fish

Stramenopile—a large group of golden and brown algae and diatoms; all are eukaryotic; also called *heterokonts* as a motile stage of their life cycle contains two different shaped flagellae.

diatom—an algal form comprising a major portion of marine plankton; eukaryotic unicellular or colonial forms; possess a unique bipartite, silica-encased cell wall.

plankton—microscopic marine and freshwater life-forms that are usually the lowest levels in the food chain; includes both photosynthetic and nonphotosynthetic forms.

water mold—a fungal-like eukaryotic filamentous microorganism; actually most forms are terrestrial; includes *Phytophthora*, a genus that causes horrible potato blights.

brown alga—mostly marine, multicellular algae containing the brown pigment fucoxanthin; includes the kelps.

Macrocystis pyrifera

Group #8: The Amoebozoa

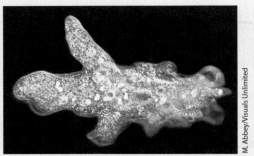
Amoeba proteus

The eighth group, whose members also vary widely in size, is the **Amoebozoa**. An example of an organism from this group is the amoeboid cell, *Amoeba proteus*. These well-known lab subjects prefer the bottom of a pond. They creep along a surface by allowing lobes of their cytoplasm to flow forward into new space. As they encounter smaller cells and organic material, they flow around and engulf them into food vacuoles. They tend to move away from light, showing themselves to be photosensitive. The Amoebozoa group consists largely of unicellular and colonial multicellular forms that are eukaryotic in structure and diverse in habitat. The group is defined by the fluidity of the shape of their cells, which result from the freedom of cytoplasmic flow in seemingly random directions. The Amoebozoa include all the unicellular amoebae as well as a number of colonial groups in which amoeboid cells swarm together to form **slime molds**.

Amoebozoa—single-celled, eukaryotic forms that move by internal flow of cytoplasm into blunt, lobe-like pseudopodial extensions of the cell membrane.

food vacuole—a membrane-bound organelle found in many ameboid and alveolate cells; contains engulfed organic solids that are eventually digested by hydrolytic enzymes.

slime mold—a collection of unicellular and colonial multicellular forms distributed within the Alveolate, Rhizaria, and Excavate groups; one stage of the life cycle involves ameboid cells coming together to form a large slime-like body called a *syncytium*.

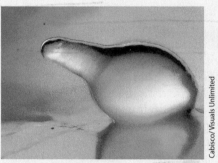
D. discoideum cells collectively form a multi-cellular migrating "slug"

Dictyostelium discoideum individual cells streaming together

The "slug" stops migrating, forms a fruiting body which will develop spores

Group #9: The Plants

Pisum sativum, the garden pea

The ninth group, whose members vary widely in size, is the Plant group. Members of the Plant group are composed largely of multicellular forms that are eukaryotic in structure and diverse in habitat. The group is defined as all autotrophic organisms whose photosynthesis occurs in chloroplasts that are surrounded by a double membrane. An example of an organism from this group is Gregor Mendel's "toy"—the common garden pea plant, *Pisum sativum*. It's a higher plant with true tissues and true flowers.

The term *higher plant* places peas above all of the *lower* (usually smaller) plant forms. These include some of the green and the red algae, the **mosses, liverworts, hornworts,** club mosses, and **ferns.** Among these lower plants, many, like the mosses, liverworts, and hornworts, do not have separate tissues like xylem and phloem that conduct fluids up or down over long distances. Lacking these tissues sorely limits the height to which a plant can grow. Mosses lie along the ground in small tufts. Liverworts grow laterally as well. Pea plants, however, can grow considerably taller than you!

Peas plants form nutritive and protective seeds—sophisticated conveyances that highly increase the success of the next generation. There are two divisions (phyla) of seed-producing plants. **Gymnosperm**s (Gk. *gymnos* = naked)

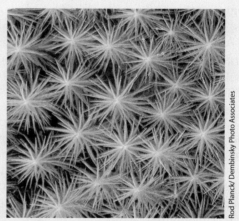

Polytrichum communae, the haircap moss, used decoratively in Japan

moss—small plants of the bryophyte group ranging from 1 to 10 cm in height; growth is in small smooth clumps; these plants lack a vascular system.

liverwort—small plants of the bryophyte group; the dominant part of their life cycle contains cells with haploid gene content; lacking a vascular system, they grow close to the surface of the substrate.

hornwort—a group of bryophyte plants lacking a vascular system; the brief diploid portion of the life cycle has a horn-like structure that extends aerially.

ferns—a division of higher plants having vascular systems but forming spores instead of seeds; the fronds have very elegant morphologies.

Gymnosperm—a division of higher plants having vascular systems and bearing seeds exposed on the surface of cone scales.

Marchantia polymorpha, the liverwort

Polystichum acrostichoides, the Christmas fern

Pinus contorta, the lodgepole pine showing male and larger female cones

generate their seeds naked on the surface of **scales** without the protection of an **ovary** in a flower. These include such plants as **conifers,** evergreen trees and shrubs, **cycads,** and gingko trees. But the pea plant is in a division called the **Angiosperms**. This means that its seeds are formed within the ovary of a flower. Corn, wheat, grasses, lilies, dandelions, cherry, oak, and maple trees are all Angiosperms.

The pea plant is a member of order Rosales, the Rose family, which includes roses, beans, peas, strawberries and many (!) other kinds of plants. The use of peas as food goes back in history to the ancient Middle East. More recently, dried peas from England kept many Massachusetts Bay colonists alive during that first terrible winter.

Arabidopsis thaliana, the thale cress plant in bloom; widely used in molecular research

scale—a structure within the cone of a Gymnosperm; in the female cone, an ovule on the surface of the scale matures into a seed.

ovary—the female part of a flower within the pistil; contains ovules within which seeds mature.

conifer—Gymnosperms that are cone-bearing vascular plants; includes firs, pines, hemlocks, spruces, larches, and redwoods.

cycad—seeding-bearing evergreen plants with vascular systems and having long, frond-like compound leaves.

Angiosperms—a large and diverse group of plants that reproduce by forming flowers and subsequently fruit containing seeds; includes much of the diversity of the plant group.

Group #10: The Opisthokonta, a Home for Humans

Zonotrichia leucophrys, the white-crowned sparrow

The tenth and last group, <u>whose members also vary widely in size, is the</u> **Opisthokonta**. The name Opisthokonta (Gk. *opisth-* = behind; Gk. *cont-* = a pole) refers to the arrangement of flagella in those cells having them. <u>The flagellum is single and oriented posteriorly, pushing the cell through the medium in which it swims.</u> This large group includes almost 2 million named species of multicellular, eukaryotic organisms of diverse habitats, including both animals and fungi. An example of an organism from this group is the white-crowned sparrow, *Zonotrichia leucophrys*. You learned about its song patterns in Chapter 11.

Sparrows, like fruit flies and people, are good animals; that is, they are <u>multicellular heterotrophs that feed by ingestion</u>. Ingestion involves taking food inside of themselves to digest it rather than secreting enzymes into their environment digesting nutrients external to themselves. Also, animal cell membranes are not enclosed within cell walls. These features and others distinguish all animal-like opisthokonts from all of the fungal forms that also populate this group. (Molecular sequence comparisons show that fungi are more closely related to animals than to plants!) The **Fungi** include all of the yeasts, some of the molds, all of the mushrooms and bracket fungi on old dead trees. To a consistent naturalist, then, the mushroom is your

distant second cousin. It requires nutrients from plants just like you do!

The sparrow's position within the animal kingdom places it among many of the simpler animal forms such as sponges, flatworms, earthworms, insects, snails, and starfish.

Polytrichum Monilinia fruticola, a brown rot of peach crops

Marchantia Morchella esculenta, the yellow morel, a delicacy among mushroom lovers

Opisthokont—a large group of eukaryotic multicellular life-forms that includes the fungi and animal kingdoms. Flagellated cells in this group have a single, posteriorly oriented flagellum.

Fungi—that kingdom of Opisthokonts characterized by cells with chitinous walls surrounding their membranes; organisms that secrete extracellular digestive enzymes and that subsequently absorb the resultant nutrients.

Antheraea polyphemus, the giant silk moth

Dendrobates pumilio, the red dart frog, whose secretions are somewhat toxic to other animals

The animal kingdom includes almost 40 different phyla. To which does the sparrow belong? Sparrows, like humans and coyotes, are included in phylum **Chordata** because of common patterns of nervous system development and their possession of gill slit-like structures for a short time during their embryonic development. This places them among the sea squirts, sharks, bony fish, snakes, lizards, frogs, salamanders, birds, and mammals.

Sparrows are found in class **Aves** because they're birds: That means they are warm-blooded, have true feathers, and can fly. They are included in the order of the **Passeriformes**, which includes all of the small songbirds with which you are familiar: flycatchers, ovenbirds, wrens, vireos, cuckoos, crows, ravens, robins, larks, warblers, thrushes, starlings, cardinals, chickadees, and many others.

White-crowned sparrows aren't the only Passeriform species whose song varies from region to region. Robins in Wales and England sing different songs. In fact, a Sussex male robin was so vexed to hear a recording of a Welsh robin that he puffed up his feathers and attacked the tape player.

Perhaps you're surprised to discover that the large group to which you belong—the Opisthokonts—grants you membership because of the way a human male's sperm cells swim using a single posterior flagellum. We will return to the classification of human beings in Section 14.7.

Chordata—a group of animals that (at some point in their development) possess a stiff, dorsal notochord that lends support to surrounding structures; includes all vertebrate organisms.

Aves—a large class of animals that have feathered wings, are warm-blooded and lay eggs; all birds.

Passeriforms—an order of smaller birds characterized by perching behavior and singing; includes some 5000 species.

Pan paniscus, a bonobo chimpanzee holding her sleeping baby

1. The Bacteria are unicellular prokaryotic life-forms, usually quite small in cell size; both autotrophic and heterotrophic forms exist, as do both unicellular and colonial forms.
2. The Archaea are fundamentally similar to bacterial forms but have different cell wall structures, different ribosomal RNA sequences, and they tend to live in environmentally extreme habitats.
3. The Excavates are all heterotrophic, microscopic in size, and eukaryotic in cell structure; they are defined by having two or more flagellae facing anteriorly that pull the cell through the medium.
4. The Rhizaria are microscopic marine forms that are unicellular and eukaryotic; they have produced most of the world's limestone.
5. The Discicristates are a collection of unicellular and colonial forms that vary widely in size; they have the same flagellar arrangement as the Excavates but their mitochondria contain disc-shaped cristae.
6. The Alveolates are microscopic, ciliated, mostly unicellular life-forms that have flattened vesicles packed into an alveolar layer beneath their cell membranes; this layer adds to their structural stability.
7. The Stramenopiles are unicellular and colonial life-forms that are eukaryotic in structure and diverse in habitat; they include the diatoms—some of the most biologically valuable and artistically beautiful parts of the marine food chain.
8. The Amoebozoa are also unicellular and colonial, multicellular eukaryotic forms that are capable of amoeboid movement; developmental biologists study the transition of some species from the unicellular to colonial mode of existence.
9. The Plant group is a diverse, multicellular collection of eukaryotic life-forms that includes mosses, ferns, conifers, cycads and flowering plants; gingko trees are in this group.
10. Opisthokonts are a very large collection of fungal and animal forms whose genetic similarity is represented by a common tendency for flagellated cells to possess just one posteriorly oriented flagellum.
11. Animals within the Opisthokonts are divided into phyla of which the Chordata contain humans and other animals with backbones.

CLASSIFICATION: PERSISTENT PROBLEMS

All of the organisms you're familiar with fit neatly into the 10 groups we just listed. But the remaining problems to be solved by this 10-group contrivance are formidable! First, by analysis of DNA sequences pulled directly from soil and water samples, we already know there are many, many organisms hidden out there in nature (mostly small ones) that we haven't discovered yet (see Figure 14.11). What is more, some of these new organisms are going to represent new groups that will fit between or completely outside of the 10 existing groups, making our current distinctions seem that much more arbitrary. So we can be disappointed about that ahead of time if we want to.

As mentioned, we will also continue to have difficulty placing currently known organisms neatly within our artificially simplistic categories. Consider the widespread angiosperm plant known as Indian Pipe (see Figure 14.12a). It lacks the most essential feature of the group it's placed in! It can't do photosynthesis. It depends on fungal connections to nearby plants to get its nutrition. Yet in all

a

Finding New Microorganisms in Nature

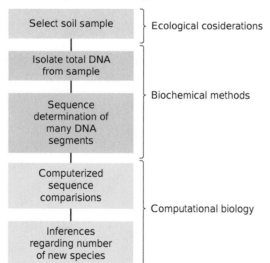

Select soil sample — Ecological cosiderations

Isolate total DNA from sample

Sequence determination of many DNA segments — Biochemical methods

Computerized sequence comparisions

Inferences regarding number of new species — Computational biology

Figure 14.11 Finding New Microorganisms in Nature. Cooperation between biologists with a variety of backgrounds and training facilitate the discovery of new species of organisms based solely on fragments of their DNA detected in samples from nature.

b

Figure 14.12 Taxanomic Enigmas. **(a)** The Indian Pipe has tissues and structures that are plant-like yet it has no chlorophyll and is heterotrophic. **(b)** the duck-billed platypus has both mammalian and avian features. How should it be classified?

other aspects of its structure, it seems clearly like other flowering plants. Do we consider it a plant? Many biologists are quick to say, "No problem, it used to do photosynthesis and by mutation it simply lost that ability. So it's just a degenerate plant." But how would such a mutant form have survived long enough to evolve a new way of efficiently doing nutrition? What if Indian Pipes were created essentially as they now are? By asking questions like this we get one step closer to a highly reasonable expectation: No system derived by a human mind can organize a biotic community created by a superhuman Mind.

Consider the duckbill platypus (see Figure 14.12b). It has a beak and lays eggs, so it must be a bird, yes? But it has hair, fur (really!), and when the young hatch, they feed on milk provided by the mother! So taxonomists classify it with the mammals but place it in a special group called the **monotremes.**

This grouping argues that the platypus is more like its supposed reptilian ancestors, the **therapsids.** But again, the platypus might have come from a Designer's hand in essentially its current form. There is no strong fossil evidence to contradict this. If this is so, then the platypus is not an advanced reptile. It is a creature in its own right and as such is another eloquent testimony to our inability to neatly classify the diversity that God enjoyed devising.

monotreme—a small group of mammals that lay eggs instead of giving birth to young alive; the platypus and spiny anteaters are the two major extant representatives.

therapsid—an evolutionary term given to modern mammals and all of their presumed immediate ancestors that are believed to find their roots in an earlier reptilian group.

IN OTHER WORDS

1. DNA samples taken from soil and water suggest that many thousands of other species of microorganisms are known to exist in nature but have yet to be isolated and cultured in the laboratory.
2. A growing variety of individual species, like the platypus, have characteristics that place them into two separate groups simultaneously, confounding our classification system.

There is one organism in particular for which classification activity appears uniquely superficial. If we wish to place human beings in relation to all other organisms, we face that huge issue of the inner nature of man that his biology supports and meshes seamlessly with. Are man's highest cognitive and emotional experiences distinct from those experienced in other places within the animal kingdom (see Figure 14.13)? As the scientific method developed, its great strength has been rooted in our ability to manipulate and objectively compare *physical* aspects of nature. So when Enlightenment man began to explore his relationship to other living organisms, it was only natural that comparisons were limited to the physical realm. And those comparisons have been made quite carefully.

Man is a mammal. This means that he is warm blooded, having a complete double circulation, with one branch that leads from the heart to the lungs and the other leading from the heart to the rest of the body. Man has hair (although some of us are becoming less mammalian all the time in this regard). The female of the species provides milk for her young, and they are supported before birth by a baby organ called the **placenta**. These features clearly place man in the class Mammalia, which represents about 4500 species (see Figure 14.14).

But man is also a **primate**. He possesses five digits on each hand, including an opposable thumb for grasping purposes. He has an increased visual dependence and a lower olfactory acuity than most other mammals. There is increased care of the young as compared to other mammals, and unlike most other mammals, he maintains an upright or semi-upright posture. (Recall that George Orwell stood his pigs up on their hind limbs to represent

placenta—an organ of fetal origin that connects the fetal circulation with the maternal circulation so as to allow molecular components to be exchanged between the two.

Primates—a taxonomic order that includes man, the apes, monkeys, tarsiers, lemurs, lorises, and galagos.

a

b

Figure 14.13 Man and Chimpanzee. Do they differ from each other only by 5% of the their DNA sequence? Or are there qualitative differences between them that range beyond the physical realm? Can science answer such a question? If not, is the question worthy of pursuit?

Class: Mammals	Warm-blooded, double circulation, placenta, hair
Order: Primates	Five digitas, opposable thumb, increased visual dependence
Family: Hominids	Larger, tailless, increased fore-limb specialization
Homo sapiens	Totally upright posture, increased intelligence, worship

Figure 14.14 Classifying Man. Genus and species *Homo sapiens* are nested within higher order categories (taxa) that group man with other organisms based on shared physical or behavioral characteristics.

their biosocial progress in *Animal Farm*.) These features place man within the order of the Primates, which includes monkeys, apes, and us.

Man is a **hominid**. Unlike monkeys, humans are large and without tails. There is more specialization in the use of the forelimbs for climbing and tool use. Man, chimpanzees, and the great apes are all members of the family Hominidae.

Finally, man is *Homo sapiens*. His totally upright posture, his increased intelligence, and his tendency to worship have been chosen as the hallmarks of our species, *Homo sapiens*. Notice that the last characteristic takes us out of the realm of the physical and into that elusive gray area that has been called the *mind*. Even nineteenth century enlightened scholars could not deny the relative richness of man's experience in these areas. Yet because the experience of worship is difficult to tie to specific neurological coordinates, it is difficult for a scientist to aver that a chimpanzee cannot experience worship.

Leaving that question to one side, let's go on to ask: Is *Homo sapiens* just a primate? Our long progression of distinctions between man and other life-forms, as outlined above, culminates with words like *intelligence* and *worship*! The question that haunts the naturalist in this quasiphysical definition is simply put: Is the difference between man and the apes one of degree or one of kind? In the naturalist's view, since the sea anemone is our distant cousin, we are forced to the conclusion that our differences from the chimpanzee are merely of degree. We are just slightly more intelligent and slightly more *person-sensitive* than the apes. And that is all. Or is it?

Can only scientific data be used to address a question pressing that data past its limits? Is there ancient wisdom from any other source that can help us here? The Hebrew Scriptures claim revelatory information complementary to the anthropologist's assertions regarding what man is. Consider the narrative in Genesis 1, verses 24 through 26. It reads: "Then God said, "Let the earth bring forth the living creature according to its kind: cattle, and creeping thing, and the beast of the earth according to its kind; and it was so. And God made the beast of the earth according to its kind. . . . .Then God said, "Let Us make man in Our image, according to Our likeness. Let them have dominion over the fish of the sea, over the birds of the air, and over the cattle . . ."

Hominids—the taxonomic family to which man and the great apes belong; does not include monkeys.

Then God said, "Let the earth bring forth the living creature according to its kind, cattle and creeping thing and beast of the earth . . . . And God made the beast of the earth according to its kind; cattle according to its kind; and everything that creeps on the earth according to its kind. And God saw that it was good.

Then God said, "Let Us make man in Our image, according to Our likeness; let them have dominion over the over the fish of the sea, over the birds of the air, and over the cattle, over all the earth . . . ..

—GENESIS 1: 24 – 26a

When God made man in His image, He was not fashioning man's physical aspect. Chimps look remarkably like us physically. But nothing is said in the text of God's image in them. The scriptures everywhere teach that God is a Spirit, and not corporeal. So this image God speaks of must be an internal thing—a reality at precisely the point where increased intelligence and worship take over from the physical traits that distinguish man from lower forms of life. Since the *in God's image* aspect of man is unique to man's creation, the text is taking us a step further than the naturalist and confidently asserting that man's uniqueness is not simply one of degree. It is one of kind as well.

This unique human standing both apart from and above the rest of creation has such far-reaching implications. It would be comforting if a second Biblical passage could be found that would support such a standing. Psalm 8, attributed to Israel's greatest king, David, returns us to this same theme. He singles out mankind saying that the Creator made man "a little lower than God and crowned him with glory and honor." Again, this sounds like a nonphysical, positional sort of reality. Finally, David says that God gives man dominion over every other kind of animal God has created. It cannot be avoided—God, Yahweh, of Hebrew scripture gives physical man a special hierarchical authority over the other forms of creation.

So if these Hebrew Scriptures are to be believed, we end with yet another reason to see glory in the works of our Designer. He has, in our species, done something truly amazing. He has combined features of the physical realm with those of the spiritual realm seamlessly into the glorious invention that is man. In fact, He then uses this unique combination of spirit and flesh to come among us Himself and rescue us from the tragedy of physical death that we know so intimately (see Chapter 16). In these passages from Genesis and Psalms, you are called to rejoice in the uniqueness of species *Homo sapiens*—the one species that has clearly been given eternity. Sola Dei Gloria!

What is man that You are mindful of him,
And the son of man that You visit him?
For You have made him a little lower than God,
And You have crowned him with glory and honor.

You have made him to have dominion over the works of Your hands;
You have put all things under his feet,
All sheep and oxen—even the beasts of the field,
The birds of the air
And the fish of the sea that pass through the paths of the seas.

—PSALM 8: 4 – 8

1. Does man possess quasiphysical or nonphysical characteristics that qualitatively separate him from other primates and all other organisms?
2. Man has been physically related to other organisms by placing him within class Mammalia, order Primata, family Homindae, and genus *Homo*.
3. While human characteristics of increased intelligence and worship are relatively easy to measure behaviorally, do they point to an aspect of man that is unquantifiable scientifically?
4. While scientific study finds Biblical assertions about man's nature untestable, does that render those assertions untrue or meaningless?

QUESTIONS FOR REVIEW

1. How many species of life-forms exist on planet Earth that we have described and named?
2. List three broad classes of challenges that face the systematist as she tries to put together an organized filing system for the living world.
3. Distinguish between the terms *taxonomy* and *systematics*. What is the focus of each discipline?
4. A Martian visiting this planet might be tempted to classify Korean humans and Norwegian humans as two separate species. What evidence would eventually disfavor this hypothesis?
5. What two-word title would be used to relate German cockroaches to spiders and scorpions? to butterflies and wasps?
6. How does the term *domain* relate to the term *kingdom*?
7. Why would an evolutionist prefer the term *primitive* to the term *fundamental* in describing a characteristic of an organism?
8. List the fundamental characteristics used to place all living organisms into approximately 10 large groups.
9. List some common molecules whose DNA base sequences have been used for classification purposes. Why were these molecules chosen for comparison?
10. What is a clade in evolutionary thinking? How would a design proponent view a clade?
11. Do all bacteria either parasitize us or compete with us for resources? Are there any bacterial species that actually support us in nature?
12. Excavates were said to be either parasitic or free-living microscopic forms. Given their structure, what would you predict about the nature of their habitat in either case?
13. What structural feature is diagnostic of all Alveolates? What is its value to the cell?
14. Compared with other microorganisms in the first five groups of our classification scheme, what appears unique about the sporozoan that causes malaria in humans? What would you expect to be true of the genome size of these Alveolates compared to other members of the group?
15. You fill your stomach three times a day. If you were the size of an amoeba, what would we call your "stomach"?
16. Use taxonomic terms provided in this chapter to classify the garden pea. Where might you find its family name?
17. The name *Opisthokonta* is not particularly attractive. What feature does it refer to (that the motile cells of boys and fruit flies have in common)?
18. Were you to divide Opisthokonts into two large groups, what would they be and what characteristics would you choose to form those two groups?
19. Make a list of five primate mammals and five non-primate mammals.
20. Use both scientific and Biblical evidence to support the following statement: "Man is a part of nature, but he stands above the rest of nature."

QUESTIONS FOR THOUGHT

1. The platypus was described as an enigma for taxonomists. Why must it be? It's clearly not a bird; it's not entirely a mammal. Why not simply create a whole new class for the platypus to reside in? What effect would this approach have on systematics in general?

2. What is the risk to the evolutionist of trying to relate all living organisms back to a single progenitor organism in the primordial soup?

3. How might the sentence "King Philip came over from German soil" be a helpful device for a Biology 101 student struggling with the terms in this chapter?

4. Which characteristic would be more useful for classification purposes, the presence/absence of a flagellum, or the presence/absence of ribosomes? Explain your response.

5. Aristotle recognized two kingdoms of organisms: plant and animal. Speculate about how he might have classified *Euglena gracilis*.

6. The systematist Thomas Cavalier-Smith's studies have contributed heavily to the groupings of living organisms used in this chapter. Why might he have placed such a heavy emphasis on the presence of and structures within the mitochondrion? (He is an evolutionist.)

7. Give a reason or two for why you should be called *Homo sapiens* if you consist of more bacterial cells than you have human cells.

8. Most enzymes denature as temperatures rise above about 40°C. How can *Pyrodictium* species survive at temperatures above 100°C? What other feature of their habitat must be assisting these enzymes to retain function?

9. "The most amazingly designed microscopic eukaryote is the diatom." What facts might you draw together to support such a claim?

10. How does our ignorance of the precise origin of the Indian Pipe hinder our attempts to classify it?

11. How might an anthropologist studying the remains of a fossil hominid skeleton look for evidence that the hominid worshipped God or a god?

GLOSSARY

Alveolate—a large group of unicellular eukaryotic forms that includes those possessing cilia and the sporozoan cells that cause malaria; possess mitochondria with tubular cristae.

alveoli—flattened vesicles just under the surface of the cell membrane in some unicelled eukaryotes; together the alveoli contribute to a sub-membrane layer called the *pellicle*.

Amoebozoa—single-celled, eukaryotic forms that move by internal flow of cytoplasm into blunt, lobe-like pseudopodial extensions of the cell membrane.

Angiosperms—a large and diverse group of plants that reproduce by forming flowers and subsequently fruit containing seeds; includes much of the diversity of the plant group.

Animalia—a taxonomic kingdom that includes all living and extinct animals.

Archaea—a large group of prokaryotic, mostly unicellular organisms that tend to inhabit extremes of environment such as high-temperature, high-pressure, or high-salt environments.

autotroph—an organism (or cell) that is capable of producing its own food either via photosynthesis or geochemical exothermic reactions.

Aves—a large class of animals that have feathered wings, are warm-blooded and lay eggs; all birds.

Bacteria—a large group of prokaryotic, mostly unicellular organisms; those with cell walls contain the polymer peptidoglycan in those walls.

brown alga—mostly marine, multicellular algae containing the brown pigment fucoxanthin; includes the kelps.

Chordata—a group of animals that (at some point in their development) possess a stiff, dorsal notochord that lends support to surrounding structures; includes all vertebrate organisms.

cilium—a narrow protuberant organelle found extending from the surface of certain eukaryotic cell types; they are usually present in large numbers on the cell surface.

clade—an evolutionary grouping of organisms that include a single ancestral species and all descendant species that have arisen from it.

class (in systematics)—a formal grouping of structurally related orders that is distinct from other such groupings.

colonial—descriptive of a multicellular aggregation (organism?) in which the relations between cells are superficial; basic cell functions are retained by each cell in the colony. Many algae fit this description.

conifer—Gymnosperms that are cone-bearing vascular plants; includes firs, pines, hemlocks, spruces, larches, and redwoods.

cristae—membranous internal folds of the inner mitochondrial membrane; these increase the surface area required for aerobic respiration reactions.

cyanobacteria—widely distributed prokaryotic unicellular and colonial life-forms that do photosynthesis, liberating oxygen to the atmosphere.

cycad—seeding-bearing evergreen plants with vascular systems and having long, frond-like compound leaves.

diatom—an algal form comprising a major portion of marine plankton; eukaryotic unicellular or colonial forms; possess a unique bipartite, silica-encased cell wall.

dinoflagellate—a group of flagellated unicellular eukaryotes most of which are marine plankton; about half of them are photosynthetic.

diplomonad—an order of parasitic flagellates that includes members of genus *Giardia*, which causes dysentery in humans; each cell has two nuclei and no functional mitochondria.

Discicristate—a large group of unicellular eukaryotes whose mitochondrial cristae are disc-like in shape; includes many euglenoid forms such as genus *Euglena*.

domain—an increasingly archaic term referring to a broad collection of organisms having a particular sequence of ribosomal RNA.

eukaryote—a type of cell or organism whose genetic information is highly organized within the confines of a membrane-bound nucleus.

Excavata—a large group of unicellular eukaryotic organisms with mitochondria that are highly modified or absent; usually possessing two, four, or more flagellae.

family (in systematics)—a formal grouping of structurally related genera that is distinct from other such groupings.

ferns—a division of higher plants having vascular systems but forming spores instead of seeds; the fronds have very elegant morphologies.

flagellum—a whip-like shaft extending from the surface of a cell that by its own internal flexion is capable of propelling the cell through a liquid medium.

food vacuole—a membrane-bound organelle found in many ameboid and alveolate cells; contains engulfed organic solids that are eventually digested by hydrolytic enzymes.

foraminiferan—a group of ameboid eukaryotes that possess strand-like pseudopodial (false feet) extensions of the cell's cytoplasm; found in marine plankton.

Fungi—that kingdom of Opisthokonts characterized by cells with chitinous walls surrounding their membranes; organisms that secrete extracellular digestive enzymes and that subsequently absorb the resultant nutrients.

genus—a collection of species that are structurally closely related to each other and distinct from other such collections.

group (in systematics)—a large, informal collection of life-forms physically distinct from other such collections.

Gymnosperm—a division of higher plants having vascular systems and bearing seeds exposed on the surface of cone scales.

Hominids—the taxonomic family to which man and the great apes belong; does not include monkeys.

Homo sapiens—the formal generic and specific name for human beings; the scientific name for mankind.

hornwort—a group of bryophyte plants lacking a vascular system; the brief diploid portion of the life cycle has a horn-like structure that extends aerially.

kingdom (in systematics)—a formal grouping of structurally related phyla (in animals, or divisions, in plants) that is distinct from other such groupings.

Life Is Diverse—the tenth principle of life on which this text is based.

liverwort—small plants of the bryophyte group; the dominant part of their life cycle contains cells with haploid gene content; lacking a vascular system, they grow close to the surface of the substrate.

mammal—a group of vertebrate animals that possess hair and nourish their young with milk; includes humans.

monotreme—a small group of mammals that lay eggs instead of giving birth to young alive; the platypus and spiny anteaters are the two major extant representatives.

moss—small plants of the bryophyte group ranging from 1 to 10 cm in height; growth is in small smooth clumps; these plants lack a vascular system.

multicellular—descriptive of a kind of organism that is composed of many cells.

nitrogen cycle—a global, bio-geo-chemical sequence of chemical reactions within and between life-forms that moves the world's nitrogen supply through a variety of compounds, including several important to living things.

Opisthokont—a large group of eukaryotic multicellular life-forms that includes the fungi and animal kingdoms. Flagellated cells in this group have a single, posteriorly oriented flagellum.

order (in systematics)—a formal grouping of structurally related families that is distinct from other such groupings.

ovary—the female part of a flower within the pistil; contains ovules within which seeds mature.

Passeriforms—an order of smaller birds characterized by perching behavior and singing; includes some 5000 species.

pellicle—a thin layer of sacs beneath the cell membrane of Alveolates that, by its stiffness, helps support the membrane and retention of cell's shape.

phylum (in systematics)—a formal grouping of structurally related classes that is distinct from other such groupings.

placenta—an organ of fetal origin that connects the fetal circulation with the maternal circulation so as to allow molecular components to be exchanged between the two.

plankton—microscopic marine and freshwater life-forms that are usually the lowest levels in the food chain; includes both photosynthetic and nonphotosynthetic forms.

Primates—a taxonomic order that includes man, the apes, monkeys, tarsiers, lemurs, lorises, and galagos.

primitive (in biology)—descriptive of a characteristic of an organism that is presumed to have great evolutionary age.

prokaryote—a type of cell whose genetic information is not organized within the confines of a nuclear membrane.

protistan—an archaic term that refers to a broad, highly heterogeneous group of unicellular and colonial eukaryotes, once lumped together into kingdom Protista.

radiolarian—a group of amoeboid eukaryotes that produce intricate extracellular skeletons of silicates or strontium sulfates; possess needle-like pseudopodial extensions of their cells.

Rhizaria—a large group of unicellular eukaryotes that includes ameboid cells as well as foraminerans and radiolarians; most have mitochondria with tubular cristae.

scale—a structure within the cone of a Gymnosperm; in the female cone, an ovule on the surface of the scale matures into a seed.

slime mold—a collection of unicellular and colonial multicellular forms distributed within the Alveolate, Rhizaria, and Excavate groups; one stage of the life cycle involves ameboid cells coming together to form a large slime-like body called a *syncytium*.

species—a collection of populations of organisms that are similar enough to each other to be able to inter-mate to produce fertile offspring.

sporozoan—a group of Alveolates that possess a unique organelle called the *apicoplast* that supports penetration of the cell into a host cell during parasitic invasion; malarial parasites belong to this group.

Stramenopile—a large group of golden and brown algae and diatoms; all are eukaryotic; also called *heterokonts* as a motile stage of their life cycle contains two different shaped flagellae.

systematics—the structuring and criticism of attempts at natural groupings of life-forms usually according to presumed evolutionary relationships.

taxonomy—the science of classifying individual varieties of organisms into an orderly system.

therapsid—an evolutionary term given to modern mammals and all of their presumed immediate ancestors that are believed to find their roots in an earlier reptilian group.

tissue—a collection of highly similar cells and their intercellular materials that associate closely with each other and carry out a common function for a larger organism.

trichomonad—an order of anaerobic, usually parasitic eukaryotic flagellated cells including parasites of humans and symbionts within termite guts.

trypanosomes—a genus of flagellated, single-celled parasites, many of which are transmitted to their host by blood-feeding invertebrates, including the agent that causes sleeping sickness in humans.

unicellular—descriptive of a kind of organism that is composed of one cell.

water mold—a fungal-like eukaryotic filamentous microorganism; actually most forms are terrestrial; includes *Phytophthora*, a genus that causes horrible potato blights.

15

Ecology: Interactivity by Design

Survey Questions

- The term *ecology* is derived from what two words? Whose household are we studying?
- How has our interaction with God's creation changed over time? Which phase are we in now?

15.1 Thinking like an Ecologist: Exploring a Lake

- What are the three zones in a lake, and how do they differ from each other?
- What is an overturn in a lake, and why does a phytoplankton bloom occur in the spring and not fall?
- Ice floats. Why is that critical to aquatic organisms?
- What interactions were seen in the lake between an organism and the abiotic environment and an organism and the biotic environment?

15.2 Hierarchical Organization in Ecology

- What is included in organismal, population, community, and ecosystem ecology?

15.3 Organismal Ecology

- What is a habitat?
- What is a niche?

15.4 Population Ecology

- What is a population?
- What parameters can we measure on populations?

Population Size and Density

- What is population size and population density?

ecology—the study of the relationships between organisms and their environment.

Life Is Interactive. What does that mean? Let's explore this by looking at the two words that the term **ecology** is derived from: *oikos*, which means "household," and *logos*, which means "study." We might ask, "Whose household are we studying?" In the biblical text, St. Paul's letter to the Colossians (1:16) states "For by Him all things were created; things in heaven and on earth, visible and invisible, whether thrones or powers or rulers or authorities; all things were created by Him and for Him." So it is God's household we are studying. What kind of interaction does God want us to have with His household? Let us examine this with two examples from that household.

Consider the Grand Canyon in Arizona (see Figure 15.1). It has massive rock walls rising up 1830 meters (6000 feet) from the Colorado River. Here you might see the recently reintroduced (in 1996) California condors with wingspans up to 3 meters (9.5 feet) across soaring down the gorge and Bighorn sheep climbing on the steep canyon walls. Or, consider the Giant sequoias of California (see Figure 15.2), which can be over 91 meters (300 feet) in height. That's a football field stood upright. They have a diameter at the tree's base of 11 meters (35 feet) and older trees would have been alive when the "Word became flesh and made his dwelling among us" (Jn 1:14). That means some of the trees are over 2000 years old. When I first saw this canyon and these trees, I recall being absolutely amazed at their size and beauty. Both were truly magnificent. These places I have just described are works of art. Psalm 104 states the glory of the Lord is displayed in his creation (verse 31a), the Lord rejoices in his creation (verse 31b), and we are invited to rejoice in it also (verse 33).

- How can we uniquely mark animals in order to identify individuals for a mark-recapture study?
- How can we use information from a mark-recapture study to estimate population size?

Population Distribution Patterns

- What is the distribution pattern called when (1) there are no strong social interactions between organisms, (2) the organisms repel each other (i.e., they are territorial), and (3) the organisms tend to congregate?

Age Structure and Sex Ratios

- What would an age pyramid look like for a country with a fast-growing population, a slow-growing population, and a population that is shrinking in number?

Population Growth

- What is the geometric growth model?
- What resources might limit animal and plant populations?
- What model is used to describe population growth that at some time slows to where birth rates equal death rates?
- What is carrying capacity?
- When birth rates decline with increasing population density, is this a density-dependent or independent process?
- Name some density-independent factors?
- What are some characteristics of an *r*-selected species, a *K*-selected species?

15.5 Community Ecology

- In the Serengeti grasslands of East Africa, how do the wildebeest, the Thomson's gazelle, and grasses affect each other?
- What is a community?
- What are some of the interactions seen between species in a community?

Interspecific Competition

- What happens when *Paramecium caudatum* and *P. aurelia* are grown together in one culture flask?
- What happens to the populations of other plankton-feeding organisms when the zebra mussel, an invasive species, is accidentally introduced into the Great Lakes?

Figure 15.1 Grand Canyon, Arizona

Is life interactive? You bet. God wants it so and wants us to revel in his creation. Each process and creature you have explored so far—photosynthesis, mitosis, muscle contraction, and man—bears the fingerprint of an awesome Designer upon them. "For since the creation of the world, God's invisible qualities, his eternal power and divine nature have been clearly seen being understood from what has been made so that men are without excuse" (Rom 1:20). God's creation is a tangible expression of His invisible qualities and it should help us respond to Him in worship.

Figure 15.2 Sequoia tree. For size scale, note the adult standing at the base of the tree in the center of the photo.

14.

- What happens in a manipulative study where the competitor is removed?
- How do five species of warbler coexist in the spruce forests of North America?
- Why is total species extinction not a typical consequence of competition in nature?

One Species Benefits and the Other Is Adversely Affected

- What are some interactions where one species benefits and the other is adversely affected?
- Why might the lion not really be considered the king of the jungle?
- How did Gause and Huffaker get sustained oscillations in their respective predator-prey lab studies?
- What are some ways predators find prey and prey avoid being eaten?
- What at are some advantages and disadvantages of biological control?
- Why is the sea star considered a keystone species in the rocky intertidal region?

Both Species Benefit

- How do both species benefit in the ant-acacia relationship?
- Mutualisms: Are they simply a few notable interactions periodically seen in the natural world, or do they profoundly affect the world as we know it?

15.6 Ecosystems: Energy Flow Through Sets of Interacting Organisms

- How does a food chain differ from a food web?
- What does *autotroph* mean and what are the trophic levels called beyond the autotrophs?
- What is an ecosystem?
- What do each of the variables in the primary production equation represent (GPP = NPP + R)?
- What do each of the variables in the consumer equation represent (I − W = A = R + P)?
- What does the 10% rule mean and does energy flow through the Silver Springs ecosystem follow this rule?
- What does a pyramid of energy depict?

Let's take the theme "life is interactive" and go back to the word *ecology*, which is defined as the interactions between organisms and their environment where the environment includes both *nonliving* (*abiotic*) and *living* (*biotic*) components. Have these interactions remained the same through time or have major events in history affected the types of interactions we see? Consider the ecology of the original creation; let's call it *Phase I: creation before the fall*, as described in Genesis.

Genesis 1:1, 20–23, 30 "In the beginning God created the heavens and the earth . . . And God said, 'Let the water teem with living creatures, and let birds fly above the earth across the expanse of the sky.' So God created the great creatures of the sea and every living and moving thing with which the water teems, according to their kinds, and every winged bird according to its kind. And God saw that it was good. God blessed them and said, 'Be fruitful and increase in number and fill the water in the seas, and let the birds increase on the earth.' And there was evening, and there was morning—the fifth day. . . .

'And to all the beasts of the earth and all the birds of the air and all the creatures that move on the ground—everything that has the breath of life in it—I give every green plant for food.' And it was so."

Genesis 2:15–17 states, "The Lord God took the man and put him in the Garden of Eden to work it and take care of it. And the Lord God commanded the man, 'You are free to eat from any tree in the garden; but you must not eat from the tree of the knowledge of good and evil, for when you eat of it you will surely die.'"

What kinds of interactions between organisms and their environment do we see? We see ourselves as being caretakers or stewards of the garden. Stewardship means managers of God's creation—not owners. God clearly states in Psalm 24:1 that the "earth is the Lord's and everything in it, the world and all who live in it." We also see that we and other living creatures were given green plants for food (this is called herbivory); reproduction also seems to be going on rather rapidly (population growth that is likely geometric or exponential).

What happened next in the biblical narrative? The ecology of the household changed dramatically after sin entered the world. I call this Phase II and we get a description of what life was like from several passages in scripture:

"Cursed is the ground because of you; through painful toil you will eat of it all the days of your life. It will produce thorns and thistles for you, and you will eat the plants of the field. By the sweat of your brow you will eat your food until you return to the ground, since from it you were taken; for dust you are and to dust you will return."

(GN 3:17–19)

542   **Chapter 15** Ecology: Interactivity by Design

- Why do eating organisms that are lower on the food chain or eating at lower trophic levels make sense energetically?
- What is biomagnification and how might it affect you?

15.7 A Final Word about Our Interaction with God's Household

- How do we make good decisions with regard to caring for God's household?

"Do you hunt the prey for the lioness and satisfy the hunger of the lions when they crouch in their dens or lie in wait in a thicket? Who provides food for the raven when its young cry out to God and wander about for lack of food?"

(JB 38)

"Everything that lives and moves will be food for you. Just as I gave you the green plants, I now give you everything."

(GN 9:3)

What do we observe from these passages about the ecology in Phase II? We continue as stewards of God's creation but keeping the garden seems to be a lot harder than what it was earlier (Gn 3:17–19). And what happened to the herbivorous lifestyle that we, as well as all other creatures, had before? Our diet expanded to include meat. Some creatures (**carnivores**) now include meat in their diets. Has God abandoned His creation in Phase II? Job 38 indicates that God is the one who provides for the carnivorous raven and lion. We will also see in this chapter that God has not abandoned prey species for He has provided them with a multitude of ways to avoid becoming dinner for a carnivore.

But Phase II is not the end of the story; we are not permanently consigned to Phase II! Creation is waiting to be "liberated from its bondage to decay" (Rom 8:21). At some future point in time, the biblical text shows us a new heaven and new earth (Rv 21:1). Even now in Phase II, God has offered redemption to all who put their trust in the Lord Jesus. What does it mean to redeem or restore? *Re* means back or returning to a previous state. Think about what this means in our fractured relationship with God, each other and His creation. We will explore this further as it relates to our relationship with His Creation (His household) at the end of this chapter.

IN OTHER WORDS

1. Ecology is the study of God's household as it relates to the interactions between organisms and their environment.
2. Our interaction with God's creation has changed over time. Prior to sin entering the world, we were charged with being stewards of God's creation and green plants were given as food to both ourselves as well as other livings creatures.
3. After sin entered the world, other forms of food acquisition are present, including carnivory. We are still in our roles as stewards of God's creation, but it is more difficult now. This is the time period we are in.
4. We will not always be locked into a world damaged by sin. In the future, God will recreate the heavens and the earth.

carnivore (carnivory)—an organism that eats animals.

Before we examine a formal, systematic description of the discipline called *ecology*, let's look at a still water system (a **lentic** system like a pond or lake) and examine it through the eyes of an ecologist. Let's start looking at the Designer's household as an ecologist might. Remember that throughout our discussion of ecology in this chapter we are describing how things work during Phase II (after the fall and before God recreates the heavens and the earth).

We'll put on some chest waders and step into a lake located in a temperate region of the world—like the continental United States or Europe. You walk into the water from the bank feeling the water pressure as it presses the chest waders against your legs. As you get into knee-deep water, you might be surrounded by cattails, sedges, and maybe water lilies. You are in the **littoral zone** (see Figure 15.3). In this zone, the rooted plants provide energy and structural complexity for a rich diversity of vertebrates and invertebrates. Poke around here a bit and you might see the immature life stage of a dragonfly, an adult fishing spider, or maybe some tadpoles and bluegill fish. As you move further away from the bank, the water is now deeper and free of rooted plants. If you scooped up a water sample with a plastic jug from near the water surface and examined it under a microscope, you would see tiny creatures called **phytoplankton** (*phyte-* = plant; *plankton* = drifter) that drift around this zone. They live in the upper layer of open water, called the **limnetic zone** because of the high amounts of solar radiation that drive photosynthesis. The limnetic zone has a high concentration of dissolved oxygen (DO) because the oxygen concentration in the air is higher than in the water; as you might recall from your previous readings in this book, you would expect diffusion

to occur with oxygen molecules entering the aqueous environment. Of the solar radiation received in this zone, only about 40% of the photons reach 1 meter in depth. Consequently, most of the photosynthesis occurs near the surface. Red wavelengths of light are lost first in the water column; blues and greens are lost last. Why do you think that is? (Recall the energy content of photons moving at different wavelengths; see Section 6.9.) In the limnetic zone, the phytoplankton provide a source—a base—of energy for the zooplankton that in turn provide energy for larger carnivores. We have just described a food chain. The water is now getting too deep for us to proceed with chest waders. We climb into a boat and move out further toward the center of the lake. How can we sample water below the surface to see what the zone below the limnetic zone is like? Remember, we just immersed a plastic jug at the surface to sample the limnetic zone. That method would not work to get a pure sample from this deeper zone since it would contain some water from the limnetic zone. You could dive down with a closed jug and then near the bottom of the lake open the jug to collect your sample. But you can actually collect your sample more simply by using a Kemmerer sampling device, an open tube with caps at both ends that are held slightly away from the tube while you lower the device into the deeper water. When you get the sampling device at the right depth, you send a weight (called a *messenger*) along the rope holding the Kemmerer; this messenger strikes a triggering device on the Kemmerer that causes the caps to seal the ends of the tube. You have just collected a sample of water from near the lake bottom. You hoist up the Kemmerer device and pour out your sample and examine it. There are no

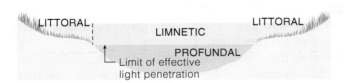

Figure 15.3 Lake zonation. The littoral zone is around the shore to where the water is too deep for rooted plants, the limnetic zone is the lighted water above the profundal zone.

lentic—pertaining to standing water like a lake.

littoral zone—the shallowest part of a lake where rooted plants can be found.

phytoplankton—microscopic organisms that drift with the currents and that can photosynthesize.

limnetic zone—open waters of a lake beyond the littoral zone.

live phytoplankton. Hmm. We must have lost too many photons at this depth to drive photosynthesis. We are now in the **profundal zone**. How does this zone get any energy since photosynthesis does not occur here? Remember that in the limnetic zone there is an abundance of life, and where you have lots of life, you also have lots of death. Dead creatures sink down to the profundal zone and provide energy to the **decomposers** that dominate this zone. In the oceans, these dead bodies are called *marine snow* because the dead organisms sinking down look like snowflakes falling on a winter day.

The decomposition of dead life-forms in the profundal zone releases compounds containing elements such as nitrogen, phosphorus, and carbon (i.e., plant nutrients), which can be recycled to the phytoplankton in the limnetic zone. If the lake is deep, these compounds accumulate in the lake bottom sediments and in the summer, this physical separation of the nutrients from the phytoplankton in the limnetic zone could actually limit phytoplankton population growth. The nutrients would remain in the bottom sediments if it were not for a process called *overturn*, which occurs in the fall and spring. During these seasons, the conditions in the lake waters are such that a light wind sweeping across the surface of the lake can set up bulk water movement that actually causes the entire lake's water to turn over. Water from the bottom of the lake rises to the surface carrying with it nutrients trapped in the sediments. When this coincides with the rising temperatures and hours of daylight during spring, all the conditions are right (i.e., nutrients, light, and warm temperatures) for an explosion of phytoplankton reproduction called a *phytoplankton bloom*. In the fall, when an overturn occurs, nutrients are near the surface, but phytoplankton blooms would not likely occur since temperatures and hours of light are declining.

Let's consider one more season in our temperate lake: winter. Here, if it gets cold enough, water will freeze. Because water is densest at 4°C and less dense at 0°C, the frozen water floats at the lake surface. This provides a layer of insulation against the cold air temperatures for the liquid water. This property of water that makes it less dense at 0°C versus 4°C is critical for most aquatic organisms (see Section 3.4). Let's review. What if water was densest at 0°C like most compounds? Would the frozen water stay at the surface or sink? It would sink and the lake would freeze from the bottom up becoming one solid block of ice. Creatures living in this lake would freeze with the water, and although there are some creatures that can handle freezing of their body tissues, most cannot. The winter season would be a death sentence for most creatures living in lentic systems. As mentioned in Chapter 3, a brilliant Designer has given water many special properties that allow for our aquatic systems to remain rich in life. "How many are your works, O LORD! In wisdom you made them all; the earth is full of your creatures" (Ps 104:24).

We have just viewed some aspects of a lentic system through the eyes of an ecologist. Next time you visit a lake, borrow some chest waders and repeat the tour we just took. Or simply gaze out over a lake with a new understanding of the dynamics that are going on in the waters below. As you look at the lake, think about the interactions between organisms and their environment (this is the definition for ecology) that you saw in the above narrative and that are summarized for you here:

profundal zone—waters below the limnetic zone.

decomposers—organisms, like bacteria and fungi, that obtain energy from the breakdown of dead organic matter.

IN OTHER WORDS

1. Examples of the interactions between an organism and the nonliving (abiotic) lake environment include:
   - Depths where photosynthesis can occur in the limnetic zone (restricts where phytoplankton are found)
   - Overturn in the spring bringing up nutrients from the lake bottom to the surface that fuels, along with increasing levels of sunlight, an algal bloom
   - Floating ice that prevents lakes from freezing from the bottom up and thus organisms in the lake waters do not freeze during the winter

2. Examples of the interaction between an organism and the biotic lake environment include:
   - Plants providing structure for animals in the littoral zone
   - Decomposers recycling nutrients to phytoplankton
   - Death in the limnetic zone providing energy to profundal zone decomposers

HIERARCHICAL ORGANIZATION IN ECOLOGY

We can begin our more formal study of ecology by considering the different levels of organization we see in words used to define ecology—interactions between organisms and their environment (see Figure 1.17). Consider first the organism. What kind of requirements does it have to survive, grow, and reproduce? Students at Liberty University have been studying the Peaks of Otter salamander, a species found only in a small area along the Blue Ridge Mountains in Central Virginia (see Figure 15.4). This species is found in mature hardwood forests typically at elevations higher than 425 meters (about 1400 feet). Discovering the factors that restrict this species to such a small area is the focus of organismal ecology. Are the temperatures too warm below 425 meters or is some other environmental factor making these lower-elevation areas uninhabitable to the Peaks of Otter salamander?

The students also considered the population ecology for this species by evaluating the changes in number over time for individuals from the same species living in a particular area. They evaluated the numbers per square meter (density) at various elevations as well as the animal's reproductive output. The number of eggs each female produced was first determined and then how frequently she produced eggs (annually, biannually, etc.). Students also considered how this salamander species fits within the montane hardwood forest salamander **community**. Here we are considering community ecology, which focuses on how populations of different species interact. Are the Peaks of Otter salamander and another similar species, the widespread Eastern Red-backed salamander, in competition with each other when they occur together along the edge of the Peaks of Otter salamander's distribution? Students could also look at ecology at the **ecosystem** level, which considers the community and its interaction with the abiotic part of the environment. This might be done by considering energy flow and nutrient recycling in the hardwood forest ecosystem, where the salamanders are one component of the ecosystem.

© 2005 A. B. Kniowski

Andrew Kniowski

Figure 15.4 Peaks of Otter salamander, *Plethodon hubrichti.*

community—interacting species in a particular area.

ecosystem—the community and abiotic components in a particular area.

ORGANISMAL ECOLOGY

How an organism relates to its environment is usually considered in terms of what conditions maximize its fitness—its ability to survive and successfully reproduce. Each organism requires certain conditions in order for it to reach maturity and produce offspring. These conditions make up the **habitat** for that organism. For example, our students doing research on the Peaks of Otter salamander find this species by looking under rocks and logs. We describe to the students the salamander's habitat requirements. We search for salamanders on days that are cool and moist because on hot, dry days, the salamanders leave the soil surface and move down vertically into the soil to escape the heat, which becomes lethal to them when temperatures exceed 33°C. So an area that provides cool, moist conditions with lots of rocks and decaying logs, such as under a hardwood forest canopy at elevations greater than 425 meters, constitutes good habitat for this species.

In organismal ecology, we also define a species' **niche**. This is the functional role of a species in its habitat. For the Peaks of Otter salamander, the niche is determined by asking: What does a salamander consume, and what consumes it? Does it compete with other species? How much energy does it store in terms of biomass? The niche is multidimensional and incorporates all of the abiotic and biotic factors that affect a species' survival, growth, and reproduction.

> **habitat**—a place where an organism lives.
>
> **niche**—the functional role of a species in a community.

IN OTHER WORDS

1. What a species needs to survive and successfully reproduce is the focus of organismal ecology.
2. In organismal ecology, we define the habitat and the niche or functional role of the species.

15.4

POPULATION ECOLOGY

A population is defined as a group of organisms of the same species in a particular area. This might include all the Bluegill fish in a specific pond, where both the species (the Bluegill fish) and the particular area (the pond) are clearly defined for this population. For a population of White-tailed deer, the species is easily defined but the particular area may not be. Are we talking about the population in a particular forest, county, state, and so on? Since the White-tailed deer habitat may be continuous over broad areas, defining a particular area might have to be done in a practical fashion. For example, if I am a wildlife biologist studying White-tailed deer in a national forest, the particular area for my deer population might simply be the national forest's boundaries. I realize the deer move about in areas beyond the national forest, but I may have only enough resources to study them in the area I am responsible for.

Once the population is defined, there are multiple population parameters we like to measure, including size, density, sex ratios, age structure, dispersion patterns, and movement patterns. Let's examine each of these in turn.

Population Size and Density

Population size is fairly easy to measure for some species. We could completely enumerate the number of *Red-spotted newts* (a type of salamander with a rough skin) in a small ditch. We would take a net of appropriate mesh size and slowly drag it through the ditch. We count the number of newts and we have our population size. Consider the same newt species but now use a pond as the particular area. There would simply be no possible way to enumerate all of the newts in the pond unless you drained it. So what do we do? We need to employ a *mark-recapture method*. A marking technique is required along with a mathematical model to estimate population size. Depending on the animal you are working with, there are a number of marking techniques available. One could inject a harmless, colored elastomer under the skin of an animal. Or it's possible to inject a passive integrated transponder (PIT) tag under the skin of an animal. We sometimes attach

Figure 15.5 Individual marking methods for population studies **(a)** Forida Key deer **(b)** Costa Rican owl butterfly (*Caligo*).

a numbered collar on larger animals, use a Sharpie to write a number on a butterfly's wing or a numbered band on the leg of a bird (see Figure 15.5). We can even use the *DNA fingerprint* of an individual as a way to identify whether the individual had been seen previously. The PIT tag is being used with many household pets. If a lost pet is recovered, it can be traced to the owner using a national database that stores the owner's contact information in a unique number encoded in the PIT tag. An animal with a PIT tag can be examined with a handheld scanner, and the unique number encoded in the PIT tag shows up on the scanner screen.

Now back to our example with the Red-spotted newt. We did a mark-recapture study on newts in a pond near Liberty University. A seine (a net strung between two poles that can be pulled through the water) was used to capture our newts. In 2009, 443 newts were collected. All these animals were marked using the colored, injectable elastomer. One week later, we ran the seine in the same area and collected 332 newts of which 174 had elastomer marks. We then use the Peterson mark-recapture method with our data to estimate the population size for the area of the pond that we seined. The method involves two ratios. The first one is a ratio of the number of newts captured in the first trip (m) divided by the total population size (N). This ratio has the one unknown in it, the total population size. The second ratio uses information from the number of the newts collected during the second seining event. It is a ratio of the number of newts recaptured (r) divided by the total number captured during the second seining event (c). By setting these two ratios equal to each other we can solve for the unknown:

$$m/N = r/c$$

For our example:

$$443/N = 174/332$$

This formula can be rearranged to solve for N:

$$N = (443 \times 332)/174$$
$$= 845$$

So the total population estimate for the area seined is 845 newts. Remember that N is just an estimate of the population size. How good the estimate is depends on many factors such as how the newly marked animals behave when released. If they now avoid the area they were initially captured in, then when we resample the same area a week later, we would recapture fewer of the marked animals than expected (i.e., our second ratio r/c would be off and our population estimate would be too high). The practical reality is that often the mark-recapture method is the only way we can estimate a species population size and we do our best to minimize any violations of the method's assumptions.

Once the population size is known for a given area, we can estimate its density. **Density** is the number of organisms per unit area. In our example, the area sampled was 150 m². With a population estimate of 845 newts in 150 m², our density estimate was 5.6 newts/m². Several other areas in the pond were seined with estimated population sizes of 876, 297, and 1008. Which area did the newts prefer? Before you say the area with the 1008 newt population estimate, you need to ask how big each area was. If they are not the same size, you should not use population estimates to determine which area the newts prefer. The corresponding areas sampled

were as follows: 99, 66, and 400 m². Calculate densities and determine which area the newts prefer. The density derived from the 876 newt population estimate divided by the 99 m² area should give you the highest density, or the area favored by the newts.

Population Distribution Patterns

Till now we have determined only how many individuals we suspect are in a given area. The next question to ask is, How are the individuals within the population spread out in the area sampled? Do the individuals repel, ignore, or attract each other? If there are no strong social interactions between organisms (i.e., they ignore each other) and the resources needed are found fairly uniformly distributed throughout an area, then the organism might have a **random distribution pattern** (see Figure 15.6). If the organism you are studying is territorial, where each individual defends a specific area (i.e., they repel each other), then the distribution pattern is more likely to be **uniform** (see Figure 15.6). A uniform distribution pattern may also result when resources are scarce, as with some desert plants like the Creosote bush, which were hypothesized to compete for below-ground resources (see Figure 15.7). Evidence for this was seen when researchers carefully dug up multiple Creosote bushes and mapped out their root zones. There was very little overlap in their root zones. This supports a competition hypothesis. Social species tend to have clumped distribution patterns (see Figure 15.6). I wonder if, like me, you have ever experienced the **clumped distribution pattern** seen in Yellowjackets and hornets. Where you find one, there are usually more! A patchy distribution of the resources needed by individuals within the population can also lead to a clumped distribution pattern. Scale is very important when considering distribution patterns. If you observe a penguin breeding

Density—number of organisms per unit area.

random distribution—a distribution pattern in a population where the spacing of individuals shows no particular pattern.

uniform distribution—a distribution pattern in a population where individuals are evenly spaced.

clumped distribution—a distribution pattern in a population where there are aggregations of individuals.

clumped

nearly uniform

random

Figure 15.6 Three population distribution patterns: clumped as in squirrel fish schools, fairly uniform as in royal penguin nesting colony, and random, as when wolf spiders live in burrows scattered throughout the forest.

Figure 15.7 Near the eastern base of the Sierra Nevada, creosote bushes show a nearly uniform population distribution. The plants compete for water which is scarce in desert regions.

colony and consider only the area that includes the colony, you might say the distribution pattern is uniform (see Figure 15.6). If you now consider the area of the colony plus the land surrounding it, you would say it's a clumped distribution pattern since the colony is located in one specific area while the rest of the area lacks birds.

Age Structure and Sex Ratios

If it's possible to determine the age of individuals in a population or use some measure that roughly corresponds to age, like length or mass, you can examine age structure in a population. Often, this information is combined with gender and reproductive information, all of which is readily available for people, but less so for other species. These data can be graphed using age structure plots (see Figure 15.8), where the width of the horizontal bar represents the number of individuals in that particular age class. Countries with a broad base of prereproductive and reproductive individuals will have rapid population growth while those with more postreproductive individuals relative to prereproductive individuals represent a population that is declining (negative population growth). You can also see in these age pyramids that the numbers for each gender are fairly similar until you reach the postreproductive years. Which gender tends to dominate in the later part of the postreproductive period? If you guessed females, you are correct. Why do you think that is?

Population Growth

Let's return to our Red-spotted newt example. I have been collecting newt population size data for over 10 years in one pond. In 2007 the population estimate for all areas seined (essentially the perimeter of the pond) was 1232. In 2008 the estimate for the same area was 1536. The observed population size increase may have been due to births or the arrival of individuals from outside the population (immigrants). Losses in a population would be due to deaths and individuals leaving the population (emigrants). In our case the additions exceeded the losses and the newt population was estimated to have increased by 304 individuals in a one-year period. This increase can be characterized by a ratio of the current year's population estimate divided by last year's population estimate. This is called the **annual finite rate of increase**, designated by the Greek letter λ (lambda):

$$\lambda = 1536/1232$$
$$= 1.25$$

A λ greater than 1 indicates population growth is positive as seen with the one we just calculated (304 newts were added to the population between years 2007 to 2008). If λ is less than 1, population growth is negative and a λ of 1 would indicate no change in population size over time.

annual finite rate of increase (λ)— ratio of the current year's population size divided by last year's population size.

Expanding Rapidly	Expanding Slowly	Stable	Declining
Guatemala	United States	Japan	Germany
Nigeria	Australia	Italy	Bulgaria
Saudi Arabia	China	Greece	Russia

■ Prereproductive ages 0–14   ■ Reproductive ages 15–44   ■ Postreproductive ages 45–85+

Figure 15.8   Human age structure diagrams for countries with rapid growth, slow and negative population growth rates.

Let's now use λ in a model to predict a future population like that for 2009 using the **geometric growth model** (note the geometric growth model is similar to the **exponential growth model**, which you may have encountered before in high school biology, but it's a little easier to work with):

$$N_t = N_0 \lambda^t$$

In this formula, N_t represents the population size in some year (t) beyond the starting population size designated as N_0. We have already calculated λ, and if we believe this λ is a good estimate for the annual finite rate of increase for the next year, then we are ready to predict a population size for the Red-spotted newt in 2009.

N_t is our unknown newt population size for 2009, N_0 is the current population in 2008 or 1536, λ is 1.25, and t would be the number of years into the future we are making our prediction. In this example, there is one year between the current population (the one for 2008) and the one we are predicting (the one for 2009). Do the substitutions and we are ready to calculate N_t.

$$N_t = 1536 \times 1.25^1$$

Punch this out on your calculator and you should get 1920. If you wanted to estimate a population two years into the future, all you have to change is t, which would be two. Your new estimate would be 2400. You can easily repeat this calculation using your calculator for three, four, five, etc., years into the future and you would get a graph like the one in Figure 15.9. The shape of the growth curve is a *J-shape* and shows how quickly some populations might increase in number. You might wonder, though, how close your estimate is to an actual population estimate from a mark-recapture study done during one of those years. Does the λ

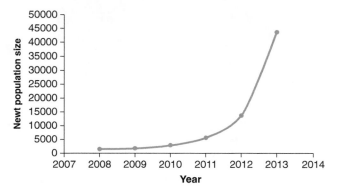

Figure 15.9 Geometric population growth curve showing characteristic J-shape. Starting newt population was 1536 and lambda was 1.25.

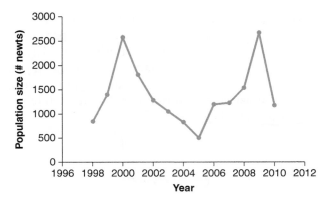

Figure 15.10 Red-spotted newt population size over time in a pond from central Virginia.

we calculated using the data from the years 2007 and 2008 provide an accurate annual population growth rate if, for example, the population size is different from what it was during the years used for our λ estimate? Every *model* has assumptions, and over short periods of time, the geometric growth model may provide reasonable population estimates if λ is fairly stable. Figure 15.10 shows estimates of our newt population sizes for a number of years. Notice that our estimate for 2009 of 1920 newts is lower than what we found (2669 newts). We predicted population growth and that was correct (recall when λ was greater than 1, population grow is occurring). But the amount of growth was lower than what actually occurred (λ was actually greater than 1.25).

Geometric growth rarely lasts for long periods of time. Typically, some kind of environmental factor slows or limits population growth. Environmental factors that might limit animal populations include food, space, nesting areas, predation, and disease. Nutrients, sunlight, space, and moisture may be limiting factors for plants. As these resources become scarce, individuals within the population begin to interact in a competitive way (intraspecific competition). In an ideal environment, a population might begin growing at a geometric rate and then growth slows as one to several environmental factors start to limit population growth. The

geometric growth—population growth in which each generation changes in size by a constant ratio.

exponential growth—population growth is where the rate of change is the product of the population size and the per capita growth rate.

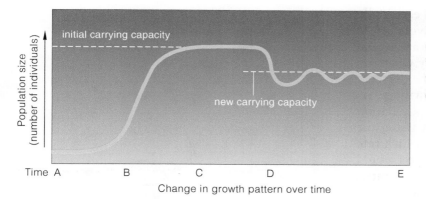

Figure 15.11 An idealized logistic growth curve. Population growth initially grows geometrically (time A to C) and then slows as carrying capacity is reached (C to D). Variations in the logistics growth occur when populations fluctuate around carrying capacity and when changes in the environment lower carrying capacity (time D to E).

growth eventually slows to where birth rates equal death rates and the population remains stable at a number that we call the carrying capacity of the environment. The population growth we just described would be following the logistic growth model where the population growth curve is sigmoidal in shape (see Figure 15.11). So what exactly happens when population growth slows due to some environmental factor(s)? We can take a look at some of these factors that alter population growth using another graph which illustrates birth and death rates in relationship to population density. Before we look at the graph, let's describe how such a graph might be derived with a hypothetical example. Picture two rooms, each 4 × 4 meters (about 12 × 12 feet). In one room you place 10 mice (5 males and 5 females), and in the second room you place 1000 mice (500 males and 500 females). You provide plenty of food and water for the mice in each room. The mice go about their normal business of eating, drinking, and reproducing (the House mouse can produce about 6 to 10 babies every six to eight weeks). If you were to take an educated guess, you might think that the birth rates (babies per female) would be highest in the room that started off with 10 mice. Here there is plenty of space to raise the babies, you can get away from any aggressive male mice, and the area is not contaminated with fecal material. In contrast, the room with the 1000 mice is crowded and soon becomes contaminated with fecal material. This is a stressful environment and birth rates (babies per female, not total babies produced) would likely be lower than in the room that started off with 10 mice. Death rates would be reversed. If you place the data points on a graph with density on the *x*-axis and death and birth rates on the *y*-axis and connect them with straight lines, you would get what is illustrated in

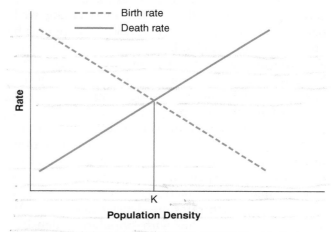

Figure 15.12 Idealized graph of density dependent birth and death rates.

Figure 15.12. The two lines intersect where birth rates equal death rates. This is also the population density for carrying capacity. Where densities are lower than the carrying capacity, you can see that birth rates exceed death rates. When that occurs, the population is growing because environmental factors are not limiting. That would be represented by the first part of the logistic growth curve, where

birth rate—the number of new individuals produced in a population; usually expressed at births per individual or births per 1000 individuals.

death rate—the number of individuals that died in a population; usually expressed as deaths per individual or deaths per 1000 individuals.

carrying capacity (K)—the maximum population size an environment can sustain.

logistic growth—population growth pattern that has an S shape where population growth levels off at the carrying capacity.

population growth is rapid and is essentially following the geometric model. Once you get to the intersection of the two lines (birth rates equal death rates), you are at carrying capacity where no population growth occurs. That would be depicted by the flat portion of the logistic growth curve. Now consider a scenario where the population density exceeded the carrying capacity. Using the graph illustrating birth and death rates, which rate would be higher? If you said death rates, you would be correct. And if death rates exceed birth rates, then the population is declining. Populations in the real world often fluctuate at times rising above the carrying capacity and at other times falling well below it (see Figure 15.11). Before we leave our birth and death rate graphs, let's use them to illustrate an important set of factors that are considered to be **density dependent** (that is, the magnitude of the effect varies with how dense our population is). If I asked you what the population's birth rate was, could you give me an answer? The answer would be "no" because I did not give you a population density value. You need to know population density in order to determine a birth rate since birth rates change with density. This is what it means when we say birth rates are density dependent. If a factor changes value with population density, then we call it a *density-dependent factor*. In our illustration, death rates for the mice are also density dependent.

There is another set of environmental factors that affects population size but is not dependent on density. These typically are things like fires, floods, severe winters, and drought that reduce population numbers regardless of the population density. While we have not devoted as much space to such **density-independent** factors, please do not think that they are not important. For example, a drought in 1977 caused an 85% decline in a population of finches in the Galapagos Islands, reducing it from about 1200 individuals to 180. Density-independent factors can have profound effects on populations.

Limiting environmental resources such as we have described previously only partially explain how population size is regulated. Another part comes from the biology of the organism itself. Some species produce few young and then provide lots of parental care, while others produce hundreds of eggs that hatch without a parent in sight. These are illustrations of differences in a species' biotic potential or capacity to produce offspring.

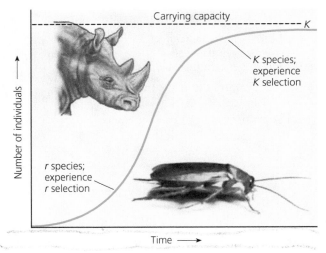

Figure 15.13   Positions of *r*-selected and *K*-selected species on the logistic population growth curve.

The extremes of biotic potential are labeled **K-selected** and **r-selected species** (see Figure 15.13). *K*-selected species have low biotic potential. They produce few young, provide parental care, develop slowly, and are strong competitors. The term *K-selected* is used because these species may typically be at or near their carrying capacity, which is often symbolized with the letter *K*. Examples of *K*-selected species are wolves, bears, sharks, and elephants. At the other extreme are *r*-selected species. These have a high biotic potential: They produce many young. They exhibit no parental care, develop quickly, and are not strong competitors. Rather, they are strong dispersers. They often inhabit recently disturbed areas before competition becomes too strong. The term *r-selected* is used because the letter *r* in many formulas represents population growth rate in

density-dependent factor—biotic factors, like competition for food resources or space, that change in response to and are dependent upon population density.

density-independent factor—abiotic factors such as a flood or a severe winter that affects populations and their effect is independent of population density.

K-selected species—species that have low biotic potential and typically follow a logistic style of population growth. They are usually regulated by density-dependent factors at a population size around carrying capacity.

r-selected species—species with high biotic potential that follow an exponential or geometric style of population growth and are often regulated by density independent factors.

the absence of limiting factors. (It is similar to λ.) Examples of r-selected species are insects and many annual plants such as dandelions. Most species fall somewhere between these two extremes.

We have just explored how populations of species are controlled primarily through characteristics of the species (biotic potential) or by way of a resource that limits individuals within the population (density-dependent, intraspecific interactions limiting population growth). All of these internal regulatory mechanisms can be trumped by abiotic factors such as weather, which can knock population numbers down (density-independent factors). Although this may seem complex enough, it is not a complete picture because we have not considered other species. Our species of interest does not live in isolation; rather it is a member of God's household. How do species interact with each other during Phase II of the Designer's historical plan? Let's explore this with a look at the spectacular migrations of wildebeest and Thomson's gazelle in East Africa as we move into a study of communities (a group of interacting species in a given area).

IN OTHER WORDS

1. When we focus on a single species and evaluate its numbers in a given area, we are looking at population ecology.
2. To understand the dynamics of a species' population, we measure various parameters on a population, including the following:
   - Size and density, where population size is usually done through mark-recapture population estimation methods where individuals in the population are marked in some fashion
   - Distribution patterns, which relate to whether individuals in a population ignore, repel, or attract each other
   - Age structure, which includes number per age category and can be used to determine whether a population is growing, stable, or declining
   - Growth rates, which can be mathematically modeled using various equations, each with its own set of assumptions (The model for growth without any limitations to population size is the geometric growth model. Population growth often slows when some environmental factor becomes limiting and this is can be modeled with the logistic growth model.)
3. The logistic growth model has a general assumption that birth rates decline and death rates increase with increases in population density due to intraspecific competition. These are considered density-dependent processes and when birth rates equal death rates, the population is at carrying capacity.
4. Other factors that can affect population size include density-independent factors, which are typically weather-related phenomena such as drought or excessive amounts of snow that can cause deaths in a population regardless of the population density.

Ecologist Sam McNaughton once estimated that more than 1 million wildebeest and 600,000 Thomson's gazelles migrate in a circular fashion through the Serengeti-Mara grasslands of Kenya and Tanzania. Wildebeest migrate through the Serengeti Plains first and graze upon the green plants. McNaughton measured *plant biomass* (g/m²) before the wildebeest arrived. Then, using a fenced area as a control, he was able to compare plant biomass in areas where the wildebeest had grazed and where they were excluded (the fenced area). Over the four days it took the wildebeest to pass through the area, McNaughton found that in the unfenced areas where wildebeest had grazed, the green plant biomass had been reduced by 85% when compared to his fenced area. For one month after the wildebeest left, he examined plant growth in grazed and ungrazed areas. He found that plant biomass increased in the grazed areas while it declined in ungrazed areas (see Figure 15. 14)! The wildebeest had prevented the grasses from going into senescence (that's what was happening in the ungrazed areas) and had stimulated new plant growth in the grazed areas. About one month after the wildebeest left the Serengeti, the Thomson's gazelles arrived. Where do you think they grazed? That was another question McNaughton had. Using additional plots, he found that the gazelles primarily grazed in areas where the wildebeest had grazed and avoided areas that were ungrazed. We are here looking at the concept of a community where our focus is on the interactions between populations of different species in a given area. There are always surprises when we do this. Consider the relationship between the grasses and the wildebeest. How should we characterize it? We must ask two questions. First, does the wildebeest benefit from the grass? The answer is "yes," since the grass provides energy and nutrients to the wildebeest. The next question is whether the grass derives any benefits from the wildebeest. If the grass was affected only negatively from the wildebeest grazing on it, we would call this relationship strictly **herbivory** (an animal that eats a plant or its products). But it is actually a bit more complicated since the plant

growth is stimulated, in our example, at the level of grazing typically experienced in the Serengeti. So with this example of herbivory, the grass is not affected strictly in a negative way. Sometimes, our categories are not so neat! The interaction between gazelle and grass would be strictly herbivory since the gazelle is eating the new growth. Now consider the wildebeest and the Thomson's gazelle. Do the wildebeest derive any benefit from the gazelles? No; they actually arrive in the Serengeti before the Thomson's gazelles. Do the Thomson's gazelles benefit from the wildebeest? Yes; the Thomson's gazelles select areas that were been grazed by the wildebeest. Here one species benefits (Thomson's gazelle) while the wildebeest is unaffected by the gazelle. This is called **commensalism**.

Other types of interactions seen in communities include ones (1) where both species are negatively affected (reduced population sizes) since they both use the same resource that is in limited supply (**interspecific competition**) and (2) where one species benefits and the other is negatively affected. This later interaction has several subcategories depending on the details of the interaction. Recall the interaction between gazelle and grass. This was considered to be herbivory since the gazelle benefited from eating the grass while the grass was negatively affected. The other subcategories would include **predation**, where one animal (predator) hunts, kills, and typically consumes all or part of another animal (prey); **parasitism,** where the parasite uses the host (the organism it lives on or in) in some fashion to benefit itself (usually nourishment) at

10.

herbivore (herbivory)—an organism that eats plants.

commensalism—an interaction between species where one benefits and the other is not harmed.

interspecific competition—competition between individuals of different species where both species are adversely affected.

predator (predation)—an organism that kills its prey.

parasite (parasitism)—an organism that lives in or on another organism (called the host) from which it derives a benefit.

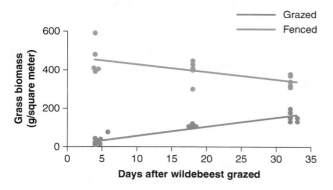

Figure 15.14 **(a)** Wildebeest grazing on an African savanna. **(b)** Growth responses of grasses in areas grazed by wildebeest and other areas where wildebeest were excluded (fenced areas).

the expense of the host; **parasitoidism**, where an insect parasitizes another insect typically resulting in the host's death; and *disease* (bacteria, viruses, fungi), where the pathogen can cause an illness in the host.

Interspecific Competition

Let's explore competition using a series of examples. In the 1930s, Russian ecologist G. F. Gause examined experimentally the outcome of competition between two species that had similar ecological requirements or niches. One set of experiments involved two species of ciliated **protozoans**, *Paramecium caudatum* and *P. aurelia*, that he first grew separately in culture flasks. The growth pattern over a series of days indicated both species followed the sigmoidal population growth pattern typical of logistic growth where a carrying capacity could be determined (see Figure 15.15). Recall that carrying capacity is where birth rates equals death rates and the population is controlled by competition between individuals of the same species for a limited resource, which in this case is food. When he grew the two species together in one culture flask, only *P. aurelia* survived (see Figure 15.15). This example illustrates that competition may lead to loss of one species when it is forced to compete for food in a culture flask.

Other evidence for interspecific competition comes from invasive species. When such a species

parasitoid (parasitoidism)—an insect whose larvae consumes all or part of its host.

protozoans—group of single-celled organisms which some classification schemes place in the Kingdom Protista.

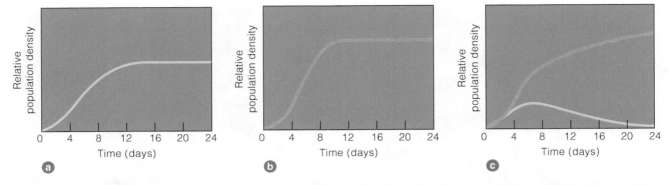

Figure 15.15 **(a)** *Paramecium caudatum* and **(b)** *P. aurelia* grown separately in culture flasks. Both follow a logistic population growth curve and reach a stable number (carrying capacity) after 10-12 days. **(c)** when grown together, *P. aurelia* (brown curve) outcompleted P. caudatum (green curve) causing its numbers to decline over time.

invades a habitat where native species with similar niches are already living, there is often a decline in numbers of the native species as the invasive species population increases. For example, the Zebra mussel was accidently introduced into the Great Lakes around 1988. This small, **filter-feeding bivalve**, about the size of a dime, is originally from Eastern Europe and Western Asia (see Figure 15.16). It is thought that ships from Europe that entered the Great Lakes must have discharged ballast water containing the larvae of this bivalve. Populations of the Zebra mussel exploded (recall the geometric growth model) in the Great Lakes while populations of native mussels and plankton-feeding fish declined during the same period of time. This study is a natural experiment where observations were made on a system without doing any direct manipulations to set up a control and treatment. Here observations were made after the Zebra mussel was introduced and then these observations were interpreted. It is possible that other factors caused the decline in native mussel populations and plankton-feeding fish. But Zebra mussels consume plankton just like native mussels and plankton-feeding fish (niche overlap with regard to food resources) and their population increased while those of the other plankton-feeding species declined. This natural study provides fairly strong evidence for interspecific competition, but the strongest support for interspecific interactions such as competition, comes from manipulative studies. Let's examine such a study.

A manipulative study to evaluate interspecific competition usually involves the removal of one or the other competitor species from test plots. Consider a study of two species of barnacles in an intertidal region. Barnacles are marine crustaceans, and as adults, they attach themselves to rocks and then use their appendages to trap plankton and other organic particles for food. The intertidal region is

(photo credit, sideways text) NOAA Great Lakes Environmental Research Laboratory

Figure 15.16 The introduced zebra mussel attached to a water current meter in Lake Michigan. Increases in this species populations have been related to declines in native mussel and plankton-feeding fish populations in the Great Lakes.

filter-feeding—a feeding process used by some organisms where material suspended in water is separated from the water by a sieving process.

bivalve—a Class of organisms characterized by having two valves (or shells) such as clams, mussels and scallops.

the area between low and high tide and exposure to air will vary depending on where in the intertidal region the organism lives. For example, if a barnacle lives in the upper part of the intertidal zone, then essentially every time the tide goes out (moving toward low tide), the barnacle would be exposed to air. Ecologist Joseph Connell observed that one species of barnacle, *Chthamalus stellatus*, was found primarily in the upper part of the intertidal region, while another species of barnacle, *Balanus balanoides*, was found in the middle to lower parts of the intertidal region. The first question you might ask is, "What is the resource that is limited for these two species?" Think of the environment where these barnacles are located. The intertidal region is an area where waves often crash against rocks. To hold your position in the intertidal region, it is helpful if you can be attached to something fairly immovable like a rock. So space is the resource that may be limited for barnacles in an intertidal region.

Connell carefully mapped out the locations of the barnacles attached to the rocks by using glass plates laid on top of four rods permanently driven into the substrate of the intertidal region. In the knee-deep water he placed a horizontal glass plate lightly on the four rods and marked on the glass the locations and species of barnacles below the plate. He returned after a period of time and placed a new glass plate on the four rods and once again marked the barnacle locations on this new glass plate. By comparing glass plates, Connell could keep track of individual barnacles in the area below each glass plate. He mapped the locations of adult barnacles in multiple locations throughout the intertidal zone during March and April, before the larvae of the barnacles settled on the rocks. Then he began removing one or the other species in different areas. When he removed *Chthamalus* from the upper part of the intertidal area, young *Balanus* settled in this area but their survival rates were essentially the same as in areas where *Chathamalus* was not removed. Do *Chthamalus* and *Balanus* compete in the upper part of the intertidal region? Since *Balanus* survival rates were similar regardless of whether *Chthamalus* was removed or not, he could not support a hypothesis of competition between these species in the upper part of the intertidal region. It appears young *Balanus* do not grow well in the upper part of the intertidal region because they are vulnerable to desiccation. So it is desiccation and not competition with *Chthamalus* that restricts *Balanus* from the upper part of the intertidal region. When *Balanus*

was removed in middle parts of the intertidal region, the *Chthamalus* that settled in these areas survived very well in comparison to *Chthamalus* settling in areas where *Balanus* was not removed. *Balanus* is a larger species than *Chthamalus* and it can smother or undercut *Chthamalus* when they are found together. So here we have evidence to support the hypothesis that interspecific competition was restricting *Chthamalus* from the middle part of the intertidal region. In the lowest areas of the intertidal region, removing *Balanus* did not affect the survival rates for *Chthamalus* (see Figure 15.17).

In summary, desiccation and not competition with *Chthamalus* restricts *Balanus* from the upper part of the intertidal region because in the upper parts of the intertidal region *Balanus* would be exposed to air for long periods of time during each tidal cycle. *Chthamalus* is found primarily in the upper parts of the intertidal region because of its ability to withstand desiccation and because it is outcompeted by *Balanus* in the middle part of the intertidal region. In the lowest parts of the intertidal region, predation apparently restricts the distribution of both species. So both biological (interspecific competition and predation) and physical conditions (desiccation) define where these two species of barnacles can be found in the intertidal region.

Our last example of competition illustrates how similar species can coexist in nature. If you consider the entire intertidal region in the previous example, two species of barnacle have essentially partitioned this resource. One species lives higher and the other lower in the intertidal region. Resource partitioning is considered to be one result of competition—a result that reduces the intensity of the competition. A classic example of resource partitioning is seen with five species of warbler in the spruce forests of North America. These birds all are similar in size and eat similar kinds of insects. Ecologist Robert MacArthur predicted that these species might coexist if they foraged in different parts of the tree. After observing these birds, he was able to quantify the zones each species foraged in, and indeed, each had a fairly distinct foraging area. For example, the Cape May warbler foraged primarily in the crowns of the trees while the Yellow-rumped warbler foraged in the lower branches and trunks of the trees (see Figure 15.18).

Let's review and compare our examples of competition. With the paramecia, one species was lost when an experiment on competition was conducted in the lab. For the zebra mussels in the

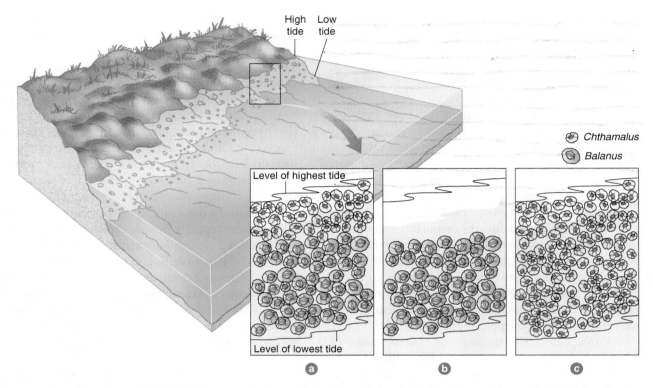

Figure 15.17 Barnacle competition: **(a)** barnacles belonging to two genera, *Chthamalus* and *Balanus* live in the rocky intertidal zone; **(b)** when *Chthamalus* was experimentally removed from the upper intertidal zone *Balanus* did not expand into this area, **(c)** but when *Balanus* was removed from lower in the intertidal zone *Chthamalus* was able to expand into this zone which indicated that the two species were competing in this zone.

Figure 15.18 Resource partitioning in five species of warblers from spruce forests in Maine. Each species minimizes interspecific competition by foraging primarily in different zones of the spruce trees.

Great Lakes, populations of potential competitors declined but extinctions have not occurred, at least to date. With the barnacles, one species was eliminated from the middle part of the intertidal region due to competition, but it flourished in the upper part of the intertidal region. Generally speaking, total species extinction is probably not a typical consequence of competition in nature because of the complexity of natural environments. Natural environments vary in time and space. One species may be eliminated in one area but flourish in another. If the limited resource is food, then one of the competing species might switch to another food source if the one jointly sought after becomes limited. In addition, competition is only one of a variety of interactions that a species may be involved in; others may include parasitism, predation, disease, as well as abiotic factors such as adverse weather. These interactions might keep populations far enough below carrying capacity so that competition happens only periodically. While interspecific competition is considered common and important, it is simply one of several interactions that structure communities. Let's move on now to the sort of interaction where one species benefits and the other is adversely affected. Predation, herbivory, parasitism, parasitoidism, and disease fall into this category.

One Species Benefits and the Other Is Adversely Affected

Imagine a pride of Lions stalking prey on the savannas of Africa. Typically, their prey would be wildebeest, Impala, Zebra, Cape buffalo, or Warthog, and under some conditions, even Giraffe or African elephant. An adult Lion has no natural predators. With this niche, you can easily imagine why it is sometimes considered to be king of the jungle (although it really lives on the savannas [tropical grasslands] of Africa and not jungles). But this top predator of the African savannas is vulnerable to parasites and pathogens. A study done by veterinarian Melody Roelke-Parker and her colleagues found 19 parasites and six viruses known to infect Lions. The viruses do not normally cause mortality in their Lion hosts, but in 1994, the canine distemper virus reduced the estimated population of 3000 Lions in the Serengeti ecosystem by 30%! So when we consider the interactions where one species benefits and the other is adversely affected, the Lion falls into both categories depending on whether it is the predator (species that benefits) or the host (species that is adversely affected). Is there really any species that can be the king of the jungle? With parasites and pathogenic organisms, there really aren't any kings of the jungle whether you are considering the Lion, Orca, Polar bear, or you and me. We are all vulnerable and subject to death in this

Phase II, postfall world. For us, though, that need not be the final word. "For if, by the trespass of the one man, death reigned through that one man, how much more will those who receive God's abundant provision of grace and of the gift of righteousness reign in life through the one man, Jesus Christ" (Rom 5:17) (see Section 16.6).

When we graph a typical model of predator-prey interactions, a pattern of oscillations in population size is seen over extended periods of time. The predator population will peak slightly after the prey population peaks. Predictions from these models were examined by Gause using ciliated protozoans. Think about the wisdom of using protozoans for these first experiments on predator and prey population cycles. With the short life cycles and small space requirements of protozoans, Gause could conduct his experiments in flasks over a matter of days! He used the predator species *Didinium nasutum*; the prey was *Paramecium caudatum* (see Figure 15.19a).

Gause started with a simple culture flask with the two species. Each species' populations increased in size and then crashed to extinction (see Figure 15.19b). Next, he added some sediment to the bottom of the flask, which provided a refuge for prey species. *Paramecium caudatum* could now escape from *D. nasutum* by hiding in the small gaps between the sediment particles. The spaces were large enough for the prey but too small for the predator. So the prey had a refuge. After the predator ate all the prey that were not hiding in the refuge, the predator populations crashed (see Figure 15.19c). Now the flask was free from predators, and the prey populations rose rapidly. The only way he was able to get sustained oscillations in population size was when he added individuals from both species on a regular basis (see Figure 15.19d). In other words, he had to complicate his experimental system by adding immigrant protozoa to his populations (not an entirely unrealistic complication).

In the 1950s, entomologist Carl Huffaker used mites in experiments designed to examine the role of environmental complexity in the oscillations predicted by the predator-prey models. He had worked with these mites in citrus groves and so he knew a lot of the biology of these two species. One kind was a prey species that fed on oranges and the other mite preyed on the herbivorous mites. The prey species could hitch a ride on wind currents using a silk thread they extruded

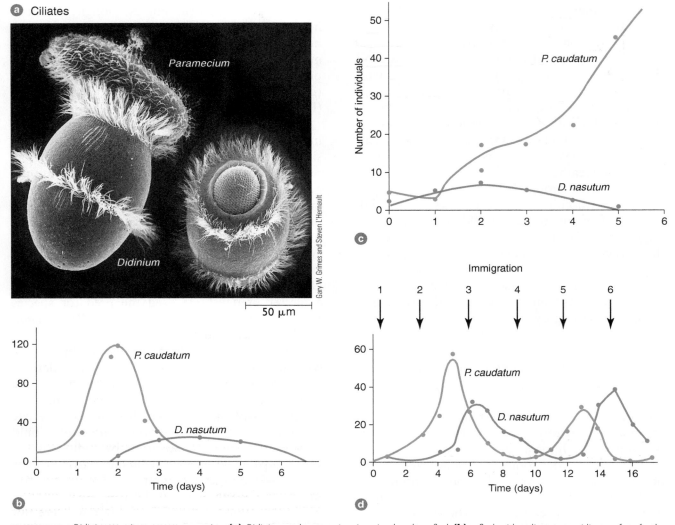

Figure 15.19 Didinium preying upon a paramecium (**a**), Didinium and paramecium in a simple culture flask (**b**), a flask with sediments providing a refuge for the Paramecium (**c**), and where immigration of predator and prey were simulated (**d**).

(referred to as *ballooning*). In this way, they could migrate quickly to new locations. In contrast, the predators had to crawl to new locations since they did not balloon. In the complex environment that he created, Huffaker had designed "rooms" with oranges where the perimeter of each room was a thin layer of Vaseline. Gaps in the Vaseline were like doors to the rooms. And in the center of each room was a wooden pole that the prey species could use to balloon from one room to the next. To simulate wind, he provided a small fan at the side of this complex design all of which covered the area of a large table. The predator could crawl between the rooms, but the prey could quickly move between the rooms by ballooning. With this design, which used a total of 120 oranges, he was able to produce three population oscillations over

a time span of seven months. With the ballooning and crawling activities of prey and predator, Huffaker essentially simulated what Gause, in the previous study, had to do manually by adding predator and prey individuals to his system (see Figure 15.20).

One of the most widely used examples of predator prey oscillations comes from the number of snowshoe hare and lynx pelts sold to the Hudson Bay Company from 1845 to 1935. When the numbers were plotted over time, they produced fairly regular oscillations with intervals lasting 9 to 11 years. Originally, it was thought that the lynx controlled the hare populations, but more detailed experimentation showed that food shortages for the hares, especially during the winter months, contributed significantly to the cycles (see Figure 15.21).

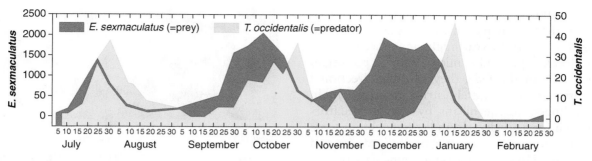

Figure 15.20 Oscillations in populations of herbivorous and predatory mites from a complex environment created in the laboratory (data from Huffaker).

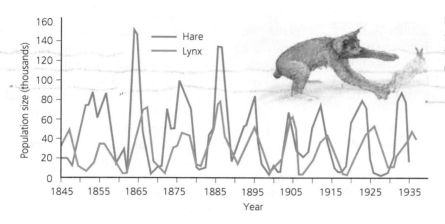

Figure 15.21 Oscillations in lynx and snowshoe hare populations based upon the number of pelts sold to the Hudson Bay Company.

So far our discussion of predator-prey relationships has focused on changes in numbers over time. Now, let's look at the biological details of how predators find prey and how prey avoid being eaten. How do predators find prey? Bats, porpoises, dolphins, and toothed whales can find prey by echolocation. They emit very-high-frequency sounds that bounce off objects and then return to the predator, who then interprets them. Essentially, it's a radar system that allows the individuals to navigate and find prey in the dark. Different bat species can find fish, frogs, and insects using echolocation. The Sperm whale, a toothed whale, also uses it to search for Giant squid in the murky, abyssal ocean depths. Giant squid can grow very large and have eyes the diameter of a car's headlamp! And you can imagine they don't give up without a fight. Large sucker marks have been found on the bodies of Sperm whale. Humpback whales belong to another grouping of whales called *baleen whales*. While these whales do not use echolocation to find prey, once prey are found, they use a superb method called *bubble netting* to concentrate them. When a pod (i.e., a group of whales) of Humpback whales finds a school of herring, some members of the pod will start swimming in a circular fashion around the herring while releasing air from their blowholes. The herring are scared by the bubbles

of air and cluster together. The whales working around the school gradually tighten the bubble net by encircling the school and working it toward the surface. When the herring are near the surface, the whales break the surface with their mouths wide open (that's a 4-meter, or 12-foot, gap from the lower to the upper jaw) and gulp in hundreds of gallons of water that are packed with fish. They don't swallow all that water. Instead, baleen, which is a sieve-like structure, drops from their upper jaw and allows the whales to strain out the fish from the water; the water then flows out of the sides of the whale's mouth. There are video clips of Humpback whales bubble netting on the Internet. It is worth checking out.

Other predators hunt cooperatively also. Wolves, Lions, porpoises, chimpanzees, and Cape hunting dogs are just a few species that are known to work as a group to hunt and capture prey. Camouflage or cryptic coloration is typically considered to be a way for prey to avoid being eaten, but it also helps predators. Think of the stripes on a tiger when crouched among tall grasses while it stalks its prey. Some praying mantis and crab spiders have the same color as the flowers of the plants on which they sit waiting patiently for an insect to come in for some nectar.

Some snakes have pit organs right in front of their eyes that can detect infrared radiation, which is sensed as heat. As you might imagine, they eat warm-blooded prey like mice. With a pit organ on each side of the face, they can get directional information and accurately strike at a rodent in total darkness. So the means by which predators secure their food are diverse and spectacular in some cases. But prey species are not typically decimated by predators. How do they avoid being eaten?

Some plants have secondary compounds (products of metabolism) that make their leaves distasteful. Other plants have thorns or fuzzy structures on their leaves that reduce their vulnerability to many herbivores. Some plants synchronize when they produce seeds. They essentially produce so many seeds that predators are unlikely to consume them all. This is called *predator satiation*. You may have seen bumper crops of acorns in deciduous forests. The forest floor seems to be covered with acorns. It's not hard to imagine that some of these acorns will survive to form a new generation of oak trees.

Animal prey may also have chemical compounds that make them toxic to a predator such as the poison arrow frogs of South America. These frogs consume ants, which contain toxins that the frogs then modify and use for their own defensive skin secretions! The Red-spotted newt discussed earlier has a terrestrial life stage, the Red eft, which is well known in the forests of eastern North America. This brightly colored salamander has skin toxins that make it unpalatable to many predators. Many prey species that have toxins are also brightly colored so predators learn to avoid them. This is called *warning* or **aposematic coloration** (see Figure 15.22).

Figure 15.22 Warning coloration of the Red eft, a species with toxic skin secretions.

Figure 15.23 Batesian mimicry where a palatable species (a fly, right photograph) mimics the unpalatable Yellowjacket (this species can deliver a painful sting, left photograph).

Left – Edward S. Ross, Right – Nigel Jones

Some species that don't have any toxins to protect them simply resemble those species that do. We call this *mimicry*. If a palatable species mimics an unpalatable species, like a fly mimicking a Yellowjacket, this is called **Batesian mimicry**. It's named in honor of the naturalist, Henry Walter Bates, who explored the Brazilian rainforests in the 1800s. For example, the harmless Virginia Yellowjacket Hover fly has bold yellow and black markings on its abdomen, and just one pair of wings. Most predators who have encountered the venomous Yellowjacket are not counting numbers of wings in order to distinguish the harmless fly from the Yellowjacket with its two pairs of wings (see Figure 15.23)! When two or more species mimic each other, and all of them are unpalatable, we call this **Mullerian mimicry**. This is most commonly seen in butterflies. This form of mimicry was named after Johann Muller Theodor Muller, a German naturalist who immigrated to Brazil in the 1800s.

Camouflage, as noted previously, can hide predators from being seen by potential prey, but we more commonly think of camouflage as a way prey can avoid being eaten. Examples of this abound. Lizards look like part of the tree they cling to. Some plants, like *Lithops*, look like rocks when they are not in flower. Walking sticks sway like a branch would in a light breeze as they move about in a tree. And the amazing squid, octopus, and cuttlefish rapidly change their colors and textures with incredible accuracy to match their environments (see Figure 15.24)!

Other ways prey avoid being eaten is by moving about in groups (flocks or herds), which confounds

aposematic coloration—a warning coloration.

Batesian mimicry—where a palatable species resembles an unpalatable species.

Mullerian mimicry—where two or more unpalatable species resemble each other.

(a)

(b)

Figure 15.24 Prey Camouflage: Stone plants **(a)** hiding out in the open from herbivores since they look like the stones surrounding them or **(b)** a katydid that looks like insect damaged leaves.

Figure 15.25 Black-tailed prairie dog barking to warn others in the colony of nearby predators.

some predators as they prefer to focus on individuals. Or, in some groups, specific individuals act like sentinels that issue a warning call if a predator is near. Prairie dogs, Meerkats, Topi antelope, and some species of monkeys use this predator defense mechanism (see Figure 15.25). Other defense mechanisms, representing last-ditch efforts to avoid being preyed upon, are collectively called *moment-of-truth defenses*. Examples of this would be a Hognose snake or Opossum playing dead, a basilisk lizard streaking on its hind legs across the surface of the water, a skunk squirting its foul musk, or an Asian Flying Dragon lizard gliding to another tree.

The interactions whereby one species benefits and another is harmed have been exploited by humans for controlling the spread of some species (biological control). *Bacillus thuringiensis* (Bt) is a soil bacterium that produces a toxin that can kill certain insects ingesting it. Once the insect ingests these microbes, their cell walls are degraded by the insect's midgut digestive activity. This releases the protein toxin and in susceptible insects, the lining of the insect's gut is destroyed resulting in a lethal infection in the body cavity. Bt has been used successfully on federal and state lands to control Gypsy moth infestations.

Since Bt is sprayed on large areas of infested forest, it has to be used carefully since it kills caterpillars not only of the Gypsy moth but also of other species of moths and butterflies. You can purchase various formulations of Bt at garden stores to control problem insects in your garden. Read over the labeling carefully before using this biocontrol agent.

The Cactus moth, *Cactoblastis cactorum*, has been used in the biological control of the Prickly Pear cactus. Prickly pear cacti were introduced in Australia in the 1800s as an ornamental plant. During the turn of the century, this plant started showing up in the wild, and it then spread quickly, eventually covering millions of acres! Why do you think it spread so quickly? Consider the sorts of relationships we have just discussed above. For most species, there exists at least one other species that can have a negative effect on it (a predator, parasite, pathogen, or competitor). But when you introduce a species to a totally new area, are there likely to be other species there that would exert such a negative effect? So what to do with species that have gotten out of control? If you are interested in biological control, the usual method is to go to the native range for the species you want to control and see what

Figure 15.26 Collapse of a Prickly Pear cactus before **(a)** and after **(b)** the introduction of the Cactus moth, a biological control agent.

The State of Queensland, Department of Employment, Economic Development and Innovation

regulates it. The Cactus moth, from South America, was found to be an effective control agent for the cactus. This moth was imported from Argentina to Australia in the 1920s, and in just a few years, the moth managed to reduce the cactus population to low numbers that were highly dispersed (see Figure 15.26). This was a huge success since the moth is now part of the Australian fauna, and it will continue to control the cactus without any additional effort on our part. The challenge with biological control, though, is that once the control organism is released into its new environment, it may have unforeseen consequences on nontarget organisms. And it is very difficult to remove once released! Unhappily, there is another chapter to our Cactus moth biocontrol story. Because of the success in controlling the Prickly Pear cactus in Australia, it was imported to other countries with the same cactus problem, including several nations in the Caribbean. The moths didn't remain in the

Caribbean but migrated to Florida and Texas, where it is now the invasive (nonnative) species with a corresponding potential negative impact on native species of cacti in the United States and Mexico. It is challenging to effectively and safely use biocontrols in a vastly complex biosphere.

We have looked at various aspects of predator-prey and competitive interactions in the last two sections. Let's look now at an example in the natural world where both processes are evident. The rocky intertidal region off the coast of Washington is home to a predaceous sea star (*Pisaster*) as well as a diverse community of sessile organisms like barnacles, mussels, sea anemones, sponges, and benthic algal species. Numerous mobile organisms like chitons, limpets, and sea urchins are found there as well. Ecologist Robert Paine removed the top predator, *Pisaster*, over a five-year period in his experimental sites in order to determine the effect of this predator. In the absence of this primary predator, mussels began to spread deeper in the intertidal region. As we noted in our earlier example of competition between two barnacles species, space is a limited resource in the intertidal region. As the mussels expanded their distribution in the experimental sites, other species that were normally found there were crowded out. Paine's control sites retained essentially the same number of species over the five years of his study while in the experimental sites, at least 25 species were eliminated by the mussel. This example illustrates both predator-prey and interspecific competition interactions. The sea star is a major predator of the mussel and when present, it keeps the mussels from dominating (out competing other species in) the intertidal region. Because the intertidal community becomes markedly different without the sea star, it is considered a keystone species (one that has far-reaching influences on a community).

Both Species Benefit

During the spring, bees and hummingbirds are busy gathering nectar from flowering plants and in the process end up transferring pollen from one plant to another. Similarly, in the tropics, hornbill birds consume fruit and then defecate the seeds, undamaged, in a location away from the tree that produced the fruit. In the ocean, many corals have dinoflagellate protozoans, called *zooxanthellae*, living within their cells (**endosymbionts**); these zooxanthellae

endosymbiont—an organism that lives within the body or cells of another organism.

(a)　　　　　　　　　(b)

Figure 15.27 Mutualism: Bull's horn acacia trees provide ants with food resources as well as enlarged thorns **(a)** which ants hollow out to live in while ants defend their acacia from herbivores and remove plants to create a space clear of competitors **(b)**.

can photosynthesize. The coral receives products of photosynthesis while the zooxanthellae receive a nitrogen source, ammonia, from the coral, which is used in the construction of their proteins and nucleic acids. We have just described three examples of **mutualisms** that are characterized by both species benefiting from the interaction.

Let's explore in some more detail two examples of mutualisms and then consider how important they are in our world. Ecologist Dan Janzen examined in detail the relationship between ants of the genus *Pseudomyrmex* and the bullhorn acacia tree, both of which range from southern Mexico to northern South America. When a mated queen ant finds an unoccupied bullhorn acacia shoot or seedling, she will bore a hole into one of the swollen thorns of the acacia plant. The interior of the thorn is hollowed out and becomes a brood chamber for the new ant colony (see Figure 15.27a). The queen feeds on acacia nectar taken from foliar nectaries, and special leaflet tips called *beltian bodies* on the leaves of the plant. As the colony grows, more thorns are hollowed out and the entire colony, which can grow to 16,000 workers in about three years, will be sustained by the nectar and beltian bodies from the acacia. So what do the acacias get out of feeding and housing their own resident ant colony?! Janzen made observations and conducted several experiments to determine this. First, he observed that about 25% of the colony was active at any time of the day. Of what benefit is this to the plant? When he examined acacia shoots with and without ants during the day, he found that 38.5% of the shoots without ants had herbivorous insects while 2.7% of shoots with ants had herbivores on them. At night when herbivorous insects are more active, 58.8% of the shoots without ants had herbivorous insects while shoots with ants had only 12.9% occupancy by herbivores. Ants will actively bite and sting any animal coming in contact with their host

mutualism—an interaction between species where both benefit.

plant, including people, cows, and herbivorous insects. Bullhorn acacias lack secondary toxic compounds to protect their foliage, but they don't need these since the ants protect them. The ants will also remove any plants growing on or nearby their host acacia that might compete for water, nutrients or solar energy (see Figure 15.27b). When Janzen assessed growth and survival rates for acacias with and without ants, as you might guess, both were much higher for acacias with ants. This is definitely a mutualism.

Another fascinating example of a mutualism exists between the Greater Honeyguide bird and people. Zoologists Isack and Reyer studied details of this interaction in northern Kenya. The earliest written accounts of this interaction date back to the seventeenth century. These accounts described how Africans could be led by Greater Honeyguides to bee colonies located in large trees, rock crevices, or termite mounds. After the people gathered the honey they desired, the bird would have an easier time eating pieces of the remaining honeycomb from which it extracted larvae and wax to supplement its normal diet of insects. Currently, the Boran honey gatherers (a people group) use a penetrating whistle, heard up to a distance of 1 km, to attract the bird. The honeyguide then gains the attention of the people by flying close to them while emitting a persistent call. It will then fly above the treetops in the direction of the bee colony, disappearing for a minute or more before returning to a conspicuous tree from which it calls to the following honey gatherers. When the people approach to within 5 to 15 meters, the bird again takes off, calling as it flies and then returns to another conspicuous tree. This pattern of leading and following is repeated until the bee colony is reached. With a bird guiding them, the search time to find a bee colony averaged 3.2 hours, while without one, the average search time was 8.9 hours. The bird benefits from this association since 96% of the 186 bee colonies to which the Boran were guided to were inaccessible to the birds without human help!

Are these examples of mutualism simply a few fascinating interactions periodically seen in the natural world, or do mutualisms profoundly affect the world as we know it? Ecologist Manuel Molles considered this. What would happen if the zooxanthellae-coral mutualism did not exist? The coral reefs—the largest biological structures on earth—would not exist (see Figure 15.28). Without these reefs, the incredible diversity of fish and invertebrates associated with them would be lost. Or suppose that on land, there were no animal-pollinated plants? Gone would be about 90% of flowering plants, including over 100 crops that make up one-third of the U.S. diet since they are pollinated by honeybees. Orchids and cacti would also be gone. Left would be wind-pollinated plants. But of these, over 90% of plants require another mutualism involving mycorrhizal fungi in order to live in all but the most fertile soils. The mycorrhizal fungus that grows on plant roots enhances the ability of the plant to harvest nutrients and, in turn, the fungus gains products of photosynthesis from the plant. So a greatly reduced number of wind-pollinated, nonmychorrhizal plants would be all that remained for herbivores to eat. But mutualisms are pervasive in herbivory as well. Many herbivores require microorganisms in order to extract nutrients and energy from plant tissues. The microbes live in the guts of the herbivores where they break down the cell walls of the plant cells—something the animals could not do without the microbes. And without these herbivores, what would carnivores do? Mutualisms: are they simply a few notable interactions periodically seen in the natural world or do they profoundly affect the world as we know it? What do you think?

Figure 15.28 The Great Barrier Reefs stretches more than 2,000 km (1,200 miles) along the Queensland coast, Australia. It covers 344,000 square kilometers (137,600 square miles) and houses more than 1,500 different species of fish.

I hope you have seen in our community ecology section that manipulative experiments in nature are quite doable and often elucidate relationships between species in a community. Manipulative experiments, which have controls, provide stronger support for a particular interspecific interaction than do observational studies or natural experiments. In many cases, manipulative studies cannot be done because they are too costly or require too much time to complete. But if it is possible, manipulative studies provide rich experimental evidence for teasing out relationships between species in a community.

IN OTHER WORDS

1. When we focus on the interactions between populations of different species in a given area, we are looking at community ecology.
2. Manipulative and natural experiments are often used to elucidate the relationships between species in a community.
3. Interspecific competition can cause reductions in species population size but rarely, in nature, completely eliminate a species.
4. Herbivory, carnivory, parasitism, disease, and parasitoidism are all examples of how one species benefits and another is harmed in the relationship. There is a rich array of ways predators find their prey and prey escape being preyed upon. Biological control capitalizes on this type of interaction by using specific pathogens or predators to control organisms we consider to be problematic.
5. When both species benefit in the interaction, we are studying mutualism. Mutualisms have a profound effect on the world as we know it.
6. All of the interactions noted above often work in concert with each other to allow a rich variety of species to live in any given community.

Consider again interactions such as predation and herbivory where one species benefits and the other is harmed. We saw examples of gazelles eating the grass that had been cropped by wildebeests, *Didinium* feeding on *Paramecium*, and lynx preying on the Snowshoe hare. These interactions focus attention on a few species in a particular community. But there are other predators eating the Snowshoe hare. Other herbivores graze on grass in the Serengeti. How can we study this more complete picture? Imagine how complex things become if we try to discover all the different types of interactions within a forest or within one of the Great Lakes.

Let's focus on feeding relationships between the species in one community: the ocean around Antarctica. In that vast region of ocean, photosynthetic phytoplankton (mainly diatoms) are consumed by herbivorous zooplankton (mainly krill, small shrimp-like animals), and krill are eaten by lots of different animals ranging in size from the small fish and squid to smaller species of penguin to huge baleen whales like the Blue whale (see Figure 15.29). Small fish are consumed by larger species of penguin like the Emperor penguin, which in turn might be eaten by Leopard seal. The top predator in the community would be the Orca or killer whale. What we have just described is a food web that links all the species in a community together by considering what each species consumes. If you follow one sequence in the food web, like diatoms, krill, Adélie penguin, Leopard seal, and Killer whale, that would be a food chain. Linking all these chains together creates a food web.

The food web concept can be simplified by grouping species into feeding categories or **trophic levels.** Diatoms photosynthesize, so they would be considered producers or **autotrophs.** They are self-feeders since they can produce energy-rich organic molecules using the sun's energy. The captured energy is stored in the chemical bonds of carbohydrates, which can then be used by the producers for their own metabolic needs, or the energy may remain stored in the chemical bonds of organic molecules collectively called *producer biomass.* Organisms that consume producers are called *herbivores* and organisms that

consume herbivores are primary carnivores (see Figure 15.30). Such feeding at increasing trophic levels involves not only the movement of energy from one level to the next but matter, in terms of the carbon, nitrogen, and oxygen atoms that make up the organic molecules, is also being transferred. Understanding and tracking the movement of energy, water, and nutrients (i.e., matter), requires not only an understanding of interactions between organisms within the community but also the interaction between the community and its physical environment. This larger context is called an *ecosystem,* which could be as narrowly defined as the biological and physical environment of a small pond, as broadly conceived as the Great Barrier Coral Reef off the coast of Australia, the Amazon rainforest, or even the entire earth!

Let's start with defining a couple of simple equations that describe energy flow through an ecosystem and then explore an example from Florida, where we will apply these equations. Our first equation describes energy flow for producers:

$$GPP = NPP + R$$

The total amount of energy captured from the sun by producers is called the **gross primary production** (GPP). Some of the GPP is then used by the producer to maintain itself; that's R in the equation, and it stands for respiration. The rest of the productivity can be converted into biomass for which the term **net primary production** (NPP) is used.

Organisms that consume producers (consumers or herbivores and carnivores), do so by ingestion (I in

> **trophic level**—a functional classification of species in an ecosystem based upon feeding relationships.
>
> **autotroph**—an organism that can synthesize organic compounds from inorganic compounds and a source of energy.
>
> **gross primary production**—the total amount of solar energy captured by autotrophs or producers.
>
> **net primary production**—the amount of energy left over after autotrophs have met their own energy needs that can be used to make autotroph biomass.

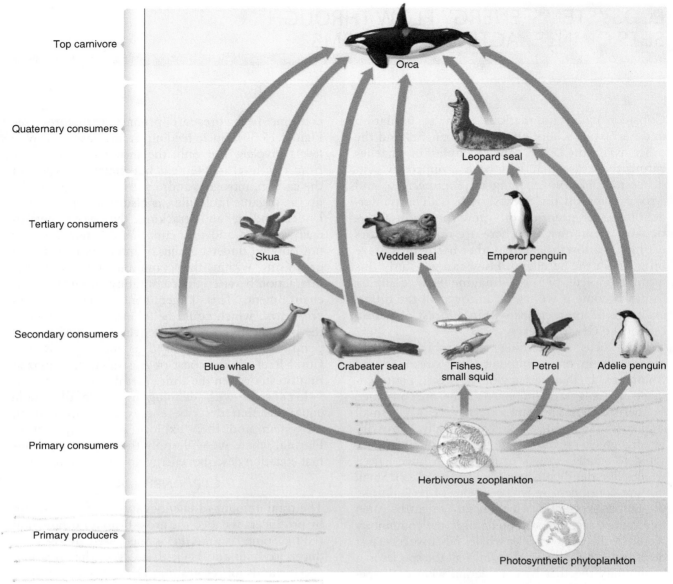

Top carnivore

Quaternary consumers

Tertiary consumers

Secondary consumers

Primary consumers

Primary producers

Orca

Leopard seal

Skua
Weddell seal
Emperor penguin

Blue whale
Crabeater seal
Fishes, small squid
Petrel
Adelie penguin

Herbivorous zooplankton

Photosynthetic phytoplankton

Figure 15.29 The food web in the marine waters off the coast of Antarctica. (Note that primary consumers can also be called herbivores, secondary consumers can be called primary carnivores, tertiary consumers, secondary carnivores, etc.).

the equation below). Not all the ingested energy can be used by the consumer, which from the consumer's perspective is called *waste* (W). The difference between I and W is called the *assimilated energy* (A) and this is the energy available to the organism. Just like with producers, the energy available to the organisms can then be used either to maintain themselves (R) or fixed into biomass (P). Energy flow through the consumer is thus expressed by the formula:

$$I - W = A = R + P$$

Ecologist Howard Odum examined energy flow in Silver Springs, a spring-fed lake in central Florida (see Figure 15.30). He measured the amount of energy that different organisms living in the lake took in, how much they used to maintain themselves, and then how much they fixed into biomass. He then multiplied these values, which were for individuals, by population size for the various producers, herbivores, and carnivores to get the total amount of energy moving through each trophic level. The final units are kilocalories/m²/year. Use Figure 15.30 right now to try to estimate the GPP for the producers in the lake. Recall that this is the total amount of energy captured by producers. If you recorded 20,810 kilocalories, you were right. This is only 1.2% of the incoming solar energy (1,700,000 kilocalories).

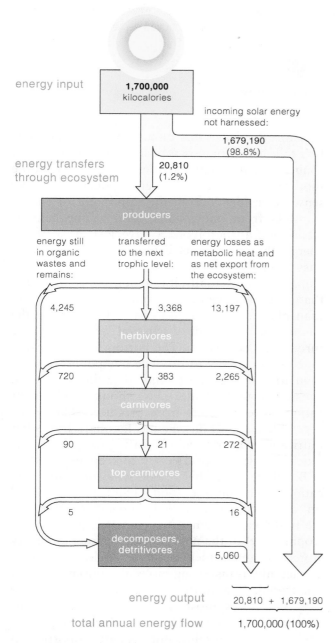

energy input — **1,700,000** kilocalories

incoming solar energy not harnessed:

1,679,190 (98.8%)

energy transfers through ecosystem — 20,810 (1.2%)

producers

energy still in organic wastes and remains: | transferred to the next trophic level: | energy losses as metabolic heat and as net export from the ecosystem:

4,245 | 3,368 | 13,197

herbivores

720 | 383 | 2,265

carnivores

90 | 21 | 272

top carnivores

5 | 16

decomposers, detritivores

5,060

energy output — 20,810 + 1,679,190

total annual energy flow — 1,700,000 (100%)

Figure 15.30 Annual energy flow through Silver Springs, Florida, as measured in kilocalories/square meter/year. The producers are primarily aquatic plants and the herbivores are snails, insects and small fish. The carnivores are invertebrates, fish and turtles and the top carnivores are large fish.

So you can see that most of the incoming solar energy is not captured by producers but rather, it warms the earth's atmosphere and surface. Now realize that the 20,810 kcal/m²/year is all the energy this particular ecosystem has to work with. The herbivores and carnivores we are about to examine do not have any additional energy source available. Energy flows in one direction from the producers to the herbivores and then to the carnivores.

What do the producers do with the 20,810 kcal/m²/year? In Figure 15.30, what is NPP and what is R? Remember R is that which the producer uses to maintain itself and this cannot be passed on to the next trophic level. The energy represented by R is critical to the producer for all the metabolic processes it conducts. But since herbivores cannot eat R, it is a complete loss from the next trophic level's perspective. R is 13,197, and it is 63.4% of GPP, which means most of the energy a producer captures from the sun is not available to the next trophic level. It's the other values associated with the producers that represent NPP—those that are available to other trophic levels. That would include 3368 and 4245. Both of these represent the biomass the producers have generated. Dead leaves would be part of the 4245 that goes to decomposers and **detritivores**. Living producer biomass (3368) would go to the herbivores. What percent of GPP is the NPP available to herbivores ([3368/20,810] × 100). Record this on a separate sheet in a table like this:

Trophic Level	Total Energy Captured by Trophic Level	% of Energy Transferred
Producers	20,810	16.2%
Herbivores		
Carnivores		
Top carnivores		

The 16.2% is a measure of the percent of energy fixed by producers that is available to the next trophic level.

Now recall the energy equation for consumers: I − W = A = R + P. Let's determine the quantities for the herbivores: I = 3368; W = 720; A = 3368 − 720, or 2648; P = 383; and R = 2265. Add R and P to see if you get A, and then add R, P, and W to see if you get I. You should because energy cannot be created or destroyed, although it is transformable. Which law of thermodynamics does this describe? (Review Section 6.2 if you can't remember; the same law operates at both the cellular and ecosystem levels!) Now determine the percent of the captured energy, which the herbivores transfer to the carnivores ([383/3368] × 100) place that value in the table. Then repeat what we just did for the carnivores.

detritivores—organisms, like earthworms and millipedes, that feed on nonliving organic matter (dead bodies and waste products.

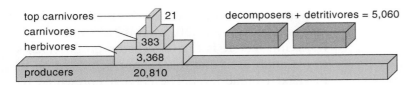

top carnivores ——— 21
carnivores ———
herbivores ———
383
3,368
producers   20,810

decomposers + detritivores = 5,060

Figure 15.31 Pyramid of energy flow through Silver Springs, Florida, in kilocalories/square meter/year. This is a summary of the data illustrated in Figure 15.30.

For all trophic levels, where does the majority of the energy taken in end up? If you said R, you would be right. So there is less and less energy available as you move through the different trophic levels. A pyramid of energy dramatically captures this fact (see Figure 15.31). Here the total energy available to each trophic level is depicted by the width of each block in the energy pyramid. Producers would have the largest block: They capture 20,810 kcal/m²/year. Of that, only 3368 is available to the herbivores, primarily because of R (energy used by the producers in metabolic activities). At Silver Springs, there are four trophic levels. From what we've just described, if you saw an ecosystem with five or six trophic levels, do you think the base of its pyramid could start out at 20,810 kcal/m²/year? How much energy would be left for the fifth or sixth level?

Let's go back to the food web for the Antarctic Ocean. How many trophic levels are there? (Trace several food chains to find which one gives the highest number of trophic levels.) The maximum you should be able to see is six. To support that number of trophic levels, you need a broader base than what we had at Silver Springs. How is that possible? During the Antarctic spring and summer, there is an abundance of sunshine (up to 24 hours per day) and nutrients. This combination creates a veritable explosion of life at the producer level. The resulting autotrophs support the large number of trophic levels seen here. In most other ecosystems, only about four trophic levels are seen.

Now take the percent of energy transferred values from your table and average them. You should get 11%. This is close to what is called the *10% rule.* That rule states that in general, about 10% of the energy taken in by any trophic level is passed on to the next level. If you don't have specific information about energy transfer in an ecosystem like what we had with Silver Springs, you can use the 10% rule. Since energy flows in one direction through an ecosystem, you might have realized that we need a constant influx of energy from the sun to sustain the energy needs of any ecosystem. When the sun burns out, life goes with it.

Before we leave this discussion of energy flow, let's talk about our own position within the food chains we participate in. Does eating lower on the food chain—eating at a lower trophic level—make sense? Consider it from the standpoint of energy transfers from one trophic level to the next. If I consume an herbivore, I have lost 90% of the energy that the plants captured since they only pass about 10% of their energy capture to the next trophic level. (Actually, it is a bit more complicated than this since we digest animal cells more easily than plant cells.) But you can still clearly see the connection with our discussion of energy flow through an ecosystem. The bottom line is it takes much more energy to produce one pound of meat than to produce one pound of grain. So as you consider your next meal, you should think about eating more products from producers like fruits, vegetables, and grains. Sound familiar? It is what nutritionists have been advocating for years. How much does it cost God's earth to keep me?

But there is another reason why some advocate eating lower on the food chain. This is based on a phenomenon called *biomagnification.* As we noted earlier, when we pass energy from one trophic level to the next, it travels along as energy stored in the chemical bonds of molecules. So we are actually transferring molecules (biomass) from one trophic level to the next. Biomass is a mixture of biomolecules, most of which is useful to us for energy (i.e., sugars) and building blocks (i.e., amino acids) for our proteins. But a small proportion of these molecules in the biomass we consume might actually be harmful to us. Some toxins like DDT degrade very slowly and can accumulate in the fatty tissues of an organism. DDT has been banned in the United States since the early 1970s, but years ago when it was widely used, it started showing up in various food webs. For example, DDT that washed into a pond from an agricultural field could be absorbed across the body wall of plankton. The DDT would then accumulate in the fatty tissues of the plankton. As organisms at higher trophic levels ate organisms at lower trophic levels, such as small fish eating zooplankton, they would acquire DDT

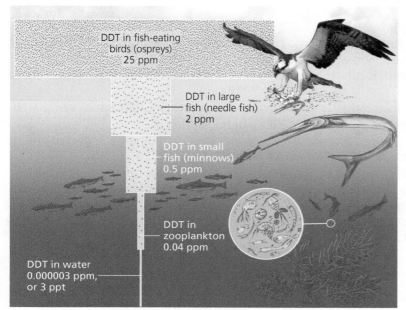

Figure 15.32 Bioaccumulation and biomagnification. DDT is a fat-soluble chemical that can accumulate in the fatty tissues of an organism. In a food chain, the accumulated DDT can be magnified in the bodies of the organisms at the higher trophic levels as they consume organisms at the lower trophic levels which have accumulated DDT.

Within the figure:

DDT in fish-eating birds (ospreys) 25 ppm

DDT in large fish (needle fish) 2 ppm

DDT in small fish (minnows) 0.5 ppm

DDT in zooplankton 0.04 ppm

DDT in water 0.000003 ppm, or 3 ppt

from each individual consumed. Consequently the concentration of DDT in the small fish rose to higher concentrations (0.5 ppm [part-per-million]) than that found in the zooplankton (0.04 ppm). As we move up into higher trophic levels, the process continues with each higher level having higher concentrations of DDT relative to the previous one (see Figure 15.32). Toxins that biomagnify are thus found at their highest concentrations in the highest trophic levels. You can see from Figure 15.32 that top predators like birds of prey (Osprey and Bald eagles) had the highest concentrations of DDT. When a bird metabolizes DDT, one of the results is that it can disrupt the physiological process of producing a shell of adequate thickness around the bird embryo. The net result was that when the eggs were incubated by the parents, they would often break. This resulted in the death of the embryo. Population declines were noted for our national emblem, the Bald eagle, as well as other raptors. Many species of birds impacted by DDT have recovered following the banning of DDT as well as the implementation of other strategies to help these birds.

As you might suspect, biomagnification is not just a reality for nonhuman food chains. We are all part of God's household! There is currently a federal advisory issued for mercury levels in fish that cautions women who may become pregnant, women who are pregnant, and nursing mothers about consuming fish such as shark and swordfish due to the concentrations of mercury—a natural element that is also a nerve poison in humans. In 1979, the U.S. Food and Drug Administration (FDA) set the action level for mercury at 1 ppm as the maximum safe limit for total mercury in fish. Shark and swordfish are top-level carnivores and mercury has biomagnified in the tissues of some individuals in these species to levels exceeding the FDA's limit. Check out the websites of the FDA or the U.S. Environmental Protection Agency (EPA) for more information about the safe consumption of fish.

In the 1950s, through biomagnification, mercury reached toxic levels in the people of Minamata, Japan. Wastewater discharged to Minamata Bay from a local chemical company contained mercury. The mercury was absorbed by phytoplankton and passed up through the food chain to shellfish and fish. Fisherman and others in Minamata whose staple food source was fish and shellfish, started experiencing signs of mercury poisoning. Symptoms include ataxia, numbness of extremities, and in severe cases, convulsions and death. Cats that ate fish scraps also experienced similar symptoms. Some called the disease *cat dancing disease* due to the erratic movements of afflicted cats. The human death toll was nearly 1800 with many more experiencing some degree of mercury poisoning. Biomagnification is a genuine threat to global biological health.

1. When we look at the movement of energy and nutrients between trophic levels (producers, herbivores, carnivores, and decomposers), we are studying ecosystem ecology.
2. The movement of energy in an ecosystem is often illustrated with a food chain or food web (cross-linked food chains).
3. Producers capture a certain amount of solar radiation (gross primary production [GPP]), which can then be allocated to either plant biomass (net primary production [NPP]) or respiration (R).
4. Consumers, such as herbivores and carnivores, assimilate (A) a certain amount of energy [ingested energy (I) minus wastes (W)] which may be allocated to either animal biomass (P) or respiration (R).
5. In general, 10% of the energy captured by a given trophic level is passed on to the next trophic level.
6. Toxins may also be passed up through the trophic levels. When a higher trophic level has a higher concentration of the toxin relative to the previous one, this is called *biomagnification*. Species at the highest trophic level may then have the highest concentrations of the toxin, which in several cases involving some people, have resulted in adverse effects.

A FINAL WORD ABOUT OUR INTERACTION WITH GOD'S HOUSEHOLD

So here we are, in Phase II of nature's history since sin entered the world. Ecological challenges like the biomagnification of toxins and species extinctions face us. During Phase II, Jesus entered His Household to redeem us. At the beginning of this chapter, you were asked to think about what it means to redeem or restore our broken relationship with God, with each other, and with His creation. Originally, Adam and Eve walked with God in His creation. No barrier existed between them and God, and they could easily follow His directives for managing His household. But the relationship was fractured by their desire to be totally in charge of the living world. They accepted uncritically Satan's deception that God was withholding something good from them. As sin entered the world, their (our) relationship with God became fractured. All generations since Adam and Eve no longer clearly understood His desires because we were focused on ourselves instead of God. When we view life with ourselves as the focus and we hear that we are to "subdue the earth and rule over every living creature" (Gn 1:28), we tend to think about it in terms of what we get out of it. But has the intent behind those words been clouded by our sin? How might we gain a proper understanding of God's desire for our lives as it relates to Himself, other people, and His household? It begins by receiving God's way for our relationship with Him to be restored—through Jesus Christ's sacrificial death on the cross (see Section 16.6). We then begin to learn what it means to abide in Christ (Jn 15:4), which means to rest in and rely on Jesus. As we grow in our awareness of our identity in Christ and his presence and power within us, we then actually "can do all things through Christ who strengthens us" (Phil 4:13). We begin to have the capacity to live life in harmony with God's desires.

Perhaps you are thinking that we don't really need to concern ourselves too much with God's creation since it is subject to decay anyway (Rom 8:21) and will eventually be recreated (Rv 21:1). But consider this: Our own bodies, similar to God's household, are subject to decay. We are not immediately transformed physically when we are redeemed. Does this then mean we should trash our current body (by consuming and/or doing things harmful to us) since we know we are going to get a new one? That would not be considered wise stewardship of our bodies. Just as we should care for our current bodies, we should also care for God's household.

How then do we care for His creation? Instead of giving you a list of things to do as a wise steward of God's creation, consider instead how you can cultivate your relationship with the Lord your God by learning to abide in Christ. With that as a focus, you will make wise decisions as it relates to loving God, other people and caring for His household.

IN OTHER WORDS

1. Loving God would include loving the things he has made, for "the glory of the Lord is displayed in his creation" (Ps 104:31a). How we practically work out caring for God's household requires us to cultivate our relationship with God by learning to abide in Christ.

QUESTIONS FOR REVIEW

1. What does the word *ecology* mean?
2. Characterize our role in the environment prior to sin entering the world (Phase I)? What type of species interaction was seen during this time as it relates to food consumption?
3. During Phase II (after sin entered the world), what other type of species interaction is now seen? Has our role changed in Phase II?
4. What lies beyond Phase II?
5. Characterize the littoral zone in a lake.
6. How does the limnetic affect the profundal zone, and what determines the depth of the limnetic zone?
7. How do nutrients in the lake sediments get to the limnetic zone, and how does this relate to a phytoplankton bloom?
8. Ice floats. Why is this fact so critical to aquatic organisms?
9. How do your answers to questions 6–8 reflect the definition of ecology—interaction between the organism and environment?
10. Describe the organismal ecology for the Peaks of Otter salamander.
11. Define the term *population*.
12. If you marked 20 box turtles during your first trip and then on the second trip one week later you found 18 turtles, 2 of which were recaptures, what would your population size estimate be? If the area you studied was 10,000 m², what would the box turtle density be in this area?
13. If you were doing a study on male white rhinoceroses and you noticed they were marking the perimeters of their territories with piles of dung, what population distribution pattern do you think they would have? If the females did not exhibit this type of territorial behavior then what distribution pattern do you think they might have?
14. If a country's population is dominated by pre-reproductive individuals, then would this country's population growth rate be—growing, shrinking, or staying the same?
15. If the current newt population is 1200 and last year it was 1100, then calculate λ. Is the population growing, stable, or declining? Using this λ, estimate a population size one year into the future and then two years into the future.
16. Name several environmental factors that might limit plant and animal population sizes.
17. What model describes population growth where environmental factors limit population growth and what shape does the population growth curve have?
18. A dandelion produces lots of seeds and typically lives one year. Is this an *r*- or *K*-selected species?
19. Define what a community is.
20. After the wildebeests leave the Serengeti, what percent of the grass biomass has been consumed? What happens to the grasses after the wildebeests leave, and then where do the Thomson's gazelles graze when they arrive in the Serengeti?
21. When Gause put *Paramecium caudatum* and *P. aurelia* together in one culture flask, what happened?
22. When zebra mussels were accidentally introduced into the Great Lakes, what happened to plankton-eating fish and native mussels? Why is this not considered a manipulative study?
23. In Connell's barnacle removal study off the coast of Washington, what happened when *Chthamalus* was removed from the upper part of the intertidal region? when *Balanus* was removed from the middle part of the intertidal region?

    So what was restricting *Balanus* from the upper part of the intertidal region, and what was restricting *Chthamalus* from the middle part of the intertidal region?
24. How can five species of warbler coexist in the spruce forests of North America?
25. Why might the lion not be considered the king of the jungle?
26. What happened when Gause put *Didinium nasutum* and *Paramecium caudatum* in a simple flask? How did things change when he added some substrate which acted like a refuge for the prey? And finally, what did Gause need to do in order to get multiple oscillations for both *Didinium nasutum* and *Paramecium caudatum*?
27. What did Huffaker show with his experiments using mites with regard to predator-prey population oscillations?
28. Name several ways predator find prey.
29. How do prey avoid being eaten (include in your answer a description of Batesian and Mullerian mimicry)?
30. How has Bt been used in biological control?

31. How do the ants benefit the Bullhorn acacias and how do the acacias benefit the ants?
32. Describe a mutualism between the Greater honeyguide and people.
33. Mutualisms: Are they simply a few notable interactions periodically seen in the natural world, or do they profoundly affect the world as we know it?
34. Define what an ecosystem is.
35. Find and list the species involved in the longest food chain in the Antarctic food web.
36. What does *autotroph* mean?
37. Determine GPP, NPP, and R for the autotrophs, and define I, W, A, P, and R for the herbivores in the Silver Springs ecosystem.
38. How much, on average, gets passed from one trophic level to the next?
39. What is biomagnification?

QUESTIONS FOR THOUGHT

1. If you were working with an endangered species, what would you want to know with regard to its organismal and population ecology?
2. Draw a graph that shows birth rates as being density dependent and death rates as density independent. Put density on the *x*-axis and rate on the *y*-axis. Determine the carrying capacity from your graph.
3.

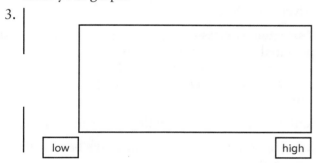

4. Why are there more females than males in the older age categories of human population age structures?
5. Why are manipulative studies stronger than natural studies?
6. Design a manipulative study to show whether the five species of warbler in the spruce forests of North America are really competing for food resources?
7. In the ant-Bullhorn acacia mutualism, how could one determine whether the two species actually need each other to survive?
8. Knowing now how complex communities are, what would you need to know about a proposed species to be used as a biological control agent before you introduced it into an area where it is not normally found so that you could control a pest species?
9. If we start using a lot more solar energy technology, would this have any adverse impact on the amount of energy available to autotrophs (justify your answer with information from the section on Ecosystems: Energy Flow through Sets of Interacting Organisms)?
10. If Phase I (before sin entered the world) lasted longer than a few days, how do you think populations could be regulated without carnivory, parasitism, and so on?
11. Think about some practical ways you can be a good steward of God's household and then do them.

SUGGESTED READING

Dewitt, Calvin B. *Earth-wise: A Biblical Response to Environmental Issues,* 2nd ed. Faith Alive Christian Resources, 2007. Grand Rapids, MI.

Merritt, Jonathan. *Green like God. Unlocking the Divine Plan for our Planet.* Faith Works, 2010. New York, NY.

Schaeffer, Francis A. *Pollution and the Death of Man: The Christian View of Ecology.* Hodder Publishing, 1974. London, England.

GLOSSARY

annual finite rate of increase (λ)—ratio of the current year's population size divided by last year's population size.

aposematic coloration—a warning coloration.

autotroph—an organism that can synthesize organic compounds from inorganic compounds and a source of energy.

Batesian mimicry—where a palatable species resembles an unpalatable species.

birth rate—the number of new individuals produced in a population; usually expressed at births per individual or births per 1000 individuals.

bivalve—a Class of organisms characterized by having two valves (or shells) such as clams, mussels and scallops.

carnivore (carnivory)—an organism that eats animals.

carrying capacity (K)—the maximum population size an environment can sustain.

clumped distribution—a distribution pattern in a population where there are aggregations of individuals.

commensalism—an interaction between species where one benefits and the other is not harmed.

community—interacting species in a particular area.

death rate—the number of individuals that died in a population; usually expressed as deaths per individual or deaths per 1000 individuals.

decomposers—organisms, like bacteria and fungi, that obtain energy from the breakdown of dead organic matter.

Density—number of organisms per unit area.

density-dependent factor—biotic factors, like competition for food resources or space, that change in response to and are dependent upon population density.

density-independent factor—abiotic factors such as a flood or a severe winter that affects populations and their effect is independent of population density.

detritivores—organisms, like earthworms and millipedes, that feed on nonliving organic matter (dead bodies and waste products.

ecology—the study of the relationships between organisms and their environment.

ecosystem—the community and abiotic components in a particular area.

endosymbiont—an organism that lives within the body or cells of another organism.

exponential growth—population growth is where the rate of change is the product of the population size and the per capita growth rate.

filter-feeding—a feeding process used by some organisms where material suspended in water is separated from the water by a sieving process.

geometric growth—population growth in which each generation changes in size by a constant ratio.

gross primary production—the total amount of solar energy captured by autotrophs or producers.

habitat—a place where an organism lives.

herbivore (herbivory)—an organism that eats plants.

interspecific competition—competition between individuals of different species where both species are adversely affected.

K-selected species—species that have low biotic potential and typically follow a logistic style of population growth. They are usually regulated by density-dependent factors at a population size around carrying capacity.

lentic—pertaining to standing water like a lake.

limnetic zone—open waters of a lake beyond the littoral zone.

littoral zone—the shallowest part of a lake where rooted plants can be found.

logistic growth—population growth pattern that has an S shape where population growth levels off at the carrying capacity.

Mullerian mimicry—where two or more unpalatable species resemble each other.

mutualism—an interaction between species where both benefit.

net primary production—the amount of energy left over after autotrophs have met their own energy needs that can be used to make autotroph biomass.

niche—the functional role of a species in a community.

predator (predation)—an organism that kills its prey.

parasite (parasitism)—an organism that lives in or on another organism (called the host) from which it derives a benefit.

parasitoid (parasitoidism)—an insect whose larvae consumes all or part of its host.

protozoans—group of single-celled organisms which some classification schemes place in the Kingdom Protista.

phytoplankton—microscopic organisms that drift with the currents and that can photosynthesize.

profundal zone—waters below the limnetic zone.

***r*-selected species**—species with high biotic potential that follow an exponential or geometric style of population growth and are often regulated by density independent factors.

random distribution—a distribution pattern in a population where the spacing of individuals shows no particular pattern.

trophic level—a functional classification of species in an ecosystem based upon feeding relationships.

uniform distribution—a distribution pattern in a population where individuals are evenly spaced.

16

Life Is Finite

Survey Questions

16.1 Definitions
- How would a biologist define terms like *life, death,* and *aging?*
- Does death result naturally and normally from aging?

16.2 Theories of Aging
- How many theories of aging are there?
- What is the substance of each theory?

16.3 Observations: Cellular Processes
- Do cells age? If so, how is aging observed in them?
- Why do some cells stop dividing and die while other cells divide perpetually?
- In what structures within the cell is aging most clearly seen?
- What does aging in these structures result from?

16.4 Observations: Organ-Systemic Processes
- How does aging at the organ or system level of the body relate to the cellular aging just described?
- In what organs or body systems is aging most clearly observed?

Loretta Pleasant never completely died. Her life began in Roanoke, Virginia, on August 18, 1920. Somehow, her Christian name got changed to Henrietta. In 1941, she married a cousin, David Lacks, and by 1950 she had given birth to five children. Henrietta Lacks spent her remaining days raising them. One dark day in Baltimore, Maryland, four months after the birth of her fifth child, Henrietta was diagnosed with cervical cancer. Without her knowledge or consent, cells were removed from a tumor in her cervical area and then localized radium treatments were begun. By February of 1951, complicating illnesses along with her cancer took Henrietta's life at age 31. But even as the family quietly buried "her" in a small Virginia town, cells extracted from her cervical tissues continued to live, indeed to thrive. (Cancerous transformation of cells often has this immortalizing effect on them.) Dr. George Otto Gey cultured Henrietta's cells and through successive transfers established a cell line called *HeLa* cells, which are still alive and in use today (see Figure 16.1). They have been subcultured, sold, and circulated to research facilities around the world. Scientists usually prefer experimental results from a well-studied system in which comparisons with other results are easily made. HeLa cells became such a system and as a result, there are more of Henrietta's cells alive today than when she was alive and well and living in Baltimore! Henrietta is

- People often die of disease. How is the immune system affected by aging?
- Elderly people often appear stiff and weakened. What is the basis for this aging effect?

16.5 Theory Evaluation

- Which of our theories best accounts for the observations made?
- Are there observations from elsewhere in the animal world that support one theory over another?

16.6 Why Do We Die? Programmed Aging from Two Perspectives

- Are we allowed to ask "why" questions in science?
- What are the two perspectives referred to in the title?
- What is the evolutionary view for why aging occurs?
- What is a Biblical view for why aging occurs?
- Are both views based on the favored theory of aging?
- Can aging and death at the cellular level bear on this question?

just one fascinating example of how biological research has complicated the meaning of naïvely simple words like life and death. How should we use these words in discussing our last principle of life?

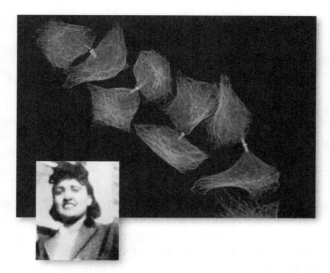

Figure 16.1 A Woman and her Cells. Henrietta Lacks has provided cervical cancer cells to molecular biologists all over the world. The cells are shown here dividing.

cells courtesy of Dr. Pascal Madaule, France   photo courtesy of the family of Henrietta Lacks

When we say **Life Is Finite,** we mean that physical life as we now know it is not eternal. The Greeks may have thought this less than ideal. Darwin's theory would never have predicted it. But macroscopic life (almost) universally ends in a process we call death. Microscopically, the humble algal cell may simply divide her cytoplasm and become two daughter cells (see Figure 16.2). But for some scientifically inexplicable reason, macroorganisms simply do not fare as well.

One of the most perplexing features of the transition from life to death in many organisms, man included, is a slow process called *aging* or **senescence.** A large collection of individual molecular, cellular, and organismal activities deteriorate to the point where death is the inevitable result. Many in the scientific community define human death as the cessation of brain activity. Yet this cessation itself is generally not a momentary event.

Death is the greatest tragedy of life (see Figure 16.3). As human beings with a concept of eternity, death's our biggest problem. Many (or perhaps most) mortals prefer or are even driven to purposefully ignore or repress the problem until one's time comes. To quote the English author Aldous Huxley, "Ignore death up to the last moment; then, when it can't be ignored any longer, have yourself squirted full of morphine and shuffle off in a coma."

In this last chapter, our purpose is to look death full in the face from a biological perspective and examine this terminus that is integral to so many living systems. At the end of the chapter we will seek to rescue the reader from despair by extending biology to a future that is simply not open to discussion in most biology texts.

> **Life Is Finite**—one of 12 principles of life on which this book is based.
>
> **senescence**—a complex process in which an organism ages, becoming less and less vital and precise in physiological function.

Figure 16.2 Life is Infinite for Desmid Cells (unless they get eaten). The mother cell simply "becomes" two cells. Nothing's left to "die".

Figure 16.3 Death. Sencescense does not always precede it.

1. Organismal life has a finite end point not preferred by ancient philosophers and not predicted by evolutionary theory.
2. This end point—death—is typically approached through a well-studied process called *senescence*.
3. Organisms capable of conceiving of eternity find death to be a tragic feature of living systems.

16.2 THEORIES OF AGING

The scientific study of aging has provided three competing, somewhat interrelated theories for how we get old and die. They are:

1. Senescence is a simple collection of deteriorative processes. It results from dysfunctional molecular changes that cause multiplying cells to divide erratically and non-multiplying cells to become metabolically unstable. Non-cellular materials like collagen also deteriorate in structure leading to loss of function. Death results ultimately from molecular disorder in all of these categories.

2. Senescence results from the failure of repair systems that combat deteriorative processes. Repair processes successfully offset the deteriorative processes of theory #1 all during the organism's adult years. It is therefore dysfunction of the repair processes that allow the organism to senesce and die.

3. Aging is an inevitable feature of the "bio-software"—the program—by which the body runs. An overall program regulates all aspects of the life cycle. After a given length of time, this program systematically attenuates repair processes so that the organism slowly ages and dies.

These three models are all complicated by the fact that disease, superimposed on the aging process, is what usually takes us. A world where there were no diseases would allow us to simply grow older and weaker without the threat that some microbe would overwhelm our weakened immune system and physiological responses. Consider for example the respiratory disease **pneumonia**: It often results from an infection

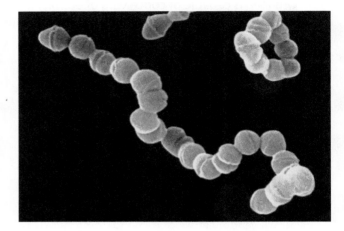

Figure 16.4 *Streptococcus* sp. There are at least 27 species in this Genus. Species *S. pneumoniae* is given the common name pneumococcus and strains of it frequently cause pneumonia in the elderly and the very young.

with the **pneumococcus** (see Figure 16.4). But the infection flourishes both because of a decreased immune response to the pathogen and an impaired **pulmonary reserve** and function.

> **pneumonia**—the results of a lung infection and/or inflammation in which the alveoli begins to fill with tissue fluid; severe cases slowly asphyxiate the individual.
>
> **pneumococcus**—common name for the bacterium *Streptococcus pneumoniae*, an opportunistic pathogen that commonly causes *pneumonia* in the elderly or immuno-compromised.
>
> **pulmonary reserve**—an additional volume of air that can be inhaled or exhaled in times of extreme need; a volume beyond the tidal air exchanged in breathing while at rest.

IN OTHER WORDS

1. There are essentially three competing but overlapping theories of aging that we present in their historic sequence of preference.
2. The first theory bases aging on the slow deterioration of cellular processes and the products of those processes.
3. The second theory bases aging on the deterioration of cellular repair processes that normally offset or undo the developing dysfunction of life processes and their products.
4. The third theory bases aging on the expression of a carefully designed program that slowly degrades processes and their products until death is the predictable result.
5. Disease usually interrupts the process of aging at some point and takes the life of the individual.

16.3 OBSERVATIONS: CELLULAR PROCESSES

Let's observe life's senescence at the cellular level. Then, we'll take a brief look at organismal aging (your aging). Finally, we'll put together our observations to see which theory is more consistent with the evidence. First, here are some observations we've made about cellular aging.

1. If human cells are grown in culture medium where they can be studied more reproducibly, an interesting phenomenon occurs. While being transferred from flask to flask, they grow and divide for many rounds of cell division (see Figure 16.5). Eventually, they cease dividing and die. We call this process cell *senescence*.

2. On rare occasions, as in Henrietta Lacks' case, a cell will **transform** to a cancerous state by a partially understood process after which it divides continuously without undergoing senescence or death. For now, let's ignore this rare event.

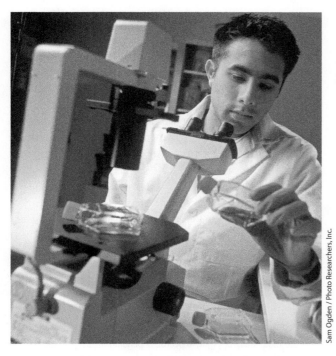

Figure 16.5 Cells in Culture. Human cells can be grown in artificial cell culture medium in plastic culture flasks with flat sides. The microscope shown here is adapted to focusing on the single layer of cells that grows on the floor of the culture flasks shown.

Table 16.1 The Number of Cell Division Events a Cell is Capable of Depending on its Tissue Source.

Cell Source	Doublings till Senescence
human:	
fetus	50
40 yr old	40
80 yr old	30
animal:	
long life span	greater
short life span	fewer

3. When we culture human cells, their source determines the number of doublings they are capable of going through (see Table 16.1)!

What do these observations mean? We doubt that cells count up exactly how many divisions they've been through. In a **clone** of cells, not all daughters go through the same number of divisions before they die (see Figure 16.6). So if there is some sort

transformation (in the context of cell physiology)—the alteration of a cell's hereditary makeup such that it is now capable of dividing continuously with no senescence or death.

clone—a collection of cells that all derive from a single, original parental cell as a result of successive cell divisions.

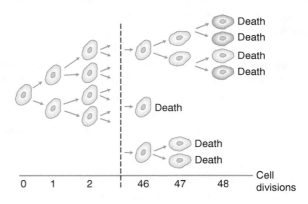

Figure 16.6 Cell Division Number. Individual human cells from the same culture were cloned to see how many cell divisions each cloned cell went through before senescence occured. The number of divisions were similar in each case but not identical.

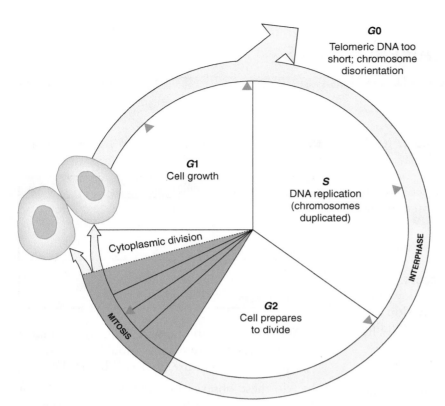

G0
Telomeric DNA too
short; chromosome
disorientation

G1
Cell growth

S
DNA replication
(chromosomes
duplicated)

Cytoplasmic division

INTERPHASE

G2
Cell prepares
to divide

MITOSIS

Figure 16.7 The Last G_0 Phase. The normal G_1 growth phase becomes a period in the cell cycle during which chromosome telomeric regions fail to be recognized properly due to telomere under-replication (after many cell generations). Instead of moving successfully into a normal S phase, the cell cycle aborts into a G_0 phase where it will senesce and die.

of internal cell division counter, it isn't as simple as was initially suspected.

One growing suspicion is that cells, in their cycling (see Section 8.3), shunt off into a G_0 stage (see Figure 16.7). They get "stuck" there because they can no longer organize and distribute their chromosomes properly prior to mitosis. This happens because the ends of the chromosomes—the **telomeres**—become unrecognizable to the machinery that normally handles and distributes them. This machinery recognizes chromosome ends by the very short, very highly **repetitive DNA** sequences found there (see Figure 16.8). Before each cell division, this DNA is replicated. But with each division the number of these repeat sequences decreases—the repeat sequence ends of chromosomes slowly become under-replicated so that the ends of chromosomes are poorly demarcated in the cell.

There is an enzyme in the nucleus of the cell that's generated specifically to replicate these repeated sequences. It's called **telomerase**. Now this. . . . is exciting! If we generate cells in culture that overproduce telomerase enzyme, they continue to divide well beyond their normal life expectancy in culture.

Might these exciting results help us to select a preferred theory of aging? Theory #1 argues that cells stop dividing because chromosome recognition has deteriorated and that is all. Theory #2 says the deterioration is caused by reduced production of telomerase. Theory #3 says that the reduction in telomerase is a programmed process—but there must be some flexibility in running the program

G_0—an abnormal stage in the cell cycle in which the cell no longer responds effectively to external signals calling for division; usually an irreversible loss of the potential to divide.

telomere—regions of large numbers of short, highly repeated DNA segments in sequence that define the ends of eukaryotic chromosomes for the machinery that positions them for mitotic division.

repetitive DNA—identical segments of DNA in sequence that are moderately or highly repeated depending on the number of iterations in the sequence in question.

telomerase—an enzyme that replicates highly repetitive DNA in the telomeres of chromosomes.

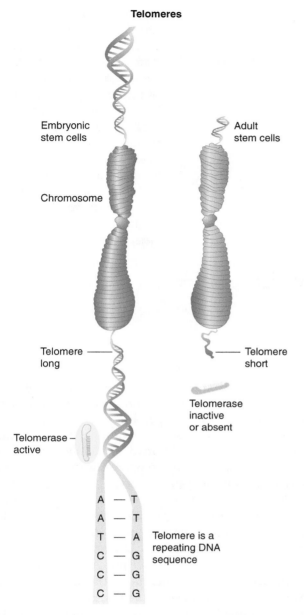

Telomeres

Embryonic stem cells

Chromosome

Adult stem cells

Telomere long

Telomere short

Telomerase inactive or absent

Telomerase – active

A — T
A — T
T — A
C — G
C — G
C — G

Telomere is a repeating DNA sequence

Figure 16.8 Telomeres. Chromosome DNA sequences end with very large numbers of identical, very short base sequences. As cells continue to divide, each round of initiation of DNA replication causes the number of base sequence repeats to decrease. Thus the length of the telomeres decreases and only the activity of a telomerase enzyme helps to retain that length. Small telomeres make the "ends" of the chromosomes unrecognizable to the cell as it alligns chromosomes in preparation for the next mitotic division.

since cells differ in the number of daughter generations they produce. Hmm.

Still another set of results suggests that rather than DNA loss being significant, mutational *change* in DNA is what causes aging. Humans are exposed to cosmic radiation in small amounts and to **mutagenic** chemicals in their environments. They also have DNA replication machinery that imperfectly incorporates nucleotide bases into the growing DNA polymer. So genetic mistakes happen (see Figure 16.9a). These mistakes code for errant proteins. Our first theory would view these mutations and resultant dysfunctional proteins as deteriorative events. The cell does have repair enzymes that remove and replace such mutations (see Figure 16.9b, c). But if the mutations are too subtle or too numerous for the repair systems of the cell to correct, then they accumulate. These changes often lead to cancer (see Section 8.6). Of course, theory #2 predicts that mutations accumulate in the genes coding for the repair system components themselves. By slowly mutating, their protein products (the green enzyme in Figure 16.9, for example) are losing efficiency in catching and correcting newly formed mutations.

These observations, however, are also consistent with the programmed aging theory (#3) if we imagine that at some point in life the genes coding for DNA repair enzymes are programmed to turn off. Error buildup in the DNA archives then slowly debilitates cell processes and death ensues.

Finally, another set of results suggests that the gradual accumulation of **free radicals** reduces cellular efficiency and increases cellular waste (see Figure 16.10). Free radicals build up as a result of cosmic radiation or simply as by-products of respiration. For example, a rare by-product of aerobic respiration is O_2^-, the **superoxide radical**. Such radicals chemically attack other cellular molecules, altering their covalent bonding and hence their structure. This destroys their functionality. The

mutagenic—any process, force, or substance that causes changes in the base sequence of an archival informational molecule such as DNA.

free radical—the result of a broken covalent bond in which an atom or functional group retains just one of the two electrons originally shared in the bond; highly reactive chemically.

superoxide radical—an oxygen atom bearing a single unpaired electron; highly reactive chemically.

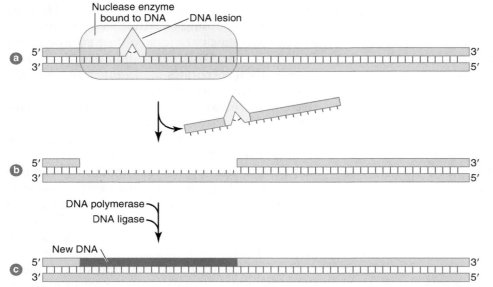

Figure 16.9 Mutations and Their Correction. **(a)** a double stranded DNA molecule in which ultraviolet light has caused two adjacent DNA bases to fuse together (yellow) in a way that will cause subsequent DNA replication to be defective at this point. Notice that a repair enzyme is poised to fix the problem. **(b)** the repair enzyme senses the error and cuts out a section of the DNA that includes the error. **(c)** Another set of repair enzymes rebuilds the DNA molecule using the complementary strand base sequence as a template against which to build.

Free Radical Generation and Destruction

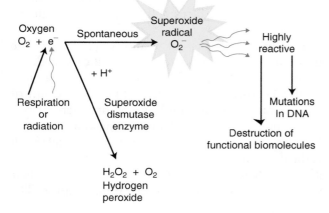

Figure 16.10 Free Radical Generation and Destruction. Free radicals react strongly and indiscriminately altering covalent bonds in a wide variety of biomolecules including DNA where they cause mutations. If the enzyme superoxide dismutase is being synthesized, it quickly converts the superoxide radical into the less reactive hydrogen peroxide and free oxygen. As we age, levels of this helpful enzyme are diminished.

enzyme **superoxide dismutase** deactivates free radicals. And it is in higher concentrations in tissues of organisms with longer life spans! Again, each theory explains these observations. Free radicals themselves are deteriorative of cellular processes. But dysfunction of the repair process—the superoxide dismutase system—would hasten the accumulation of such radicals. Finally, the third theory of aging envisions a program shutting down the production of enzymatic protection against free radical accumulation.

Which of these observed processes might most influence aging and death at the cellular level? Some workers believe that telomere shortening is the principle reason for aging. Others favor the process of free radical accumulation. Still other workers see a combination of all of these factors at work. The study of animal models of aging has yet to yield a clear-cut answer to this question.

superoxide dismutase—an enzyme that binds to two superoxide anions (radicals) and covalently combines them with protons to form less harmful hydrogen peroxide and free oxygen.

1. Animal cells grown in liquid culture medium go through a fairly reproducible number of divisions after which they senesce and die.

2. The total number of divisions that cells go through is characteristic of the kind of organism, the kind of tissue involved, and the age of the organism from which the cells are taken.

3. Cells appear to senesce and die because they become unable to organize and distribute their chromosomes properly into daughter cells.

4. The inability to organize and replicate chromosomes results from deterioration of the telomeric regions of the arms of each chromosome.

5. As they approach senescence, cells appear to accumulate mutations in their DNA and produce defective protein products as a result.

6. Accumulation of mutations indicates that the system designed to repair them is no longer functioning properly, perhaps because it is programmed to decline in function.

7. Free radicals appear to accumulate at higher levels in aging individuals; these highly reactive ions make random changes in the body's functional chemistry.

8. There is no clear consensus regarding which of these deteriorative processes is the primary cause of aging. Do all three processes contribute equally?

16.4 OBSERVATIONS: ORGAN-SYSTEMIC PROCESSES

If the process of cellular aging is only partially understood, its relationship to aging of the organism is *poorly* understood. This is disappointing. Do humans age just because their cells are limited in the number of times they can divide (see Figure 16.11)? This seems unlikely because nerve and muscle cells do not divide at all in adult life, yet they continue to live. But they show deterioration with age. We've searched for body systems or whole-body processes that might cause aging and have come up with the following observations.

Our immune systems begin to malfunction (see Section 10.4, Figure 10.12). This takes two different forms. First, our response to disease and cancers begins to decline seriously with age. At age 60, our thymus gland is a mere 5% of the volume it had when we were born. We simply don't process as many **T lymphocytes** as we used to. Hence, our responses to foreign intruders are weaker.

Another variable is that we become more **autoimmune**. As a result of mutational changes in cells, our cell surfaces begin to exhibit surface proteins that are novel (mutant). As such, they begin to appear foreign to our own immune surveillance system. We begin to attack our own tissues. This predisposes us to suffer even more from diseases and cancers as our defenses are increasingly distracted by our own deteriorating cell surfaces.

Meanwhile, our tendons, ligaments, bones, cartilage, blood vessels, and other connective tissues are constantly generating **collagen**, a molecule that helps gives structural strength to these tissues (see Figure 16.12). With age, adjacent collagen polymers begin to become more cross-linked, that is, more covalently bonded together; they become less able to function separately. This leads to profound loses in elasticity, and hence functions like cardiac muscle recoil (heart strength). Cross-linkage of collagen in vessel walls can contribute significantly to hypertension (high blood pressure). Some workers think that cross-linkage of vessel wall proteins alters the walls' permeability to nutrients and wastes. Such changes could have far-reaching potential effects on many organs and tissues.

Once again, deterioration of the immune system or of collagen integrity can be viewed as simply that: a slow deterioration process. But if such loss of function is in any way prohibited in early life by some compensatory process, the programmed-aging theory has only to posit the turning off of the compensatory process in order for aging and death to be inevitable.

Figure 16.11 Aging. Can the disabilities the elderly face all be the result of cellular senescence? Are organ-level or organismic processes contributory as well?

T lymphocyte—a cellular product of the bone marrow that, through maturation in the thymus gland, becomes able to attack cells that have been invaded by foreign pathogens or to aid cells producing antibodies.

autoimmune—the state of actively responding immunologically to one's own molecular surfaces; rheumatoid arthritis is a common example.

collagen—protein polymers in long fibrils found in the connective tissues of mammals; they add strength and elasticity to connective tissue.

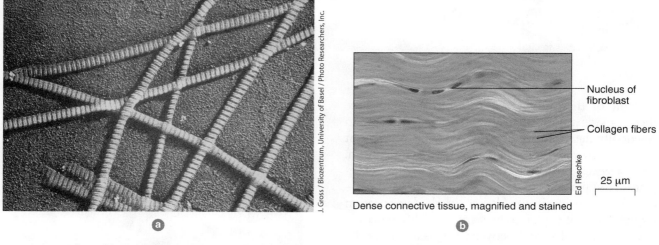

a — J. Gross / Biozentrum, University of Basel / Photo Researchers, Inc.

Nucleus of fibroblast

Collagen fibers

Ed Reschke

25 μm

Dense connective tissue, magnified and stained

b

Figure 16.12 Collagen. Fibers of this protein make up about one fourth of all the protein in the body. **(a)** Individual fibrils each of which is composed of numerous collagen molecules, each of which is, in turn, composed of 3 intertwined polypeptide chains. **(b)** a section of dense connective tissue such as would be found in the dermis of the skin or within a ligament.

IN OTHER WORDS

1. There is no unified understanding of how cellular aging relates to and/or causes organismal aging.
2. The human immune system deteriorates in two fundamental ways: Its responses begin to lack effective intensity, and they start to become more directed against self-antigens.
3. With age, collagen fibrils become increasingly cross-linked; this decreases elasticity in critical tissues such as cardiac muscle and vascular system walls.

In light of these observations, which of our three theories seems more plausible? The first theory—an essentially deteriorative description—fails to account for the many repair processes built into the organism. Repair systems exist. Dead and damaged cells get replaced, trauma and wounds heal, infections clear up—even hair regrows itself. Also, a simple deterioration model does not explain why significant differences in life spans are observed between very similar species that should have very similar experiences with such common deteriorative processes. Why does a leopard have a life expectancy of 17 years while a lion's is 35 years (see Figure 16.13)? A simple deterioration theory also does not explain why mammals kept at

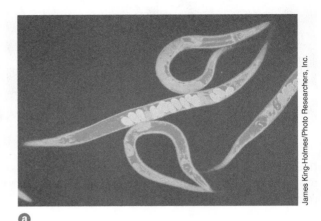

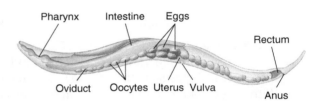

(b) Structures in the adult hermaphrodite. The sperm-producing structures are not shown.

Figure 16.14 *Caenorhabditis elegans*. At about 1.5 mm in length, this tiny nematode round worm is a truly elegant system for the study of animal development. Several amazing mutations in this worm are capable of doubling the worm's life span. **(a)** false color optical micrograph of several adults; eggs are light blue in color **(b)** structural diagram.

near starvation conditions have an increased life span by nearly half!

Our second theory is more realistic because it accounts neatly for the wide range of repair systems built into most organisms. It might also be able to explain species life span differences if repair systems differ in number or quality among species. Perhaps different systems dominate the deteriorative process in different species. But our second theory is insufficient to explain still another recent set of observations regarding genes such as *age-1* in the **nematode** worm, *Caenorhabditis elegans* (see Figure 16.14).

nematode—a large phylum of worms; most are free-living found in soil; some are parasitic to higher life-forms; commonly called *roundworms*.

Figure 16.13 Similar Species, *Panthera leo* (**(a)** the lion) and *Panthera pardus* (**(b)** the leopard) with radically different life expectancies.

Programmed Aging

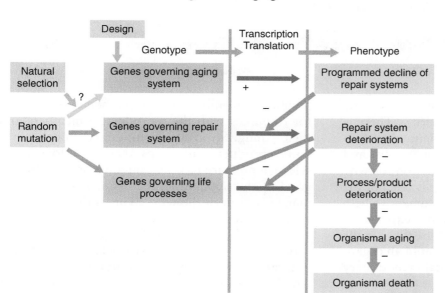

Figure 16.15 Programmed Aging. Designed, coordinated gene products unleash a programmed deterioration of repair mechanisms that result in the accumulation of defective processes and gene products that age the individual.

A recessive allele at this locus has been found to double the worm's life span! How could a single mutation in one gene have such a sweeping and positive effect on a wide range of repair functions in the animal?

The third theory—programmed senescence—seems capable of facing up to all of these observations (see Figure 16.15). The program would ultimately cause the deterioration posited by theory #1 through its systematic shutdown of the repair mechanisms posited by theory #2. Different programs in different species would explain the disparity in life spans of related species. The *Caenorhabditis* mutations would then be in genes central to the control of the entire program. We have a suspicion that such programming genes exist in humans because genetic diseases like **progeria** show us a human body that appears to neatly and coordinately age itself much more rapidly than normal (see Figure 16.16).

progeria—a rare disease state in humans in which the individual begins to age prematurely; most sufferers die by age 13, usually of heart attack or stroke.

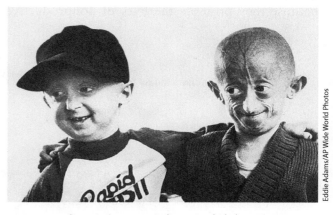

Figure 16.16 Progeria. A rare genetic disease in which the entire coordinated aging process begins prematurely in an individual whose life usually ends by age 13.

IN OTHER WORDS

1. The deterioration theory of aging appears simplistic; it fails to account for the variety of repair processes integral to the macroorganism.
2. The decline in repair process theory accounts for more observations but fails to explain the existence of simple point mutations that can radically alter the individual's life span.
3. The programmed aging theory is currently able to explain the highest number of observations we have regarding aging in animals.

WHY DO WE DIE? PROGRAMMED AGING FROM TWO PERSPECTIVES

As human beings, our sex cells "live on" in the lives of our offspring and their offspring. There is a pleasing if sobering character of immortality to this biological reality. But both the materialist and the design proponent need an explanation for why the organisms producing these sex cells die. For the naturalist, organismal death must somehow help the species to survive at the extreme expense of the individual. For design proponents, there is the quandary of why a Designer would build an organism that *must* die. Consider a typical evolutionary response to organismal death:

First, our developmental program causes us to mature to a reproductive age, at which time we begin to pass our genetic traits on to the next generation. Any mutations that favor or strengthen this part of our life spans will be preserved in the population (see Figure 16.17). Once the reproductive years are over, mutations that promote longevity and health are harmful to the population because they promote the lives of nonproductive

population members. These members then compete for resources with the reproductive members and their young. So in an evolutionary model, when your reproductive life stops, there is no longer any selective pressure to keep you alive. In fact, for the good of the population, it's better if you are permanently "out of the way". This is the reason that aging and death are inevitable.

But there are some serious questions for this evolutionary model to answer: First, why hasn't natural selection preserved mutations that would lengthen the reproductive years of the individual? Such individuals would leave more offspring that would perpetuate those mutations in the population. Second, wouldn't mutations that lengthen total life span help to create a context in which mutations lengthening the reproductive years would be more beneficial? In fact, why don't we all live to the age of 969 years, reproducing all the way? Some organisms are apparently further along at this than we are! One variety of giant tortoise has a measured maximum life span of 255 years. *Sebastes aleutianus,* the rougheye rockfish, has a life span approaching 200 years. Isn't this what evolutionary theory would predict should happen? Certainly such individuals leave more offspring, capable of more reproduction! In fact, evolutionarily, why do we die at all? Those individuals whose aging processes get interrupted and who therefore reproduce longer certainly must be the fittest for survival! Evolutionary theory has yet to produce a convincing explanation for why we die. So why *do* we die?

Consider a biblical response to why we die. Genesis 1 asserts that man was made in God's image. God does not die. Therefore a physical body supportive of this eternal human spirit would best not die. This is clearly implied in Genesis 2:17, where man is told what voluntary behavior might cause him to die. St. Paul interprets death as a novelty added to human life in his Roman letter (5:12). Amazing . . . you were designed *not* to die, just as evolutionary theory would predict! But the Genesis account (3:19) describes a phenomenon that scientists cannot measure or even characterize. There Adam is told that as a result of his *sin,* he will now

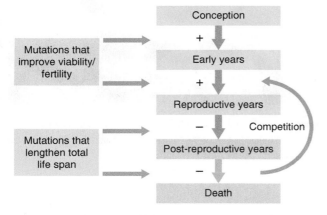

Evolutionary Model for Aging

Figure 16.17 Evolutionary Model for Aging. If mutations occur that would positively lengthen the post-reproductive life span, they would have a negative effect on the population because increased longevity of aging individuals would add to local competition for food and perhaps compromise the viability of the young that have yet to reproduce or are currently of reproductive age.

wrestle with a creation whose population interactions are all fallen, and he will eventually return to the same dust of which he is composed. Death is not, then, an inevitable characteristic of life (see Figure 16.19). (Actually, bacteria have taught us this.) Rather, death is imposed on life! If God is the Imposer, and He does everything perfectly, then we can just *assume* that death is programmed and theory #3 is almost certainly the best one. Our developmental program has death built into it.

How do we die? In some soon-to-be-understood way, the program of life in our bodies enters a death loop: Cellular divisions reach a disorganized terminus, immune function becomes autoimmune, functional proteins slowly lock into intractable positions, and life gives way to death.

The cellular world has revealed to us how death happens at that level. In normal development of a palm frond or a human hand, the organism purposely cuts out patterns within the frond or between the fingers. This tissue destruction requires killing of the organism's own cells—a process called **apoptosis** (see Figure 16.18). Apoptosis is a step in a complex program that furthers development of the final

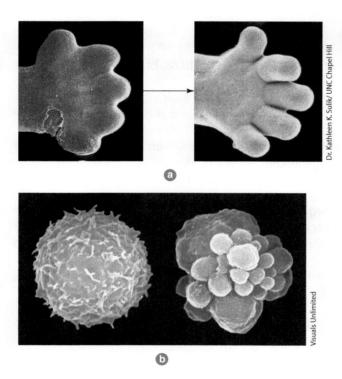

(a)

(b)

Figure 16.18 Apoptosis. **(a)** Programmed cell death is required for normal human development. Notice how the cellular "webbing" between the primordial fingers dies out to achieve spaces between the digits. **(b)** Electron micrographs of a normal cell (left) and one undergoing apoptosis (right).

Dr. Kathleen K. Sulik/ UNC Chapel Hill

Visuals Unlimited

John V. A. F. Neal / Photo Researchers, Inc.

Figure 16.19 Life after Death. Science cannot verify the resurrection of Christ from death because no human observed the event. Historical research supports the event however, because his facial identity and wounds were preserved in a living individual for observation by hundreds of individuals that included skeptics.

masterpiece. Programmed organismal death may be a logical though tragic extension of this concept.

So here we are, in a course devoted to the arduous celebration of life, stuck in a program of death—forced to admit that Life Is Finite. St. Paul's words come to mind:

"Oh wretched man that I am! Who will deliver me from the body of this death?!"

apoptosis—a process of programmed cell death usually contributing in some way to the normal development of a multicellular organism.

"Well, Paul, evolutionary theory won't because it can't explain how we got into this lethal web in the first place!"

But then Paul doesn't turn to evolutionary thinking to extricate himself from his body of death. Nor does he adopt Greek philosophy, looking hopefully toward some Socratic unknown. He's not stoical; he's not cynical. What is he in the face of death? What are we in the face of death? Let's return to his commentary. He says:

"I thank God through Jesus Christ our Lord." And not two paragraphs later we find him saying (with a bit of paraphrasing added):

> *"If the Spirit of God raised Christ from the dead, and that Spirit lives in you, He will raise your (death-programmed) body and delete forever that death loop that you could not escape."*

He uses the historically verifiable return of Christ from physical death to argue that such a return is possible for Christ's follower as well.

In fact, Paul teaches that a return to infinite life will happen to every person reading these words. The death loop will be deleted! For some, it will be deleted so that they can, for the rest of eternity, be painfully confronted with the results of their own worst sin—willful, irrational, practical atheism. Physical torment in a milieu called Hell then becomes a persistent remedy protecting a determined atheist from a horrific spiritual and intellectual pathology: denial of a Designer God.

Other readers of these words have submitted their wills to Christ. They have uncovered before Him all of their inner hates and greed. His own suffering on their behalf allows Him to forgive and heal them. For those individuals, loss of a death loop restores in them His image. They will glorify and enjoy Him forever.

Life is finite—but only for a finite time. Biology will change. May that change find the reader in the arms of Christ, returning the smile of Christ, living an infinite life in His joy.

IN OTHER WORDS

1. Our genetic information retains its integrity into the lives of future generations, but its expression at the organismal level includes aging and death.
2. A naturalistic explanation for death is that organisms who've lived past their reproductive years now compete with younger reproducing organisms for food and other resources; this is detrimental to the population as a whole.
3. There is no acceptable naturalistic explanation for why evolution does not lengthen the reproductive years of the organism until it has the same potential longevity as cancer cells.
4. A nonscientific reason for organismal death is the moral decay of the human organism as recorded in the Mosaic literature of the Bible.
5. Because of humanity's immorality, then, a human organism designed for eternal physical life is reprogrammed to undergo death before his moral character becomes too highly destructive of nature.
6. Organismal death is as neatly programmed as apoptosis—cellular death; the program is simply executed at a higher organizational level.
7. The Biblical text speaks of a person-to-person relationship with God that obtains for the individual a new physical body that lacks the aging and death programs we now have.

QUESTIONS FOR REVIEW

1. Give a biological definition for the term *death*.
2. What is senescence? Give an example of a cell type in which it occurs. Give two examples of cell types in which it does not occur.
3. "We do not die as a result of aging." In what important sense is this sentence true?
4. Name and describe three competing theories of aging.
5. Describe the behavior of normal cells placed in cell culture medium and kept by sequential transfers to fresh medium. What happens to these cells?
6. What is the G_0 stage in the cell cycle? How does a cell enter it? How does a cell leave it?
7. How might the introduction of mutations into the DNA sequence of the genome result in aging?
8. What is a free radical? From what does it result? Why is its prolonged presence in a cell considered dangerous?
9. How does increased cross-linking of collagen fibrils contribute to the aging process?
10. Defend the notion that the programmed aging theory is a superior explanation of aging and death as compared with the two competing theories.
11. Give an evolutionary explanation for why a human being ages and dies. What major challenge does the explanation face?
12. What is apoptosis? What value might it have to the organism?

QUESTIONS FOR THOUGHT

1. Recall your studies in Chapters 8 and 9 of this text. What changes would be necessary in HeLa cells in order to regenerate the body of Henrietta Lacks? HeLa cells have about 82 chromosomes/cell, with four copies of one chromosome and three copies of three other chromosomes/cell. The genome also contains numerous sites where human papilloma virus has inserted within the chromosomes. How would these data affect your answer?
2. Why can we not give a terse definition for the term *life?*
3. HeLa cells have what is described as a highly active telomerase gene. How might this explain the immortality of this cell line?
4. T lymphocytes are immune system cells that attack foreign molecules (antigens) found on the surfaces of our own cells. This is what helps us destroy virally infected cells, for example. As T lymphocytes mature in the thymus gland in preparation for deployment, all T lymphocytes that would recognize our own molecules are deleted (destroyed) so that only T cells recognizing foreign molecules are allowed to complete the maturation process. How is it then, that we can become autoimmune as we age?
5. What sort of molecular studies should be performed on individuals having the disease progeria? What would be the major setback in doing such studies?
6. What feature of the Biblical explanation of the origin of an aging program would be most distasteful to a naturalistic scientist who studies aging?
7. The existence of apoptosis in normal development could be used as a powerful argument by evolutionists for the existence of aging and death in the individual. How would that argument be stated? How would a design proponent respond to it?

GLOSSARY

apoptosis—a process of programmed cell death usually contributing in some way to the normal development of a multicellular organism.

autoimmune—the state of actively responding immunologically to one's own molecular surfaces; rheumatoid arthritis is a common example.

clone—a collection of cells that all derive from a single, original parental cell as a result of successive cell divisions.

collagen—protein polymers in long fibrils found in the connective tissues of mammals; they add strength and elasticity to connective tissue.

free radical—the result of a broken covalent bond in which an atom or functional group retains just one of the two electrons originally shared in the bond; highly reactive chemically.

G_0—an abnormal stage in the cell cycle in which the cell no longer responds effectively to external signals calling for division; usually an irreversible loss of the potential to divide.

Life Is Finite—one of 12 principles of life on which this book is based.

mutagenic—any process, force, or substance that causes changes in the base sequence of an archival informational molecule such as DNA.

nematode—a large phylum of worms; most are free-living found in soil; some are parasitic to higher life-forms; commonly called *roundworms*.

pneumococcus—common name for the bacterium *Streptococcus pneumoniae*, an opportunistic pathogen that commonly causes pneumonia in the elderly or immuno-compromised.

pneumonia—the results of a lung infection and/or inflammation in which the alveoli begins to fill with tissue fluid; severe cases slowly asphyxiate the individual.

progeria—a rare disease state in humans in which the individual begins to age prematurely; most sufferers die by age 13, usually of heart attack or stroke.

pulmonary reserve—an additional volume of air that can be inhaled or exhaled in times of extreme need; a volume beyond the tidal air exchanged in breathing while at rest.

repetitive DNA—identical segments of DNA in sequence that are moderately or highly repeated depending on the number of iterations in the sequence in question.

senescence—a complex process in which an organism ages, becoming less and less vital and precise in physiological function.

superoxide dismutase—an enzyme that binds to two superoxide anions (radicals) and covalently combines them with protons to form less harmful hydrogen peroxide and free oxygen.

superoxide radical—an oxygen atom bearing a single unpaired electron; highly reactive chemically.

T lymphocyte—a cellular product of the bone marrow that, through maturation in the thymus gland, becomes able to attack cells that have been invaded by foreign pathogens or to aid cells producing antibodies.

telomerase—an enzyme that replicates highly repetitive DNA in the telomeres of chromosomes.

telomere—regions of large numbers of short, highly repeated DNA segments in sequence that define the ends of eukaryotic chromosomes for the machinery that positions them for mitotic division.

transformation (in the context of cell physiology)—the alteration of a cell's hereditary makeup such that it is now capable of dividing continuously with no senescence or death.

Page numbers followed by *f* indicate figures.

A

Abiotic environment, 445
ABO gene
   in humans, 420
Absorption, 308
Accessory pigments, defined, 146
Acetylcholine, 114–116, 116*f*, 291
   defined, 114
Acetyl-CoA
   defined, 138
   in Krebs cycle, 138, 138*f*
Acinar cells, 113–115, 114*f*
   amylase production in, 113–116,
      114*f*–116*f*
   defined, 113
Acrosome, 389
Actin, 231
Action potential, 291
Activation energy
   defined, 129
   enzymes and, 130–131, 130*f*
Active site, 130–131, 130*f*
   defined, 130
Active transport, 357
Ada gene, 204
Adaptation, 483
Adaptive immune response
   antibody-mediated, 304
   cell-mediated, 305
   characteristics of, 303
Adaptive immunity, 303
Adenine, 83, 84
   molecular structure, 59*f*
Adenosine, 331
Adenosine diphosphate (ADP), 83*f*
Adenosine triphosphate (ATP), 16, 83,
      135, 135*f*
   in aerobic respiration, 137, 140
   structure, 83*f*
   synthases, defined, 140
Adhesin gene expression, of
      M. genitalium, 444, 445*f*

Adhesins, 444
   defined, 102
ADP. *See* Adenosine diphosphate (ADP)
Adventitious, 377
Aerobic respiration, 136–137,
      136*f*, 137*f*
   defined, 136
   glycolysis in, 137
   stages of
      electron transfer phosphorylation,
         139–140
      glycolysis, 137
      Krebs cycle, 137–139
   summary of, 137*f*
Afferent, 270
Age structure, population, 551, 551*f*
Aging, 582, 590, 590*f. See also*
      Senescence
   evolutionary model for, 594, 594*f*
   observations
      cellular processes, 585–588
      organ-systemic processes, 590
   programmed, 593, 593*f*, 594–596
   theories of, 584
   theory evaluation, 592–593
Agnosticism, 439
Air, 38
Airfoil, 454
Alanine
   molecular structure, 59*f*
Alcohol
   ethanol, 328
   invades the synapse, 329
Algorithm, 468
Alleles, 380
Allo-lactose, 352
Allosteric site
   defined, 132
   of enzyme, in metabolic pathways,
      132–133, 132*f*
Alpha-linolenic acid, 69
Alveolata, 521–522, 521*f*–522*f*
Alveoli, 521
Amino acids, 59*f*, 75
   coding for, 181

L and D forms of, 447, 447*f*
   monomer, structure of, 76, 76*f*
Ammonia (NH_3), 446, 446*t*
Amoeba proteus, 524, 524*f*
Amoeboid movement, 512
Amoebozoa, 524, 524*f*
Amylase, 66
   defined, 113
   production, in acinar cells, 113–116,
      114*f*–116*f*
Amylopectin, 65
Amylose, 65, 66*f*
Anaerobic conditions, defined, 137
Anal canal, 265
Analogous (in biology), 475
Anaphase, 225
Androgenic steroid hormone, 73, 73*f*
Angiosperms, 526
Animalia, 506
Animal life cycle, 387
Animals
   defined, 14
Annual finite rate of increase (λ), 551
Antheraea polyphemus, 528*f*
Antibiotic, selective effect of, 462, 462*f*
Antibody, 305
Anticodon, 183
Antidiuretic hormone (ADH), 314
Antigen, 303
Antigen-presenting cell (APC), 304
Apical meristem, 254
Apical ridge, 266
Apoptosis, 595, 595*f*
Aposematic coloration, 564
Appendix, 264
Arabidopsis thaliana, 348, 356, 357
Archaea, 517
   defined, 14
Arginine
   molecular structure, 59*f*
Aristotle, 12, 12*f*, 13, 14, 20
Art, defined, 435, 436
Artery, 294
Arthropoda, 473
Arthropods, 506

Asexual reproduction, 376
  extreme, 378
  in plants, 377
Asparagine
  molecular structure, 59f
Aspartate
  molecular structure, 59f
Assimilated energy, 570
Atheism, 439
Atherosclerosis, 69, 70f
ATM, 237
Atom(s), 43f
  Bohr model of, 43f
  components, 43, 43f
    arrangement of, 44–46, 45f
  defined, 7, 8f, 41, 43
  differentiating, 43–44
  in living systems, 44t
  number of neutrons in, 44, 44f
ATP. See Adenosine triphosphate (ATP)
ATP molecule, 310
  evolutionary origin of, 335
  internal integration of, 334–335
Atrium, 296
Autoimmune, 590
Autonomic nervous system (ANS),
  320, 326
Autonomy, 434
Autosome, 425
Autotroph, 509, 569
  defined, 144
Auxin, 252, 356
Auxin-induced cell elongation, 359
Auxins behavior
  in plant shoot tips, 357
Avery's experiment, 165
Aves, 528
Axon, 315

B

Bacillus thuringiensis (Bt), 565
Bacteria, 14, 516
  biosynthesis, 62f
  comparison of, 443, 443f
  defined, 97
  internal structure of, 100f
Bacterial cell, 348
  RNA polymerase, 193
Balanus balanoides, 559
Baleen whales, 563
Ballooning, 562
Barbicel, 456–457, 456f
Barbs, 455, 456f
Barbules, 456, 456f, 457
  pattern, hypothetical evolution of,
    460–461, 461f
Basophil, 301
Batesian mimicry, 564, 564f
Behe, Michael, 460, 469
Bible, 33, 34
Bile, 308

Biological classification, 13–14, 14f
  domain-based scheme, 15f
  kingdom-based scheme, 15f
Biological information
  application of, 190
  in chromosomes, 170
  expression of, 162, 163, 173
    as problem solving, 191
  nature of, 164
  need for, 160–163
  physical nature of, 162
Biology, defined, 1
Biomagnifcation, 571, 572
Biomolecules, 7, 8f
  carbohydrates, 64–67, 64t
  classes of, 64t
  hemoglobin, 80–82
  lipids, 64t, 68–74
  nucleic acids, 64t, 83–85
  proteins, 64t, 75–79
Biosphere, defined, 9–10, 10f
Biosynthesis
  activities, 219
  defined, 124
Bird feather. See Feather, bird
Bird preening, 457, 457f
Bird songs
  composite response, 367
  environmental change, 368
  variations within species, 367
Birth control
  altering body function, 405–406
  avoiding intercourse, 406–407
  commonly used method, 405
  condoms, 405
  contraception, 406
  copper IUD, 406
  permanent surgical methods, 407
  pregnancy rates for, 404
  sperm blockage, 404–405
  sterilization, 407
  vaginal rings, 406
Birth rates, 553
Bivalve, 558
Bladder, 312
Blastocyst, 259
Blattella germanica, 506
Blattellidae, 506
Blood, composition of, 294
Blood-brain barrier, 323, 332
Blood vessels, 245, 295
Bluegill fish, 548
B lymphocyte, 304
Body system
  life is internally integrated, 284
  smooth muscle, role of, 292
Bog, 354
Bohr model of atom, 43f
Bomb calorimeter, 41
Brain, 317
  adult brain regions, 270

development, 268
  organogenesis of, 267–270
Bronchi, 301
Brooklyn Bridge
  structural design of, 2
Broth culture, 442
Brown, Robert, 94
Brown algae, 523
Bubble, 218
  netting, 563
Budding, 216
Buffer, 334
Bulbourethral gland, 399
Bullhorn acacia tree, 567

C

Cactoblastis cactorum, 565
Cactus moth, 565, 566
Caenorhabditis elegans, 592, 592f
Caffeine, 331
Calamus, 455, 456f
Calmodulin, 292
Calories, defined, 140
Camarhynchus pallidus, 438f
Cambrian explosion, 471–474
Canalization, in development, 488, 489f
Cancer
  genes, 234
  mutation, 233
  unifying basis of, 233
Candida, 189
Capillaries, 294
Capsules, defined, 103
Carbohydrate monomers, 310
Carbohydrates, 7, 64–67, 64t
  polymers, 65–67, 66f
  sugars, 64–65, 64f, 65f
Carbon-12, 44, 44f
Carbon-14, 44, 44f
Carbon (C), 58
  atomic structure, 58, 58f
Carbon cycle, defined, 153
Carbon dioxide (CO₂)
  binding in hemoglobin, 81–82, 82f
Carboxysome, defined, 100
Cardiac muscle, 292
Cardiac patient
  effects of prayer on (experimental
    study), 31
Cardiovascular system, 283, 293, 298
  blood, 293–294
  blood vessels, 294–295
  heart, 296–299
Carnivore (carnivory), 543
Carotene, purification of, 41
Carrier molecule, 202
Carrying capacity, 553
Cashew nut, fat energy in, 70, 70f
Cat dancing disease, 573
Cathedrals, 160
Causality in Nature, 440f

Cell division, 217, 220
    in context, 216
    control of, 234
    protein control of, 236
    ras protein control of, 235
    regulating, 222
Cell-mediated immune response, 305
Cell membrane
    defined, 98
    of eukaryotic cells, 104–105
    of prokaryotic cells, 98–99, 98f, 99t
    at resting potential, 290
Cell plate, 231
Cell respiration
    defined, 109
Cell(s), 90–118, 91f
    in artificial culture, 6f
    ATP in, 135
    body, 315
    complexity, 97, 97f
    culture, 202
    cycle, 220
    defined, 5, 93, 93f
    Elodea, 123f
    energy change in, categories of,
        124–125, 124f
        biosynthesis, 124–125, 124f
        concentration of substance,
            124f, 125
        electrical potential, 124f, 125
        heat, 124f, 125
        movement of materials, 124f,
            125, 125f
    eukaryotic. See Eukaryotic cells
    expression of, 162, 163
    growth, 220
    prokaryotic. See Prokaryotic cells
    size of, 95–96, 95f
    theory, 93–94
        elements of, 94t
        generalizations of, 95–96, 95f
Cell's genotype, 173
Cell's growth, 219
Cell's nucleus, 237
Cellular life
    Earth's history and, 452–453, 452f
Cellular masterpiece, 161
Cellular predation, 237
Cellular processes, 585–588
    cell division number, 585f
        source and, 585t
    senescence, 585, 585f
Cellular relationships, 392
Cellulose, 66–67, 66f
Cell wall, 162
    defined, 99
Central dogma, 174
Central nervous system (CNS), 291, 321
Centromere, 171, 225
Centrosome, 225
Cerebellum, 269

Cerebral hemispheres, 362
Cerebral-spinal fluid (CSF), 321
Cerebrum, 269
Certhidea olivacea, 438f
Cervix, 395, 399
Chargaff's data, 167
Chase experiment, 166
Chatton, Edouard, 512
Chemical bonding, 46, 46f, 47
    covalent bonding, 48–49, 49f
    effects of, 47
    hydrogen bonding, 50, 50f
    ion formation and ionic bonding,
        47–48, 48f
    polar covalent bonding, 49–50, 49f
Chemical reactions
    activation energy for, 129, 129f
    characteristics of, 128–129
    defined, 128
    endergonic, 128
    energy flows in, 128–129
    exergonic, 128
Chitin, 474
Chlorophylls, 16
    defined, 144
Chloroplast, 162
    defined, 111
    in eukaryotic cells, 110f, 111
Cholesterol, 73, 73f
Choline
    molecular structure, 60f
Chordata, 528
Chordates, 472–473
Chromatid, sister, 225
Chromatin, 6f, 7, 171
    defined, 106
Chromatography, 40
    discovery of, 40, 40f
Chromosomal replication, 218
Chromosomes, 7, 171, 219, 384, 385,
        386, 423
    defined, 106
Chronic infection, defined, 444
Chthamalus stellatus, 559
Chylomicron, 70f
Chyme, 308
Cilia, 301
Cilium, 521
Circadian, 364
Circulatory system, 4f, 314
    heart, 4–5, 5f
Clades, 515
Class, in systematics, 506
Classes, 14f
    defined, 13
Clone, 377, 585t
Clumped distribution pattern, 549, 550f
CNS processes, 318
Codominance, 419, 420
Codons, 182
Cohesion, defined, 53

Cohesiveness, of water, 52–53, 53f
Coiling
    of DNA, 171, 172
Collagen, 590, 591f
Collar, 459
Colliculi, 269
Colon, 264
Colonial, 512
Commensalism, 556
Community(ies)
    defined, 9, 9f
    ecology, 546, 556–568
Compounds, 40f
    defined, 40
Computer chip, 4f
Condensation reaction, 61, 63f
    between glucose and fructose, 65, 65f
    peptide bond formation, 76–77, 76f
Condom, 405
Cone cell, 258, 334
Conifers, 526
Conjectured early atmospheres,
        compounds in, 446t
Conjoined twins, 410
Connective tissue, 246
Constrict, 295
Contraceptive, 404
Contractile ring, 231
Control conditions, 29
Core temperature, 362
Corona radiata, 401
Corpus luteum, 396
Cotransmitter, 334
Covalent bonding, 48–49, 49f
Covert feather, 454
Cranial nerves, 324
Creosote bushes, 549, 550f
Crick, Francis, 452–453
Cristae, 110–111, 110f, 512
    defined, 110
Cuvier, George, 471
Cyanobacteria, 516
    defined, 154
Cybernetics, 468
Cycads, 526
Cyclic adenosine monophosphate (cyclic
        AMP), 83–84, 84f
Cyclic AMP. See Cyclic adenosine
        monophosphate (cyclic AMP)
Cyclins, 222
Cysteine
    molecular structure, 59f
Cytokinesis, 221, 230
    in animal cells, 231
    mitosis, 230
Cytokinins, 255
Cytoplasm, defined, 99
Cytoplasmic molecules, 186, 259
Cytosine, 84, 168
    molecular structure, 59f
Cytotoxic T lymphocyte, 305

D

D and L forms of amino acids, 447, 447*f*

Darwin, Charles, 15, 436–440, 437*f*, 460
  model of evolution, 437, 438*f*, 438*t*. *See also* Evolution; Neo-Darwinian synthesis
  smallest cell, 442–445
  theory of homology, 475–476. *See also* Homology, evidence from
  theory of microevolution and macroevolution, 439, 440*f*

Da Vinci, Leonardo, 435–436, 435*f*, 440

Dawkins, Richard, 464

DDT, 572–573, 573*f*

Death, 582*f*
  defined, 582
  life after, 595, 595*f*
  rates, 553

Decomposers, 545

Degeneracy, 188

Degeneration, 444

Deletion, 483–484, 484*f*

Dendrite, 315

Dendritic cells, 304

Dendrobates pumilio, 528*f*

Density, population, 549

Density-dependent factor, population, 554

Density-independent factor, population, 554

Deoxyribonucleic acid (DNA), 17, 17*f*, 84–85, 84*f*
  base sequence of, 164
  biomolecules, 8*f*
  cell's genome, 217
  chromosome, 172
  coiling
    bacterial cell, 172
    chromosome, 170
  complementarity, 177
  double helix, 168, 169, 171, 172
  hereditary molecule, 166
  isolation, 195
  KRAS proto-oncogene, 235
  lipid carrier, 202
  Miescher, Friederick, 164
  nucleotides of, 167
  overview/discovery, 17
  polymerases, 200, 217
  recombinant, 191, 195
  replication, 169, 217, 387
    enzymes of, 218
  segment mixture, 197
  structure of, 168
  synthesis, 221
  technology, 162
  tetra-nucleotide model for, 34, 34*f*
  thymine, 177

transcription
  processes, 354
  into RNA, 176
  X-ray diffraction analysis of, 167

Dermal layer, 458

Dermal tissue, 253

Design
  glory of, 1–2
  at multiple levels, 4–11
    macrobiological system, 8–11
    microbiological architecture, 4–7
  talkability, 1–3

Design, of life
  rational experimentation, 29–32
    effect of prayer on cardiac patient, 31
    effect of sleep on disease resistance, 29–31
  truth
    characterization, 33, 33*f*
    comparing sources of, 33–34
    limits to, 34
    value of sources, 34–35
  understanding, 25–28

Detritivores, 571

Dialect, 366

Diaphragm, 405

Diastolic pressure, 298

Diatom, 523

Didinium nasutum, 561, 562*f*, 569

Diencephalon, 267, 321

Diet(s)
  high in saturated fats, 69, 70*f*

Differentiation, 216, 245

Diffusion
  defined, 96, 96*f*
  rates, 214

Digestive system, 246, 284

Dihybrid, 417

Dilate, 294

Dimer
  defined, 61
  formation of, 63*f*

Dinofagellates, 522

Dioecious, 250

Dionaea muscipula, 354

Diplococcus, 164

Diplococcus bacterium, 165

Diplomonads, 518

Directed panspermia, 453

Directional selection, 488–489, 488*f*. *See also* Natural selection
  in *Drosophila melanogaster*, 488, 488*f*

Disaccharide, 65, 65*f*

Discicristates, 520, 520*f*

Disease resistance
  sleep effect on, 29–31

Disruptive selection, 487, 487*f*. *See also* Natural selection

Dissolved oxygen (DO), 544

Distribution pattern, population, 549–551, 550*f*
  clumped, 549, 550*f*
  random, 549, 550*f*
  uniform, 549, 550*f*

Disulfide bonds, 457

Diversity, of life. *See* Life is Diverse

Diversity of styles, 12–14

DNA. *See* Deoxyribonucleic acid (DNA)

DNA polymerase, 17, 17*f*, 75, 76*f*

DNase, 165

DO. *See* Dissolved oxygen (DO)

Domain, 177, 477
  systematics, 506, 514, 514*f*

Domain-based scheme, 15*f*

Dominant, 415

Dopamine, 328

Down feathers, 459

Drosophila karyotype diagram, 425

Drosophila melanogaster, 425
  directional selection in, 488–489, 488*f*M, 489*f*
  mutational studies, 463

Duodenum, 264

Dyneins, defined, 109

E

E. coli, 172, 351
  Mycoplasma genitalium vs., 443, 443*f*

Earth's history
  and cellular life, 452–453, 452*f*
  "Mars Jars" experiments, 86, 86*f*, 446

Ecology, 540–575
  community. *See* Community ecology
  defined, 18, 540
  levels of organization and, 546–547
  limnetic zone, 544–545
  organismal, 547
  population. *See* Population

EcoR1, 196

Ecosystems, 546, 569–573
  defined, 9, 9*f*

Ectoderm, 260
  differentiation, 265

Ediacarans, 472

Effector, 318

Efferent, 271

Egg, fertilized, 242
  frog, 244

Egg cell, 251, 392

Electrical gradient, 289

Electric potential, 354
  defined, 125

Electroencephalograph, 410

Electromagnetic spectrum, defined, 146

Electron microscope
  defined, 7

Electrons
  defined, 43, 43*f*

Electron transfer phosphorylation
   in aerobic respiration, 139–140, 139f
Elements, 40f
   defined, 41
Ellerbeckia arenaria, 523
Elodea cells, 123f
   energy change in, 124–125
   movement of materials in, 124f,
      125, 125f
Elongation, 177, 186
Ely Cathedral, 122, 123f
Embryo, 243
   differentiation, 253
   Ginkgo biloba, 253
   primitive gut, differentiation, 264
   Spemann, Hans, 274
Embryonic differentiation
   of organ systems, 262–266
Embryonic disc, 264
Embryonic induction, 248
Empiricism, 33
Empiricist, 412
Endergonic reaction
   defined, 128
   in metabolic pathways, 132, 135
Endocardial tubes, 265
Endocrine system, 283, 314, 315, 327
   hormones of, 310
Endocytosis
   defined, 104
   in eukaryotic membrane,
      104–105, 105f
Endoderm, 260
Endometrium, 396
Endosperm, 252
Endosymbionts, 566
Endosymbiosis, 117–118
   defined, 117
Energy
   ATP, in cells, 135
   within cell, 124–125, 124f
      for biosynthesis, 124–125, 124f
      for concentration of substance,
         124f, 125
      for electrical potential, 124f, 125
      for heat, 124f, 125
      for movement of materials, 124f,
         125, 125f
   defined, 122
Energy flow(s), 16f, 153–155, 153f, 154f
   from carbohydrates to ATP, 136–143
   in chemical reactions, 128–129
   enzymes direct, 130–131
   for fermentation. *See* Fermentation
   laws, in living world, 126–127
   for living systems, 122–125
   in metabolic pathways. *See*
      Metabolic pathways
   from photons to carbohydrates,
      144–152
   for photosynthesis. *See*
      Photosynthesis

in reaction pathways, 132–134
for respiration. *See* Respiration
Energy of concentration, defined, 125
Enlightenment, 437
   thinking, features of, 439t
Environmental change, 348
   daily light-dark cycle, 363
Enzymes, 61
   and activation energy,
      130–131, 130f
   active site in, 130–131, 130f
   in cell nucleus, 192
   defined, 17, 130
   direct energy flow, 130–131
   in glucose breakdown, 130–131,
      130f–131f
   ligase, 196
Eosinophils, 301
Epidermis, 458
Epididymis, 398
Epistasis, 420–421
Epistatic control
   of coat color, 421
Epithelial cells, 444
Epithelial tissue, 246
Erectile tissue, 398
Erythrocytes. *See* Red blood cells
Escalator, 301
Escherichia coli, 99, 516, 516f
Esophagus, 264, 308
Essence, unity in, 14–17
Estrogen, 73, 73f, 395
Ethanol, 328
   defined, 143
Euglena gracilis, 520, 520f
Eukarya
   defined, 14
Eukaryotes, 174, 189, 512
Eukaryotic cells, 174
   component parts of, 111t–112t
   defined, 97, 97f
   DNA, inserting methods, 193
   intricacies of, 103–113, 104f
      cell membrane, 104–105
      chloroplast, 110f, 111
      dyneins, 109
      Golgi complex, 107, 107f
      intermediate filaments, 109
      kinesins, 109
      lysosome, 108, 108f
      microtubules, 109, 109f
      mitochondrion, 109–111, 110f
      nucleoli/nucleolus, 106
      nucleus, 105–106, 106f
      in pancreas, example, 113–116
      RER. *See* Rough endoplasmic
         reticulum (RER)
   organization of, 113–116
   photosynthesis in, 111
Eukaryotic chromosomes, 172
Eukaryotic malarial parasite, 305
European corn borer, 191

Evolution, 489–492
   biological activity, spatial ordering
      of, 451–453
   Cambrian explosion, 471–474
   Darwin model of, 437, 438f,
      438t, 442
   geochemical models, 445–447
   homology, evidence from,
      474–482
   information flow in an RNA world,
      448–450
   life history, Biblical constraints, 490f
   model for aging, 594, 594f
   mutations. *See* Mutations
   naturalistic hypothesis, 469, 470f
   natural selection. *See* Natural
      selection
   neo-Darwinian synthesis, 460–462
   pre-life Earth, 442f
   product and value of, 483–492
   smallest cell as first goal of,
      442–445. *See also Mycoplasma
      genitalium*
   theistic, 461
Excavata, 518
Exergonic reaction
   defined, 128
   in metabolic pathways, 132, 135
Exocytosis
   defined, 105
Expansin, 354
Experiment
   defined, 26
Experimental conditions, 29
Exponential growth model, 552
Extinct organisms, 471
Extracellular process, 442

F
FADH$_2$. *See* Flavin adenine dinucleotide
      (FADH$_2$)
Fagellum, 510t, 512
Fallopian tubes, 395, 400
Family, in systematics, 506
Fat energy, in a cashew nut, 70, 70f
Fats, 309
   saturated, 69, 70f
   unsaturated, 69
Fatty acids, 60f, 68–70
   saturated, 69, 69f
   unsaturated, 69, 69f
Feather, bird
   anatomy, 455–457, 456f
   development of, 458–460, 458f
   fossilized, 459, 459f
   mutations for generation of,
      463–464, 463f
   naturalistic hypothetical evaluation
      of, 469, 470f
   primary flight feathers, 454
      evolutionary changes,
         454–455, 455f

Feather, bird (*Contd.*)
    primitive feather keratinocytes
        mutation in, 460–464
        natural selection in, 464–469
Feces, 309
Feedback inhibition, 133*f*
    defined, 133
Female reproductive system, 395
Fermentation, 142–143, 142*f*
Ferns, 525
Fertilization, 251, 392, 397, 400
    cell fusion, 392
    early development, anatomy of, 402
Fertilized egg, 243
Fertilized human egg cell, 216
Fetology, 409
Fetus, 409
Fibril, 360
Fimbriae, 102*f*, 395
    defined, 102
Flavin adenine dinucleotide (FADH$_2$)
    defined, 138
Flower, 258
Flow of energy, 16*f*
Flter-feeding, 558
Fluoxetine, 332
Follicle, 393, 458
Follicle-stimulating hormone (FSH), 394
Food vacuoles, 524
Foraminiferan, 519
Forelimbs, vertebrates
    comparison of, 475–476, 476*f*
    diversity, origin of, 481–482, 481*f*
Fossils, 471, 471*f*
Fraction, 164
Franklin, Rosalind, 167
    DNA diffraction pattern, 167
Free radicals, 587, 588*f*
Freshwater pond community, 9*f*
Fructose, 64, 64*f*
Function
    defined, 29
Fungi, 14, 527

G

Galactose, 64*f*
Galapagos Islands, 438*f*
Galileo, 34
Gallbladder, 264, 309
Gamete, 389
    formation, 388
Gamma amino butyric acid (GABA), 330
    receptors, 329
Gap junctions, 296
Gastrulation, 259
Gene expression, 174
Gene modification, 192
Gene therapy, 203
    approaches, 204
    augmentation, 204
    history of, 204–206
    specific replacement, 204

Genetic information flow, 375
Geneticists use, 415
Genetic recombination, 384
Genetic variability, 378
Genetic variation, 380
Genome alteration, 191
Genome cycling, 219
Genomes, recombining, 201
Genomic potency, 275
Genotype, 173, 415
Genus, 504
    defined, 13
Geochemical model, of evolution,
    445–447
Geometric growth model, 552
Geospiza magnirostris, 438*f*
Geospiza scandens, 438*f*
Geothermal vents, 446–447, 447*f*
German cockroach, systematics
    of, 506*f*
Germination, 250, 255
Germ line cells, 193, 194
Gey, George Otto, Dr., 580
Giardia lamblia, 518*f*
Gibberellins, 256
Gilbert, Walter, 448
Ginkgo biloba, 250, 254, 256
    root, 253
    seed, 252
    stem development, 256
Ginkgo reproduction, 251
Ginkgo trees, 250
Globigerina bulloides, 519, 519*f*
Glucose, 8*f*, 16, 61, 64, 64*f*
    molecular structure, 60*f*
Glucose breakdown
    enzymes in, 130–131, 130*f*–131*f*
Glutamate, 330
    molecular structure, 59*f*
Glutamine
    molecular structure, 59*f*
Glycerol, 68–69
    molecular structure, 60*f*
Glycine
    molecular structure, 59*f*
Glycogen, 66, 66*f*
Glycolysis, 518
    in aerobic respiration, 137
    defined, 137
    NADH in, 137
    pyruvate in, 137
Glycoproteins, 79, 79*f*
Golgi complex, 187
    defined, 107
    in eukaryotic cells, 107, 107*f*
Gonadal ridge, 387
Good mutations, 485, 485*f*. *See also*
    Mutations
Gould, Steven J., 489
G$_0$ phase, 220
G$_1$ phase, 220
G$_2$ phase, 220

GPP. *See* Gross primary production
    (GPP)
Grant, Peter, 467–468
Grant, Rosemary, 467–468
Gross primary production (GPP), 569
Ground tissue, 253
Group, in systematics, 514, 516–528
    Alveolata, 521–522, 521*f*–522*f*
    Amoebozoa, 524, 524*f*
    Archaea, 517
    Bacteria, 516
    Discicristates, 520, 520*f*
    Excavata, 518
    Opisthokonta, 527–528,
        527*f*–528*f*
    Plant, 525–526, 525*f*–526*f*
    Rhizaria, 519
    Stramenopiles, 523, 523*f*
Growth curve
    J-shape, 552
G$_0$ stage, 586, 586*f*
Guanine, 84
    molecular structure, 59*f*
Guanosine triphosphate (GTP), 186
Gurdon, John, 276
Gymnosperms, 525–526
Gypsy moth, 565

H

Habitat, 547
Haeckel, Ernst, 510
Harmful mutations, 483–484, 483*f*,
    484*f*. *See also* Mutations
Harris, William, Dr., 31
HCL1 genes, 380
Heart, 5*f*
    functions, 4–5
    muscle tissues, 5*f*
Heart development, 266
Heart disease
    high fat diet and, 69, 70*f*
Heat capacity, 51
    of water, 51, 51*f*
HeLa cells, 580, 581*f*
Helium, 47*f*
Heme group, 80, 80*f*
Heme's breakdown
    urobilinogen, 312
Hemoglobin, 80–82, 173
    CO_2 binding, 81–82, 82*f*
    heme group, 80, 80*f*
    oxygen binding in, 81*f*
    structure, 80–81, 81*f*
Hemolysins, 102*f*
    defined, 102
Henslow, John, 436
Hepatic portal system, 309
Hepatic vein, 310
Herbivore (herbivory), 556, 569
Hershey-Chase experiment, 166
Hershey experiment, 166
Heterozygous, 415

High-energy phosphate bond, 83, 83f
Histamine, 301
Histidine
    molecular structure, 59f
HIV invasion, 307
HIV viruses, 300
    infections, 307
Holy Bible, 2, 21
Homeobox genes, 476–477, 477f
    in insects and mammals, 478–479, 478f
    mutation in *Drosophila*, 480–481, 480f
    in sponges, 479
Homeoprotein, 477
Homeostasis, 345, 354
    fails, 346
    organism's response, 349
Hominid, 533
Homologous chromosomes, 380
Homologous (in biology), 476
Homologous information, 380
Homology, evidence from, 474–482
    homeobox genes. *See* Homeobox
        genes
    oxygen distribution in animals
        and, 475f
    vertebrates forelimbs
        comparison of, 475–476, 476f
        diversity, origin of, 481–482, 481f
Homo sapiens, 380, 504–505, 533–534
Homozygous, 415
Hooke, Robert, 93, 93f
Hooklet, 456–457, 456f
Hormonal gradient
    in embryo, 253
Hormonal response
    melatonin effects, 364
Hormone melatonin
    in bloodstreams, 362
Hormone(s), 73, 73f, 252
    effects on tissues, 73f
    receptors, 345
Hornworts, 525
Host cell, 442
HoxC6, 479
Human being
    development of, 259
        early, 260
Human body
    common elements in, 44t
    organ systems in, 248
Human brain, 321
    regional diagrams of, 322
Human cardiovascular system, 295
Human circulatory system, 297
    pulmonary circuit, 297
    systemic circuit, 297
Human development
    cellular events in, 410
    early, 260
    embryo, 261
    primary tissue layers and
        structures, 261

Human digestive system, 308–310
Human egg, 259
Human gestation, 409
Human heart, 299
Human hepatic portal system, 310
Human immune system
    cells of, 302
    infection, inflammation, 302
Human kidney, 313
Human nervous system, 320–327
    central nervous system, 321–323
    internal integration, 327
    peripheral nervous system, 323–327
    responsiveness, in tools, 369
Human sensation, 1–2
Human sperm banks, 389
Human spinal cord, 322
Human urinary system, 312–315
Huxley, Aldous, 582
Hydrogen atom, 8f
Hydrogen bonding, 50, 50f
    polarity in water molecules and,
        49–50, 49f
Hydrogen (H_2), 44, 44t, 58, 446, 446t
    atomic structure, 58f
Hydrolysis, 61, 63f
Hydrophobicity
    of amino acids, 76
    of lipids molecules, 68
Hydroxyl radical, 364
Hypothalamus, 269, 362
Hypothesis
    defined, 26

I
Icarus, 452
Ileum, 264
Immune cells, 304
Immune response, 284
Immune system, 293
Immunity, basic concept of, 300–307
    lines of defense, 300
Implantation, 395
Index fossils, 471
Indian Pipe, 530, 530f
Indole-3-acetic acid (IAA), 357
    wall synthesis response, 360
Induction, 246
    embryonic, 248
    neural tube, 269
Inflammation, 301
Influenza (flu), 29
Information preservation, 373
    radical, 374
Information storage
    human understanding of, 170
Initiation, 177, 185
Innate immunity, 303
Instinctive behaviors, 366
Insulin, 191
Insulin gene, 198
Integrase, 200

Integration center, 318
Integumentary system, 283, 300
Intermediate filaments, defined, 109
Interphase, 220
Interpretation
    defined, 26
Interspecifc competition, 556, 557–561
Interstitial fluid, 296
Intrauterine device, 406
Ion
    defined, 43
Ion channels, 289, 316
Ion formation/ionic bonding, 47–48, 48f
Irreducible complexity, 460
Isoleucine
    molecular structure, 59f
Isotopes, 44f
    defined, 44

J
Jejunum, 264
J-shape growth curve, 552

K
Kalanchoe plants, 377
Karyotype, 425
Keel, 468
Kennedy, John F., 18
Keratin, 455, 457
Keratin fibers, 457, 457f
Keratinocytes, 459. *See also* Primitive
    feather keratinocytes
Kidneys, 312
Kinase enzyme, 222, 234
Kinesins, defined, 109
Kinetochore, 225
Kingdom, in systematics, 506,
    514, 514f
Kingdom-based scheme, 15f
KRAS, 234
Krebs, Hans, 137
Krebs cycle
    acetyl-CoA in, 138
    in aerobic respiration, 136f,
        137–139
    defined, 137
    $FADH_2$ in, 138
    summary, 138f
K-selected species, 554

L
Lacks, David, 580
Lacks, Henrietta, 580–581, 581f, 585
Lactase, 351
Lactose, 65, 65f, 351
Lactose operon, 352
L and D forms of amino acids,
    447, 447f
Lantern, 160, 161
Large intestine, 309
Laryngeal, 266
The Last Supper, 435

Lateral bud, 256
Lateral meristem, 254
Lateral mesoderm, 265
Leaf development, 257
Leaf variation, 257
Learned behavior, 366
Lentic, 544
Leptins, 345
Leucine
    molecular structure, *59f*
Leukocytes, 293
Leydig cells, 398
Library, 197
    construction, 198
Life
    defined, 90, 92
    diversity. *See* Life is Diverse
    interactive. *See* Ecology
Life, responsiveness, 346, 348
    organism control, 346
Life Can Be Understood, 34
Life Is Complex, 7, 41, 56
Life is Diverse, 12, 500–534. *See also*
        Evolution
    classification, 504–506
        characteristics in, 508–514, 508*t*,
            509*t*, 510*t*, 511*t*
        groups. *See* Group, in systematics
        man, 532–534, 532*f*–533*f*
        problems, 530–531
    defined, 501, 501*f*
    groups. *See* Group, in systematics
    priorities/presuppositions, 514–515
    as ultimate accident, 436–440
    as ultimate art, 435–436
Life Is Energy-Driven, 15
Life Is Finite, 21, 582, 582*f*
Life Is Informational Continuity, 17
Life Is Information Expressed, 16
Life Is Interactive, 18
Life is internally integrated, 5
Life Is Responsive, 18
Life Is Significant, 3
Life Is Ultimate Art, 20
Life/living organism. *See also* Design
    described, 17–19
    interactivity between, 18
    responsive quality of, 18, 18*f*
Life's essential resources, 214
Life's informational continuity, 214
Ligase enzyme, 196
Ligation, 196
Light-dependent reactions
    defined, 144
    in photosynthesis, 145–149, 145*f*,
        147*f*, 148*f*, 149*f*, 150*f*
Light-independent reactions
    defined, 144
    in photosynthesis, 145*f*, 149–152,
        151*f*, 152*f*
Limbic system, 321

Limnetic zone, 544–545
Lin 39, 479
Linkage, 426
    behavior of, 426
Linoleic acid, 69, 69*f*
Lipids, 7, 64*t*, 68–74
    fats, 68–71, 69*f*, 70*f*
    functions, 68
    hydrophobic nature of, 68
    phospholipid, 71–72, 71*f*–72*f*
    testosterone, 72–74, 73*f*
    water exclusion of, 71, 71*f*
Littoral zone, 544, 544*f*
Liver, 308
    caffeine, 313
Liver cells, vertebrate, *2f*
Liverworts, 525
Living matter
    common elements, 44*t*
    and nonliving, continuity
        between, 41
Logistic growth model, 553
Lumen, 398
Lungs, vertebrate, 468*f*
Luteinizing hormone (LH), 394
Lyell, Charles, 437, 439
Lymph. *See* Interstitial fluid
Lymphatic system, 284, 298
Lymph node, 296
Lymphocytes, 303
Lysine
    molecular structure, *59f*
Lysosome
    defined, 108
    in eukaryotic cells, 108–109, 108*f*

M

Macrobiological system, 8–11
    organizational levels, 11*f*
Macroevolution, 439, 440*f*
Macromolecular bodies, 70*f*, 71
Macromolecular structures
    defined, 6–7, 6*f*
Macrophages, 301
    defined, 102
Male nervous system, 398
Male reproductive system, 399
Malthus, Thomas, 437
Mammals, 502
    man as, 532
Man, classification of, 532–534,
    532*f*–533*f*
Marchantia Morchella esculenta, 527*f*
Marine snow, 545
Mark-recapture method, Peterson,
    548, 549
"Mars Jars" experiments, 86, 86*f*, 446
Mast cell, 301
Mastigonemes, 523
Materialism, 439
Maternal tissues, 253

Matter
    atomic structure, 43–46. *See also*
        Atom(s)
    chemical bonding, 47–50
    complexity (historical perspectives),
        38–41
    living and nonliving, continuity
        between, 41
    water, 51–53
Mcnaughton, Sam, 556
Medulla oblongata, 270
Meiosis
    genetic variability, 384
    genome reduction, 384
    life without, 382
    stages of, 384–385
Melatonin, 363, 364
Melatonin's widespread
        distribution, 364
Melospiza melodia, 367
Membrane repolarization, 316
Memory lymphocyte, 306
Mendel, Gregor, 412, 460
    dihybrid cross – genotypes, 418
    first generalization, 416
    law of segregation, 415, 416
    pea plants, 414
    Punnett square representation, 416
Mendel's laws, 424, 425
    first law, 418
    second law, 419
    as therapy, 417
Meningitis, 322
Menstrual cycle, 393, 394
Mental tools, scientific, 26
Meristem, 254, 255
Mesencephalon, 267
Mesoderm, 260
Mesodermal tissue, 265
Mesoderm differentiation, 265
Mesophyll tissue, 246
Messenger RNA (mRNA), 174
    to amino acids, 188
    codon, 182
    to cytoplasmic ribosomes, 174
    genetic code, 182
    proteins, transcripts code, 179
    ribosome shifts, 186
Metabolic pathways, 132*f*
    allosteric site, of enzyme,
        132–133, 132*f*
    cyclical, 132*f*
    defined, 132
    endergonic, 132
    exergonic, 132
    feedback inhibition, 133, 133*f*
    inhibition by enzyme
        phosphorylation, 133, 134*f*
    linear, 132*f*
Metabolism
    defined, 16–17, 94

Metaphase, 225
  duplicated chromosome, 226, 227
  plate, 227
Metencephalon, 267
  differentiates, 269
Methane (CH₄), 446, 446t
  molecular formation, 48–49, 49f
Methionine
  molecular structure, 59f
Micrasterias, 207
Micrasterias cell, 160, 161
Microbiological architecture, 4–7
Microcompartments
  defined, 100
  in prokaryotic cell, 98f, 100
Microevolution, 439, 440f
Microfossils, 452, 472
Micrometer, 172
  defined, 95
Micron, 172
Microorganisms
  in nature, 530, 530f
Microtubules, 109f
  defined, 109
Mid-America Heart Institute, 31
Miescher, Friederick
  DNA, discoverer of, 164
Mifepristone
  pregnancy, termination, 411
Miller, Stanley L., 86, 446, 451
Millivolt, defined, 140
Mimicry, 564
Mitochondria, 389, 511t, 512
Mitochondrion
  defined, 109
  in eukaryotic cells, 109–111, 110f
Mitosis, 221
  cytokinesis, 230
  process of
    sequence of stages, 224–228
  reason for, 224
    chromosomes, 224
  stages, 226
  telophase of, 231
Mitotic spindle, 225
Mixture
  defined, 40
Model
  defined, 26
Molecular weight, 217
Molecules, 40f. *See also* Biomolecules
  defined, 40
  organic
    centrality of carbon to,
      58–60, 58f
    construction and degradation of,
      61, 62f–63f
    form and function (overview),
      56–57
Moment-of-truth defenses, 565
Mona Lisa, 435

Monomers. *See also specific types*
  condensation of, 61, 63f
  defined, 58
  molecular structures, 59f–60f
Monosaccharides, 64, 64f
Monotremes, 531
Morphogenesis, 245, 246, 255
  origin of leaves, 256–257
  origin of reproductive structures,
    257–258
  origin of roots, 255–256
Morula, 259
Moses, 12, 12f
Mosses, 525
Motor neuron, 315
Motor proteins, 225
Mouth, 308
Mullerian mimicry, 564
Multicellular hand, servicing, 245
Muscle tissue, 247
Muscular system, 282, 286–292
  contraction, control of
    cardiac and smooth muscle, 292
    ion gradient, 288–290
    membrane potential, 288–290
    nervous system, 290–291
  diffusion, 289
  muscle contraction, 287–288
  muscle structural organization,
    286–287
  potential, 289
  sodium-potassium ATPase pumps, 289
Mutagenic chemicals, 463, 463f,
    587, 588f
Mutations, 188
  cancer, 233
  effects on populations, 461, 462f
  features, 461–462
  good, 485, 485f
  harmful, 483–484, 483f, 484f
  neutral, 484–485, 485f
  in primitive feather keratinocytes,
    460–464
  threatening design, 233–237
Mutualisms, 567–568
Mycoplasma genitalium, 442–445, 443f
  adhesin gene expression, 444, 445f
  tip structure, 443, 444
  translation from different reading
    frames, 444f
  ultrastructure, 451, 451f
  vs. *E. coli*, 443, 443f
Mycoplasmas, 442
  defined, 95
Myelencephalon, 267
  differentiates, 270
Myoglobin, 77, 79f

N
NADH. *See* Nicotinamide adenine
    dinucleotide (NADH)

Na-K-ATPase pumps. *See* Sodium-
    potassium ATPase pumps
Nanogram, 193
Naturalism, 434, 439
Naturalistic hypothesis, evolution of,
    469, 470f
Natural killer cell, 301
Natural selection, 378, 454–460, 465f
  directional selection, 487–488,
    487f, 488f
  disruptive selection, 487, 487f
  limits to, 465–468, 466f–467f
  in primitive feather keratinocytes,
    464–469
  role in Cambrian deposition begins,
    479–480, 480f
  roles in forelimb evolution, 479, 479f
  stabilizing selection, 486–487, 486f
Nature
  causality in, 440f
  microorganisms in, finding,
    530, 530f
Nectar, 354
Nematode, 592
Neo-Darwinian synthesis, 460–462
Neon, 47f
Nephron, 312
Nerve, 316
Nerve cell signal, 291
Nervous reflexes, 318
Nervous signals, 315
Nervous system, 271, 283, 327, 369
  and drugs, 328–333
    alcohol, 328–330
    caffeine, 331–332
    fluoxetine hydrochloride,
      332–333
  internal integration of, 327
  role in, 317
Net primary production (NPP), 569
Neural fold, 262
Neural groove, 262
Neural inputs converge, 316
Neural tube, 262, 267
  cells throughout, 269
  induction, 269
Neurons, 315, 316
  defined, 114
  receptors, 316
  structure, 315
Neurotransmitter, 291
  glutamate, 330
Neutral mutations, 484–485, 485f. *See
    also* Mutations
Neutrons
  defined, 43
Neutrophil, 301
Niche, 547
Nicotinamide adenine dinucleotide
    (NADH), defined, 137
Nitrogen cycle, 516

Nitrogen (N), 58
  atomic structure, 58f
Nonhomologous chromosomes, 427
Nonliving matter
  and living matter, continuity
    between, 41
Notochord, 265
NPP. See Net primary production (NPP)
Nucleases, restriction, 196
Nuclei, 362
Nucleic acids, 7, 64t, 83–85
  discovery of, 17
  nucleotides, 83–84, 83f–84f
  polymers (DNA and RNA), 84–85,
    84f, 85f
Nuclein, 164
Nucleoid, 172
Nucleoid region
  defined, 99
  of prokaryotic cells, 98f, 99–100
Nucleoli/nucleolus, defined, 106
Nucleolus, 6f
Nucleoplasm, defined, 105
Nucleoside triphosphate, 217
Nucleosome, 171, 172
Nucleotides, 83–84, 83f–84f
Nucleus, 6f
  accumbens, 328
  of atom, defined, 43, 43f
  defined, 14, 94
  in eukaryotic cell, 105–106, 106f
Numenius phaeopus. See Whimbrel
Nymphae odorata, 257

O
Observations
  cellular processes, 585–588
  organ-systemic processes, 590
Oligosaccharides, 78–79, 79f
Oncogene, 233
Oocyte
  primary, 387
  secondary, 388
Oogonium, 387
Oparin, A. I., Dr., 446
Operator, 351
Operon, 351
Opisthokonta, 527–528, 527f–528f
Optic chiasm, 362
Optic nerve, 362
Oral contraceptive, 405
Orbitals, 43f
  arrangement of, 45, 45f
  defined, 44–45
Order, in systematics, 506
Organelles, 6f
  defined, 5–6, 105
Organismal ecology, 547
Organism's response, 349
  environmental change, 349
  homeostasis, 349

Organization
  levels of, ecology and, 546–547
Organogenesis
  of brain, 267–270
Organs, 246
  defined, 4
Organ systems, 246
  cooperation of organs, 270–272
  direction, terms for, 262
  early gut differentiation, 264
  early organogenesis, 263
  embryonic differentiation, 262–266
Orgel, Leslie, 453
The Origin of Species, 437
Ornithologist, 367
Ovary, 387, 526
Overlap, defined, 443
Overturn, 545
Oviduct. See Fallopian tubes
Ovulation, 395
Ovule, 251
Owen, Richard, 475
Oxidized molecules, 446
Oxygen (O₂), 58, 446
  atomic structure, 58f
  binding in hemoglobin, 81f
  distribution in animals, 475f

P
P21, 237
P53, 236
Pancreas, 264, 308
  acetylcholine by, 114–116, 116f
  acinar cells. See Acinar cells
  amylase production, 113–116,
    114f–116f
  defined, 113
  eukaryotic intricacies, example,
    113–116
  neurons, 114
Pando the Trembling Giant, 377
Pan paniscus, 528f
Panthera leo, 592f
Panthera pardus, 592f
Paradigm, 440
Paramecium aurelium, 521, 521f, 557
Paramecium bursaria, 117, 117f, 376
  symbiosis in, 117–118
  Zoochlorella cells and, 117, 118f
Paramecium caudatum, 557, 558f,
    561, 562f
Parasite (parasitism), 442, 556
Parasitoidism, 557
Parasympathetic system, 320
Passeriformes, 528
Passive integrated transponder (PIT)
    tag, 548
Pathogen, 300
Paul of Tarsus, 2, 3
PCR amplification
  therapeutic gene, 201

Peaks of Otter salamander, 546, 546f
Peas plants, 525–526
  Mendel observation, 414
Peduncles, 269
Pellicle, 521
Penis, 398
Peptide bond
  formation, by condensation reaction,
    76–77, 76f
Peripheral nerves, 270
Peripheral nervous system (PNS), 320,
    323–327
  somatic portion of, 325
Periplasmic space, 98f
  defined, 99
Phagocytic leukocytes, 302
Pharyngeal arch, 266
Pharynx, 264
Phenol, 195
Phenotype, 173, 415
Phenylalanine
  molecular structure, 59f
Phloem, 255
Phospholipid, 71–72
  bilayer of, 72, 72f
  structure, 71f
Phosphorus, 164
Phosphorylation, 222
Photoreceptor, 359
Photosynthesis, 144–152, 144f, 247,
    509, 509t
  defined, 111, 144
  light-dependent reactions in,
    145–149, 145f, 147f, 148f,
    149f, 150f
  light-independent reactions in, 145f,
    149–152, 151f, 152f
Photosystem, defined, 146
Phototropic response, 358
Phototropism, 357
Phylum, 472–473
  in systematics, 506
Physarum polycephalum, 95, 95f
Phytophthora infestans, 18
Phytoplankton, 544
Phytoplankton bloom, 545
Pigment molecules, defined, 146
Pineal gland, 269, 362
Pisaster, 566
Pisum sativum, 412, 525, 525f
  life cycle of, 414
PIT tag. See Passive integrated
    transponder (PIT) tag
Pituitary gland, 269, 394
Placenta, 243, 259, 532
Planar, 459
Plankton, 436, 523
Plant group, in systematics, 525–526,
    525f–526f
Plant hormones, 356
  response, 356

Plants
    defined, 14
Plant shoot tips
    auxins behavior, 357
Plant's root system, 377
Plant tissue culture, 379
Plaque, 70f, 458
Plasma, 293
Plasmid, 196, 197
Plasmodium falciparum, 305
Platelet, 293
Plato, 408
Pleiotropic effects
    of abnormal hemoglobin, 422
Pleiotropy, 421
Plinian Society, 436
Ploidy, 382
    problem solving, 382–383
Pneumococcus, 584
Pneumonia, 584
Polar body, 388
Polar covalent bonding, 49–50, 49f
Polar transport, 357
Pollen grain, 251
Poly(A) tail, 179
Polymerase chain reaction (PCR),
        198, 199
Polymerase genes
    protein products of, 217
Polymers
    carbohydrate, 65–67, 66f
    defined, 58
    formation of, 61, 63f
Polypeptides, 75
Polytrichum Monilinia fruticola, 527f
Pond ecosystem, 9
Pons, 269
Population, sex cells, 193
Population(s), 9f
    age structure, 551, 551f
    birth rates, 553
    death rates, 553
    defined, 8–9
    density, 549
    distribution pattern, 549–551, 550f
    ecology, 548–554
    growth, 551–555
    sex ratios, 551
    size, 548–549
Porifera, 473
Portal vein, 309
Potato. See Solanum tuberosum
Prairie dogs, 565, 565f
Prayer
    effects on cardiac patient
            (experimental study), 31
Predator (predation), 556
Predator satiation, 564
Prediction
    defined, 26
Preening, bird, 457, 457f

Pregnancy, termination
    mifepristone, 411
Pre-mRNA
    processing of, 179
Prickly Pear cactus, 566, 566f
Primary flight feathers, 454
    evolutionary changes, 454–455, 455f
Primary germ cells (PGCs), 387
Primary structure, of proteins, 77, 78f
Primate, 532
Primer, 198
Primitive feather keratinocytes
    mutation in, 460–464
    natural selection in, 464–469
Primitive features, organism
            structure, 508
Primitive streak, 259
Producer biomass, 569
Product, defined, 128
Profundal zone, 545
Progeria, 593, 593f
Progesterone, 396
Progestogen, 406
Programmed aging, 593, 593f, 594–596
Prokaryotes, 174, 189, 512
Prokaryotic cells, 172, 174
    component parts of, 111t–112t
    defined, 97, 97f
    intricacies of, 98–100, 98f, 100f
        cell membrane of, 98–99, 98f, 99t
        cell walls in, 98f, 99
        cytoplasm of, 99
        nucleoid of, 98f, 99–100
        Streptococcus pyogenes, example.
            See Streptococcus pyogenes
    organization of, 101–103
Proline
    molecular structure, 59f
Promoter, 175, 351
Pronucleus, 401
Prophase, 225
Prostaglandin, 399
Prostate gland, 399
Protein
    human intracellular protein
            factory, 187
    photoreceptor, 359
    proto-oncogenes, 234
    regulatory pathways, activation, 233
    α-Tropomyosin gene, 180
    tumor suppressor genes, 234
Proteinase, 166
Proteins, 7, 75–79
    alternate, 180
    defined, 17
    functional classes of, 75t
    structural features, 75–77, 76f
        levels of complexity, 77, 78f, 79f
Protein structure
    DNA mutation, effect of, 188
Protein synthesis, 175, 181

Protistans, 506, 520
    defined, 97
Protists
    defined, 14, 15f
Protocell, 448f
Protons
    defined, 43
Proto-oncogene, 233
Protozoan cells
    defined, 117
Protozoans, 237, 557
Pseudomyrmex, 567
Psi sequence, 201
Pulmonary circulation, 296
Pulmonary reserve, 584
Pulp, 459
Pulse, 298
Purines, 59f
Pyrimidines, 59f
Pyrodictium occultum, 517, 517f
Pyruvate, defined, 137

Q

Quaternary structure, of proteins,
        77, 78f
Questions
    defined, 26
Quickening, 408
Quinone, defined, 146

R

Rachis, 455, 456f
Radiation (in evolutionary theory), 473
Radioactive decay processes, 44
Radiolarian, 519
Ramus, 324
Random distribution pattern, 549, 550f
Ras, 234
Rb, 235
Reactant, defined, 128
Reading frames, 443
    translation from, 444f
Receptor, 318
Receptor proteins, defined, 99
Recessive, 415
Rectum, 264
Red blood cells, 293
Red-spotted newts, 548, 552f, 564
Reduced molecules, 446
Reduction division, 385
Reflex, 318
Reflex arc, 318
Regional differentiation, 260
Remak, Robert, 94, 94f
Renaissance, 435
Repetitive DNA sequences, 586, 587f
Replication
    origin of, 218
Repressor, 351
Reproduction
    Gingko's unique mode of, 258

Reproduction (*Contd.*)
in human, 391–403
follicle, 393
menstrual cycle, 393, 394
ovary, 393
Reproductive cells
challenge of, 382
differentiation of, 387
Reproductive potential, 437
Reproductive system
egg ruptures, 396
female, 395
hormones, 396
male, 399
physical and spiritual, 402
sperm formation, 397
RER. *See* Rough endoplasmic reticulum (RER)
Resource partitioning, in species, 559, 560*f*
Respiration, 136–140
aerobic. *See* Aerobic respiration
Respiratory ciliary, 301
Respiratory system, 283
Resting potential, 289
Restriction nuclease, 195
Results
defined, 26
as puzzle pieces, 27–28
Retina, 362
Retroviral genome, 201
Retroviral infection, 201
Retroviruses, 200
Revealed truth. *See also* Truth
value of, 34–35
vs. scientific knowledge, 33–34
Revelation, 33, 33*f*
Reverse transcription, 200
R groups, 76, 76*f*
Rhizaria, 519
Rhythm method, 406
Ribonucleic acid (RNA)
complementarity, 177
Ribonucleic acid (RNA), 85, 85*f*
Ribonucleotide, 177
Ribose
molecular structure, 60*f*
Ribosomal RNAs (rRNAs), 178
Ribosomes, 184
defined, 100
in RER, 106–107, 107*f*
Ribulose 1,5-bisphosphate, defined, 150
RNA. *See* Ribonucleic acid (RNA)
RNA genome, 200
RNA molecule
functional classes of, 179
RNA polymerase, 175, 176, 178, 351, 353
RNA polymerase enzyme, 353
RNase, 166
RNA world system, 448
difficulties, 449, 449*f*

evolution of information flow in, 448, 448*f*
tRNA synthetases, 450, 450*f*
Rod cell, 334
Root, 252
Root cap, 255
Root development, 255
Rough endoplasmic reticulum (RER)
defined, 106
in eukaryotic cells, 106–107, 107*f*
R-selected species, 554
"Rule of law," concept of, 35

S
Saliva, 308
Salivary gland, 308
Salmonella, 516
Sarcomere contraction
regulation of, 290
Saturated fats, 69
diets high in, 69, 70*f*
Saturated fatty acid, 69, 69*f*
Scales, 526, 549
Schleiden, Mathew, 94, 94*f*
Schwann, Theodor, 94, 94*f*, 95
SCID patient lymphocytes, 205
Scientific knowledge. *See also* Truth
value of, 34–35
vs. revealed truth, 33–34
Scientific method, 33, 33*f*
Sciurus carolinensis. See Squirrel
Seasonal affective disorder, 364
Sebastes aleutianus, 594
Secondary structure, of proteins, 77, 78*f*
Sedative, 328
Sedgewick, Adam, 472
Sedimentary rock, 471
Seed, 250
Segmentation, 410
Selection pressure, 467–468
Seminal vesicle, 398
Senescence, 582, 584. *See also* Aging
at cellular level, 585, 585*f*
Sensory neuron, 317
Serine
molecular structure, 59*f*
Serotonin, 332
Serotonin-specific reuptake inhibitor (SSRI), 332
Severe combined immunodeficiency (SCID), 204
Sex chromosome, 425
Sex ratios, population, 551
Sexual display, costly, 378
Sexual exchange, 379
Sexuality, maintenance of, 379
Sexual reproduction, 378
Sheath, 455, 456*f*
SHH. *See* Sonic hedgehog
Shoot, 252

Silver Springs
energy flow in, 570–572, 571*f*, 572*f*
Single-celled life-forms, 21
Size, population, 548–549
Skeletal muscle, 292, 316
Skeletal system, 283
Sleep study
control group, 29*f*
effect on disease resistance, 29–31
experimental group, 30*f*
results, 30, 30*f*, 30*t*
Slime molds, 524
Sly pathogens, 303
Small intestine, 308
absorption, 309
Smith, William, 471
Smooth muscle, 292
Snail populations, genetic diversity in, 486, 486*f*
Snapdragon flower color, 420
Socket wall, 459
Sodium chloride (NaCl)
ion formation, 47–48, 48*f*
as solute in water, 51–52, 52*f*
Sodium-potassium ATPase pumps (Na-K-ATPase pumps), 289
Soil
complexity, 38, 39*f*
Solanum lycopersicum, 13, 13*f*
Solanum tuberosum, 13, 13*f*
Solute
defined, 51
Solvent
defined, 51
water as, 51–52, 52*f*
Somatic cell, 193
Somatic mesoderm, 265
Somatic system, 320
Somites, 265
Sonic hedgehog, 267, 268
Sparrows, 527–528
Speciation, 468, 491*f*
Species, 504
defined, 12
resource partitioning in, 559, 560*f*
Spemann, Hans, 274
Sperm
swimming ability of, 400
Spermatid, 389
Spermatocyte
primary, 389
secondary, 389
Spermatogenesis, 397
Spermatogonia, 389
Sperm banks, 389
Sperm cell repartee, 401
Sperm cells, 259, 389
Sperm formation, 397
Spermicides, 404
Sperm production, 398
Sphere of hydration, 52, 52*f*

Spinal cord, 270, 322
Spinal nerves, 324
   anatomy of, 325
Splanchnic mesoderm, 265
Spleen, 304
Spontaneous abortion, 410
Sporozoans, 522
Squirrel, 56–57, 57*f*
Stabilizing selection, 486–487, 486*f*.
   See also Natural selection
Staining cells, 171
Staphylococcus aureus, 300
Starch, 65, 66*f*
   defined, 150
   granules, 162
Starch synthase, 61
Start codon, 185
Stearic acid
   molecular structure, 60*f*
Stem cells, 191, 254
Stem development, 256
Sternum, 468
Steroids, 73, 73*f*
Stomach, 246, 308
Stomata, defined, 150
Stramenopiles, 523, 523*f*
Streptococcus pyogenes, 101–103,
   101*f*–103*f*
   adhesins, 102
   capsules, 103
   fimbriae, 102, 102*f*
   hemolysins, 102, 102*f*
   macrophages, 102
Stroma
   defined, 111, 150
Structural gene, 351
Structure
   defined, 29
Sucrose, 65, 65*f*, 77, 79*f*
   defined, 150
Sugars, 60*f*, 64–65, 64*f*, 65*f*
   disaccharide, 65, 65*f*
   monosaccharides, 64, 64*f*
Sulfur, 164
Superoxide dismutase, 588
Superoxide radical, 587–588
Suprachiasmatic nuclei, 362
Symbiosis, 117–118
Sympathetic system, 320
Synapse, 291
   alcohol, invades, 329
   caffeine, invades, 331
   serotonin-specific reuptake inhibitor
     (SSRI), 333
   signal conversion, 316
Synaptic gap, 291
Systematics, 504, 504*f*
   of German cockroach, 506*f*
   group in. *See* Group, in
     systematics
Systemic circulation, 296

Systems
   defined, 4
Systolic pressure, 298

T

Taxonomy, 504, 504*f*
T2 bacterial virus, 166
T cell, helper, 304
Telencephalon, 267
Teleology, 20–21
   defined, 20
Telomerase, 587
Telomeres, 586, 587*f*
Telophase, 225
Termination, 178, 186
Tertiary structure, of proteins, 77,
   78*f*, 79*f*
Testis, 387
Testosterone, 72–74, 398
   structure, 73*f*
Tetranucleotide hypothesis, of DNA,
   34, 34*f*
Tetrapods, 476
Thalamus, 269
Theism, 439, 440*f*
Theistic evolution, 461
Theory(ies)
   defined, 27
   in science, 28*t*
Therapsids, 531
Thomas hunt morgan
   work of, 424
Thoracic, 265
Thorax, 488
Threonine
   molecular structure, 59*f*
Threshold, 316
Throat infection
   Streptococcal cells in. *See*
     Streptococcus pyogenes
Thylakoids
   defined, 111, 146
   in eukaryotic cells, 110*f*, 111
Thymine, 84
   molecular structure, 59*f*
Thyroid gland, 363
Thyroxin, 363
Tissue(s), 512
   defined, 5
   heart, 5*f*
Tissue structure
   of organ, 247
T lymphocytes, 304, 590
Tomato. *See Solanum lycopersicum*
Topological structure, 459
TP53, 236
Trachea, 474
   of insects, 475*f*
Transcription, 174, 175–180
   factor, 477
   level of, 351

Transduction, 200
Transfection, 193
Transfer RNA, 183
   binding site, 186
Transformation, 164, 193, 585
   heat-killed virulent "S" cells, 165
   in mice, 165
Translation, 174, 185
   from different reading frames, 444*f*
   making proteins, 181
   protein synthesis, 181
   termination of, 186
   tRNA for, 183
Transporter protein, 332
Trichomonads, 518
Trichomonas vaginalis, 518
Triglycerides, 309
   composition, 68–69
   structure, 69*f*
Trimester, 409
Triturus, 273
TRNA synthetases, 450, 450*f*
Trophic levels, 569
Trophoblastic cells, 401
Tropomyosin, 290
α-Tropomyosin gene, 180
Troponin, 291
Truth
   characterization, 33, 33*f*
   comparing sources of, 33–34
   limits to, 34
   revealed *vs.* scientific knowledge,
     33–34
   value of sources, 34–35
Trypanosomes, 520
Tryptophan
   molecular structure, 59*f*
Tsvet, Mikhail, 40, 40*f*, 41
Tubal ligation, 407
Tumor suppressor gene, 233
   functions, 236
Turgid, 334
Tyrosine
   molecular structure, 59*f*

U

Ultrastructure, 451
Unconscious reflex, 318
Unicellular, 510
Uniform distribution pattern, 549, 550*f*
Uniformitarianism, 437
Unity in essence, 14–17
Unity within diversity
   diversity of styles, 12–14
   life, described, 17–19
   unity in essence, 14–17
Unsaturated fats, 69
Unsaturated fatty acid, 69, 69*f*
Uracil, 85
   molecular structure, 59*f*
Uranium-238, 44

Urea, 41f
Ureter, 312
Urethra, 312
Urey, Harold C., 86, 446, 451
Urinary system, 284
Urine, 312
Uropygial gland, 457
Uterine tube, 259. *See also* Fallopian tubes
Uterus, 395

V

Vaccination, 307
Vagina, 396
Vaginal rings, 406
Valine
    molecular structure, 59f
Valve, 296
Variable
    defined, 29
Vascular cylinder, 255
Vascular tissue, 253
Vas deferens, 398
Vasectomy, 407
Vein, 294
Ventricle, 296
Venus fly trap
    response, 355
Verrocchio, 435
Vertebra, 265
Vertebrates, 454
    forelimbs
        comparison of, 475–476, 476f
        diversity, origin of, 481–482, 481f

genome differences, 474t
    liver cells, 2f
    lungs, 468f
Vesicles, 108f
    defined, 106
Viral genes, 195
Viral reproduction, 201
Virchow, Rudolph, 94
Virulent, 164
    bacteria, 164
    heat-killed, 165
Virulent cells
    transforming factor, 165
Viruses, 190
Virus packaging cell, 202
Vitamin, 309
Von Linne, Carl, 13, 13f
    biological classification, 13–14, 14f

W

Washington monument, 283
Water, 38
    cohesiveness of, 52–53, 53f
    exclusion of lipids by, 71, 71f
    high heat capacity, 51, 51f
    molecules, polar covalent bonding in, 49–50, 49f
    as solvent, 51–52, 52f
Water diffuses, 313
Water lilies, 3f
Water molds, 523
Weismannian border, 194
Weismannian boundary, 194
Whale, origin of, 472f

Whimbrel
    feathers on, 455f
White blood cells, 293
Withdrawal method, 405
Wnt, 267
    signal protein, 272
Woese, Carl, 448
Wohler, Friedrich, 41, 41f

X

X chromosome, 425
Xenopus laevis, 275, 478
    Gurdon, John, 276
Xylem, 255

Y

Y chromosome, 426

Z

Zebra mussel, 558, 558f
Zona pellucida, 401
Zonotrichia leucophrys, 366, 527, 527f
Zoochlorella cells
    Paramecium bursaria and, 117, 118f
Zooxanthellae, 566–567
Zygote, 243, 252, 387
Zymogen granules, 113